Power and Safety.

SLM has a record of unusual engineering accomplishments such as manufacturing rack-and-pinion rail
vehicles for gradients of up to 480 per mill. Or for
making combined rack-and-pinion/adhesion railways.
Be it electric or diesel motor vehicles or locomotives, or
ecologically-compatible oil-fired steam locomotives for
tourist purposes, all types of SLM vehicles have the following in common: technically perfect running gears, safe
interaction between toothed wheels and rack rails, and
appealing looks. And, of course, SLM's rail vehicles are
customized in both engineering and design to meet the
individual needs of mountain railway operators.
Rack-and-pinion rail vehicles by SLM operate successfully
throughout the world, wherever reliability and safety
for passengers and material take first priority.

SLM develops innovative rail vehicles
for today's markets to put people on
the move.

SLM

Member of the Sulzer Corporation

SLM Swiss Locomotive and
Machine Works Ltd
CH-8401 Winterthur, Switzerland
Phone +41 (0) 52 264 10 10
Fax   +41 (0) 52 213 87 65

SLM
the power of moving

Our Experience Travels The World.

As an internationally recognized designer and manufacturer of innovative products for the urban, suburban and intercity rail passenger transportation markets, Bombardier's proven technologies and transit system delivery experience continue to travel across — and reshape — the rail transportation world.

 TRANSPORTATION GROUP

PROFESSIONAL IN RAIL TRANSPORT

In the rail transport sector, GEC ALSTHOM is advancing and applying technology in the design, manufacture and supply of rolling stock and signalling equipment for main line commuter and light rail systems.
To date, in more than 50 countries, GEC ALSTHOM has on order or in service 571 TGV high speed trains, more than 14,000 electric and diesel electric locomotives, over 30,000 single and double-deck passenger coaches, and metro systems in over 40 major cities worldwide.

▼

GEC ALSTHOM

SIEMENS

Always a step ahead –
The ICE leads the way to a
future without limits

The challenge: The ICE® started the mega-trend to rail, and sparked the demand for advanced train concepts for specific market needs. To meet these needs, the ICE family is now being extended.

Our solution: By the end of this year the ICE 2 will be on the rails, with a versatile half-length concept for economical service on lines with fewer passengers. The ICE 3 will follow in 1999. Its new power car concept will take it to 330 kph (210 mph) and let it handle steeper grades, while making room for more seats and lowering life-cycle costs. Designed for all four European operating voltages, it has an outstanding international career ahead of it. Meanwhile, on conventional lines the ICT will get passengers where they´re going ultra-fast and in complete comfort with active tilt technology.

Speed. Comfort. Economy. These are the keys to success for the ICE family. The Deutsche Bahn AG and the Royal Dutch Railways have already chosen it.

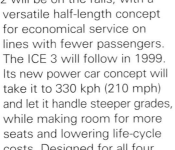

Looking straight ahead into the future: the ICE 3 extends national high-speed train routes into a European high-speed network.

Mobility for a moving world.
Siemens Transportation Systems

More Info? Siemens AG, Transportation Systems Group,
Infoservice VT/Z 039, Fax (++49) 9 11 / 9 78 - 33 21

Contents

The Power Behind
MotivePower
Industries

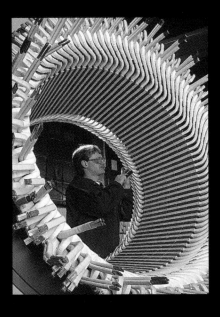

Boise Locomotive Company

Manufacturers of the world's most efficient switcher locomotives. Boise Locomotive also overhauls and rebuilds locomotives, and provides fleet maintenance.

Phone: 208.389.4800

Motor Coils Manufacturing Company

A premier manufacturer of traction motors and related components – from field coils to armatures.

Phone: 412.273.4900

Engine Systems Company

The nation's leading supplier of turbochargers and turbocharger components to the rail aftermarket.

Phone: 518.783.0545

RAILWAY SYSTEMS

AFGHANISTAN

Ministry of Transport

PO Box 2509, Ansari Walt, Kabul
Tel: +93 21015

Key personnel
Minister of Transport: Syed Anwari

Political background
In 1982 the first railway tracks appeared in Afghanistan with completion, after three years' work by Afghan and Soviet labour, of an 816 m combined rail and road bridge over the Abu Darja river, the border with the former USSR, now Uzbekistan, and the projection over it of a rail link from the Bukhara—Dushanbe line near Termez to Hairaton in Afghanistan. This penetration was to be continued into Afghanistan, beginning with a 200 km line to Pali—Khumri, some 160 km north of Kabul, but progress was blocked by the mountainous terrain, the long annual periods in which the area is blanketed by heavy snow and the unstable political situation within the country.

A new prospect that would place Afghanistan astride a Central Asian railway was opened up in 1992 when Pakistan's Economics Minister offered the Central Asian republics aid for the construction of a railway through Afghanistan to an emergent Arabian Sea port in Baluchistan at Pasni. Later, a revised plan emerged for an 800 km trans-Afghan line linking the existing Pakistan Railways route at Chaman with Kushka in Turkmenistan, via Herat and Kandahar. This has been accorded priority by the Pakistan government, and was the subject of an accord signed in March 1994 between the Pakistan, Afghan and Turkmenistan governments.

VERIFIED

ALBANIA

Ministry of Industry, Trade & Transport

Rruge Myslym Shyri 42, Tirana

Key personnel
Minister: Suzana Panariti
Director, Railways: M Dizdari

VERIFIED

Albanian Railways (HSH)

Hekurudhat Shqiptare
Drejitoria e Pergjithshme e Hekurudhave Shqiptare, Rue Skenderbeg, Durrës
Tel: +35 55 222311   Fax: +35 55 222037

Key personnel
Director General: Arben Keci
Assistant Directors General: Aleksander Sheldia, Petraq Pano
Directors
Finance: Petrit Tafili
Rolling Stock: Nderim Kasa
Commercial: Dhimiter Karanxha
Infrastructure: Cesk Radovani
Passenger: Fadil Kaja
Planning, Personnel: Shkelzen Xava
International Relations: Miranda Jani

Gauge: 1,435 mm
Route length: 447 km

Political background
Following deposition of the hardline Communist government, consideration was given in the early 1990s to abandonment of the badly rundown state railway system. Following a study on the future of the railway by CIE Consult of Ireland under World Bank auspices, it was decided that efforts would be made to revitalise HSH.

One of the first decisive moves was to cut the 9,000-strong workforce of HSH by almost half: by 1995, only 4,700 employees remained. The aim was to cut this again, to 3,500, by the end of 1996.

In 1997 the political situation in Albania was unstable; it was unclear how this would affect the rehabilitation of the railway.

Organisation
Following the CIE Consult report, HSH was restructured into two business units (passenger and freight) and two service units (infrastructure and rolling stock).

Finance
Revenue from operations covers only about 30 per cent of HSH's overall costs, with the balance coming in the form of government subsidy and subventions from international bodies.

Passenger operations
From a peak of 12 million passengers annually in the 1980s, carryings collapsed following the economic reforms of 1990-91. In 1993, 4 million passengers were carried; passenger-km stood at 223 million.

Freight operations
The upheavals in the Albanian economy which attended the collapse of Communism drained away most freight traffic from the railway. The mining sector, including chrome, nickel and phosphates, was formerly the mainstay of HSH rail freight.

Tonnage declined from an annual average of 8 million tonnes in the 1980s to approximately 0.5 million tonnes in 1994. HSH's management's aim is to attract freight back as the economy is rebuilt.

New lines
A link from the northern Albanian railhead at Shkodër into Montenegro was finished in 1986. This was Albania's first rail connection with a foreign railway, but it fell foul of the United Nations 1991 embargo on trade with Yugoslavia and in early 1997 had not been reopened to traffic.

An agreement is in place to extend the line from Pogradec into Greece; design work was completed in 1995, but no physical construction has taken place. A line is also planned from Pogradec to Bitola in Macedonia, where it would link with an existing line to Skopje and form part of a proposed new route to Sofia in Bulgaria. This will require 3 km of new construction in Albania and 50 km in Macedonia. Planning for both projects continues in the 1996-2000 plan period (see 'Improvements to existing lines').

Improvements to existing lines
Italy has financed upgrading of the 40 km route from the capital, Tirana, to the port at Durrës, with a Lire6 billion credit supplementing a government contribution of US$2 million. The work, undertaken by Italian contractor Fersalente, involves upgrading the line and improving signalling and telecommunications systems. Renewal of the 28.2 km from Durrës to Kashar to 70 km/h standards was completed in early 1997.

HSH is hopeful that further credits from the Italian government will fund reconstruction of the Durrës—Rrogozhinë section.

Traction and rolling stock
The only serviceable locomotives are 29 Czech-built 1,007 kW (1,350 hp) T669 Co-Co diesels.

T669 locomotive with Chinese-built carriages (Stephen R L Phillips)   **1997**

Most passenger trains are composed of HSH's 63 coaches of 1960 manufacture obtained second-hand from Italy; two sets of Chinese-built stock are also in use. The railway is seeking to obtain another 10 second-hand coaches plus a railcar.

Total freight vehicle stock is around 2,100, but only about 400 wagons are serviceable.

Signalling and telecommunications

As there is a problem with theft of exposed cables, all stations are equipped with radios and are in contact with the control office in Durrës; train order tickets are given to drivers. An underground cable is planned for the main line between Tirana and Durrës.

Track

Rail: 38, 43, 48, 49 kg/m in 12 to 24 m lengths
Sleepers: Wood, duo-bloc concrete
Min curve radius: 300 m
Max axleload: 21-24 tonnes
Max speed: 60 km/h

UPDATED

ALGERIA

Ministry of Transport

Algiers

Key personnel
Minister: Essaid Bendakir
Secretary-General: A Brachemi
Director, Infrastructure and Rail Transport:
   A Benallegue

VERIFIED

Algerian National Railways (SNTF)

Société Nationale des Transports Ferroviaires
21-23 Boulevard Mohamed V, Algiers
Tel: +213 2 711510   Fax: +213 2 748190

Key personnel
Director General: Abdelhadim Lalaimia
Secretary General: Ahmed Halfaoui
Directors
   Operating: Brahim Sebaa
   Human Resources: Abderrahmane Belkadi
   Infrastructure: Mourad Soliman Benameur
   Rolling Stock: Rafik Djouadi
   Finances: Djamel Djenas
   Planning: Ali Leuimi
   Purchasing: Abdelhamid Moudjebeur
External Relations Manager: Bachir Ghalous

Gauges: 1,432 mm; 1,055 mm
Route length: 3,616 km; 1,156 km
Electrification: 301 km at 3 kV DC

Organisation
The network consists primarily of two standard-gauge coastal lines running east and west from Algiers: about 550 km westward to the railhead at Akid Abbès (where a connection with Moroccan Railways, broken in 1976, was reactivated in 1989), and about 370 km eastwards to a connection with the 520 km north—south line at El Guerrah. In addition to standard-gauge spur lines, a 300 km (partly electrified) 1,435 mm gauge line runs parallel with the Tunisian border, providing international connecting services at Souk-Ahras with Tunisian National Railways (SNCFT) from the port of Annaba to Djebel Onk. Major narrow-gauge lines run from Tizi to Béchar and Blida to Djelfa; conversion to standard gauge is proposed.

None of SNTF's main lines were built to handle present passenger and freight traffic volumes, which trebled during the 1980s. The government is committed to a heavy investment in SNTF to fit rail transport for the demands both of new industry and of the agricultural development now accorded considerable priority. Importance is also attached to enlargement both of long-haul and suburban rail passenger capacity.

In 1987 a number of subsidiaries were formed to free the railway's management for full attention to transport. EIF and EST are the infrastructure and signalling/telecommunications subsidiaries; the others include EMF, covering rolling stock modernisation; Infrarail, new construction and tracklaying; Informatique Service, computerisation; Restau-Rail, on-train catering; Rail-Express, small freight consignments door-to-door; Promolmmobilière, housing; and SIM, multimodal transport.

Improvements to existing lines
Besides lengthening existing passing loops on single-track routes to permit operation of trains up to 1,200 m long instead of the previous 800 m maximum, and also laying in additional loops, SNTF has carried out some large-scale projects to double-track single lines which were quite inadequate for current industrial development.

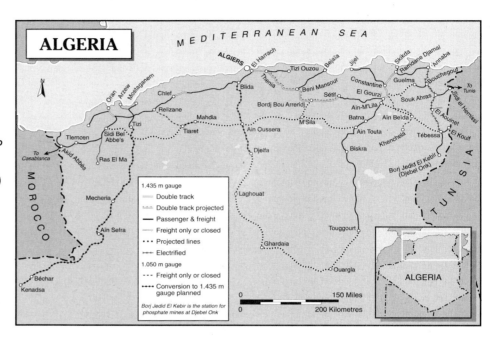

The first was between Ramdane-Djamel, 67 km north of Constantine and El Gourzi, 38 km south of Constantine. This vital link between Algiers and the petrochemical port of Skikda, as well as Annaba, was previously double-track only for 18 km between Constantine and El Khroub, and handicapped in its negotiation of the Constantine mountains by gradients as steep as 1 in 50 and curves sharper than 200 m radius. With an axleload limit of 18 tonnes, it could carry only 9,000 tonnes of freight a day. Under a scheme estimated to cost AD2.2 billion and managed by Cogifer and Italconsult, the line has been doubled throughout the 67 km from Ramdane-Djamel to Constantine and the 20.6 km south from El Gourzi to El Khroub, along with realignments.

In conjunction with installation of heavier UIC 54 welded rail on concrete sleepers of SL Type U (1,722 per km), this scheme has raised permissible freight speed from 60 to 90 km/h and wagon axleload from 18 to 28 tonnes. Following installation of modern automatic signalling, the line's train operating capacity has doubled and a throughput of 7 million tonnes a year is possible.

To create a relief route between Constantine and Annaba, resuscitation of the 95 km El Khroub—Guelma connection, abandoned in the 1950s, is under way. In 1989 local contractors began the double-tracking of 65 km between Khemis Miliana and Oued Fodda; and a six year upgrading has been put in hand between Mohammadia and Bechar.

West of Constantine some double track already exists on the littoral main line to Algiers and Oran, and the creation of more is among the projects funded by a US$477 million loan obtained from Austria for infrastructure modernisation in 1981. The credit was for drawing over a period of 15 to 20 years. A 16-company Austrian group, including Simmering-Graz-Pauker, Jenbachertransportsysteme, Plasser & Theurer and Voest-Alpine, is one of the largest concerns collaborating in SNTF modernisation.

The first double-tracking scheme to be undertaken with these funds, supervised by DE-Consult, covered the 43.5 km from El Harrach, on the outskirts of Algiers, to Thenia. A further US$157 million contract provides for reconstruction planning of 350 km of trunk routes from Thenia eastward to Setif, and between Skikda and Annaba.

In 1991 tenders were invited for construction of a 7.6 km cut-off on the Algiers—Constantine line involving a new 5.2 km tunnel at El Achir.

In 1986 the Indian Railway Construction Company was given the contract to upgrade the 80 km from Thenia east towards El Esnam. Threading the foothills of the Atlas Mountains, this section is imposing some substantial tunnelling on the realignments planned as part of the upgrading. The scheme, which is part-financed by India's Export-Import Bank, includes the remodelling of three marshalling yards for prospective enlargement.

Traffic	1992	1993	1994
Passenger journeys (million)	58.4	58	56
Passenger-km (million)	2,904	2,768	2,524
Freight tonnes (million)	11.1	9.7	9.9
Tonne-km (million)	2,522	2,291	2,400

New lines
The El Hadjar steel complex gets its ore in 1,500-tonne trains from mines at Quenza and Bou Khedra, about 190 km south of Annaba (whence the imported coal for its coking plant is also ferried by unit train). The ore line was electrified at 3 kV DC before the Second World War and most of the ore trains, plus trains of phosphates from the mines at Djebel Onk further south, are powered by 32 2,700 hp electric locomotives procured from East German builder LEW in the early 1970s and 14 new locomotives from GEC Alsthom (see 'Traction and rolling stock' section below). As the rail input and output at El Hadjar grew, SNTF became concerned to avoid choking the approaches to Annaba and the rail area in the port itself. That prompted the first steps toward construction of Algeria's biggest long-term rail construction project — a second east—west transversal line deep inland, the so-called High Plateau route from the area of the phosphate deposits in the east to Sidi Bel Abbes, south of Oran. The total distance involved is over 800 km.

In 1980 a series of agreements with India led to a contract with RITES, the Indian Railways consultancy, for provision of technical and management assistance and staff training services. That has been twice extended, latterly for the period to the end of 1992. A joint Algerian-Indian study group was formed to plan a first section of the High Plateau route, the 146 km from Ain Touta, on the line south from Constantine to Biskra, to M'Sila, where a new aluminium plant was in urgent need of rail service. A 60 km line from M'Sila to the existing east-west transversal at Bordj Bou Arreridj was also committed to study.

Construction of a 160 km line from further northeast on the Constantine—Biskra route, at Ain-M'Lila, to Tebessa was subsequently added to the forward programme. Work on this scheme began in 1988 and is in the hands of Cosider, a local company. RITES is supervising the Ain Touta—M'Sila operation, but the Ain-M'Lila scheme is being overseen by EIF and EST.

The Ain Touta—M'Sila line is being engineered for 160 km/h with long-welded 54 kg/m rail on twin-block sleepers, the latter manufactured in a plant established at Ain Touta. The Ain-M'Lila—Tebessa section is being engineered for 150 km/h.

SNTF contemplates extension of its standard-gauge system across the heart of the Sahara, looping southward from Touggourt, in the southeast, through Ouargla then northwest via Ghardaia and Laghouet to Ain Quessara, on the projected High Plateau route. DE-Consult was commissioned to design the first section of this project, from Touggourt via the oil region of Hassi Messaoud and Ouargla to Ghardaia, and to draft tender documents for construction.

Much of the work previously started has been in abeyance, but in late 1994 the Transport Minister announced a AD120 billion plan to revive the project, in part as a job-creation measure. Part of the money is earmarked for conversion to standard-gauge of the remaining 1,055 mm gauge routes.

Passenger and freight traffic growth has seriously outstripped capacity in the four principal cities and ports, above all in Algiers. The main Algiers Maritime station is a terminus, hemmed between the port and the cliffs which the city surmounts, so that the station cannot be enlarged. SNTF aims to convert the terminus into a branch leaving a new cross-city suburban line at Place Emir Abdel Kader. The cross-city line is being created by driving a line underground westward beneath the densely populated Casbah to Bab el Oued. The tunnelling is a delicate job, because of the high water table in the area. New stations will be built on the extension, which will parallel and be integrated with Line 1 of the Algiers metro, the first phase of which is scheduled to open in 2000.

At the same time SNTF intends to divert traffic from the centre of Algiers by creating a rail-road passenger interchange at Dar el Beida, in a thriving development area to the south, with a branch to the adjacent Houari Boumedienne Airport. The works at Dar el Beida, which would become Algiers' main passenger station with nine island platforms and a five-storey passenger facility, will also open a route for east-to-west freight traffic via the existing transversal that will give it a through run avoiding the centre of Algiers between Thenia and Blida. Intercity trains on the Oran—Constantine axis would transfer Algiers passengers to and from local trains at Dar el Beida.

Further relief for Algiers Maritime station will be obtained by constructing a new station in the city's downtown business area at Tafourah. A new chord line will enable through running between Tafourah and Blida. SNTF plans to accompany these developments by redeveloping installations in the port area and shifting the centre of freight handling and train marshalling from Agha to a new yard and depot further east at Rouiba, near Dar el Beida. Completion of the entire Algiers network development is not expected until the next century.

Traction and rolling stock

On 1,432 mm gauge SNTF operates 24 electric and 154 diesel locomotives, 59 locotractors and 13 twin-unit diesel railcars. Coaching stock totals 674, and there are 10,042 wagons of which 3,727 are adaptable to either gauge. The narrow-gauge traction fleet comprises 33 diesel locomotives and there are 41 coaches.

In 1992 SNTF contracted with Breda of Italy to establish a local company, ALFRED, for manufacture and reconditioning of passenger rolling stock, not only for SNTF but for neighbouring countries' railways. Rehabilitation of existing stock is a pressing concern for SNTF, which has many vehicles immobilised through age and lack of adequate maintenance.

Algeria already has its own freight wagon producing plant, Ferovial, at Annaba, with capacity to produce for export as well as SNTF demand. Recent contracts have included 150 wagons for Iraq, 500 for Germany and orders from several African countries.

On the diesel front, General Motors has supplied 10 Co-Cos rated at 2,400 kW, the first of which was delivered in 1994. A further 50 units of various types were supplied by GM through to 1996, some as kits for assembly locally. An order is also expected for a new fleet of 30 diesel multiple-units for Algiers suburban services.

New electric locomotive for the Djebel Onk—Annaba ore haul built by GEC Alsthom **1996**

Diesel locomotives

Class	Builder's type	Wheel arrangement	Output kW	Speed km/h	Weight tonnes	No in service	First built	Mechanical	Builders Engine	Transmission
Standard gauge										
060 DD	GT 26 W	Co-Co	2,400	120	120	27	1971	GM	GM	E GM
060 DF	GT 26 W	Co-Co	2,400	120	120	25	1973	GM	GM	E GM
060 DG	GT 26 W	Co-Co	2,400	120	120	15	1976	GM	GM	E GM
060 DH	GT 22 W	Co-Co	1,600	120	120	24	1976	GM	GM	E GM
060 DL	GT 26 W	Co-Co	2,400	120	120	25	1982	GM	GM	E GM
060 WDK	GL 18 M	Co-Co	800	100	78	5	1977	GM	GM	E GM
060 DJ	U 18 C	Co-Co	1,400	100	96	25	1977	GE	GE	E GE
060 DM	GT 26 HCW-2A	Co-Co	2,400	125	125	10	1985	GM	GM	E GM
040 DH	GL 18 B	Bo-Bo	800	80	80	5	1990	GM	GM	E GM
040 DH	GL 18 B	Bo-Bo	800	80	80	8	1993	GM	GM	E GM
060 DP	GT 26 HCW-2A	Co-Co	2,400				1994	GM	GM	E GM
1,050 mm gauge										
040 YDA	GL 18 M	A1A-A1A	800	80	72	24	1977	GM	GM	E GM
060 YDD	GL 18 2C/2M	Co-Co	1,200	80	80	5	1989	GM	GM	E GM

Diesel railcars

Class	Builder's type	Cars per unit	Motor cars per unit	Power/car kW	Speed km/h	No in service	First built	Mechanical	Builders Engine	Transmission
ZZN 200	ALN 668	2	2	286	120	14	1972	Fiat (Iveco)	Fiat (Iveco)	Fiat (Iveco)

Electric locomotives

Class	Wheel arrangement	Power kW	Speed km/h	Weight tonnes	No in service	First built	Builders Mechanical	Electrical
6CE	Co-Co	1,492	80	130	17	1972	LEW	Škoda
—	Co-Co	2,400	—	132	14	1995	GEC Alsthom Transporte	ACEC

East German-built Class 6CE locomotive with a phosphate train (Marcel Vleugels) **1997**

A new fleet of electric locomotives came into service in 1996 on the Djebel Onk—Annaba ore haul. GEC Alsthom ACEC Transport has supplied 14 Co-Cos rated at 2,400 kW, designed to haul trains of up to 2,700 tonnes.

Signalling and telecommunications
Resignalling and a complete renewal of the telecommunications network ranks high. Among other things, the railway aims to make track-to-train radio communication a standard feature on its principal routes. Electrically operated mechanical signals are gradually being replaced by colourlight displays throughout the system. On new lines and upgraded tracks automatic signalling is being installed. SNTF has signed an agreement in principle with Siemens for formation of a joint company to manufacture and install signalling equipment.

UPDATED

Class 060DL locomotive and Oran-Algiers train at Relizane (Marcel Vleugels)

ANGOLA

Ministry of Transport and Communications

PO Box 1250-C, Luanda
Tel: +244 337793/337744
Tx: 3108 Mitrans AN

Key personnel
Minister of Transport: André Luis Brandao
Deputy Minister, Transport: Dr A de Sousa e Silva

Direcçao Nacional dos Caminhos de Ferro

PO Box 1250-C, Luanda
Tel: +244 339794/330233   Fax: +244 339976
Tx: 3108 Mitrans AN

Key personnel
Director: R M da C Junior

Gauge: 1,067 mm; 600 mm
Route length (four railways combined): 2,648 km; 123 km

Organisation
Three previously independent railways (the Amboim, Luanda and Namibe Railways) are now amalgamated in a national system, while the Benguela Railway is supervised by the Ministry of Transport but retains its own administration. Because of the country's continuing guerrilla warfare the four railways have so far been unable to integrate operations fully or handle international traffic consistently.

Freight and passenger operations
Despite operating difficulties, in 1991 the four railways carried a total of 3.6 million tonnes of freight, 45.3 million tonne-km. Passenger journeys amounted to 5 million, for 246 million passenger-km. Passenger traffic held up well through to 1993, but freight was 20 per cent down at 2.8 million tonnes.

Traffic	1991	1993
(All four railways)		
Passenger journeys (million)	5.0	5.0
Passenger-km (million)	246.2	n/a
Freight tonnes (million)	3.6	2.8
Tonnes-km (million)	45.3	n/a

VERIFIED

Amboim Railway

Caminho de ferro do Amboim
Estaçao Puerto Amboim

Key personnel
General Manager: A Guia

Gauge: 600 mm
Route length: 123 km

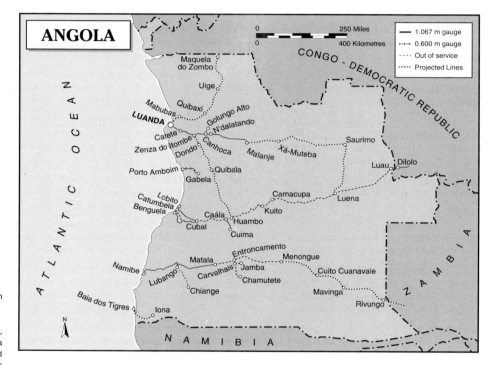

ANGOLA (map)

Organisation
The railway is a single line between the port of Amboim and the coffee-growing region at Gabela. The first 40 km out of Amboim is fully operational, the remainder intermittently so. All trains are steam hauled.

Improvements to existing lines
A partial rehabilitation has been accorded priority, and a new telecommunications system is urgently required.

Traction and rolling stock
There are 6 steam locomotives, 12 wooden-bodied coaches and 60 freight wagons, around 50 per cent of which are operational.

VERIFIED

Benguela Railway

Caminho de ferro de Benguela
PO Box 32, Lobito
Tel: +244 22645   Fax: +244 22865
Tx: 2922 cf bang anv

Key personnel
Chairman: Eng Jorge Bastos Viegas
Deputy Chairman and General Manager:
   Cleofas Silinge
Managing Director: Guilherme Pratas

Gauge: 1,067 mm
Route length: 1,302 km

Organisation
The Benguela Railway should be a major traffic route to the sea for Zambian and Congolese copper, but the connection from the port of Lobito across Angola to the Congo Democratic Republic border at Dilolo, where it is connected with SNCC, has been disrupted by guerrilla action since 1975. Since then the only section in regular use has been the 33 km from the port of Lobito to Benguela, with trains running occasionally to Cubal (154 km) 'when circumstances permit'. Elsewhere, some bridges have been destroyed and sections of track have been removed.

In late 1996, an Italian company, Tor di Valle, won a contract to reconstruct the out-of-use section of the railway. The company will be paid by the exploitation of eucalyptus forests.

Benguela Railway diesel locomotives

Wheel arrangement	Power kW	Speed km/h	Weight tonnes	No in service	First built	Builders Mechanical	Electrical
C	317	27	40	1	1960	NB	H Paxman 8RPHXL
C	317	27	41	1	1972	Andrew Barclay	H Paxman 8RPHXL
Co-Co	1,604	109	90	8	1972	GE	E GE 7FDL12
Bo-Bo	448	94	60	6	1987	GE	E 2 × Cummins NT855L4

Traction and rolling stock
The current fleet comprises 19 steam and 22 diesel locomotives, but the serviceable proportion is smaller and variable. The line-haul diesels are GE Type U20C. The 37 passenger cars, including four sleeping and four restaurant cars, were supplemented in 1992-93 by 24 supplied second-hand from South Africa. The railway owns 1,761 wagons.

Type of coupler in standard use: AAR M201/10A
Type of braking in standard use: Vacuum
Track
Rail: BS 60A/N 30 kg/m, BS 80A 40 kg/m, BS 90A 45 kg/m, CFB 60 30 kg/m
Sleepers: Wood 2,000 × 250 × 140 mm, spaced 1,392/km in plain track, 1,491/km in curves
Fastenings: Elastic spike
Min curve radius: 150 m
Max gradient: 2%
Max axleload: 19 tonnes

UPDATED

Luanda Railway

Caminho de ferro de Luanda
PO Box 1250-C, Luanda
Tel: +244 70061/73270

Key personnel
Director: A Alvaro Agante

Gauge: 1,067 mm
Route length: 479 km

Organisation
The line runs from the port of Luanda to Malanje serving an iron, cotton and sisal producing region. A branch runs 55 km south from Zenza to Itombe and Dondo. The 600 mm gauge line from Canhoca to Golungo Alto has been closed.

Passenger and freight traffic
The main freight flow is of agricultural produce to Luanda, which amounted to 2.5 million tonnes in 1993. Passenger traffic is also of some importance, in particular a suburban service into Luanda from Viana and Baia (36 km).

Improvements to existing lines
Rehabilitation of the line started in 1989, but only a few short sections have been completed. Poor track conditions and inoperable signalling render train working problematic to the east of Ndalatando.

Traction and rolling stock
Of the 35 steam locomotives, only one-third is available at any time; these work the Luanda suburban service. The diesel situation is worse, with no more than a few of the 50-strong fleet in operating condition. All four Fiat diesel railcars are out of service. In addition, there are 50 coaches and about 1,800 wagons.

VERIFIED

Namibe Railway

Caminho de ferro do Namibe
Caixa Postal 130, Sá de Bandeira, Moçâmedes

Key personnel
General Manager: J Salvador

Gauge: 1,067 mm
Route length: 858 km

Organisation
The Namibe Railway consists of a 756 km line running from Namibe inland to Menongue via Lubango, Matala and Entroncamento. A line of some 150 km linking Lubango with Chiange was destroyed in the war.

Freight and passenger operations
In normal times the Cassinga ore fields yielded traffic of some 6 million tonnes annually, but at last report in late 1994 only the 424 km from Namibe to Matala was in operation and trains were still being affected by military action. Only some 500,000 passengers were carried in 1993, plus less than 100,000 tonnes of freight.

Traction and rolling stock
In 1993 only six or eight diesel locomotives were in operational condition. The programme announced in 1990, under which 11 locomotives, 59 passenger cars and 50 freight wagons were to be rehabilitated, had still not been completed. Currently about 20 coaches are in working order, along with 60 wagons.

VERIFIED

ARGENTINA

Secretariat of Works and Public Services

Avenida 9 de Julio 1925 1322, 1002 Buenos Aires
Tel: +54 1 381 8911   Fax: +54 1 814 1823

Key personnel
Minister: O Pritz
Secretary: Armando Guibert
Under-Secretary: Eduardo Sguiglia
Metropolitan Transport & Long Distance:
　Armando Canasa
UPDATED

Unidad de Coordinación del Programa de Reestructuración Ferroviaria

Avenida José María Ramos Mejía 1302 — piso 5°, 1104 Buenos Aires
Tel: +54 1 318 3548   Fax: +54 1 318 3662

Key personnel
Director: Juan Pablo Martínez

This organisation oversees the operation and undertakes inspections of the Buenos Aires suburban network, where passenger numbers grew from 220 million in 1993 to 350 million in 1995 and 410 million in 1996.

As from 1 August 1996, all government subsidies to suburban train operators were withdrawn — these have recouped the loss of funding by raising fares by up to 30 per cent.

NEW ENTRY

Argentinian Railways (FA)

Ferrocarriles Argentinos
Avenida Ramos Mejia 1302, 1104 Buenos Aires
Tel: +54 1 312 4713   Fax: +54 1 312 2872

Key personnel
Trustee: M Ordoñez
Assistant Trustee: A Pigliacampo
Comptrollers: N Dilerna, O A Diaz, A Papazian
General Manager: P Suárez
Deputy General Manager: R Chandler

Manager, Concessions: L Chiapori
Manager, Legal Affairs: H Borré

Gauge: 1,000 mm; 1,435 mm; 1,676 mm
Route length (before start of privatisation and excluding FEMESA (qv)) — 33,821 km

Political background
Between November 1991 and August 1993 operation of freight services on the former Mitre, San Martín, Roca, Sarmiento and Urquiza networks that formed Argentinian Railways (FA) was transferred to private sector companies for a period of 30 years, with a negotiable 10 year extension at the end of that period. The various consortia now operating the former FA lines are composed of Argentinian companies, many of whom are regular customers of the railways, with expertise on day-to-day operations provided by North American railway companies.

The government required that FA was granted at least a 15 per cent interest in any consortium winning an operating concession. The consortia pay rental for use of FA locomotives and rolling stock (some private operators have purchased additional resources from outside Argentina), but maintenance of these and of the infrastructure is the group's responsibility. Concessionaires may modify existing workshops, but are forbidden to close them. Almost US$2 billion was to be invested in Argentina's railways by these new consortia in the first 10 to 15 years of the new concessions, while the government was to receive an additional US$2 million a year in fees.

FA continues to exist, on a much-reduced scale, until it completes its present task of selling surplus railway land and buildings across Argentina. A separate state-owned company, Ferrocarril General Belgrano SA (qv), was brought into being on 1 October 1993, created from the railway of the same name.

In 1997, a political row erupted over the rate at which the private sector companies which took over from FA were investing. Members of parliament were demanding more and stricter controls over how government subsidy for infrastructure projects is used by the new operators. In 1997, the subsidy was due to jump by 55 per cent to 338 million pesos, which is more money than was annually transferred to the former state railway, FA. Some politicians consider this poor value for money, as railway employment has dropped from 90,000 under FA to 10,000 in the new structure, and long-distance passenger trains have virtually all gone.

The main concern of the MPs is that investment by the private sector companies is proceeding too slowly; they seem unable to follow the agreed investment timetable set down in the original concession conditions.

Passenger operations
As part of the privatisation process, responsibility for funding passenger services outside the Buenos Aires suburban area has passed from federal government to provincial government. With only a few provinces willing or able to subsidise services operating within their boundaries, the majority of long-distance and local passenger services in Argentina were withdrawn in March 1993. Buenos Aires suburban services had become the responsibility of FEMESA (qv) in April 1991.

As of late 1995, long-distance passenger services remained in operation between the capital Buenos Aires and San Carlos de Bariloche (see SEFEPA entry), Tucumán (withdrawn in April 1996) and several towns in the provinces of Buenos Aires and La Pampa (see UEPFP). Efforts to restore Buenos Aires–Rosario and Buenos Aires–Córdoba services were continuing. Isolated passenger services of a more local nature funded by provincial government or geared to the tourist market were reported in operation on Ferrocarril Córdoba Central (qv), on the Salta–Socompa route of the Ferrocarril General Belgrano and on the 750 mm gauge 402 km steam-operated line from Ingeniero Jacobacci to Esquel in the province of Chubut. In 1996 the province of Chaco announced its intention to restore passenger services on Ferrocarril General Belgrano routes by the end of that year.

UPDATED

Buenos Aires al Pacífico (BAP)

Avenida Santa Fe 4636 — piso 3, 1425 Buenos Aires
Tel: +54 1 777 2884   Fax: +54 1 777 2877

Key personnel
President: H O Vivacqua
Vice-President and General Manager: L P Magistocchi
Technical Manager: J Miranda

Gauge: 1,676 mm
Route length: 5,254 km

An Alco Co-Co locomotive hauls a BAP mineral train through Empalme Villa Constitución
(Angel Ferrer)   *1997*

Diesel locomotives

Class	Builder's type	Wheel arrangement	Output kW	Speed km/h	Weight tonnes	No in service	First built	Builders Mechanical	Engine
Alco RSD 16	Alco USA	Co-Co	1,380	90	118	21	1968	Alco 321-B	E GE
Alco RSD 35	Alco Canada	Co-Co	930	90	98	50	1962	Alco 321	E GE
Alco 321	Alco Spain	Co-Co	1,570	120	119	20	1979	Alco 321-C	E GE
Gaia	Argentina	Co-Co	1,380	75	99	4	1968	Alco 321-B	E GE
Loco Tractor	Argentina		520	40	50	9		Detroit Diesel	M

Organisation

On 5 June 1992 the Consorcio Ferrocarril Central group was awarded the 30 year concession to operate 5,400 km of the General San Martín railway and 706 km of the Sarmiento railway (both 1,676 mm gauge). This was the third freight concession to be granted, considered to be potentially very profitable.

The CFC consortium was headed by Industries Metalúrgicas Pescarmona (IMPSA), which held a 60 per cent stake and whose main manufacturing plant in Mendoza is connected to BAP lines. IMPSA was also the main partner in the CFM consortium later awarded the Urquiza concession. Other members of CFC were Román Maritima (25 per cent), Transapelt and Hugo G Bunge. Railroad Development Corporation (which controls the Iowa Interstate Railroad between Chicago and Omaha, USA) was chosen as operator, with Conrail as technical consultant.

Freight operations

Operations as the Buenos Aires al Pacífico commenced on 26 August 1993, several months later than planned due to problems with the transfer of staff from FA. The lines covered by the concession link the provinces of Mendoza and San Juan in the Andean foothills to Buenos Aires, crossing the provinces of San Luís, Córdoba and Santa Fe in the process. In 1996 BAP began direct services to the Río de la Plata terminal in the port of Buenos Aires following completion of a new link.

BAP's traffic base inherited from FA consisted mainly of trainload movements of petroleum, coke and stone. The new operators have made efforts to develop wagonload, intermodal (both container and piggyback) and door-to-door services and to broaden the range of commodities carried. In 1994 BAP carried 2.47 million tonnes (1.92 million tonnes were carried in 1991 before privatisation) and recorded 1.976 billion tonne-km. In total 2.81 million tonnes were carried and 2.471 billion tonne-km recorded in 1995.

Trains are operated by a crew of two and have end-of-train telemetry devices. At the end of 1995, BAP had 954 employees.

Traffic	1995	1996
Freight tonnes (million)	2.81	3.19
Freight tonne-km (billion)	2.471	2.652

Improvements to existing lines

At the commencement of BAP operations the maximum permitted speed on the San Martín east—west main line was 120 km/h, although many branch lines were only

suitable for speeds of 12 km/h. Of the US$150 million BAP intended to invest in the first five years of the 30 year concession period, US$45 million was to be spent on track improvements and a continuous-rail welding programme. An infrastructure analysis matrix has been deployed to assess the commercial desirability of infrastructure improvements and to determine those which should take priority over others.

Traction and rolling stock

A fleet of 71 ageing Alco RSD16 and RSD35 Co-Co diesel-electric locomotives was to have passed to BAP from FA, but by the start of 1994 only 70 per cent of this figure had been transferred with many in poor condition. Intending to spend US$34.4 million on rolling stock in the first five years of the concession, BAP subsequently acquired 20 Alco-engined Class 321 Co-Co diesel-electric locomotives from Spanish National Railways (RENFE). At the start of 1996 other BAP motive power included 55 Alco diesel-electrics, four Gaia diesel-electrics and nine 900 kW diesel-mechanical locomotives inherited from FA.

At the start of 1997, BAP operated 5,072 freight wagons. Recent acquisitions included 46 high-capacity wagons for palletised goods, 130 container wagons and 148 general purpose freight wagons.

Signalling and telecommunications

The old British semaphore and staff block signalling system has been replaced by a North American radio-based track warrant system. BAP trains are dispatched from the computer-equipped Mendoza control centre, and satellite links between regional centres are planned. Investment in signalling and telecommunications was to total US$34 million over the first five years of the concession.

UPDATED

Ferrocarril Austral Fueguino (FAF) (Tranex Turismo SA)

Avenida Corrientes, 538 — piso 5°, 1043 Buenos Aires
Tel: +54 1 325 0681   Fax: +54 1 326 3540

Passenger operations

FAF runs a 500 mm gauge tourist line linking Ushuaia and the Tierra del Fuego National Park. It is the world's most southerly railway.

NEW ENTRY

Ferrocarril Córdoba Central (FCC)

Estación R del Busto, 5009 Córdoba, cba
Tel: +54 51 822252   Fax: +54 51 822252

Gauge: 1,000 mm
Length: 158 km

Organisation

FCC operates freight and passenger (including the *Tren de las Sierras* tourist operation) services between the city of Córdoba and Cruz del Eje, on a route closed by FA in 1977. FCC came into being in response to the call for tenders issued by the province of Córdoba, and began operations on 5 December 1993.

UPDATED

Ferrocarriles Del Chubut (FCH)

Avenida 25 de Mayo 550, 9103 Rawson, Chubut
Tel: + 54 9 658 2263   Fax: +54 9 658 2261

Passenger operations

This company operates passenger services between El Maitén and Esquel on a 750 mm gauge branch line.

NEW ENTRY

Ferrocarriles Metropolitanos SA (FEMESA)

Bartolomé Mitre 2815, 1201 Buenos Aires
Tel: +54 1 864 5601   Fax: +54 1 865 4135

Key personnel

President: Luis A Laguinge
Vice-President: Guillermo Crespo
Directors: Fulvio Arias, Daniel Cerino, Santos Reali

Political background

FEMESA, which came into being on 1 April 1991, initially as the suburban train operator for commuter services into Buenos Aires, is now charged with monitoring service quality and supervising the investment programmes drawn up by private sector operators who have assumed operational control of the 184-station network, a role it shares with Unidad de Coordinación del Programa de Reestructuración Ferroviaria (qv). The network comprises the electric services of the Sarmiento, Mitre, Urquiza and Roca divisions and diesel-powered services on the Belgrano, San Martín and Roca divisions.

Metrovías has a 20-year concession to run suburban services on the Urquiza line and the Buenos Aires metro and the TBA consortium has a 20-year concession to run services on the Mitre and Sarmiento lines.

The Roca, San Martín and Belgrano South 10-year concessions were awarded in January 1993 to the Trainmet consortium.

A 10-year concession to operate the Belgrano North line was signed by the government and the Ferrovías consortium on 3 February 1994.

UPDATED

Ferrocarril General Belgrano SA (FGB)

Maipú 88, 1084 Buenos Aires
Tel: +54 1 343 7220/29   Fax: +54 1 343 7220/29

Key personnel

President: Ignacio Ludueña
General Manager: Rubén Galanis

Gauge: 1,000 mm
Route length: 10,811 km

Political background

The metre-gauge General Belgrano system, serving the far northwest of Argentina with routes to the Chilean and Bolivian borders, attracted no offers from the private sector when bids were invited in 1991. It became a separate state-owned company on 1 October 1993. On

Refurbished (left) and unrefurbished Japanese-built trains at the terminus at Tigre (Angel Ferrer)   **1997**

Trenes de Buenos Aires (TBA)

Avenida Ramos Mejía 1358 — piso 2°, 1104 Buenos Aires
Tel: +54 1 317 4400   Fax: +54 1 317 4446

Key personnel
President: S C Cirigliano
Vice-President: J Crawford
General Manager: C A Orseg Schor
Director, Operations: H Payne

Gauge: 1,676 mm
Route length: 352 km
Electrification: 93.9 km at 800 V DC

Organisation
Trenes de Buenos Aires (TBA) was formed by the members of the Metrovias consortium (qv), which had been awarded the concessions for suburban services on the Mitre and Sarmiento systems in 1993.
    TBA's shareholders are Morrison Knudsen (41.65 per cent), Cometrans (41.65 per cent) and Burlington Northern Santa Fe (16.7 per cent).

Passenger operations
TBA began operating the Mitre and Sarmiento systems on 29 May 1995. FEMESA had carried 37.8 million fare-paying passengers on the Mitre system and 59.9 million on the Sarmiento system in 1994. However, by 1996, TBA had boosted patronage on the Mitre line to 69.8 million passengers and on the Sarmiento route to 99.3 million.

Improvements to existing lines
TBA was to invest US$405 million over the 10-year life of the concession. Rolling stock was the immediate priority, but TBA has also made provision for track renewal, the elimination of 10 level crosssings and station modernisation. World Bank funding was secured by the government in 1995 for the rebuilding of the Caballito—Liniers section of the Sarmiento system to eliminate 18 level crossings. In 1996 TBA proposed a larger US$800 million investment programme, including new links and electrification, in return for a larger concession and permission to raise fares.
    TBA signed a US$95 million contract with Siemens Argentina in 1995 for the renewal and maintenance of traction power supply equipment, including substations at Floresta and Morón on the Sarmiento network. In the longer term, TBA intended to re-lay 3.6 km of the four-track Mitre main line; re-lay the double-track route to José León Suárez (19 km); upgrade 56.9 km of the single-track Victoria—Capilla del Señor route; and renew 15 km of the four-track Sarmiento main line. It is also hoped to carry out a track rationalisation programme, subject to agreement from freight operators and other authorities.

Traction and rolling stock
TBA inherited 367 electric multiple-unit cars, 43 hauled passenger coaches and 96 diesel multiple-units from FEMESA. Refurbishment of 362 emu cars and 43 coaches has been made an investment priority, with 130 emu cars to be refurbished by the end of 1997. In 1995

TBA purchased 15 Class 313 Co-Co diesel-electric locomotives from RENFE of Spain, and it was reported that Cometrans and Daewoo were examining the possibility of building between 80 and 100 emus a year in TBA workshops for TBA and the Buenos Aires metro.

Signalling and telecommunications
TBA drivers have been issued with radios to communicate with dispatchers, and on lightly used diesel-operated routes track warrant control has replaced manual block signalling. From 1997, TBA hoped to replace semaphore signals on 5 km of the Mitre main line from Retiro to Empalme Maldonado and carry out signalling improvements at Once, Caballito, Flores, Floresta, Liniers and Moreno on the Sarmiento system.

UPDATED

Unidad Ejecutora del Programa Ferroviario Provincial (UEPFP)

General Hornos 11 — piso 4°, 1084 Buenos Aires
Tel: +54 1 305 5174   Fax: +54 1 305 5933

Key personnel
Chairman: Alberto Trezza
Transport Co-ordinator: Héctor Dumas

Gauge: 1,676 mm
Route length: 4,690 km

Political background
UEPFP was established by Eduardo Duhalde, governor of the province of Buenos Aires, after the federal government ceased to support long-distance passenger services in March 1993. The company initially contracted FA to run services, and on 27 August 1993 began operations itself with a fleet of ex-FA locomotives and coaches.

UEPFP Mar del Plata—Buenos Aires service at Kilo 5, Buenos Aires (N P Slocombe)   **1995**

Initial plans for the eventual privatisation of UEPFP operations envisaged inviting separate bids for the network's Atlantic and Pampas zones. The Atlantic zone is considered to be potentially profitable, but services in the Pampas zone require subsidy. It was later decided, in the light of UEPFP's improving financial performance, to put the operation of the whole network out to tender without offering any subsidy.

Finance
By late 1994 UEPFP operations had become self-financing; subsidies paid by UEPFP to FA before August 1993 to cover 50 per cent of operating losses amounted to some US$1 million a month. UEPFP implemented a cost-cutting and efficiency programme which included better utilisation of rolling stock through changes to the timetable and passing responsibility for ticket sales and station cleaning and maintenance to local authorities.
    Through stricter revenue protection and the abolition of free passes for railway staff and government employees, UEPFP has been able to generate 30 per cent more revenue than FA while operating 25 per cent fewer train-km. UEPFP began operations in August 1993 with 1,400 employees; 561 operating staff had been transferred from FA. Track access charges were reduced through bargaining (backed by political pressure) with the freight concessionaires, with FEPSA reducing its charges by 53 per cent from US$2.50 per train-km. Purchasing is undertaken as required, with cash payment on delivery.

Passenger operations
UEPFP passenger operations are marketed as 'Ferrobaires' and comprise the Atlantic and Pampas zones. The Atlantic zone comprises services from Buenos Aires to Mar del Plata, Tandil, Quequén, Bahía Blanca, Carmen de Patagones and Bolivar; the Pampas zone comprises services from Buenos Aires to Darreguiera, Toay, General Pico, Pasteur, Cuena, Iriarte and Rojas. Monthly ridership is around 250,000 passengers, doubling during the summer months (December to March).
    The Atlantic zone is considered to be potentially profitable, serving coastal resorts south of Buenos Aires and attracting much holiday traffic. To serve the principal resort of Mar del Plata, UEPFP operates 'El Marplatense' featuring refurbished air conditioned rolling stock and a service carrying private cars. By late 1994, eight trains were in operation daily (with an extra return service at weekends) in each direction between Buenos Aires and Mar del Plata, covering the 400 km in 4 hours 50 minutes.
    On 21 May 1994 UEPFP reopened the 72 km General Guido—General Madariaga route, closed in 1978. A new branch to Pinamar opened in 1996 and the company intended to refurbish the General Madariaga—Vivoratá line for summer 1998 opening using 80 km/h dmus. Ferrobaires declares the Pinamar service a great success, exceeding all expectations, with 27,000 tickets sold in January 1997 alone.

New lines
In 1996, UEPFP and Spanish National Railways began conversations regarding the creation of a high-speed rail link between Rosario and Mar del Plata. Similar plans have also been advanced by Japanese, Italian and German interests.

Traction and rolling stock
UEPFP received 70 diesel locomotives and 320 passenger coaches from FA. Seven diesel multiple-units (each seating 170 passengers) have been purchased from RENFE of Spain for US$1.3 million, for possible use on routes with low traffic.
    Workshops at Avellaneda, Coronel Maldonado and Mecho were transferred to UEPFP, in addition to four locomotive depots and seven coach yards. Rolling stock refurbishment has been undertaken by UEPFP using its own facilities.
    In July 1995 an agreement was signed with GEC Alsthom Transporte and RENFE of Spain to form a company to maintain traction and rolling stock at La Plata. A separate agreement between RENFE and UEPFP covered the possible sale of Spanish locomotives and Talgo coaches.

Signalling and telecommunications
The agreement signed with RENFE in 1995 also made provision for Spanish assistance with the resignalling of the Buenos Aires—Mar del Plata route.

UPDATED

Yacimientos Carboníferos Río Turbio SA (RFIRT)

Gdor Lista 790, 9400 Río Gallegos
Tel: +54 9 662 0874   Fax: +54 9 662 0874

Freight operations
RFIRT is a privately owned company running coal trains on 750 mm track between the Andes Australes mines and the ports of Río Gallegos and Loyola. Two return services a day are operated using four FAUR diesel-hydraulics acquired second-hand from Bulgaria in 1996, replacing former steam traction, which had held sway for more than 40 years. Two of the 1,000 hp locomotives have been remotored using Caterpillar D379 traction motors, while the other two retain their Romanian originals. A fifth Faur has been cannabilised.

The service is operated by fewer than 100 workers. Attempts to introduce radio signalling were defeated by the topography; crews are now contacted by cell phone.

NEW ENTRY

ARMENIA

Ministry of Transport and Communications

10 ul Zakian, 375015 Yerevan
Tel: +374 2 528810   Fax: +374 2 560528

Key personnel
Minister: H Kochinian
Director of Rail Transport: V Asriants

VERIFIED

Armenian Railways

Tigrana velikogo ul 50, 375005 Yerevan
Tel: +374 2 540428

Key personnel
President: V V Asriyants

Gauge: 1,520 mm
Route length: 830 km
Electrification: 818 km at 3 kV DC

Political background
Following easing of tensions in Azerbaijan and the surrounding area, railway traffic has shown signs of increasing.

Organisation
The rail network has existed as a separate entity since January 1992. It comprises a southern portion of the former SZhD's Trans-Caucasus Railway and is fully electrified. Backbone of the system is a mountainous double-track route running from the Georgian capital Tbilisi via Alaverdi, Kirovakan, Leninakan and Oktemberyan to Nakhichevan and Baku in Azerbaijan. The capital, Yerevan, lies on a secondary line just off this main line. At Leninakan another main line strikes eastwards to Erzurum in Turkey.

Passenger services between Yerevan and Tblisi resumed in October 1996.

Passenger and freight traffic
In 1991, the railway carried 29.1 million tonnes of freight for 4,200 million tonne-km, while passenger traffic amounted to 2.8 million journeys and 300 million passenger-km. Unrest in the area prompted dramatic declines in subsequent years: in 1996, 1.7 million tonnes were carried for 351 million tonne-km and passenger traffic was 1.9 million journeys, 84 million passenger-km.

Traction and rolling stock
Electric locomotive classes include the VL8, VL10 and derivatives (46 in service), while main line diesels include the M62 and TEM3 types (11 in service). There are 28 emus, 134 coaches and 1,250 wagons in use and large amounts of rolling stock stored unserviceable.

UPDATED

AUSTRALIA

Department of Transport

PO Box 594, Canberra, ACT, 2601
Tel: +61 6 274 7111   Fax: +61 6 257 2505

Key personnel
Minister: Hon John Sharp, MP

Political background
The Australian railway industry, in the past year, has continued its evolution from a number of government departments to privately owned competing transport organisations.

Railways in Australia were built initially by state governments (to four different gauges) to serve local needs. When it was necessary to connect Western Australia with South Australia by rail, the Commonwealth government built the line across the Nullarbor Plain (to standard gauge). As the tracks extended to state borders, there arose the problem of the break of gauge. Whilst interstate trade grew, each state had a vested interest in retaining as much industry and trade as possible within their state boundaries.

The Second World War showed the folly of a change of gauge each time a border was reached. Post war, efforts were slowly made to convert track (or provide new track as between Albury and Melbourne) to standard gauge. It was only in 1995 that all state capitals were directly connected by standard gauge, although they had been connected via Broken Hill since 1970.

Whilst much of the difficulty of not having one standard gauge has been overcome, the disadvantage of having geographically based railways all with different standards is just beginning to be addressed. In 1991, National Rail Corporation Ltd was established to provide interstate (only) freight services over the tracks of the state systems. All governments have now agreed (to a greater or lesser degree) to introduce competition to their activities.

By 1997, a couple of private organisations were operating passenger services over the tracks of others. Each state is working towards providing third-party access to their tracks whilst the commonwealth government is indicating that it will establish a body (Track Australia) to regulate interstate standard gauge third-party access. So it is now theoretically possible for any company (which meets acceptable standards) to run train services on any government organisation's tracks.

Each state (except Queensland) is dividing its passenger, freight and track businesses into discrete operations, though the problem of freight trains getting rail access at commuting times is yet to be addressed. Yet to happen is any attempt to standardise safe working practices, accounting systems or access agreements. Fortunately, the physical train aspects (coupler height, braking systems, locomotive multiple-unit compatibility) have, by chance, been uniform.

There is still a tendency for each system to 'reinvent the wheel'. One railway introduced its own ticket vending machine (after considerable delays) but it only accepts coins, while the next system has had machines that accept notes for many years. Another railway has not been able to introduce Train Order working, yet other systems have used it safely for more than a decade. The new National Rail NR Class locomotives could not initially operate in New South Wales due to different environmental standards decided upon by that state.

So in 1997, we see the following permutations of railways:
(a) Railways that provide everything including track, locomotive, crew and wagons (the State railways and AN)
(b) Railways that provide locomotive, crew and wagons but run on another's track (NR, WCR, NSWRTM)
(c) Operators that provide wagons but hire locomotives and crews and run on another's tracks (TNT, SCT)
(d) Operators that provide locomotives and crews but haul others wagons over another's tracks (currently operators providing terminal shunting only).

There have been occasions when NR trains south from Adelaide have had five locomotives, all in the colours of different owners. Other problems involve allocating the costs of the trains of one operator delaying those of another or even 'Control' taking the locomotive of one operator to rescue the train of a competitor!

Schemes for new lines are being promoted. These currently include the Alice Springs—Darwin route, an additional track to link Victoria through western New South Wales with Brisbane or Darwin, 'ultra-fast' trains between Sydney, Canberra and Melbourne and schemes to link capital city airports with the rail network. Although these proposals have supporters with good credentials, only the Sydney airport scheme has, to date, been able to move to the construction phase.

The South Australian and Northern Territory governments have formed a joint statutory body, AustralAsia Railway Corporation, to progress proposals to finance and build the Alice Springs—Darwin railway. Each government has committed A$100 million to fund acquisition of the corridor. The route, which would require eight major bridges and 120 minor ones, has been pegged. If built, the line is expected to be privately owned with the various levels of government contributing to the initial cost.

UPDATED

Australian National Railways Commission

1 Richmond Road, Keswick, South Australia 5035
Tel: +61 8 217 4111   Fax: +61 8 231 9936

Key personnel
Chairman: J Smorgon
Deputy Chairman: J W McArdle
Group General Manager, Finance & Commercial:
   J D Gilbert
Group General Manager, Engineering & Operations:
   A L Neal
Group General Manager, Marketing & Business
   Development: B T Conroy
General Managers
   AN Tasrail: R Blaszak
   Passenger: C Cramerie
Human Resources Director: P J Moran
Corporate Business Manager: L Black
Public Affairs Manager: C Holmdahl
Group Financial Controller: G Hosking

Gauges 1,435 mm; 1,067 mm; 1,600 mm
Route length: 4,016 km; 1,481 km (of which 733 km is in Tasmania); 621 km

Political background

Australian National (AN) is the business name of the Australian National Railways Commission, a commonwealth government business enterprise formed in 1975. Under the Australian National Railways Commission Act 1983, AN has powers to provide supplementary non-rail as well as rail passenger and freight services. When National Rail was formed in 1991, NR was 'given' the profitable freight segment while AN was 'left' with the corresponding debt and insufficient income to service the debt. The coalition government elected in 1996 has announced its intention to sell AN after acquiring AN's debt. It is expected that Tasrail (including track) would be sold to one buyer as a going concern; the mainland track would come under the control of a new national track infrastructure authority while the various business activities would be sold individually.

Organisation

AN is responsible for the management and operation of railways owned by the commonwealth government and functions as a commercially oriented enterprise. Its principal businesses are:

(a) freight rail services in South Australia and in the island state of Tasmania

(b) tourist rail travel on the world renowned 'Indian Pacific', 'Ghan' and 'Overland' passenger trains

(c) engineering design and project management services and front line rail wagon maintenance

(d) wagon construction and heavy locomotive servicing

(e) construction and maintenance of railway infrastructure, including track, signalling, and associated civil engineering works

(f) provision of locomotive fleet and its front line maintenance

(g) management of access to and passage over track owned by AN.

AN-controlled track comprises: standard-gauge (1,435 mm) main lines from Broken Hill (NSW) via Port Augusta (South Australia) to Kalgoorlie (Western Australia) (2,173 km), with a connecting line from Crystal Brook to Adelaide (197 km) and on to the Victorian Border (313 km) with several broad-gauge connecting lines and a standard-gauge branch to Loxton; the Central Australia Railway from Tarcoola to Alice Springs (831 km); and important branch lines from Port Augusta to Telford (Leigh Creek) (251 km) and Whyalla (75 km).

There are also isolated narrow-gauge (1,067 mm) networks on Eyre Peninsula (South Australia) (748 km) and in the island state of Tasmania (AN Tasrail – 733 km).

Staff numbers fell from 4,228 in 1993 to 2,435 at November 1996.

Finance

When National Rail was established it acquired much of AN's income-producing assets leaving AN with little ability to service its remaining debt. The government has announced a A\$2 billion funding package to retire the debt which was accumulated upgrading infrastructure, and to provide payouts to employees who will lose their employment when the organisation is sold.

Financial statistics since 1995 have not been disclosed.

Business Segment Profit and Loss Statement (A\$000) 1994-95

	AN Freight	AN Tasrail	AN Passenger and Travel
Revenue*	54,262	23,496	55,365
Expenditure	56,571	30,777	64,206
Surplus**	(2,309)	(7,281)	(8,841)

* includes revenue supplements and grants
** before abnormal items

Passenger operations

AN operates the 'Indian Pacific' service which travels twice weekly the 4,350 km across Australia between Sydney, Adelaide and Perth; the weekly 'Ghan' between Adelaide and Alice Springs (1,559 km); and the overnight (now standard-gauge) daily 'Overland' service between Adelaide and Melbourne (about 830 km). Upgrade of the 'Indian Pacific' vehicles and corridor management will improve cost recovery from its 61 per cent in FY1993-94. On occasions, the 'Indian Pacific' comprises 30 vehicles. (One passenger has made the journey 42 times.) Cost recovery of the 'Ghan' was similar to the 'Indian Pacific'. The 'Overland', which was cancelled while gauge conversion works took place, has suffered a large reduction in patronage. In all, 244,000 journeys were made in FY95-96. All three of AN's passenger trains run on 1,435 mm gauge.

With the completion of the Adelaide-Melbourne standard-gauge conversion, AN ran a special service in June 1995 from Perth to Brisbane (not usually an AN destination) (5,300 km) which attracted significant publicity and about 10,000 visitors in both Melbourne and Brisbane. Expectations that regular services might be extended to Brisbane have not been fulfilled due to the uncertain future of the organisation.

Passenger traffic (000)

	1993-94	1994-95	1995-96
	223.1	190.7	243.6

Freight operations

Mainland

AN's interstate freight business has been transferred to National Rail leaving AN with only intrastate traffic in South Australia and the island state of Tasmania. Coal traffic from Leigh Creek (mine) to Port Augusta (power station) (250 km) is hauled in 160 wagon trains grossing 9,600 tonnes, AN's heaviest regular trains. This traffic has now been opened to competitive tender. AN withdrew from involvement in the Trailerail service between Melbourne and Perth as interstate traffic is now the responsibility of NR. Isolated broad-gauge grain trains continue to operate on the branch from Pinnaroo to Tailem Bend with grain transferred to silo there. The 1,600 mm gauge branch between Wolseley and Mount Gambier (183 km) and Snuggery and the Victorian

Border, which was isolated by the standardisation of the Melbourne—Adelaide track in April 1995, remains unused. An unusual train runs weekly from Adelaide to Cook in the Nullabor Plain with fuel tankers for loco refuelling as all locomotives need refuelling there. The isolated Eyre Peninsula 1,067mm gauge network transports about one million tonnes of gypsum and 600,000 tonnes of grain annually.

Tasrail — 1,067mm gauge

The freight-only system in the island state of Tasmania has shown major advances in operational efficiency, productivity and financial performance since it became part of AN in 1978. In FY1994-95 Tasrail's freight task was 283 million net tonne kilometres. Most trains require two or three locomotives with lines seeing two or three trains on weekdays. Staff numbers were reduced further to 283, down from 1,686 in 1978. About a third of the traffic is bulk cement from Railton. New workshop facilities for wagon and locomotive maintenance at East Tamar Junction, Launceston, were completed in September 1993. Improvements in productivity and maintenance efficiency have resulted, reducing delays in returning locomotives and rolling stock to traffic.

Track west of Burnie sees no traffic following damage. Haulage of woodchip logs has virtually ceased. This traffic was a major part of Tasrail's task for many years.

Freight traffic (million)

	1992-93	1993-94	1994-95
Tonnage	13.9	14.9	7.8
Tonne-km	8,480	9,159	1,500

New lines

AN has been contracted by the commonwealth government to complete survey work on the long-proposed Alice Springs—Darwin rail link over two years. Present indications are that construction of the line will be dependent on financial support from the private sector or the opening of mining operations along the route. The commonwealth government has offered the Tarcoola—Alice Springs section free to a builder of the line.

Improvements to existing lines

The line between Adelaide and Wolseley (and Melbourne) was converted to standard-gauge on time and within budget. This left four isolated broad-gauge branch lines in southeast South Australia. The branches to Apamurra and Loxton have been converted to standard-gauge while the Pinnaroo line remains as broad-gauge. All these lines see seasonal grain traffic but the isolated branch from Wolseley to Mount Gambier, Snuggery and the Victorian Border remains as broad-gauge and unused.

Traction and rolling stock

Mainland and Tasmania

At June 1995 the fleet comprised 181 locomotives: 34 on broad-gauge; 100 on standard-gauge; 15 on the narrow-gauge Eyre Peninsula network; and 32 in Tasmania. The carriage fleet comprised 36 broad-gauge, 151 standard-gauge and 3 narrow-gauge. AN owned 1,069 broad-gauge, 3,359 standard-gauge and 1,055 narrow-gauge freight vehicles. AN had four locomotives converted to 'traction effort booster units' (without engines) to be used between powered units but the conversion has not proved successful and they are out of service. The run of the AN special passenger service to Brisbane in June 1995 saw the only run of AN locomotives (CLP class) to Brisbane. Twenty-one HA wagons have been shipped from Tasmania to the Eyre Peninsula to assist with the haulage of gypsum between Kevin and Thevenard.

Signalling and telecommunications

A data-radio-based Centralised Traffic Control (CTC) system between Dry Creek and Coonamia was commissioned. Signalling rationalisations at Gladstone, Cockburn and Bordertown were designed.

In Tasmania, a communications upgrade has been completed with cellular telephones and UHF radios being installed in all locomotives and track vehicles.

Track

The final 208,200 concrete sleepers have been inserted in the Trans Australia Railway marking the end of a 20-year project to install concrete sleepers in the main line between Kalgoorlie, Adelaide and Broken Hill. The project was completed ahead of time and below budget due to the sustained high performance of an SMD80-AN concrete sleepering machine and its crew.

CLP locomotive at the head of the 'Indian Pacific' at Lithgow, New South Wales (Brian Webber)   **1997**

Standard rail: Flat bottom throughout, weighing 53, 47, and on some branch lines 40, 31.2, 30 and 25kg/m
Joints: Fishplates, bolts: but all main lines are cwr
Rail fastening: Dog and screw spikes, Pandrol and McKay Safelok elastic rail spikes and clips, T-headed bolts and nuts
Crossties (sleepers): 1,600 mm gauge: impregnated hardwood 2,600 × 250 × 125 mm; 1,435 mm gauge:

untreated hardwood 2,500 × 230 × 115 mm; CR2 prestressed concrete 2,514 × 264 × 211 mm; AN3/AN4 prestressed concrete 2,500 × 264 × 211 mm; AN6 prestressed concrete 2,500 × 264 × 240 mm; 1,066 mm gauge: hardwood 1,900 × 200 × 115 mm
Spacing: 1,600 to 1,300 per km
Filling: Crushed stone and gravel ballast
Min curve radius: 14.5°

Max gradient: 2.5%
Longest straight: 478 km — Nullabor Plains
Max axleload: 23 tonnes
Highest station: Peterborough, South Australia (532 m)

Type of coupler in standard use: Alliance
Type of braking in standard use: Westinghouse air

Australian National (Powerail) locomotive fleet available for interstate services, July 1996

Class	First built	No	Power (kW)	Total power (kW)
ALF	1994	8	2,460	19,680
CLF	1993	7	2,460	17,220
CLP	1993	10	2,460	24,600
700	1970	5	1,490	7,450
GM	1967	9	1,390	12,510
Total		**39**		**81,460**

UPDATED

Diesel locomotives

Class	Builder's type	Wheel arrangement	Power kW	Speed km/h	Weight tonnes	No in service	First built	Mechanical	Builders Engine	Transmission
AN		Co-Co	2,984	155	132	11	1992	Clyde	EMD 16/	E EMD D77
BL		Co-Co	2,238	115	130	10	1983	Clyde	EMD 16/645	E EMD D77B
DL		Co-Co	2,259	140	122	15	1988	Clyde	EMD 12/710	E EMD D87
EL		Co-Co	2,380	140	114		1990	Goninan	GE FDL-12	E GE 761-AN
81	JT26C-255	Co-Co	2,240	125	129	13	1985	Clyde	EMD 16/645	E EMD
C	GT26C	Co-Co	2,238	115	134	10	1977	Clyde	EMD 16/645	E EMD
G	JT26C-255	Co-Co	2,238	115	127	7	1985	Clyde	EMD 16/645	E EMD
Dash 9	Dash 9	Co-Co	2,998		132	120	1996	Goninan	GE FDL-16	E GE

BHP Iron Ore Railroad

PO Box 231, Nelson Point, Port Hedland, Western Australia 6721
Tel: +61 91 736888   Fax: +61 91 736209

Key personnel
Group General Manager: G Wedlock
General Manager, Railways and Ports: D J Miller
Railroad Manager: W Walker
Superintendent, Track Maintenance: G Offereins
Superintendent, Rolling Stock Maintenance: A Cowin
Superintendent, Technical Services: M Moynan
Superintendent, Locomotive & Vehicle Maintenance: B Green
Superintendent, Operations: B Gale

Gauge: 1,435 mm
Route length: 643 km

Organisation
The railway has two operations: the Mount Newman mine operation and the Yarrie mine operation. These lines were previously operated as separate entities but are now amalgamated with common management.

Freight operations
One line runs from Mount Newman to Port Hedland, on the northwest coast, with 35 tonne axleloadings, one of the highest figures in the world. Trains are of 240 wagons, but the company has operated trains of up to 300 wagons.

The single-track route has two 1.64 km and twelve 3 km passing loops. It is scheduled to carry seven trains a day, of which all are 240-wagon Locotrol trains. Maximum speed of a fully loaded train is 75 km/h. The sophisticated facilities at the Mount Newman railhead allow a train to be fully loaded in only 70 minutes, so that a trainset can be turned, loaded and remanned within 120 minutes. Each

return journey over the 426 km route from Port Hedland to Mount Newman and back is scheduled to take less than 19 hours; ore dumping at the port takes 4-5 hours for a 240-wagon train.

The railway operated Australia's heaviest train on 28 May 1996 when it ran a 5.9 km long ore train with 540 wagons; it was controlled by one driver using Locotrol equipment to control remote locomotives. Ten GE Dash 8 locomotives were required with this train configuration: three locomotives, 135 wagons, two locomotives, 135 wagons, two locomotives, 135 wagons, locomotive. Gross mass was 72,191 tonnes and average speed was about 58 km/h with a maximum of 75 km/h. The train was run to test the new-generation GE Harris Locotrol 3 control system which will allow trains with four remote locomotive sets.

The other line is from Yarrie to Finucane Island (near Port Hedland) over a route length of 217 km. Three train-rakes of 88 wagons each (6,700 tonnes per train) run daily.

Traction and rolling stock
The company operates 48 diesel locomotives and 2,057 ore wagons, 95 other freight wagons and has one lounge/dining car.

The locomotive fleet replacement programme has been completed. There are now 40 2,984 kW Dash 8 locomotives (of which three are cabless) and eight Dash 7 locomotives. The three cabless locomotives are employed as mid-train helpers.

Traffic	1994	1995
Freight tonnes (million)	48.718	53.617

Signalling and telecommunications
The railway is controlled by CTC, supplemented by track-to-train radio, from a control centre at Port Hedland. Interlockings can function automatically in the event of

any failure in the CTC telemetry.

Five hot box detectors, three hot wheel detectors and 39 dragging equipment detectors are used on the main line.

Automatic Car Identification (ACI) transponders are fitted to each ore wagon and readers are located at three positions on the track.

Track
A contract has been signed with Barclay Mowlem to replace 250 km of rail and 500,000 sleepers in the next four years. The Newman line will comprise concrete sleepers when the contract is completed.
Newman line: concrete sleepers are fitted to 31 per cent of main line track; steel is under 15 per cent, timber under 54 per cent.
Yarrie line: Jarrah timber sleepers are used.

Rail: 66 and 68 kg/m continuous welded rail (standard carbon on tangent and head-hardened on curves and some tangents)
Sleepers: Concrete: 300 wide × 240 deep × 2,600 mm long
Steel: 120 mm deep × 9 or 10 mm thick
Timber: 225 × 150 × 2,600 mm
Spacing: Timber 1,875/km; steel/concrete 1,667/km
Fastenings: Concrete : Pandrol
Steel : Traklok
Timber: Pandrol or dogspikes
Min curvature radius: 528 m
Max gradient: Newman line : 1.5% (empty); 0.55% (loaded); Yarrie line : 1.04%
Max axleload: 35 tonnes

Type of brake: Air
Type of coupling: Alliance automatic

UPDATED

A Dash 8 locomotive approaches the terminus at Port Hedland (Wolfram Veith)

CityRail, New South Wales

PO Box 349, Haymarket, NSW, 2000
2nd floor, Sydney Rail Terminal, Sydney, NSW, 2000
Tel: +61 2 9379 4331   Fax: +61 2 9379 1631

Key personnel
Group General Manager CityRail: Richard Middleton

Gauge: 1,435mm

Political background
Under the restructure of railways in New South Wales, CityRail is a business group within the State Rail Authority (qv).

Organisation
CityRail is responsible for passenger operations in an area around Sydney, extending to Lithgow in the west, Scone/Dungog in the north, Nowra on the south coast and Goulburn in the Southern Highlands.

Finance
Farebox revenue improved in 1995-96 to A$314.1 million; A$20.1 million more than the previous year.

Passenger operations
CityRail operates an extensive service in Australia's largest city, Sydney, and adjacent residential areas. With 8,278 staff, CityRail has 298 stations and runs a fleet of 1,535 carriages providing 2,200 electric and diesel services each weekday and carrying 850,000 passengers over 1,700 km of track. Most lines receive either four or six services per hour off-peak. Patronage has continued to grow from a low of 229.8 million journeys in 1992-93 to 256.4 million journeys in 1995-96, the highest such figure for 30 years.

The railway pioneered the use of double-deck emus in 1968. Most services are now provided by double-deck trains (about 340), many being 'Tangara' trains (about 90). The last of 450 Tangara carriages (placed in service from 1988) has been delivered. About one in four services are provided by air conditioned stock. Some 80 double-deck Outer Suburban Tangara (OST) cars have been introduced to join 370 Tangara cars already in service. Some Blue Mountains services utilising these (OST) cars have been altered to run through the city underground rather than terminating at Sydney Terminal, providing the first direct access to the Central business district.

Fourteen two-car Endeavour air conditioned diesel-hydraulic railcars have been introduced. They are similar to the previously introduced Countrylink Xplorer cars. ABB Transportation (now Adtranz) built the cars, which have a maximum speed of 145 km/h and seat 177 passengers. They work most non-electrified outer-suburban services around Sydney and Newcastle. With the 14 Endeavour units in traffic, there is still a requirement for some two-car diesel railcars of the 620/720 class to operate on Newcastle—Maitland services.

In FY94-95, work was completed on a A$60 million scheme for installation of automatic ticket machines. Large stations have a combination of booking office facilities and vending machines, while smaller stations have machines capable of selling the entire range of CityRail tickets. Low-patronage stations will be equipped with authority-to-travel machines. Ticketing gates are now installed at 29 stations with more than 80 per cent of passengers passing through the gates on their journeys. It is estimated that fare evasion has dropped by A$5 million since the installation of the gates.

Security has been enhanced on CityRail trains with the introduction of the Nightsafe programme where only the two last carriages are open and lit on late evening services. This ensures all passengers travel in the same or adjacent carriage to the guard. High-technology mini-cameras have also been installed in some trains and closed-circuit television surveillance of stations has been introduced to deter vandalism and enhance security.

New lines
A$50 million has been spent on the construction of the new double track 1.6 km Y Link between Harris Park and Merrylands which allows through running between the west and southwest suburbs of Sydney, a population growth area. The new link opened on 2 November 1996. A new half-hourly passenger service, advertised as the 'Cumberland Line', has been provided between Blacktown and Campbelltown which saves up to 8,000 passengers daily changing trains at Granville. The link, which includes three bridges, will also provide more

Endeavour dmu at Dungog (Brian Webber)   *1997*

Double-deck suburban electric multiple-units

Class	Cars per unit	Trailer cars per unit	Motor cars per unit	Motors per car	Power/motor kW	Speed km/h	No in service	First built	Builders Mechanical	Electrical
Trailer car T4799-T4895	4	2	2*	—	—	—	56	1964	Tullochs	—
Motor car C3805-C3857	4	2*	2	4	135	115	52	1972	Comeng	Mitsubishi
Motor car C3858-C3911	4	2*	2	4	135	115	52	1973	Comeng	Mitsubishi
Control trailer D4011-D4020	2	—	1*	—	—	—	8	1974	Comeng	—
Trailer car T4921-T4962	4	2	2*	—	—	—	41	1974	Comeng	—
Motor car C3912-C3986	4	2*	2	4	135	115	75	1976	Comeng	Mitsubishi
Control trailer D4021-D4070	2	—	1*	—	—	—	50	1976	Comeng	—
Trailer car T4963-T4987	4	2	2*	—	—	—	25	1978	Comeng	—
Motor car C3001-C3080	4	2*	2	4	135	115	79	1978	Goninan	Mitsubishi
Trailer car T4101-T4170	4	2	2*	—	—	—	70	1978	Goninan	—
Motor car C3741-C3765	4	2*	2	4	135	115	25	1979	Comeng	Mitsubishi
Control trailer D4001-D40102	2	—	1*	—	—	—	25	1978	Comeng	—
Air conditioned motor car C3501-C3504 & C3550-C3580	4	2*	2	4	135	115	35	1981	Goninan	Mitsubishi
Air conditioned control trailer D4096-D4099	2	—	1*	—	—	—	4	1981	Goninan	—
Air conditioned trailer T4216-T4246	4	2	2*	—	—	—	31	1982	Goninan	—
Motor car C3505-C3549	4	2*	2	4	135	115	45	1981	Goninan	—
Trailer car T4171-T4215	4	2	2*	—	—	—	45	1981	Goninan	Mitsubishi
Air cond motor car chopper C3581-C3608	4	2*	2	4	150	115	28	1986	Goninan	Mitsubishi
Air cond trailer car T4247-T4274	4	2	2*	—	—	—	28	1986	Goninan	—
Air cond Tangara motor car Chopper/GTO N5101-N5285	4	—	2	4	170	115	225	1988	Goninan	Mitsubishi
Air cond Tangara control trailer D6101-D6285	4	—	2*	—	—	—	225	1988	Goninan	

* These cars do not belong to the class concerned

Air conditioned double-deck outer suburban Tangara electric multiple-units

Class	Cars per unit	Motor cars per unit	Motors per car	Power/motor kW	Speed km/h	No in service	First built	Builders Mechanical	Electrical
Motor car†	4	2	4	170	115	11	1994	Goninan	Mitsubishi
Motor car	4	2	4	170	115	11	1994	Goninan	Mistubishi
Control trailer	4	2*	—	170	115	22	1994	Goninan	—

* These cars do not belong to the class concerned   † with toilet

Tangara double-deck emu at Circular Quay station, near the Opera House in Sydney (Brian Webber)   *1997*

Air conditioned double-deck interurban electric multiple-units

Class	Cars per unit	Trailer cars per unit	Motor cars per unit	Motors per car	Power/motor kW	Speed km/h	No in service	First built	Builders Mechanical	Electrical
Trailer car DMT9201-DMT9207	4	2	2*	—	—	130	7	1970	Converted from motor car 1982	
Trailer car DDT9208-DDT9211	4	2	2*	—	—	130	4	1970	Converted from control trailer 1982	
Trailer car DFT9212-DFT9215	4	2	2*	—	—	130	4	1970	Converted from trailer 1982	
Motor car DCM8021-DCM8036	4	2*	2	4	140	130	15	1977	Comeng	Mitsubishi
Control trailer DCT9031-DCT9044	2	—	1*	—	—	130	14	1977	Comeng	Mitsubishi
Motor car DIM8037-DIM8092	4	2*	2	4	140	130	54	1981	Comeng	Mitsubishi
Trailer car DIT9101-DIT9184	4	2	2*	—	—	130	84	1981	Comeng	Mitsubishi
Motor car, chopper DJM8093-DJM8138	4	2*	2	4	140	130	46	1986	Comeng	Mitsubishi
Trailer car DKT9185-DKT9191	4	2	2*	—	—	130	7	1989	Comeng	Mitsubishi
Motor car, chopper DKM8139-DKM8145	4	2*	2	4	140	130	7	1989	Comeng	Mitsubishi
							242			

* These cars do not belong to the class concerned

Diesel railcars or multiple-units

Class	Cars per unit	Motor cars per unit	Motored axles/car	Power/motor kW	Speed km/h	Vehicles in service	First built	Builders Mechanical	Engine	Transmission
620/720	2	1	2	164 × 2	105	3	1961	NSWGR	Cummins BC	H Voith
620/720	2	1	2	212 × 2	122	2	1964	NSWGR	Cummins NTA855R2	H Twin Disc
620/720	2	1	2	227 × 2	122	5	1961	NSWGR	Cummins NTA855R4	H Voith
Endeavour	2	2	2	353	145	30	1994	ABB	Cummins KTA-10R	H Voith

flexibility in freight train running. An additional platform face has been provided at Glenfield which will enable trains to terminate there.

Major new stations
Major station upgradings were completed at Gosford, Epping, Sutherland, Strathfield, Moss Vale and Summer Hill. At Gosford, the fifth busiest station on the network, the work made special provision for disabled people to use the station without inconvenience. Adjoining the station are a 700 space car park and bus interchange which were federally funded at a cost of A$13 million. Another A$4.1 million was spent providing 453 car parking spaces at Seven Hills station.

New stations have been constructed and opened at Metford and Warrabrook on the Newcastle—Maitland line. They incorporate easy access to streets, lifts to platform level, closed circuit television surveillance, covered and well-lit waiting areas and ticket vending machines.

Traction and rolling stock
The CityRail electric fleet (at June 1996) comprised 770 double-deck suburban cars; 367 double-deck suburban Tangara cars; 80 double-deck outer suburban Tangara cars; 240 double-deck intercity cars; and (since withdrawn) 32 single-deck intercity cars. 1996 saw the withdrawal of the last single-deck interurban electric trains; these had operated on Newcastle area services. They have been replaced by two-car double-deck trains. The last of 30 new Endeavour railcars were placed in service in February 1996, joining 16 older railcars.

Type of coupler: Passenger, automatic
Type of braking: Air

NEW ENTRY

Comalco Railway

Post Office, Weipa, North Queensland 4874
Tel: +61 70 698416   Fax: +61 70 698321

Key personnel
Railway Superintendent: R Pritchard

Gauge: 1,435 mm
Route length: 19 km

Freight operations
Owned by Comalco Minerals and Alumina, the railway connects Andoom (mine) with Weipa (port) and carries some 18 million tonnes of ore annually. It was opened in 1972 and in earlier years carried about 8 million tonnes annually. The line includes a 1 km long concrete bridge.

Traction and rolling stock
The railway is operated with a Clyde-EMD GT26C 3,000hp/2240kW diesel-electric locomotive, 128 bottom-

discharge ore (124 tonne gross) wagons and nine freight wagons. The locomotive R1001 was shipped to New South Wales for a rebuild and on return in August 1994 a sister locomotive was sold to Westrail to become an L class there.

Track
Rails are 67.5 kg/m on hardwood sleepers at 2,020/km spacing.

Countrylink

PO Box 349, Haymarket, NSW, 2000
1st floor, Sydney Rail Terminal, Sydney, 2000
Tel: +61 2 9379 1298   Fax: +61 2 9379 4836

Key personnel
General Manager Countrylink: Kim Finnimore

Gauge: 1,435mm

Political background
Under the restructure of railways in New South Wales, Countrylink is a business group of the State Rail Authority (qv).

Organisation
Countrylink has access to 4,338 kilometres of track.

Finance
Countrylink experienced strong revenue growth in 1995-96 with a nine per cent increase in customer revenue to A$61.7 million.

Passenger operations
Countrylink employs 1,111 (of whom half are permanent part-time) and operates a daily Xplorer railcar service between Sydney and Moree/Armidale; three daily Xplorer services between Sydney and Canberra; two daily XPT services between Sydney and Melbourne and daily XPT

services between Sydney and Murwillumbah; Brisbane; Grafton and Dubbo. A loco-hauled train has been re-introduced to run weekly services to Broken Hill and Griffith.

In 1995-96, Countrylink generated A$61.76 million in revenue and carried 1.8 million rail passengers, both figures up on the previous year. Productivity improved, with passenger kilometres per employee rising 4.2 per cent to 867,000. Some 72 per cent of passengers (mainly pensioners) either do not pay a fare or pay half-fares, being subsidised by the state government.

Traction and rolling stock
Countrylink owns 19 XPT power cars, 52 XPT trailer saloons and eight XPT sleeping/seating cars generally run as seven seven-carriage trains and one five-carriage train (the Dubbo service). Countrylink has been operating the XPT trains for 15 years. The original power cars have now run over four million kilometres. Fourteen Xplorer power twins and seven trailers provide interurban services. A loco-hauled set operates the Broken Hill and Griffith services. A shunting locomotive is employed at the Sydney servicing depot.

Satellite pay phones have been installed in the eight XPT sets for passenger use. Four new intermediate Xplorer cars were added to Armidale—Sydney—Canberra services, resulting in a 36 per cent increase in patronage on Canberra services.

State Rail trialled three carriages of a Swedish X2000 tilt train on its network for several months in mid-1995, to

In 1996, an XPT power car was repainted in an Olympic Games promotional livery   **1997**

assess the feasibility of tilting trains as successors to the 15-year-old XPTs. The carriages were hauled by SRA XPT power cars (which could not tilt). Tilt trains have been shown to be capable of slashing existing travel times by 40 per cent.

Type of coupler: Passenger, automatic
Type of braking: Air

NEW ENTRY

Diesel railcars or multiple-units

Class	Cars per unit	Motor cars per unit	Motored axles/car	Power/motor kW	Speed km/h	Units in service	First built	Builders Mechanical	Builders Engine	Transmission
XPT	7-9	2	4	1,500	160	*	1981	Comeng/ABB	Paxman Valenta	E Brush
Xplorer	2-3	2-3	2	353	140	21	1994	ABB	Cummins KTA-19-R	H Voith

* 19 power cars, 60 trailers

Emu Bay Railway (EBR)

A subsidiary of Pasminco Ltd
PO Box 82, Wilson Street, Burnie, Tasmania 7320
Tel: +61 6 430 4211   Fax: +61 6 430 4230

Key personnel
Managing Director and Executive Director: D H Stewart
Manager: R P Evetts

Gauge: 1,067 mm
Route length: 133 km (145 track-km)

Organisation
The company is a subsidiary of Pasminco Ltd, the world's largest zinc producer. The railway celebrated 100 years of hauling minerals (and general freight and passengers in earlier times) on the remote Tasmanian west coast in 1997.

Freight operations
In 1996 the railway hauled 582,319 tonnes of mineral concentrate to the port at Burnie. The cessation of mining at Mount Lyell was short-lived with Copper Mines of Tasmania replacing the Mt Lyell Mining and Railway Company. Production recommenced in December 1995 with the first trainload of copper leaving Melba Flats on 16 December 1995. Production from that mine is expected to reach 120,000 tonnes annually. With the new operation, EBR is responsible for the road-haul operation from Queenstown to Melba Flats; the company uses an outside trucking contractor to handle this task.

Normal train services are two trains from Hellyer, one from Primrose on weekdays and three trains a week from Melba Flats. The running of weekend extra trains is not unusual. All trains are operated by a driver only and most are hauled by three or four locomotives.

Improvements to existing lines
The major Pieman River bridge has been given a complete overhaul.

Traction and rolling stock
The railway operates 12 diesel-hydraulic locomotives, 79 bulk ore wagons and 14 general freight wagons. 11 Class locomotives, all now fitted for driver-only operation, lead trains while 10 Class units are used as trailing units only. PVH21 machine shunts at Burnie.

Signalling and telecommunications
All operations are now under radio control from the signalling centre at Burnie.

Track
Rails are 31 and 41 kg/m, permitting a 14.5 tonnes maximum axleload. Sleepers are untreated wood of 130 mm thickness, spaced 1640/ km and rails are fastened with elastic spikes. Maximum gradient is 1 in 33 and minimum curvature is 100 m radius. The highest point (703 m) is at 71 km from Burnie.

UPDATED

FreightCorp

Locked Bag 90 PO, 126 Church St, Parramatta, NSW, 2150
Tel: +61 2 9843 9111   Fax: +61 2 9843 2124

Key personnel
Group General Manager: Lucio Di Bartolomeo

Gauge: 1,435 mm

Political background
FreightCorp was established following the restructure of the previous State Rail Authority at 1 July 1996 (see New South Wales Department of Transport and Roads entry for details).

Organisation
FreightCorp conducts two core businesses: the transport of commodities and the provision of services. Bulk commodities such as coal, grain and minerals are transported in unit trains and general freight train services carry a range of products including cement, petroleum

82 Class locomotive hauling containers near Telegraph Point (Brian Webber)   **1997**

and export containers. FreightCorp provides services to other rail operators including locomotive and wagon maintenance and hire, train crew hire and terminal services. Although FreightCorp currently operates in New South Wales only, consideration will be given to operating in other states where this makes commercial sense. Under the restructure, this unit employed 3,891 employees at October 1996.

Freight operations

At October 1996 FreightCorp operated 415 locomotives and 6,108 wagons over 7,469 km of track in the state. The tonnage hauled in 1995-96, 63.8 million tonnes, represented a significant increase over the previous year when 58.8 million tonnes were hauled. The freight hauled in 1995-96 included 51 million tonnes of coal and 1.8 million tonnes of grain.

To meet the growing international demand for NSW coal, FreightCorp took delivery of 399 high-capacity 120 tonne coal wagons in 1994-95; a contract has been awarded for 400 additional wagons. Also during 1994-95, FreightCorp took delivery of the final high-horsepower 82 Class and 90 Class locomotives, allowing FreightCorp to increase locomotive productivity significantly. Average train loads increased by 8 per cent to 1,841 tonnes with locomotive availability at 85 per cent.

The state government has announced that it has adopted an open access policy to infrastructure which allows any company which can meet the standards of the 1993 Rail Safety Act to run trains over tracks previously used exclusively by FreightCorp. This could introduce competition in the very important Hunter Valley coal haulage market. The rail freight component of coal costs is significant and is seen by the coal industry as having a potential for cost reduction.

Coal hauls commenced from Stratford Mine (north of Dungog) to Newcastle in 1995, with nearly one million tonnes hauled in the first year.

FreightCorp has conducted a noise and vibration study of Hunter Valley operations comparing different locomotive and wagon types and driving techniques. As a result, modifications are being made to locomotives and wagons to reduce dynamic brake noise and the booming noise of empty wagons.

Diesel locomotive trains hauled 43.1 million tonnes of coal to Newcastle's terminals and about six million tonnes to Port Kembla in 1995. This is assisted by the introduction of 120 tonne wagons. FreightCorp expects to haul 70 million tonnes by 2000.

Important contracts won include a contract to transport 180,000 tonnes annually of copper concentrate from the North Parkes Mine to Newcastle and a five-year contract to haul two million tonnes annually of limestone and clinker between plants.

Interstate freight hauls are now the responsibility of the National Rail Corporation. The 1996 grain harvest was the largest for 15 years. FreightCorp converted some coal hoppers to haul grain and hired wagons from interstate. Some mothballed branch lines were returned to service and temporary crews (often recently retired locomen) were employed. FreightCorp has signed a contract to haul 130,000 tonnes of sugar annually from Grafton to Sydney.

Improvements to existing lines

The first stage of redevelopment of the Enfield marshalling yard in Sydney is nearing completion. A$60 million has been spent providing an appropriate layout for longer trains. The section track will remain under FreightCorp control.

90 Class locomotives operate FreightCorp's prime coal trains   *1996*

Diesel locomotives

Class	Builder's type	Wheel arrangement	Power kW	Speed km/h	Weight tonnes	No in service	First built	Mechanical	Builders Engine	Transmission
422	J26C	Co-Co	1,490	124	110	20	1969	Clyde	EMD 16-645 E	*E* EMD
48	DL531G	Co-Co	710	120	75	114	1959	Goodwin	Alco 6-251 B	*E* GE/AEI
49	G8C	Co-Co	650	124	81	4	1960	Clyde	EMD 8-567 C	*E* EMD
80	CE615A	Co-Co	1,492	130	121	49	1978	Comeng	Alco 12-251 CE	*E* Mitsubishi
81	JT26C-2SS	Co-Co	2,240	125	129	84	1982	Clyde	EMD 16-645E3 B	*E* EMD
82	JT42C	Co-Co	2,259	115	132	55	1994	EMD	EMD 710G3A	*E* EMD
90	GT46CW-M	Co-Co	2,836	115	165	31	1994	EMD	EMD 710G3A	*E* EMD

Electric locomotives

Class	Wheel arrangement	Output kW continuous/ one-hour	Speed km/h	Weight tonnes	No in service	First built	Builders Mechanical	Electrical
85	Co-Co	2,700/2,880	130	123	10	1979	Comeng	Mitsubishi
86	Co-Co*	2,700/2,880	130	119	50	1983	Comeng	Mitsubishi

* One locomotive is Bo-Bo-Bo

Traction and rolling stock

1995 was a significant year for operations following the introduction of 90 Class and 82 Class locomotives to traffic. These were the first new locomotives for over a decade. An indication of the efficiency gains achieved by the introduction of the 90 Class locomotives has been the use of one of the class on coal trains previously hauled by four 48 Class (branch line) units.

Maintenance of the new 82 and 90 Class locomotives is the responsibility of Clyde Engineering under a Ready Power agreement, the first of its kind in Australia. The agreement requires 100 per cent availability of 84 locomotives. To meet this requirement 89 locomotives were built. These were all based at Clyde Engineering's Newcastle Ready Power facility by June 1994.

In April 1996, FreightCorp owned 1,935 coal wagons, 1,429 grain wagons, 326 mineral wagons and 1,512 general freight/container wagons.

In May 1997, 98 new-generation coal wagons built by ABB/ANI Bradken entered service on Newcastle coal shipments. Owned by Novacoal Nominees, a wholly owned subsidiary of RTZ-CRA, the wagons will be hauled by FreightCorp.

FreightCorp has ordered 25 cement wagons of 75 tonne capacity.

A new 110 tonne capacity mobile recovery crane arrived by ship from Clarke Chapman Ltd of Carlisle, UK. The crane can be hauled at 120 km/h and run on 30 kg/m track, if required.

Type of coupler: Freight cars, AAP
Type of braking: Air

NEW ENTRY

Hamersley Iron Ore Railway

PO Box 21, Dampier, Western Australia 6713
Tel: +61 9 143 6300   Fax: +61 9 143 6345

Key Personnel

General Manager: G Neil
Manager, Railway Operations: to be announced
Manager, Rolling Stock and Signals Maintenance:
    G D Ingram

Gauge: 1,435 mm
Route length: 541 km

Organisation

The railway operates solely to convey iron ore from the mines to the port at Dampier in the remote Pilbara area of Western Australia. The original section of 288 km to Tom

Price opened in 1966, with the line being extended a further 94 km to Paraburdoo in 1972. Since then 56 km have been duplicated and a 40 km spur was constructed to serve Brockman Mine in 1991. In 1994, another spur line was constructed to a new mine at Marandoo. Temperatures in the area exceed 38°C for extended periods in summer.

Freight operations

Trains from the mines at Tom Price, Brockman and Marandoo consist of two diesel-electric locomotives hauling 226 wagons each of 105 tonnes nominal capacity. This results in gross train weights of 28,000 tonnes. Wagons are coupled in pairs by a solid drawbar with rotary couplings connecting each pair. A train is approximately 2.3 km in length and is the heaviest and

longest employing head-end locomotive power operating anywhere in the world. The main line configuration permits following train movements at 15 minutes headway. The ore trains are operated by one driver only.

The maximum opposing grade to loaded trains on the Mount Tom Price to Dampier section is 0.33 per cent whilst empty trains returning to the mine negotiate a maximum adverse grade of 2 per cent. These grades and the gross loads of trains permit an exact balance of locomotive power. On the Mount Tom Price to Paraburdoo section, there is a constant compensated grade of 0.42 per cent against the loaded trains. Two head-end and two banker locomotives are required by loaded trains for the 100 km journey between Paraburdoo and Mount Tom Price to overcome this adverse grade. At Dampier, trains are unloaded in rotary dumpers at either

A Citytrain SMU crossing the world's longest prestressed concrete railway bridge over the Coomera River on the new Gold Coast Railway **1997**

(d) two spurs located near Gladstone to transport limestone from East End quarry to the cement clinker factory at Fishermans Landing (which was due to open late 1997)

(e) a 2 km siding near Cloncurry and 3 km unloading balloon loop at Townsville port to handle mineral concentrates from Cannington Mine (which was due to open end 1997)

(f) a 7.3 km spur to Moranbah North coal mine near Moranbah (to open mid-1998).

Improvements to existing lines
Citytrain network
An additional two tracks, four new tunnels and additional platforms through inner Brisbane from Roma Street to Bowen Hills were commissioned in June 1996. The A$164 million project included reconstruction of Roma Street's platforms, completed in February 1997.

Dual gauging involving track upgrade and electrification of the previous standard-gauge track between South Brisbane and Salisbury (11 km) is due for completion in early 1998. Stage 1 (South Brisbane—Yeerongpilly, 7 km) was commissioned to coincide with the introduction of additional Helensvale services in February 1996.

Provision of a fourth track between Bowen Hills and Northgate (11 km) commenced in 1996 and is due to be completed in late 1998.

Coal and minerals network
The A$114 million reconstruction of the Blackwater network in Central Queensland, involving rerailing of 369 km of track with new 60kg/m rail on prestressed concrete sleepers, was completed in May 1996. Further upgrading works, including strengthening of bridges to minimum 25 tonne axleload, upgrading of the power signalling system to allow increased coal train speeds from maximum 60 km/h to 80 km/h, and upgrading of the power supply to the overhead traction system, are under way on this corridor.

Duplication of 16 km of track between Bajool and Midgee (south of Rockhampton) was completed in May 1996 and duplication of the last 8.6 km of single track between Gladstone and Rockhampton has commenced, for planned completion in 1998. The total cost of this project is A$40 million.

Upgrading of the 190 km Gladstone—Moura line and the 30 km Callide branch commenced in 1996. The A$95 million investment involves replacement of track with 60 kg/m rail on prestressed concrete sleepers, stabilisation of extensive soft clay foundation areas and resignalling and upgrade of communication links. Completion is scheduled for mid-1998 and will permit

higher speed coal train operation and increased axle-loads to 25 tonnes.

Upgrading of the Goonyella rail system to meet increased coal tonnages included duplication of 10 km of track between Coppabella and Broadlea in April 1996, whilst upgrade of the power signalling to allow increase in train speeds to 80 km/h and upgrading of the power supply to the overhead traction system is under way.

Freight network
The Mainline Upgrade project, involving investment of A$440 million on the 1,658 km North Coast Line between Brisbane and Cairns, commenced in 1992 and was completed in mid-1997. Works included replacement of 673 timber bridges with prestressed concrete structures; strengthening of 155 steel or timber bridges to minimum 20 tonne axleload (previously 15.75 tonnes); realigning curvature and grades on 118 km of track in 51 separate deviations; and installation of about 400,000 steel sleepers interspersed with timber between Rockhampton and Cairns to improve track stability. Welding of remaining rail joints to provide continuously welded rail was due to be completed during 1997.

The 970 km line between Townsville and Mount Isa is being upgraded to allow increased axleloads (20 tonnes) and higher operating speeds (80 km/h for mineral trains). Works completed include the replacement or upgrading of bridges, steel resleepering of the 590 km between Hughenden and Mount Isa and commencement of heavy duty turnouts to all main line loops. A programme to replace all timber sleepers between Townsville and Hughenden with prestressed concrete sleepers and to install heavier rail cascaded from other lines will be completed by late 1998.

The remaining 102 km of timber sleepers on the North Coast Line between Bundaberg and Gladstone was resleepered with prestressed concrete sleepers in 1996.

A deviation in suburban Cairns has taken the North Coast Line away from housing areas and given direct access to the freight yard.

Other branch lines being upgraded include 146 km between Goondiwindi and Thallon, the Western Line between Roma and Charleville and the Atherton branch to service a new sugar mill at Atherton.

Traction and rolling stock
The stock of locomotives in service at December 1996 comprised 180 electric and 360 diesel locomotives. There were 283 coaches, 7 diesel railcars/trailers, 329 emu cars and 11,976 wagons (of which 5,765 are for coal traffic).

Twelve suburban electric multiple-units (SMUs) and four interurban 140 km/h electric multiple-units (IMUs) entered traffic between November 1994 and May 1996.

They were built by Walkers-ABB Pty Ltd and are the first AC-motored units on QR. Six additional IMUs are being built by the same joint venture and were due to enter service during 1997.

In April 1997, QR ordered 18 new three-car electric trains from Walkers of Maryborough. The new trains will allow the phasing out of locomotive-hauled carriages on suburban services by 2001.

In February 1995, QR signed a contract worth A$62.5 million with Walkers EDI-Hitachi-Itochu for two six-car tilt trains to operate on the 'Spirit of Capricorn' daylight services between Brisbane and Rockhampton. The trains will operate at 160 km/h maximum and will reduce the 638 km journey time by 2½ hours to 7 hours by their ability to run faster than the existing ICE trains round the many curves. The two sets, each seating 323 passengers in five economy cars and one first class car, will feature videos, faxes, radio and telephones. It was expected that the trains would enter service in early 1998.

The 40 diesel-electric locomotives worth A$110 million ordered from Goninan North Queensland Pty Limited were all delivered by early 1997. The locomotives are Dash 8 type, weighing 116 tonnes, and are far more powerful than any previous QR diesel locomotives by generating 3,000 hp/2,280 kW. They are the first QR locomotives with a hood section between full width cabs. Deliveries commenced in mid-1995 and they now power passenger and freight services on the non-electrified main lines primarily between Rockhampton, Cairns and Mount Isa. The class haul a through load of about 2,000 tonnes between those centres. A further 10 locomotives of the same class have been ordered.

All of the 22 new 33/34 Class electric locomotives built by Clyde Engineering at Bathurst NSW for Central Queensland coal traffic are in traffic.

Some 400 stainless steel bodied VSH (100 tonne gross) coal wagons are being delivered while 100 PCZY container wagons are under construction.

Signalling and telecommunications
On the 9,222 km of regularly used 1,067 mm gauge track, the following signalling and traffic control systems are in use: Suburban/Urban Traffic Control: 279 km; Centralised Traffic Control: 2,725 km; Manual Train Order: 2,198 km; Computer Assisted Train Order: 2,322 km; Ordinary Staff: 801 km; Electric Staff: 58 km; Direct Traffic Control: 839 km.

Radio is used extensively, with a UHF system on suburban electric stock providing continuous driver-to-control communications, VHF for driver wayside communications in country areas, a variety of UHF yard systems for shunting applications in major marshalling yards, and VHF and UHF car-to-base systems. All electric and most diesel locomotives are at least VHF radio-fitted and have direct access with train controllers while en route.

Centralised Traffic Control is in use between Brisbane and Townsville and between Ipswich and Toowoomba, allowing improved running times and withdrawal of employees from remote crossing loops. Train Order (by radio to the driver) has been introduced on many lightly trafficked lines. Direct Traffic Control (a lap-top computer/ code system) has been introduced between Charters Towers and Mount Isa.

The former standard-gauge track between South Brisbane and Yeerongpilly has been relaid as dual gauge and equipped with computer-controlled signalling via a solid state interlocking, the first such installation on QR.

To allow the new tilt train to run at higher speeds than presently allowed, A$28 million has been spent upgrading level crossing protection and signalling between Brisbane and Rockhampton.

Electrification

Most Brisbane suburban services (over six million kilometres annually) are run by electric multiple-units, while most passenger and freight services between Brisbane and Rockhampton are hauled by electric locomotives. Central Queensland coal services from the Blackwater area or from the Goonyella area are hauled by up to five electric locomotives, including two or three mid-train controlled by the driver with Locotrol remote equipment. The original 88 emu units date from 1979 and are now receiving a technology upgrade.

Track

A A$42 million re-equipping of the on-track maintenance fleet is at an advanced stage, with deliveries of three new high-production continuous-action tampers, ballast regulators, sleeper-inserting machines and on-track welders. A new 72 tonne rail grinder has been supplied by Speno Australia.

Standard rail: Flat bottom 60, 53, 50, 47, 41, 40, 31, 30 and 20 kg/m rail has been used throughout the state, dependent on line class. New construction has been standardised to 60 kg/m rail for heavy-haul lines, 50 kg/m as the normal main line standard and 41 kg/m for lighter trafficed lines.

Joints: 6-hole bar fishplates

Welded rail: Rails are purchased in 27.4 m lengths and flashbutt welded at depot into lengths up to 110 m. Long-welded rails are laid in lengths up to 220 m on unplated track and to unrestricted lengths in plated track. Heavy-haul lines and other lines with prestressed concrete sleepers are continuously welded. Site welding is generally by the thermite process though extensive work using a mobile flashbutt welding machine has been undertaken.

Tracklaying: Relay of track is predominantly carried out by tracklaying machine

Sleepers: Mostly unimpregnated local hardwood timber 2150 × 230 × 115 mm or 150 mm thick on the older heavy-

haul lines. Prestressed concrete sleepers are used extensively for new construction including heavy-haul lines. Steel sleepers are being installed on a continuous face for over 450 km between Hughenden and Mount Isa and on shorter sections of other lines. They are also replacing timber sleepers on a 1 in 3 or 1 in 4 pattern for almost 1,000 km between Rockhampton and Cairns. Extensive installation of treated timber sleepers has also been undertaken in recent years.

Sleeper spacing: Normally 610 mm in main line or heavy-haul tracks for timber, 685 mm for concrete and steel

Fastenings: Normal standard 16 mm square dogspikes and springspikes with 115 mm thick timber sleepers; 19 mm square dogspikes used with 150 mm thick timber sleepers and indirect fasteners on curves used on older heavy-haul lines. The use of elastic rail spikes has now been discontinued. Indirect fastenings are used with concrete and steel sleepers.

Ballast: Mainly crushed rock in new work but river gravel used on some branch lines

Max curvature: Generally minimum radius of 100 m though new construction to 300 m radius at least

Max gradient: Generally not exceeding 1 in 50

Max altitude: 925 m near Cairns, North Queensland

Max permitted speed: Freight trains: 80 km/h. Long-distance passenger trains: 100 km/h for the premium 'Queenslander' service and 80 km/h for other services. Suburban EMUs: 100 km/h. Interurban EMUs: 120 km/h. Interurban IMUs: 140 km/h on Helensvale line.

Max axleload: 26 tonnes on some mineral wagons

Bridge loading: All bridges on important lines can carry loading equivalent to Coopers E25-E30. Many equivalent to Coopers E35 and most new construction to this standard. Heavy-haul mineral lines have bridges built to carry Coopers E50 loading. Australia's longest pre-stressed concrete bridge is the 856 m Coomera River bridge on the Helensvale Line, opened in 1996.

Tunnels: 51

UPDATED

Electric railcars

Class	Cars per unit	Motor cars per unit	Motored axles/car	Power/motor kW	Speed km/h	Units in service	First built	Builders Mechanical	Electrical
1979 emu	3	2	4	135	100	67	1979	Walkers	ASEA
1982 emu	3	1.5	4	135	100	20	1983	Walkers	ASEA
1988 ice	2	2	4	135	120	8 + 4	1988	Walkers	ASEA
1994 smu	3	2	4	180	100	12	1994	Walkers	ABB
1995 imu	3	2	4	180	140	4	1995	Walkers	ABB

Electric locomotives

Class	Wheel arrangement	Output kW	Speed km/h	Weight tonnes	No in service	First built	Builders Mechanical	Electrical
3100/3200	Bo-Bo-Bo	2,900	80	110	84	1986	Comeng	Hitachi/GEC
3300/3400	Bo-Bo-Bo	2,900	80	113	22	1994	Clyde	Hitachi/GEC
3500/3600	Bo-Bo-Bo	2,900	80	110	50	1986	ASEA/Walkers	ASEA/Clyde
3900	Bo-Bo-Bo	2,900	100	110	28	1988	ASEA/Walkers	ASEA/Clyde

Diesel locomotives

Class	Builder's type	Wheel arrangement	Power kW	Speed km/h	Weight tonnes	No in service	First built	Builders Mechanical	Engine	Transmission
1502	G 22C	Co-Co	1,119	80	91	23	1967	Comeng/Clyde	GM 12-645 E	E EMD/Clyde
1550	GL 22C		1,119	80	91	104	1972	Comeng/Clyde	EMD 12-645 E	E EMD/Clyde
2400		Co-Co								
2450	GL 22C									
2470	GL 22C									
1700	GL 8C	Co-Co	652	80	60	10	1963	Comeng/Clyde	EMD 8-557CR	E EMD/Clyde
1720	GL 18C	Co-Co	746	80	62.5	56	1966	Comeng/Clyde	EMD 8-645E	E Clyde
2100		Co-Co	1,492	80	97	100	1970	Comeng/Clyde	EMD 16-645E	E EMD/Clyde
2130										
2141	GL 26C									
2150										
2170										
2600	U 22C	Co-Co	1,640	80	97	13	1983	Goninan	GE	E GE
2800	CM 30-8	Co-Co	1,074	80	91	40	1995	Goninan	GE 7CDL12	E GE

Rail Access Corporation (New South Wales)

GPO Box 47, Level 16, City Centre Tower, 55 Market St, Sydney, NSW, 2000
Tel: +61 2 9224 3000   Fax: +61 2 9224 3900

Key personnel

Chief Executive Officer: Judi Stack

Gauge: 1,435 mm
Route length: Freight : 7,181 km; CityRail : 1,700 km
Electrification: 618 km at 1.5 kV DC overhead

Political background

Following the restructure of the previous State Rail Authority from 1 July 1996 (see New South Wales Department of Transport and Roads entry for details), the Corporation has become an organisation independent of other government-owned rail organisations.

Organisation

The Corporation has four divisions: Operations, Finance, Assets and Access. The Corporation owns essential rail-related infrastructure and facilitates the opening of the network to competition among train operators. It sets standards for operators and funds the upkeep of track. Initially a staff of about 70 will be employed by this unit.

The Assets Division is responsible for rail corridors (track and overhead wiring) but not facilities required by one operator (eg station buildings). Construction and maintenance work was contracted initially with the Rail Services Authority but this work will be progressively put out to competitive tender.

A Heritage unit has been established and has accepted responsibility for some 2,000 assets. It is investigating ways to make these assets more available to the public.

The Access Division is required by the NSW government to generate adequate revenue to cover its operating costs. All train-operators are guaranteed access to track on individually negotiated confidential pricing terms. Passenger trains have priority over freight trains. A tourist passenger train operator has commenced running on a scenic freight route between Wollongong and Moss Vale.

New lines

The state government announced in July 1994 its intention to construct two new Sydney suburban lines before 2000 (when the Olympic Games will be held in Sydney). A new line will join Sydney Central with the airport at Botany and Southern lines near Tempe, giving airport users the opportunity to connect with existing routes either in the city or in the near-southern suburbs. The line, known as the New Southern Railway and due to be opened in 2000 (for the Olympic Games) will be owned

by Rail Access Corporation and operated by CityRail. However, four stations (Rosebery, Mascot, Domestic Terminals and International Terminals) will be built, controlled and operated for 30 years by the Bouygues joint venture Airport Link company which will finance the construction of the stations. Since January 1997, a A$33 million tunnel boring machine has been excavating a 6 km tunnel as part of the 10 km route of the New Southern Railway connecting Sydney Central station with the Airport and East Hills line. It is the biggest railway project in Sydney in two decades and will cost A$600 million.

To transport attendees to the proposed Olympic Stadium, a freight branch line is to be extended to serve a new station at the stadium. It will be unusual in that there will be three parallel tracks, each with a platform on each side to assist queueing and expedite loading/unloading. After the Games, it will be used to service the nearby showgrounds. The A$50 million contract has been awarded to Leighton Contractors, which is to complete the project by March 1998.

Expressions of interest have closed for proposals to finance, design, build and operate a single-track extension of the Eastern Suburbs passenger line an additional 3 km to Bondi Beach. The extension would help relieve road traffic congestion in the area.

The single-track Clyde—Carlingford branch may be extended to Epping if a current proposal eventuates to provide better access to Parramatta from areas north of that suburb. Parramatta has become increasingly important as Sydney's geographic and commercial centre has moved west as the population has spread to areas of available land.

Improvements to existing lines
A new double-track 1.6 km Y Link constructed in Sydney's western suburbs has enabled a passenger service to be introduced between Campbelltown (South line) and Blacktown (West line), saving passengers changing trains at Granville.

GHD-Transmark is to be project manager for the rehabilitation of the Casino—Murwillumbah branch line which sees daily XPT and freight services. Track upgrading and bridge reconstruction will be supervised for two years.

An 1896 cast-iron lattice bridge over the Parramatta River on the suburban Carlingford branch has been replaced by a 119 m fully welded continuous truss bridge, the first in New South Wales.

The railway has been accurately mapped using a system based on the Global Positioning System and satellites. The record created will be accurate to within a metre and will detail all features of the railway including signals and turnouts.

A$9.8 million has been spent rehabilitating an elderly viaduct at Stanwell Park on the Illawarra Line in an area of instability.

A significant milestone was the replacement of the last timber underbridges in the CityRail system.

Additional track was provided between Flemington and Rhodes in Sydney's busy western suburbs area to enable segregation of freight and passenger services running between the west and north.

Work is progressing on a 6.6 km third bidirectional line between Glenfield and Ingleburn in Sydney's southwestern suburbs to provide paths for freight services amongst the heavy passenger services.

Several crossing loops on the North Coast line north of Grafton have been extended to about 1,500 metres and other shorter loops closed. Two deviations (with 60kg/m rail) were opened to reduce grades and ease curves. Longer loops to provide 1,500 metres standing room are to be provided at four crossing loops south of Junee.

Signalling and telecommunications
Signalling systems in use as at 31 December 1995 were:
Ordinary train staff: 3,800 km
Electric train staff: 1,500 km
Double line automatic: 500 km
Centralised traffic control (CTC): 1,000 km
Manual block telegraph: 55 km.

Work in progress at that date included:

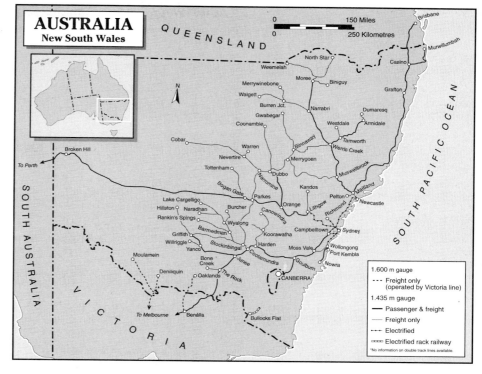

Bi-directional signalling: Picton—Mittagong: 45 km
CTC: Wallerawang—Tarana : 27 km (replacing double-track)
CTC: Mt Owen and Stratford balloon loops: 7 km.

Train-to-ground radio is being provided on 400 locomotives and 530 CityRail and Countrylink electric trainsets. A$22 million has been expended on improved train radio facilities.

Several locomotives have been fitted with radio equipment for trials of FreightCorp's train radio system. The project is designed to give radio coverage of all interlockings and most of the distance between. Initial trials of the system are taking place in the Orange—Dubbo area. Commissioning of the radio system will allow introduction of a new train order system.

A new interlocking for the Dartbrook coal mine saw the commissioning of the state's first screen-based PC operating system. A similar system has been introduced between Wallerawang and Tarana, where the previous double track has been singled following diversion of

much of the line's traffic via the Southern line. The systems are being supplied by Union Switch and Signal and mark a change to North American practice from the British practice previously followed.

The Granville area is being resignalled in connection with the new Y Link. The new signalling will be a computer-based Solid State interlocking.

A significant improvement in train operation is expected to flow from the provision of bidirectional signalling between Cowan and Hawkesbury River on the North Line. The section involves a steep climb with several tunnels.

CityRail's first computer-based interlocking system has been installed at Liverpool. Resignalling has been carried out in the Sydenham area, between Westmead and Seven Hills and on the North Shore Line to Hornsby. A programme to renew 200 km of cabling has been completed.

NEW ENTRY

Railway Services Authority of New South Wales

GPO Box 29, 7th floor, Transport House, 11-31 York St, Sydney, NSW, 2000
Tel: +61 2 9224 3702   Fax: +61 2 9224 3777

Political background
The Authority has been created as an independent unit following the restructure of the previous State Rail Authority from 1 July 1996 (see New South Wales Department of Transport and Roads entry for details).

Organisation
The Authority will provide track and infrastructure maintenance and rolling stock maintenance and construction services. It will continue activities under way at June 1996 but in future will be subject to competition for projects of the other entities. The Authority is now looking beyond New South Wales for work and has already obtained a major contract with Indonesian Railways to recondition traction motors. A workforce of 6,500 will be employed by the Authority initially.

Traction and rolling stock
Around the time the State Rail Authority was split up, 50 new NDFF class ballast wagons with pneumatically operated doors were supplied by ABB Construction Pty Ltd at a cost of A$4.5 million to enable improved productivity during track upgrading. They are the first wagons to carry the new organisation's colour scheme. A 48 Class locomotive used to shunt Chullora Workshops has also been painted in the Authority's colour scheme. It is expected that further locomotives will be acquired so that hiring of locomotives from FreightCorp can be avoided.

NEW ENTRY

Robe River Iron Associates (Railroad)

PO Box 21, Wickham, Western Australia 6720
Tel: +61 9 159 2150   Fax: +61 9 159 2184

Key personnel
Manager, Railroad: E E Girdler
Superintendent, Rail Maintenance: D G Higgins
Train Master: A H Cullen

Gauge: 1,435 mm
Route length: 203 km

Freight operations
The railway provides transport of ore from Pannawonica to Cape Lambert port. Ore tonnage totalled 20.7 million

tonnes in 1993-94 and 25.2 million tonnes in 1994-95. A significant milestone was the haulage of the 400 millionth tonne of ore in May 1997. The first haul was in August 1972 and the 300 millionth tonne was hauled in January 1992. Average net freight train load is around 17,450 tonnes.

Improvements to existing lines
Replacement of timber with concrete sleepers throughout the main line was completed in 1991.

During 1992-93 main line track was extended, a new loadout facility installed and a new rail yard constructed to service a new ore deposit.

Traction and rolling stock
At the end of 1995, the railway used 18 diesel locomotives, 822 ore wagons and 21 service vehicles.

A pair of Dash 8 locomotives head empty ore wagons over the Northern Highway (Wolfram Veith)   ***1997***

A 2,983 kW General Electric Dash 8 CM40-M locomotive was ordered in October 1995 for delivery in April 1996.

Couplers in standard use: Fixed and rotary
Braking in standard use: Westinghouse air

Track
Standard rail: Head-hardened 1,130 mpc 68 kg/m
Crossties (sleepers): Concrete 2,600 × 280 × 235 mm

Diesel locomotives

Class	Wheel arrangement	Power kW	Speed km/h	Weight tonnes	No in service	First built	Mechanical	Builders Engine	Transmission
GE Dash 8 CM40-8M	Co-Co	2,983	110	190	18	—	GE	GE7FDL16	E GE

Spacing: Concrete 1,538/km
Fastenings: Concrete, Mackay Safelock
Min curvature radius: 3°

Max gradient: 1.29% (empty); 0.50% (loaded)
Max axleload: 36 tonnes

UPDATED

Specialized Container Transport

51- 55 City Rd, South Melbourne, Victoria 3000
Tel: +61 3 9686 1444   Fax: +61 3 9686 1288

Political background
Specialized Container Transport decided that it should operate its own trains after experiencing difficulties dealing with the existing operators. It introduced a private weekly freight service between Melbourne and Perth in July 1995 and since then patronage has necessitated that trains be run twice-weekly.

Freight operations
SCT is to build a A$19 million freight terminal in Perth. The company is committed to the long-term but is concerned that it get track access on an economically acceptable basis. Quotations for track access have varied considerably between the various railways, with the company indicating that New South Wales' rates currently preclude economic operations into that state. Loadings have surprised the company, with its trains regularly requiring three locomotives through the Adelaide Hills. The largest train had a 5,500 tonne trailing load. The

company has been able to provide a reliable transit time of 2½ days between Melbourne and Perth.

Traction and rolling stock
The company has leased box cars from AN, while locomotives and crews are provided by V/Line between Melbourne and Adelaide, AN between Adelaide and Kalgoorlie and Westrail between Kalgoorlie and Perth. About 160 box cars, 20 open vans and 40 container flats are available for traffic.

NEW ENTRY

Speedrail

Speedrail Pty Ltd, PO Box 3169, Canberra, ACT 2601
Tel: +61 6 247 8898   Fax: +61 6 247 8989

Key personnel
Managing Director: Dale Budd

Organisation
Speedrail is a proposal for a new high-speed rail service between Sydney (Australia's largest city) and Canberra (the national capital), serving major centres along the route. The service is planned to bring world-best practice to Australian passenger railways, similar in concept to the high-speed rail systems which are successful and profitable in other countries. Speedrail is a 50:50 joint venture between GEC Alsthom Australia Ltd and Leighton Contractors.

Studies aimed at determining the financial viability of the project were initiated in 1994 and were funded by the

proponents and by the commonwealth, Australian Capital Territory and New South Wales governments. The overall finding of the study was that the link could be commercially financed. The project would cost about A$1.6 billion, with predicted demand estimated as 4.3 million one-way trips in 2000. The population of the Sydney-Canberra region is 3.4 million with Canberra's Parliament House visited by 2 million people annually. Financial forecasts (based on a fare half the present air fare) indicate that Speedrail would be debt-free 12 years after opening.

Speedrail responded to an advertisement placed by the relevant government organisations in March 1997 for 'Registrations of Interest' in building a new high-speed line on the Sydney—Canberra route. Other organisations bidding were Capital Rail; Goninan Consortium; InterCapital Express Ltd; Talgo/Rail Services Australia; and Thyssen Transrapid. After a bidding process, a preferred proposal was expected to be selected in November 1997.

The project involves building a 270 km route capable of supporting 350 km/h trains (initially 300 km/h trains similar to French TGVs) to provide a journey time of 80 minutes — faster than air when terminal times are taken into account. Within Sydney, the project would build additional tracks in the existing rail corridors but elsewhere a new route would use 5,500 m minimum radius curves compared with 240 m curves on the existing railway. Speedrail trains would be compatible with the existing Sydney electric rail system so that they could, if desired, run to multiple destinations within Sydney. It is envisaged that an hourly service would be provided.

To date, the only significant private railways in Australia have been mineral railways. There are few private passenger trains and no wholly privately owned rail passenger routes (other than a couple of short-distance monorails).

UPDATED

State Rail Authority/SRA (New South Wales)

Level 8, 201-207 Kent Street, Sydney, NSW 2000
GPO Box 29, Sydney, NSW 2001
Tel: +61 2 9379 3000   Fax: +61 2 9224 4711

Key personnel
Board Chairman: Michael Sexton
Chief Executive: Len Harper
Acting Chief Financial Officer: Bill Pascoe

Political background
With the restructure of the former State Rail Authority (see

New South Wales Department of Transport and Roads entry for details), the new SRA has responsibility for passenger services and support services. The passenger services are operated by the CityRail and Countrylink groups.

Organisation
Under the restructure, SRA will employ approximately 9,770 employees split within the various elements: Network Control — 700; passenger fleet maintenance — 350; Business Services Group — 700; CityRail — 7,200; and Countrylink — 820.

The revenue-raising businesses are supported by a corporate group which provides centralised services.

Rationalisation of staff continues and all non-core businesses have been discontinued. Productivity improvements continue to reduce the organisation's dependence on government funding.

Passenger operations
Details appear under headings CityRail and Countrylink.

NEW ENTRY

TNT

654 Footscray Rd, West Melbourne, Victoria 3000
Tel: +61 3 9688 7000   Fax: +61 3 9688 8414

Political background
TNT Ltd is one of Australia's major transport organisations. To complement its extensive road transport operations it introduced a private rail freight service between Melbourne and Perth in June 1996. The company wished to gain control of its customers' freight over the entire movement from pick-up to delivery.

Traction and rolling stock
The company has leased wagons from AN, while locomotives are provided by AN and crews are provided by V/Line between Melbourne and Wolseley, AN between Wolseley and Kalgoorlie and Westrail between Kalgoorlie and Perth.

NEW ENTRY

TNT container yard, Melbourne (Brian Webber)

1997

TransAdelaide

136 North Terrace, Adelaide, South Australia 5000
Postal: GPO Box 2351, Adelaide, SA 5001
Tel: +61 8 218 2200   Fax: +61 8 211 7614

Key personnel

Minister for Transport: Hon Diana Laidlaw
General Manager: Kevin Benger
Group Managers
  Corporate and Business Development: Carolyn Barlow
  Finance and Information: Rodger Seaman
  Human Resources: Sue Filby
  Technical Services: George Erdos

Gauge: 1,600 mm
Length: 119.63 route-km

Political background

Following the dissolution of the State Transport Authority, TransAdelaide was launched on 4 July 1994. It operates services under contract to the Passenger Transport Board, which has responsibility for policy and planning aspects of public transport. The state government's reform agenda requires a reduction of costs. To provide a more efficient, effective and responsive transit system, a competitive tendering process has been devised.

Organisation

TransAdelaide operates extensive bus services, one tram route and six train routes in the state capital, Adelaide. Since the 1978 transfer of the country railway system from the state to Australian National Railways, the Authority controls only the metropolitan passenger railway system of Adelaide. Some track is used by freight services to and from the country system as well as by suburban rail services.

The rail system and two other fixed components, a tramway and a guided busway, form the spine for much of the outer suburban bus network.

Diesel railcars or multiple-units

Class	Cars per unit	Motor cars per unit	Power/car kW	Speed km/h	Vehicles in service	First built	Mechanical	Builders Engine	Transmission
2000	2/3	1	390 × 2	135	M12	1980	Comeng	Cummins KTA 19R	H Voith
2100	2/3	1	–	–	T18	1980	Comeng	–	–
3000	1	1	354	100	M26	1987	Comeng/Clyde	Mercedes OM444LA	E Stromberg
3100	2	2	354	100	M40	1987	Comeng/Clyde	Mercedes OM444LA	E Stromberg

Passenger traffic (million)

	1993-94	1994-95	1995-96
Vehicle-km	6.30	6.52	6.55
Journeys	8.72	8.40	8.27

Passenger operations

The Authority operates six suburban rail routes providing 30 minute railcar services to 85 stations. An ongoing steady decline in public transport patronage in Adelaide, a city of about one million residents, has continued.

The Authority continues to encourages passengers to purchase tickets 'off-board' from licensed ticket vendors. However, in an acknowledgement that this is not convenient for all travellers, in 1996 TransAdelaide awarded a contract to Camms Systems Pty Ltd to manufacture 130 ticket vending machines for fitting to railcars.

Improvements to existing lines

As part of the creation of standard-gauge line for freight trains between Adelaide and Melbourne, one of the previous broad-gauge tracks between Goodwood and Belair was converted to standard-gauge. The remaining single broad-gauge track, used by TransAdelaide services, has been provided with four crossing loops. New stabling sidings have been provided for four trains at Belair.

Traction and rolling stock

At December 1996, the fleet comprised 100 railcars. This coincided with the completion of an order for 50 new 3000/3100 Class railcars placed with Clyde Engineering in May 1989. The last of the older 300 and 400 Class railcars (circa 1955) have been withdrawn. During 1995-96 railcars were equipped with ticket vending machines, security cameras and closed circuit TV to allow drivers to observe passengers boarding and alighting.

Signalling and telecommunications

The signalling system on both Belair and Noarlunga Centre lines has been upgraded to include uninterruptible power supply (UPS) systems to improve service reliability.

Coupler in standard use: Knuckle automatic; and Scharfenberg fully automatic

Track

Resleepering and other major work is now done by outside contractors.
Rail: Australian Standard 47, 50, 53 and 60 kg/m rail
Crossties (sleepers): Hardwood timber 2,600 × 260 × 130 mm; steel (BHP M7-5 section) 2,595 × 260 × 98 mm
Spacing: 1,400/km plain track and curves
Fastenings: 19 mm² dogspike with sleeper plates. Elastic fastenings on steel sleepers, points and crossings
Min curvature radius: 200 m
Max axleload: 23 tonnes
Max grade: 1 in 45

UPDATED

TransAdelaide service formed with 3000 Class railcars

1997

Victoria Public Transport Corporation

589 Collins Street, Melbourne 3000
Tel: +61 3 9619 1111   Fax: +61 3 9619 2343

Key personnel

Chief Executive: I Dobbs
Director, Finance: R Mendes
  Personnel: J Carlisle

Acting Managing Director, V/Line Freight: T Spicer
Managing Director, Met Trains: S Lane
Acting Managing Director, V/Line Passenger: G Tighe
Director, Infrastructure: J Sutton
  Rail Vehicle Maintenance: J Barry

Gauges: 1,600 mm; 1,435 mm
Route length: 4,582 km
Electrification: 385 km of 1,600 mm Melbourne suburban routes - 1.5kV DC overhead

Political background

Legislation of July 1989 amalgamated Victoria's Metropolitan Transit and State Transport authorities as the Public Transport Corporation.

Organisation

The Victoria Public Transport Commission is divided into five business units: MET Trams; MET Bus; MET Trains; V/Line Passenger; V/Line Freight. The old trading names are retained and all freight and country and interstate passenger services are marketed as V/Line, while Melbourne metropolitan passenger services (buses, trams, light rail and trains) are marketed as The Met.

Staff employed by all units reduced from 20,027 in 1991 to 11,608 on 30 June 1994 to 9,516 on 30 June 1996.

Finance

The current Victoria government embarked on a major reform programme focusing initially on ensuring financial viability and subsequently focusing on service quality. Between 1990/91 and 1994/95, the PTC reduced its call on government funding by A$250 million. During this period, productivity measures showed a marked improvement, with a total of 9,800 staff leaving the Corporation.

Revenue (A$ million)

	1996	1997
Pasenger and freight	443.7	418.7
Other	83.1	110.4

Victorian govt contribution towards:

Operating expenses	183.5	183.6
Termination payments	21.9	46.6
Capital works/maintenance	14.8	204.1
Other	15.0	1.5
Superannuation	–	97.1
Total revenue	762.0	1,062.0

Expenditure (A$ million)

Salaries and wages	368.7	387.0
Associated labour costs	49.7	61.9
Services/supplies	205.1	228.5
Other	260.3	223.0
Termination payments	26.0	50.3
Superannuation costs	8.7	166.8
Total expenses	918.5	1,117.5
Deficit for year	156.5	55.5

Passenger operations
The Met

During FY1995-96 staff numbers were reduced by 18 per cent. Single person operated trains and the new classification of Customer Service Employee were successfully introduced. The boardings per employee statistic improved from 16,661 in 1991-92 to 29,953 in 1995-96.

The Melbourne suburban rail network extends to 427 km of 1,600 mm gauge route, of which 343 km is electrified at 1.5 kV DC overhead. Limited Met suburban operation extends a further 42 km from Pakenham to Warragul, over a V/Line electrified route (though V/Line no longer operates electric trains). There are 19 routes, 15 of them electrified, serving 209 stations. The four-track underground city loop line, completed in 1984, provided three additional city-centre stations and reduced the need for terminating facilities at Flinders Street station.

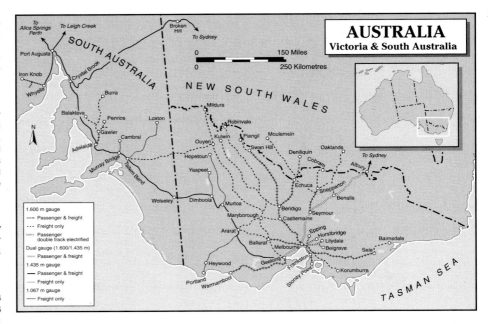

In 1995-96, 109 million boardings were recorded compared with 105 million in the previous year. Patronage rose more rapidly in FY1995-96 than at any time in the past 20 years. Passengers travelled in 907 emu carriages of which four are the double-deck Tangara test train. Suburban electric trains ran 14.5 million kilometres in 1995-96.

During 1994-95 services were extended 13.4 km from Dandenong to Cranbourne, one of Victoria's fastest growing areas, following upgrading and electrification costing A$27 million. The project included construction of two new stations (Merinda Park and Cranbourne) and coincided with the redevelopment of Dandenong (the junction station and a busy suburban centre). The line is single-track with a crossing loop and provides for 115 km/h running, the maximum allowed for Melbourne's suburban trains. More frequent off-peak and Sunday services were introduced on the busiest lines.

A number of major stations are being upgraded as 'premium stations' by provision of improved lighting, closed circuit television, an audio train information system and enclosed waiting area. The intention is to concentrate passengers to these stations during off-peak times making it practical to provide passengers with a secure environment.

The previously threatened suburban electric service to Upfield is to be retained and will receive a A$25 million upgrade over the next two years. Services will be provided additionally on Sundays and 13 manually operated level crossing gates will be replaced with automatic boom gates.

V/Line
Broad gauge: The V/Line division of the PTC operates country passenger services between Melbourne and Geelong (approximately 22 daily); Ballarat (approximately eight daily); Bendigo (six); Traralgon (seven); Stony Point (seven); Albury (two); Shepparton (two); Swan Hill (one). Sprinter railcars work many services including a new twice-weekly service to Echuca, which had not seen a passenger rail service since 1981. Most off-peak Geelong line sevices have been extended through a tunnel to South Geelong.

In 1995-96, seven million journeys were undertaken on V/Line passenger trains. Punctuality was over 93 per cent on time and driver-only operation has been extended to 80 per cent of services.

Passenger services between Melbourne and Warrnambool (267 km) have, since August 1993, been taken over by West Coast Railway (qv) using ex-V/Line rolling stock including four S Class locomotives running over V/Line track.

Standard gauge:
There are now two daily XPT services between Sydney and Melbourne while the overnight 'Overland' services provided by Australian National between Melbourne and Adelaide now run on standard gauge.

Freight operations

V/Line provides intrastate freight services on two gauges and resources and safe-working for services run by other operators. V/Line runs few trains on the Albury—Melbourne—Wolseley standard-gauge lines as most services are run by other operators. Reference to the accompanying map shows that effectively there are two independent systems, broad-gauge and standard-gauge.

Some 6,877,000 tonnes were hauled during 1995-96 comprised of 3,896,000 tonnes of grain, 366,000 tonnes of cement, 550,000 tonnes of minerals/quarry and

'G' Class diesel-electric locomotive on a grain train

Sprinter diesel railcar at South Geelong (Brian Webber)   **1997**

Diesel locomotives: 1,600 mm or 1,435 mm gauge

Class	Builder's type	Wheel arrangement	Power kW	Speed km/h	Weight tonnes	No in service	First built	Mechanical	Builders Engine	Transmission
A	AAT22C-2R	Co-Co	1,840	115	121	11	1983*	Clyde	GM 12-645E3B	E GM
G	JT26C-255	Co-Co	2,460	115	127	20	1984	Clyde	GM 16-645E3B	E GM
H	G188	Bo-Bo	820	100	81	5	1968	Clyde	GM 8-645E	E GM
N	JT22C HC-2	Co-Co	1,840	115	124	25	1985	Clyde	GM 12-645E3B	E GM
P	G18HB-R	Bo-Bo	826	100	77	13	1984*	Clyde	GM 8-645E	E GM
T	G88	Bo-Bo	710/ 826	100	69	13	1959	Clyde	GM 8-567CR or 8-645E	E GM
X	—	Co-Co	1,450/ 1,640	115	118	23	1966/ 74	Clyde	GM 16-567E or 16-645E	E GM
Y	—	Bo-Bo	480	64	68	21	1963	Clyde	GM 6-567C or 6-645E	E GM

* Rebuilt

Diesel railcars: 1,600 mm gauge

Class	Cars per unit	Motored axles	Power/motor kW	Speed km/h	No in service	First built	Mechanical	Builders Engine	Transmission
Sprinter	1	4	235 kW	130	22	1993	Goninan	Deutz	H Voith

* Two motors per car

Electric multiple-units: 1,600 mm gauge

Class	Cars per unit	Motor cars per unit	Motored axles/car	Power/motor kW	Speed km/h	Units in service	First built	Builders Mechanical	Electrical
Hitachi	6	4	4	112	115	56	1972	Martin & King	Hitachi
Comeng	6	4	4	137	115	93	1981	Comeng	GEC
Tangara	4	2	—	—	130	1	1992	Goninan/ Mitsubishi/ Westinghouse	Mitsubishi

1,116,000 tonnes of containers. The Australian Wheat Board has signed a five-year contract with V/Line to haul most of the state's grain to Melbourne for domestic use or to Geelong or Portland for export. There has been strong growth in container traffic at several provincial centres.

Interstate services have been taken over by other operators, mainly National Rail although two non-government operators now run trains (with hired Australian National locomotives and crews) between Melbourne and Perth. The Geelong—Adelaide route has been converted to standard gauge and an additional standard-gauge track provided between Geelong and Melbourne. Train lengths between Albury and Wolseley may now reach 1.3 km. NR commenced responsibility for Long Island (east of Melbourne) broad-gauge trains in January 1994.

The broad-gauge lines from Ouyen and Heywood into South Australia see no trains. The new standard-gauge line provides an alternative for any traffic offering.

Driver-only operation of freight trains commenced in December 1993 and V/Line was planning for 50 per cent driver-only operation in 1996. The number of locomotive and fuelling depots has been reduced from 14 to three.

Improvements to existing lines
Former 1,600 mm gauge lines in the west of the state (Murtoa—Hopetoun; Dimboola—Yaapeet; Ararat—Portland), isolated by the conversion to standard gauge of

the Geelong—Adelaide route, have been converted to standard gauge at a cost of A$20.4 million, to enable continued haulage of grain. Ararat—Maryborough (88 km) was standard-gauged in April 1996 while Maryborough—Dunolly (22 km) will be dual-gauged. The former broad-gauge main line between Ballarat and Ararat now has siding status.

A new A$9 million station has been opened at Traralgon. It is part of a new commercial development, one of the largest in that area of Victoria in the past decade.

Traction and rolling stock
At 30 June 1996, V/Line used 128 diesel locomotives, 23 shunting rail tractors, 158 passenger carriages, 22 'Sprinter' railcars, 149 six-car electric multiple-units and an eight-car 1,435 mm gauge XPT train (used in a pool with NSWSRA vehicles). V/Line owns 2,535 freight wagons with 191 freight vehicles leased by National Rail.

V/Line purchased Australia's first Road Transferable Locomotive (RTL) in February 1996. This is a large convertible road/rail prime-mover (354 kW/475 hp) which can shunt or haul several wagons and then be driven along a road to another location. Conversion between modes can be performed by one person in about 5 minutes. The RTL has a maximum rail speed of 60 km/h and can haul a 1,000 tonne load in dry weather on 1 in 100 grades.

V/line has made its fleet of 'classic carriages', including the royal carriage and a retired 'Red Rattler' suburban electric train, available for charter work.

In 1996 structural repairs and interior enhancements were completed on 15 older Hitachi three-car suburban electric trains and the 94 six-car Comeng trains (dating from 1981) will be overhauled in the next four years at a cost of A$49 million.

Signalling and telecommunications
Most of the V/Line system is controlled by a simple train order working system. Other systems are CTC (577 km), staff and ticket (336 km), automatic block signalling (322 km), electric staff (318 km), double line block (240 km) and automatic track control (194 km).

A new computer-based signalling system was commissioned at the important junction at Sunshine.

Electrification
Work was completed on the A$27.1 million Cranbourne electrification conversion and suburban services commenced in March 1995.

Track
The 35-year-old standard-gauge line between Albury and Melbourne, with its 47kg/m rail and old timber sleepers, is worn out and costly to maintain. About 20 per cent of this line has been upgraded to current standards of 60kg/m rail suitable for 25 tonne axleloads and 115 km/h speeds.

In 1995-96, 166,000 sleepers were replaced in the state. 1,100 km of track were rehabilitated and 31 bridges were upgraded or strengthened. The 1876 Geelong Tunnel was reconditioned, apparently for the first time, in mid-1996.

Standard rail: Flat-bottomed 47, 53 and 60 kg/m rail rolled in 13.72 m lengths

Crossties (sleepers)

Timber: Non-treated Australian hardwoods (Red Gum, Ironbark, Box Stringbark and Messmate)

Dimensions: 1,600 mm gauge 2,705 × 250 × 125 mm; 1,435 mm gauge 2,590 × 250 × 125 mm

Spacing: 685 mm centres

Concrete: Prestressed concrete with cast-iron shoulders to take Pandrol rail clips

Dimensions: 2,670 × 275 × 145 mm at midspan (208 mm deep at ends). Rail seat canted at 1 in 20

Spacing: 670 mm centres

Fastenings
Timber: Most track fastened with dogspikes. Sleeper plates used on all tracks except 60 lb/yd branch lines, double-shouldered and canted at 1 in 20. 'Fair' deep bow one-piece rail anchors used instead of pads. Approximately 150 km of track relaid in 60 kg/m rail on rolled double-shoulder sleeper plates with Pandrol clips and three lock spikes per rail foot

Concrete: Pandrol rail clips, rail pads and insulators used on 53 and 60 kg/m rail laid on concrete sleepers

Ballast: Generally broken stone, usually basalt, but granite, rhyodicite and diabase also used. For rail lengths up to 27 m, 250 mm bearing depth with 50 mm shoulder width. For long or continuously welded rail, 300 mm deep with 405 mm shoulder width

Maximum gradient
Main line: 2.08% = 1 in 48

Branch line: 3.33% = 1 in 30

Trackwork design standards: Curves of less than 2,400 m radius transitioned. Main line curves for 100 km/h traffic to be 830 m radius minimum, while for 50 km/h main line traffic minimum radius should be 400 m

Max altitude: 591.3 m near Wallace, Melbourne–Ballarat line

Longest straight: 38.3 km between Glenorchy and Murtoa, Western line

Welded rail: Standard 13.72 m rail lengths welded into 27.5 to 82 m lengths at the central flashbutt welding depot, Spotswood. Once laid, rails thermit-welded into 328 m lengths or continuously welded rail. Stress-control measures taken during field welding to ensure the continuously welded rail is in an unstressed condition within the temperature range of 33 to 38°C

Max speeds: 130 km/h — Sprinter railcars, 115 km/h — locomotives

Max axleload: 22.36 tonnes on Class C diesel-electric locomotives

UPDATED

West Coast Railway

The Victorian Railway Company Pty Ltd
Level 3, 75-77 Moorabool St, Geelong, Victoria 3220
Tel: +61 3 5222 5900   Fax: +61 3 5222 5966

Key personnel
Directors: Donald M Gibson
  Gary G McDonald
  Michael J Menzies

Gauge: 1,600 mm
Route km: 267 km

Political background
In January 1993, the state government of Victoria called tenders for private operation of most of the long-distance passenger services throughout rural Victoria. West Coast Railway (the trading name of The Victorian Railway Company Pty Ltd) was the successful tenderer for the operation of the Melbourne—Warrnambool service.

Passenger operations
The railway provides the rail passenger service of 36 services weekly between Melbourne and Warrnambool, a distance of 267 km. Trains ran about 500,000 km in 1995-96 carrying 296,149 passengers, with trains usually comprising four or five vehicles. Some 55 staff are employed. Government contracts prohibit publication of revenue statistics.

In addition to connecting with V/Line trains at Geelong and Melbourne, WCR trains connect with road coach services providing travel to locations throughout south-western Victoria and to Mount Gambier in South Australia. Payphones have been installed on all trains.

Traction and rolling stock
Until 7 April 1995, all locomotives and carriages were leased from V/Line; however, since then West Coast Railway has purchased 15 diesel and three steam locomotives, 26 carriages and 16 vans. Six diesel locomotives and 15 air conditioned carriages were available for service at December 1996. Maintenance staff

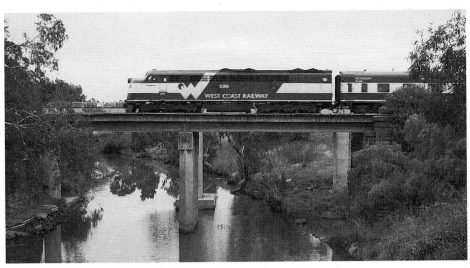

Warrnumbool passenger service at Werribee (Brian Webber)   **1997**

Class	Builder's type	Wheel arrangement	Power kW	Speed km/h	Weight tonnes	No in service	First built	Mechanical	Builders Engine	Transmission
B	ML2	Co-Co	1190/1120	133	123	1	1952	Clyde	EMD16-567C	E EMD
S	A7	Co-Co	1450/1340	133	123	4	1957	Clyde	EMD 16-567C	E EMD
T	G8B	Bo-Bo	710/650	100	70	3	1962	Clyde	EMD 8-567CR	E EMD

carry out heavy maintenance and overhaul at workshops at Ballarat East while a servicing facility has been established at Warrnambool where routine checks and the servicing of rolling stock occurs.

Signalling and telecommunications
Some safe-working and signalling duties are carried out by WCR staff and some by V/Line freight staff at Colac and Warrnambool. WCR employees staff stations at Winchelsea, Colac, Camperdown and Warrnambool. Train conductors carry mobile phones for emergency

use. Fees are paid to V/Line for the use of its train control and for operation at its stations between Melbourne and Geelong.

Track
West Coast Railway runs its trains over the tracks of V/Line, by contract with the Public Transport Corporation of Victoria.

UPDATED

Western Australian Government Railways (Westrail)

Westrail Centre, West Parade, Perth, Western Australia 6000
(PO Box S1422, GPO Perth, WA 6001)
Tel: +61 9 326 2222   Fax: +61 9 326 2648

Key personnel
Minister of Transport: Hon Eric J Charlton MLC
Commissioner: R Drabble
General Manager, Business Development: J Goodall
  (Acting)
Civil: W James (Acting)
Engineering: G J Willox
Finance: R D Collister
Operations: M G Baggott
Urban Passenger: H Smith (Acting)
Passenger Services: C A Field
Manager, Human Resources: B Mortmore

Gauge: 1,067 mm; 1,435 mm; dual-gauge
Route length: 4,170 km; 1,212 km; 172 km
Electrification: 63 km of 1,067 mm gauge at 25 kV 50 Hz
AC — Perth suburban passenger network

Transperth
Metropolitan (Perth) Passenger Transport Trust
10 Adelaide Terrace, PO Box 6122, Hay Street, East Perth, Western Australia 6000
Tel: +61 9 425 2525   Fax: +61 9 325 2063

Key personnel
Chairman: A Middleton
Chief, Rail Operations: R Campbell

Political background
Westrail is the trading name of The Western Australian Government Railways Commission which is established under the (State) Government Railways Act 1904.

Transperth is responsible for provision of Perth's public transport system.

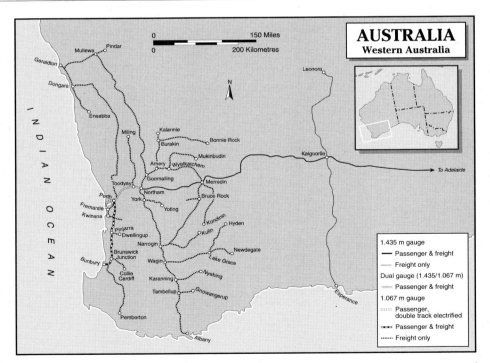

Organisation
Westrail is a statutory authority that competes in the freight, passenger and related transport markets of southern Western Australia. Westrail's primary activity is rail freight, which is segregated into three business units: Agriculture, Forestry and General; Ores and Minerals; and Intersystem. For passengers, Westrail provides interstate and country trains, and country road coaches. The Perth metropolitan rail service is owned by Westrail and operated for Transperth under contract.

Westrail is a partner in two joint venture companies, Total Western Transport Pty Ltd and Western Quarries Pty Ltd, which complement its transport activities.

There was a further reduction in the number of staff employed with numbers falling from 3,053 at June 1995 to 2,283 at June 1996.

Finance
In FY95-96 Westrail declared a profit of A$13.1 million. Revenue increased due to the start of iron-ore haulage from Koolyanobbing to the port of Esperance.

A$9.1 million was spent on the Swan River bridge in Perth and A$4.3 million was expended on an underfloor wheel lathe. The A$20.5 million upgrade of the track between Leonora, Kalgoorlie and Esperance for iron-ore haulage was completed.

timetable and the planned increase from 90 to 150 freight trains daily. The case for this and other north–south operating capacity increase projects was further strengthened by the political liberalisation of eastern Europe.

There has been an extensive double-tracking, realignment, and resignalling programme. Only the final 9 km summit section of the 62 km between Selzthal and St Michael remains to be doubled. A new curve at Selzthal to save Graz–Salzburg trains reversal there will also contribute to a prospective saving of 25 minutes on their present 160 minute timing between Leoben and Bischofshofen. Total cost of all the works, including elimination of level crossings, is put at Sch4.7 billion, of which some two-thirds has already been spent.

South of the Schober Pass, the 28 km section between St Michael and Bruck-an-der-Mur, over which north–south Schober Pass trains share the route with east–west Südbahn trains, is being quadrupled. Boring of a 5.4 km Galgenberg Tunnel for a Leoben avoiding line is the first step. North of the pass, the Pyhrnbahn from Selzthal north to Linz is due to be doubled and resignalled before the end of the century.

Meanwhile, a 13 km single-track Linz avoiding line was completed in May 1994 to link the Pyhrnbahn at Traun with the Westbahn at Marchtrenk, at the approach to Wels, at a cost of some Sch700 million.

Class 5047 railcar

1997

Tauern line

The trans-Alpine north–south line from Salzburg through the Tauern Tunnel to Rosenbach on the Slovenian border, where trains can go on further south via the Karawanken Tunnel route, is being doubled at a cost of Sch600 million.

Enlargement of the 280 m Untersberg Tunnel near Schwarzach St Veit in a Sch46 million scheme has permitted Tauern route piggybacking of 4.05 m high road vehicles.

Long-term plans cover improvements to the north of the Tauern route between Salzburg and Schwarzach St Veit (already double-track, but where curves are being eased) and to the south of it between Spittal-Milstättersee and Rosenbach. Realignments where feasible will lift maximum speed to 130 km/h, 140 km/h over parts of the southern section. The aim is to raise freight train capacity from 110 to 150 a day.

Arlberg line

The Arlberg is the key east–west trans-Alpine route in the west of Austria, linking Innsbruck and points to the east with Switzerland. Progressive double-tracking continues, with attention now focused on the 25 km segment between Ötztal and Landeck on the eastern approaches to the Arlberg Tunnel. Associated work aims to raise line-speed to 140 km/h, provide extra capacity for an S-Bahn service, and eliminate the railway's division of some communities by rerouteing, principally in the Ötztal to Kronburg section. Given the steep sides of the valley, this necessitates tunnelling, and eventually 12 km of the 25 km section will be underground. Preliminary work on the Schnann to St Jakob section has begun and plans are under way for the Langen to Klösterle section.

The Arlberg Tunnel itself was built with two tracks. Work has been undertaken to enlarge its clearances for RoLa piggybacking of 4.05 m-high road vehicles. In places the additional clearance could be secured only by lowering the trackbed because the tunnel walls were not thick enough for reduction, and in one area the clearance was obtained by the use of 3.7 km of slab track on one of the two lines.

Links with Eastern Europe

In 1995 the governments of Austria, the Czech Republic, and Germany agreed a programme to upgrade of the Vienna–Prague–Berlin corridor for speeds of 200 km/h north of Dresden, 160 km/h elsewhere. The Czech tilting trains will deliver a 3 ¾ hour Berlin–Prague timing in 1998. For ÖBB the lines concerned are Vienna–Gmünd–České Velenice and Vienna–Břeclav. Electric working on the first of these was extended from Sigmundsherberg to Gmünd in September 1995 after extensive modernisation work, but the line remains single north of Absdorf-Hippersdorf.

Feasibility studies are to be undertaken into new infrastructure construction, involving substantial tunnelling, to allow the Berlin–Prague–Vienna journey time to be cut to 4 hours by the second decade of the next century.

Co-operation between ÖBB and the Hungarian railway MÁV remains close. Major investment has been put into the Vienna–Hegyeshalom–Budapest line (see Ostbahn section above). ÖBB bought 18 new dual-voltage locomotives for the cross-border traffic.

Three lines will improve links with the Slovak capital, Bratislava. The Pressburger Bahn to the east of Vienna is

to be developed as line S7 of the Vienna S-Bahn, providing a much-increased frequency to Vienna International Airport. The Vienna and Lower Austria administrations are anxious to see double-tracking throughout and a link with the new Vienna station. Beyond the airport at Schwechat more double-tracking and some new construction are proposed to extend the line beyond its present terminus at Wolfsthal to Kittsee, where it would join the line from Parndorf, extension of which to Bratislava began in late 1994. The airport section is likely to be finished in 1997, but the remainder will not be ready before the end of the decade.

The Parndorf route uses the Budapest main line as far as Parndorf, whence the existing single-track branch to Kittsee is being rebuilt for 160 km/h speeds and later doubling. A 2.5 km extension suitable for 140 km/h will lead on to the border, and on the Slovak side the line is to be linked to Petržalka, across the Danube from Bratislava, with first a bus connection to the centre, later an underground railway.

The third route into Slovakia already exists and runs from Vienna via Marchegg to Bratislava.

Major new stations

The *Neue Bahn* plan provides for Sch650 million to be spent on 32 stations, to create public transport interchanges, parking space and station garages, and a wide range of other passenger services and amenities.

A massive scheme is planned for Vienna, where the Südbahn at Meidling (where there will also be a junction with the Donauländebahn for freight traffic use) is to be linked by a 14 km new line, with all but 2 km in tunnel, under the Lainzer Tiergarten and the city's southwestern residential area, with the Westbahn at Purkersdorf Sanatorium. There is to be a new Vienna station on the site of the present Südbahnhof. Plans approved in 1995 involve a major urban redevelopment as well as the station works. The new main entrance will be on the Sütiroler Platz, considerably improving the links with local transport, and there will be four through platforms on the curve between the Ostbahn and the Sübahn main lines. The work is to be staged, the first part starting in 1998 and lasting five years. Completion of the whole project is not expected until 2020.

Traction and rolling stock

At the end of 1994 ÖBB owned 732 electric locomotives (of which 15 were 760 mm gauge), 468 diesel locomotives (of which 28 were 760 mm gauge) and 16 steam locomotives (of which 12 were metre-gauge and four were 760 mm gauge). The railway owned 225 emus and 137 dmus (of which nine were 760 mm gauge and two were metre-gauge), 3,639 passenger cars (including 84 restaurant, and 113 sleeping and couchette cars) and 23,871 freight wagons.

In early 1997 ÖBB opened Europe's new depot at Villach, where 110 staff look after 160 locomotives, 250 passenger coaches and 4,000 freight wagons. This is a third major modern installation, alongside Knittelfield and Linz. The Linz works are being extensively modernised and will, in future, look after all ÖBB's high-performance

Class 2068 Bo-Bo diesel locomotive heads a container train from Vienna's container port on the Danube River (David Haydock)

1997

Siemens SGP double-deck coach for Vienna local services   *1997*

passenger equipment. The railway aims in the future to exploit its modern facilities more extensively by tendering for international work.

Locomotives
The last Class 1044 locomotive was delivered in 1995, bringing the class total to 200. The first three locomotives of Class 1012, the 82 tonne, 6,000 kW, Bo-Bo successor to Class 1044, were due to be delivered in June 1996. However, the locomotives were not actually acquired until December 1996, after considerable negotiation about costs, the price paid being Sch 70 million per machine instead of the Sch 90 million originally asked. They will be used in place of Class 1044s on domestic services, so they have only been authorised for 160 km/h operation instead of the design speed of 230 km/h.

Since May 1994 Vienna—Budapest EuroCity trains have been worked through by the new dual-voltage Class 1014 locomotives, of which ÖBB is taking delivery of 18. These 72 tonne 3,500 kW machines have 170 km/h capability and are designed for high curving speeds. Mechanical parts by SGP are derived from Class 1044 and the electrical equipment, by Elin, from Class 1146. Designed for light and middle-weight fast passenger and freight trains and cross-border traffic, they are also suitable for push-pull operation of suburban trains. They have three-phase asynchronous motors with microprocessor-controlled thyristor systems.

For through freight working between Germany and Italy via the Brenner, an Adtranz-Siemens-SGP consortium has delivered five prototypes of a dual-voltage (15 kV AC/3 kV DC) 82 tonne Class 1822 Bo-Bo rated at 4,300 kW with a top speed of 140 km/h.

In 1994, ÖBB took delivery from SGP of the first of 20 three-phase AC Class 1163 electric Bo-Bos. These 80.5 tonne, 1,600 kW locomotives are intended primarily as yard shunters, but they have a maximum speed of 120 km/h so that they can be used on short-haul train operation.

The June 1996 timetable saw the introduction of push-pull working on ÖBB, for which 75 Class 1042 locomotives have been converted to form a new Class 1142 which can be driven from a driving trailer or from another locomotive (for heavy freight work). The conversion work was carried out in the railway-owned works at Linz. Deployment will be in the Vienna area at first.

In early 1997 ÖBB was seeking tenders for 200 high-performance locomotives, with installed power of 6.5 MW and a top speed of 230 km/h, to be used on both fast passenger and heavy freight services. In view of the fall in prices of recent years, it hopes to be able to obtain a purchase price of only Sch40 million per locomotive.

Passenger vehicles
The first phase of *Neue Bahn* investment earmarks Sch1.6 billion for new traction and rolling stock (though over the whole *Neue Bahn* programme forecast expenditure in this area totals Sch12.5 billion). Most of the first-phase money is going on development and

evaluation of new 200 km/h passenger car prototypes with sophisticated amenities. ÖBB eventually aims to have trains capable in international service of using the 300 km/h new lines in neighbouring states. SGP has developed an SGP-300 range of guided-wheelset bogie designs including a model with 300 km/h capability.

In late 1994, ÖBB took delivery of 40 SGP coaches of a new modular design in an Sch718 million contract; a further 19 have been ordered. The interiors are readily adaptable to a range of designs, from day and overnight to restaurant, buffet, and children's nursery layouts. Major assemblies, such as braking equipment, are modularised, allowing quick replacement in the event of a defect.

Although ÖBB was one of the original partners in the DACH company, the Austrian sector felt that it would be best to withdraw in September 1996. They bought the *Wiener Walzer* (Vienna—Zurich) service, which they believe can be worked without loss, from DACH and now run it as a EuroNight train, and they also bought 16 modern DACH vehicles at a cost of SF43 million.

In September 1995 the railway works at St Pölten rolled out ÖBB's first push-pull driving trailer, designated Class 80-75. ÖBB long resisted the move to push-pull working, but the pace has now been forced by the need to save on personnel costs; the aim is to operate regional trains with a driver alone, for which various technical preparations such as side-selective door-release, automatic brake-test, remote monitoring of handbrakes, and so on are required. The initial production-run is 14 vehicles, and 75 are to be built by 1999 by conversion of 26.4 m Jenbacher vehicles built between 1982 and 1987 at a total cost in the order of Sch615 million.

Tenders were sought in 1994 for 50 bilevel coaches and 10 bilevel driving coaches. The contract went to ARGE Doppelstockwagen (a consortium of Siemens Verkehrstechnik/SGP and Jenbacher) in March 1995 for a sum of roughly Sch700 million. Add-on orders took the total number of vehicles on order to 240. For 33 trailer vehicles the interior fitting out will be undertaken in the railway-owned works at Simmering, and ÖBB will deliver some parts to ARGE.

ÖBB's new SGP Class Rh 4090 narrow-gauge electric (6.5 kV AC 25 Hz) multiple-units can be used in three- or four-car formations, two powered vehicles and two trailers, or a power-car, a trailer, and a driving trailer. Two sets can be coupled. Maximum speed is 70 km/h. They have modern seating, enclosed gangways, and closed-system toilets.

ÖBB's new Design Committee has produced a completely new livery for passenger vehicles which is now being applied to new stock on delivery. The left-hand-side of a coach, as seen from the front, is painted red, the right-hand-side being grey, with the border between the two painted areas being slanted. The doors are white.

Signalling and telecommunications
Electronic signalling installations are being developed by two companies, Alcatel Austria and Siemens AG. Each is pursuing its own software technology.

With the commissioning of new signalling and LZB (the

Diesel locomotives

Class	Wheel arrangement	Power kW	Speed km/h	Weight tonnes	No in service	First built	Mechanical	Builders Engine	Transmission
1,435 mm gauge									
2043	B-B	1,035	110	70	72	1964	JW	JW 400 (01-4) LM 1500 (5+)	H Voith
2143	B-B	1,035	110	68	76	1965	SGP	SGP T 12c	H Voith
2048	B-B	808	100/65	64	34	1991	MAK	CAT3512DI	H Voith
2050	Bo-Bo	1,140	100	75	16	1958	Henschel	GM 12-567c	E GM
Shunting locomotives									
2060	B	129	30/60	27	23	1954	JW	JW 200	H Voith
2062	B	250	40/60	32	65	1958	JW	JW 400	H Voith
2067	C	398	65	49	111	1959	SGP	S 12a/S12na	H Voith
2068	B-B	820	50/100	68	60	1989	JW	JW 480D	H Voith
760 mm gauge									
2090	Bo	72	40	13	1	1930	SGP	Saurer BXD	E Syst Gebus
2190	Bo	86	45	13	1	1934	SGP	SGP SU8	E Syst Gebus
2091	1-Bo-1	114	50	22	6	1936	SGP	SGP R 8	E Syst Gebus
2092	C	88	20	17	3	1943		Deutz ABM 517	H Voith
2095	B-B	405	60	32	15	1958	SGP	S 12a	H Voith

Electric locomotives

Class	Wheel arrangement	Output kW continuous/ one-hour	Speed km/h	Weight tonnes	No in service	First built	Builders Mechanical	Electrical
1010	Co-Co	3,260/3,990	130	110	19	1955	SGP	ABES
1110	Co-Co	3,260/3,990	110	110	29	1956	SGP	ABES
1014/1114	Bo-Bo	3,000/3,400	160	74	18	1993	SGP	BES
1040	Bo-Bo	1,980/2,020	80	80	15	1950	Lofag	ABES
1041	Bo-Bo	1,980/2,020	80	83	23	1952	SGP	ABES
1141	Bo-Bo	2,100/2,400	110	80	30	1955	SGP	ABES
1042	Bo-Bo	3,336/3,600	130	84	60	1963	SGP	BES
1042.5	Bo-Bo	3,808/4,000	150	84	193	1966	SGP	BES
1043	Bo-Bo	3,600/4,000	135	83	10	1971	ASEA	ASEA
1044	Bo-Bo	5,000/5,310	160	84	122	1974	SGP	BES
1044.2	Bo-Bo	5,000/5,310	160	84	88	1989	SGP	BES
1044.5	Bo-Bo	5,000/5,310	220	84	1	1987	SGP	BES
1245	Bo-Bo	1,504/1,780	80	83	2	1934	Lofag	ABES
1046	Bo-Bo	1,360/1,550	125	67	13	1956	Lofag	ABES
1146	Bo-Bo	2,400	140	73	2	1987	Lofag	Elin
1163	Bo-Bo	—/1,600	120	80	6	1994	Graz	Adtranz
1822	Bo-Bo	4,400/—	140	83	1	1991	SGP	ABB
Shunting locomotives								
1063	Bo-Bo	1,520/2,000	100	82	50	1983	SGP	BES
1064	Co-Co	1,520	100	113	10	1985	SGP	BES
760 mm gauge, 6.5 kV 50 Hz								
1099	C-C	310/405	45	50	15	1911	Krauss	Siemens

German form of automatic train protection) in March 1993 over the 25 km between Linz and Wels, 200 km/h running became possible for the first time in Austria. Later that year LZB was commissioned from Wels to Lambach and Attnang Puchheim. The new Salzburg electronic signalling control centre was brought into use in May 1996. This is an Alcatel installation replacing five previous signalboxes.

In July 1996 ÖBB Telekom Service GmbH was established and a few months later the railway signed up with United Telecom Austria as its preferred partner for future developments which will aim to exploit the railway network to take full advantage of the newly liberalised telecommunications regime, not only in Austria but also internationally.

Track
Standard rail
Standard-gauge: 60.34, 53.81, 49.43 kg/m
Narrow-gauge: 35.65 kg/m
Length
Standard-gauge: 30 and 60 m
Narrow-gauge: 20 m
Crossties (sleepers)
Standard-gauge: impregnated wood 2,600 × 260 × 160 mm; concrete 2,600 × 300 max × 200 mm max; also some steel
Narrow-gauge: impregnated wood 1,600 × 200 × 130 mm; concrete 1,500 × 200 max × 160 mm max
Crossties spacing
Standard-gauge: 600-700 mm (1,667-1,429 per km)
Narrow-gauge: 700-810 mm (1,429-1,235 per km)
Rail fastening
Standard-gauge: resilient fastening, ribbed slabs, clips and bolts
Narrow-gauge: ribbed plates and elastic clips
Filling
Standard-gauge: broken stone ballast 30-65 mm
Narrow-gauge: broken stone ballast 25-35 mm

Diesel railcars or multiple-units

Class	Cars per unit	Motor cars per unit	Motored axles/car	Power/motor kW	Speed km/h	Units in service	First built	Mechanical	Builders Engine	Transmission
1,435 mm gauge										
5046	1(2)	1	2	375	100	8	1954	SGP	SGP S12a	H Voith
5047	1	1	2	419	120	100	1987	JW	OM444 LA	H Voith
5145	2(3)	2	2	405	115	8	1954	SGP	SGP S12a	H Voith
5146	1(2)	1	2	375	100	4	1959	SGP	SGP S12a	H Voith
5147	2	1	4	838	120	10	1992	JW	OM444LA	H Voith
760 mm gauge										
5090	1	1	4	235	70	14	1986	Knotz	MAN-D 2,866 LUE	E BBC
1,000 mm gauge										
5099	1	1	2	350	20	2	1964	SGP	S8 Bna	H Voith

Electric railcars or multiple-units

Class	Cars per unit	Motor cars per unit	Motored axles/car	Output/motor kW	Speed km/h	Units in service	First built	Builders Mechanical	Electrical
4010	6	1	4	620	150	29	1964	SGP	BBC
4020	3	1	4	300	120	120	1978	SGP	BES
4030.1/2	3	1	4	250	100	50	1956	SGP	BES
4030.2	3	1	4	315	120	22	1962	SGP	BES
4130	3	1		315	120	2	1958	SGP	Siemens
4855*	1	1		480	120	2	1989		Elin

*15kV/800 V DC

Thickness under sleepers
Standard-gauge: 200-300 mm
Narrow-gauge: 150 mm
Min or sharpest curvature
Standard-gauge: 9.7° = min radius of 180 m
Narrow-gauge: 29.1° = min radius of 60 m
Max gradient compensated
Standard-gauge: 4.6 per cent
Narrow-gauge: 2.5 per cent

Gauge width with max curvature
Standard-gauge: 20 mm
Narrow-gauge: 20 mm
Max super elevation
Standard-gauge: 160 mm
Narrow-gauge: 60 mm
Max axleload
Standard-gauge: 22.5 tonnes
Narrow-gauge: 12 tonnes   **UPDATED**

Graz-Köflach Railway

Graz-Köflacher Eisenbahn- und Bergbau-
Gesellschaft mbH (GKB)
Köflacher Gasse 41, A-8020 Graz
Tel: +43 316 5987   Fax: +43 316 5987 16

Key personnel
Managing Director: Mag Ing Josef Baumann

Gauge: 1,435 mm
Length: 96.5 km

Organisation
The railway, which, although a subsidiary of the Alpin-Montan group, is operated as an autonomous entity, heads south from its own station at Graz to Lieboch, where it branches northwest to Köflach and south to Wies. In addition, the company operates 28 bus routes in West Steiermark.

Passenger operations
The GKB operates a diesel railcar service.

Freight operations
Total freight tonnage in 1995 was 629,000, falling to 460,000 in 1996. Tonne-km were 11.1 million in 1995, falling to 9.0 million in 1996.

Improvements to existing lines
In 1988 a modernisation plan was formulated. Its main aims were double-tracking, an increase in maximum speed to 100 km/h, introduction of track-to-train radio, signalling renewal, acquisition of bilevel passenger cars, and electrification from Graz to Köflach and Lieboch to Wies/Eibiswald.

Traction and rolling stock
The company operates two steam locomotives, 13 diesel locomotives, 13 VT70 diesel trainsets, three VT10 diesel railcars and three trailers, 33 passenger coaches, including 15 bilevel passenger cars, three trailers, 15 two-axle passenger cars, and 138 freight wagons. The VT70 dmus are articulated twin-units with MTU engines and ABB electric transmissions, built by Simmering-Graz-Pauker to Linke-Hofmann-Busch design under licence.

GKB double-deck car

Diesel line-haul locomotives

Class	Wheel arrangement	Power kW	Speed km/h	Weight tonnes	No in service	First built	Builders Mechanical	Engine	Transmission
1500.1-6	B-B	1,103	100	64-72	6	1975	Jenbacher/ Henschel	Jenbacher LM1500	H Voith L720rU2
700	C	515	48	6	1	1977	MaK	MaK	H Voith L4r4U2
600	C	441	60	48	3	1973	Jenbacher	Jenbacher JW600	H Voith L26StV
1500.7	B-B	1,120	90	72	1	1992	MaK	MTU 12V 396 TC14	H Voith HDHL4r425tvz
1100	B-B	808	100	64	2	1961	Henschel	Caterpillar 3512DI-TA	H Voith HDHL 216rs

Diesel railcars

Class	Cars per unit	Motor cars per unit	Motored axles/car	Power/motor kW	Speed km/h	Units in service	First built	Mechanical	Builders Engine	Transmission
VT70	2	2	2	228	90	5	1980	SGP/LHB	Büssing BTYUE	E BBC AC-DC
VT70	2	2	2	237	90	8	1985	SGP/LHB	Büssing D2866 LUE	E BBC AC-DC
VT10	1	1	2	2 × 110	90	3	1953	Uerdingen	Büssing U10	M ZF-Gmeinder

Signalling and telecommunications
Track-to-train radio communication, supplied by AEG-Westinghouse, became operational in 1992.

Type of coupling: UIC-coupler, railcars and railbuses excepted
Type of braking: Compressed air

Track
Rail: (B) (S49) 49.43 kg/m
Crossties (sleepers): Wood, thickness 160 mm
Concrete, thickness 200 mm
Spacing: 1,538/km plain track and curves
Fastening: Rippenplatte and Pandrol
Min curvature radius: 181.25 m

Max gradient: 0.015%
Max axleload: 20 tonnes

UPDATED

Stern & Hafferl Light Railways

Verkehrsbetriebe Stern & Hafferl
PO Box 122, A-4810 Gmunden
Tel: +43 7612 33410   Fax: +43 7612 334 1202

Key personnel President: I Stern
General Manager, Railways: J Berger

Organisation
The group operates the following railways:
Gauge: 1,435 mm
Linz—Eferding—Waizenkirchen, 42.4 km, electrified at 800 V DC
Neumarkt—Waizenkirchen/Peuerbach, 16.5 km, electrified at 800 V DC
Bürmoos—Trimmelkam, 8.8 km, electrified at 1.1 kV DC
Lambach—Vorchdorf, 15.5 km, electrified at 800 V DC

Lambach—Haag am Hausruck, 26.3 km, electrified at 800 V DC and 15 kV 16⅔ Hz
Gauge: 1,000 mm
Gmunden—Vorchdorf, 14.7 km, electrified at 800 V DC
Vöcklamarkt—Attersee, 13.4 km, electrified at 800 V DC

Traction and rolling stock
The group owns 11 electric locomotives, 29 passenger cars, 40 light rail vehicles and 53 freight wagons.

UPDATED

Styrian Provincial Railways

Steiermärkische Landesbahnen
PO Box 893, Radeyzkystrasse 31, A-8011 Graz
Tel: +43 316 812 5810   Fax: +43 316 8125 8125

Key personnel
General Manager: F Brünner
Managers
    Finance: H Wittmann
    Traffic: A Pint

Chief Engineers
    Mechanical and Electrical: H J Schwab, R Zeller
    Track: F Brünner

Organisation
The group operates the following railways:
Gauge: 1,435 mm
Feldbach—Bad Gleichenberg, 21 km, electrified at 1.8 kV DC; Gleisdorf—Weiz, 15 km; Peggau—Übelbach, 10 km, electrified at 15 kV AC.

Gauge: 760 mm
Weiz—Birkfeld, 24 km; Kapfenberg—Aflenz, 13 km; Unzmarkt—Tamsweg, 65 km; Mixnitz—St Erhard, 10 km, electrified at 800 V DC.

Traction and rolling stock
The group owns seven steam, five electric and 17 diesel locomotives, five electric and six diesel railcars, three diesel railbuses and seven trailers, 25 passenger cars, eight baggage and postal cars, and 325 freight wagons.

VERIFIED

Vienna-Baden Railway (WLB)

AG der Wiener Lokalbahnen
PO Box 73, Eichenstrasse 1, A-1121 Vienna
Tel: +43 1 554910/554909   Fax: +43 1 5549 1050

Key personnel
General Managers: R Köhler, G Zimmerl

Gauge: 1,435 mm
Length: 28 km
Electrification: 28 km at 850 V DC

Traction and rolling stock
The railway operates four diesel locomotives, 31 electric railcars and 10 other passenger cars.

VERIFIED

AZERBAIJAN

Azerbaijani Railways (AZR)

ul Mustofaeva 230, 370010 Baku
Tel: +994 12 984467   Fax: +994 12 988547

Key personnel
President: V M Nadirli
Director General: Z A Mamedov
Deputy Director: M S Panakhov
Manager, International Affairs: R T Zeinalov

Gauge: 1,520 mm
Route length: 2,122 km
Electrification: 1,278 km at 3 kV DC

Political Background
Having borders with Russia, Georgia, Armenia and Iran, Azerbaijan gained independence from the USSR in 1991. The dispute with Armenia concerning the territory of Nagorno-Karabakh has affected railway operations though traffic to/from Russia resumed early in 1996.

Organisation
The network comprises the whole of the former SZhD's Azerbaijani Railway. Two main lines extend from the capital, Baku: the northern runs along the Caspian coast to Makhachkala in Russia, the other heads south to Alyat before turning inland to serve Kyurdamir, Yevlakh,

Kirovabad and Akstafa before reaching Tbilisi in Georgia. Both lines are double-track and electrified.

A third main line, only partially electrified, follows the Iranian border to Nakhichevan, from where there is an electrified link to Iran at Djolfa.

AZR operates a cross-Caspian ferry from Baku to Krasnovodsk in Turkmenistan.

Passenger operations
In 1989, traffic stood at 2,020 million passenger-km. By 1996, this had declined to 560 million passenger-km.

Freight operations
The country is rich in oil, ore and other resources, and agrarian produce and chemicals have also been important in freight shipments. The collapse of the Soviet Union hit traffic levels hard: down from 92 million tonnes (44,900 million tonne-km) in 1989 to 7 million tonnes (2,100 million tonne-km) in 1996. Early in 1996, traffic to/from Russia resumed on a limited scale, particularly for deliveries of Russian food and construction materials.

New lines
A second route into Iran has been long planned from the Astara port terminus of the line south from Baku. Its immediate goal is a mere 7 km across the border, to a site where customs and warehousing facilities are to be provided for Iranian imports which currently languish

awaiting clearance at Astara. Preliminary works started in early 1993, and some construction was undertaken in 1994-95.

Traction and rolling stock
At the end of 1996 the fleet comprised 152 electric and 142 diesel locomotives, 44 emus, 300 coaches and 13,000 freight wagons. Among the main line electric classes are the VL23, VL8 and VL11M, while diesel designs include the 3TE3, 2M62, and ChME3 types. Large amounts of stock in addition to those listed above were stored unserviceable.

In 1997, it was estimated that half the locomotive fleet was in need of replacement. New and refurbished oil tank wagons were also required, both for export of Azerbaijani oil and for transit oil from Turkmenistan and Kazakhstan.

Electrification
Azerbaijan was one of the pioneers of Soviet electrification, with the 33 km from Baku to Sabunchi and Surachami energised at 1.2 kV DC in 1926. Conversion to 1.5 kV followed in 1940, and to 3 kV in the 1960s. The most recent project was the Djolfa—Nopachen line, energised in 1989.

UPDATED

speed train services on the west side of the station. As all passengers for Eurostar services to London must first pass through security checks, an airport-style enclosed departure area for terminal platforms 1 and 2 has been created, with its own bar and toilet facilities. This departure area was ready for the start of Eurostar operation on 14 November 1994, and three more rebuilt platforms were brought back into service by May 1995.

It is intended that the through platforms will be used mainly by 'Thalys' (Paris—Brussels—Cologne/Amsterdam) four-voltage TGV trains, when they enter service in 1998. Already, however, the main concourse, a wide gallery with the usual offices and facilities along each flank, including a travel centre with 32 open counters, has been rebuilt to more spacious proportions. Overall roofing is being provided for all platforms. In 1993, Midi's adjoining four-level tram and metro station was remodelled and expanded to improve its interchange function.

Traction and rolling stock

At the end of 1996 SNCB traction and rolling stock comprised 376 electric locomotives, 590 diesel locomotives, 1,398 emu vehicles, four Eurostar trainsets, one Thalys high-speed trainset, 20 diesel railcars, 1,843 passenger coaches and 13,611 freight wagons.

Due to the increasing need for dual-voltage locomotives, in December 1995 SNCB and CFL (Luxembourg Railways) ordered a total of 80 3 kV DC/25 kV AC locomotives from GEC Alsthom ACEC. The locomotives cost BFr140.5 million each and deliveries were due to begin in December 1997, for completion in 2001.

By mid-1995, all the 140 two-car emus of so-called 'Break' Classes 80, 82 and 83 had been enlarged by the addition of central trailer vehicles. The trailers were built by Bombardier Eurorail with Fiat bogies. This capacity increase allowed many 1950s two-car emus to be withdrawn.

In 1997 deliveries were due to be completed for 163 Type I11 air conditioned cars, capable of 200 km/h operation between Ostend and Eupen and between Antwerp and Charleroi. They were constructed by Bombardier Eurorail.

Also placed with Bombardier Eurorail was an order for 120 three-car air conditioned 160 km/h Type AM96 emus with three-phase AC drives by ACEC, regenerative braking and comprehensive diagnostics. Delivery began early in 1996. Each unit has a single power car, motored on all axles for a total output of about 1,300 kW. Cab design follows that of Danish IC-3 trains. For operation to Lille—Flandres and through northern Luxembourg, 50 of the AM96 units are dual-voltage (3 kV DC/25 kV 50 Hz AC) versions and these were expected to enter service in 1997.

SNCB has acquired 84 second-hand type K4 passenger coaches from SNCF (French Railways) so that the oldest locomotive-hauled stock can be scrapped. From NS (Netherlands Railways), SNCB has purchased 25 diesel shunting locomotives for hauling works trains on the new high-speed lines.

In the freight sector, in 1995 SNCB received the final vehicles of 300 bilevel auto-transporter wagons ordered from Vagonka Poprad in Slovakia.

In 1997, SNCB ordered 100 Type Shimmns wagons from its own workshops.

High-speed rolling stock

SNCB owns four of the 38 Eurostar trainsets used jointly with SNCF and Eurostar UK Ltd for the London—Paris/Brussels high-speed operation (for details see the United Kingdom entry). A secure maintenance depot for these sets has been built at Brussels-Forest.

In March 1997 SNCB's first four-voltage Thalys trainset, numbered 4321, was delivered to the Forest Midi depot. It is part of an order for 17, jointly ordered by SNCB, NS, SNCF, and DB AG from GEC Alsthom. The rest of the fleet was due to arrive later in 1997; as a prelude, some tri-voltage TGV-R units were painted in the red Thalys livery and equipped to deal with the Dutch signalling system. They began working Paris—Brussels—Amsterdam services in June 1996.

Signalling and telecommunications

A serious fire at Brussels North signalbox on 5 December 1995 caused severe disruption to traffic. A temporary cabin was brought into service at the end of December 1995, and the new box was due to be completed early in 1997.

The first AM96 emu was delivered in 1996   *1996*

Eurostar at Brussels South   *1996*

Liquid crystal display inside new type I11 coach   *1997*

New boxes at St Ghislain and Leuven using advanced electronic technology were commissioned in 1995.

SNCB is progressively installing a track-to-train radio system, employing equipment supplied by Alcatel-Bell. Because of the country's dual language and the need for drivers to use the system with facility in both French- and Flemish-speaking territory, the system uses illuminated cab displays of pictogram codes rather than telephonic speech communication between control centre and train crew.

SNCB is in the course of replacing its traditional ATC (Automatic Train Control) system, based on contact between brushes mounted beneath traction units and track-mounted 'crocodiles', with an inductive transponder system known as Train-Balise-Locomotive (TBL). The TBL system — being installed first on the new high-speed lines — brakes the train automatically if the authorised speed is exceeded.

Signalling and track circuits have been modified on the Tournai—St Ghislain, Brussels—Mons, Brussels—Liège and Brussels—Antwerp routes to enable high-speed trains with three-phase drive to operate over these lines.

Modernisation of switching technology for Antwerp marshalling yard is being carried out by Siemens and the Duisburg-Wanheim unit of Thyssen AG. The work includes delivery of the MSR32 guidance system (a radio-controlled system for shunting locomotives) as well as systems installation.

Electrification

Over two-thirds of the SNCB network is electrified, and 85 per cent of trains are electrically hauled.

The St Ghislain—Quiévrain line was energised at 3kV DC in 1995. The 70 km Deinze—De Panne 3kV DC electrification was brought into service in June 1996.

While the Belgian network has thus far used the 3 kV DC system, the 88 km high-speed line from Lembeek to the French border is being electrified on the 25 kV AC system. The 142 km Dinant—Athus 'Athus—Meuse' line — an important freight artery between Antwerp and Luxembourg — is also programmed for 25 kV electrification. Work began on this project in 1995; it is due to be finished by the end of the decade.

Electrification of the 68 km from Rivage, 24 km out of Liège, to Gouvy has long been sought by Luxembourg Railways (CFL), so as to create a seamless electrified connection with CFL's own electrification. Agreement was reached in March 1997 for this to be effected, with the European Union bearing Bfr400 million, SNCB Bfr295 million and CFL Bfr150 million out of a total cost of Bfr 845 million. Like CFL's, the Belgian section's electrification will be at 25 kV 50 Hz AC. Completion was scheduled for 1999.

Track

Three-quarters of the SNCB network has been laid with continuously welded rail. Some 93 km of cwr were installed in 1995.

Standard rail: Flat bottom, 50 and 60 kg/m main track, 50 kg/m secondary track

Length: Main track: 243 m rails long-welded. Secondary track: jointed 28 m rails

Joints: 4-hole fishplates

Rail fastenings: Sole plates and screws, mostly K-fastenings on wood sleepers. New track Pandrol fastenings. Pads are inserted under the rail when concrete sleepers are used.

Crossties (sleepers): Existing track: generally oak, 2,600 × 280 × 140 mm. Sections of welded-rail track have been laid with three types of concrete sleeper: Type RS (two blocks joined by a steel bar) with Type RN flexible rail fastenings; Type VDH (two blocks joined by a steel bar) with Pandrol fastenings; and Type DMD (monobloc prestressed) with Pandrol fastenings.

Spacing: 1,667/km on main line track; 1,370-1,590/km secondary routes

Filling: Broken stone or slag

Min curvature radius

Main line: 2.18° = 800 m

Secondary line: 3.5° = 500 m

Running lines: 8.75° = 200 m

Sidings: 11.7° = 150 m

Max gradient: 2.5%

Max altitude: 536 m at Hockai on Pepinster—Trois Ponts line

Max axleload: Certain locomotives have axleloads of 24 tonnes. Except for certain bridges they can operate anywhere on the system, subject to speed restriction.

UPDATED

SNCB Class 09 emu   *1997*

Diesel locomotives

Class	Wheel arrangement	Power hp	Speed km/h	Weight tonnes	No in service	First built	Builders Mechanical	Builders Engine	Builders Transmission
51	Co-Co	1,950	120	117	79	1961	Cockerill-Ougrée	Cockerill-Ougrée	E ACEC/SEM
59	Bo-Bo	1,750	120	87	10	1955	Cockerill/B&M	Cockerill (licence Baldwin)	E ACEC (licence Westinghouse)
52/53/54	Co-Co	1,720	120	108	33	1955	AFB	GM	E GM/Smit
55	Co-Co	1,950	120	110	39	1961	BN	GM	E ACEC/SEM (licence GM)
62	Bo-Bo	1,425	120	80	104	1961	BN	GM	E GM
75	B-B	1,460	120 82	79	6	1965	BN	GM — 2 speed Type 12-567DI	H Voith L216
71	B-B	900	80 50	74	3	1962	ABR	ABC	H Voith L217
91	B	335	35 40	36	33	1961	Cockerill/BN ABC	GM	H Twin-Disc Q Cockerill
84	C	550	30 50	55.8	9	1958	ABR/B&M	ABC 6 DUS	H Voith L37U
85	C	550	30 50	57.3	25	1956	Haine St Pierre	ABC 6 DXS	H Voith L37U/ SEMT.B.122
80	C	650	30 60	52.1	39	1960	BN/ABR	Maybach GTO 6A	H Voith L37
70	Bo-Bo	700	50	83	6	1954	B&M	ABC	E ACEC (licence Westinghouse)
82	C	650	60	57	75	1965-66	BN/ABR	ABC 6 DXS	H Voith L217U
73	C	750	60	56	95	1965-68	BN	Cockerill-Ougrée 6 TH 695 SA	H Voith L217U
74	C	750	60	59	10	1977	BN	ABC 6 DXS	H Voith L217U
76	B-B	660	100	72	25	1955	Allan	Storelf	H Heemaf

B&M = Baume & Marpent

Electric multiple-units

Class	Cars per unit	Motor cars per unit	Motored axles per car	Power/car kW	Speed km/h	Units in service	First built	Builders Mechanical	Builders Electrical
00/1	2	2	2	310	130	21	1956	La Brugeoise Nicaise	ACEC/ SEM
00/3	2	2	2	310	130	117	1962	BN/Ragheno	ACEC
05	2	2	4	170	140	63	1967	BN/Ragheno/ABR	ACEC
05 Airport	2	2	2	340	140	6	1970	BN/Ragheno/ABR	ACEC
06	2	2	2	340	140	118	1970	BN/SNCB	ACEC
08	4	2	4	1,360	140	44	1975	BN	ACEC
03 ('Break')	3	1	4	1,240	160	137	1981	BN	ACEC
09	2	1	4	680	120	52	1988	BN	ACEC
96*	3	1	4	1,400	160	10	1996	BN	ACEC

*Dual-voltage 3 kV DC/25 kV

Electric locomotives

Class	Wheel arrangement	Output kW continuous/ one-hour	Speed km/h	Weight tonnes	No in service	First built	Builders Mechanical	Builders Electrical
20	Co-Co	5,130/5,150	160	110	24	1975	BN	ACEC
22	Bo-Bo	1,740/1,880	130	87	49	1954	BN	ACEC/SEM
23	Bo-Bo	1,740/1,880	130	93.3	83	1955	AM	ACEC/SEM
25	Bo-Bo	1,740/1,880	130	83.9	14	1960	BN	ACEC/SEM
25.5[1]	Bo-Bo	1,740/1,880	130	85	8	modified 1973	BN	ACEC/SEM
26	B-B	2,240/2,355 * 2,470/2,590	130	82.4	34	1964	BN	ACEC
28	Bo-Bo	1,620/1,985	130	85	2	1949	B&M	ACEC/SEM
15[2]	Bo-Bo	2,620/2,780	160	77.7	5	1962	BN	ACEC
16[3]	Bo-Bo	2,620/2,780	160	82.6	7	1966	BN	ACEC
18[3]	C-C	4,320/4,450	180	113	6	1973	BN	ALSTHOM
27	Bo-Bo	4,150/4,250	160	85	60	1981	BN	ACEC
21	Bo-Bo	3,130/3,310	160	84	59	1984	BN	ACEC
11	Bo-Bo	3,130/3,310	160	84	12	1985	BN	ACEC
12	Bo-Bo	3,130/3,310	160	84	12	1986	BN	ACEC
19	Bo-Bo		160		1	1994	BN	ACEC

* First five locomotives only
[1] Dual-current 1.5 kV/3 kV DC
[2] Tri-current 1.5 kV/3 kV DC/25 kV AC
[3] Quadri-current 1.5 kV/3 kV DC/15 kV 16⅔ Hz/25 kV 50 Hz

BENIN

Ministry of Public Works and Transport

PO Box 16, Cotonou
Tel: +229 313380

Key personnel
Minister: Georges Kédou
Director General: A Glele

VERIFIED

Organisation Commune Benin-Niger des Chemins de Fer et des Transports (OCBN)

PO Box 16, Cotonou
Tel: +229 313380   Fax: +229 314150
Tx: 5210

Key personnel
Director General: Enidé Krilanyossi
Director of Motive Power and Rolling Stock:
   Edmond Agbla
Director of Way and Works: Alzouma Younsa
Director of Operations: Gabriel Alaye
Director of Supplies: J Hinson

Director of Finance: M Ousseini
Director of Personnel: A Sonon

Gauge: 1,000 mm
Route length: 578 km

Organisation
OCBN operates, on behalf of Niger and Benin, a single-track metre-gauge railway consisting of the Northern line from Cotonou to Parakou via Pahou (438 km), the Eastern line from Cotonou to Pobé (107 km), and the Western line linking Pahou and Ségboroué (33 km). From Parakou freight traffic is transported by road to the Niger capital of Niamey.

Passenger operations
In 1994 the railway carried 600,000 passengers (107 million passenger-km).

Freight operations
In 1994 OCBN carried 250 million tonne-km of freight.

New lines
A cherished project is the extension of the Northern line from Parakou to Niamey, Niger's capital, a distance of 650 km. At present, Niger traffic has to be road-hauled to Parakou. An agreement was signed in 1976 between Niger and Benin for construction of a rail link, since three-quarters of Niger's exports are channelled through

Cotonou, and work was started in 1978 but made scant progress. Neither the World Bank nor any other aid agency has been prepared to help finance the scheme.

Improvements to existing lines
A successful application was made in 1991 to France's Fund for International Co-operation (CCCE) for a loan worth US$8.6 million. It was to be applied to rehabilitation of the Benin segment of the Cotonou—Parakou Northern line.

Further rehabilitation work was undertaken using fresh supplies of new rail delivered from British Steel in 1994.

OCBN has so far been unsuccessful in gaining external finance for modernisation of the Cotonou—Pobé Eastern line and its extension to a cement factory at Onigbulo with a projected output of 500,000 tonnes a year. Half the output would be for Nigeria, and Belgian finance has been offered for construction of a railway from the cement plant to Ilaro, northwest of Lagos, in Nigeria.

Traction and rolling stock
At last report, locomotives in operation totalled eight Alsthom BB500 and 12 Alsthom BB600 diesel-electrics, plus six shunting tractors. Soulé railcars totalled seven and other stock consisted of 31 Soulé passenger coaches and trailers and 296 freight wagons.

VERIFIED

BOLIVIA

Ministry of Economic Development

Palacio de Comunicaciones, piso 18, Avenida Mariscal Santa Cruz, La Paz
Tel: +591 2 377320   Fax: +591 2 371347

Key personnel
Secretary of Transport: A Revollo

VERIFIED

Bolivian National Railways

Empresa Nacional de Ferrocarriles (ENFE)
ANDEAN NETWORK
PO Box 428, Estación Central, Plaza Zalles, La Paz
Tel: +591 2 327401/354756
Fax: +591 2 392677/392106

Key personnel
General Manager: R Suarez M
Manager, Administration: L Rivera S
Manager, Commercial: R Soria R
Manager, Operations: P Adrian C

EASTERN NETWORK
PO Box 108, Santa Cruz
Tel: +591 33 348467   Fax: +591 33 327507

Key personnel
General Manager: J Baldivieso H
Manager, Administration: M A Villarroel M
Manager, Commercial: J Mercado B
Manager, Operations: H Zumaran P

Gauge: 1,000 mm
Route length: 3,652 km

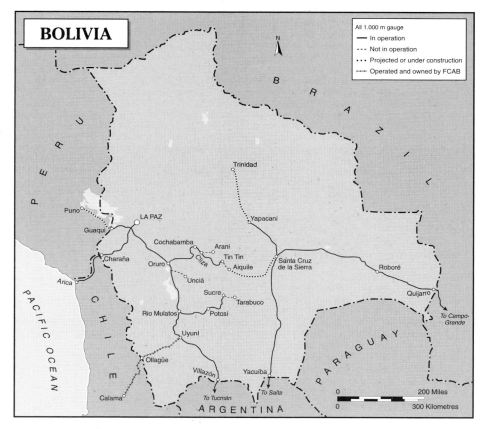

Political background
In 1995 the Ministry of Capitalisation invited bids for a 50 per cent shareholding in a new public/private corporation holding ENFE's assets. Seven bidders came forward, namely Antofagasta and Bolivia Holdings, Cruz Blanca and FEPASA of Chile and Anacostia and Pacific, CSX, Railroad Development Corporation and RailTex of the USA. Cruz Blanca subsequently paid US$39 million for the shares, with the remainder retained by the government to form the basis of private pension funds for its citizens.

Management of the railway passed to Cruz Blanca for 40 years. In 1996 Antofagasta and Bolivia Holdings, parent of Chile's Antofagasta, Chili and Bolivia Railway (FCAB), purchased a 73 per cent stake in Cruz Blanca's share of ENFE's Andean network and 23 per cent of its share of the Eastern network. FCAB connects with the Andean network at Ollagüe.

Cruz Blanca believes that the former Eastern network of ENFE has the most potential, because of strategic links with Brazil and Argentina. Cruz Blanca has signed an agreement with the government which will see the phased withdrawal of subsidies for soya bean traffic.

Organisation
Bolivia is a landlocked country and lack of communications has made virtually impossible the sort of economic development which the country needs. ENFE's two railways, the Andean (2,275 km) and Eastern networks (1,377 km) connect only via Argentina. They are of major importance as a means of access to ports on the Pacific and Atlantic Oceans via neighbouring countries. These international railway connections, some of which have fallen into disrepair, are as follows: with Chile to the Pacific ports of Arica and Antofagasta; with Argentina to the Atlantic ports of Rosario and Buenos Aires; with Brazil

Santa Cruz Estacion on Bolivia's Eastern Network   *1997*

to the Atlantic port of Santos; with Peru (by ship across Lake Titicaca to Puno) to the Pacific port of Matarani.

In 1995 ENFE employed 3,894 staff, with 2,454 assigned to the Andean network and 1,440 to the Eastern network. The Andean network carried around 40 per cent of ENFE's total freight traffic in 1994 and around 42 per cent of total passenger traffic.

Traffic

	1993	1994
Passenger journeys (000)	854.6	750
Passenger-km (million)	348.9	285
Freight tonnes (000)	—	1,400
Freight tonne-km (million)	761.9	778

New lines
There are long-term aspirations to bridge the 300 km gap between ENFE's Andean network at Tin Tin and its Eastern network at Santa Cruz.

Diesel locomotives

Class	Wheel arrangement	Power kW	Speed km/h	Weight tonnes	No in service	First built	Mechanical	Builders Engine	Transmission
950	Bo-Bo-Bo	970	70	81.6	9	1968	Hitachi/ Mitsubishi	MAN VGV 22/30 ATL	E Hitachi/ Mitsubishi
1000	Bo-Bo-Bo	1,550	100	90	7	1978	Hitachi/ Mitsubishi	MTU 12 V 956TB 11	E Hitachi/ Mitsubishi
521	Bo-Bo	280	25	30	1	1968	Hitachi	Hitachi MAN RGV 18/12 TL	H Hitachi
841	Bo-Bo	395	40	55	1	1980	Hitachi Mitsubishi	MTU V396 TC 12	H Hitachi
U 20C	Co-Co	1,550	103	89.9	6	1977	GE	FDL 12 GE	E GE
U 10B	Bo-Bo	590	103	50.8	7	1977	GE	Caterpillar D 398	E GE
980	Bo-Bo	551	60	66.5	1	1987	Sulzer	MTU	E Sulzer
846	Bo-Bo	480	60	66.4	2	1950	Sulzer	Sulzer	EM Sulzer

Diesel railbuses

Cars per unit	Motor cars per unit	Motored axles/car	Power hp per motor	Speed km/h	No in service	First built	Mechanical	Builders Engine	Transmission
2	1	2	340/240	80	8	1967/78	Ferrostaal	Cummins NHHRTO-6	M Zahnfabrik
2	1	2	335/240	90	3	1978	Ferrostaal	Cummins	H Voith T 211 R

Japanese-built Class 1000 diesel locomotive (foreground) at Guaracachi   *1997*

Traction and rolling stock
In 1995 ENFE operated 52 diesel locomotives, 12 diesel railbuses, 95 passenger coaches and 1,949 freight wagons. The Andean network operated 27 locomotives, seven railbuses, 53 passenger coaches and 1,280 freight wagons, with the remainder allocated to the Eastern network. Poor diesel locomotive availability forced ENFE to bring two steam locomotives out of retirement at the end of 1995.

Signalling and telecommunications
In 1992, UN-funded procurement agency OSP called for tenders to supply a radio and telephone communications system for ENFE. The railway's 1994 budget included US$2 million for signalling and telecommunications.

Track
Rail: ASCE 29.76, 37.2 and 39 kg/m
BSS 32.24 and 37.2 kg/m
Crossties (sleepers): Wood and steel
Spacing: 1,400-1,640/km
Min curvature radius: 15°
Max gradient: 3% compensated on curves
Max axleload: 18 tonnes

UPDATED

La Paz station

1997

BOSNIA-HERCEGOVINA

Railways of Bosnia-Hercegovina

Željeznice Bosne i Hercegovine (ŽBH)
Omladinska 2, Sarajevo
Tel: +387 871 618 448   Fax: +387 871 144 6255

Key personnel
President of the Board of Administration:
    Dragutin Kosovac
Director General: Dipl Ing Brankovic
Assistant Director General: Jasminko Aksamija
Technical Manager: Midhat Terzic

Gauge: 1,435 mm
Route length (1991): 1,021 km
Electrification (1991): 795 km at 25 kV 50 Hz AC

Political background
ŽBH was formed out of the Bosnian division of the unified railways of Yugoslavia when Bosnia-Hercegovina declared its independence in 1992. The railways were severely affected by the war with Serbia. In February 1995 a service was restored on the 7 km route to the suburb of Alipasin Most.

A through service from Sarajevo to Mostar and Ploče resumed in 1997. Trains started running between Sarajevo and Mostar in July 1996, the first since 1992. Much of the funding for replacement of bridges and rolling stock came from Germany. The line via Ploče has been named as Bosnia's main route to the sea, and has been granted free trade zone status.

In July 1996, ŽBH and Yugoslav Railways (JŽ) agreed to resume cross-border services between the two states.

Passenger and freight operations
In 1991, 554 million passenger-km were travelled on the railways of Bosnia, and 1,946 million tonne-km of freight hauled.

Improvements to existing lines
The electrified main line from the capital, Sarajevo, to the port of Ploče, was reopened in July 1996. Two major bridges on the Neretva river were rebuilt, catenary replaced, and trackbed restored on a stretch south of Sarajevo. Rebuilding was carried out with German assistance.

Traction and rolling stock
In 1991 there were 87 diesel locomotives, 87 electric locomotives, 434 passenger coaches (including two dining cars, 28 couchettes and 14 sleeping cars), 9,405 freight wagons, 7 two-car dmus and 24 three-car emus. During the conflict, some stored steam locomotives were revived to provide local services. In 1996, 25 Class 232 diesel-electrics (ex-DR of 1973 vintage) were supplied by a DB AG (German Railway) following refurbishment at Cottbus, along with components and equipment to help improve rolling stock availability.

VERIFIED

BOTSWANA

Ministry of Works, Transport and Communication

Private Bag 007, Gaborone
Tel: +267 358500   Fax: +267 313303

Key personnel
Minister: D K Kwelagobe
Permanent Secretary: A V Lionjanga
Deputy Permanent Secretary: M J M Moatshe

Botswana Railways (BR)

Private Bag 52, Mahalapye
Tel: +267 411375   Fax: +267 411385

Key personnel
Chairman: A V Lionjanga
Chief Civil Engineer: E C C Chimidza
General Manager: A Ramji
Chief Signals and Telecommunications Engineer:
    B R Gaiceleboise
Assistant General Manager (Finance): Bajrang L Bagra
Assistant General Manager (Human Resources):
    Batlhatswi S Tsayang
Assistant General Manager (Rolling Stock):
    Bennet M Katai

Assistant General Manager (Business Management):
    Babe C Botana
Number of staff employed: 1,217

Gauge: 1,067 mm
Route length: 888 km

Political background
The country is traversed by 640 km of main line between Ramatlabama (north of Mafikeng, South Africa) and Bakaranga (south of Plumtree, Zimbabwe) with three branch lines, formerly managed by National Railways of Zimbabwe. Botswana Railways took over operation of the railway in 1986 and the following year took control of the assets and administrative services. The 175 km branch from Francistown to serve soda ash deposits at Sua Pan was opened in 1991.

Economic and political changes in southern Africa have led to a reduction in transit traffic moving through Botswana, while drought-induced recession caused further decline. An integrated transport policy to assist the railway in competing with road hauliers on an equitable basis was being looked at.

Traffic	1992-93	1993-94	1994-95
Freight tonnes (million)	2.85	1.71	1.75
Freight tonne-km (million)	1,266	585	626
Passenger journeys (000)	355.1	330.8	525

Finance (million pula)			
Revenue	*1992-93*	*1993-94*	*1994-95*
Passengers	6.5	5.6	7.2
Freight	90.1	60.2	66.6
Other income	13.6	15.6	12.9
Total	111.28	82.29	86.85
Expenditure			
Total	100.15	100.58	89.87

Passenger operations
FY93-94 saw a further decline in passenger traffic, with continued poor demand for the *Blue Train* day service launched in 1991 between Gaborone and Francistown. Accommodation on this service was reduced as a result. On the other hand, the new commuter railcar service between Lobatse and Gaborone was immediately successful, and a similar train has been introduced from Pilane to Gaborone.

Through-running to South Africa was resumed in early 1995 when the Bulawayo—Lobatse train was extended to Mafikeng.

Freight operations
As a result of crop failures brought on by drought, large quantities of imported grain were handled during 1991-92. This traffic continued into 1993, helping to produce a record haul of 2.85 million tonnes for FY92-93.

By contrast, 1993-94 was disappointing, with shortfalls against budgeted volumes in all commodities. Transit traffic, 386,000 tonnes, was at an all-time low, and while salt and soda ash moved from Sua Pan increased in absolute terms, this was still well below budget.

There continued to be serious concern over the low levels of traffic on the Sua Pan line, which serves the Soda Ash Botswana development, with levels of traffic much below those contracted for. With high interest payments necessary on the assets acquired to move the traffic, BR was forced to levy guaranteed minimum charges for 1991-92 and 1992-93, and in 1994-95 made a provision of 24 million pula for losses likely to arise from the liquidation of SAB.

Improvements to existing lines
Following completion of track re-laying for the 88 km between Francistown and Serule, and the 87 km between Gaborone and Artesia, a further 214 km is being rehabilitated with financial and technical aid from China. This enables maximum speed to be raised from 90 km/h to at least 100 km/h. At the same time, 11 crossing loops have been extended to accommodate longer trains.

Traction and rolling stock
Botswana Railways operates 10 Krupp diesel-electrics, 19 Type GT22LC-2 diesel-electrics and 10 short-haul/shunting diesel locomotives. Freight wagon stock totals 1,026; there are 47 passenger coaches and a railcar.

Recent deliveries include: 330 wagons for soda ash traffic over the Sua Pan line, and coal haulage from Morupule; and 41 air conditioned passenger cars, including five buffet and six sleeping cars. The wagon contract was awarded to China National Machinery Import & Export Corporation, and the passenger car contract to Mitsui (but the vehicles were built in South Africa).

Signalling and telecommunications
Technical assistance from Sweden, which started in 1986, came to an end in 1993, and the S&T department is now managed almost entirely by local engineers.

The Radio Electronic Token Block system now controls the 878 km of line. A modification and improvement plan was implemented in 1993 and work continues to improve reliability. A back-up VHF radio system has been installed to help keep trains moving when there is a communications breakdown. In progress early in 1997 was an automatic block signalling scheme between Rakhuna and Mafikeng, a distance of 34.5 km.

Operation of Gaborone station and the immediate area was improved by installation of relay/programmable logic controller hybrid interlocking, completed in 1993. The

A pair of GM-built locomotives head-up a freight train leaving Francistown for Zimbabwe (D Delaney)
1996

Diesel locomotives

Class	Builder's type	Wheel arrangement	Power kW	Speed km/h	Weight tonnes	No in service	First built	Mechanical	Builders Engine	Transmission
BD 1	UM 20C	Co-Co	1,500	103	96	10	1982	Krupp	GE 7FDL 12	E GE
BD 2	GT22LC-2	Co-Co	1,700	107	96.6	19	1986	GM	GM 645E3B-12	E GM
BD 3	U15C	Co-Co	1,120	65	97.9	10	1991	GE	GE FDL8	E GE

project was carried out by Telkor of South Africa, with the interlocking itself supplied by Spoornet.

A network of microcomputers has been installed using Novell Netware. A vehicle control system has been written 'in house', primarily to calculate vehicle hire charges and produce operational statistics, and the first phase of a personnel management system implemented. Systems to monitor vehicle utilisation, schedule preventive maintenance and automate the daily operating diary have been developed by the railway as an adjunct to the vehicle control system. A new stock control system was implemented in 1994.

Type of coupler in standard use
Passenger cars: Alliance 8X6 vacuum
Freight cars: Alliance 8X6

Type of braking in standard use, locomotive-hauled stock: Vacuum

Track
Rail type and weight: Flat-bottom 40, 50 kg/m
Sleepers: Concrete, spaced 1,429/km in 50 kg/m cwr; steel, spaced 1,445/km in 40 kg/m jointed track
Fastenings: Fist on concrete sleepers, clip bolt on steel
Min curvature radius: 200 m
Max gradient: 1.6%
Max permissible axleload: 16.32 tonnes

UPDATED

BRAZIL

Ministry of Transport

Esplanada dos Ministérios, Bloco R, 6° Andar, 70044-900 Brasilia DF
Tel: +55 61 224 0185   Fax: +55 61 225 0915

Key personnel
Minister of Transport: O Klein
Executive Secretary: C Ivanov Lucarevschi
Director, Rail Transport: C B Motta e Silva
VERIFIED

Carajás Railway (EFC)

Estrada de Ferro Carajás
Avenida dos Portugueses s/n, Praia do Boqueirão, São Luís, Maranhão, CEP 65085-850
Tel: +55 98 218 4444   Fax: +55 98 218 4520

Key personnel
General Manager: R M Figueira
Managers
Administration: S J B da Silva
Transportation: L E de O Neto
Permanent Way: N B da Silva
Mechanical and Electrical: P L Bernhard
Assessor: R M Figueira

Gauge: 1,600 mm; 1,000 mm
Route length: 892 km; 105 km

Political background
EFC is owned by the state-owned mining group Companhia Vale do Rio Doce (qv), which has been proposed for privatisation, with the company's railway assets being sold off separately.

Traffic (million)	1993	1994
Freight tonnes	38.22	43.85
Freight tonne-km	36,825	42,008
Passenger-km	9.91	13.017

Finance (US$ million)		
Revenue	1993	1994
Passengers	1.76	2.38
Freight	328.79	316.94
Other	0.12	0.13
Total	330.67	319.45

Expenditure		
Staff/personnel	35.38	40.56
Materials and services	69.87	97.42
Depreciation	60.22	58.04
Total	165.47	196.02

Passenger operations
Principally a freight railway, EFC operates three trains (of around 16 coaches) a week in each direction between São Luís and Parauapebas (850 km). EFC has improved station facilities and lengthened platforms, and was reported to be considering the purchase of additional passenger coaches to operate six or seven trains a week in each direction.

Three trains with passenger accommodation also operate each week in both directions on the Açailândia—Imperatriz branch.

Freight operations
EFC's principal traffic is iron ore, moved from the mine at Carajás to Ponta da Madeira in trains comprising 202 ore wagons with a total capacity of 20,400 tonnes, hauled by three locomotives. A return trip, including crew changes, refuelling, loading and unloading, usually takes 56 hours and on average six loaded and six empty trains are in operation each day. EFC moves around 40.5 million tonnes of ore each year.

Other freight traffic amounts to around 3.5 million tonnes a year. Soya products, fertiliser, pig iron, cement, petroleum products, road vehicles and other commodities are carried on freight trains composed of around 60 wagons.

New lines
CVRD has contemplated the construction of a 200 km branch to a bauxite mine and more recently a 1,000 km extension into the grain-producing Cerrado area to the southeast.

Improvements to existing lines
EFC plans to construct an additional crossing loop on its trunk route between the points Km 422 and Km 457. This

EFC diesel locomotives

Builder's type	Wheel arrangement	Power kW	Speed km/h	Weight tonnes	No in service	First built	Mechanical	Builders Engine	Transmission
C30-7B	Co-Co	2,465	80	180	41	1984	GE	GE 7FDL16	E GE
C40-8	Co-Co	3,018	80	180	4	1989	GE	GE FDL16	E GE
SD40-2	Co-Co	2,429	80	180	29	1985	GM	EMD 645E3C	E EMD
SD60M	Co-Co	3,056	80	180	2	1991	GM	EMD 16-710G3A	E EMD
GT26-CU2	Co-Co	2,208	80	180	2	1984	GM	EMD-16-645E3B	E EMD
U26	Co-Co	2,024	80	180	2	1982	GE	GE 7FDL12-Turbo AL	E GE

EFC iron ore train   **1995**

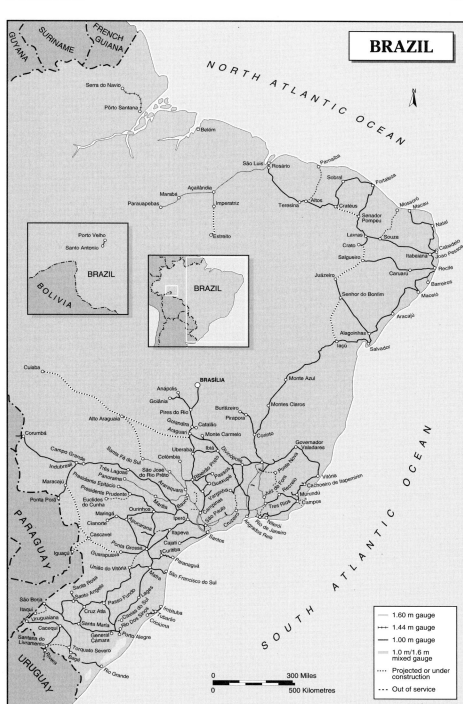

would allow the amount of ore moved in a year to be increased from the current maximum of 43.6 million tonnes. EFC's 1996 investment budget made provision for US$1.26 million to be spent on freight yards.

Traction and rolling stock
Rolling stock comprises 80 diesel-electric locomotives, 35 passenger coaches (including two buffet cars and three luggage vans), 2,974 ore wagons and 629 other freight wagons.

Operations on the 1,000 mm gauge Açailândia–Imperatriz branch are conducted with two diesel-electric locomotives, one passenger coach and 12 freight wagons.

At the end of 1994, EFC had received 25 hopper wagons from FNV as part of an order for 80 wagons, each with a capacity of 97 tonnes. EFC's 1996 investment budget made provision for the purchase of two diesel-electric locomotives (US$4.84 million) and 36 freight wagons (US$2.34 million).

Signalling and telecommunications
Ansaldo Trasporti of Italy gained the contract to equip EFC's main line with a comprehensive CTC and ATC system (all locomotives are ATC fitted), controlled from a centre at Ponta de Madeira. EFC's 1996 investment budget made provision for US$4.24 million to be spent on signalling and train control systems.

Track
Rails: 68 kg/m long-welded
Fastenings: Pandrol or Denik
Crossties (sleepers): Timber, creosote-treated, thickness 170 mm, spaced 540 mm between centres
Min curve radius: 860 m
Max gradient: 0.4% loaded trains, 1% empty trains
Max axleload: 30 tonnes

UPDATED

Centre Atlantic Railway

Political background
In June 1996, the second concession under the government's privatisation programme for RFFSA (qv), for the Centre-East Network, was sold. The network connects such cities as Goiânia, Brasília, Salvador, Vitória, Belo Horizonte and Rio de Janeiro. The so-called Tacumã Consortium, which bought the concession, consists of CVRD subsidiary Tacumã Mining, Valia (the CVRD pension fund), intermodal operator Interférrea, local steel and cement producers, plus the Varbra investment group. From the US come shortline operator Railtex, the Bank of Boston and investment group Ralp Partners. The buyer was the only bidder at the auction and paid the minimum price of Cr316.9 million (US$316.87 million). The concession covers an area running from Rio de Janeiro in the southeast to the northeastern state of Sergipe and inland to the capital Brasilia. Connection is possible with CVRD's own railway (qv).

Under the terms of the sale, the consortium must invest at least Cr900 million over the first 30 years of the concession, including Cr300 million in the first six years. CVRD said investments might exceed this minimum, as much of the network's rolling stock is in poor condition, with 126 of the concession's 394 locomotives out of service. Of the 9,380 wagons, 85 per cent are under 25 years old.

In 1993, this former RFFSA region had net operating revenues of US$200 million and handled 6.8 billion tonne/km, which dropped to only 6.3 billion tonne/km in 1995. Main traffic is limestone, grain, iron ore and steel products.

NEW ENTRY

Companhia Brasileira de Trens Urbanos (CBTU)

Estrada Velha da Tijuca 77, Rio de Janeiro RJ, CEP 20531-080
Tel: +55 21 288 1992   Fax: +55 21 571 6149

Key personnel
President: Paulino Talarico Correa
Finance and Administration Director:
  Carlos Alberto Capelleti Sarmento

Gauge: 1,600 mm; 1,000 mm
Route length: 38 km; 210 km
Electrification: 52 km at 3 kV DC

Political background
CBTU was formed in 1984 as the urban transit management subsidiary of RFFSA, but has operated independently of the national railway since 1994. President Collor took up the intention of his predecessor to break up CBTU and pass control of its urban railways to the relevant state governments. He indicated that if the transfer were achieved, he would seek, in consort with the local authorities, to invest US$3,500 million in development of CBTU services. In the interim he proposed in 1990 complete withdrawal of state financial support for CBTU.

The dissolution of CBTU took a step further when, in late 1991, President Collor signed an agreement with the Governor of São Paulo state for the latter to take over responsibility for CBTU's 170 km network in the São Paulo metropolis. In 1994 São Paulo services passed to CPTM (qv) and CBTU's Rio de Janeiro network was also transferred to state control, henceforth operating under the name Flumitrens (qv).

At the start of 1996, CBTU continued to operate suburban services in Belo Horizonte, Recife, Fortaleza, Salvador and João Pessoa, Natal and Maceió. Agreements had been signed with the state governments of Minas Gerais and Pernambuco for the transfer of the Belo Horizonte and Recife systems to local companies, with negotiations continuing over the transfer of the remaining five systems.

Finance
CBTU earned US$18.8 million in passenger revenue in 1995, with a further US$1.2 million in income from other sources. Total expenditure was US$395 million; personnel costs made up US$281 million of this total.

CBTU electric multiple-units

Class	Cars per unit	Motor cars per unit	Motored axles/car	Output/motor kW	Speed km/h	Units in service	First built	Builders Mechanical	Electrical
Belo Horizonte									
BH	4	2	4	315	90	5	1985	Cobrasma	MTE
Recife									
REC	4	2	4	280	90	25	1985	CISM/MAN	GEC/Villares

Passenger operations
Belo Horizonte
A Franco-Brazilian group headed by Francorail won a contract worth FFr900 million to establish the first 12.5 km Belo Horizonte Central—Eldorado stage of a 3 kV DC, 1,600 mm-gauge, electrified suburban system that was planned eventually to total 55.5 km. By the start of 1996 the system had reached 17 km, linking Eldorado with Santa Inês and employing a staff of 546. In 1995 over 15.3 million passengers were carried using a fleet of eight four-car emus.

Bids have been called for the construction of four extensions totalling 6.6 km. These form part of a US$100 million project to improve Belo Horizonte services; three four-car emus were delivered by Cobrasma in 1995 to enable a service to be run every 10 minutes using 15 units in total. Tenders have been called for an automatic ticketing system and CBTU has been negotiating finance for a US$198 million extension project to link Minas Shopping with Venda Nova.

Recife
CBTU's 53 km Recife network carried 37.2 million passengers in 1995, employing 1,612 staff. A fleet of 17 four-car emus is in use on the electrified portion (21 km) of the system. Other services are hauled by five diesel-electric locomotives. In 1995 CBTU was negotiating finance with the World Bank for a US$204 million upgrading programme for Recife.

Fortaleza
The Fortaleza network carried over 7.7 million passengers in 1995. Services were operated with a staff of 439 over 46 route-km using a fleet of 45 passenger coaches and seven General Electric U-10B diesel-electric locomotives.

Salvador
CBTU operates a single 14 km electrified line in Salvador

which carried over 1.5 million passengers in 1995. A total of 221 staff were employed at the end of 1995.

Maceió
Maceió's suburban system consists of a single non-electrified 32 km line serving seven stations, which carried over 2.7 million passengers in 1995. Operations were conducted with two diesel-electric locomotives, 21 passenger coaches and 104 employees.

João Pessoa
João Pessoa's 30 km, eight-station non-electrified system carried over 1.7 million passengers in 1995. The rolling stock fleet comprised two Alco RS-8 diesel-electric locomotives and 17 passenger coaches and a total of 98 staff were employed at the end of 1995.

Natal
Natal's 56 km suburban system serves 17 stations and operated with two Alco RS-8 diesel-electric locomotives, 20 passenger coaches and 124 employees in 1995. A total of 1.3 million passengers were carried in 1995.

Improvements to existing lines
In 1995 over US$168 million was spent on track renewal, rolling stock, capacity improvements and new equipment, including CTC. In connection with the agreed transfer of the Belo Horizonte network to the state of Minas Gerais and Recife operations to Pernambuco, CBTU was negotiating in mid-1995 with the World Bank and the federal government for US$196 million for upgrading the Belo Horizonte system and US$204 million for improvements in Recife.

Traction and rolling stock
At the end of 1994, the CBTU fleet comprised 12 diesel-electric locomotives, 41 electric multiple-units and 20 electric railcars.

UPDATED

Companhia Paulista de Trens Metropolitanos (CPTM)

Avenida Paulista 402, São Paulo SP, CEP 01310-903
Tel: +55 11 281 6000   Fax: +55 11 285 0323

Key personnel
President: José Roberto Medeiros da Rosa
Administration and Finance Director: Ismar Lissner
Operations and Maintenance Director:
  Telmo Giolito Porto
Engineering and Works Director: José Aurélio Brentari

Gauge: 1,600 mm; 1,000 mm; dual 1,600 mm/1,000 mm
Route length: 192 km; 18 km; 60 km
Electrification: 270 km at 3 kV DC

Political background
CPTM was brought into being by the São Paulo State Government on 2 July 1993 to run the city of São Paulo's suburban passenger services, with a view to better integration with the city's metro system. CPTM began operation of FEPASA's (see separate entry) suburban routes in August 1993, and took over the former CBTU (see above) system on 27 May 1994. CPTM aims to modernise and integrate the two systems and boost rail's share of the São Paulo travel market. This currently stands at some one million passengers a day for the 270 km network, whereas São Paulo's 43.6 km metro system carries twice that number.

Finance
In 1995 CPTM had total revenue of US$162.58 million, with US$101.01 million generated by its passenger operations, US$48.44 million provided in subsidy and US$13.12 million derived from other sources of income. Total expenditure for 1995 was US$178.12 million, with

Refurbished Class 160 electric multiple-units   **1996**

staff costs totalling US$90.34 million, materials and services US$69.82 million and depreciation US$18 million.

Passenger operations
West System
CPTM assumed ownership of FEPASA's 78 km electrified network in February 1996. Known as the West System, the

former FEPASA network comprises a 42 km trunk route (the West Line) from the city centre at Julio Prestes to Itapevi and the 36 km South Line from Oscaso to Jurubatuba. Extensions from Itapevi to Amador Bueno and from Jurubatuba to Vargihna have recently been added to the system, which serves 35 stations. In 1995, the West System recorded a total of 105 million passenger-journeys, with some 350,000 passengers carried daily. Services operate with 6-minute headways in peak hours.

East System
The former CBTU routes form the 192 km East System, serving 59 stations. The East System includes a 109 km route across the São Paulo metropolitan area from Jundiaí in the northwest to Paranapiacaba in the southeast, via Barra Funda in the city centre. Known as the Northwest-Southeast Line, this route provides interchange with the West Line at Lapa, Agua Branca and Barra Funda. Roosevelt is the terminus for the East Line (50 km) which runs to Estudiantes; The East Line has a 33 km loop leaving the main route at Eng Gualberto to rejoin it at Calmon Viana.

In total 150 million passengers were carried on the East System in 1995, at a rate of 411,000 passengers per day. Most lines have 10-minute headways in operation.

Improvements to existing lines
In mid-1996 work had begun on a US$32 million upgrade of CPTM's West System, funded by the São Paulo State Government. The programme includes investment in permanent way, electrification equipment, signalling and telecommunications systems and rolling stock.

A US$281 million investment programme was under way on the East System, funded by a US$126 million World Bank loan secured in 1992 and federal support of US$155 million. In an effort to increase capacity to 1.25 million passengers per day, headways are to be reduced, rolling stock is to be refurbished and 19 stations upgraded.

PITU investment programme
Drawn up by the state government, the Plan for Integrated Urban Transport (PITU) aims to increase public transport usage and includes three major suburban rail projects. CPTM's East Line is to be upgraded between Roosevelt and Calmon Viana, with a new 6 km cut-off between Itaquera and Guaianazes, new stations and interchanges with metro and bus routes. New rolling stock is to be

acquired and infrastructure improvements undertaken to allow peak-hour headways to be lowered from the present 10 minutes to 3 minutes, enabling up to 400,000 passengers to be carried daily.

For CPTM's South Line, PITU makes provision for capacity improvements to meet rising demand and cater for up to 450,000 passengers daily. Seven new stations are to be built on the 14.8 km Pinheiros—Jurubatuba section and new bus/metro interchanges provided. The upgrading of the South Line would form part of a transport programme to be financed by the Interamerican Development Bank, which also includes the construction of Line 5 of the São Paulo metro between Capão Redondo and Santo Amaro (9.4 km), interchanging with CPTM's South Line at João Dias.

In the São Paulo city centre, PITU hopes to use World Bank funding to construct two extra tracks over the 6 km from the present terminus of the East Line at Roosevelt westwards to Barra Funda for interchange with the West Line. This project would also involve further upgrading of existing infrastructure.

CPTM electric multiple-units

Class	Cars per unit	Motor cars per unit	Motored axles/car	Output/motor kW	Speed km/h	Units in service	First built	Builders Mechanical	Builders Electrical
101	3	1	4	306	100	6	1956	Budd/ Mafersa	GE
160	3	1	4	259	100	20	1981	Mafersa/ Soreframe	Villares/ ACEC
400M	3	1	4	315	100	22	1964	FNV/ Cobrasma	Hitachi/ Toshiba
401	3	1	4	344	90	18	1976	Mafersa	GE
431	3	1	4	344	100	19	1978	Mafersa	GE
431M	3	1	4	344	120	2	1987	Mafersa	GE
700	4	2	4	315	120	20	1987	Mafersa	Hitachi/ Toshiba
5000 U	3	1	4	207	90	68	1978	Cobrasma	Brown Boveri/ MTE
5500 U	3	1	4	250	90	4	1978	Mafersa/ Sorefame	Villares/ ACEC
5800 U	3	1	4	—	90	5	1958	Nippon/ Kawasaki/ Kinki	Toshiba

Traction and rolling stock
At the start of 1996, CPTM operated a fleet of 185 electric multiple-units and 18 diesel-electric locomotives for infrastructure maintenance trains. Following refurbishment, 10 Class 400M and two Class 160 emus had returned to traffic by the start of 1996.

In 1996 CPTM signed a contract for 30 new emus for the East Line in a transaction to be financed through a Eurobond issue, subject to the approval of the state legislature. The first of the new trainsets will be delivered within 18 months, with the remainder arriving over a 10-month period. CPTM's new trainsets will be built by a Franco-Spanish consortium (including CAF, GEC Alsthom and Adtranz) known as COFESBRA, to a design similar to the Class 447 for RENFE of Spain.

Signalling and telecommunications
A contract to supply an ATP system for CPTM's Eastern line was awarded to CMW Equipamentos in 1995. The new equipment will allow headways to be reduced from 8 minutes to 3 minutes.

UPDATED

Companhia Vale do Rio Doce (CVRD)

Key personnel
Transport Director: José Carlos Marreco

CVRD, the biggest producer of iron ore in the world, owns the Vitória a Minas Railway (EFVM) and since 1977 has been in sole control of the Carajás mining development and the Carajás Railway (EFC) built to serve it.

In 1996 it was reported that the Brazilian Government intended to privatise the state-owned CVRD, with EFVM and EFC sold off separately, but political presssure has effectively postponed a sell-off. In 1996 CVRD formed part

of a consortium that was unsuccessful in its bid for RFFSA's Western Network (see Novo Oeste Railway), but in June 1996 a CVRD-led consortium was successful in bidding for the Centre-East Network (see Centre Atlantic Railway).

New lines
The so-called North-South Railway, a 1,600 km line extending from the Carajás Railway (EFC) at Açailândia to Anapolis, 115 km southwest of Brasilia, was approved in 1987. Starting in Maranhão state, it would thread the sparsely populated agricultural state of Goiás en route to the vicinity of the national capital, Brasilia. The aim of the project was to open up the neglected interior and provide

a rail route to the northern ports for the agriculture, principally soya beans and maize, which the venture would foster in Goiás.

President Sarney opened the first 105 km section from Açailândia to Imperatriz in 1989. This 1,000 mm gauge route is operated as a branch of the 1,600 mm gauge Carajás Railway (EFC) by CVRD, who were approached in 1994 by a consortium of farmers from the state of Mato Grosso with a view to reactivating the rest of the project, dormant since 1989. However, there seems little hope that it will restart given that local agricultural production would be inadequate to sustain such an ambitious railway.

UPDATED

Ferroeste

Estrada de Ferro Paraná Oeste SA
Avenida Iguaçu 420, 7° Andar, Curitiba PR, CEP 80230-902
Tel: +55 41 322 1811   Fax: +55 41 233 2147

Key personnel
President: Osiris Stenghel Guimarães
Works and Maintenance Director:
   Leo Casela Bittencourt
Finance and Administration Director:
   José Haraldo Carneiro Lobo

Gauge: 1,000 mm
Route length: 248 km

Political background
Promoted by the state of Paraná to serve the agricultural industry in its western portion, Ferroeste aims to lower the cost of exporting products such as maize, wheat and soya via the port of Paranaguá. The Ferroeste project principally comprises 419 km of new construction between Guarapuava and Guaíra, undertaken in two phases (248 km Guarapuava—Cascavel and Cascavel—Guaíra).

As a corporate entity, Ferroeste was created by the state of Paraná in December 1987 to build and operate the new route. The project was approved by the federal

government in 1988. Ferroeste was originally a mixed private/public sector company with the state of Paraná holding 92.25 per cent of the shares. However, at the end of 1996, a 30-year concession (with a possible 30-year extension) was awarded to a consortium comprising Brazilian companies Gemon, FAO, Banco Interfinance and Pouna, as well as Comazor of South Africa which will act as operator. The consortium paid Reias 25.68 million of which 5 per cent had to be put down up front. The new owners also agreed to invest Reias 117.7 million in an initial five-year period, part of which will fund acquisition of 20 diesel locomotives and 300 wagons. Projections for traffic suggest 4.7 million tonnes will be carried in the next three years.

The sell-off was hotly contested by Brazil's Socialist Party, since the purchase price was only 10 per cent of the construction cost. Expansion of the network to Foz do Iguaçu (179 km) and Guaira (171 km) will be taken forward by the private sector with Paraná state incentives.

New lines
Construction work on the initial Guarapuava—Cascavel section of Ferroeste began in August 1992, undertaken by the Brazilian Army. Infrastructure work was complete by September 1994 and commercial operations commenced on 4 April 1996, with through running over RFFSA metals. Up to December 1996, about 250,000 tonnes of soya bean, bran, wheat, corn, cement and

fertilisers had been carried. In 1997, it was expected that one million tonnes of soya bean and bran exports would be carried to the port of Paranaguá.

Estimated demand for 2000 is 5.7 million tonnes. Terminals will be served at Cascavel and Vila Flórida and a warehouse complex has been constructed at Guarapuava by an agricultural co-op.

The new line features a minimum curve radius of 250 m and maximum gradients of 1.5 per cent for loaded (Cascavel—Guarapuava) trains and 1.8 per cent for empty (Guarapuava—Cascavel) trains. Track comprises TR 45 rail welded in 270 m sections and attached to concrete sleepers using Deenik fastenings. Engineering design has been managed by CPCS of Canada.

The second 169 km Cascavel—Guaíra phase of the Ferroeste project includes a road, rail and water terminal at Guaíra, across the river Paraná from Paraguay. The terminal would aim to funnel the agricultural output of the neighbouring portions of Paraguay and Argentina and the Brazilian states of Mato Grosso and Mato Grosso do Sul down Ferroeste for export from the port of Paranaguá.

Construction of the Cascavel—Guaíra section is expected to take some three years, at an estimated cost of US$120 million. Funding arrangements had yet to be clarified by mid-1996, when the construction of a 165 km branch from Cascavel to Foz do Iguaçu (on the borders with Argentina and Paraguay) was under consideration, estimated to cost US$140 million.

Improvements to existing lines

From the eastern limit of new construction at Guarapuava, Ferroeste trains will reach Paranaguá over existing RFFSA infrastructure via Ponta Grossa and Curitiba. Upgrading of this 490 km route has been proposed, due to sharp curves and the 3.9 per cent ruling gradient as it traverses the the the central Brazilian plateau between Paranaguá and Curitiba. Upgrading the Guarapuava–Ponta Grossa

section would cost US$150 million. A new alignment has also been proposed for this section and between Paranaguá and Curitiba.

Traction and rolling stock

For its first two years in service, the initial Guarapuava–Cascavel section was to be used by RFFSA trains under an operating agreement as Ferroeste attempted to

acquire its own fleet of 60 locomotives and 925 freight wagons. Ferroeste's operating plans have made provision for moving bulk cereals in trains of 54 hopper wagons (each with a capacity of 60 tonnes) hauled by six 2,540 hp diesel-electric locomotives employing the Locotrol remote-control system.

UPDATED

Ferronorte

A soya farming magnate in the states of Mato Grosso and Goiás who also fronts one of the country's major banks, Olacyr Francisco de Moraes, has formed a company, Ferronorte, to build a line from FEPASA at Santa Fé do Sul, northwest of São Paulo, into Mato Grosso. The new railway would eventually be 4,000 km long and two-pronged, forking at Cuiabá (Mato Grosso) into lines heading northwest to Porto Velho and north to Santarém, on the Amazon. The distance from Santa Fé do Sul to Cuiabá would be 1,038 km. En route, at Alto Araguaia, a 550 km branch will run to Uberlandia, where there are soya processing plants. In early 1995 Ferronorte's founder announced further plans to construct a railway from Santarém to the western extremity of the Carajás Railway (EFC).

However, Mr de Moraes has put 70 per cent of his shares up for sale, worth an estimated Reias 354 million. Some 60 per cent of the shares were acquired in July 1996 by Brazilian pension funds Previ, Petros and Sistel.

Subsequently, Brazil Rail Partners, a private investment group, signed a memorandum of understanding to take over responsibility to fund Ferronorte's completion, as well as taking on full management responsibility. BRP will initially invest Reias 25 million out of a total package of Reias 131 million, with up to Reias 150 million also pledged by Brazil's National Bank for Economic and Social Development (BNDES).

Ferronorte's purpose is the movement of rice, soya and grain for export to the Atlantic ports of Santos (near São Paulo) and Rio de Janeiro. Soya production in particular is expanding fast in Mato Grosso, and at present its only outlet is by road transport, which is markedly more expensive than rail for bulk movement. The cost of the complete project has been assessed as US$2,500 million, including a requirement of 196 locomotives and 4,510 wagons.

The company has been granted a 50-year franchise by the federal government. In 1992, the National Bank for Economic and Social Development signed an agreement with the Grupo Itamarati to finance the first 311 km of the

project. Work began the following month between Aparecida do Taboado and Chapadão do Sul, and in early 1995 it was reported that tracklaying was under way on this section.

Traffic predictions for the first year of operations suggested that 7.3 million tonnes would be carried, consisting mostly of soya, containers and forestry products. For the initial Aparecida do Taboado–Chapadão do Sul segment, Ferronorte expected to call tenders for 40 locomotives and 1,300 wagons, including 72 five-section articulated container wagons. Of the US$624 million total cost of the first section of the Ferronorte system, US$120 million is to be spent on rolling stock.

The Ferronorte prospectus envisages 2,630 kW diesel locomotives handling 12,000 tonne trains. Ruling gradients would be 1 to 1.3 per cent. For traction, Ferronorte has been discussing with Villares a version of the GM-EMD SD60, and with General Electric do Brasil a variant of the GE C40-8.

UPDATED

Ferrovia Paulista SA (FEPASA)

Rua Mauá 51, São Paulo SP, CEP 01218-900
Tel: +55 11 223 7211   Fax: +55 11 223 0227

Key personnel
President: R C Pavan
Directors
    Administration: L C Leite da Silva
    Finance: A F G Andrade
    Marketing: S A Minciotti
    Logistics: J R Zaniboni
    Engineering: L M S Biazotti

Gauge: 1,600 mm; 1,000 mm; dual 1,600/1,000 mm
Route length: 1,491 km; 2,517 km; 336 km
Electrification: 463 km of 1,600 mm gauge, 581 km of 1,000 mm gauge and 78 km of dual gauge, all at 3 kV DC

Political background
Tenders were called in early 1997 for the privatisation of FEPASA. A 30-year concession covering freight services should be awarded in June or July, to be followed by a second concession for passenger services. The entire company has been valued at US$390 million, but the new owners will need to invest nearly four times that amount in order to win concessions. The government wants Reias 306 million to be invested in the northern, metre-gauge network, Reias 661 million in the broad-gauge central network and Reias 497 million in the metre-gauge southern network.

Finance
FEPASA's accumulated debt was reckoned to have reached US$3.6 billion at the start of 1995. It was reported that in an effort to cut costs prior to privatisation, FEPASA's workforce of 11,900 was to be cut to 6,800 and electrified 1,600 mm gauge routes turned over to diesel traction.

Funded by the World Bank, BNDES and São Paulo state, a US$285 million Railway Recovery & Modernisation Plan (PRMF) was deemed to be 76 per cent complete at the start of 1994 with US$191 million having been spent. Under FEPASA's provisional spending plans for 1996, US$9.71 million was allocated to PRMF. The money has funded infrastructure and rolling stock development to raise maximum trainloads from 2,000 to 5,000 tonnes and to enable 30 million tonnes of freight a year to be carried upon completion of the plan.

Passenger operations
At the end of 1994, services were in operation on the following 1,600 mm gauge routes: São Paulo–Campinas–Itirapina-Panorama; Itirapina–Araraquara–Santa Fé do Sul; and Araraquara–Barretos. Long-distance services were in operation on the following

FEPASA 'Bandeirante' passenger service hauled by GE-built electric locomotive (F F Lage)   **1997**

sections of FEPASA's 1,000 mm gauge network: Campinas–Ribeirão Prêto–Araguari; São Paulo–Sorocaba–Assis–Presidente Prudente; Santos–Samaritá–Juquiá; and Samaritá–Embú Guaçú.

Diesel-hauled local services were in operation between Santos and Samaritá, with tourist services provided between São Paulo, Campinas and Peruíbe; Águas da Prata and Poços de Caldas; and Pedregulho and Rifaina. FEPASA operates the Campinas LRT system and suburban services have been proposed for Campinas, Itapevi, Sorocaba and Ribeirão Prêto.

In 1995, FEPASA unveiled a new strategy aimed at raising ridership. Renewable five-year concessions were to be offered to private companies to manage and market services largely operated with a dedicated FEPASA fleet of 11 locomotives and 84 coaches. To cater for the different sectors of the travel market, FEPASA intended to provide luxury trains and a basic daily 'Expresso Bandeirante' service, catering for the less well-off and providing ample space for passengers' belongings.

Freight operations
In 1994 FEPASA moved 18.4 million tonnes of freight and recorded 6.541 billion tonne-km. Freight traffic largely consists of commodities moved in bulk, including oil, agricultural produce (such as fruit pulp and soya beans) phosphates, cement, sulphur and alcohol.

Intermodal operations
Container train services have been revived, along with establishment of intermodal terminals at key centres.

FEPASA has studied the possibility of establishing new container terminals outside São Paulo and at Campinas for traffic to and from Santos port.

New lines
As part of FEPASA's connection with the projected Ferronorte system (qv), construction has begun of a 2,600 m double-deck road and rail bridge over the river Paraná between Rubinéia and Aparecida do Taboado. A new 15.6 km line to link Rubinéia with the present FEPASA railhead at Santa Fé do Sul forms a complementary part of the project.

Funding for the US$500 million project has come in part from the São Paulo state government. FEPASA's provisional investment budget for 1996 included US$80 million for the Santa Fé do Sul–Rubinéia link.

Traction and rolling stock
At the end of 1995, FEPASA operated 84 electric and 217 diesel locomotives, four diesel railcars, 252 passenger coaches (including 25 restaurant and 32 sleeper cars) and 11,585 wagons.

In 1995, four rebuilt U20C diesel-electric locomotives were delivered by Gevisa. FEPASA's provisional 1996 investment budget included US$0.47 million for diesel locomotive modernisation and US$0.5 million for workshop and repair facilities.

Signalling and telecommunications
A modern telecommunications system is being installed across the FEPASA network in conjunction with Embratel.

A fibre optic network will provide telephone links and carry commercial and management data. A radio communications system will be provided for the use of dispatchers and train crews. It was hoped to have the necessary equipment in place to serve the routes linking São Paulo with Campinas, Araraquara, Sorocaba, Santos and Pinhalzino by July 1994. Santa Fé do Sul, São Josē do Rio Preto, Itirapina and Campinas would be served by the new network by July 1997. FEPASA was to invest US$1 million in signalling systems during 1996, according to its provisional investment budget for that year.

Electrification

In 1980 a US$322 million contract was concluded with the 50 c/s Group for 3 kV DC electrification of some 600 track-km between Ribeirão Prêto and Mairinque. The programme has been beset by contretemps, mostly financial, but by 1991 continuous wiring was in place from Boa Vista to the limit of earlier electrification at Mairinque.

After a somewhat protracted renegotiation process, agreement was reached between FEPASA and the supplying consortium in 1993 that the latter would proceed to electrify the remaining Ribeirão Prêto—Guaianā section, install substations at Louveira, Campinas, Sumaré, Aterrado, Torrinha and Jaú, and replace track circuits between Amador Bueno and Ourinhos.

However, at the start of 1994 work had not yet started as the agreement had not been fully ratified. In early 1995, FEPASA president Renato Pavan proposed abandoning the scheme as part of the railway's drive to tackle its mounting debt. It was reported in 1996 that electric operations on the 1,600 mm gauge network were to cease, but those on the 1,000 mm gauge network were to be retained.

Track
Rail
Type: TR 37, TR 45, TR 50, TR 55, TR 57, TR 68
Weight: 37, 45, 50, 55, 57, 68 kg/m
Crossties (sleepers)

Diesel-electric locomotives

Class	Wheel arrangement	Power kW	Speed km/h	Weight tonnes	First built	Builders Mechanical	Builders Engine	Transmission
3100	C+C	447	80	64	1948	GE	CB	GE
3200	B-B	894	138	71.2	1957	GE	CB	GE
3500	C-C	671	95	68.1	1957	GE	Alco	GE
3600	B-B	652	100	56.7	1961	GM	GM	GM
3600	B-B	652	100	60.5	1960	GM	GM	GM
3650	B-B	976	100	74.9	1957	GM	GM	GM
3700	B-B	574	90	70	1969	LEW	SACM	LEW
3750	B-B	835	100	74	1968	LEW	SACM	LEW
3800	C-C	1,491	103	108	1974	GE	GE	GE
7000	B-B	1,304	105	110.6	1958	GM	GM	GM
7050	B-B	976	124	80	1958	GM	GM	GM
7760	B-B	574	90	74	1967	LEW	SACM	LEW
7800	C-C	1,491	103	108	1977	GE	GE	GE

Electric locomotives

Class	Wheel arrangement	Output kW	Weight tonnes	First built	Builders Mechanical	Builders Electrical
2000	1-C+C-1	1,729	130	1943	GE	GE
2050	1-C+C-1	1,729	130	1943	Westinghouse	Westinghouse
2100	B-B	1,371	72.7	1968	GE	GE
6100	2-C+C-2	2,846	165	1982	Westinghouse	rebuilt FEPASA
6150	2-C+C-2	2,846	165	1982	Westinghouse	rebuilt FEPASA
6350	C-C	3,269	144	1967	GE Brasil	GE Brasil
6370	2-C+C-2	2,846	165	1940	GE	GE
6410	C+C	1,134	107	1927	Westinghouse	Westinghouse
6450	2-D+D-2	3,470	242.6	1951	GE	GE
6500	B-B	341	55.5	1924	GE	GE
6510	B-B	341	55.5	1947	GE	GE
EC362	B-B	2,480	100	1984	50 c/s Gp	50 c/s Gp

Wood: 1,000 mm gauge 2,000 × 220 × 160 mm; 1,600 mm gauge 2,800 × 240 × 170 mm
Spacing: 1,000 mm gauge 1,600/km; 1,600 mm gauge 1,667/km
Rail fastenings: GEO or K; ML
Concrete block: 1,000 mm gauge 680 × 290 × 211 mm; 1,600 mm gauge 680 × 290 × 239 mm
Spacing: 1,500/km
Fastenings: FN

Concrete (monobloc): (1,000 mm gauge only) 2,000 × 220 × 210 mm to 2,000 × 320 × 242 mm
Spacing: 1,500/km
Fastenings: RN
Min curve radius: Main lines 150 m; branches 90 m
Max gradients: Main lines 2%; branches 3%
Max axleload: 1,000 mm gauge 20 tonnes; 1,600 mm gauge 25 tonnes

UPDATED

Flumitrens

Companhia Fluminense de Trens Urbanos
Praça Cristiano Ottoni, Sala 445, Rio de Janeiro RJ, CEP 20221
Tel: +55 21 233 8594   Fax: +55 21 253 3089

Key personnel
President: Murilo Siqueira Junqueira
Production Director: Jose Carlos Martins Lopes
Administrative Director: Gilberto Martins Velloso
Engineering Director: Ronaldo da Silva Cotrim
Human Resources Director: Marluce M S M Tavares

Gauge: 1,600 mm; 1,000 mm
Route length: 228 km; 152 km
Electrification: 167 km of 1,600 mm gauge at 3 kV DC

Political background
The suburban network serving the city of Rio de Janeiro passed from CBTU control to the state of Rio de Janeiro on 22 December 1994. Services are now marketed under the name Flumitrens. In 1996, it was decided to initiate privatisation of the network based on the Buenos Aires model, being franchised to either one or more operators based on the lowest subsidy requested.

Passenger operations
Flumitrens operates the largest suburban system in Brazil, with electrified 1,600 mm gauge routes from two city-centre termini, Dom Pedro II and Barão de Mauá, to Santa Cruz, Paracambi, Belford Roxo, and Gramacho. The Santa Cruz—Itaguaí section is diesel-worked. The 1,000 mm gauge network comprises routes from Gramacho to Vila Inhomirim and Guapimirim and from

Flumitrens electric multiple-units

Class	Cars per unit	Motor cars per unit	Motored axles/car	Output/motor kW	Speed km/h	No in service	First built	Builders Mechanical	Builders Electrical
400M	3	1	4	315	90	50	1964	FNV/Cobrasma	Hitachi/Toshiba
400	3	1	4	255	90	12	1964	FNV/Cobrasma	GE
500	4	2	4	315	90	28	1977	Nippon Sharyo	Hitachi/Toshiba
700	4	2	4	315	90	29	1980	Mafersa	Hitachi/Toshiba
800	4	2	4	280	90	55	1980	Santa Matilde	GE
900	4	2	4	279	90	60	1980	Cobrasma	MTE
1000	3	1	4	315	90	22	1954	Metro-Vick	Hitachi/Toshiba/ Villares

Barreto on the east side of Guanabara Bay to Visconde de Itaboraí.

In 1994 Flumitrens recorded 133 million passenger journeys. In 1995, 114 million passenger journeys were recorded, and at the end of that year Flumitrens employed 7,871 staff.

Improvements to existing lines
Using loan funds secured upon the creation of Flumitrens, an upgrading programme has been planned for the system. This comprises station rebuilding, rolling stock refurbishment expansion of the system's workshop facilities and a grade-separation programme. An estimated US$60 million per year in investment is required to modernise the existing, rundown network, which has an annual operating deficit of US$252 million.

Traction and rolling stock
At the end of 1995, the 1,600 mm gauge fleet comprised 37 diesel-electric locomotives, 251 electric multiple-units and 86 railcars. The 1,000 mm gauge fleet comprised 23 diesel-electric locomotives and 92 passenger coaches.

Using World Bank/BNDES funding, Flumitrens hoped to undertake rolling stock refurbishment in 1996 and 1997. Poor emu availability has recently been a problem, and in 1996 it was reported that tenders had been invited for the refurbishment of 21 Series 500 emus.

Signalling and telecommunications
At the end of 1995, Centralised Traffic Control (CTC) was in operation on 150.1 route-km of the Flumitrens system, with train staff operation in place on 75 route-km. CTC was being installed on the Dom Pedro II—Lauro Muller (2.3 km), Marechal Hermes—Deodoro (1.5 km) and Mesquita—Japeri (29.8 km) sections of the 1,600 mm gauge network, and Automatic Train Control (ATC) on the Dom Pedro II—Deodoro (22 km), Deodoro—Japeri (39.7 km) and Deodoro—Santa Cruz (32.7 km) sections.

Electrification
At the end of 1995, electrification of the 10.8 km Gramacho—Saracuruna section (1,000 mm gauge) at 3 kV DC was under way.

UPDATED

New West Railway

Key personnel
Director: Glen Michael
Transport Director: Sergio Julian Cardoso
Administration and Finance: Homero Boretti Elias
Logistics and Permanant Way: Edmundo Dias do Amaral
Marketing: Ricardo Lopes
Engineering: Melvin Jones

Political background
The privatisation of the RFFSA network as six 30-year regional freight operating concessions began in earnest in 1996, when the concession for the 1,000 mm gauge route from Bauru to Corumbá and its branch to Ponta Porã (known as the Western Network) was auctioned at the Rio de Janeiro stock exchange on 5 March. The concession was acquired for Cr62.36 million (US$63.4 million) by a consortium of Brazilian and US

investors, led by the Noel Group (owners of Illinois Central) and including Chemical Bank, Bank of America, Brazil Railway Partners and Western Rail Investors.

The concession for the 1,600 route-km Western Network is renewable for a further 30 years, with the concessionaire leasing infrastructure and rolling stock from RFFSA. As of March 1996, the Western Network's rolling stock fleet comprised 88 diesel-electric locomotives and 2,600 freight wagons, with half of the locomotives and some 7 per cent of the wagons out of service for want of maintenance and spare parts. Under the terms of the concession, the government requires some Cr359 million to be invested in the Western Network, with rolling stock, track maintenance and the upgrading of structures and communications regarded as priorities. In 1995 the Western Network made a loss of Cr18 million and the principal commodities carried included petroleum products, ores, grain and fertiliser and manufactured products bound for Bolivia via Corumbá. Of the Western Network's 2,750 employees, the new operators were to take on 1,800.

NEW ENTRY

North-Eastern Network

Political background

Bids for this 4,629 km RFFSA (qv) network were due to be submitted in early 1997, to be followed by a public auction. US$74 million raised from World Bank funds and revenue received from the sell-off of other networks will be used to upgrade track, expand radio communications and rebuild locomotives. Fleet improvements were made by transferring 20 locomotives and 240 wagons to this region from the Centre-East Network before its privatisation, to increase capacity from 900 million net tonne km/year to 1.2 billion.

By 1996, the workforce had already been cut from 4,800 a few years earlier to 1,600.

New lines

A new line projected in the 1980s was the Trans-nordestina Railway. As its name suggests, this would traverse the country's far northeast inland, linking up three metre-gauge lines that head inland from the Atlantic coastal line between Salvador and Recife. New single-track line would extend 342 km from Petrolina through Crato and Salgueiro to Ingazeiras, making access to Salvador and Fortaleza much simpler for inland cities in this area. Complementary rehabilitation would be required over the existing 594 km between Salgueiro and Recife, and over the 550 km between Ingazeiras and Fortaleza.

In a second phase, a new 178 km link would be built between Cratéus and Piquet—Carneiro. Further upgrading would be carried out on the 296 km from Cratéus to Tresina Altos and the 131 km from Petrolina to Senhor de Bonfin.

Construction work on the US$815 million project began in 1991, although stopped again at the year end for want of finance. In 1992, the Treasury made more funding available, making it possible for work to begin once again. Completion of the first 117 km was scheduled for 1993-94. However, by the start of 1994, another halt had been imposed by the lack of finance.

NEW ENTRY

Rede Ferroviaria Federal SA (RFFSA)

Praça Procópio Ferreira 86, 20224-900 Rio de Janeiro
Tel: +55 21 233 5795   Fax: +55 21 263 3128

Key personnel

President: I Popoutchi
Directors
    Administration and Finance: J A Schmitt de Azevedo
    Marketing and Development: J A Resende
    Operations: B J de Lima
Superintendents
    Commercial: J A R Rios
    Financial: F A E Cavour
    Transport: F Lemos
    Logistics: L C Andrade Junior
    Planning: L A A Bordallo
    Human Resources: L M Gonçalves
    Legal Affairs: P de Oliveira
    Communications: R Guerrante
    Engineering: R S da Silva Lucas

Gauge: 1,600 mm; 1,000 mm; 762 mm
Route length: 1,740 km; 20,247 km; 13 km
Electrification: 65 km of 1,600 mm gauge at 3 kV DC

Political background

The state owned operator RFFSA is being privatised in the form of six 30-year freight operating concessions. By early 1997, four RFFSA regions had been transferred to the private sector. The New West Railway (qv) and Centre Atlantic Railway (qv) were carved out of the former Western and Centre-East railways respectively in early 1996, followed by the transfer of the South-Eastern railway (see SUDFER) to MRS Logística in September of the same year and the Southern Network, renamed the South Atlantic Railway (qv), to a US/Brazilian consortium in December.

Still to be auctioned in mid-1997 were the hopelessly uneconomic North-Eastern network, as well as the smaller (169 km) Tereza Cristina network, which serves coal mines in the state of Santa Catarina and has so far attracted interest only from its existing workforce.

All down payments by each concession holder, plus any charges above the minimum bid price, have gone to RFFSA to improve its cash flow during the privatisation process, while an additional US$350 million loan has been secured from the World Bank to enable 230 diesel locomotives to be repaired and excess staff laid off.

Finance

Privatisation of RFFSA was prompted by the withdrawal of most former subsidies and compensations as desperate efforts were made in the early 1990s to stabilise the national economy, driving the railway into technical bankruptcy in the process. By 1991 the daily loss had soared to US$1 million and accumulated debt stood at US$1.2 billion. The latter had reached US$1.84 billion in 1994 and was expected to rise to some US$2.56 billion in 1995, when the intention was that funds generated by the auction of operating concessions would go towards settling RFFSA's accumulated debt.

UPDATED

South Atlantic Railway

Key personnel

President: José Paulo Oliveira Alves

Political background

In December 1996, RFFSA's (qv) Southern Network was sold for US$208 million, 37 per cent higher than the reserve price, to a consortium of Railtex and Ralph Partners of the US and Banco Garantia, Judore and Interferrea of Brazil. Reias 300 million is to be invested in the 6,586 km metre-gauge railway within the first two years of the concession period, aimed at boosting revenue by 50 per cent. Some 100 locomotives will be rebuilt in this period. Oil traffic will account for 45 per cent of the total hauled.

The new railway operates in the states of Paraná, Santa Catarina and Rio Grande do Sul and carried 50 per cent of all RFFSA traffic.

NEW ENTRY

SUDFER

Political background

In September 1996, sole bidder MRS Logística was awarded a concession to operate RFFSA's (qv) 1,633 route-km South-Eastern Network, paying the reserve price of US$875.6 million. The consortium consisted of several of the railway's major customers, notably Companhia Siderúgica Nacional, Usiminas, Minerações Brasileiras Reunidas (Caemi group) and Gerdau group member Cosigua. Other members are Ferteco, Interférrea, Lachman, Ultrafértil, and the pension funds of CSN and Caemi employees. Existing RFFSA employees will continue operating the railway.

MRS Logística must invest US$227 million during its first five years in charge and up to US$1.4 billion throughout the 30-year concession period.

However, the new owner has plans to spend US$400 million in an initial three-year period. Some 130 of the present 401 diesel locomotive fleet look set to be scrapped, while the rest will require extensive rebuilds. MRS Logística is talking to manufacturers with a view to leasing more machines. In early 1997, the company signed a contract with TECFER, Hatch & Kirk and Montana Raillink to overhaul six SD38 locomotives.

A budget of US$50 million is also available for a computerised information system needed to control all the company's day-to-day functions. Productivity has to be raised, which means upping train speeds to improve equipment utilisation and also that of crews.

The company wants to increase tonnage from the 1995 figure of 46 million to one of 50 million tonnes by 2000.

Operation of the network has been subcontracted to a company formed by redundant RFFSA employees and known as SUDFER, whose members will subsequently take a 10 per cent stake in MRS Logística costing Reias 9 million, to be financed by the National Bank for Social & Economic Development.

The 1,633 km network is believed to be the most profitable part of RFFSA, linking São Paulo to the mining district around Belo Horizonte in Minas Gerais province. The concession includes the 300 km Steel Railway.

SD40-2 locomotives on the Steel Railway, Minas Gerais (F F Lage)   **1996**

Freight operations

There had been some growth in imported oil traffic in the early 1990s, accounting for much of the meagre freight business, and trial hauls were made of manganese ore brought by road from Tambao to the Kaya railhead for forwarding to Abidjan. Tonnage carried in Burkina in 1995 amounted to about 200,000, about 92 million tonne-km. Early indications were that tonnage was on the increase as a result of the concessioning agreement.

Sitarail's freight plans are based on development of the export manganese traffic and exploitation of zinc mined at Perkoa, some 30 km from the railway at Koudougou.

Improvements to existing lines

In late 1995, Sitarail called tenders for supply of rail and sleepers to begin a programme of upgrading throughout the railway. Spare parts to refurbish GM locomotives were also sought.

New lines

Construction of the Tambao extension has begun, with the aim of tapping rich manganese deposits in the region. The government bought 6,000 tonnes of used rail from Canadian National and in 1989 funds were obtained from the UN Development Programme for engagement of consultants to manage work on the initial 105 km from Ouagadougou to Kaya, which was opened in 1993.

The Burkina Faso government then advanced CFAFr6.2 billion for construction of the remaining 271 km from Kaya to Tambao. In 1990 Canac International was contracted by the UN Development Programme to oversee the first stage and assist in planning the second.

Earlier, in 1988, Canac International had secured a C$2.3 million turnkey contract to supply and install a telecommunications network over the new line. The work included installation of five microwave sites between Ouagadougou and Kaya. In addition, a VHF/FM communications network would be installed to link train stations and train crews.

These works are currently in abeyance on account of the need to concentrate on rehabilitation of the existing line. Finance totalling some US$5 million for this was agreed by the West African Development Bank in 1996 (see Ivory Coast entry).

Traction and rolling stock

At the start of 1996, the Sitarail combined operation had available 20 diesel locomotives, 17 shunters, 40 coaches and 600 wagons. Burkina's 1994-96 plan provided for purchase of three diesel-electric locomotives and 30 mineral wagons, while 60 tank wagons were acquired through the national oil company Sonabhy.

A deal has been agreed with Projects & Equipment Corporation of India for launch of local freight wagon production. The Indians are to set up a manufacturing plant at Bobo Dioulasso, get it going with a supply of wagon kits for assembly, then oversee transition to local manufacture from scratch.

UPDATED

CAMBODIA

Royal Railways of Cambodia

Chemins de Fer Royaux du Cambodge
Ministry of Public Works and Transport, Phnom Penh
Tel: +855 25156

Key personnel
Director: Pich Kimsreang

Gauge: 1,000 mm
Route length: 603 km

Organisation

Because of the country's internal unrest most of the rail network was out of use during the 1970s and 1980s, but in 1993 trains were operating on all sections except for the 48 km between Sisophon and the Thai border at Poipet. There are two main lines. The Old line runs westwards from Phnom Penh to Sisophon (339 km), whence the route to Poipet was removed in the 1970s. The New line, opened in 1969, links Phnom Penh with the country's only deep water port at Kompong Som, 263 km distant.

Passenger and freight operations

Operations are severely hampered by the poor condition of the track, and security problems. In 1993 only one train daily was running on each line, with a separate train plying between Battambang and Sisophon because of the particularly poor state of the track and bridges on that section. Maximum speed was 35 km/h and trains ran generally during daylight hours only. Passengers and freight are carried on each train, the locomotive often propelling several flat wagons in front of it as protection against mines. Armed guards are also carried.

Freight traffic comprises rice (20 per cent), oil and other fuels (15 per cent), construction materials (12 per cent), forest products (10 per cent), sea salt (10 per cent), engineering supplies (5 per cent), with the balance accounted for by imported goods. Tonnage, which never exceeded 190,000 annually during the 1980s, declined to a low of 64,000 tonnes in 1991, but rose to 113,000 tonnes for 27.6 million tonne-km the following year, when 1.2 million passengers were carried.

Upgrading of the New line (see below) has included enlargement of the loading gauge, thus permitting introduction in 1996 of a container service between Kompong Som and Phnom Penh, using a rake of 30 refurbished flat wagons on a six-hour timing. It is planned to purchase or refurbish a further 100 wagons to augment the service.

New lines

A 450 km line linking Phnom Penh and Ho Chi Minh City (formerly Saigon) has been projected for a number of years but consistently cancelled owing to hostilities. The line would fill one of the missing links in the Trans Asian Railway Project. In 1996, Malaysia offered to finance and carry out a feasibility study for this route and reopening from Sisophon to Poipet; the two projects would close the missing links in a 5,500 km Singapore-Beijing dual-gauge route.

Daily coast-bound train leaves Phnom Penh (P F Wickenden)

Improvements to existing lines

The United Nations Development Programme's Office for Project Services financed a detailed examination of the railway in 1992-93 to assess the work necessary to raise line speed. Engineers seconded from the State Railway of Thailand were accompanied by French experts who looked at the motive power situation. It soon became clear that any remedial work would have to be directed merely at keeping the system running, in particular through the wide areas still affected by mines — some 148 km of the Old line and 90 km of the New.

As a result of these studies, some damaged rail was replaced, a bridge repaired and a few tank wagons rehabilitated. A small supply of rail and steel sleepers from the Sisophon—Poipet line was purchased, but this was quickly exhausted and fresh supplies were sought from Malaysia and Thailand.

The experts proposed a four-stage track rehabilitation programme, starting with a pre-operational phase that would include mine clearance. Equipment has been acquired to reactivate ballast quarries, repairs made to track tampers and works cars, and 40 ballast wagons repaired or purchased. Excluding mine clearance, for which no cost estimate can be made, this stage is costing US$2 million. Funds have been provided by the World Bank and the Asian Development Bank.

In the second phase, lasting about a year and costing at least US$6.5 million, emergency works would be carried out to keep the railway in operation, including replacement of 42 track-km on the Old line where rail length is down to 2 m and thus fishplates cannot be used. Both routes would be reballasted and some reprofiling of embankments and cuttings carried out. Training of CFRC staff in track repair techniques would pave the way for longer term complete rehabilitation of the track at a cost of US$18 million. This would involve stabilisation of weak formations, strengthening of turnouts, rehabilitation of buildings, and welding of rail.

In the fourth phase, a signalling system would be installed, probably radio electronic tokenless block, and technical manuals and standards data provided to replace documentation lost during the war.

In 1993 the French government granted US$1.7 million in aid towards track improvements and rehabilitation of motive power.

Traction and rolling stock

At the start of 1993 CFRC's serviceable fleet amounted to 13 diesel and five steam locomotives. Backbone of the diesel-electric fleet were nine Alsthom-built BB 900 kW units fitted with MGO-V12 BZSHR engines delivered in 1967-69. There were also two 750 kW units supplied by CKD Prague in 1991 and two French-built shunters of 1956 vintage.

The 25 coaches comprised former Chinese vehicles supplied by Vietnam and seven trailers from German-built dmus of 1969; there were around 250 wagons.

Signalling and telecommunications

Both the former telegraph and radio signalling systems have been destroyed and the current service is designed on a non-conflicting basis with trains normally running in each direction on alternate days.

UPDATED

CAMEROON

Ministry of Transport

PO Box 8043, Yaoundé
Tel: +237 232236

Key personnel
Minister: Issa Tchiroma
Director of Land Transport: M Mundi Kengnjisu

VERIFIED

Regie Nationale des Chemins de Fer du Cameroun (Regifercam)

Bonanjo, PO Box 304, Douala
Tel: +237 406045/407159   Fax: +237 423205

Key personnel
Director General: Samuel Minko
Deputy Director General: Paul Djoko Moyo
Directors
   Traffic: S Ebata
   Technical Adviser: René Kamo
   Commercial: E Ngankou
   Personnel: R H Soulemanou Danbaba
   Infrastructure: J P Moudourou
   Finance: Guillaume Wamal
   Traction and Rolling Stock: Ebelle Mbedi
   Infrastructure: Jean Pierre Moudourou
Assistant Directors
   Information Systems: Ignace Ntjono
   Internal Audit: Jeannette Dissak
   General Administration: F Moutome
   Planning and Studies: E Ndoufa

Gauge: 1,000 mm
Route length: 1,006 km

Organisation
The Cameroon system consists of two single-track lines: the West line running from Bonaberi to Nkongsamba operated by Regifercam; and the much longer Transcameroon line, opened in 1974, between Douala and Ngaoundéré.

Political background
Moves towards railway privatisation started in 1994, when 15 state enterprises were considered for sale into the private sector. Bidding closed at the end of May 1996 for prequalification for a 20-year operating concession which would also demand investment in modernisation and maintenance of the infrastructure. Railway equipment suppliers and construction companies were prohibited from bidding.

In the short term, up to June 1997, expenditure of some CFAFr13.4 billion was planned on infrastructure improvements, including track upgrading and bridge strengthening. Purchase of three diesel shunters was also planned.

Freight operations
Freight traffic, which had been diminished since the 1985 opening of a highway from Douala to Yaoundé, rebounded with an increase of 21 per cent in FY88-89, but fell back to around 1.1 million tonnes in the years following. There was a very slight increase to 1.2 million tonnes in 1992-93, though tonne-km fell by 6 per cent to 592 million.

Passenger operations
Passenger traffic grew by 14 per cent in the five years to 1991-92, but fell back below 2 million journeys in 1992-93.

Improvements to existing lines
Following completion of the Transcameroon line to Ngaoundéré (935 km from Douala), it was decided to realign the Douala—Yaoundé section to match the standard of the Yaoundé—Ngaoundéré extension. The work was phased in four stages.

The most difficult stretch, the 27 km from Eséka to Maloumé, which entailed construction of three tunnels aggregating 3,295 m in length and five viaducts with a total length of 875 m, took much longer than expected. It was not until 1991 that the project was completed. The works doubled the line's capacity to 40 services a day, raised single-locomotive trainloads to 1,000 tonnes and increased annual throughput potential to over 14 million tonnes. Solar-powered colourlight signalling with interlockings at intermediate stations and track-to-train radio have been installed.

Foreign credits have been sought for purchase of track maintenance equipment, to resleeper the Yaoundé—Ngaoundéré extension and to realign an 8 km section of it. Sofrerail has signed a personnel management contract to train local staff.

New lines
A new port is proposed for Grand Batanga, and in 1988 the Transcameroon Authority commissioned from French consultants a feasibility study of a 136 km freight line from the Regifercam main line near Eséka to Grand Batanga and Kribi, on the coast some 20 km north of the new port's site. Kribi is the starting point of a proposed 1,100 km new line running east to the Central African Republic. No decision to build has yet been taken.

Traction and rolling stock
In 1993 Regifercam operated 69 diesel locomotives, two locotractors, one diesel railcar, 84 coaches and 1,647 wagons.

Signalling and telecommunications
The task of resignalling the remaining sections of the main line was some 80 per cent complete at the end of 1993. Main stations are being equipped with colourlight signalling and manual single-track block.

Track
Rail: Vignole 30 and 36 kg/m
Crossties (sleepers): Timber and steel, thickness 130 mm
Spacing: 1,500/km plain track; 1,714/km curves
Fastenings: Sleeper screw (stiff); sleeper screw and Nabla (elastic)
Min curvature radius: 120 m
Max gradient: 1.9%
Max axleload: 20 tonnes

UPDATED

Diesel locomotives

Class	Wheel arrangement	Power kW	Speed km/h	Weight tonnes	No in service	First built	Builders Mechanical	Engine	Transmission
3600	Bo-Bo-Bo-Bo	2,650	80	132	4	1975	MTE	SACM AGO V16E	E Alsthom
2200	Co-Co	1,540	107	101	29	1980	Bombardier	Alco V1225 IC4	E CGE
1200	Bo-Bo	805	70	56	8	1969	Alsthom	SACM MGO V16 ASHR	E Alsthom/MTE
1100	Bo-Bo	650	60	60	20	1981	Alsthom	SACM MGO V12 ASHR	E Alsthom/MTE
1000	Bo-Bo	580	60	60	5	1978	Moyse	SACM MGO V12 ASHR	E Moyse
300	Bo-Bo	520	70	70	6	1955	Alsthom	SACM MGO V12 SHR	E Alsthom

CANADA

Transport Canada

Place de Ville, Ottawa, Ontario K1A 0N5
Tel: +1 613 998 2689   Fax: +1 613 998 2686

Key personnel
Minister: David Anderson
Deputy Minister: Nick Mulder
Assistant Deputy Minister, Policy: Moya Greene

Political background
The most recent efforts to modernise the legal framework of Canada's transport industry are embodied in the Canada Transportation Act of 1996. The emphasis of the Act is on enhancing trade and the viability and competitiveness of the Canadian transport system, reducing regulatory intervention and encouraging more innovative transport services. A new Canadian Transportation Agency (CTA), which is answerable to parliament through the minister, will replace the present National Transportation Agency (NTA). In the area of rail freight, the Act is designed to enhance the long-term viability of Canada's railways, foster the creation of short lines, preserve key shipper rights and reduce the regulatory burden on railways. The rail elements of the complicated package will complement the strategy of privatising Canadian National (qv) which happened in November 1995.

In addition the legislation is designed to encourage the rationalisation of Canada's over-dense rail system by streamlining the current regulatory process for sale of lines and for abandonment, while simultaneously providing incentives for the expansion of a short line industry in Canada.

The dramatic changes in the rail industry since passage of the Act are evidence of its effectiveness.

These measures at federal level to liberalise downsizing are mirrored by a series of legislative initiatives at the provincial level. A law was due to be passed by Ontario's parliament freeing railways from the successor provisions associated with the transfer of rail assets, leaving only Saskatchewan and British Columbia with laws protecting workforces in rail sales. In the case of the former this is expected to impair the disposition of many grain-hauling branches, but in the latter it is not much of an issue since there is little mileage that lends itself to downsizing.

Rail Policy Branch
The Rail Policy Branch of the Transport Department is responsible for providing railway expertise and policy advice for federal interests in the various fields of railway activity, including freight and passenger issues and grain transport.

The Branch monitors, analyses and evaluates rail freight issues and the impact of regulatory reforms and overall transport legislation on carriers, shippers, provinces and regions. As part of the Branch mandate, it also develops, maintains and provides expertise and information on infrastructure and operations; capital investment; service availability; railway economics and carriers' financial performance; technology and systems concepts; energy and alternative fuels.

The Branch also manages certain federal expenditure programmes in respect of VIA Rail passenger services (including policy advice on the operating, capital, and legal requirements of rail passenger services in Canada within the context of overall government objectives) and programme delivery in respect of the federal involvement in grain transport and handling.

The Branch has been involved in a number of major policy initiatives including the privatisation of CN and introduction of transport legislation, especially the Canada Transportation Act. The Branch has also represented the department in, *inter alia*, the Agri-Food Policy Review regarding grain transport and the removal of the rail subsidy programme for the transport of western grain to export. With the expiration of the very low Crows Nest Pass rates for the export of grain (embodied in the now-defunct Western Grain Transportation Act), the future of the national government's 13,000 hopper car fleet will need to be decided.

Rail Safety Branch
The Rail Safety Branch works with the industry and the Transportation Safety Board of Canada to investigate all aspects of the business. One result is the 1996 initiative CANALERT, a programme sponsored by CN, CP, VIA and the BLE (Brotherhood of Locomotive Engineers) to understand operator fatigue and to provide input to future rule-making and the identification of fatigue countermeasures to complement, or replace, some rules.

Algoma Central Railway

Algoma Central Railway Inc
PO Box 9500, Sault Ste Marie, Ontario P6A 6Y1
Tel: +1 705 541 2850

Key personnel
President: Edward A Burkhardt
Vice-President, Passenger Operations: Keith White
Vice-President, Marketing: William R Schauer

Gauge: 1,435 mm
Route length: 518 km

Organisation
Following approval in December 1994 from Canada's National Transportation Agency, the rail assets of the Algoma Central Corporation were purchased by Wisconsin Central Transportation Company (WCTC) (qv in the US section) through a wholly owned subsidiary WC Canada Holdings Inc. Algoma Central Railway Inc has been the operating subsidiary since February 1995. Some 200 Algoma Central employees were retained by the new owners. Work rules similar to those in effect on WCTC were introduced.

Finance
In acquiring the Algoma Central, WCTC paid US$16.1 million for property and rolling stock, including 23 locomotives and 879 passenger coaches and freight wagons. Additionally, WCTC paid US$8.2 million for the rights of way in a partnership transaction involving the province of Ontario. Algoma Central's financial results are now consolidated with those of parent WCTC.

Passenger operations
ACRI provides the thrice-weekly passenger service each way between Sault Ste Marie and Hearst, complemented by seasonal tourist trains (of which the best known is the Agawa Canyon service).

Freight operations
Under WCTC management, daily freight service operates between Sault Ste Marie and Oba, and on the Michipicoten branch. Service north of Oba to Hearst is Monday-Friday only. Marketing and customer service functions are now integrated with WCTC. Iron ore, steel and forest products are the dominant commodities.

Traction and rolling stock
The 23 diesel locomotives absorbed into WCTC ownership comprised a mix of EMD 2,200 kW Type SD40, EMD 1,500 kW Type GP38-2, EMD 1,100 kW Type GP7 and one switcher. Several of the higher-power locomotives have been redeployed; 11 ex-VIA steam-generator equipped EMD FP9 units have been acquired for the passenger trains and seven are in service.

Coupler in standard use
Passenger cars: AAR Type E, F, H
Freight cars: AAR Type E, F, H
Braking in standard use, locomotive-hauled stock: Air Type 26
Track
Rail type: 115 RE, 100 RE, 85 CPR, 80 ASCE
Sleepers: Wood
Spacing: 1,822/km
Fastenings: Splice bars
Minimum curve radius: 1°
Max gradient: 1.7%
Max axleload: 30.4 tonnes

UPDATED

BC Rail

BC Rail Ltd
PO Box 8770, Vancouver, British Columbia V6B 4X6
Tel: +1 604 986 2012   Fax: +1 604 984 5428
Web site: www.bcrail.com/bcr

Key personnel
President and Chief Executive Officer: Paul McElligott
Vice-Presidents
   Finance and Information Technology: Roger Clarke
   Human Resources and Strategic Planning: Eric Lush
   Customer Services and Sales: Wayne C Banks
   Support Services: J C Trainor
   Service Integration and Corporate Secretary:
      R W Young
   Business Development: Michael Cornellison
   Properties, Investments & Passenger Services:
      Jim C Cox

Gauge: 1,435 mm
Route length: 2,314 km
Electrification: 129 km at 50 kV 60 Hz

Organisation
BC Rail Ltd is the railway operating unit of the BC Railway Group; the BC Railway Group is a crown corporation, wholly owned by the province of British Columbia, and has five business units including BC Rail. One unit, British Columbia Railway Company, owns 25 per cent of BC Rail. Another, BCR Properties Ltd, which is the property-owning unit of the Group, owns the other 75 per cent. In 1995 the Group added a unit called BCR Ventures for the purpose of developing business and pursuing a diversification strategy since several major coal contracts are up for renegotiation in 1998 and 1999, plus projections for traffic from the forest products industry show few growth prospects.

   The railway's principal yard facilities are at North Vancouver, Squamish, Lillooet, Williams Lake, Quesnel, Prince George, Fort St James, Mackenzie and Fort St John. Rail-served industrial parks are situated at Williams Lake, Prince George, Mackenzie, Fort St John, Dawson Creek, Fort St James and Fort Nelson.

Vancouver Wharves
During the first quarter of 1993 BC Rail acquired 100 per cent ownership of Vancouver Wharves Ltd, for an investment of C$15.75 million. Vancouver Wharves is a deep-water storage and handling facility (adjoining BC Rail's North Vancouver yard) for bulk commodities, including sulphur, potash, mineral concentrates, methanol, pulp and paper. Throughput in 1995 totalled 6 million tonnes. The terminal occupies 45 ha of land, of which 40 are leased long-term from BCR Properties.

   Ownership by BC Rail will secure existing traffic and enhance the railway's ability to contend for new business. It will also relieve congestion in the North Vancouver terminal and yard, which was the subject of a four-year C$15 million upgrade in the early 1990s. Ownership of Vancouver Wharves does not affect the Group's plan to develop the port facilities in Squamish when the business climate calls for it. Vancouver Wharves created a subsidiary known as Wharves Leasing in 1994 which assumed ownership and management of BC Rail's locomotive and car fleet. Vancouver Wharves produced its first operating profits in late 1994, and the unit was profitable in 1995.

Other subsidiaries
BC Rail formed a wholly owned subsidiary known as Westel in 1993; the subsidiary operates in the telecommunications market.

   BCR Ventures is involved with two partners, Mitsui-Matsushima and Globaltex Industries Inc, in exploring potential for a new open-cast coal mine 50 km west of Chetwynd. BC Rail would be the transport provider and Pine Valley Coal Company, which is one-third owned by the Ventures unit, would be the operator. Start-up plan is for 600,000 tonnes/year (approximately one unit train weekly) with a future plan to double that volume.

   International Rail Consultants (IRC) is a joint venture formed in 1985 between BC Rail and Sandwell Inc. During 1996, it hosted visitors from China, India, Bangladesh and Myanmar.

Finance
BCR Group reported consolidated net income of C$47.1 million for 1995 on record revenues of C$425.1 million. Comparative figures for 1994 were C$40.5 million on C$385.5 million. This was the second year of strong rebound from a dismal 1993 of depressed world commodity prices. Preliminary results for 1996 indicated a pre-tax net income of C$36.3 million, with a fall in rail revenue being offset by growth in the subsidiaries. The traffic mix comprises coal (at 34 per cent of total tonnage), sulphur, lumber and pulp as the main commodities.

   In 1996 a Canadian government subsidy approximating C$1.3 million per annum for handling export grain was terminated.

   Rail operating ratio (expenses as a percentage of turnover) for 1995 was 81.3.

   BC Rail's capital investment programme for the period 1990-95 was C$450 million, with C$132 million set aside for 1996. Principal items of expenditure have been for high-power traction; new and remodelled wagons; infrastructure improvements; signalling; telecommunications; and train-end technology for ensuring continuity

SD40-2 diesels (railway's own designation: GF30) outside maintenance shop in the Tumbler subdivision.
Note catenary for electric locomotives used in this area

of brake lines, which has enabled BCR to operate with two-person crews since 1995.

Passenger operations

BC Rail provides passenger service on three days each week over the 740 km from North Vancouver to Prince George via Lillooet; journey time is 13½ hours. North of Prince George local services are by bus. Regularly scheduled services are provided with trains composed of Budd RDC diesel railcars.

BC Rail runs excursions to Squamish in the summer season using the 'Royal Hudson' steam locomotive, owned by the province of British Columbia. In 1997, BC Rail experimented with a dinner train between Vancouver and Porteau.

Freight operations

BC Rail serves some 700 shippers (150 on BCR Properties sites) in the province of British Columbia. The railway's traffic volume for 1995 totalled 17.9 million gross revenue tonnes and 8.2 billion tonne-km (up from 7.7 billion in 1994).

Forestry products

In 1995, a good year for the forestry industry, 52 per cent of BC Rail's total freight traffic was accounted for by forestry products, namely woodchips, lumber, pulp and miscellaneous. BC Rail serves some 70 planer and sawmills, six major plywood and veneer manufacturers and seven pulp mills. The eastern USA and Japan are major markets for much of BC Rail's forestry traffic but, in 1996, a US lumber quota went into effect; this, combined with depressed wood chip prices, led to a 50 per cent fall-off of chip carloads compared to 1995.

Refinery moved

One of BC Rail's more remarkable accomplishments in 1996 was to transport a disassembled refinery 1,200 km from Taylor, near Fort St John, to a quayside in North Vancouver, using 60 intermodal trailers, flatcars, bolster well cars and 'spacers'. The move took a month. Ultimately, the refinery was reassembled in the United Arab Emirates.

Intermodal operations

In addition to rail services, BC Rail's Intermodal Division provides motor cartage and dry storage warehousing. Business is expected to grow significantly in the future. During 1995, the division received 55 twin-unit container wagons worth C$8 million to add to its fleet, which already includes some triple-unit wagons.

Improvements to existing lines

In 1996 BC Rail finished realigning the track that allows access to the port of Roberts Bank; a new two-berth container-handling pier to be called Delta Port opened in June 1997.

Traction and rolling stock

In mid-1997 BC Rail rostered seven electric and 120 diesel locomotives (including 10 'slugs'); 12 Budd diesel railcars; eight passenger coaches; and 10,450 freight

RDC on service from North Vancouver to Prince George at Lillooet (John Sully)   ***1996***

wagons. BC Rail took delivery of four 3,300 kW GE Dash 9-44CWL locomotives in 1995 at a cost of C$9 million, and also purchased 16 second-hand GE model B36-7 machines.

The GEF40 series is due for an overhaul. BC Rail and GE will work together to upgrade the units to 3,300 kW with Dash-9 electronics.

A five-year remanufacturing programme of 25 MLW Alco-engined yard/transfer locomotives was completed during 1996. The programme introduced to these units a Caterpillar 3516 engine package and has extended their useful life for 15 years. The rebuilds, classified CRS20, are uprated from 1,350 kW to 1,500 kW. They feature electric drive of all auxiliaries and microprocessor control of excitation and adhesion levels.

BC Rail will next convert its M420 and 420B units into slugs to pair with the B36-7 GE locomotives which are being put through the Squamish shops for component evaluation.

Wagon fleet investment

At the end of 1996 the wagon fleet totalled 9,428 (62 more than a year earlier). During 1996, 200 60 ft, 100 tonne boxcars were added to the fleet to haul orientated strand board (OSB). BC Rail is converting in its own workshops older boxcars to take 100 tonne loads. It is also converting flatcars to haul logs, as well as buying new.

When the Crowsnest Pass Rate legislation (officially the

Western Grain Transportation Act), which has subsidised the transport of export grain from the Prairies, expired in 1996, hopper cars from other parts of Canada were expected to become surplus to requirements. BC Rail was expected to endeavour to secure a share of the government grain hopper fleet for use in the province. By mid-1997 the sell-off had still not taken place.

Major wagon repairs and rebuilding are undertaken by BC Rail's Squamish workshop facility, which performs similar work on locomotives. Lighter running repairs are undertaken by workshops at Prince George, where a 9,500 square foot addition was constructed in 1995.

Signalling and telecommunications

The train order system of dispatching was eliminated in 1990. Operations are now conducted with CP Rail's Computerised Manual Block System, the software for which BC Rail secured from CP Rail under a lease agreement.

BC Rail's 1995 capital investment programme included C$3 million to install hot axlebox and dragging equipment detectors and train-end devices.

Electrification

Development of British Columbia's northeast coalfields prompted construction in 1983 of the 129 km Tumbler Ridge branch line into the coalfield area. It was the fourth line in the world to be electrified at 50 kV AC.

Seven Type GF6C 4,400 kW Co-Co electric locomotives were built by General Motors of Canada, using ASEA (now Adtranz) licensed technology to operate in back-to-back pairs. The standard operation is for 13,000-tonne trains of export coal (Japan is a major customer), consisting of 98 rotary coupler-fitted 118 tonne hopper wagons, to travel 720 km to the deep-water port at Ridley Island, near Prince Rupert. BC Rail shares the operation with CN, employing CN diesels from the end of the electrification at Tacheeda Junction (Anzac). At Prince George, CN crews take over for the remainder of the journey over CN trackage to Ridley Island. BC Rail provided one-third of the 913-car fleet. The operating plan provides for nine trains to be in use, each on a 75 hour cycle for the round trip.

Track

Rail: 50, 60 and 68 kg/m
Crossties (sleepers): Softwood, 178 × 228 × 2,400 mm; steel, 130 × 300 × 2,500 mm
Spacing: Wood 510 mm; steel 610 mm
Fastenings: Cut spikes and anchors on timber sleepers, elastic clips on steel sleepers
Min curve radius: 110 m
Max gradient: 2.2 per cent
Max axleload: 29.9 tonnes

Diesel locomotives

Class	Wheel arrangement	Power kW	Speed km/h	Weight tonnes	No in service	First built	Mechanical	Builders Engine	Transmission
MRS18	Bo-Bo	1,350	105	111.6	3	1957	MLW	MLW Alco 251-12	E GE
M420 & 420B	Bo-Bo	1,500	105	112.5	12	1973	MLW	MLW Alco 251-12	E GE
C420	Co-Co	1,500	105	119.3	2	1966	Alco	Alco 251-16	E GE
SD40/GMF30	Co-Co	2,200	105	192.5	23	1978	GM	EMD 645-16	E EMD
Slug	Bo-Bo	1,200	105	109	10	1981	MLW	—	E GE
CRS20	Bo-Bo	1,500	105	113.6	25	1990 R	MLW/BCR	Caterpillar 3516	E KATO/GE
GEF36	Bo Bo	2,700	105	n/a	16	1980	GE	GE 7FDL16	E GE
GEF40	Co-Co	3,000	105	192.5	26	1990	GE	GE 7FDL16	E GE
GEF44	Co Co	3,000	105	n/a	4	1995	GE	GE 7FDL16	E GE

Diesel railcars

Class	Cars per unit	Power kW	Speed km/h	Weight tonnes	No in service	First built	Mechanical	Builders Engine	Transmission
RDC1	1	520	129	53.5	8	1956	Budd	Cummins	Twin Disc

Electric locomotives

Class	Wheel arrangement	Output kW continuous/ one hour	Speed km/h	Weight tonnes	No in service	First built	Builders Mechanical	Electrical
GF6C	Co-Co	4,400/6,480	90	178	7	1983	GMC	ASEA

UPDATED

BC Transit

Government of British Columbia Transit
815 West Hastings Street, Suite 800, Vancouver, British
Columbia V6C 1B4
Tel: +1 604 689 3641   Fax: +1 604 689 3896

Key personnel
General Manager: Lecia Stewart

Passenger operations
In May 1994 BC Transit entered into an agreement with
CP Rail to undertake development work for the
introduction of commuter services serving Vancouver.
Marketed as West Coast Express (WCE), services began

on 1 November 1995 over a 65 km CP route which is now
all double-track and equipped with CTC (centralised
traffic control) between Mission and central Vancouver.
Journey time (with six intermediate stops) is 77 minutes,
compared to two hours by bus. WCE attests to 75 per
cent of riders previously being motorists. The service
contract winner was CP Rail, which beat Burlington
Northern and Herzog Transit Services (see under Tri-Rail
in the US entry) in a tender competition; VIA was awarded
the maintenance contract. Inclusive cost of introducing
the West Coast Express service has been estimated at
C$117 million.
Initial service frequency is five trains in the direction of
peak flow only. Opening daily ridership was targeted at
7,000 but the actual figure realised was 5,100. By late

1996, this figure had risen to 5,800. All fare/ticket types
have provision for use on other BC Transit properties
(bus; Sea Bus; SkyTrain); 60 per cent of train riders make
a transfer. WCE issues a smartcard usable for any ticket
purchase. A C$100 deposit to the card earns a 5 per cent
dividend.

Traction and rolling stock
West Coast Express is operating with five 2,200 kW GM
model F59PHI locomotives each in push-pull mode with
GO Transit-style double-deck passenger coaches; 25
coaches were leased by BC Transit pending delivery of its
own fleet.

UPDATED

Canadian American Railroad

Canadian American Railroad Co
RR2, Box 45, North Maine Junction Park, Bangor, Maine
04401-9602, USA
Tel: +1 207 848 4240   Fax: +1 207 484 4343

Key personnel
Senior Operating Officer: Ted Michon

Gauge: 1,435 mm
Route length: 461 km

Organisation
The Canadian American Railroad Co (CARC) began

operating in November 1994; the company works the
former Canadian Pacific Rail System (CPRS) route from
Sherbrooke, Québec, into the US state of Maine. The
293 km line is a part of what was previously operated by
CPRS as the Canadian Atlantic Railway, and since March
1995 has been owned by Iron Road Railways Inc of
Washington DC (qv in US short line section).
The eastern 168 km of the former Canadian Atlantic
from Brownville Junction, Maine, to St John in New
Brunswick is owned by J D Irving Ltd, under the name of
the Eastern Maine Railway in the USA and the New
Brunswick Southern Railway on the Canadian side of the
border. CARC has access to customers on the Irving-
owned segment in the US.

The St Lawrence & Hudson Railway (St L & H) sold
substantial trackage to Iron Road Railways in September
1996. The latter bought 391 km east from St Jean,
Québec, to the CAR at Sherbrooke, together with short
branches, and named these the Québec Southern. A
196 km line south from Farnham into the state of Vermont,
US, is now the Vermont Northern Railroad, also in the IRR
portfolio.
CARC is receiving a dozen rebuilt GP40s in order to
return leased units to CPRS.

UPDATED

Canadian National

Canadian National Railway Company
935 de la Gauchetière Street Ouest, Montréal, Québec
H3B 2M9
Tel: +1 514 399 5430   Fax: +1 514 399 5479
Web site: http://www.cn.ca

Key personnel
Chairman: David G A McLean
President and Chief Executive Officer: Paul Tellier
Executive Vice-President, Operations: Jack McBain
Executive Vice-President, Marketing: Gerald K Davies
Executive Vice-President and Chief Financial Officer:
  Michael Sabia
Senior Vice-Presidents
  Line Operations: Keith Heller
  Corporate Services: Robert F Dolon
Secretary and Chief Legal Officer: J P Ouellet
Vice-Presidents
Public Affairs and Advertising: Wes Kelley
  Government Affairs: Dave Todd
  Merchandise: James W Foote
  Investor Relations: R E Noorigian
  Bulk Commodities: Peter Marshall
  Market Planning: Sandi Mielitz
  Intermodal and Automotive: Craig Littzen
  Corporate Development & Special Projects:
    André Couture
  Strategic & Financial Planning: Claude Mongeau
  Vice President & Corporate Comptroller: S Pharand
President and Chief Executive Officer, CN Investment:
  Tulio Cedraschi
President and Chief Executive Officer, CANAC
  International Inc: Allan R Pozniak
Treasurer: Jean-Paul Beaulieu

Gauge: 1,435 mm
Route length: 25,900 km, including US properties (see
below)
Electrification: 27 km at 25kV AC (Deux Montagnes line,
Montréal)

Political background
A Crown Corporation wholly owned by the government of
Canada since its incorporation in 1919, CN entered the
private sector on 28 November 1995 when the CN
Commercialisation Act took effect. The government sold
all its shares in the company to private investors in
Canada, the United States and overseas. About two-thirds
of shares were placed with US buyers. No restriction was
placed on foreign acquisition, but individual investors
were limited to a holding of no more than 15 per cent. CN
privatisation involved the single largest initial public

3R International intermodal system operated by CN's Ecorail subsidiary   **1996**

In 1996, CN announced the acquisition of 105 SD751 locomotives from General Motors Diesel Division
1997

offering in Canadian history. The sale of 83.8 million common shares in CN generated gross proceeds to the government of C$2.26 billion.

CN is now free to pursue business rather than public policy objectives.

In conjunction with the offering, CN executed a financial restructuring plan that cut long-term debt by more than half. Debt fell from C$2.8 billion at the end of 1994 to C$1.3 billion at the end of the first quarter of 1996.

CN entered the private sector as Canada's only 'pure' rail company, having earlier divested itself of non-rail businesses. CN Real Estate and CN Tower in Toronto were transferred to the government (for future sale) in 1995, while the oil and gas unit, CN Exploration, was sold to the private sector early in the same year for C$43 million. In March 1996, CN sold its Montréal-based locomotive remanufacturing unit, AMF Technotransport, to GEC Alsthom Canada, with an agreement to place C$100 million in work with the facility over the next five years. CANAC, another subsidiary, continues to offer consulting and contract management services both in the Americas and further afield.

Organisation

Canadian National is Canada's largest and North America's sixth largest railway, based on 1996 revenues of C$4.16 billion. It operates approximately 25,900 km of track in Canada and the United States. The network serves all four of Canada's major ports (Halifax, Montréal, Vancouver and Prince Rupert) and includes strategic connections through the Chicago gateway to much of the rest of North America.

Until the second quarter of 1997, the railway comprised two administrative units: CN East and CN West; in 1997 CN amalgamated the two and eliminated a management layer that had been responsible for the two units. As of 1 January 1996 the Grand Trunk and the Duluth, Winnipeg & Pacific have been officially absorbed and results are consolidated.

Finance

After three years of losses in the early 1990s, CN produced income of C$264 million in 1994. Income excluding special charges rose to C$361 million in 1995. However, because the company incurred special charges

totalling C$1.453 billion, principally to cover for asset impairment write down, compliance with environmental laws, debt repayment and other provisions, CN showed a net loss of C$1.091 billion.

Revenues in 1995, at C$4.159 billion, were 1.5 per cent improved over the previous record year. CN succeeded in reducing expenses by 3 per cent, even while fuel increased in price by 13 per cent over 1994 levels.

In 1995 CN brought its operating ratio (expenses as a proportion of income) down sharply from 94.9 per cent in 1994 to 89.4 per cent; 85 per cent was the declared target and by the fourth quarter of 1996 85.3 had been achieved. Now 80.0 per cent by the year 2000 is the restated goal.

CN continues to trim its workforce, down to 24,064 at the close of 1996 (a reduction of 2,897 on the year).

Cost reduction

CN's cost reduction strategy targets labour costs, network costs, and asset utilisation. Early in 1995 CN successfully concluded a three-year downsizing that aimed at eliminating 11,000 positions, or about one-third of the workforce. By this initiative, labour costs as a percentage of revenue were reduced from 43 per cent in 1992 to 36.3 per cent in 1995. Process change and administrative streamlining made possible the rapid reduction in employment ranks. The company plans to continue downsizing at a rate of approximately 1,000 to 1,500 positions annually over the next five years.

Advances in technology and changes in traffic patterns prompted CN to consolidate three locomotive maintenance shops in eastern Canada during 1996, thereby saving C$30 million per annum. Because of its central location and the quality of the existing shop, Toronto was chosen as the primary maintenance site. The shops at Montréal and Moncton are now servicing facilities. Major locomotive shops are also at Winnipeg, Edmonton, Vancouver. The ex-Grand Trunk shops at Battle Creek were to be evaluated during 1996. Similarly, Toronto is designated as the heavy wagon repair shop in the east; Halifax, Moncton, Montréal, Senneterre and Hamilton are assigned to routine upkeep.

During 1995, CN implemented extended runs, which essentially doubled the distance over which train crews can travel before a crew change, thereby eliminating up to 36 per cent of crew change points. Once fully

Fourteen new sets of aluminium coal wagons were integrated into CN's wagon fleet in 1996   **1997**

implemented by the end of 1996, the practice was expected to result in net annual savings of C$17.2 million.

Also playing a part in reducing costs is CN's patented Beltpack system, developed at CN's research centre based in Montréal. Beltpack enables CN to operate yard locomotives by remote control and an estimated 70 per cent of yard activity is now directed in this fashion. It facilitates the replacement of up to four locomotive drivers and reduces the risk of workplace accidents and

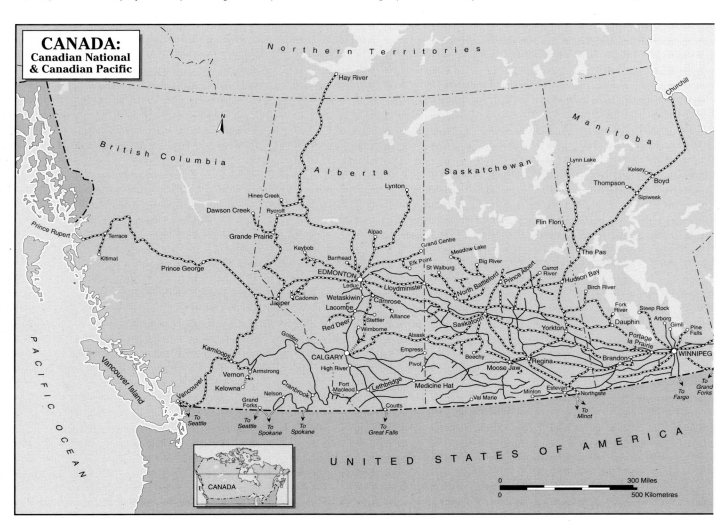

The Brampton Intermodal Terminal in Toronto   **1997**

injuries. By the end of 1996 CN had 105 Beltpack units in service and operational; the annualised savings per application are C$300,000. CN's attention to supply chain management (just-in-time delivery for its own materials inventory and services) has yielded C$30 million in savings.

Rationalisation

CN continues to advocate plans to reduce trackage significantly. CN has established that 39 per cent of its network carries 92 per cent of volume, and that west of Winnipeg the railway (along with its rival CP) is profitable. In November 1995 CN sponsored a first, for Canada, national short lines symposium at which there were 15 operators or holding companies represented. There have since been repeat symposia. The government's decision

in February 1995 to proceed with privatisation brought a halt to negotiations over proposed joint CN and CP use of 440 km of CN trackage in the Ottawa Valley.

In recent years, progress in network rationalisation included: sale of 147 km of line to the Société des Chemins de Fer du Québec which now operates it as Le

Chemin de Fer de Charlevoix; sale of the Central Vermont Railway in the US to RailTex (qv in the US section), bringing in C$39 million; abandonment of the 277 km Graham Subdivision. The new law passed by parliament (refer to section on Transport Canada) provides that either CN or CP may put a line up for abandonment and must accept any offer presented within seven months that equals or exceeds net liquidation value. The Canadian Transportation Agency (CTA) will arbitrate if that value is disputed. In the absence of such an offer within the stipulated seven months, the parent company may abandon the branch line in question.

CN has created a semi-autonomous, 1,855 km internal short line operation in northern Québec. It came into being on 1 May 1995 under a five-year memorandum of agreement with CN's labour unions. Flexible working methods and remuneration policies have been introduced and the workforce reduced from 329 to 223. The new operation connects with CN proper at Garneau and its end points are Arvida, Chibougamau, Noranda, La Sarre and Matagami.

Lines sold, offered, or abandoned during 1996-97 totalled 5,440 km. One such sale was the former Detroit, Toledo and Ironton, which was sold to RailTex in February 1997. In November 1996, CN declared the OmniTRAX company (qv in USA section) the preferred buyer for 1,295 km of track in northern Manitoba, made up of the Flin Flon subdivision, the Sherridon subdivision and the Bayline, 865 km between The Pas and Churchill. Minerals, forest products and grain are the bulk of 1.2 million in revenue tonnes moved. OmniTRAX has committed to continue VIA Rail passenger services. By the end of the century, CN plans to have sold, abandoned or converted to internal short lines an additional 6,400 km of track.

Finance (Consolidated, restated)

Results (C$ million)	*1992*	*1993*	*1994*	*1995*	*1996*
Operating Revenue	3,897	3,956	4,305	4,098	4,159
Operating Expenditure	3,785	3,754	3,548	3,658	3,549
Special charges	951	49		1,453	381
Income/(loss)	(1,018)	(60)	263	(1,091)	229

Traffic	*1992*	*1993*	*1994*	*1995*	*1996*
Revenue tonne-km (million)	155,939	158,728	175,387	169,729	171,936

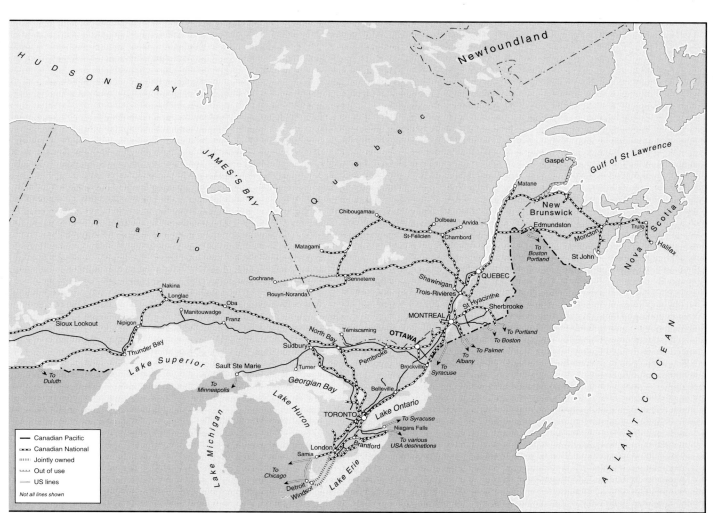

Freight operations

CN's six commodity-based marketing business units reflect a diversified traffic mix. The Industrial Products unit generates 22 per cent of CN freight revenue; the Forest Products unit contributes 20 per cent; the Grain and Grain Products unit 14 per cent; Coal, Sulphur and Fertiliser 16 per cent; Intermodal (qv) 18 per cent; Automotive 10 per cent.

CN's freight revenue also reflects Canada's status as a major trading nation, especially the high volume of trade with the US. The largest proportion of CN revenues — 39 per cent — comes from transborder and US domestic traffic. A further 26 per cent derives from goods exported overseas, while 35 per cent is attributable to domestic Canadian traffic.

The Industrial Products unit includes chemicals, petroleum products, metals and construction materials. Revenue from this sector in 1996 grew by 2 per cent to C$866 million, with liquefied petroleum gas still in strong demand.

Revenue from the Forest Products sector rebounded from C$774 million to C$790 million in 1996. The Forest Products group comprises four commodities — lumber, fibres, paper and panels.

Most of the grain that CN hauls originates in the prairie provinces and is destined for overseas markets via the ports of Vancouver, Prince Rupert or Thunder Bay. A haulage arrangement with BNSF facilitates movement of Canadian grain to US markets or to US export locations. Revenue from the Grain and Grain Products business unit declined by 5 per cent in 1996 to C$570 million.

The Coal, Sulphur and Fertiliser unit earned higher revenues in 1996, totalling C$622 million compared to C$603 million in 1995. Much of the traffic originates in western Canada and is exported to the US or overseas. Higher axleloading for unit coal trains, together with the introduction of low tare weight aluminium cars, has increased productivity in the coal sector by 28 per cent, but both coal and sulphur exports declined, offset in this sector by new potash business.

The Automotive unit, based in southern Ontario and Michigan, experienced lower revenue in 1996: C$402 million as opposed to C$412 million in 1995 but volume was up 6 per cent in spite of two strikes during the year. The Ontario-Michigan region produces 40 per cent of vehicles made in the US and Canada. CN has access to 10 of 14 assembly plants in Canada and 8 of the 17 in Michigan.

CN's CargoFlo service caters for powdered/liquid commodities such as flour, cement and petrochemicals. The railway operates hub centres for transhipment of heavy freight such as steel and lumber.

Information systems

Phase I of CN's three-phase Service Reliability Strategy (SRS), a project that focuses on tracking shipments rather than carloads, was completed in July 1995. CN purchased a tracking program from US railway Santa Fe which can pinpoint the location and status of any shipment anywhere along the chain of distribution. Since May 1996, a shipper has been able to obtain real-time data on a shipment via the Internet on CN's home page. Full implementation of the SRS system will eventually cost C$100 million.

SRS also equips CN to participate in the North American rail industry's new Interline Settlement System (ISS) for electronically allocating revenue between carriers involved in a shipment. In 1994 CN became the first Canadian railway (only the third overall) to become ISS-certified.

Winter Operations Plan

To improve customer service and satisfaction, CN has developed a Winter Operations Plan, a mix of technology, storm management and response techniques, and customer advice.

Intermodal operations

CN's intermodal division accounted for 18 per cent of the company's revenues in 1996. The division comprises three product segments. Retail, which accounts for 31 per cent of revenues, handles consumer products and miscellaneous manufactured items, and provides complete door-to-door service in direct competition with trucks. The overseas segment, which accounts for 31 per cent of revenues, handles import/export container business on behalf of shipping companies. The wholesale segment, which accounts for 18 per cent, handles motor carrier business and carload freight-forwarder business. Intermodal revenue rebounded to C$710 million from

C$669 million, a 6.1 per cent improvement over 1996. The increase is attributed to both an improving domestic ecomony and increases in overseas traffic.

The MonTerm facility in Montréal, HalTerm in Halifax, the Brampton Intermodal Terminal in Toronto and ConPort have all been improved in the last two years. On the West Coast, CN is a partner in the new DeltaPort container facility under development at Vancouver, BC and invested C$2 million in the project in 1996. DeltaPort has doubled capacity at the port of Vancouver, enabling CN to expand intermodal services to central Canada and the US midwest and northeast. The intermodal group has a strong base of negotiated strategic alliances with trucking companies and rail carriers to promote seamless service throughout North America. Among CN's partners are J B Hunt, Kleysen Transport and Reimer Express.

The company has seven intermodal hubs at Moncton, Montréal, Toronto, Chicago, Winnipeg, Edmonton and Vancouver. Satellite hubs are at Halifax, Windsor, Saskatoon and Calgary terminals. The Halifax—Chicago traffic lane achieved an 87 per cent on time performance in 1996 compared to a company-wide 78 per cent, itself 10 per cent improved over 1995.

3R Intermodal system

CN has a shareholding in Innotermodal, a company which has developed the 3R International intermodal system. The latter comprises railborne command and power units coupled to bogie-mounted road trailers to form rail trains, and is aimed at short haul markets. CN created a subsidiary known as Ecorail to operate the 3R International system. A first, largely experimental,

Diesel locomotives: Canadian operations

Class	Builder	Model	No in service	First built	Modified	Rating kW	Speed km/h
Road							
GR-12m	GM	GMD-1	10	1958	1983-88*	895	105
GR-12s	GM	GMD-1	3	1959	1983-88*	895	105
GR-12t	GM	GMD-1	8	1959	1983-87*	895	105
GR-12w	GM	GMD-1	11	1959	1983-87*	895	105
GR-12z	GM	GMD-1	5	1960	1987-90*	895	105
GR-12zc	GM	GMD-1	5	1959	1986-90*	895	105
GR-12u	GM	SW-1200RS	14	1959		895	105
GR-12y	GM	SW-1200RS	25	1960		895	105
GR-412a	GM	GMD-1B	24	1989 (Rebuilds)		895	105
GR-612a	GM	GMD-1A	15	1988 (Rebuilds)		895	105
GRG-12n	GM	GMD-1	2	1958		895	105
GR-12n	GM	GMD-1	6	1958-59		895	105
MR-20a	MLW	M-420	18	1973	1986-87‡	1,492	105
MR-20b	MLW	M-420	26	1974	1986-87‡	1,492	105
MR-20c	MLW	M-420	16	1976	1986-87‡	1,492	105
MR-20d	MLW	HR-412	7	1981	1986-87‡	1,492	105
GR-418a	GM	GP-9RM	12	1981-82 (Remanufactured)	1987‡	1,343	105
GR-418b	GM	GP-9RM	10	1982-83 (Remanufactured)	1987‡	1,343	105
GR-418c	GM	GP-9RM	15	1984 (Remanufactured)	1987‡	1.343	105
GR-418d	GM	GP-9RM	17	1984 (Remanufactured)		1,343	105
GR-418e	GM	GP-9RM	12	1989-90 (Remanufactured)		1,343	105
GR-418f	GM	GP-9RM	15	1991 (Remanufactured)		1,343	105
GR-420b	GM	GP-38-2	34	1972-73	1982-83‡	1,492	105
GR-420c	GM	GP-38-2	45	1973-74	1982-83‡	1,492	105
GR-430a	GM	GP-40	8	1966		2,238	105
Road Freight							
MF-32a	MLW	HR-616	14	1982		2,238	105
MF-36b	MLW	M-636	3	1971		2,685	120
EF-640a	GE	8-40CM	30	1990		2,984	105
EF-640b	GE	8-40CM	25	1992		2,984	105
EF-644a	GE	9-44CWL	23	1994		3,282	105
GF-30c	GM	SD-40	7	1967		2,238	105
GF-30d	GM	SD-40	51	1967-68		2,238	105
GF-30e	GM	SD-40	35	1969		2,238	105
GF-30h	GM	SD-40	39	1969-71		2,238	105
GF-30k	GM	SD-40	47	1971		2,238	105
GF-30m	GM	SD-40	13	1971		2,238	105
GF-30n	GM	SD-40-2	20	1975		2,238	105
GF-30p	GM	SD-40-2	16	1975		2,238	105
GF-30q	GM	SD-40-2	15	1976		2,238	105
GF-30r	GM	SD-40-2	19	1978		2,238	105
GF-30s	GM	SD-40-2	10	1979		2,238	105
GF-30t	GM	SD-40-2	30	1980		2,238	105
GU-30u-y	GM	SD-40-2	42	1980		2,238	105
GF-636a	GM	SD-50F	40	1985-86		2,685	105
GF-636b	GM	SD-50F	20	1987		2,685	105
GF-638a	GM	SD-50DAF	4	1986		2,835	105
GF-638b	GM	SD-60F	59	1989		2,835	105
GF-640a	GM	SD-70I	1	1995		4,000	70
GF-643a	GM	SD75I	105	1996		3,208	112
GF-620a	GM	SD-38-2	4	1976		1,492	105
GF-630a-c	GM/CN	SD-40Q	29	1992-95 (Remanufactured)		2,238	105
GF-430a	GM	GP-40-2L	74	1974		2,238	105
GF-430b	GM	GP-40-2L	38	1974		2,238	105
GF-430c	GM	GP-40-2L	65	1975		2,238	105
GF-430d	GM	GP-40-2	72	1977		2,238	105
GF-430e	GM	GP-40-2	3	1974**	1991-2	2,238	130
GF-430f	GM	GP-40-2	3	1974**	1991-2	2,238	130
GF-430g	GM	GP-40-2	4	1975**	1991-2	2,238	130
Switchers							
MHL-410a	MLW-CN	DL-411RB	1	1982-85 (Rebuild)		746	65
MHT-410a	MLW/CN	DL-411RB	1	1984 (Rebuild)		746	65
GS-418a	GM/CN	GP-9RM	14	1985 (Remanufactured)		1,343	105
GS-418b/c	GM/CN	GP-9RM	70	1990-93 (Remanufactured)		1,343	105
GS-413a	GM/CN	SW-1200RM	2	1986 (Remanufactured)	1987	1,007	105
GS-413b	GM/CN	SW-1200RM	6	1987 (Remanufactured)		1,007	105
GY-418a	GM/CN	GP-9RM	14	1985-86 (Remanufactured)		1,343	105
GY-418b	GM/CN	GP-9RM	18	1986 (Remanufactured)		1,343	105
GY-418c	GM/CN	GP-9RM	8	1987/90 (Remanufactured)		1,343	105
GY-418d-f	GM/CN	GP-9RM	40	1988-90 (Remanufactured)		1,343	105
GS-412a	GM/CN	SW-1200RB	17	1987 (Rebuild)		895	105
GH-20b	GM	GP-38-2	27	1973	1977-85	1,492	105
MS-410a/b	MLW/CN	DL-411RB	10	1983-85 (Rebuild)		746	65
Boosters							
MH-00a	CN		1	1964-105		–	65
GY-00b	GM	YBU-4M	8	1980	1985-86	–	105
GY-00c	GM/CN	YBU	4	1986 (Remanufactured)		–	105
GY-00d	GM/CN	YBU	18	1986 (Remanufactured)		–	105
GY-00e/f/g	GM/CN	YBU	42	1987-90 (Remanufactured)		–	105
GH-00a	GM	HBU-4	19	1978		–	105
GH-00b	GM	HBU-4	4	1980		–	105
GH-00c	GM	HBU-4M	4	1980	1986	–	105
GY-00m	MLW-CN	MS-7	7	1964-66	1990-91	–	105

* Rebogied from A1A-A1A to B-B
‡ Weight reduced
** Former GO Transit locos converted for freight haulage

Central Western Railway

Central Western Railway Holdings
Suite 1165 Weber Center, 5555 Calgary Trail South,
Edmonton, Alberta T6H 5P9
Tel: +1 403 448 5855   Fax: +1 403 439 5658

Key personnel
President: Gordon Clanachan
Vice-President: Thomas Payne

Vice-President and General Manager: S I Smith
Chief Engineer: R L Garrett

Gauge: 1,435 mm
Route length: 384 km

Organisation
The Central Western Railway (CWR) began operations in
1986 as Canada's first 'home-grown' short line spinoff
with the purchase of the Stettler subdivision (Dinosaur-

Ferlow Junction, Alberta) from Canadian National; in 1993
CWR added the former CP Stettler-Compeer branch. The
locomotive roster comprises two GP8 and two GP9 units.
(See also RaiLink.)

UPDATED

Goderich-Exeter Railway

Goderich-Exeter Railway Co Ltd
PO Box 214, Goderich, Ontario N7A 3Z2
Tel: +1 519 524 4024   Fax: +1 519 524 4026

Key personnel
General Manager: A E Parker
Operations Manager: L D Freeman

Gauge: 1,435 mm
Route length: 111 km

Organisation
The Goderich & Exeter (GEXR) was the first RailTex (qv in
United States entry) property developed outside the USA.
GEXR operates the former CN Goderich (72 km) and
Exeter (39 km) subdivisions.
The locomotive fleet comprises four GP9 units.

Total freight handled in 1994 was 9,100 carloads; the
dominant commodity was salt outbound. Interchange is
made with the CN at Stratford, Ontario.
In 1997 the GEXR provided locomotives for the start-up
of another RailTex acquisition from CN, namely the
Ontario L'Original Railway, 40 km, based on Hawkesbury,
Ontario.

UPDATED

GO Transit

Government of Ontario Transit
20 Bay Street, Suite 600, Toronto, Ontario M5J 2W3
Tel: +1 416 869 3600   Fax: +1 416 869 3525

Key personnel
Chairman: David G Hobbs
Managing Director: Richard C Ducharme

Gauge: 1,435 mm
Route length: 360 km

Political background
GO Transit, set up in 1967, was Canada's first interregional transport system created and funded by a
provincial government. Since 1974 it has been under the
control of the Toronto Area Transit Operating Authority,
an Ontario Crown agency on which five regional
municipalities are represented as well as Metropolitan
Toronto and the Province of Ontario (which appoints the
chairman). GO (an abbreviation of Government of
Ontario) Transit serves a territory of over 8,000 km² with a
population of 4.5 million, which continues to increase. It
runs an integrated bus and rail passenger network with a
total annual ridership of 33.5 million.

Finance
In FY1995-96, GO experienced a year-to-year decrease in
ridership of 0.75 per cent to 24.8 million boardings. The
operating cost recovery ratio in FY1995-96 rose from 64.2
to 65.3. Annual train-kilometres operated in 1995-96 were
2.155 million, compared to 2.21 million in 1994-95.

Passenger operations
Starting with a single rail route along Lake Ontario, GO
now operates seven lines (taking into account that the

Lakeshore line has been split into East and West lines),
with Toronto's Union station as the system's hub. In
addition to 151 trains run daily, GO Transit operates 1,060
bus trips. In recent years several proposals for service
expansion have been deferred due to lack of funds.
Limited parking at several stations continues to be a
deterrent to ridership growth.
In 1996 a new consolidated Hamilton GO Center
opened in Hamilton using the restored Toronto, Hamilton
& Buffalo Railway structure; this facility replaces separate
GO Train and GO Bus terminals.
Train services are run under contract over Canadian
National tracks (in six corridors) and Canadian Pacific
(one corridor) by CN and CP crews to GO Transit
specification, but GO Transit owns the infrastructure of
the Lakeshore East line between Pickering and Whitby. A
rolling stock maintenance contract valued at

C$97.4 million has been awarded to Bombardier for a six-
year period, 1997-2003.

Traction and rolling stock
GO Transit operates a standardised fleet consisting of 49
F59PH diesel-electrics from GM-Canada (jointly designed
by GM and GO Transit) and a 331-strong passenger
coach fleet exclusively composed of double-deck
vehicles, built by UTDC (now Bombardier).

Coupler in standard use (passenger cars): H-tightlock
Braking in standard use (locomotive-hauled stock):
26L, 26LUM and 26C

UPDATED

Go Train on the Richmond Hill line near downtown Toronto

Montréal Urban Community Transport Commission

Société de Transport de la Communauté Urbaine de Montréal (STCUM)
800 rue de la Gauchetière Ouest, CP 2000, Bureau 1-4500, Montréal, Québec H5A 1J6
Tel: +1 514 280 5150   Fax: +1 514 280 5193
Web site: http://www.cum.gc.ca/cum-fr/stcum/accustcf.htm

Suburban rail operations office:
STCUM Trains de Banlieue
800 Place Victoria, Bureau 2118, Montréal, Québec H4Z 1H9
Tel: +1 514 280 5133   Fax: +1 514 280 6198

Key personnel
Chairman: Yves Ryan
President and General Manager: Trefflé Lacombe
Executive Directors
  Finance: Michel Rhéaume
  Planning: André Haddad
  Metro and Commuter Rail: Jacques Rompré
  Commuter Rail: Marcel Grégoire
  Construction and Maintenance: Roger C Chocotte
Secretary and Manager, Legal Dept: Daniel Robert
Gauge: 1,435 mm
Route length: 91 km
Electrification: 27 km at 25 kV AC

Political background
STCUM formerly oversaw all public transport for the city of Montréal: bus, metro and two commuter rail lines connecting Montréal with Rigaud and Deux-Montagnes. From the beginning of 1996, the two commuter lines were taken over by the newly created Agence Métropolitaine de Transporte.

In 1992, CP Rail proposed the Bonjour Montréal Inc concept to introduce several new services totalling about 190 km, including restoration of some discontinued in the last 25 years. In 1993, CN endorsed the concept in general. The Province of Québec secured and 'mothballed' 94 coaches from GO Transit's surplus stock with a view to realising the CP plan; details of service standards and the possible required subsidy have yet to be established.

Passenger operations
CP operates diesel push-pull service on the line from Montréal's Windsor station to Rigaud (64 km). The route has been significantly upgraded over the last 10 years and daily ridership currently is 8,000 (16,000 trips). Rolling stock consists of conventional and double-deck coaches hauled by seven FP7 and four GP9u diesel-electric locomotives. The latter are ex-CN GP9 units remanufactured by CN's Pointe St Charles workshops (later AMF Technotransport, now GEC Alsthom AMF) and operate with head-end power generator vans converted from standard box cars.

Reconstruction of Windsor station began in 1994: CP and Molson Breweries (owner of the Canadiens ice hockey club) are undertaking the redevelopment. A first stage opened in March 1996, creating direct access to Montréal's Metro and pedestrian footpath network.

Bombardier emu car for STCUM's Deux-Montagnes line   **1995**

Diesel locomotives

Class	Wheel arrangement	Power kW	Speed km/h	Weight tonnes	No in service	First built	Builders
FP7	B-B	1,500	105	113	1	1951	E GM
FP7	B-B	1,500	105	113	6	1952	E GM
GP9u	B-B	1,800	105	112	4	1959	E GM/AMF

Electric multiple-units

Class	Cars per unit	Motor cars per unit	Motored axles/car	Output/motor kW	Speed km/h	No in service	First built	Builders Mechanical	Electrical
MR 90	2	1	4	284	120	29	1994	Bombardier	GE

Improvements to existing lines
The electrified Canadian National route from Montréal's Gare Centrale to Deux-Montagnes (27 km) has been entirely rebuilt and re-electrified under a three-year modernisation project managed by CANAC International, with SNC-Lavalin as electrification engineers.

As part of the modernisation, the line has been extended 5.3 km at its outer end from Deux-Montagnes to Autoroute 640. The new yard is between Deux-Montagnes and Route 640. The extension was energised at 25 kV 60 Hz AC in 1994 to permit testing of the first deliveries from an order for 29 two-car emus built by Bombardier and costing C$99 million. Each new car has a crush load of 233 passengers.

In 1994 the Val Royal-Gare Centrale section was rebuilt, and some 5,000 parking spaces were provided at stations out past Val Royal. Three stations in Laval were consolidated into one at Sainte-Dorothée; two others were repositioned, and all were equipped with 10-car-length platforms. Services operated by the new emus were introduced in October 1995, at which time the surviving Z-class locomotives and heavyweight passenger coaches were retired. Fully restored service levels, including weekend and evening service, were attained by December 1995. There was a period of three weeks in early 1996 when the service was suspended while a traction motor fault was rectified on the new emus. A new CTC (centralised traffic control) installation has increased peak direction route capacity from nine trains to 14. Train speed has been raised from 55 km/h to 105 km/h; journey time from Gare Centrale to Deux-Montagnes has been cut from 55 to 30 minutes. The proposed double-track extension from Val Royal to Am-A-Baie has been deferred for the immediate future. The all-inclusive cost is estimated at C$300 million.

UPDATED

New Brunswick Southern

New Brunswick Southern Railway Co Ltd
11 Gifford Road, PO Box 5666, Saint John, New Brunswick E2L 5B6
Tel: +1 506 632 5813   Fax: +1 506 632 5818

Key personnel
General Manager: B L Bourgeois

Gauge: 1,435 mm
Route length: 190.5 km

Organisation
As part of the January 1995 disposal of the Canadian Atlantic Railroad by Canadian National, 190.5 km located in New Brunswick were acquired by the J D Irving Company and are now operated as the NBSR using, in early 1996, six GP9 units overhauled either by OmniTrax (qv in the US section) or by AMF Technotransport. The property consists of a 136 km line from the border at McAdam to Saint John, plus a 55 km branch from McAdam to Saint Stephen. The line continues as the Eastern Maine Railroad (also owned by Irving but served by the Candian American Railway (qv) for 168 km into the US from McAdam to Brownville Junction.

UPDATED

Ontario Midwestern Railway Company

Organisation
This company was formed in the first half of 1997 to buy or lease 175 km of CP track within Ontario, from Mississauga to Owen Sound.

NEW ENTRY

Ontario Northland Rail Services

555 Oak Street E, North Bay, Ontario P1B 8L3
Tel: +1 705 472 4500   Fax: +1 705 476 5598

Key personnel
President and Chief Executive Officer (of the ONTC):
   K J Wallace
Vice-Presidents
   Finance and Administration: S G Carmichael
   Telecommunications: R S Hutton
   Transportation Services: R G Leach
Superintendent, Train Operations: J Thib

Gauge: 1,435 mm
Route length: 1,211 km

Organisation
Ontario Northland Rail Services is a component of the multimodal Ontario Northland Transport Commission's operations. ONRS lies at the eastern rim of the province. It runs from North Bay, where it connects with Canadian National and CPRC routes westward from Ottawa, to Moosonee on James Bay, the southward-probing neck of Hudson Bay. In addition to rail services, ONTC offers bus services, ferry services on the Great Lakes, and telecommunications. It exited the air passenger business in March 1996.

In 1991 agreement was reached for the transfer to Ontario Northland of 240 km of CN line between Cochrane and Calstock. This section connects with Ontario Northland at Cochrane. The Ontario Northland main line has four additional short branches.

Passenger operations
Ontario Northland runs the Northlander passenger service from Cochrane to Toronto Union station daily except Saturdays, travelling over 367 km of CN track between Toronto and North Bay. North of Cochrane, to

Moosonee, a mixed train runs three times a week September-June and twice-weekly in July and August when it is augmented by a tourist train, the Polar Bear Express. 1995 ridership was 42,485 on the Northlander, up 31 per cent on 1994. A total of 37,535 passengers travelled on the Cochrane—Moosonee section.

With the passing of the Canada Transport Act, eliminating train service subsidies (except, so far, VIA's), and the province of Ontario now scheduling bus deregulation for January 1998, some hard business decisions may face the ONTC, which has, in the past, cross-subsidised its services out of profits in the telecommunication sector, now called ONTel. Based on 1995 data, the ONTel profit is less than the combined federal and provincial subsidies for rail services.

Freight operations
Freight, chiefly lumber, pulp, newsprint and ores, is the backbone of Ontario Northland's business. 1995 carload shipments totalled 41,500 and contributed C$43.3 million in revenue to the commission. ONTC anticipates there may be a future, large, market in transport of solid waste from metropolitan Toronto.

Traction and rolling stock
The railway rosters 27 line-haul and six switching diesel-electric locomotives, 46 passenger coaches and 692 freight wagons. The passenger fleet includes 26 single-level commuter coaches acquired from GO Transit (the

last six were purchased in 1994) and comprehensively renovated as first-class long-haul coaches in Ontario Northland workshops.

One FP7A locomotive was rebuilt in 1994 with a Caterpillar 3516 engine rated at 1,529 kW; a second was outshopped in 1995 and ONRS has a further five FP7s, some out of service, that are available for similar repowering. Seven diesel locomotives without cabs have been acquired for conversion to provide Head-End Power for ONRS's refurbished passenger coaches.

The 1995 capital programme included nine miles of replacement rail; 47,000 new sleepers; further rebuilding of the 100-tonne gondola car fleet; and construction of two new loading ramps, one in Moosonee, one in Rouyn-Noranda.

Track
Rail: 125.77 kg/m
Crossties (sleepers)
Wood: Thickness: 180 mm
Spacing: 1,886/km
Fastenings: 4 spikes per sleeper on tangent, 8 spikes per sleeper on curves
Min curvature radius: 300 m
Max gradient: 1.5 per cent
Max axleload: 29.5 tonnes (65,000 lb)

UPDATED

Diesel locomotives

Class	Wheel arrangement	Power kW	Speed km/h	Weight tonnes	No in service	First built	Mechanical	Builders Engine	Transmission
SD40-2	C-C	2,237.1	104.6	170.7	7	1973	GM	645E3	E GM Main Gen
GP38-2	B-B	1,492.5	104.6	115.67	10	1974	GM	645E	E GM Main Gen
FP7-A	B-B	1,118.55	113.0	117.11	2	1951	GM	567BC	E GM Main Gen
GP-9	B-B	1,304.97	104.6	117.34	6	1956	GM	567C	E GM Main Gen

Québec North Shore & Labrador Railway

Québec North Shore & Labrador Railway Co
100 rue Retty, Sept-Iles, Québec G4R 3E1
Tel: +1 418 968 7495   Fax: +1 418 968 7498

Key personnel
President and Chief Executive Officer: M D Walker
General Manager: Marc Duclos
Manager, Materials and Services: John Turnbull
Superintendents
   Transport and Traffic: Michel Lamontagne
   Equipment Maintenance: Gilbert Sarazin
   Maintenance of Way, Signals and Communications:
   Louis Gravel

Gauge: 1,435 mm
Route length: 639 km

Freight operations
Begun in 1950 by its then newly formed owners, the Iron Ore Company of Canada (IOCC), with the shareholding support of several US steelmakers, the 573 km main line of the Québec North Shore & Labrador (QNS&L) runs from Schefferville south to Sept-Iles on the St Lawrence River. Schefferville, the railhead for the Ungava ore tract in the Labrador peninsula, is just inside the Québec border, but otherwise the northern half of the route is enclosed by Newfoundland. Within this section a 58 km branch was run from Ross Bay westward to Labrador City in 1960.

IOC stopped mining in the Schefferville area in 1982, but still serves the railhead as there are no roads north of Sept-Iles. Mining is now concentrated in the Carol Lake area, at the extremity of the Labrador City branch.

Despite the savage winters in the region, QNS&L functions all year round. In winter, however, it only moves processed (beneficiated) ore in pellets, because of raw ore's propensity to freeze.

QNS&L runs loaded ore trains varying from 117 to 265 wagons in length; the latter trail about 3.3 km behind their lead locomotives and gross over 33,700 short tons, but a 117-wagon train weighs at least 14,000 short tons. Normal power is two 2,200 kW GM-EMD SD40 locomotives at the front end, but when a train is made up to 165 wagons or more mid-train helper units, radio-controlled by the Locotrol system from the lead locomotive, are added. Twenty-two of the type SD40-2 units were Locotrol-equipped by AMF Technotransport in 1994 and redesignated SD40-2CLCs. In 1997, IOCC announced a C$14 million contract with GE/Harris Railway Electronics for a train control system aimed at enhancing performance of a train powered by multiple locomotives.

Tonnage moved in 1994 was 20.5 million, an increase of almost 8 per cent on 1993.

Traction and rolling stock
Resources consist of 55 diesel-electric locomotives, 2,400 freight wagons, 11 passenger coaches and six Budd RDC diesel railcars bought used from VIA in 1994. In 1994 the QNS&L acquired its first GE locomotives, three Dash 8-40C units bought new.

Signalling and telecommunications
Centralised Traffic Control (CTC) is in operation on 416 km of QNS&L's 573 km main line. The railway is controlled from Sept-Iles.

Track
Rail: 65.5 kg/m
Crossties (sleepers)
Treated hardwood: 177.8 × 228.6 × 2,743.2 mm
Spacing: 2,080/km
Fastenings: Standard track, 165 mm (5½ in)
Min curvature radius: 220 m
Max gradient: 1.32%
Max axleload: 32.5 tonnes

VERIFIED

Diesel locomotives

Class	Wheel arrangement	Power kW	Speed km/h	Weight tonnes	No in service	First built	Mechanical	Builders Engine	Transmission
SD40/40-2	C-C	2,238	114	174	48	1968	GM	GM	E GM
GP-9	B-B	1,305	114	109	4	1954	GM	GM	E GM

Québec Railway Corporation

1130 Sherbrooke Street West, Suite 310, Montréal, Québec, H3A 2M8
Tel: +1 514 849 1214/+1 514 982 9944
Fax: +1 514 849 2319

Key personnel
Chairman of the Board: Pierre Martin
General Manager: Serge Belzile

Gauge: 1,435 mm
Route length: 325 km in two segments

Freight operations
The QRC bought 233.6 km of line from CN in 1995. It is operated as the Chemin de Fer Charleroix Inc.

In November 1996, the company bought CN's line between Matapedia and Chandler (235 km) which it will operate as the Chemin de Fer Baie des Chaleurs, interchanging with CN at Matapedia. The CFBC will host

passenger trains operated by VIA (qv) which must now secure the orphaned section Chandler — Gaspé (90 km).

NEW ENTRY

RaiLink Investments Ltd

100 Ferguson Street, North Bay, Ontario PIB 1W8
Tel: +1 705 472 6200   Fax: +1 705 472 2527

Organisation
RaiLink is the new holding company for the Central Western Railway (qv). In addition to the CWR, RaiLink has a 25 per cent equity position in the Québec Railway Corporation (qv) and, in October 1996, formed the Ottawa

Valley RaiLink to lease and operate 550 km of CP track from Coniston, near Sudbury, to Smiths Falls under long-term lease, plus a branch from Mattawa Ontario, to Temiscaming.

NEW ENTRY

RailTex Canada Inc

Organisation
This company is a wholly owned subsidiary of RailTex Inc (qv in the US section) formed in 1996 to finance

acquisitions within Canada. Operations are listed under the name of the operating company.

NEW ENTRY

Southern Railway of British Columbia

Southern Railway of British Columbia Ltd
2102 River Drive, New Westminster, British Columbia V3M 6S3
Tel: +1 604 521 1966   Fax: +1 604 526 0914

Key personnel
President: Richard J Stoeckly

Gauge: 1,435 mm

Organisation
Formerly the property of the British Columbia Hydro & Power Authority, the Southern Railway of British Columbia (SRY) assumed its current name in September 1988 when it was sold to the Itel Rail Corporation. In October 1994 it was acquired by an Alberta company controlled by Washington Companies, a natural resources conglomerate that owns the US Montana Rail Link system (qv).

SRY's main line connects Vancouver (New Westminster) and Chilliwack, a distance of 130 km. There are several branches, including one to the industrial centre of Annécis Island. Some 41 per cent of SRY's current 47,000 annual wagonloads of traffic is made up of cars imported through Annécis. SRY has 19 locomotives, which are mostly switchers and 385 freight wagons and employs 170. Interchange is made with CN, CP and with the Burlington Northern.

VERIFIED

VIA Rail

VIA Rail Canada Inc
PO Box 8116, Station A, Montréal, Québec H3C 3N3
Tel: +1 514 871 6000   Fax: +1 514 871 6003

Key personnel
Chairman: Marc LeFrançois
President and Chief Executive Officer: Terry W Ivany
Vice-Presidents
  Customer Services and Government Relations:
  Michael Gushue
  Marketing and Information Services:
  Christena Keon-Sirsly
  Equipment Maintenance: John Marginson
  Public Affairs & Human Resources: Paul Côté
  Planning and Finance: J R Paquette
  Education and Corporate Enhancement:
  Richard McConnell
General Counsel and Corporate Counsel: Carole Mackay

Gauge: 1,435 mm
Route length operated: 6,524 km

Political background
VIA Rail Canada Inc came into being as a Crown Corporation in January 1977 as a creation of the then Trudeau administration. At that time it took over management of all rail passenger services previously operated by CN and CP Rail, except commuter services. Since then its fortunes have been inextricably tied to the cabinet of the government in office because the law requires only an order in council rather than a vote in Parliament to alter VIA's future. The current mandate is clearly to apply private industry principles to administration of the corporation with the intent of determining how close it can come to self-sufficiency. For all its performance gains in the last few years VIA is still considered expendable in some quarters of Canada's political spectrum.

VIA contracts with the Canadian government for the provision of those rail passenger services specified by the Minister of Transport. In turn, VIA contracts with railway companies for the operation of these services and with non-railway companies for the provision of incidental goods and services; 92 per cent of track used is contracted from CN.

By comparison with its US counterpart, Amtrak, VIA was launched with a less specific political mandate and on unsatisfactory terms of relationship with its host Canadian railways, paying considerably more in user fees than Amtrak on a pro rata basis. In 1995 some progress was made in renegotiating user fees and rents with CN until 2008.

In the last few years, VIA has begun to generate useful income (altogether C$11 million in 1995) from sources other than passenger fares, examples being the sale of some locomotives to Algoma Central (qv) and the lease of some power to freight carriers, especially on weekends.

F40PH locomotive and LRC coaches on Toronto—Ottawa service at Whitby, Ontario (Neil Sprinks) **1996**

Traffic	1993	1994	1995
Passenger journeys (000)	3,570	3,586	3,597
Passenger-km (million)	1,311	1,334	1,375

Finance
From a high annual subsidy of C$650 million in 1989 the figure was cut to C$295 million in 1995 and the target for 1997 is C$233 million. During 1995 the company reduced the workforce by 540, and has now shed 23 per cent of payroll in the last three years.

Revenues in 1995 were C$175 million, while expenses totalled C$397.3 million; the Canadian government made a contribution of C$295.4 million for operating deficits, capital improvements and reorganisation charges. The revenue/cost ratio in 1995 was 44 per cent, up from 40 per cent a year earlier.

Passenger operations
Following cuts in the early 1990s, VIA's network is now down to the Québec City—Windsor corridor, some service to the Maritimes and Vancouver, plus a handful of 'rump' services.

Transcontinental service between Toronto and Vancouver (the 'Canadian') is now thrice-weekly each way with a Jasper—Prince Rupert connection (the 'Skeena').

In the Maritimes, the 'Ocean' still goes from Montréal to Halifax on the CN route six days a week. St John is connected by bus service to Moncton.

The 'International' Toronto—Chicago service now uses Amtrak Superliner coaches since the opening of the St Clair border tunnel (see Canadian National entry), and a

VIA F40PH locomotive, having used an Amtrak locomotive and VIA LRC coaches for some years.

The rump services are thrice weekly Winnipeg—Churchill (the 'Hudson Bay'); Sudbury—White River; Québec—Jonquière (the 'Saguenay'); Québec—Senneterre (the 'Abitibi'). Additionally, in Manitoba, a mixed train connects The Pas with Lynn Lake.

Total systemwide ridership has stabilised in the region of 3.6 million annually (see table), with 3 million of that riding on Québec City—Windsor corridor services. This contrasts with 8 million in 1981.

Short line impact
The accelerating trend to short-line spinoffs by CN & CP, and the new liberal attitudes toward abandonment proceedings, are beginning to affect VIA. CN's internal Québec short line has reduced the Senneterre—Cochrane section to 15 km/h and filed an abandonment petition for it. It is unlikely this will continue as passenger-only. More than 1,400 km of track in northern Manitoba have been sold by CN to OmniTRAX, with which VIA will have to negotiate in future for continuation of service, and the section Matapedia—Chandler has been sold by CN to line Québec Railway Corporation, which leaves VIA to negotiate over the future of the outlier section, Chandler to Gaspé, which carries the 'Chaleur'.

New lines
There are hopes of instituting a high-speed rail service between Montréal, Ottawa and Toronto. Much of the drive to institute such a service comes from equipment

manufacturers; VIA hopes to be (but is not assured of being) the operator of any high-speed service that is introduced. So far, efforts to get beyond the proposal stage have been unsuccessful.

Traction and rolling stock

At the close of 1996 VIA Rail's locomotive fleet consisted of 59 GM F40PH diesel-electric locomotives, 29 LRC power cars (of which eight were active). A handful of FP9s retained for services using steam-heated stock was withdrawn in 1996 and made available for sale; several have been bought by Wisconsin Central for use on Algone Central services.

The LRC coach fleet consists of 99 vehicles: 50 LRC-2 coaches, delivered between 1978-80; and 49 LRC-3 cars, delivered in 1982-83; 10 LRC-1 cars were in store. VIA's coaching stock is 214 stainless steel long-distance cars and five Budd RDC diesel railcars. Four of the RDCs are in use on the 'Malahat' service on Vancouver Island; the fifth is used between Sudbury and White River, Ontario.

Equipment modification and standardisation projects have served to increase reliability by 80 per cent for coaches and 20 per cent for locomotives, resulting in an estimated C$15 million in annualised savings.

LRC improvements
A C$16.9 million interior refurbishment of the 100 coaches and club cars in the LRC fleet was completed in December 1993. Designed for 200 km/h operation, LRC power cars have been limited to 160 km/h due to high

Diesel locomotives

Class	Builder's type	Wheel arrangement	Power kW	Speed km/h	Weight tonnes	No in service	First built	Builders Mechanical	Engine	Transmission
GPA 30 a	F40 PH2	Bo-Bo	2,238	153	129	20	1986	GMD	16-645E3C	E GMD
GPA 30 b	F40 PH2	Bo-Bo	2,238	145	129	10	1987	GMD	16-645E3C	E GMD
GPA 30 c	F40 PH2	Bo-Bo	2,238	145	129	29	1989	GMD	16-645E3C	E GMD
MPA 27	LRC	Bo-Bo	2,760	153	125	8	1978	B/MLW	16 Cyl 251-F	E CGE

GMD General Motors Diesel (Canada)   CGE Canadian General Electric   B/MLW Bombardier/Montréal Locomotive Works

unsprung weight. Two power cars were due to be fitted with body-mounted traction motors by the end of 1995 for 200 km/h in-service tests in 1996.

The tilting mechanism fitted to LRC coaches (the power cars do not tilt) has proved unreliable. In 1994 two coaches and one power car were loaned to Bombardier to undertake a test programme with a view to upgrading the tilting mechanism. A more reliable mechanism with a self-diagnostic capability is sought by VIA.

Coach refurbishment
The 181 stainless steel coaches constructed in the 1950s and used on long-haul services were comprehensively refurbished in 1990 for C$200 million. Besides complete internal renovation and refurnishing, the coaches have been equipped for Head-End Power (HEP) with electric heating, electric kitchen equipment and new air conditioning. Bogies have been rebuilt and fitted with

modern braking and wheel-slide protection equipment. The original 1950s ambience of the interiors has been retained in the complete refurnishing with new wall carpets, wall coverings and upholstery, and a special feature is mural artwork specially commissioned from Canadian artists. All sleeping cars now have showers. The rebuilding was executed by AMF Technotransport. This was dubbed the HEP-I project.

A similar programme (HEP-II) to upgrade 33 Budd-built stainless steel coaches used on services in southwestern Ontario was concluded during 1996. These will replace all non-LRC vehicles used in this area and a handful were assigned to the 'Skeena'. The contract, with GEC Alsthom AMF, has an option for treatment of a further 12 vehicles.

These programmes, coupled with judicious shortening of trains, have allowed VIA to climinate steam-heated stock from its fleet.

UPDATED

Windsor & Hantsport Railway

Windsor & Hantsport Railway Co Ltd
PO Box 578, 2 Water Street, Windsor, Nova Scotia
ON 2TO
Tel: +1 902 798 0798   Fax: +1 902 798 0816

Key personnel
General Manager: James Taylor
Chief Mechanical Officer: Peter Johnstone

Gauge: 1,435 mm
Route length: 96 km

Organisation
The Windsor & Hantsport began operations in August 1994 after CP Rail sold 96 km of line, eight RS23 diesel locomotives and 76 80-ton hopper wagons to Iron Road Railways (qv in US short line section). Connection is made with the CN system at Windsor Junction, Nova Scotia. The Windsor & Hantsport is the last working vestige of CP Rail

in Nova Scotia and had previously formed part of CP's Dominion Atlantic Railway subsidiary. Carloadings in 1994 were 22,000, with gypsum representing 90 per cent of the traffic carried. The railway was evaluating replacement power during 1997.

UPDATED

CHILE

Ministry of Transport & Communications

Amunategui 139, Santiago
Tel: +56 2 672 6503   Fax: +56 2 699 5138

Key personnel
Minister of Transport: N Irueta

VERIFIED

Chilean State Railways (EFE)

Empresa de los Ferrocarriles del Estado
Avenida Libertador Bernardo O'Higgins 3322, Santiago
Tel: +56 2 779 0707   Fax: +56 2 776 2609

Key personnel
President: Sergio Gonzalez
General Manager: Osvaldo Sepulveda
Planning and Development Manager: Jorge Max
Administration and Finance Manager: Jaime Moncada
Managers
  Human Resources: Patricio Corvalan
  Legal Affairs: Patricio Morales
  Operations: Jaime Contreras
  Passenger: Alejandro Uribe
  MERVAL: Andres Link
  Arica-La Paz: Eduardo Espinoza
Comptroller: Ernesto Opazo

Gauge: 1,676 mm; 1,000 mm
Route length: 3,045 km; 402 km
Electrification: 1,351 km at 3 kV DC

Political background
Under legislation passed in 1992 which established the company in its present form, EFE was granted some measure of autonomy and allowed to meet its objectives by means of contracts, concessions and joint ventures with third parties. Under this legislation, EFE's objectives were to be set out in three-year development plans agreed

with the Chilean government, the first of which was approved in August 1993.

As required by the 1993-96 plan, a controlling 51 per cent interest in EFE's freight subsidiary FEPASA (qv) was sold to the Transportes del Pacífico consortium in January 1995. As well as disposing of its non-core activities, EFE has been charged with increasing the involvement of the private sector in the railway system it currently operates. This was to take the form of concessions to operate passenger services, and concessions to upgrade and maintain sections of track to specified standards. It was expected that concessions for passenger services and track maintenance on a particular route could, if advantageous, be awarded to the same bidder.

EFE invited bids for a track maintenance concession on the Santiago—Chillán (to allow speeds of 140 km/h) and Chillán—Temuco/Concepción—Valdivia sections of its Santiago—Puerto Montt main line in 1996, so that work could begin in 1997. FEPASA will undertake maintenance on those lines and branches where there are no passenger services.

Three separate passenger concessions were due to commence operation in 1997, covering the Santiago—Chillán, Chillián (including the Concepción branch) and Temuco—Puerto Montt routes. Bids were also invited in 1996 for the operating and maintenance concessions covering the Santiago—Maipú—Talagante route.

Maintenance concessionaires were to receive subsidy where the track standard required by EFE was above that which could be funded through access charges. It was reported that EFE was to retain responsibility for electrification, major bridges, signalling and dispatching.

Overseeing the project is the state-appointed Transport Investment Infrastructure Planning Commission (Sectra), which will set standards for track maintenance on all routes. Sectra will also determine minimum passenger services, covering such aspects as speed, frequency, capacity and standards of accommodation. Eleven companies or groups are known to have entered bids.

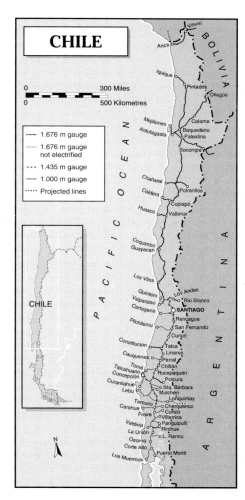

CHILE

0	300 Miles
0	500 Kilometres

-⊶- 1.676 m gauge
—— 1.676 m gauge not electrified
---- 1.435 m gauge
—— 1.000 m gauge
····· Projected lines

Organisation

On 29 September 1995 EFE reorganised its activities as six subsidiary limited companies; a property management company was later established on 3 October 1995. With the exception of Ferrocarril de Arica–La Paz SA, all are concerned with the trunk 1,676 mm gauge Valparaíso–Santiago–Puerto Montt route and its 1,000 mm and 1,676 mm gauge branches. Most of the trunk route is electrified, as far south as Temuco.

Ferrocarril de Arica–La Paz SA (Arica–La Paz Railway Ltd) operates passenger and freight services on a 206 km route in the far north of Chile, isolated from the rest of the EFE network. Linking the Pacific port of Arica with the Bolivian system at Visviri, this 1,000 mm gauge diesel-worked route reaches a maximum height of 4,257 m and features spectacular civil engineering. A private operator for the Chilean section of this railway was due to be selected from 10 bidders in late 1997; the Bolivian section is already privately operated, by a joint venture of Cruz Blanca's Ferrocarril Oriental de Bolivia and FCAB. The separate 1,000 mm gauge system extending from La Calera, near Valparaíso, north to Iquique has been operated by a separate state-owned company, Ferronor (qv), since 1990.

With the exception of some 900 route-km placed under the responsibility of FEPASA, infrastructure maintenance and management on the core EFE system has been undertaken since September 1995 by Infraestructura y Tráfico Ferroviario SA (Infrastructure and Railway Traffic Ltd). Suburban passenger services are operated in the Valparaíso area by MERVAL (Metro Regional de Valparaíso SA - Valaparaíso Regional Metro Ltd) and in the Santiago area by Ferrocarriles Suburbanos SA (Suburban Railways Ltd). Long-distance passenger services between Santiago and Puerto Montt are operated by Ferrocarril de Pasajeros SA (Passenger Railway Ltd). A second subsidiary with the same responsibility, Ferrocarril del Sur SA (Southern Railway Ltd), was formed in September 1995.

Finance

Legislation passed in 1992 placed EFE on a new financial footing, following a steady deterioration in the company's finances during the 1980s which had left it with an accumulated debt of US$100 million by 1990. The consequent neglect of essential expenditure on the railway saw much of its track fall into disrepair, and 40 per cent or more of its locomotives and passenger cars become unserviceable.

Under the 1993-96 development plan, which came into force on 31 August 1993, the government has agreed to guarantee bonds to allow EFE to renegotiate its debt or obtain funds for infrastructure renewal. EFE was also to receive subsidy for providing socially necessary services, and funding to enable a staff reduction programme to be brought into effect. At the start of this programme, staff numbers stood at 4,000 (excluding freight operations) and had been brought down to 2,237 by the end of 1995.

EFE's first three-year development plan also established that subsidy was to be paid by the government as long as road users were not meeting their true infrastructure costs. During 1994, EFE was to receive 2.65 pesos (then 0.65 US cents) for every tonne-km of freight traffic carried and 0.23 pesos (0.056 US cents) for every passenger-km, with payments of 2.39 pesos (0.58 US cents) per tonne-km and 0.13 pesos (0.032 US cents) per passenger-km scheduled for 1995. It was anticipated that this subsidy would provide EFE with an extra US$10 million a year, with freight subsidy continuing to be paid after the privatisation of FEPASA in the hope that track access charges would be kept at a reasonable level.

Traffic	1994	1995
Freight tonnes (000)*	275.9	233.8
Freight tonne-km (million)*	73.4	63.7
Passenger journeys (million)	10.2	10.1
Passenger-km (million)	814.5	689

*Arica–La Paz Railway only

Passenger operations

EFE has tended to concentrate on the more lucrative portions of its passenger network, such as suburban services around Santiago and Valparaíso and the Santiago–Temuco route. Services beyond Temuco to Puerto Montt operate at a heavy loss and are supported by profitable operations elsewhere. EFE's desire to confine itself to profitable routes has in part been frustrated by political pressure to maintain services on the Temuco–Puerto Montt route.

Passenger operations in 1995 were hampered by a shortage of emus and locomotives, the latter made worse by the privatisation of FEPASA and subsequent transfer of a portion of the EFE locomotive fleet. Fares had to be revised downwards after being pitched too high for the peak period at the start of the year.

Although initially concentrating on the trunk Santiago–Puerto Montt route, where long-distance passenger services have been operated under the VIA Sur brand, it was hoped that the system of concessions for passenger operations and track maintenance unveiled in 1996 would in turn be applied to the MERVAL network, linking Valparaíso with neighbouring towns such as Quilpué, Limache and Quillota. The existing suburban service between Santiago and Rancagua (80 km) is operated by three refurbished 25-year-old emus and has been unreliable. EFE has therefore bought five Class 440 rebuilt emus from Spanish National Railways (RENFE) costing US$8 million. The company is seeking permission to implement a service on the 61 km line to Melipilla, costing US$180 million.

Freight operations

Freight operations on the main EFE network passed out of state ownership in January 1995 with the privatisation of FEPASA, leaving EFE responsible only for those undertaken by its Arica–La Paz Railway subsidiary.

New lines

In October 1994, provincial and central government in Argentina agreed public funding for the first 60 km of a proposed 220 km rail link from Zapala to Lonquimay in Chile. Private finance was sought for the Chilean portion (60 km) of the US$120 million project.

Private finance was also envisaged for a scheme unveiled in 1995 to build a new 123 km Santiago–Valparaíso–Viña del Mar rail link, initially costed at US$511 million. The new electrified route would be engineered for 160 km/h and make use of an existing alignment between Valparaíso and Viña del Mar.

Improvements to existing lines

At the start of 1996, branches from the Valparaíso–Santiago–Puerto Montt trunk route totalling 418 route-km of 1,676 mm gauge and 73 route-km of 1,000 mm gauge were out of use.

In 1992 the Chilean government approved a rehabilitation plan, subsequently included in the 1993-96 development plan, which aimed to make good many years of deferred maintenance at a cost of US$67.37million. The principal source of funding for this project was a US$51 million loan to EFE from the Overseas Economic Corporation Fund of Japan, agreed in November 1992. The remainder has been provided by the sale of surplus railway property and government grants.

The first work began at the start of 1994, with the rehabilitation programme scheduled for completion in 1997. Track repairs have formed a major part of the

programme, and were due by 1997 to have received total investment of US$30.62 million with spending of US$17.63 million budgeted for 1996.

Finances (US$ million)

Revenue	1994	1995
Passengers	17.3	14.9
Freight	22.9*	8.6
Other	40.5	30.6
Total	80.7	54.1

*Includes US$15.1 million of FEPASA income

Expenditure		
Personnel	43.5	34.3
Materials and services	27.7	27.2
Depreciation	12.9	9.7
Other	10.3	7.3
Total	94.4	78.5

Traction and rolling stock

Under EFE's rehabilitation programme, started in 1994, a total of US$13.43 million was to be spent on passenger rolling stock by the end of 1997, with investment of US$8.72 million budgeted for 1996. At the start of 1996, 86 of EFE's 147 passenger coaches were available for traffic and the railway's resources (following the sale of FEPASA) totalled:

Locomotives	Total
Steam	2
Diesel	21
Electric	11
Diesel railcars	2
Electric multiple-units	19
Passenger coaches*	147
Freight wagons	347

*Including 12 dining, six video bar and 22 sleeping cars

Coupler: Automatic
Braking: Air

Signalling and telecommunications

At the start of 1996, the following signalling systems were in use on the EFE network: Alameda–Puerto (187 km), mechanical signalling with electromechanical interlocking and track circuits; Alameda–Talca (249 km), mechanical signalling and interlocking, track circuits; Talca–Cabrero (208 km), mechanical signalling with electrical interlocking, track circuits; Cabrero–Temuco (233 km), electric signalling and interlocking, train staff working; San Rosendo–Talcahuano (83 km), electrical interlocking and train staff working; Temuco–Puerto Montt (389 km) and various branches (971 km), train staff working.

Under EFE's 1994-97 rehabilitation plan, signalling was to receive investment totalling US$3,52 million and telecommunications US$5.62 million. EFE and Chilesat (a private communications company) were to install an optical fibre network between Santiago and Temuco and

Diesel locomotives

Class	Builder's type	Wheel arrangement	Power kW	Speed km/h	Weight tonnes	No in service	First built	Mechanical	Builders Engine	Electrical
D-16 000	253/253	C-C	1,305	120	114.5	5	1954	GE	Alco 244	E GE USA
Dt-13 100	U-13-C	C-C	1,063	95	85	5	1967	GE	GE FDL-8	E GE USA
D-7100	040 DE	B-B	615	90	72	5	1963	B&L	SACM-MGO 12V-175-A5	Various European builders
Dt-6000	–	C-C	492	80	64	3	1954	GE	CB FWL-6T	E GE USA
D-5100	U-5-B	B-B	447	70	50	2	1963	GE	Caterpillar D-379	E GE USA
Dt-3000	–	B-B	223	48	40	1	1953	GE	Cummins HBI-600	–

Electric railcars or multiple-units

Class	Cars per unit	Motor cars per unit	Motored axles/car	Output/motor kW	Speed km/h	No in in service	First built	Builders Mechanical	Electrical
AEZ	4	2	4	225	160	4	1973	Kawasaki	Toshiba
AEL	4	2	4	310	130	3	1973	Kawasaki	Toshiba/ Hitachi
AES	2	1	4	190	130	12	1977	Fiat-Concord	SEL/ Siam di Tella

Electric locomotives

Class	Wheel arrangement	Output kW	Speed km/h	Weight tonnes	No in service	First built	Builders Mechanical	Electrical
E-32	C-C	3,400	130	136	4	1962	Breda	Marelli
E-30	B-B	2,265	130	98	5	1962	Breda	Ansaldo-Marelli
E-17	B-B	1,950	90	76	2	1973	Breda	Ansaldo-Marelli

San Rosendo and Concepción. The scheme was to receive US$1.75 million from EFE's rehabilitation budget and was to be used for ground-to-ground and later ground-to-train communication.

Electrification

A total of US$5.27 million was to be spent on EFE's 3 kV DC electrification system under the company's 1994-97 rehabilitation plan. This investment was intended to compensate for several years of deferred maintenance, rather than fund any further electrification.

Track	Lengths
Rails	*laid 1995*
(kg/m)	*(km)*
60	563.3
50	972.9
40	1,453.7
30	457.1

Crossties (sleepers): Wood
Cross-section: 250 × 150 mm
Spacing: 1,800/km

Min curvature radius, main lines: 1,000 mm gauge, 80 m; 1,676 mm gauge, 180 m
Max gradient: Adhesion, 6%; rack, 8%
Max permissible axleloading: 18 tonnes (1,000 mm gauge), 25 tonnes (1,676 mm gauge)

UPDATED

FEPASA

Ferrocarril del Pacífico SA
La Concepción 331, Providencia, Santiago
Tel: +56 2 235 1686   Fax: +56 2 235 0920

Key personnel

General Manager: E Valdatta
Chief Operating Officer: Paul Victor
Chief Mechanical Officer: David L Powell
Director, Operations: Robert G Muilenberg
Transportation Superintendent, Southern Division:
    J David Wallace

Political background

FEPASA was created in 1993 to operate freight services on EFE routes, excluding the Arica—La Paz Railway. It was initially a 99 per cent-owned EFE subsidiary, with the Chilean government holding the remaining 1 per cent. In January 1994, parties interested in bidding for a 51 per cent (including the government's 1 per cent) stake in FEPASA were invited to prequalify. After an extended tendering process, the 51 per cent stake was sold to the Transportes del Pacífico consortium for US$30 million. The consortium formally took control of FEPASA on 23 January 1995.

The Transportes del Pacífico consortium comprised the Chilean holding company Cruz Blanca, Estrella Americana (a Chilean pension fund company) and San Pablo Bay Railway Company. The last is an affiliate of the US Anacostia and Pacific Company, which was to provide financial, technical and operating expertise.

Organisation

FEPASA operates freight services over EFE infrastructure, excluding the Arica—La Paz Railway. Responsiblity for scheduling and track maintenance remains with EFE for the core Valparaíso—Puerto Montt route, its branch to Concepción and between San Rosendo and Talcahuano, Paine and Talagante and Santiago and San Antonio. On these routes, FEPASA pays track access fees to EFE. On some 900 km of routes where no EFE passenger trains operate, FEPASA is responsible for scheduling and track maintenance.

Finance

Bidders for the 51 per cent stake in FEPASA were required to provide details of the development strategies, operational and investment plans as far as 2000, commercial and financial policy and equipment maintenance programmes they intended to implement. Transportes del Pacífico has undertaken to invest US$88 million in FEPASA by 2000, with US$28 million earmarked for freight wagons, US$20million for locomotives and US$28 million for track improvements.

Of the US$30 million Transportes del Pacífico offered to pay for its stake in FEPASA, 40 per cent was to take the form of a down payment, with the balance to be paid over a period of five years. At the time of the sale, FEPASA's annual revenue was reported to be around US$40 million.

FEPASA General Electric diesel locomotive at Temuco (Bryan Philpott)   *1996*

The company's new owners expected to make a loss of some US$1 million in their first year of operations (1995), and move into profit thereafter.

Freight operations

In 1994, prior to privatisation, FEPASA carried 5.132 million tonnes of freight on the EFE system and recorded 1.104 billion tonne-km. In total 4.295 million tonnes were carried in 1995, when 903 million tonne-km were recorded.

Bulk products, such as minerals (copper) and forest products (cellulose), form the principal component of FEPASA traffic base. The new owning consortium aimed in the short term to cut operating costs and raise productivity, and train weights were to rise from 630 tonnes to around 1,100 tonnes, with a maximum of 3,000 tonnes. This was to require the use of locomotives operating in multiple.

FEPASA's new owners hope to increase traffic to over 2 billion tonne-km a year by 2000. Staff numbers were to be reduced through the introduction of new operating methods, equipment and technology (including an information system to track wagon movements), as developed in the USA and subsequently introduced to Argentina. EFE freight operations had required a staff of 2,600, which fell to 1,900 upon the creation of FEPASA in 1993. At the start of 1996, FEPASA had a staff of 700, including 400 formerly employed by EFE.

Improvements to existing lines

The raising of train weights in the short term was to require the lengthening of some passing loops. In the long term, conversion of the 1,000 mm gauge Los Andes—Río Blanco branch (the remaining 34 km of the former Transandine Railway to Argentina via Juncal) to 1,676 mm gauge was projected. This would eliminate the present transhipment of copper concentrate containers at Los Andes.

Traction and rolling stock

FEPASA passed into private ownership with 19 electric locomotives, 90 diesel locomotives (of 13 different models) and 4,800 wagons. Due to financial constraints, EFE had been deferring maintenance for some years and FEPASA's new owners intended to rationalise and modernise the locomotive fleet with a view to obtaining 100,000 km a year from each unit. Abandonment of electric operation has been mooted to lower track-access charges paid to EFE, which in 1995 began trials of a microprocessor-based onboard system to measure and record traction current consumption by electric locomotives and multiple-units.

In January 1996 FEPASA signed a contract with National Railway Equipment Company, USA, for the supply of eight remanufactured General Motors SD39-2M Co-Co diesel-electric locomotives.

Signalling and telecommunications

Responsible for regulating train movements on routes with no EFE passenger service, FEPASA's new owners intend to convert to a train warrant system, install train radio and replace brake vans with end-of-train devices.

VERIFIED

Ferronor

Ferronor SA
Ferrocarril Regional del Norte de Chile
J Smith Solar 426, Providencia, Santiago
Tel: +56 2 233 5321   Fax: +56 2 233 2676

Key personnel

President: José Luis Ramaciotti F
General Manager: José E Miranda
Commercial Manager: Ramón Silva
Operations Manager: A Zarate
Marketing: Victor López

Gauge: 1,000 mm
Route length: 2,224 km

Political background

Ferronor and the Chilean government have examined the possibility of creating separate infrastructure and operations administrations for the system, with Ferronor's management proposing privatisation of operations. Privatisation of Ferronor was undertaken in 1997 when the Andrés Pirazzoli construction and transport company bought Ferronor for US$12 million, double the bid of its nearest rival. The Chilean company plans to enter into a joint venture with Rail America to operate the network. Rail America is a US short line operator.

Organisation

Ferronor's Calera—Iquique main line crosses the Antofagasta (Chili) and Bolivia Railway (FCAB) at Palestina and Baquedano. Ferronor's route from Augusta Victoria to Socompa and the Ferrocarril General Belgrano (FGB) of Argentina is connected to its main line at Palestina via FCAB.

Finance

In 1995 revenue from freight operations was US$10.358 million and Ferronor made a profit that year. Unlike its southern neighbour EFE, Ferronor receives no government subsidy to offset competition from trucks which do not fully bear their road-use costs.

Passenger operations
Ferronor occasionally operates passenger trains on a charter basis for tourist groups.

Freight operations
In 1995 Ferronor carried 2.75 million tonnes of freight and generated 299.967 million tonne-km. Copper concentrates (0.144 million tonnes) accounted for 29 per cent of freight revenue, iron ore (1.143 million tonnes) 19 per cent and other domestic traffic (0.073 million tonnes) 8 per cent.

Copper concentrates and iron ore are moved from mines at the northern end of the system to the Pacific ports of Chañaral, Caldera, Huasco and Coquimbo.

Traffic levels are subject to fluctuation in line with the market price of these commodities, but the temporary closure of the Cerro Colorado iron ore mine was offset by a contract to carry 2,000 tonnes/month of El Melón cement from La Calera to Copiapó and limestone in the reverse direction. A subsequent rise in iron ore prices and the reopening of the Cerro Colorado and Copiapó mines have recently boosted Ferronor traffic levels, with a 20-year contract signed in 1996 to transport ore from Los Colorados mine to a pellet plant at Husaco.

International traffic interchanged with FGB of Argentina at Socompa amounted to 0.112 million tonnes (31.249 million tonne-km) in 1995 and generated 28 per cent of Ferronor's total freight revenue. A 1996 contract

should see 38,000 tonnes pa of liquefied gas transported from Socompa to Baquedano. Tolls charged to FCAB for the use of the Augusta Victoria—Socompa route totalled US$1.675 million in 1995, 16 per cent of freight revenue. FCAB bridge traffic over the Ferronor system was 1.278 milion tonnes (34.879 million tonne-km).

Traction and rolling stock
At the end of 1995, Ferronor's fleet comprised 31 diesel locomotives (including nine for yard service) and 550 wagons. Ferronor's workshops at Coquimbo carry out repairs for other railways as well as non-railway work.

UPDATED

Antofagasta (Chili) and Bolivia Railway plc (FCAB)

Ferrocarril de Antofagasta a Bolivia
Bolívar 255, Casilla ST, Antofagasta
Tel: +56 55 206200   Fax: +56 55 206220

Key personnel
General Manager: Miguel V Sepúlveda
Planning and Development Manager:
    Marcelo Contreras
Services (Traffic) Manager: Bernardo Schmidt
Commercial Manager: Carlos Yanine
Financial Manager: Pablo Ribbeck
Human Resources Manager: Victor F Maldonado

Gauge: 1,000 mm
Route length: 903.57 km

Organisation
FCAB is entirely self-supporting financially. Founded in 1888, the company is listed on the London Stock Exchange. The railway runs from the Pacific port of Antofagasta to the Argentine border at Socompa on one route (over Ferronor track between Augusta Victoria and Socompa), and to the Bolivian border at Ollagüe on the second. FCAB has also become the operator of the former Bolivian state railway's (ENFE) Andean rail network, which did once belong to the Chilean company and connects with FCAB's own network. In 1996, this 2,082 km network had 1,417 wagons and 28 diesel-electric locomotives in service and transported 507,665 net tonnes.

Finance
In 1994 FCAB recorded total revenue of US$25.192 million, with freight operations generating US$22.254 million. Total expenditure for 1994 was US$21.069 million, comprising staff costs of US$6.791 million, materials and services costs of US$12.072 million and depreciation of US$2.205 million. At the end of 1996, FCAB had 516 employees.

Passenger operations
At the end of 1995, a passenger service was operating weekly in both directions between Calama and Uyuni in Bolivia via Ollagüe. In total 1.805 million passenger-km were recorded in 1994, rising to 1.848 million in 1995 and jumping to 3.123 million in 1996.

Freight operations
In conjunction with FCAB's bulk trainload and wagonload business, door-to-door service has been offered since 1988 in conjunction with the company's road haulage subsidiary, Train Ltd Company. The year 1996 was a significant one in that it was the first time FCAB had transported 2 million tonnes, thanks to two new contracts to transport new flows of sulphuric acid and copper cathodes.

Traffic	1994	1995	1996
Freight tonnes (million)	1.328	1.717	2.007
Freight tonne-km (million)	407.5	477.1	577.9

New lines
At the start of 1995 FCAB signed a contract with Compañía Minera El Abra to move 840,000 tonnes of sulphuric acid each year from Mejillones to a mine at El Abra, 330 km northeast of Antofagasta, and 225,000 tonnes of copper cathodes each year from El Abra to

Antofagasta. The construction of a new 16 km branch from the railway at Conchi to El Abra formed part of FCAB's US$40 million investment for this new traffic.

Traction and rolling stock
At the end of 1995, the FCAB fleet comprised 37 diesel-electric locomotives (including seven Class 600/900 units for yard service) and 1,413 freight wagons. During 1995, six NF210 locomotives, originally built for Canadian National's Newfoundland system, were acquired from CANAC International and refurbished by FCAB's Antofagasta workshops.

For the new El Abra branch, 13 Class 1400 locomotives have been refurbished at Antofagasta, receiving a new digital control system and engine modifications to increase power output. A fleet of 124 sulphuric acid tank wagons (43 tonnes capacity) and 50 wagons for the transport of copper cathodes were designed and built at Antofagasta in 1995.

FCAB's future traction policy is to acquire turbo diesel-electric locomotives to overcome the 40 per cent power loss that conventional diesel-electric locomotives face on FCAB's mountain lines. Height above sea level on FCAB lines varies from 51 m to 3,954 m.

Coupler in standard use, freight and passenger cars:
Henricot and Sharon

Refurbished diesel locomotives outside FCAB's Antofagasta workshops. No 1413 is an ex-Newfoundland NF210 unit   *1996*

Diesel locomotives

Class	Builder's type	Wheel arrangement	Power kW	Speed km/h	Weight tonnes	No in service	First built	Builders Mechanical	Builders Engine
600		Bo-Bo	373	55	45	2	1958	GM	E Cummins NT.855
900	GA 8	Bo-Bo	708	55	52	3	1965	GM	E EMD 8-567C
900	GA 18	Bo-Bo	820	57	54	1	1969	GM	E EMD 8-645-E
900	G 18U	Bo-Bo*	820	96	72	1	1977	GM	E EMD 8-645-E
1400	GR 12U	Co-Co	1,063	95	90	6	1961	GM	E EMD 12-567C
1400	GR 12UD	Co-Co	1,063	95	90	4	1962	GM	E EMD 12-567C
1400	G 22CU	Co-Co	1,230	97	90	1	1969	GM	E EMD 12-645E
1400	GR 12	Co-Co	1,063	95	90	2	1962	GM	E EMD 12-567C
1400	NF210	Co-Co	1,044	96	103	17	1957	GM	E EMD 12-567C

* Formerly AIA-AIA; centre axles removed

Braking in standard use, locomotive-hauled stock: 26L
and 65L with straight control

Signalling and telecommunications
Train control is by VHF radio throughout the system. FCAB introduced a computerised communications (Intranet) and control system linked to customers in 1991 and cabooseless train working with the aid of telemetry in the same year. Intranet is also being used as a communications and internal training tool.

Track
Rail: 24.83 kg/m, 176.84 km; 32.24 kg/m, 274.96 km; 37.2 kg/m, 231.03 km; 37.22 kg/m, 3.02 km; 42.16 kg/m, 6.45 km; 42.21 kg/m, 108.83 km
Crossties (sleepers): Wood (Coigüe) 188 × 254 × 1,027 mm
Spacing: In plain track: 1,422/km; in curves: 1,422/km, 1,490/km
Fastenings: Screw spikes, Pandrol clips
Min curvature radius: Main line 10°, branches 15°
Max permissible axleload: 15 tonnes
Max gradient: 3.4%

UPDATED

CHINA, PEOPLE'S REPUBLIC

Chinese People's Republic Railways (CPPR)

Ministry of Railways, 10 Fuxing Men, Beijing 100844
Tel: +86 10 632 46 915   Fax: +86 10 639 81 065

Key personnel
Minister of Railways: Han Zhubin
Vice-Ministers of Railways: Fu Zhihuan, Sun Yong Fu,
   Cai Qinghua, Liu Zhijun
Chairman: Hua Maokun
General Manager: Zhang Zhengqing
Chief Economist: Wang Zhaocheng
Technical Director: Zhou Yumin
Planning Director: Cao Qing
Operations Director: Chang Guozhi
Workshops Director: Tan Datong
Manager, International Co-operation:
   Mrs Tang Wensheng

Gauge: Almost entirely 1,435 mm, some 750 mm
Route length: 54,000 km approx
Electrification: 8,434 km at 25 kV 50 Hz AC

Political background
The Ministry of Railways controls 12 railway administrations, as well as most of the country's 35 locomotive and rolling stock factories via China National Railway Locomotive & Rolling Stock Industry Corporation. The railway administrations are Harbin, Shenyang, Beijing, Hohhot, Zhengzhou, Jinan, Shanghai, Guangzhou, Liuzhou, Chengdu, Lanzhou, and Urumqi.

Current policy is for progressive devolution of authority to individual railway regions, and in 1993 the Guangzhou area administration was reconstituted as the first autonomous railway organisation — the Guangzhou Railway Corporation — with almost 4,000 route-km and 172,000 staff.

In a further move in 1993, it was announced that the state railway monopoly would be ended, and new operating standards and pricing structures introduced to enable the railway to gear itself more closely to the needs of a fast growing economy. Five regions were selected in 1996 as the first batch of autonomous railways.

A separate administration, the Guangshen Railway, runs the Chinese section of the Kowloon—Canton Railway, the 147 km line from Guangzhou (Canton) to the Hong Kong border's end-on junction with the former British section. This railway was allowed to produce its own timetables and set its fares independently in April 1996, prior to the offer of shares on the Hong Kong stock market and in the USA the following month. Funds raised by the flotation will finance purchase of high-speed trains for the Guangzhou—Kowloon route; an X2000 train from Adtranz was due to arrive for trials in early 1998.

The government has also encouraged local authorities to build and operate their own railways of up to 2,000 km length, where such investment would stimulate regional economic development. Local railway systems operate in 11 of the country's provinces, their route length amounting to nearly 7,000 km in 1996. Further growth may be restrained by the early 1995 government decision to forbid provincial authorities from raising finance in foreign markets, in a bid to rein-in rapid growth in the country's foreign debt. Nevertheless, some 2,000 km of new local railways are proposed in the 1996-2000 ninth plan.

Following an accord reached with the government of Vietnam in December 1995, the border between the two countries was reopened in February 1996 after a gap of 17 years, permitting resumption of passenger service from Beijing to Hanoi, with change of train at the Dong Dang border. Work continues on refurbishment of the other link to Vietnam — the Kunming—Lao Cai—Hanoi metre-gauge line — which the Vietnamese will promote as a through freight route to Yunnan province from the port of Haiphong.

Passenger operations
Demand for passenger and freight transport considerably outstrips both infrastructure and rolling stock capacity. Between 1968 and 1989 passenger traffic quadrupled, whereas the number of trains run rose by only 1.7 per cent. Consequently, severe overcrowding was common. To relieve this congestion, fares were abruptly doubled in 1989, while a 50 per cent rise was implemented in October 1995. The daily average of passenger journeys has dropped sharply from 3.5 million at the end of the 1980s to 2.7 million. Further decline was recorded in 1995-96, causing some alarm amongst CR officials.

Yet more capacity was to be squeezed out of the network under a 1996 proposal for closure of more than 1,500 little-used passenger stations and freight depots.

To cope with demand, passenger trains of 20 to 25 cars are operated on some routes, such as Beijing—Guangzhou. The aim is to standardise 20-coach trains on other lines, such as Beijing—Shanghai and Beijing—Dalian, but progress is dependent on the rate at which station layouts can be enlarged.

In another move to ease pressure a prototype 16-car bilevel trainset was introduced to Shanghai—Nanjing service in 1989. Built by the Puzhen works in Nanjing, the air conditioned train seats over 3,000 and operates at 120 km/h. A substantial improvement in the timings between these cities was made by two pairs of trains running at up to 170 km/h, introduced in 1996, cutting the best time from 3 hours 50 min to 2 hours 30 min. More high-speed trains are in prospect for the route once a batch of 22 Dong Feng 11 diesel locomotives with 160 km/h capability is delivered from Qishuyan works.

A fleet of cars capable of 120 km/h now operates the busiest services between Beijing and Tianjin, while a 160 km/h variant was used in high-speed trials on the Guangzhou—Shenzhen line during 1994. Regular high-speed service between Guangzhou, Shenzhen and Kowloon is scheduled to start during 1997.

Separation of passenger and freight traffic is now put forward as the solution to congestion on the busiest axes. Consequently, studies began of a pilot scheme for a 200 km/h line reserved to passenger trains. The two routes reviewed for the experiment were Beijing—Tianjin (137 km) and Guangzhou to the Hong Kong border at Shenzhen (143 km). Upgrading of the latter route for 160 km/h running was completed in 1994, and public service at that speed was inaugurated in March 1995. Initially, only one train was available capable of the new top speed, and this is running a daily return trip between Guangzhou and Kowloon in 2 hours 1 min.

Freight operations
Freight tonnage has been rising with similar rapidity, spurred by recent growth in the economy of some 12 per cent annually. In 1988 movements grossed 1,405 million tonnes, 40 per cent of it coal, and 986,019 million tonne-km. By 1992, tonnage had risen further to 1,523 million, for 1,491,115 million tonne-km. Attempts to slow economic growth began to bear fruit at the end of 1993, when daily wagon loadings were down by some 20 per cent. But there is still a substantial shortfall in capacity and consequent inability to supply raw materials regularly to some manufacturing plants, driving them to temporary closure.

The Ministry of Railways aims to raise individual train weights by a third, to a norm of 3,000 to 4,000 tonnes, which has been achieved on nine trunk routes. The development has been fraught with several problems, such as restricted yard siding and loop capacities, and not least the limitations of most of the existing wagon stock. These are largely fitted with plain bearings and restricted to maximum speeds of 60 km/h. To accelerate development of a more modern fleet, a roller bearing works has been established to speed conversion of existing wagons as well as to supply new wagon construction.

In both new line construction and electrification, expansion of coal-carrying capacity is of paramount importance. China's domestic energy needs are 70 per cent met by coal and at the same time exports are rising steadily. From one coalfield alone, in the Shanxi province, where reserves are put at almost 200 billion tonnes, shipments abroad are expected to top 150 million tonnes. The principal coalfields are found in Shanxi, Inner Mongolia, Henan, Shandong, Ningxia, Guizhou, Anhui and Heliongjiang provinces. Coal flows are predominantly north-to-south and west-to-east, and form over half the traffic on some main lines.

A 10-year programme, aimed to raise rail coal-carrying capacity to over 600 million tonnes a year, has involved the upgrading of 12 existing coal routes and construction of eight more, plus a lift of maximum trainloads on key routes from 3,500 to as much as 10,000 tonnes. The requirements of the coal traffic dominated the double-tracking, new line building and electrification programmes executed in the 1980s.

Canadian Pacific Consulting Services was contracted to study the feasibility of a North American-type unit train working between the Shanxi coalfield and the port of Qinhuangdao; 10,000-tonne trains were tested on this route prior to introduction of 6,000-tonne loads between Beijing and Shanghai in 1993.

Completion of double-tracking and electrification of the 1,800 km lateral route from Lanzhou to the port of Lianyungan, and completion of the 498 km Zhongwei—Baoji line, opened up export opportunities for coal from the Gansu and Ningxia fields. Provincial governments provided part of the investment in this scheme, completed in 1994-95, as it brings substantial benefits to their coalfields.

Intermodal operations
Following the launch of through service on the Alatau Pass route to Russia in 1992, nine container terminals for landbridge traffic have been established by the Chinese. These are at the port of Lianyungang, and inland at Tanggu, Hohhot, Erlianhot, Zhengzhou, Xi'an, Lanzhou, Urumqi and Druzhba. Using this route, transits to European destinations from Japan are 2,700 km shorter

8K Class Bo-Bo+Bo-Bo 25 kV electric locomotive (Murray Hughes)   *1996*

than via the Trans-Siberian. Japanese industry has access to the new international route via the ports at Lianyungang and Shanghai. Lianyungang port is being extended to raise capacity from 14 to 18.5 million tonnes a year, financed by a loan from the Japanese government.

But traffic growth has been hampered by bureaucratic problems, and freight tonnage actually declined in 1993. This prompted a 1994 agreement between seven interested countries — China, Russia, Kazakhstan, Kirghizia, Tajikistan, Turkmenistan and Uzbekistan — to sweep away border controls for transit traffic, unify their freight rates, and co-ordinate strategies to attract new business.

Container movement within China is hampered by the scarcity of handling equipment, with many consignments having to be transhipped from containers to ordinary wagons at the ports. In 1994 a new initiative, involving the World Bank, was begun, with the aim of improving rail transport of maritime containers within China. A number of US corporations — including American President Lines and CSX — were to form a team to upgrade service between Xingang, a deep-sea port near Beijing, and Wuhan, an industrial city in the interior. US-built locomotives would haul Chinese-built wagons, moving 100 TEU each way per week. After experience on this route, it was planned to expand the service and add a Wuhan—Hong Kong route.

In 1994, a Hong Kong—Zhengzhou container service was launched jointly by the Railway Ministry's China Railway Container Centre subsidiary and the Kowloon—Canton Railway. The 70 hour journey time is half that of road haulage.

Prospects for a nationwide intermodal network were raised by a 1994 agreement between the US manufacturer Wabash National and the Chinese Railway Ministry's Sinorails subsidiary to develop RoadRailer service using bimodal trailers to obviate the need for transfer cranes at inland container terminals.

Co-operation with Russia's RZD should also benefit from another accord, signed between the two countries in 1994 and intended to stimulate cross-border traffic on the Trans-Siberian route. New transhipment facilities are to be provided at border points on the Harbin—Chita and Harbin—Vladivostok lines.

New lines

New lines are coming on stream all the time, partly to relieve pressure on the heavily occupied trunk routes in the east of the country, where the bulk of the network is concentrated, and partly to extend railways into the western provinces, which are almost without rail transport. The target is an 80,000 route-km network by the end of the century, capable of handling projected annual traffic of nearly 1.5 billion passengers and 2.1 billion tonnes.

The ninth Five-Year Plan, covering the period 1996-2000, will see 8,100 km of new lines completed at a cost of 330 billion yuan. The total includes several routes already under construction; the remaining lines will further improve access to the Shanxi and Inner Mongolia coalfields, and to the Tarim Basin oil deposits. The greater portion of new construction (6,100 km) will be funded by the state, while 2,000 km will be paid for by regional authorities.

Dong Feng 4 (left) and 'Beijing' Class diesels at Beijing station (Wolfram Veith)   **1996**

China's busiest artery is the north-south route of 2,313 km from Beijing via Zhengzhou to Guangzhou, and a priority has been this line's relief by construction of links between other existing routes to its east and west so as to create two additional and parallel trunk lines from north to south. The main line itself is now double track throughout.

An Asian Development Bank loan of US$110 million was agreed in 1993 to part-finance construction of one of these links — the 347 km Hefei—Jiujiang line to exploit mineral deposits in Anhui province.

In the southwest, construction began in 1990 of a 851 km transversal line from Kunming eastward to Nanning to provide a direct route to the port of Fangcheng. To be single track and electrified initially, with capacity put at 20 million tonnes annually, the route is being constructed on a wide solum that will allow easy double-tracking in future. Substantial engineering works are necessary to take the line over three mountain ranges, including 250 tunnels totalling 190 km and 390 bridges. Tracklaying started in 1992 and was completed in March 1997; opening was scheduled for late 1997.

Another new route has been created out of the great Shanxi coalfield by construction of an electrified double-track line 270 km eastward from Shenmu, south of Baotou, to Suzhou, on the main north-to-south route from Datong to Taiyuan. The aim is to give direct access from the developing Shenmu coalfield to the port of Huanghua. Tracklaying was in progress in 1995. Forecasts are that the completed route will be carrying 50 to 60 million tonnes of coal a year in the late 1990s.

Elsewhere in Shanxi a 170 km coal-carrying branch is being built from Yan'an south to Tongchuan, for access to the Baoji—Zhengzhou transversal in the area of Xi'an.

Another new west-to-east coal route of some 800 km is being assembled further south. It involves new construction, started in 1987 and completed in early 1995, from Houma in Shanxi province to Yueshan in Henan province (246 km). From Henan there is already a

lateral line to Xinxiang. More new construction will project the route 150 km from Xinxiang to the existing railway linking Heze with the heart of the Shandong coalfield at Yanzhou.

Other lines recently proposed include a 207 km link to transport coal to a new generating station at Zhenglan in the Inner Mongolian autonomous region, and a connection in Jilin province which would provide a link to the expanding Russian port of Zarubino avoiding North Korean territory. This latter route would be a prolongation of the line already under construction from Tumen to Hunchun and would extend 1,435 mm gauge beyond the Russian border at Changlingzhi to Zarubino. Once across the border, the line would be paralleled by a 1,524 mm gauge track as far as Kraskino.

Also now proposed for completion at the turn of the century is the long-planned South Xinjiang line in the west. Starting at Kuerla, a branch off the Alatau Pass route, the route would skirt the northern edge of the Taklaman Desert to reach Kashi, 975 km distant and close to the Tajik border. While the objective is to tap mineral deposits in the border region, the line could be extended in to Tajikistan or Afghanistan at a later date.

It is now proposed to develop the Shangqui—Fuyang new line, mentioned above, as the start of an alternative trunk route some 1,100 km long to the Shanghai area, to the further benefit of Shanxi coal output. The single-track line from Fuyang to Hefei and Yuxikou will be upgraded. The outstanding item of the project occurs in the next section of the route: that is supersession of the present train ferry crossing of the great Yangtze river to Wuhu with a bridge to rival the Shanghai main line's 12 km spanning of the river further east at Nanjing. Completion of the new route to the port of Hangzhou, southwest of Shanghai, involves upgrading of existing single-track lines from Wuhu to Xuancheng, and from Hangzhou northwestward to Niutoushan; and closure of the gap between them with a new 125 km line around the mountains. Construction was to start in 1996.

November 1995 saw opening after a long gestation of the Jitong line, built by the Inner Mongolia Autonomous Region. This extends 943 km from Jining, north of Datong, through Inner Mongolia to a rich mineral area around Tongliao, in the northeast.

The country's first major joint venture railway construction project is for a line running from the port of Wenzhou to the Shanghai—Zhuzhou southern trunk route at Jinhua, some 250 km distant. This is a local railway being built by a company owned 80 per cent by Hong Kong-based Profita Development and 20 per cent by the Zhejiang provincial government. In compensation for the high construction cost — 177 bridges and 63 tunnels are required — the developers have been granted rights to exploit land alongside the railway for a period of 75 years, and will also be permitted to deal in oil and other commodities normally traded solely by the government.

This line will not be completed for some time, and the first public/private scheme actually in operation is a 50 km line opened in August 1994 to link the ports of Shekou, Chiwan and Mawan to the Guangzhou—Shenzhen artery.

Two small schemes for pilot running at 200 km/h (mentioned above) are to be the precursors for a major

ND5 Class General Electric-built Co-Co diesel hauling a coal train (Wolfram Veith)   **1996**

Dong Feng 4 Class diesel at a crossing in eastern Beijing (Wolfram Veith)   **1996**

US$170 million. For the previous two plans credits totalling more than US$2 billion in total were secured from the World Bank and the Japanese government.

For the 1996-2000 plan period, projected investment of 330 billion yuan will require a much greater proportion of foreign funding, and joint ventures are to be sought with overseas investors.

Traction and rolling stock

At 1 January 1996, the railway had 15, 146 locomotives in operation, of which 4,347 were steam, 8,282 were diesel and the rest electric.

The railway operates a large fleet of the locally built 2,640 kW Dong Feng 4 freight Co-Co diesels. Over 4,000 are expected to be in use by the century's end. Other standard Chinese-built types are the Beijing passenger locomotive and the Sifang-built Dong Feng 5, a heavy shunter which also handles local passenger and freight haulage. A 2,984 kW Dong Feng 6 has been developed for freight haulage by Dalian works, along with a Dong Feng 8 version produced by Qishuyan works. The latest products are the Dong Feng 10, rolled out in early 1995, a 4,476 kW prototype for hauling the new 5,000 tonne coal trains, and the Qishuyan-built Dong Feng 11 for 160 km/h passenger service.

In recent years imports have developed rapidly, both of diesel and electric units. The most high-profile agreement with a western company in recent years was a deal signed in November 1996 with Adtranz, whereby China will rent a 25kV AC version of the Swedish X2000 tilting high-speed train for two years from early 1998, possibly purchasing it thereafter.

In 1997, 40 three-phase AC electric locomotives were ordered from SGP, the Austrian subsidiary of Siemens. The first six of this 6,400kW, eight-axle design will be built in Austria, the rest in China under a technology transfer agreement; they will be put to work on freight trains on the 670 km Baoji—Chengdu route in southwestern China. Earlier import contracts include one in the mid-1980s with General Electric (USA), which supplied 420 of its Type C36-7 2,984 kW Co-Co diesel-electrics (designated Class ND5 in China) for freight haulage. In 1989 Electroputere of Romania, already the supplier of close on 300 diesel and 45 5,400 kW Co-Co electric locomotives, was contracted to supply 20 more diesel locomotives of similar design to those the Romanian factory has supplied in great quantity to its home railway.

To serve newly electrified lines, local builders (mainly the Zhuzhou Electric Locomotive Works in Hunan province) have expanded output substantially. The Shaoshan SS3 Co-Co, a development of the preceding SS1 and SS2 designs offering enhanced adhesion and equipped with single-arm pantographs, has itself been superseded by SS4, SS5 and SS6 variants. Most of the Shaoshan series have a one hour rating of 4,200 kW at 44.6 km/h (continuous rating 3,780 kW at 45.9 km/h) and employ silicon rectifiers with tap-changer control of power, but the latest SS6 is rated at 4,800 kW and, though still equipped with silicon rectifiers, has thyristors to regulate motor excitation.

A Bo-Bo + Bo-Bo development of the SS3 Co-Co is in

---

high-speed route unveiled in 1993. Now planned for 250 km/h running, though designed for 350 km/h, the proposed 1,300 km Beijing—Tianjin—Shanghai line will be a dedicated passenger route catering for some 60 million journeys annually. Current Beijing—Shanghai journey times of 17 to 21 hours would be cut to around 7 hours. Considerable capacity for additional freight movements would be freed up on the existing main line.

Funding for the high-speed line, to be built in several stages, would come from central government and the four provinces through which it would run, as well as from foreign manufacturers and investors. Studies of various aspects of the proposed route and technology are under way, and funding for preparatory works has been allocated in the Ninth Plan. Apart from a substantial bridge over the Yangtse river at Nanjing, construction would require little in the way of major infrastructure works.

A more immediate prospect was for a Japanese-financed Shinkansen-style operation — the Fuzhou—Xiamen Express Railway, a proposal launched in 1992 by the Fujian provincial government as a means of stimulating industrial and commercial development locally. Linking cities with substantial populations and serving six large towns intermediately, the line would be engineered for eventual 270 km/h running. A joint venture has been formed with a consortium of Japanese banks led by the Ikawa Trust and a feasibility report on the 280 km route was adopted at the end of 1992.

Construction started in early 1997 of a 10.6 km combined road/rail bridge across the Yangtze river to replace the existing Wuhu train ferry. Completion is scheduled for 2000.

Improvements to existing lines

As China's economy grew, the limitations of the railway network were exposed, with capacity strained to handle much more than 40 per cent of traffic offering on the most heavily congested north-south routes. Accordingly, the 1991-95 Five-Year Plan, the railways' eighth, had as its centrepiece a rapid expansion of capacity. Its most striking component was creation of a 2,370 km route from Beijing to Kowloon, largely comprising new infrastructure engineered for at least 200 km/h by passenger trains.

New construction extends from Beijing through Heng-shui and Shangqui to Fuyang, where the route appropriates the recently finished line to Hefei, with further new construction thence to Jiujiang. To complete the line, existing track is being upgraded from Jiujiang to Nanchang, while new further construction, including part of the Guangdong Guangmeishan administration's scheme, takes the line to Guangzhou. An Asian Development Bank loan of US$200 million agreed in mid-1994 helped maintain the project's momentum, and completion was brought forward. The first through trains on the new route ran in September 1996.

Rapid progress produced record achievements in 1992, when 475 km of new route was opened and 347 km of double-tracking completed. Nevertheless, such was the pressure on capacity that in late 1992 a substantial revision of the plan was announced. Now the aim was to

---

complete 10 key construction projects totalling 7,000 route-km within the last three years of the plan. Apart from the Beijing—Kowloon project, the other major schemes still to be completed are:

• construction of an 851 km transversal through virgin rail territory in the southwest of the country between Nanning and Kunming, which was begun in 1990 and will open in 1997 (qv);

• to provide relief for the important electrified Chengdu—Deyang—Baoji—Xi'an trunk from the southwestern provinces to the industrial northeast, a 310 km west-to-east line opened in 1995 from Deyang via Nanchong to Da Xian, on the electrified south-to-north Guiyang—Chongqing—Xiangfan trunk. From the latter route at Ankang, construction started in 1994 of a 200 km line north to Xi'an. The Ankang—Xi'an line will thread the Shanxi province's Qinling mountains in an 18 km tunnel that will be China's longest. Its boring will delay opening of the line throughout until the turn of the century;

• double-tracking of the routes from Wuwei to Urumqi (1,622 km, completed late 1994), Hangzhou to Zhuzhou (938 km, completed late 1995), and Lanzhou—Baotou (990 km, completion 1996);

• electrification of the Beijing—Zhengzhou (697 km, completed 1995), Chengdu—Kunming (989 km, completed late 1996), and Wuwei—Zhongwei (244 km, completed 1994) lines.

The eighth Five-Year Plan again relied on significant foreign borrowing to raise the necessary 142 billion yuan, in this case to the extent of about US$1 billion. In 1991 a World Bank loan of US$330 million was negotiated and the government was seeking foreign funding of a further

SS1 Class 25 kV Co-Co electric locomotive hauls a mixed freight on the eastern part of Beijing's half-circle railway (Wolfram Veith)   **1996**

QJ Class steam locomotive at Zhaoqing (Chris Heaps)

1997

series production at the Zhuzhou plant. With thyristor control, it weighs 184 tonnes, is rated at 6,490 kW and has a top speed of 100 km/h. The SS4b 6,400 kW variant is the standard traction of the new Daqing coal line, hauling 6,000 tonne trains single-handed or 10,000 tonne trains in tandem, and is being built in quantities for other heavy-haul applications. A prototype 4,800 kW SS6 mixed traffic Co-Co emerged in 1991 and was followed by series production batch of 52. Latest offspring is the Bo-Bo-Bo SS7 rated at 4,800 kW, designed for heavy haulage on steeply graded and sharply curved routes. By late 1994 three prototypes had been delivered for testing on the difficult Baoji–Chengdu line prior to series production. Prototype SS8 (high-performance DC traction motors) locomotives for 160 km/h running were on trial in 1996, while the SS9, with three-phase AC traction based on German technology, is expected shortly.

Steam locomotive production at Datong works was terminated in 1988; it had been necessary until then since expansion of diesel traction and electrification was unable to keep pace with fast-rising traffic demand. Modest construction of the Class JS 2-8-2 has continued elsewhere, but the railway's stock was set to reduce by about 3,000 units in the 1990s.

In 1992 traction stock comprised 5,498 steam, 6,582 diesel and 2,003 electric locomotives.

The country's four coach manufacturing plants have recently been manufacturing about 2,500 vehicles a year, while wagon builders turn out around 30,000 units annually. The Changchun plant, modernised in the 1980s with technical assistance from the former Brel, now builds exclusively Type 25 air conditioned coaches based on the Brel 'International' design. At the beginning of 1995, Germany's DWA subsidiary WBA was building 100 passenger coaches for CR, while South Korea's Hanjin Heavy Industries Co Ltd supplied 30 coaches suitable for 200 km/h running in 1996.

Coach production is set to expand following establishment of a joint venture between the China National Railway Locomotive and Rolling Stock Industry Corporation (LORIC), Canadian manufacturer Bombardier and Power Corp. A new coach-building works will be set up at Qingdao.

At last official report in 1992, rolling stock comprised 28,464 passenger cars (including 1,427 restaurant and 4,233 sleeping cars) and 373,000 wagons.

On local railways in 1991, rolling stock amounted to 264 steam and 125 diesel locomotives, 279 passenger coaches and 3,748 wagons.

Signalling and telecommunications

Overall control of all signalling and telecommunications systems and projects is in the hands of the China National Railway Signal & Communication Corporation, with a staff of 23,000. Nevertheless the scale of work has led to joint ventures and contracts with foreign suppliers. Elin of Austria has supplied a track-to-train radio system embracing some 600 route-km south of Beijing. The country's first solid-state interlocking is being supplied by GEC-General Signal; it will be installed at Xiao Li Zhang, on the Zhengzhou–Wuchang line.

A technology transfer agreement was concluded between the Fengtai signal factory and French supplier CSEE-Transport in 1989, and in 1994 contracts were awarded for supply of CSEE's TVM300 continuous ATC system for installation on the Beijing–Guangzhou main line. Supply of similar equipment and hot box detectors is under discussion for the Beijing–Shanghai line.

Ansaldo and its US subsidiary Union Switch & Signal are installing computerised interlockings for 13 stations on the new Beijing–Guangzhou line, along with a hump computer process control system for a marshalling yard on the route.

In 1996, trials were made of US company Rockwell's advanced data communications system using satellite global positioning.

In 1997, the China Academy of Railway Sciences

Diesel locomotives

Class	Wheel arrangement	Power kW	Speed km/h	Weight tonnes	First built	Mechanical	Builders Engine	Transmission
DF	Co-Co	1,350	100	126	1958	Dalian	10E207	E ZQFR 1350
DF2	Co-Co	750	95.3	113	–	Dalian	6E207	E
DF3	Co-Co	1,350	120	126	1972	Dalian	10E207	E ZQFR 1350
DF4	Co-Co	2,680	100/ 120*	138	–	Dalian	16,240 Z/ZA	E TQFR 3000†
DF5	Co-Co	1,230	100	–	1976	Tangshan	8240Z	E †
DF6						Dalian		
DF7	Co-Co	1,500	–	–	1981	Beijing February 8	12 240Z	E †
DF8	Co-Co	3,000	120	–	1987	Qishuyan	–	H
DF10		7,476			1995			
DF11			160		1997	Qishuyan		
DFH1	B-B	1,350	140	84	–	Qingdao	2 × 12 175Z	H 2 × SF 2010
DFH2	B-B	750	50	60	–	Qingdao	12 180Z	H SF 2010
DFH3	B-B	2,000	120	84	–	Qingdao	2 × 12 180ZL	H 2 × SF 2010Z
DFH5	B-B	930	40/80	84	–	Qingdao	12 180ZL	H SF 2010
DFH	B-B	450	35/72	–	1964	Qingdao	–	H
BJ 3000	B-B	2,000	120	92	1975	Beijing February 7	12 240Z	H EQ 2027
BJ 6000	D-D	4,000	–	–	1969	Beijing February 7	2 × 12 240Z	H 2 × EQ 2027
ND2	Co-Co	1,540	100	120	1974	Electroputere	Sulzer 12LDA288	E Electroputere
ND4	Co-Co	2,945	100	138	1973	Alsthom	AGO 240V16 ESHR	E MTE†
ND5 (C36-7)	Co-Co	2,980	120	210	1984	GE	GEFDL16	E GE
ND15	Bo-Bo	450	80	62	1958	Ganz-Mávag	16 JV 17/24	E Ganz
NY5	C-C	2,760	160	130	1966	Henschel	2 × MB 839B6	H Voith L830rU
NY6	C-C	3,200	120	138	1972	Henschel	2 × MB 16V 652	H Voith L820
NY7	C-C	3,740	120	138	1972	Henschel	2 × MA 12V 956	H Voith L820
NY14	B-B	690	100	65	1973	LEW	MJW 12 KVD 21 A111	H GRS 30/57
NY16	B-B	870	110	68	1975	23rd August	Sulzer 6LDA 28B	H TH2

* Nos 2001 onwards   † Alternator

Electric locomotives

Class	Wheel arrangement	Output kW	Speed km/h	Weight tonnes	First built	Builders Mechanical	Electrical
SS1	Co-Co	4,200	95	138	1958	Zhouzhou	–
6Y2	Co-Co	4,800	100	138	1960	Alsthom	Alsthom
6G1	Co-Co	5,400	110	126	1971	Electroputere	ASEA
6G5O	Co-Co	5,600	110	138	1972	Alsthom	Alsthom
SS3	Co-Co	4,800	100	138	1975	Zhouzhou	–
SS4	Bo-Bo + Bo-Bo	6,400	100	184	1986	Zhouzhou	–
8K	Bo-Bo + Bo-Bo	6,400	100	184	1986	50 c/s Group	50 c/s Group
6K	Bo-Bo-Bo	4,800	100	138	1987	Kawasaki	Mitsubishi
SS4b	Bo-Bo + Bo-Bo	6,400	100	184	1987	Zhouzhou	
SS5	Bo-Bo	3,200	140	86	1989		
SS6	Co-Co	4,800	100	138	1991	Zhouzhou	Hitachi
SS7	Bo-Bo-Bo	4,800	100/120	138	1993	Zhouzhou	
SS8	Bo-Bo	3,600	160		1996	Zhouzhou	
SS9					1997	Zhouzhou	

COSTA RICA

Ministry of Public Works and Transport

San José
Tel: +506 222 8681   Fax: +506 255 0242

Key personnel
Minister: Rodolfo Silva
Director, Transport Division: H Blanco

UPDATED

Costa Rica Railways (Incofer)

Instituto Costaricense de Ferrocarriles
PO Box 1, 1009 F E al P Estación, Zona 3, San José
Tel: +506 221 0777   Fax: +506 222 3458
Telex: 2393 fecosa cr

Key personnel
President: F Bolaños
Administration Manager: A Rodriguez
Operations Manager: Oscar Brenes Alpízar
Projects Director: Hannia Cruz Calderón
Financial Director: Iris Torres Casco
Operations Director, Pacific Division:
   Rolando Rivera Rodríguez
Operations Director, Atlantic Division:
   Francisco Vargas
Maintenance of Way Director, Pacific Division:
   Herbert Schlager Irias
Maintenance of Way Director, Atlantic Division:
   Arnold Dennis
Chief Electromechanical Engineer, Pacific Division:
   Carlos Ceciliano Camacho
Chief Electromechanical Engineer, Atlantic Division:
   Rafael A Molina

Gauge: 1,067 mm
Route length: 950 km
Electrification: 128 km at 15 kV 20 Hz AC, 132 km at
25 kV 50 Hz AC

Political background
Incofer was created in 1985 to undertake the modernisation of the system created by the merger of the National Atlantic and Pacific railways (Incofer's Atlantic and Pacific divisons) in 1977. In 1987 it took over the 250 km Ferrocarril del Sur network formerly operated by the Compania Bananera de Costa Rica.

Due to its worsening finances the government ordered Incofer to cease operations in June 1995 and put the railway into a care and maintenance regime while private sector participation was sought.

In November 1996, the government invited bids to operate and maintain parts of the national rail network, with concessions to be granted based on promised levels of private sector investment.

The Atlantic network, serving the Caribbean ports and banana-growing region centred on Limón province, is available for a period of 25 years. The concessionaire will have to rehabilitate existing track and also offer both freight and passenger services.

Of the former 1,000-strong workforce for Incofer, only

an administrative core of 65 still survives, with a further 80 employed on short-term maintenance contracts. Incoming operators will be free to source their own workers.

The concessionaire will have to bid on the basis of a monthly hire fee for both track and rolling stock, plus give an indication of proposed passenger and freight tariffs. All investment will have to be supplied by the incoming company, with the rebuilding of three major river crossings a priority. Atlantic network assets are valued at US$75.3 million, with track alone valued at US$31.1 million, comprising San Cristóbal—Limón—Ley River main lines, plus assorted branch lines serving banana plantations. Trackage totalling 300 km is on offer, 219 km of which were operating in 1995.

Although the Atlantic network is electrified at 25 kV 50 Hz AC, the concessionaire will be allocated 15 GE diesel locomotives valued at US$7.4 million. Additionally, 215 box cars and 257 flat wagons valued at US$14 million will also be transferred. Four workshops form part of the total package.

Traffic projections for the Atlantic network suggest the new concessionaire would be handling 405,460 tonnes of freight in 1997, which is expected to rise to 485,420 tonnes by 2000, most of which will be Standard Fruit traffic.

A second concession covering the 150 km Pacific network is also to be let. This links the port of Caldera to San José.

The government is also being pressurised to implement suburban services in four cities, including San José. The World Bank has made funding available to future concession holders to buy new equipment or improve infrastructure. Incofer's property may be ceded to concessionaires for use as security on loans.

Passenger operations
Before Incofer operations ceased in June 1995, passenger service had dwindled to a pair of trains in each direction between Heredia and San José (12 km), catering mainly for university students. Tourist trains were reported to be in operation between Síquirres and Guápiles.

Freight operations
In 1994 Incofer carried a total of 661,349 tonnes of freight, having carried 739,000 tonnes in 1993. The Atlantic division carried 360,711 tonnes in 1994, mostly bananas produced by Standard Fruit for export, with smaller amounts of inbound fertiliser and packaging materials. Wheat and maize accounted for over 50 per cent of the 300,638 tonnes carried on the Pacific division in 1994, with iron, steel and fertiliser making up the bulk of the remainder.

New lines
A major outstanding project, discussed for some time past, is the construction of an effective link between the Atlantic and Pacific divisions, latterly connected only by a steeply graded line through the streets of San José. At Alajuela, close to the country's International Airport, the two divisions are only 3 km apart and an elevated single-track connection has been proposed at an estimated cost of US$70 million, including rolling stock for suburban passenger services.

Traction and rolling stock
When Incofer operations ceased in June 1995, the traction and rolling stock fleet included three diesel-electric locomotives formerly employed on Canadian National's Newfoundland system; two 14 tonne railbuses with 200 hp Cummins engines assembled by Incofer in its own workshops; a Romanian-built diesel-hydraulic B-B shunter converted to a 15 kV 20 Hz electrohydraulic unit by Incofer; and a pair of two-car diesel multiple-units acquired from FEVE of Spain in 1993.

The initial 15 kV 20 Hz AC electric system was operated by AEG locomotives of 1929 and Siemens locomotives of 1956. The diesel locomotive fleet was chiefly General Electric, with the newest 825 and 1,100 hp units dating from 1979, but including some 950 hp diesel-hydraulic units supplied by the 23 August works of Romania in 1971.

Incofer had received 13 diesel locomotives and some 500 freight wagons when it took over the Ferrocarril del Sur system in 1987.

Electric locomotives	16
Diesel locomotives	22
Diesel railcars	19

Rolling stock

Passenger coaches	82
Freight wagons	1,331

Type of coupler: Standard
Type of braking in standard use: Westinghouse air

Signalling and telecommunications
Incofer had hoped to install automatic block signalling throughout the main routes of the Pacific and Atlantic divisions. A new operating control centre was also planned to replace Incofer's radio dispatching system.

Electrification
The former Pacific Railway running 128 km from San José to Puntarenas was electrified at 15 kV 20 Hz AC in 1929-30. Between 1977 and 1982 modernisation and electrification of the Atlantic Railway was put in hand; the 132 km Limón—Río Frío main line was completely relaid with 43 kg/m long-welded rail on concrete sleepers, new yards were installed at both ends, bridges strengthened for 16-tonne axleloads, and electrification at 25 kV 60 Hz AC executed.

A fleet of 12 dual-voltage (25 kV 60 Hz/15 kV 20 Hz AC), 62 tonne 1,200 kW Bo-Bo electric locomotives was supplied by electrification contractors 50 c/s Group. It was hoped to eventually convert the former Pacific Railway to 25 kV 60 Hz AC operation when its generating plant became due for renewal.

Track
Rail: ASCE 42.5
Sleepers: Wood or concrete spaced 1,600/km
Fastenings: Pandrol, Nabla RN, spikes
Min curve radius: 80 m
Max gradient: 4.25%
Max permissible axleload: 18 tonnes

UPDATED

CROATIA

Ministry of Maritime Affairs, Transport and Communications

Prisavlje 14, 41000 Zagreb
Tel: +385 41 517000   Fax: +385 41 610691

Key personnel
Minister: Ziljko Luzavec

VERIFIED

Croatian State Railway

Hrvatske Željeznice (HŽ)
Mihanovićeva 12, 41000 Zagreb
Tel: +385 1 45 77 111   Fax: +385 1 45 77 730

Key personnel
Chairman: Josip Bozicevic
Managing Director: Marijan Klarić
Deputy Director: Durica Misin
Directors
   Commercial: Zvonko Podvorac
   Finance: Mirjana Pejkovic
   Operating: Marijan Klaric
   Planning: Zrinka Ivanovic
   Traction and Rolling Stock: Ive-Vice Cukrov
   Civil Engineering: Zlatko Dokaza
   Electrification: Ivica Kucan
   Information Technology: Drago Kikic
   International Affairs: Maja Stepcevic
   Public Relations: Vlatka Skoric

Interior of the 'Mimara' Zagreb—Berlin EuroCity train   **1997**

Gauge: 1,435 mm
Length: 2,296 km
Electrification: 796 km, most at 25 kV AC, about 10 per cent at 3 kV DC

Political background
A week after Croatia declared its independence from Yugoslavia in October 1991 the new republic severed its railway system from Yugoslav Railways (JZ).

The railway sustained serious damage in the war in the region in the early 1990s; full reparations are expected to take many years to complete. Through traffic with Serbia resumed in July 1996 when the Vincovici—Mirkovci route was reopened.

In response to financial pressures, staff have been shed. HŽ had 21,800 employees in 1996, down from over 36,000 five years previously.

Organisation
At the beginning of 1995, infrastructure and operations within HŽ were separated. Infrastructure is still managed by HŽ, but the government takes financial responsibility for it.

Passenger operations
In 1995, 17.5 million passenger journeys were made (a 9.3 per cent decrease on the year before); passenger-km stood at 943 million (2 per cent down).

Freight operations
In 1995, freight tonnage stood at 13.3 million tonnes, 17.9 per cent up on the year before. Freight tonne-km were 19.2 per cent up, standing at 1,974 million. HŽ freight traffic is reckoned to have fallen by 71 per cent between 1989 and 1993, and stayed roughly level thereafter.

Intermodal operations
In 1995, HŽ was admitted as a shareholder member of the Intercontainer international intermodal group. Hungary and Italy are the two most important countries with which container traffic is exchanged. Total intermodal traffic on HŽ in 1996 was estimated at 34,000 TEU, comprising 7,000 TEU imports, 3,000 TEU exports and 24,000 TEU transit traffic; this was down from a high of 41,000 TEU in 1994.

Improvements to existing lines
Following the reopening of the Zagreb—Split route in September 1995, a major strategic aim is repairing the Zagreb—Belgrade trans-Yugoslav main line. A 32 km war-damaged section of this line, between Vinkovci and Tovarnik on the Serbian border, was reopened in January 1997.

In early 1995, HŽ officials agreed with their counterparts in Hungary to upgrade the Zagreb—Budapest route to cut the intercapital journey below four hours.

Traction and rolling stock
At the beginning of 1996, HŽ was operating 440 locomotives (about a quarter of the fleet electric, the rest diesel) and 96 multiple-units (mostly diesel). The hauled coaching stock fleet stood at 798 vehicles and there were 11,543 wagons.

Electrification
The line serving Rijeka in the northwest of the country is electrified on the 3 kV DC system. HŽ aims to convert this line to its standard 25 kV 50 Hz system by 1998.

Signalling and telecommunications
In May 1997, HŽ invited tenders for a ground-to-train radio system along the Lika line. Radio exchanges would be located at Ostarije, Gospic, Knin and Split.

Track
Rail: 60 UIC, 65 UIC, S 49
Sleepers: Beechwood, prestressed concrete

Diesel locomotives

Class	Wheel arrangement	Transmission	Power kW	Speed km/h	Weight tonnes	No in service	First built	Builders Mechanical	Engine
2041	Bo-Bo	DE	606	80	67	34	1962	Brissoneau et Lotz	Duro Daković
2042	Bo-Bo	DE	680	80	67.2	3	1966	Brissoneau et Lotz	Duro Daković
2043		DE	1,454	124	100	3	1960	General Motors	Janko Gredelj
2044		DE	1,845	124	102.2	31	1981		
2061	Co-Co	DE	1,454	124	114	44	1959	General Motors	General Motors
2062	Co-Co	DE	1,640	124	103	58	1973	General Motors	General Motors
2063	Co-Co	DE	2,461	124	120.1	14	1972	General Motors	General Motors
2131	C	DH	294	60	42.5	29	1958	Jenbacher Werke	Duro Daković
2132	C	DH	441	60	45.1	83	1963	Jenbacher Werke	Duro Daković
2133	C	DH	511	60	54	15	1956	MaK	MaK
2141	B-B	DH	1,176	120	68.2	1	1977	Duro Daković	Duro Daković

Electric locomotives

Class	Wheel arrangement	Output kW	Speed km/h	Weight tonnes	No in service	First built	Builders Mechanical	Electrical
1061*	Bo-Bo-Bo	2,640/3,150	120	112	31	1960	Ansaldo	Ansaldo
1141†	Bo-Bo	3,860/4,080	140	82	98	1968	Rade Končar	ASEA
1142†	Bo-Bo	4,400/4,400	160	82	16	1983	Rade Končar	
1162†	Bo-Bo-Bo	3,869/4,386	120	129	2	1960	Janko Gredelj	Ansaldo

*3 kV †25 kV

Diesel railcars or multiple-units

Class	Cars per unit	Motor cars per unit	Motored axles/car	Transmission	Power/motor kW	Speed km/h	No in service	First built	Builders Mechanical	Engine
7021	5	2	4	DE	386	120	6	1972	B&L	B&L
7121	2	1	4	DH	103	120	35	1981	Macosa	Duro Daković
7221	2	1	1	DM	110	90	39	1955	Uerdingen	Goša

Electric railcars or multiple-units

Class	Cars per unit	Motor cars per unit	Motored axles/car	Power/motor kW	Speed km/h	No in service	First built	Builders Mechanical	Electrical
6011*	2	2	4	174	120	8	1964	Pafawag	Pafawag
6111†	2	1	4	300	120	27	1977	Ganz-Mavag	Ganz-Mavag

*3 kV †25 kV   *UPDATED*

CUBA

Ministry of Transport

Avenida Rancho Boyeras y Tulipán, Havana
Tel: +53 7 814505/814780   Fax: +53 7 335118

Key personnel
Transport Under-Secretary: Amador del Valle Portilla
Director of Rail Transport: Aguiar Castro

UPDATED

Cuban National Railways (FdeC)

Ferrocarriles de Cuba
Edificio Estación Central, Egido y Arsenal, Havana
Tel: +53 7 621530   Fax: +53 7 338628

Key personnel
Director-General: Ing Pastor Pérez Fleites
Directors
Locomotives and Rolling Stock: J Noya
Finance: N Marrero
Traffic: R Boffil
Permanent Way: J C Miranda
Signalling: R Morales
Personnel: L Pereda

Gauge: 1,435 mm
Route length: 4,807 km
Electrification: 147 km at 1.2 kV DC

Traffic (million)	1992	1994
Freight tonnes	6.9	4.4
Freight tonne-km	1,059	644.5
Passenger journeys	30	30.5
Passenger-km	2,593	2,346.7

Passenger operations
Since 1992, passenger traffic is reckoned to have increased by some 20 per cent due to the rationing of petrol for road vehicles, a measure resulting from the end of Comecon trading arrangements and the US blockade.

USSR-built Type TE114K diesel locomotive at Ranchuelo (Philip Cotterill)

Standard-gauge sugar railway at Mal Tiempo mill (Philip Cotterill)

Freight operations

Freight traffic comprises mostly sugar and its by-products of rum and molasses, tobacco and citrus fruit.

Improvements to existing lines

Reconstruction of the Havana—Santiago de Cuba line is believed to have been brought to a halt by the worsening economic situation, having been undertaken as far as Camaguey. The total length of new track to be installed under this project was 1,170 km, comprising 837 km of main line, 224 km of sidings and passing loops and 109 km of feeder branch lines. The line has been laid with Soviet-supplied Type P50 (50-48 kg/m) rail; sidings have been laid with 43 kg/m rail, also from the Soviet Union. Sleepers are prestressed monobloc concrete.

The project involves reconstruction of 400 bridges, 511 km of realignment, which will reduce distance by 15 km, and closure of over 50 small stations. The ruling gradient will be 1.2 per cent, except for a short section of 2 per cent on the exit from Santiago. The aim is to run trains of up to 1,800 tonnes gross initially, but later of 2,600 tonnes, with maximum speed raised to 100 km/h for freight trains, 140 km/h for passenger. The end result should be a cut of the best Havana—Santiago de Cuba passenger train schedule from 14 hours 45 minutes to 10 hours.

Traction and rolling stock

At the end of 1993 FdeC operated 348 diesel and 12 electric locomotives, 74 diesel and 16 electric railcars, 609 passenger cars and 8,838 freight wagons. In 1995 it was estimated that at least one-third of the rolling stock fleet was out of service for want of spare parts.

FdeC diesel traction is an eclectic assortment of French, East German, Hungarian, Canadian and, more recently, Soviet types. The Canadian machines are 20 Bombardier-MLW Type MX 624 supplied in the mid-1970s. Dominant model is the Soviet 1,912 kW Type TE-114K Co-Co, of which the stock is 96.

The diesel railcars are mostly of Fiat design with 409 kW engines, built in the mid-1970s by Concord of Argentina under licence. FdeC is now required by national policy (and economic and political circumstance) to seek local rolling stock manufacture and a local company, Empresa Productora de Equipos Ferroviarios of Cardenas, began supply of diesel railbuses based on the Ganz-Mávag design. The plant's first 85 passenger cars have been delivered to FdeC. The Ministry of Steel, Iron & Machine Industry has produced two 'Taino' trains at its Cardenas works; these have run in Las Tunas province and can carry 300 passengers.

In 1997, ZSR of Slovakia was negotiating with Cuba over the supply of 55 refurbished second-class coaches and 10 diesel railcars to FdeC.

Type of coupler in standard use: Semi-automatic
Type of brake in standard use: Air (50% Matrosov, 30% Westinghouse and 20% DAKO)

Diesel locomotives

Class	Wheel arrangement	Power kW	Speed km/h	Weight tonnes	No in service	First built	Mechanical	Builders Engine	Transmission
TE114K	Co-Co	1,912	120	121	88	1978	Voroshilov-grad	5D49	*E* Jaricov
MLW	Co-Co	1,912	135	112	43	1975	Bombardier	Alco 251E	*E* GE Canada
M62-K	Co-Co	1,234	100	120	17	1974	Voroshilov-grad	14D4DT2 PDIT	*E* Kharkov
TEM-4	Co-Co	735	100	120	27	1965	Bryansk		
TEM-2	Co-Co	757	100	120	77	1974	Bryansk	PDITM	*E* Kharkov
DVM-9	Bo-Bo	735	90	76	35	1969	Ganz-Mávag	16VCE17/24	*E* Ganz Electric
GMC G8	Bo-Bo	662	124	72	32	1955	GM	8-567C	*E* GM
BB63000	Bo-Bo	606	90	72	7	1965	B&L	MG0V12BSH 22	*E* B&L
TGM-25	C	294	50	46	8	1970	—	—	*H* —

B&L = Brissoneau & Lotz

Electric locomotives

Class	Wheel arrangement	Output kW	Speed km/h	Weight tonnes	No in service	First built	Builders
GE 7230B	Bo-Bo	588/882	60	55	12	1920	GE

Diesel railcars or multiple-units

Class	Cars per unit	Motor cars per unit	Power/motor kW	Speed km/h	No in service	First built	Mechanical	Builders Engine	Transmission
Fiat Concord	2	1	2 × 184	110	15	1976	Fiat Concord	Fiat 8217	*H* Fiat
Budd	1	1	2 × 184	128	2	1957	Budd	Leyland	*H* Leyland
Brill	1	1	132	70	10	1930	Brill	Taino	*M* Taino

Electric railcars or multiple-units

Class	Cars per unit	Output/motor kW	Speed km/h	No in service	First built	Builders
Brill	1	4 × 55	70	16	1923	Brill

Signalling and telecommunications

On the main Havana—Santiago da Cuba line, replacement has proceeded of its almost exclusively manual point and block-telephone operation. Hitherto only nine of some 100 stations have had central point working, but track-to-train and train-to-train radio has been provided. Installation of a semi-automatic block system and relay interlockings has been completed on the 16-station section between Havana and Santa Clara (207 km) and in 1991 was continuing to Santiago de Cuba.

Electrification

The 147 km 1.2 kV DC electrified section on FdeC links Havana with Matanzas.

Track

Rail: P50 51 kg/m
Sleepers: Prestressed concrete: 2,460 mm, spaced

1,520-1,840/km; creosoted pine: 2,750 mm, spaced 1,520-1,840/km
Fastenings: Elastic and rigid with track rails and screw bolts
Min curvature radius: 150 m
Max gradient: 3.0%
Max permissible axleload: 23 tonnes over 230 km

Sugar railways

The numerous railways linking the sugar plantations and factories are in sum of greater extent than FdeC and at latest report totalled 7,742 km. Of the total some 65 per cent is standard-gauge. Serving over 100 of the island's 154 sugar plants, these railways employ around 900 locomotives, 380 of them steam, and over 30,000 wagons. The diesel fleet mixes locomotives of US and USSR derivation.

UPDATED

CZECH REPUBLIC

Ministry of Transport

Nábřeží Ludvíka Svobody 12, CZ-110 15 Prague 1

Key personnel
Minister: Martin Říman
Under-Secretary for Economy and Transport Policy:
  Miroslav Sylla
Under-Secretary for Trade Unions: Ivan Foltýn
Under-Secretary for Railways: Michal Tošovský
Director, Railways: Karel Sellner

UPDATED

Czech Railways (ČD)

České Dráhy
Nábřeží Ludvíka Svobody 12, CZ-110 15 Prague 1
Tel: +420 422 23 03 1111   Fax: +420 422 81 08 12

Key personnel
General Manager: Vladimír Sosna
General Supervisor: Jaroslav Vrána
General Manager's Office
  Director: František Nykles
  Under-Secretary for International Affairs:
    Milan Matoušek
  Under-Secretary for Economy: Michael Dvořák
  Under-Secretary for Property Administration:
    Jiři Macháček
Management Board
  Strategy: Josef Beran
  Personnel:Jiři Šponer
  Economy: Vladislav Zeman
  Finance: Vojtěch Knop-Kostka
  Operations: Jaroslav Svoboda
  Transport: Jaroslav Vrána
  Privatisation: Kamil Řezníček
  Law: Vladislav Škvrna
  Ecology: Jiři Fiala
  Planning: Michal Ružička
  Technical Development: Jan Bartek
  Permanent Way: Josef Kotaška
  Passenger Traffic: Luďka Hnulíková
  Freight Traffic: Milan Dvořáček
  Traction and Rolling Stock: Karel Novák
  Signalling and Telecommunications: Karel Plachetka
  Electrification: Jan Matějka
  Tracks: Jan Ježek

Buildings: Pavel Novák
Safety: Miroslav Kochaň
Control: Jan Merta
International: Antonın Brož
UIC: Ivo Malina
Public Relations: Karel Grulich
Division Managers
  Commercial Division: Václav John
  Operations Division: Jaroslav Svoboda
  Infrastructure Division: František Nykles

Regional Managers
  Prague: Radimır Hofta
  Plzeň: Josef Chaloupka
  České Budějovice: Václav Svoboda
  Ústı nad Labem: Václav Válek
  Hradec Králové: Martin Koleš
  Česká Třebová: Jiři Vencl
  Olomouc: Jan Mrkva
  Brno: Pavel Novák
  Ostrava: Miroslav Klich

Gauge: 1,435 mm; 760 mm
Route length: 9,344 km standard-gauge; 96 km narrow-gauge
Electrification: 1,616 km at 3 kV DC; 46 km at 1.5 kV DC;
1,081 km at 25 kV 50 Hz AC

Political background
Mirroring the severance of Slovakia from the Czech Republic, the Czechoslovak railway system was formally divided on 1 January 1993. Three of the former State Railways' four regions, the Midland based on Olomouc, the Northeastern based on Prague and the Southwestern based on Plzeň, are embodied in the new Czech Republic Railways (ČD), which has taken over 72 per cent of the State Railways' network. Slovak Railways (ŽSR) is essentially the old Eastern region based on Bratislava.

Privatisation
The Czech government has continued to examine ways of introducing private capital to the running of the railways, with the aim of rectifying an investment backlog, rendering ČD more competitive against other modes and reducing the level of state support. ČD's electrification, intermodal (ČSKD-Intrans) and dining and sleeping car divisions have been privatised, in addition to nine major workshops and fringe activities such as restaurants and

the railway health service. During the first phase, privatisation earned Kcs3.6 billion and by 2005, ČD wants to sell off further property valued at Kcs6.57 billion.

Under legislation passed in 1994 ending the monopoly of the state railways, private companies holding a licence from the Ministry of Transport's Railway Authority are now able to bid to operate closed or unprofitable sections of the ČD network. A new organisation, the Railway Authority (DÜ — Drážni Úřad), was established under the Ministry of Transport in April 1994, charged with awarding operating licences to private sector companies and harmonising their operations with those of ČD.

A radical plan was put forward which would have seen a third of the network transferred to private owners, but following criticism from railway unions the plan has been toned down. It is now unlikely there will be much private sector operation before the end of the decade, and it now seems that only a fifth, at most, of the network will be privatised.

Private sector operations on ČD tracks have made more progress. On 10 August 1994 Škoda Doprava Plzeň, a subsidiary of the Czech Republic's largest industrial company, began operating two daily refuse trains over 12 km of ČD tracks in Plzeň, using its own diesel-electric locomotives and wagons. Škoda has a 35 per cent shareholding in ČMDS, a transport company established in conjunction with mining companies on 23 November 1994. ČMDS intends to take over operation of some 30 per cent of the country's coal trains, and plans in the long term to operate other freight services and passenger trains. Škoda signed contracts with two coal companies in 1994 to operate unit trains in the Ostrava-Karviná area and around Nové Sedlo (on routes totalling 102 km), and plans to operate 30-wagon coal trains over the 135 km Sokolov-Plzeň route.

Organisation
Management of infrastructure has been divorced from that of operations and there are three divisions: commercial, operations and infrastructure. There are plans to merge the operations and commercial divisions into one.

Finance
For 1996, the government budgeted support of Kcs5.15 billion, compared with Kcs5.14 billion in 1995. For 1997, state support has been increased to Kcs5.6 billion.

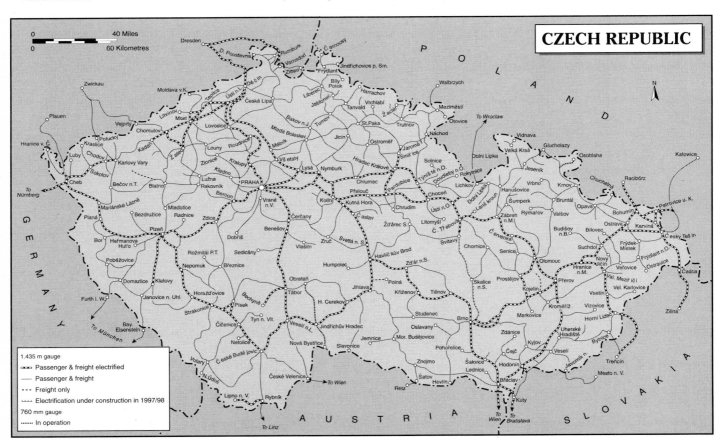

Revenue from freight traffic reached Kcs18.361 billion in 1995, earning the railway a net profit of Kcs3 billion. Owing to the highly unprofitable passenger operation, however, ČD showed a total loss of Kcs8.38 billion in 1995 and a deficit of not less than Kcs9.4 billion was recorded in 1996.

In an attempt to improve the railway's finances, in early 1997 ČD announced plans to cut 40,000 jobs from the total workforce of 101,000 (ČD is the country's biggest employer). However, this provoked a damaging strike which led to the management backing off from the more radical parts of the proposed plan.

Passenger operations

Passenger traffic has suffered both from economic recession, and competition from private bus companies offering cheaper fares over routes such as Prague–Brno and Prague–Ústí nad Labem. ČD now accounts for only 7.4 per cent of passenger journeys in the Czech Republic. The response to this position has been to attempt to strengthen services on the main lines, while cutting back on unprofitable branch line services.

The first EuroCity train in Czechoslovakia, the Vienna–Prague 'Antonín Dvořák', was introduced in June 1991. The number of such international trains has subsequently increased, with daily services connecting Prague with Vienna, Budapest, Warsaw, Berlin, Hamburg, Interlaken, Košice, Nuremburg, Dortmund and Paris. The Vienna–Warsaw EuroCity service serves the east of the Czech Republic.

Internally, service on the Prague–Bohumín route has been improved with introduction of InterCity services Nos 504/505 'Ostravan' and Nos 506/507 'Jan Perner', using refurbished coaches. ČD is attempting to attract more passengers to this route, which as yet has no firm highway competition.

In January 1997, ČD introduced a high-quality service, the 'Manažer', on the route between Prague and Ostrava (358 km). Train SC 1500/1501 consists of three first-class coaches and a restaurant car. Free at-seat refreshment, newspapers and free parking at Ostrava's main station area are provided.

Freight operations

ČD forms the Czech Republic's principal means of transporting bulk commodities, principally coal and lignite from North Bohemia and Moravia, but also petroleum products, ore, wood, cereals and other foodstuffs. Transit traffic moving between the central European countries is also carried.

Over 85 per cent of ČD's tonnage is electric hauled.

There was a serious loss of freight traffic after the demise of Communism, and the decline continued after Czechoslovakia was split in two. Some of the traffic loss was due to a combination of demand for cheaper transport from newly privatised industries, and successive devaluations of the Czech currency. For international transits the railway was forced to pay neighbouring railways in convertible currency, which inevitably inflated tariffs. Cross-border road transport had no such handicap.

ČD has attempted to make itself more competitive by maximising opportunities for block train operation and leasing modern wagons from neighbouring railways, and drop-off in traffic slowed in the mid-1990s. In 1995, revenue rose slightly and ČD's freight operations were profitable for the first time for some years, but a strike in early 1997 set back prospects for a sustained return to financial health.

In 1996, 250 Type Gagns four-axle covered wagons were ordered.

Traffic (million)	1995	1996
Freight tonnes	108.26	104.79
Freight tonne-km	NA	NA
Passenger journeys	226	219
Passenger-km	NA	NA

Intermodal operations

Container trains operate between Lovosice and Hamburg (three times a week), Prague and Rotterdam (twice a week) and Ostrava and Moscow (a weekly service begun in September 1996). In September 1993, an international piggyback operation began on the 411 km route from České Budějovice to Villach, Austria. Three piggyback companies — ČSKD-Intrans, Bohemiakombi and Ökombi — run six trains a week on this route, alleviating pressure from lorry traffic on the E55 international motorway and reducing exhaust emissions in the forests of south Bohemia. During the first two years

Class 371 electric locomotive for 3 kV DC / 15 kV AC dual-voltage working between Prague and Dresden, rebuilt for 160 km/h operation in 1997 (Michal Málek)
1997

of operation, a total of 12,700 trucks were carried, and in September 1995 another pair of trains per week was added on the route.

Although traffic has risen following a tariff reduction in January 1994, capacity is constrained by the single-track 58 km České Budějovice–Horní Dvořiště line and the need to change locomotives at the border with Austria. There are plans to double-track and electrify České Budějovice–Horní Dvořiště, but lack of finance for the estimated Kcs1 billion cost of the project means that it is unlikely to be undertaken before 1998 at the earliest.

An international piggyback service was introduced in September 1994 on the 118 km route between Lovosice and Dresden, Germany; 12 pairs of trains each carrying 25 trucks are in operation daily, and journey time is 3½ hours. Haulage is provided by ČD/DBAG Class 372/180 dual-voltage locomotives. This service is operated by Bohemiakombi, ČD, ČESMAD Bohemia, SSČR and Ökombi Wien.

The service ran initially for a trial period of six months, but due to healthy traffic levels it is likely to stay in place until at least 2002, when a new international highway is due to be completed. The Kcs25 million investment required for the introduction of the Lovosice–Dresden piggyback service, including the construction of the Czech terminal, was provided by the German Land of Saxony in an attempt to reduce traffic on the existing parallel highway.

New lines

A re-examination has taken place of plans formulated in 1988 for a high-speed (VRT) network. The move was prompted by claims that ČD's projected investment programme for its four principal corridors (see below) will be less than adequate, aiming as it does to raise line speeds to 160 km/h. The VRT network would be some 700 km long, engineered for 250-300 km/h operation and electrified at 25 kV AC. Total cost is estimated at up to Kcs180 billion.

The first section of the VRT network would be the Czech part of the Berlin–Prague–Vienna route. The Prague–Vienna via Gmünd route was one of three that was the subject of a trilateral agreement between the Czech minister of transport and his German and Austrian counterparts in July 1995, providing for construction of high-speed lines in future. The other routes in the agreement were the Prague–Nuremberg and Prague–České Budějovice–Linz lines.

At the start of 1994 a private company, PRaK, was formed to construct a Kcs8.37 billion railway between Prague and Kladno, a distance of 35.7 km. The proposed new route has been approved by Prague's Municipal Council and would both provide commuter services and serve the international airport at Ruzyně, where an expansion programme was due to be finished in 1997.

ČD intends to construct a new alignment between Březno and Chomutov on the Prague-Chomutov main line to replace existing infrastructure affected by mining subsidence. The new alignment would be 7.1 km long

with 1.6 km in tunnel, and would be electrified at 3 kV DC. Completion is pencilled in for May 2004, with the Kcs0.5 billion cost of the project being met by the mining company active in the area.

Improvements to existing lines

Since 1993, ČD has been taking the first steps towards upgrading its principal transit lines, known as Corridors 1-4, for 160 km/h operation. These lines currently attract significant quantities of transit traffic, but it is feared that unless they are upgraded some flows could be diverted around the country, losing ČD revenue. The upgrading covers relaying of track, installation of new signalling and other improvements required to meet international parameters laid down by the UIC.

Electrification is necessary on 280 route-km and installation of a second track on 392 route-km.

Corridor 1

In February 1994, the Czech government authorised upgrading of the main 454 km Děčín–Prague–Břeclav route, known as Corridor 1, making it fit for 160 km/h running throughout. The project includes electrification of the 81 km between Opatov (south of Česká Třebová) and Brno. Involving modernisation of 697 bridges, 14 tunnels, installation of supporting walls and other structures, this is the biggest investment undertaking on the Czech railways this century. Upon completion in 2001, the present 10 hour Berlin–Prague–Vienna journey time will be cut to 7 hrs 15 mins, while a Prague–Brno trip will take 90 mins.

The Czech government ratified financing of the Corridor 1 project in November 1994, with Kcs9 billion coming from the budget and Kcs21.7 billion from credits guaranteed by the government. During 1994-5, ČD gained credits from the European Investment Bank (ECU200 million), the European Bank for Reconstruction and Development (ECU125 million), Japan's EXIM Bank (ECU100 million) and Germany's Kreditanstalt für Wiederaufbau (DM25 million) to finance upgrading of the corridor and the purchase of new equipment. In March 1996, a further credit for Kcs2 billion was agreed with Česká Spořitelna. However, there is now a funding gap as the cost of the project is estimated to have risen to Kcs36.1 billion.

Some 24 km of the corridor have already been upgraded for 160 km/h running and in 1996 work began on a further five sections totalling 126 km. In 1997 work is due to begin on another 38 km.

Work is under way on electrifying the only gap in the Corridor's wires, between Opatov and Brno (81 km); this should be completed in late 1998.

Corridor 2

In August 1995, the government announced the go-ahead for a similar upgrade of the Břeclav–Přerov–Ostrava–Petrovice u Karviné corridor, a total of 320 km. Top speed will be 160 km/h.

Corridor 2 runs north-south in the east of the country, linking Austria and Poland; it accounts for some 40 per cent of ČD's freight transit traffic. It is the Czech section of 'Crete Corridor VI', a route running from the Baltic ports of Gdynia and Gdansk to the east-west Vienna–Bratislava–Budapest rail corridor. A multinational team of consultants, including Gibb of the UK, was appointed in 1997 to investigate ways in which it might be upgraded.

On the Czech section, upgrading of the main corridor was due to start in 1997 and be finished in 2003, while the Přerov–Česká Třebová branch will be tackled in the years 1998-2003.

Financing was agreed with the government in March 1996 with a mix of funds similar to the Corridor 1 package; total cost is expected to be Kcs25 billion. Late 1996 saw signatures on credit agreements with the European Investment Bank and Germany's Kreditanstalt für Wiederaufbau; agreements have also been reached with a number of other foreign and Czech financial institutions.

When the Corridor 2 works are completed, the journey time between Prague and Ostrava will be cut from 4 hours to around 2 hrs 30 mins, while an international transit from Vienna in Austria to Katowice in Poland will be able to be accomplished in about 4 hours.

Work was due to begin on the first section, between Hodonín and Moravský Písek (20 km) in April 1997, followed by the start of work on another 20 km section (between Břeclav and Hodonín) in August 1997.

Corridors 3 and 4
Feasibility studies have been commissioned for upgrading to the same standard two other corridors traversing the Czech Republic, namely: Cheb–Plzeň–Prague–Česká Třebová–Přerov–Petrovice u Karviné (Corridor 3); and Děčín–Prague–Horní Dvořiště/České Budějovice (Corridor 4). While the aspiration is to upgrade both these routes to 160 km/h running, a shortage of finance rules out any early start to the work.

Border crossing reopenings
Since 1991, several cross-border routes closed under the Communist regime have been reopened to traffic. These include routes into Germany (Železná Ruda–Bayerische Eisenstein; Potůčky–Johanngeorgenstadt; Jiříkov–Ebersbach; Dolní Poustevna–Sebnitz; Vejprty–Bärenstein/Cranzahl), Austria (Šatov–Retz) and Poland (Bohumín–Chalupki; Meziměstí–Mieroszów; Petrovice–Zebrzydowice; Černousy–Zawidów; Královec–Lubawka; Český–Těšín–Cieszyn). Another two routes may reopen if sufficient finance can be found: these are Kořenov–Szklarska Poreba, Poland, and Kraslice–Klingenthal, Germany. Bavaria's ministry of transport has expressed interest in restoring service on the closed line between Haidmühle and Nové Údolı.

Traction and rolling stock
At the start of 1997, ČD operated 1,096 electric locomotives (692 DC; 259 AC; 145 dual voltage), 1,691 diesel locomotives, 745 diesel railcars, 84 emus, 5,265 passenger cars and around 73,900 freight wagons. An extensive modernisation programme for the ČD fleet is under way; expenditure of Kcs6.5 billion was budgeted for the period 1995-97. Kcs1.5 billion of this was due to come from the railway's own resources, and the remainder from the government.

Pendolinos ordered
In August 1995, ČD ordered 10 seven-car Class 680 tilting trains for use on the Berlin–Prague–Vienna route; with the new trains, the German and Austrian capitals will be 6hr 35min apart. The Kcs4.115 billion financial package for the acquisition of the trains was put together by a consortium comprising ČSOB of the Czech Republic, Creditanstalt Finanziaria Milano of Italy and Kreditanstalt für Wiederaufbau Frankfurt of Germany.

The trains will be based on the ETR460 Pendolino trains in use in Italy. The Czech trains, to be known as 'Integral', will be tri-voltage versions, capable of operating on 25 kV 50 Hz AC, 15 kV 16⅔ Hz AC and 3 kV DC; output will be 4,000 kW and maximum speed 230 km/h. Axle loads will be limited to 13.5 tonnes; bodies will be made from aluminium profiles. The active tilt system will tilt the cars at up to eight degrees.

The trains will be supplied by a consortium of Fiat of Italy (bogies and tilting mechanisms), ČKD Praha of the Czech Republic (bodies), Siemens of Germany (electrics) and Czech firm MSV Studénka (interiors). Final assembly will take place at the ČKD works in Prague-Zličín.

The first unit was due to be rolled out in December 1997 to allow comprehensive tests during 1998; four more sets were due to follow in 1999 and the remaining five in 2000.

Class 843 railcar delivered in March 1997 by MSV Studénka (Michal Málek)   **1997**

Locomotives
In May 1995, ČD took delivery of a batch of 40 Class 163 3 kV DC electric locomotives which had been held in the Škoda works at Plzeň for three years due to the railway's inability to pay for them. The 3,480 kW, 120 km/h machines have been allocated to Ústı nad Labem depot.

ČD has embarked upon a programme to rationalise and modernise its diesel fleet, disposing of obsolete designs and locomotives made redundant by falling freight traffic. Older shunting types have been replaced with new Class 704 and Class 731 locomotives. Class 781 heavy-haul units have been progressively withdrawn since 1989, with numbers down to 45 by the beginning of 1997.

Recent modernisation programmes have included the refurbishment in the period 1991-94 of 119 Class 753 diesel locomotives to create Class 750, and a similar modernisation of 60 Class 751 and 753 locomotives into a new Class 749 between 1992 and 1995. Steam heat

equipment in these machines has been replaced by electric heating.

Refurbishment of Slovak-built Class 735 locomotives into a new Class 714 is well under way. The first two machines emerged in 1992, and the total number refurbished was expected to reach between 100 and 125 by the time the programme is complete, probably during 1997. A notable feature of these machines is dynamic braking rated at 1,020 kW.

Two prototypes of a new two-axle 300 kW diesel-electric locomotive design for local services, the Class 708, emerged in the second half of 1995. They are fitted with a Type M1.2C engine from Liaz and a 472 kW electric brake. In December 1995, ČD awarded ČKD a Kcs450 million contract for another 40 Class 708 locomotives, to be delivered in 1997-98; the first three machines in the series production emerged from works in February 1997.

Principal diesel locomotives

Class	Wheel arrangement	Power kW	Speed km/h	Weight tonnes	No in service	First built	Builders Mechanical	Engine	Transmission
701	B	147	40	22	18	1977	ČKD	Tatra 930-51	M ČKD
702	B	147	40	24	36	1968	ZTS Martin	Tatra 930-51	M ČKD
703	B	170	40	24	26	1969	ZTS Martin	Tatra 930-51	HM ČKD
704	B	250	65	28	20	1988	ČKD	Liaz M2-650	E ČKD
710	C	302	60/30	42	11	1961	ČKD	ČKD 12V 170 DR	HD ČKD
714/714.2*	Bo-Bo	520	80	64	52	1992	ČKD	Liaz 6Z 135 T	E ČKD
720	Bo-Bo	551	60	61	46	1958	ČKD	ČKD 6S 310 DR	E ČKD
726	B-B	625	70	56.6	3	1963	ZTS Martin	ČKD K12 170 DR	HD ČKD
730	Bo-Bo	600	80	69.5	19	1978	ČKD	ČKD K6S 230 DR	E ČKD
721	Bo-Bo	551	80	74	63	1963	ČKD	ČKD K6S 310 DR	E ČKD
735	Bo-Bo	926	90	64	158	1973	ZTS Martin	Pielstick 12PA 4185	E ČKD
742	Bo-Bo	883	90	64	354	1977	ČKD	ČKD K6S 230 DR	E ČKD
751	Bo-Bo	1,102	100	75	108	1964	ČKD	ČKD K6S 310 DR	E ČKD
751.3†	Bo-Bo	1,102	100	74	19	1969	ČKD	ČKD K6S 310 DR	E ČKD
753	Bo-Bo	1,325	100	73.2	171	1968	ČKD	ČKD K12V 230 DR	E ČKD
750**	Bo-Bo	1,325	100	73.2	119	1991	ČKD	ČKD K12V 230 DR	E ČKD
754	Bo-Bo	1,460	100	74.4	58	1975	ČKD	ČKD K12V 230 DR	E ČKD
770	Co-Co	993	90	114.6	59	1963	ČKD	ČKD K6S 310 DR	E ČKD
771	Co-Co	993	90	115.8	124	1968	SMZ Dubnica	ČKD K6S 310 DR	E ČKD
781	Co-Co	1,472	100	116	45	1966	KMZ	VSZ 14 D 40	E CHZE
731	Bo-Bo	880	70	72	51	1988	ČKD	ČKD K6S 230 DR	E ČKD
749***	Bo-Bo	1,102	100	75	60	1992	ČKD	ČKD K6S 310 DR	E ČKD
743	Bo-Bo	800	90	66	10	1987	ČKD	K65 230 DR	E ČKD
708	B	300	80	34	2	1995	ČKD	Liaz M1.2C M640D	E ČKD
799††	B	37	10	22	17	1992	ČKD	Zetov 5301	Battery/DE ČKD

* Rebuilt from Class 735   ** Rebuilt from Class 753   *** Rebuilt from Class 751 and 752   † Ex Class 752
†† Rebuilt from Class 700-703

Diesel railcars or multiple-units

Class	Motored axles/car	Power/motor kW	Speed km/h	No in service	First built	Builders Mechanical	Engine	Transmission
810/809	1	156	80	508	1975	Studénka	Liaz ML634	HM/Praga
820	2	206	70	18	1963	Studénka	Tatra T 930-4	HD ČKD
830	2	301	90	62	1949	Studénka	ČKD 12V 170 DR	E ČKD
831*	2	308	90	37	1952	Studénka	6L 150 PV-3	E ČKD
842	2	408	100	37	1988	Studénka	Liaz ML640F	HM Allison 4TB 741R
843	2	600	110	1	1995	Studénka	Liaz M1.2C-ML640D	E ČKD
850	2	515	110	15	1962	Studénka	ČKD 12V 170 DR	HD ČKD
851	2	588	110	16	1967	Studénka	ČKD 12V 170 DR	HD ČKD
852	2	588	120	18	1968	Studénka	ČKD 12V 170 DR	HD ČKD
853	2	588	120	31	1969	Studénka	ČKD 12V 170 DR	HD ČKD
860	4	442	100	2	1975	Studénka	6PA 4 H 185	E ČKD

* Re-engined Class 830 (1981-91)

Principal electric locomotives

Class	Wheel arrangement	Line voltage	Output kW continuous/ one hour	Speed km/h	Weight tonnes	*No in service	First built	Builders Mechanical	Electrical
100	Bo-Bo	1.5 kV	360/440	50	48	4	1956	Škoda	Škoda
113	Bo-Bo	1.5 kV	400/960	50	64	6	1973	Škoda	Škoda
110	Bo-Bo	3 kV	800/960	80	72	28	1971	Škoda	Škoda
111	Bo-Bo	3 kV	800/880	80	72	35	1981	Škoda	Škoda/ČKD
121	Bo-Bo	3 kV	2,032/2,344	90	88	63	1960	Škoda	Škoda
122	Bo-Bo	3 kV	1,990/2,340	90	85	51	1967	Škoda	Škoda
123	Bo-Bo	3 kV	1,990/2,340	90	85	29	1971	Škoda	Škoda
130	Bo-Bo	3 kV	2,040/2,340	100	86.8	40	1977	Škoda	Škoda
140	Bo-Bo	3 kV	2,032/2,344	120	82	9	1953	Škoda	Škoda-Sécheron
141	Bo-Bo	3 kV	2,032/2,344	120	84	47	1957	Škoda	Škoda
150	Bo-Bo	3 kV	4,000/4,200	140	84	23	1978	Škoda	Škoda
151⁺	Bo-Bo	3 kV	4,000/4,200	160	84	3	1978	Škoda	Škoda
163	Bo-Bo	3 kV	3,060/3,400	120	85	88	1984	Škoda	Škoda/ČKD
163.2*	Bo-Bo	3 kV	3,060/3,480	120	85	9	1991	Škoda	Škoda/ČKD
162	Bo-Bo	3 kV	3,060/3,480	140	85	29	1991	Škoda	Škoda/ČKD
181	Co-Co	3 kV	2,790/2,890	90	120	119	1961	Škoda	Škoda
182	Co-Co	3 kV	2,790/2,890	90	120	105	1963	Škoda	Škoda
210	Bo-Bo	25 kV	880/984	80	72	37	1973	Škoda	Škoda
230	Bo-Bo	25 kV	3,080/3,200	110	88	94	1966	Škoda	Škoda
242.2	Bo-Bo	25 kV	3,080/3,200	120	84	91	1975	Škoda	Škoda
240	Bo-Bo	25 kV	3,080/3,200	120	85	34	1968	Škoda	Škoda
263	Bo-Bo	25 kV	3,060/3,400	120	85	2	1984	Škoda	Škoda/ČKD
362*	Bo-Bo	3 kV/25 kV	3,060/3,400	140	87	9	1980	Škoda	Škoda/ČKD
363	Bo-Bo	3 kV/25 kV	3,060/3,400	120	87	121	1980	Škoda	Škoda/ČKD
372	Bo-Bo	3 kV/15 kV	3,060/3,400	120	84	15	1991	Škoda	Škoda/ČKD

* Bogies exchanged 1993-94
⁺ Reconstructed from Class 150 for 160km/h operation 1992-95

Principal electric multiple-units

Class	Cars per unit	Line voltage	Motor cars per unit	Motored axles/car	Output/motor kW	Speed km/h	No in service	First built	Builders Mechanical	Electrical
451	4	3 kV	2	4	165/190	100	38	1961	Studénka	MEZ
452	4	3 kV	2	4	165/190	100	9	1974	Studénka	MEZ
460	5	3 kV	2	4	250/270	110	26	1974	Studénka	MEZ
470	5	3 kV	2	4	240/260	120	2	1990	Studénka	MEZ
560	5	25 kV	2	4	420/465	110	9	1966	Studénka	MEZ

Shunting locomotive refurbishment is being undertaken at a private maintenance shop in Jihlava, where old Class 700-703 designs from the 1950s and 1960s are being turned into Class 799 battery/diesel-electric shunters.

Multiple-units and railcars
In September 1995, ČD placed an order with MSV Studénka for five bilevel 3 kV DC emus of five cars each, designated Class 471, for suburban services around Prague. Based on the two Class 470 trains supplied in 1990, the new units will have lightweight aluminium bodyshells, a top speed of 140 km/h and a total output of 3,000 kW. The five emus, with a spare trailer, were due to be finished by the end of 1997; there is an option for more trains, possibly in dual- or triple-voltage configuration.

In early 1989, MSV Studénka delivered two prototype Class 842 408 kW 100 km/h diesel-hydraulic railcars, with Liaz M1.2 ML640F engine and Allison HTB 741R transmission. Some 35 production models were delivered between 1993 and 1994 for branch line service.

In June 1995, MSV (in co-operation with ČKD) completed a prototype of a new Class 843 railcar, a diesel-electric version of the Class 842. It is equipped with two Type Liaz M1.2C ML640D engines, giving an output of 600 kW; maximum speed is 110 km/h, and weight is 56 tonnes. Total seating capacity is 60 and there is space for 60 standing.

In late 1995, ČD ordered 30 Class 843 railcars; all these were due to be delivered by the end of 1997. In addition, 11 Class 943 driving cars and 20 Class 043 trailers were ordered; pre-production vehicles emerged in 1996, with series production during 1997.

Passenger coaches
In 1995, ČD ordered 45 new 200 km/h coaches from a consortium of MSV Studénka and the Austrian firm SGP for the Berlin—Prague—Vienna artery. The Kcs2 billion order comprises 26 second class and nine first class coaches, along with 10 dining cars. First deliveries were scheduled for 1997. Financing has been arranged by a consortium of domestic banks, led by Konsolidační Banka.

Refurbishment of 100 Type Bh Hungarian-built coaches from the 1960s and early 1970s began in mid-1996, with the work being undertaken by MOVO Plzeň in conjunction with DVJ Dunakeszi, Budapest. Improvements include replacement of brake blocks by discs and new seats. The first 20 coaches, which will be used on international services, left works in 1996; the other 80 were due to be finished in 1997.

Other refurbishing projects include upgrading of Type Bmee and Aee coaches into a 160 km/h Type BMee-RIC design, modernisation of 29 Type B second class coaches into a new Type Beer, and refurbishment of Type A and AB East German-built coaches into a new Class Aee design with seats from Fainsa of Spain. Domestic companies involved in this work include MOVO Plzeň, ŽOS České Velenice and MSV Studénka.

Freight wagons
ČD expects to invest Kcs8 billion in freight wagons in the period up to 2003. The investment programme foresees purchase of 8,140 Type Gagns, 200 Type Tdns, 65 Type Sgnss, 200 Type Hbbillns, 70 Type Habbillns and 90 Type Zans wagons. Also in the programme is refurbishment of 250 Type Gbgkks wagons, with the modernised vehicles to be designated Type Hbills.

Signalling and telecommunications
Automatic block signalling has been installed on 18 per cent (1,747 route-km) of the ČD system. Some 12.5 per cent of route-km is equipped with train radio.

Electrification
Electric traction is available over 29 per cent of ČD route-mileage and hauls 86 per cent of all traffic. The north operates at 3 kV DC, the south at 25 kV AC. There are five junctions of the electrification systems: at Kutná—Hora, 73 km east of Prague; Králův Dvůr on the Prague—Plzeň route; Nedakonice on the Přerov—Břeclav route; Benešov on the Prague—Tabor route; and Nezamyslice on the Přerov—Brno route.

In the 1980s, little electrification took place due to plentiful supplies of cheap oil from the Soviet Union favouring diesel haulage. In 1991, the government of the former Czechoslovakia endorsed a rolling programme of electrification that would see 347 km electrified by 1995. Some slippage has taken place on this timetable due to a shortage of finance, but a number of projects are proceeding, principally the electrification of Brno—Nezamyslice—Olomouc/Přerov routes.

In January 1993, 3 kV DC electric trains started running on the 40 km line between Olomouc and Nezamyslice, and in December 1993 on the 27 km between Nezamyslice and Přerov. In November 1993, work began on 25 kV AC electrification of the 63 km single-track Brno—Vyškov—Nezamyslice section; this was completed in June 1995. Total cost for the three sections was Kcs776.5 million.

In October 1995, work was started on a 25 kV AC electrification of a 23 km double-track connection between Holubice and Brno-Židenice; work was completed in October 1996. The final value of the project was Kcs236 million.

In a Kcs737 million project, the 41 km Plzeň-Klatovy route has been electrified at 25 kV AC to improve links with southern Germany; electric trains commenced operation in September 1996. ČD was proposing making a start in 1997-98 on the final 49 km to the German frontier.

April 1996 saw the start of electrification work between Opatov and Brno (81 km) as part of ČD's upgrading programme for the Děčín-Břeclav Corridor 1 (see 'Improvements to existing lines' section above). Completion at 25 kV AC is scheduled for late 1998.

Preparatory works began in late 1996 on 58 km of single-track route in Corridor 4. Completion is expected in 2000, and will include conversion of the 22 km Lipno Railway from 1.5 kV DC to 25 kV AC.

Track
Main lines are generally laid with 49 kg/m rail, secondary lines with 30 to 40 kg/m. However, almost 10 per cent of all route-km has been relaid with 65 kg/m rail, since the lines concerned, carrying freight trains of increasing weight, are recording 60 to 80 million tonne-km of traffic a year. Most of the system allows maximum axleloads of 20 tonnes.

Rail is welded in long sections, fastened to wood or concrete sleepers spaced 1,450 to 1,500 per km. New Type B-91 200 km/h sleepers have been laid on upgraded sections in southern Moravia and east of Prague since 1993. On main lines, minimum curve radius is 300 m and maximum speed 160 km/h.

Type of rails: S49, R65, UIC60
Sleepers: SB8, U94, B91
Fastenings: Vossloh, Pandrol

UPDATED

DENMARK

Ministry of Transport

Frederiksholms Kanal 27, DK-1220 Copenhagen K
Tel: +45 33 92 33 55   Fax: +45 33 12 38 93

Key personnel
Minister: Bjørn Westh
Permanent Under-Secretary of State: Ole Zacchi

UPDATED

Banestyrelsen

Banestyrelsen - National Railway Agency
Solvgade 40E, DK-1349 Copenhagen, Denmark

Tel: +45 3315 0400   Fax: +45 3311 2038

Key personnel
Chief Executive: Erik Elsborg

Directors
Safety Department: Bent Nygaard
Administration and Strategic Planning: Lene Grønfeldt
Traffic Management: Eigil Sabroe
Infrastructure Management: Torben Kronstam
Consulting Engineers and Planners: Preben Olesen
Infrastructure Services: Jesper Toft

Gauge: 1,435 mm

Route length: 2,865 km
Electrification: 170 route-km at 1.5 kV DC (Copenhagen suburban system), 270 route-km at 25 kV 50 Hz AC

Political background

Following legislation in the Danish parliament, DSB (Danish State Railways) was split in two on 1 January 1997, with infrastructure and operations companies replacing it. The new organisation Banestyrelsen — comprised essentially of the old DSB Infrastructure Management Division — has taken responsibility for the infrastructure, while DSB continues to operate trains, paying Banestyrelsen for the use of the tracks. Banestyrelsen is responsible for traffic control as well as infrastructure management. Provision has been made in the legislation for 'open access' train operators to use Banestyrelsen tracks, providing competition to DSB. The legislation does not affect the small private railways in Denmark, which are operated by local authorities with government subsidies.

Under the Act, Banestyrelsen must open tenders for work on the infrastructure to outside companies. Two contracting units within Banestyrelsen — Consulting Engineers and Infrastructure Services — have been set up at 'arm's length' from the main company and will compete with outside organisations for the work.

Finance

Under the former DSB Group, in 1996 DSB Infrastructure Management had turnover of approximately DKr3 billion, with capital expenditure accounting for about one-third of the total. The unit had some 3,500 employees.

New lines

Great Belt fixed link

The long-cherished scheme for a fixed crossing of the 18 km Store Bælt (Great Belt) waterway, which interrupts communications between Copenhagen on the island of Zealand and the rest of the country, opened to trains in April 1997. The fixed link will feature both road and rail, with the rail link opened in advance of the road link. The link features three elements: *West Bridge*, a 6.6 km low bridge shared by the railway and the motorway, running from Funen to the island of Sprogø; *East Tunnel*, an 8 km twin-bore railway tunnel between Zealand and Sprogø; and *East Bridge*, a 6.8 km elevated motorway bridge between Zealand and Sprogø. Completion of East Bridge in mid-1998 would allow road vehicles to use the link.

The railway tunnel has been the most problematic section, and construction difficulties mean opening was later than originally planned. The two bores, 25 m apart, are connected by lateral passageways spaced 250 m apart. The rail tunnels have raised trackside walkways on which passengers from an incapacitated train can be evacuated, via a cross passage, to a train in the other tunnel. The rail tunnels, each 8 km long, have been bored to a diameter of 7.7 m. This slightly exceeds the girth of the Anglo-French Channel Tunnel, though there are no plans to run anything other than standard DSB trains through them.

The construction difficulties on the tunnel mean that DSB's window of competitive advantage over road has been reduced to about one year instead of the three intended. This has resulted in the government agreeing to a reduction in DSB's payment for use of the link by DKr880 million in the first two years, 1997 and 1998. Future levels of payments will be reviewed in 1998 in the light of two years' experience.

The link permits a dramatic improvement in journey times. Whereas a ferry crossing of the Great Belt took trains an hour, they can span the waterway in a mere seven minutes via the fixed link.

The cost of the fixed link has escalated almost 50 per cent beyond original estimates. DSB is not directly involved in the construction cost. For 30 years it is to pay an annual rental to the Great Belt company (qv) for use of the rail tracks. Thereafter ownership will pass to Banestyrelsen.

Fixed link with Sweden

After many years of debate, an agreement to create a fixed crossing of the Øresund waterway was signed by the Danish and Swedish Transport Ministers in 1991. Completion was programmed for 2000, at an estimated cost of some DKr18 billion.

A Danish-Swedish consortium, Øresund Consortium (qv) was formed to design, build and operate the link; by 1995, construction work was well under way on the Danish side between Copenhagen and the city's airport on the Øresund coast.

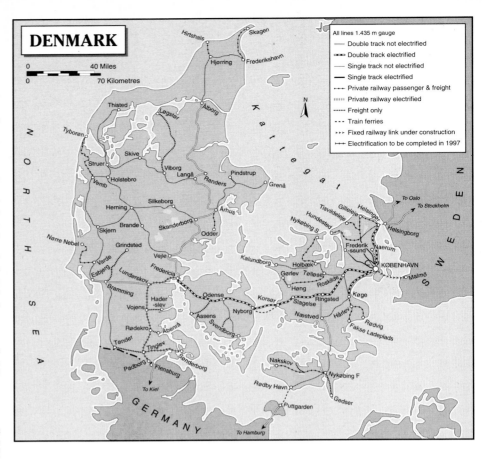

Like the Great Belt link, the 16 km Øresund crossing will combine double-rail tracks and a four-lane motorway. The centrepiece will be an 8 km-long bridge lifting the railway and road 57 m above the waterway at its 1.1 km-wide centre span.

This will have inclined bridge approaches totalling 6.4 km in length. On the Danish side, rail and road will cross artificial islands connected by a 3.85 km-long bridge designed especially to improve water flow and circulation in the low-water areas south of the island of Saltholm. The link will enter a 3.5 km submerged tunnel under the eastern channel of the Sound before surfacing immediately east of Copenhagen's Kastrup airport, on an artificial peninsula.

Here the line will divide into a northerly cut-off for freight services and a southern branch for passenger services — the latter will pass through a two-platform subsurface airport station built under a new airport terminal building, being financed and built by the Copenhagen airport authorities. West of the station the branches will rejoin to run mainly on the surface for a further 10 km into Copenhagen's Central station.

A 4 km-long cut-off will allow freight trains to avoid the city centre on their way to Jutland and central Europe, via the Great Belt link.

It is also planned to build reversing tracks and a servicing centre for Danish InterCity trains terminating at the airport on the artificial peninsula.

Upon completion of the link, DSB and SJ plan to run a joint interregional train service linking not only the centres of Copenhagen and Malmö but also the other larger towns in the region such as Elsinore and Roskilde in Denmark and Lund and Helsingborg in Sweden.

The journey time from Copenhagen Central to Malmö Central via Kastrup airport will take 25 minutes.

The connection from Copenhagen Central to Kastrup Airport is to be completed ahead of the project as a whole, so that from 1998 the two should be only 10-12 minutes rail journey time apart. DSB intends to serve Kastrup with limited-stop express train services from the rest of Denmark, as well as the Øresund Regional trains. SJ will extend all of the X2000 services from Oslo/Gothenburg and Stockholm to Malmö across the link to Copenhagen.

The fixed link is to be electrified at Banestyrelsen's 25 kV AC 50 Hz. This will give way to the Swedish 15 kV AC 16 Hz immediately west of a new Malmö South station, which will also be the limit for the Malmö suburban services (Påga trains) through the new tunnel being built under Malmö in conjunction with the Øresund link. Four dual-system trains, similar to the ER units already in service with DSB, were ordered from Adtranz in late 1996.

The Danish and Swedish railways will pay a fixed annual rental, amounting to DKr300 million each per year, for unlimited use of the fixed link. This is not enough to cover the construction costs of the railway part of the link; the motorway side of the link will be cross-subsidising the railway side, as part of the two governments' policy of promoting rail transport.

Rødby-Puttgarden fixed link

In 1992 the German, Danish and Swedish Railways published a stategic plan for traffic links between Scandinavia and the Continent. The plan describes a number of successive improvements, coupled to opening of the Great Belt link in 1997, the Øresund link in 2000 and the proposed fixed link across the Fehmarn Belt between Rødby and Puttgarden, to open at some time in the new century.

The new link would provide a direct Copenhagen—Hamburg route of 345 km, as opposed to 550 km via the Great Belt link, Fredericia and Padborg. The distance could be further shortened, given the intent of the railways to create 250 km/h approaches to the proposed underwater tunnel. On the Danish side, new infrastructure is proposed that would cut the distance between Vordingborg, at the southern tip of Zealand, and Køge, south of Copenhagen, by 25 km. Ultimately, a two hour journey time between Copenhagen and Hamburg is proposed for passenger trains; most freight traffic would continue to be routed via Padborg, Fredericia and the Great Belt.

A working group under the Danish and German Departments of Transport is now studying different models for the link, ranging from a Channel Tunnel-style rail link with an auto-transporter shuttle and classic passenger trains, to an Øresund-style combined rail/road link. The railways believe that in combination the Fehmarn Belt, Øresund and Great Belt fixed links, plus improvements to inshore lines, will boost annual rail passenger traffic between northwest Europe and Scandinavia. Another working group is making a detailed analysis of the expected traffic growth; the study was due to be completed in 1997. It is uncertain that the project will be sufficiently remunerative to warrant a go-ahead, and ferries may be retained for the long term.

Improvements to existing lines

Denmark has two links with Germany: by ferry across the Baltic between Rødby and Puttgarden and overland across the border at Padborg. In 1991 Denmark and Germany signed a framework agreement outlining a schedule for co-ordinated electrification and capacity

speed of 140 km/h. The non-motored car of the set has a low-floor section 600 mm above the track. There are 129 seats in each set and a section for bicycles, prams and wheelchairs.

The 13 sets were due to be delivered in 1997 and would cost approximately DKr18 million per set. They will be allocated as follows: Hillerød—Hundested Railway, three sets; Gribskov Railway, three sets; Lolland Railway, four sets; the Høng—Tølløse and Odsherreds Railway will share three sets.

The remaining private railways have lighter loadings and/or shorter runs than the ones that will be using Flexliners, and hence require simpler replacement trains. In 1995, four companies were invited to bid against this requirement: ABB Scandia in collaboration with ABB Henschel (Regioshuttle design); AEG (Regioliner); Siemens-Duewag (Regiosprinter); and Bombardier Eurorail's Talbot arm. In 1996 a Regiosprinter was bought for trial running on the 8 km Lyngby—Naerum line, which runs an intensive 10-minute interval service feeding into Copenhagen's S-Bane network.

Århus—Odder Railway

Hads—Ning Herreders Jernbanen (HHJ)
Banegårdsgade 3, DK-8300 Odder
Tel: +45 86 540944   Fax: +45 86 544170

Key personnel
Director: Ole Johansen
Manager: Ole Mikkelsen

Gauge: 1,435 mm
Route length: 26.5 km

HHJ runs from the DSB station in Denmark's second largest city, Århus, south to the town of Odder.

Traction and rolling stock
HHJ owns two diesel locomotives, six Duewag railbuses and seven coaches.

Eastern Railway

Østbanen (ØSJS)
DK-4652 Hårlev
Tel: +45 53 686019   Fax: +45 53 686570

Key personnel
Managing Director: N Munch Christensen

Gauge: 1,435 mm
Route length: 49.6 km

The Østbanen starts from a junction with DSB at Køge, which is served by Copenhagen S-Bane services. The line runs from Køge to Hårlev where it divides, with one line going to Fakse Ladeplads on the south Zealand coast and the other to Rødvig. Each branch has an hourly service, giving a half-hourly service on the common section.

Traction and rolling stock
ØSJS owns three 1961 Nohab-built A1A-A1A diesel-electric locomotives. It also owns eight diesel Duewag railcars and eight driving trailers.

Gribskov Railway

Gribskovbanen (GDS)
Ndr Jernbanevej 44, DK-3400 Hillerød
Tel: +45 42 260123   Fax: +45 48 240911

Key personnel
Managing Director: N Møller
Manager: Henrik Henriksen

Gauge: 1,435 mm
Route length: 42 km

The Gribskovbanen starts from a junction with DSB at Hillerød, which is served by S-Bane services from Copenhagen. The line runs north to Kagerup where it divides into branches to the seaside towns of Tisvildeleje and Gilleleje. In 1994, traffic statistics were: 1.8 million passenger journeys, 31 million passenger miles; 2,800 tonnes of freight were carried.

Traction and rolling stock
The Gribskovbanen owns one diesel locomotive, a 1952 Frichs-built A1A-A1A diesel-electric, plus seven Duewag dmus.

Helsingør—Gilleleje Railway

Helsingør—Hornbaek—Gilleleje Banen
Grønnehave Station, DK-3000 Helsingør
Tel: +45 49 210383   Fax: +45 49 210701

Key personnel
Director: Ole D Johanson

Gauge: 1,435 mm
Route length: 24.5 km

The line starts from Helsingør, terminus of DSB's coast line. It runs via several seaside towns to Gilleleje, terminus of the Gribskov Railway.

It is purely a passenger railway; in summer, it hosts Sunday steam services run by a local museum.

Traction and rolling stock
Six Duewag dmu power cars, five driving trailers.

Hillerød—Hundested Railway

Hillerød—Frederiksvaerk—Hundested Jernbane (HFHJ)
Ndr Jernbanevej 44, DK-3400 Hillerød
Tel: +45 42 260123   Fax: +45 48 240911

Key personnel
Chairman: Per Nygaard
Manager: Niels Møller
Assistant Manager: Henrik Henriksen

Gauge: 1,435 mm
Route length: 39 km

The line runs from the DSB station at Hillerød west to Frederiksvaerk and Hundested, from where there is a ferry service to Jutland.

Passenger operations
Traffic statistics for 1995 were 1.7 million passenger journeys, 38.6 million passenger-km.

Freight operations
In contrast to most of the other Danish private lines, HFHJ has considerable freight traffic: the steelworks at Frederiksvaerk generates 150,000 tonnes of freight per annum. Total tonnage in 1995 was 166,000 for 4.3 million tonne-km.

Traction and rolling stock
HFHJ owns four 1961-built A1A-A1A Nohab diesel locomotives, eight Duewag dmu power cars and nine trailers.

Hjørring—Hirsthals Railway

Hjørring Privatbaner (HP)
Banegårdspladsn 6, DK-9800 Hjørring
Tel: +45 98 920600   Fax: +45 98 926635

Key personnel
Managing Director: Søren Petersen

Gauge: 1,435 mm
Route length: 16.5 km

HP runs from the DSB station at Hjørring in the north of Jutland to the port and fishing town of Hirsthals, from where there is a train ferry service to Kristiansand in Norway. The line is part of the Scan Link service from Scandinavia via Jutland to the Continent.

Traction and rolling stock
HP owns three diesel locomotives and four two-car Duewag trainsets.

Høng—Tølløse Railway

Høng—Tølløse Jernbane A/S (HTJ)
Jernbaneplads 6, DK-4300 Holbaek
Tel: +45 53 432080   Fax: +45 59 442340

Key personnel
Managing Director: F B Henningsen

Gauge: 1,435 mm
Route length: 50 km

The line lies in the west of Zealand and runs between the DSB line from Copenhagen to Kalundborg (connection at Høng) and the main line from Copenhagen to Jutland via the Storebaelt (connection at Slagelse). Some trains run from Høng to Holbaek on the DSB line.

In 1995, HTJ purchased 12.5 km of line previously owned by DSB but served only by HTJ trains.

Traction and rolling stock
Five Duewag diesel railcars and two driving trailers.

Lolland Railway

Lollandsbanen A/S (LJ)
Banegårdspladsen 5, DK-4930 Maribo
Tel: +45 54 791700   Fax: +45 54 791760

Key personnel
General Manager: Erling Strøm
Manager: Karl Vestergaard

Gauge: 1,435 mm
Route length: 66 km

The Lolland Railway runs east-west across the island of Lolland from Nykøbing Falster on the main Copenhagen—Hamburg via Rødby line, to Nakskov, an industrial town in the west. The line also owns a 7.5 km infrequently used freight line, from Maribo to the port of Bandholm; this line is used by a railway museum.

Traction and rolling stock
LJ owns 11 diesel locomotives, seven Duewag motor coaches, 14 trailer coaches and 27 wagons.

Lyngby—Naerum Railway

Lyngby—Naerum Jernbane (LNJ)
Firskovvej 28, DK-2800 Lyngby
Tel: +45 45 870708   Fax: +45 45 933315

Key personnel
Manager: L A Jensen

Gauge: 1,435 mm
Route length: 8 km

Passenger operations
LNJ runs a 10-minute interval service linking Naerum with the Copenhagen S-Bane service at Jaegersborg. Traffic statistics for 1996 were 1.2 million passenger journeys, 7.2 million passenger-km.

Traction and rolling stock
The Lyngby—Naerum Railway owns four Duewag diesel railcars. A Regiosprinter lightweight diesel railcar was put into trial service on this line in May 1996 (see Association of Danish Private Railways entry) and LNJ has ordered four of these units to replace the 28-year-old railcars on this route by 1998.
UPDATED

Odsherreds Railway

Odsherreds Jernbane A/S (OHJ)
Jernbaneplads 6, DK-4300 Holbaek
Tel: +45 53 432080   Fax: +45 59 442340

Key personnel
Managing Director: F B Henningsen

Gauge: 1,435 mm
Route length: 50 km

OHJ runs from a junction with DSB at Holbaek on the Copenhagen—Kalundborg line to Nykøbing Sjaelland on the north Zealand coast. It is jointly managed with the Høng—Tølløse Railway.

Passenger operations
Hykøbing is a popular destination in summer, with through trains to Copenhagen at busy times. Through running will be facilitated by the purchase of Flexliner trains (see Association of Danish Private Railways entry).

Traction and rolling stock
OHJ owns five diesel locomotives, eight diesel railcars and 12 coaches.

Skagen Railway

Skagensbane (SB)
Sct Laurentivej 22, DK-9990 Skagen
Tel: +45 98 441015   Fax: +45 98 441837

Key personnel
Managing Director: Aage Jensen
Manager: Kirsten Jacobsen

Gauge: 1,435 mm
Route length: 40 km

The Skagensbanen runs from a junction with DSB at Frederikshavn to Skagen, a tourist destination and fishing port at the very northern tip of Jutland.

Traction and rolling stock
SB owns two 1,445 hp ex-DSB Mx Class diesel-electric

locomotives, one 1952 Frichs-built A1A-A1A 750 hp diesel-electric, and some shunters. It also has five Duewag diesel railcars, two driving trailers and four intermediate coaches.
VERIFIED

Vemb—Thyborøn Railway

Vemb—Lemvig—Thyborøn Jernbane (VLTJ)
Banegårdsvej 2, DK-7620 Lemvig
Tel: +45 97 823222   Fax: +45 97 810810

Key personnel
Managing Director: Knud Vigsø
Manager: Kurt Petersen

Gauge: 1,435 mm
Route length: 58 km

The line runs from the DSB station at Vemb on the remote western Jutland coast line to the town of Thyborøn; a chemical works south of Thyborøn generates freight traffic.

Traction and rolling stock
The Vemb-Thyborøn Railway owns two diesel locomotives: one ex-DSB Mx Class machine, plus one diesel-hydraulic. It has five Duewag diesel trainsets.

Western Railway

Vestbanen A/S (VNJ)
Svinget 11, DK-6800 Varde
Tel: +45 75 221722   Fax: +45 75 221910

Key personnel
Managing Director: B A Christensen
Manager: Michael Langager

Gauge: 1,435 mm
Route length: 38 km

VNJ runs from a junction with DSB at Varde on the west Jutland coast line to Nørre Nebel; the military training camp at Oxbøl generates freight traffic for the line.

Traction and rolling stock
VNJ owns two diesel-hydraulic locomotives, two Duewag trainsets and two elderly Swedish railbuses.

DOMINICAN REPUBLIC

Ministry of Works and Communications

Avenida San Cristobal, Santo Domingo

Key personnel
State Secretary: E Williams

UPDATED

Central Romana Railroad

Central Romana, La Romana

Key personnel
President: C Morales T
Vice-President and General Superintendent: R J Rivera
Director, Purchases: B R Grullon

Gauge: 1,435 mm
Route length: 375 km

Freight operations
The railway operates 13 locomotives and 950 freight wagons for the transport of sugar cane.

A further 240 km of 558 mm, 762 mm and 1,067 mm gauge track is operated by the private Angelina, CAEI and Cristobal Colon sugar cane systems.

Dominica Government Railway

Santo Domingo

Gauge: 762 mm
Route length: 142 km

Freight operations
The railway operates four locomotives and 72 freight wagons. The main freight traffic comprises bananas from Guayubin moved to the port of Pepillo for export.

A total of eight sugar cane systems are operated by the semi-nationalised CEA group, totalling 986 km on 762 mm, 889 mm and 1,067 mm gauges.

ECUADOR

Ministry of Public Works & Communications

1184 Avenida 6 de Diciembre y Wilson, Quito
Tel: +593 2 242666

Key personnel
Minister: P J López T
Under-Secretary: G Uzcátegui P

VERIFIED

State Railways of Ecuador (ENFE)

Empresa Nacional de los Ferrocarriles del Estado
PO Box 159, Calle Bolivar 443, Quito
Tel: +593 2 216180

Key personnel
Director-General: Mario Arias Salazar
Traffic Manager: Vicente Cevallos Cazar
Directors
   Administration: S Gudino C
   Finance: G Vintimilla
   Technical: M Herrera R
Motive Power Superintendent: E Benavides
Transport and Telecommunications Engineer: W Idrovo
Permanent Way Engineer: Marco Redrobán A
Managers
   Quito-San Lorenzo Division: G Gallo
   Sibambe-Cuenca Division: M Montalvo

Gauge: 1,067 mm
Route length: 965.5 km

Political background
In 1996 Ecuador's National Modernisation Council (CONAM) invited banks to assist with the privatisation of ENFE. Passenger services were reported as withdrawn in 1996 due to ENFE's railcars being unserviceable, and freight traffic had dwindled to insignificant levels. In 1997, the government announced that the network would be privatised as a 30-year concession, during which US$120 million would have to be spent on rehabilitating infrastructure and rolling stock.

Organisation
ENFE is composed of three divisions. The main line (the 446.7 km Guayaquil—Quito Division) connects Durán, located on the opposite bank of the river from Ecuador's main port of Guayaquil, with Quito, which lies at some 2,800 m altitude in the the Andes. From Durán the line runs across low-lying plains for 87 km to Bucay, at the foot of the western slopes of the Andes. Over the next 79 km the line climbs 2,940 m at an average grade over the whole section of 3.7 per cent (1 in 27). The line strikes many sharp curves, and several stretches are laid on a grade of 5.5 per cent (1 in 18), including a double zigzag which was required to negotiate a particularly awkward mountain outcrop known as the Nariz del Diablo (Devil's Nose). Once the summit of this section is reached at Palmira, 3,238 m in altitude and 166 km from Durán, the

A GEC Alsthom Bo-Bo-Bo locomotive heads a mixed train through the streets of Huiga (Bob Avery)

line remains in the high Sierra, never falling below 2,500 m, and rising to 3,609 m at the overall summit of Urbina, 264 km from Durán.

The 373.4 km Quito—San Lorenzo Division runs northwest from Quito to the coastal town of San Lorenzo, near the border with Colombia. At the start of 1996, traffic had yet to be restored between Quito and Otalvo after a decade or so of abandonment.

ENFE's Sibambe—Cuenca Division links Sibambe, 131 km from Durán on the main line, with Cuenca, an important provincial capital in the southern part of the country. Service was reported as suspended at the start of 1996.

Improvements to existing lines
Following a visit to Ecuador by President Mitterrand in 1989, France offered a gift of FFr4.2 million and a credit of FFr165 million for rehabilitation of the railway. On this basis GEC Alsthom was, in early 1991, contracted to supply nine Bo-Bo-Bo locomotives, plus spares and assistance in local staff training; and Sofrerail began a 16-month reorganisation of ENFE's operating practices and rolling stock maintenance. Also in 1989, Ecuador received a US$20 million credit from Spain, which helped to buy track maintenance equipment and freight wagons.

In April 1994, the ENFE board approved a 212 billion sucres investment programme which included track improvements and resleepering on the San Lorenzo—Ibarra and Riobamba—Durán sections of the system, as well as station modernisation.

New lines
The principal ambition of ENFE has been to build a new north—south axis connecting the oil port of Esmeraldas, in the north of the country on the Pacific coast, with Machala, the inland centre of banana plantations south of Guayaquil. It would not entail difficult civil engineering. There would be a case for up to three branches to the line, one to serve a major economic development area based on prawn farms at Manta.

ENFE has also undertaken studies to improve rail access to Guayaquil. Both transhipment by either lorry or river barge and a new rail barge were considered. In 1996 US oil company Occidental Exploration & Production commissioned a feasibility study for a new 100 km 1,435 mm gauge route to bring freight and passengers to oilfields under development in the Amazon basin. This would have 300 tonne freight trains running at 50 km/h.

Traction and rolling stock
The nine new Bo-Bo-Bo locomotives ordered from GEC Alsthom in 1991 with French aid began trials in Ecuador in August 1992. Designated Class 2400, each machine cost US$3.3 million; they are powered by SEMT Pielstick Type 12 PA4 V200 VG engines with a UIC rating of 1,780 kW.

ENFE's other motive power comprises a mix of Alco DL535B Co-Cos and GEC Alsthom 960 hp B-B-Bs, steam locomotives and a handful of diesel railcars. There have been problems with all the older traction and the diesel railcars have had to be withdrawn.

In 1992, ENFE's workshops overhauled three steam locomotives and four wooden-bodied coaches for use on tourist specials.

At latest report, the fleet stood at:

Locomotives: 13 diesel-electric; 9 steam; 31 railcars; 50 passenger coaches; 205 freight wagons

Type of coupler in standard use: Automatic
Type of brake in standard use: Air

Track
Rails: 35, 30, 27.5 and 22.5 kg/m
Sleepers: Wood, 2,000 × 200 × 180 mm
Spacing: 1,700/km
Max curve radius: 20°
Max gradient: 5.5%
Max axleload: 15 tonnes

UPDATED

EGYPT

Ministry of Transport and Communications

Cairo
Tel: +20 2 355 5566   Fax: +20 2 355 5564

Key personnel
Minister: Soliman Metwali

UPDATED

Egyptian Railways (ER)

Station Building, Ramses Square, Cairo
Tel: +20 2 575 1000/1388   Fax: +20 2 574 0000

Key personnel
Chairman: Mahmoud Marei
Deputy Chairmen
    Operation and Regions: Eng Mohamed Raafat Mostafa
    Permanent Way and Signalling:
    Eng Mohamed Talat Khattab
    Technical and Engineering:
    Eng Zakaria Abd El Hamid Youssef
    Construction: Eng Nawal Taha Mahmoud
    Financial: Bahgat Fayed
    Administration: Mohammed Ezaat Badway

Gauge: 1,435 mm
Route length: 4,810 km
Electrification: 42 km at 1.5 kV DC

Organisation

Egyptian Railways extends from the Mediterranean up the Nile Valley, serving the Nile Delta, Cairo, Alexandria, Port Said, Ismailia, Suez and connecting at Shâllal, its southernmost point, with the river steamers of Sudan Railways. From El Quantara, on the Port Said—Ismailia line, a branch runs east following the coast and connects with Israel Railways; it has been disused for many years.

Passenger operations

In modern times ER has been primarily a passenger railway. Passenger traffic grew to some 462 million journeys by 1990 (compared with 313 million journeys in 1980) and jumped substantially thereafter to reach 1.06 billion journeys in 1995 (52.41 billion passenger-km). This was due largely to the huge success of the cross-city tunnel linking Cairo's two busiest commuter lines.

On main line services, ER has expanded train lengths substantially, with the aid of 700 main line day cars and 605 suburban cars acquired since the mid-1970s. In 1992 and 1993 there was a slackening in passenger demand,

as the tourist business felt the full force first of the Gulf War and later of terrorism within Egypt itself. Little recovery has been evident since.

Three 10-car turbotrain sets built by ANF Industrie provide prime service over the 208 km between Cairo and Alexandria. It is hoped eventually to exploit this equipment's 160 km/h capability to achieve a Cairo—Alexandria transit in 1 hour 30 min, with each of the trains completing three round trips daily. At present, however, they are confined to 140 km/h, and that only over certain sections. In the Cairo area speed cannot exceed 60 km/h for some 25 km distance.

Luxury air conditioned overnight trains using refurbished stock operate on the Cairo—Luxor—Aswan

route. Infrastructure upgrading on this popular tourist route has included double-tracking and resignalling. Daytime services will benefit considerably from the track upgrading, which will permit operation at 140 km/h of four trainsets ordered from ABB Henschel (now Adtranz) and Hyundai.

Consideration is being given to resumption of passenger operations on the line running into Israel.

Freight operations

Freight too has advanced, though ER has a market share of only around 12 per cent. In 1990, 8.6 million tonnes were hauled for 2,827 million tonne-km, but this had increased to 10.2 million tonnes (3,627 million tonne-km) by 1995. The main constituent is ore carried on the Baharia—Helwan line, with wheat and oil next in importance.

New lines

Freight carryings will receive a further boost of some 7 million tonnes annually with opening of the long-planned line to tap phosphate deposits at Abu Tartour, which was being pushed forward for 1997 completion. The 227 km initial section of this export corridor, linking the Cairo—Aswan main line at Qena with the Red Sea port of Safaga, was opened in 1984, but construction of the western portion up to Abu Tartour was not started until much later. Work on this difficult project, which includes a crossing of the Nile at Nag'Hammadi, is nearing completion, and the 220 km section to El Kharga was scheduled to open in October 1996.

The infrastructure of a 70 km line from Port Said to the Nile Delta has been completed from Mansura to Matareyya, and is in operation over 24 km to Dikernis, but the final 24 km into Port Said entails a crossing of the Manzala lake and that is taking time to execute.

Another long-standing project is that for construction of a line into neighbouring Libya from ER's northwestern terminal at El Salloum, now revived as a joint venture between Egyptian and Libyan interests. Feasibility studies of the 130 km alignment have been made by ER and in 1996 it was announced that Libya would build the line to El Salloum from Tobruk with technical assistance from Egypt.

A start is also being made on re-establishing the long-closed link across the Sinai peninsula to Israel, with award in 1996 of a contract to build a new rail/road swing bridge

New Adtranz/General Motors Type DE2250 for Abu Tartour phosphates traffic at the Adtranz factory in Kassel, Germany in November 1996 (Ken Cordner)   *1997*

across the Suez Canal at El Ferdan. At 600 m, this will be the world's longest swing bridge. It will be built by Consortium El Ferdan Bridge, led by Krupp Stahlbau of Hannover, and should be open in early 1999.

Improvements to existing lines

A priority is renovation of the 350 km line built shortly after the Second World War with Soviet aid from Helwan to Baharia, which is primarily an ore and coal carrier. The present alignment is prone to interruption by drifting sand at several points and needs rerouteing. Revival of passenger traffic is planned after the route's rehabilitation.

An agreement was signed with the German Kreditanstalt für Wiederaufbau in 1994, under which German companies will undertake the rehabilitation jointly with local firms.

Another upgrading scheme in progress concerns the line to the Libyan border, where a 100 km section between Kabani and Marsa Matrûh was completed in early 1995.

Signalling and telecommunications

Bids were sought in early 1995 for installation of tokenless block on the remaining 208 km unmodernised section of the Luxor—Aswan line. Upgradinging of the Cairo—Alexandria main line continued, with Siemens Transportation Systems undertaking resignalling between Kobri El Leimoun and El Tawdeep. Bids were called in January 1997 for tokenless block signalling for the Qabbari—Matrough line.

Traction and rolling stock

At the beginning of 1996, rolling stock totalled 835 diesel locomotives, three turbotrains, 149 multiple-units, 3,210 passenger cars, 30 diesel railcars and 11,671 freight wagons.

A fleet of 700 bottom-discharge wagons for the Abu Tartour phosphates traffic is being delivered by Semaf. They will be hauled by 45 diesel-electrics delivered during 1995-96 by Adtranz Germany. These Co-Cos are rated at 1,845 kW.

Semaf and General Electric of the USA were involved in talks in late 1996 with a view to establishing a joint venture for the supply of locomotives to ENR.

UPDATED

GM-built diesel-electric in passenger service (Michal Málek) ***1997***

Diesel locomotives

Class	Wheel arrangement	Power kW	Speed km/h	Weight tonnes	First built	Mechanical	Builders Engine	Transmission
JT22MC	Co-Co	2,238	140	111	1983	EMD	645E3-12	*E* EMD
AA22T	Co-Co	2,238	140	121	1983	Henschel	645E3-12	*E* EMD
AA22T	Co-Co	2,238	120	121	1975-84	Henschel	645E3-12	*E* EMD
G26CW	Co-Co	2,163	140	98	1973-76	EMD	645E-16	*E* EMD
G22W/AC	Bo-Bo	1,641	105	80	1980	EMD	645E-12	*E* EMD
G22W	Bo-Bo	1,641	105	80	1978	EMD	645E-12	*E* EMD
AA22T/DB	Co-Co	2,238	80	122	1979	Henschel/EMD	645E3-12	*E* EMD
DE2250	Co-Co	1,845	80	132	1995	Adtranz	645E3-12	*E* EMD

EL SALVADOR

Ministry of Public Works

1a Avenida Sur 630, San Salvador
Fax: +503 271 0163

Key personnel
Minister: Jorge Alberto Sansivirini
Deputy Minister: Roberto Bara Osegueda

VERIFIED

El Salvador National Railways (FENADESAL)

Ferrocarriles Nacionales de El Salvador
PO Box 2292, Avenida Peralta 903, San Salvador
Tel: +503 715632   Fax: +503 715650

Key personnel
President (CEPA): C H Figueroa
Managers
  General (CEPA): A German Martinez
  Operations (CEPA): J A Nunez
Jose Eriberto Erquicia
  General (FENADESAL): Tulio Omar Vergara
  Purchasing: Luis Antonio Guzmán
  Finance: Fredy Antonio Mayora
  Traffic: R Marín
  Personnel: Wilfredo Ciudad Real
  Transportation: L A Carballo
  Rolling Stock and Equipment: Julio Fernando Pienda
  Maintenance of Way: Andres Abelino Cruz

Gauge: 914 mm
Route length: 562 km

Organisation

FENADESAL was formed from two railways which were formerly the property of overseas companies: the Salvador Railway, which passed to the state in 1965 under the name of Ferrocarril de El Salvador (FES); and the International Railways of Central America (IRCA), a railway undertaking that included the railway system and port at Cútuco, which was nationalised in 1974 under the name of Ferrocarril Nacional de El Salvador (FENASAL).

The two undertakings were merged under state control in May 1975 (together with the port of Cútuco) and became FENADESAL, which is administered by the port authority CEPA.

The railway is divided into three districts: District No 1 which comprises San Salvador (the capital) to the port of Cútuco in the east of the country (252 km); District No 2 which runs from San Salvador to the frontier of El Salvador with Guatemala (146 km), and a branch to Santa Ana, in

Diesel locomotives

Class	Builder's type	Wheel arrangement	Power kW	Speed km/h	Weight tonnes	No in service	First built	Mechanical	Builders Engine	Transmission
850	GA-8	Bo-Bo	595	57	61	10	1965	GM	GM 567 CR	E EMD
700	U6B	B-B	280	60	47	2	1956	GE	Caterpillar D-397	E GE

the west of the country (20 km); District No 3 which runs from San Salvador to the port of Acajutla, on the Pacific Ocean (104 km), and includes a branch from Sitio del Niño to Santa Ana in the west (40 km).

Finance

The railway is heavily subsidised. In 1994 its revenues from passenger and freight traffic totalled ¢8 million and from other sources ¢4 million, against total expenditure of ¢41.5 million. Subsidy of ¢21.9 million did not fully close the gap.

By the start of 1996, FENADESAL had ceased to operate passenger services. International traffic, principally exported coffee and imported fertiliser, makes up well over half the railway's freight business.

Investment totalling ¢3.07 million was planned for 1996, with ¢1.25 million to be spent on major track improvements, ¢0.28 million on telecommunications,

¢0.24 million on computer systems and ¢1.3 million on a locomotive fuelling facility.

Finance (¢ million)

Revenue	1993	1994
Passengers	0.4	0.3
Freight	8.4	7.6
Parcels and mail	0.008	0.003
Other	3.2	4.0
Subsidy	22.5	21.9
Total	34.5	34.0

Expenditure	1993	1994
Staff/personnel	22.1	24.8
Materials and services	14.1	15.5
Depreciation	0.6	0.8
Financial charges	0.5	0.2
Total	37.5	41.5

Traffic (million)

	1993	1994
Freight tonnes	0.310	0.204
Freight tonne-km	35.3	29.6
Passenger journeys	0.391	0.357
Passenger-km	6.0	5.5

Traction and rolling stock

Operational resources at the end of 1994 totalled: 12 diesel-electric locomotives; 3 steam locomotives; 2 railcars; 16 passenger coaches; 374 freight wagons.

Track

Rail: ASCE 54, 60, 70 and 75 lb/yd
Sleepers: Hardwood 7 ft x 6 in by 8 in
Fastenings: Standard, spike and angle bar
Spacing: 1,725/km in plain track 1,850/km in curves
Min curvature radius: 328 ft
Max gradient: 3%
Max axleloading: 12.5 tonnes

UPDATED

ERITREA

Ministry of Transport

PO Box 204, Asmara
Tel: +291 1 114307   Fax: +291 1 127048

Key personnel
Minister: Dr Giorgis Teklemikael

VERIFIED

Eritrean Railways

PO Box 569, Asmara
Tel: +291 1 114307   Fax: +291 1 127048

Gauge: 950 mm
Route length: 306 km

Political background
Following achievement of independence from Ethiopia in 1993, the government moved to revive parts of the former Northern Ethiopia Railway. This 306 km line, linking Agordat with the capital Asmara and the Red Sea port of

Massawa, has been out of use since 1978. Consultants have determined that the original alignment could be rehabilitated, and a small fleet of rolling stock rebuilt using existing spare parts.

Initial efforts have been concentrated on two short sections, 5 km at Massawa and a length around Asmara. These will be operated by three locomotives — two diesel and one steam — and a handful of coaches and wagons restored by former railway staff. The aim was to have the 117 km between Massawa and Asmara fully operational by late 1996, but by June 1996 only some 43 km of track had been rebuilt.

UPDATED

ESTONIA

Ministry of Transport and Telecommunication

Viru 9, EE0 100, Tallinn
Tel: +372 6 397613   Fax: +372 6 397606

Key personnel
Minister: K Kallo
Head of Railways Section: J Värk

VERIFIED

Estonian Railways (EVR)

Riigiettevote 'Eesti Raudtee'
EE0 100 Tallinn, Pikk Str 36
Tel: +372 640 1610/1676   Fax: +372 640 1710/1593

Key personnel
Director-General: Parbo Juchnewitsch
Directors
   Infrastructure: Kaido Simmermann
   Strategic Marketing: Aivar Urm
   Financial Operations: Vahur Karniol
   Quality Control: Ivan Kappanen
   Real Estate: Jaanus Page
Managers
   Rolling Stock: Anto Looken
   Passenger: Peep Öim
   Legal: Kersti Valge
Head of Foreign Relations Department: Rein Löokene

Route length: 1,021 km
Gauge: 1,520 mm
Electrification: 132 km at 3 kV DC

Political background
Following the declaration of independence by the three Baltic states of the former USSR in 1991, each country set up its own railway organisation. Estonian Railways

became functional at the start of 1992, and their subsequent performance and planning have been in the context of Estonia's rapid drive towards a market economy and proposed eventual membership of the European Union.

In June 1995 EVR signed up to the Baltrail-2000 project, which proposes higher line speeds, better rolling stock, and co-ordinated timetables and marketing. In January 1996 the government approved a draft five-year development programme for the railway system.

EVR relies heavily on transit traffic to/from the Russian Federation, but relations with the Russian Federation are cool and there is growing competition from neighbouring countries.

In early 1997, press reports indicated that the US short line company Omnitrax was interested in purchasing a majority share in EVR from the government.

Traffic (million)

	1995	1996
Freight tonnes	23.7	24.8
Freight tonne-km	36.10	39.01
Passenger-km	420.6	309.2

Finance (000 EEK)

Revenue		
Passengers	103,053	108,938
Freight	463,412	597,209
Other income	216,779	155,361
Total	783,277	861,508

Expenditure		
Staff/personnel	328,051	379,340
Materials and services	241,632	255,000
Depreciation	53,837	56,031
Total	783,311	846,581

Finance
Freight traffic continues to produce an operating profit. However, passenger services suffer heavy losses and in

1995 they were receiving a cross-subsidy from freight earnings plus a government subsidy of approximately one third of the loss. An operating profit of EEK2 million was recorded in 1994, including losses on passenger traffic of EEK80 million. Despite fare increases, this loss on passenger services grew to EEK100 million for January-September 1995 (US$13.7 million for the year).

The 1996 state budget included major cuts in subsidies, and EVR was planning service and line closures as a result. This is politically controversial, and railway workers have threatened strike action.

Reorganisation and privatisation are seen as the way forward. Following Finnish, Belgian and Irish consultancy studies in 1993-94, proposals were published in early 1995 envisaging the sale of most routes. However, a change of government has produced a different emphasis, eradicating cross-subsidies from the freight to the passenger businesses while retaining some state subsidisation of passenger services. The draft five-year programme would transfer the management and financing of suburban passenger services to the local municipalities, whilst EVR would manage freight and international passenger services. EVR would eventually be privatised, probably after the train fleet.

As for related enterprises, a factory at Valga for maintaining refrigerated wagons was offered for privatisation in December 1994, and the important Balti Laevaremonditehas ship and diesel works was offered for sale in early 1996.

A new joint venture between EVR and a German company will invest up to DM30 million in railway maintenance equipment and facilities.

The current EVR payroll is 7,500 people.

Passenger operations
Most passenger traffic is now local, especially around the capital, while the main international routes are to St Petersburg, Moscow and Warsaw. Since independence in 1991, some passenger services have

been speeded up and there are a few new services such as the Tallinn–Warsaw 'Baltic Express'. But severe bus competition and income cuts are a major threat, with rail services loading to only 10 to 15 per cent of capacity in 1995. In the three years to 1996, services on seven lines were withdrawn, partly due to deteriorating track.

A new state-owned company, South Western Railways, has been set up to run services in the southwest of the country. The new company has been allocated some of EVR's rolling stock and will receive subsidies from the state for running socially necessary services.

Services to Belarus have been discontinued.

Freight operations

Freight traffic is mainly concentrated on the through routes to/from Moscow and St Petersburg. Congestion at border stations with the Russian Federation is now reported as 'critical', and finance is wanted for extra sidings. Development of this transit traffic is a key priority, but there are fears of a 30 per cent decrease as competitors Finland, Latvia, Lithuania and the Russian Federation modernise their facilities.

Domestic freight shipments mainly concern oil shale and oil products from the Kohtla-Jarve and Johvi mines eastwards to Narva.

In early 1997, EVR offered for sale the section of line in the northwest of the country between Happsalu and Riisipere to any freight operator interested in maintaining the line. Passenger services have been withdrawn on this section.

New lines

Despite being considered utopian by the EVR, a 1994 Finnish proposal for an undersea tunnel between Tallinn and Helsinki is being studied seriously by a working group established by Helsinki municipal council. The tunnel would be 67 to 84 km long depending on the route chosen, would take some 10 years to construct and would cost FMk 10 billion (1994 prices).

Improvements to existing lines

In 1993 it was proposed to double the remaining single-track sections of the crucial Tallinn–Narva line on the St Petersburg route, possibly using European Bank for Reconstruction and Development (EBRD) funding, and by 1995 the overall improvement of the lines to Riga and St Petersburg formed a key part of the Baltrail-2000 project. Provisional agreement was subsequently reached with the EBRD for an ECU50 million modernisation loan, the priorities being the Tallinn–Narva line and a new freight terminal at Narva, and also for an ECU16 million loan from the European Investment Bank, particularly for track repairs on the same route between Tapa and Johvi.

Traction and rolling stock

At 31 December 1996, EVR was running 120 diesel and 23 steam locomotives; there were 14 emus and 27 dmus. Six-car emu sets are being split into more flexible three-car sets.

The hauled passenger coaching stock fleet amounted to 133 cars, and there were around 6,500 freight wagons. New passenger coaches are being obtained from Finland, and a 10-car luxury train has been introduced between Tallinn and Valga.

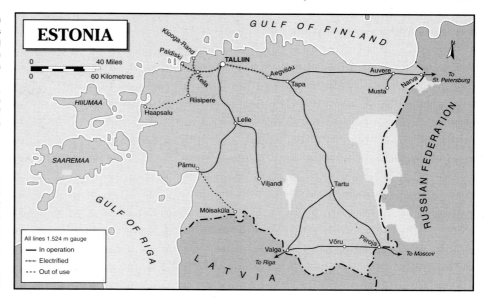

Diesel locomotives

Class	Builder's type	Wheel arrangement	Power kW	Speed km/h	Weight tonnes	No in service	Mechanical	Builders Engine	Transmission
TEP60		Co-Co	2,205	160	129	4	Kolomna	Kolomna 11D45A	E Harkov
TEP70		Co-Co	2,940	160	136	4	Kolomna	Kolomna 2A5D49	E Harkov
M62	TE112	Co-Co	1,470	100	116	30	Lugansk	Kolomna 14D40	E Harkov
2M62	2M625	Co-Co × 2	1,470 × 2	100	240	34.5	Lugansk	Kolomna 14D40	E Harkov
ČME3	T669.1	Co-Co	1,000	95	123	40	ČKD-Sokolovo	ČKD K65310DR	E ČKD-Trakce
TGM3		BB	550	30/60	68	4	Ljudinovo	Zvezda M753B	H Kaluga
TGM40	TU7M	BB	294	40	40	2	Kambarka	Barnaul 1D2-400B	H Kaluga
TGK2		B	184	30/60	28	1	Kaluga	Sverdlovsk U1D6-250TK	H Kaluga

Diesel railcars or multiple-units

Class	Builder's type	Cars per unit	Motor cars per unit	Motored axles/car	Power/car kW	Speed km/h	Units in service	Mechanical	Builders Engine	Transmission
D1		4	2	1B-2	537	120	5	M: Ganz-MAVAG T: Györ	Ganz-Jendrassec 12YFE17/24	HM Ganz
DR1A	63-349	6	2	B-2	736	120	10	Riga	Zvezda M756B	H Kaluga
DR1B	reco DR1A	6	2	B-2	745	120	4	reco Tallinn	MTU 8V396TC14	H SMI
DR1B	reco DR1A	3	1	B-1	745	120	8	reco Tallinn	MTU 8V396TC14	H SMI

Electric railcars or multiple-units

Class	Builder's Type	Cars per unit	Line voltage	Motor cars per unit	Motored axles/car	Output/motor kW	Speed km/h	Units in service	Builders Mechanical	Electrical
ER1		4/6	3.3 kV	2/3	Bo-Bo	200	130	7	M: Riga (RVR) T: Kalinin	Riga (RER)
ER2	62-61	4/6	3.3 kV	2/3	Bo-Bo	200	130	4	Riga (RVR)	Riga (RER)
ER12	62-251	4/6	3.3 kV	2/3	Bo-Bo	200	130	3	Riga (RVR)	Riga (RER)

Class ER2 emu on Tallinn-Riisipere suburban service at Tallinn station (Michal Málek)

In 1993 EVR borrowed EEK90 million to begin upgrading the locomotive fleet. In 1994 MTU (Germany) was contracted to supply diesel engines for Estonian dmus and SM (Germany) to produce the hydraulic transmissions for them, funded by a World Bank loan.

EVR's initial lack of heavy repair workshops has been remedied by contracts with two ship repair yards at Tallinn where a diesel locomotive depot has also been built.

Electrification
The Tallinn suburban lines to Riisipere and Paldiski (62 km) are electrified on the 3 kV DC system, as is the 77 km line east towards Tapa. There are plans to complete the electrification of the Tallinn—Narva route.

Track
Rail type: R43, R59, R65
Sleepers: wood, concrete
Min curvature radius: 600 m
Max gradient: 1.6 per cent
Max permissible axleload: 22.5 tonnes

UPDATED

Class 2M62 Lugansk-built twin-unit diesel-electric locomotive (Michal Málek)
1997

ETHIOPIA

Ministry of Transport and Communications

PO Box 1238, Addis Ababa
Tel: +251 1 516166   Fax: +251 1 158045

Key personnel
Minister: Dr A Hussein

NEW ENTRY

Chemins de Fer Djibouti-Ethiopien (CDE)

PO Box 1051, Addis Ababa
Tel: +251 1 517250   Fax: +251 1 513997

Key personnel
President: A Waberi Gedie
General Manager: B Hussien
Deputy General Manager: M Farah Bader
Directors
   Technical: M K Roble
   Commercial: A D Absie
   Finance: Ms F Asrat

Gauge: 1,000 mm
Route length: 781 km

Alsthom-built B-B locomotive at Addis Ababa
1996

Organisation
The railway runs from the port of Djibouti to Addis Ababa, a route length of 781 km, of which 100 km are in Djibouti. Since 1982 the railway has been under joint control of the republics of Djibouti and Ethiopia, with headquarters in Addis Ababa. The Transport Ministers of the two countries occupy the positions of President and Vice-President.

Improvements to existing lines
Since 1987 a rehabilitation programme has been under way with aid from several European countries, notably Italy. It features relaying with 36 kg/m rail over 80 km, with the aim of raising maximum axleload to 17.2 tonnes, increasing maximum freight train speed to 70 km/h and improving traffic regulation (at present affected by telephone dispatching). Before this work was begun only the first 171 km of the route were laid with 30 kg/m rail; the objective now is to install 36 kg/m over 300 route-km.

In 1992 the French government advanced funds to begin a five-year programme costed at FFr450 million which would embrace rolling stock purchases as well as repairs to track and communications.

Traffic
Both rail and highway traffic and development have been severely affected by guerrilla activity since the 1970s. Rail traffic volumes have also been depressed by economic factors and poor availability of traction. In FY91-92 freight tonnage amounted to 185,000, with 616,000 passenger journeys, rising to 240,000 tonnes and 710,000 journeys the following year.

Traction and rolling stock
At the end of 1993 the fleet comprised 13 diesel locomotives, six diesel railcars, 31 coaches and 591 wagons.

Line-haul locomotive stock consists of Alsthom units delivered between 1955 and 1985. There are seven locotractors and six 400 to 700 kW diesel railcars, all supplied from France, two by Soulé in 1984-85.

Track
Rail type: 20 kg, 25 kg, 30 kg
Sleepers: Metalbloc
Fastenings: Clips and bolts
Max axleloading: 13.7 tonnes

UPDATED

This bridge carries the TGV Nord line across the River Oise and adjoining countryside in Picardy (Philip Wolmuth) **1997**

over the Versailles—Massy—Savigny and Grigny—Corbeil—Essonnes lines; a completely new Roissy—Melun line via Villeparisis, Vaires and Torcy; Pontoise—Roissy, largely over the Pontoise—Epinay sur Seine and Grande Ceinture lines; Cergy—Massy, largely over the Grande Ceinture freight orbital line via Versailles; and Massy—Orly—Roissy, again largely using the Grande Ceinture. In the case of the last, use of the Grande Ceinture would necessitate creation of a new freight line to the east of Paris. SNCF estimates the total investment necessary at FFr55 billion.

Apart from EOLE, extensions to the RER network included in the 25-year plan include:
— Extension of line B from Mitry-Claye to Dammartin;
— Extension of line C from Montigny-Beauchamp to Pontoise;
— Creation of line F through a new tunnel between the Montparnasse and St Lazare termini, linking their respective suburban services.

In the long term, SNCF plans to invest FFr22 billion to increase capacity. FFr1.5 billion per year will allow all stock to be bilevel by 2005. Track capacity increases still required are: four to six tracks Boulevard Masséna—Brétigny (RER C), four to six tracks Maisons Alforts—

Pompadour (RER D) and two to four tracks Viry—Grigny (RER D). Also desirable are capacity increases on Poissy—Mantes, Argenteuil—Mantes, Epinay—Monsoult, Noisy—Trilport, Nogent—Emerainville, Plaisir—Saint Cyr and Melun—Fontainebleau stretches of track.

Also under way is restoration of passenger service over two stretches of the orbital Grande Ceinture line, from St-Nom-La Breteche to Noisy-le-Roi and to Saint-Germain-en-Laye. Cost of the first stage of this project is FFr300 million.

Regional upgrading
Work has started on the upgrading of the L'Aigle—Granville section (186 km) of the Paris—Granville line. The work is aimed at raising speeds from between 110 and 140 to 160 km/h over 80 per cent of the route, thus reducing journey times from the capital below 3 hours — half an hour better than at present. Much of the work will involve track singling and realignment within the existing formation. Of the FFr782 million cost, FFr658 million is being financed by the Basse-Normandie regional council and other local authorities. The Region will also pay FFr413 million of the FFr493 million cost of 15 Class X72500 160 km/h dmus for the line. Work will be completed by February 1998.

Another provincial upgrading project is Tours—Vierzon (113 km), which will have line speed pushed up from between 110 and 140 to 160 km/h to allow Class X72500 dmus to reach their maximum speed. Work will cost FFr175 million, of which FFr67 million will come from the state and FFr61.5 million from the Centre region.

Signalling and telecommunications
In 1988, following a sequence of serious accidents early in the year, SNCF announced a FFr4.1 billion five-year programme of expenditure on signalling and safety measures. Of this sum, FFr2.2 billion was assigned to the first phase of an automatic train protection programme. SNCF selected a version of the L M Ericsson automatic train and speed control system developed jointly with MTE-Alsthom. SNCF designates the system as KVB (*Contrôle de Vitesse par Balises*).

In the first phase KVB was to be operative at 5,000 signals on electrified main lines by 1993 and on their electric locomotives by 1995. The system, employing track-mounted transponders, identifies temporary speed restrictions as well as signal aspects. The second phase, costing a further FFr2.4 billion and to be achieved by the end of 1998, is equipping a further 12,000 signals on all electrified lines, and also (by June 1997) some 700 diesel locomotives which frequently traverse them.

ASTREE
SNCF started trials with a system of computerised real-time control of train movement with the acronym ASTREE in 1990. The principle of the concept is radiotelephone communication between onboard train microprocessors

and a central control. Traction units were fitted with Doppler radar apparatus that both computed a train's speed and established its location to an accuracy of ±0.1 per cent. This information was associated with data prefed into an onboard computer concerning the train's consist, destination, weight, braking capacity and other commercial data derived from intelligent systems on each of the train's vehicles. The results were radio-transmitted to a control centre. A control centre, equipped with a computer-banked map of operational trackage computer-processed the data received from moving trains and determined the desirable headway to be maintained between those on the same line of route or on converging paths, and thus the speed at which they should move. This was transmitted and received as driving commands on visual displays in traction unit cabs.

The ASTREE project has now been halted and results gained so far are being used in the development of the European Train Control System which is being developed together with other European railways.

Electrification
Electrification was completed in 1996 from Mantes-la-Jolie, near Paris, to Caen and Cherbourg (314 km), together with the branch from Lisieux to Trouville-Deauville (29 km), which has been single-tracked. Late 1997 should see energisation at 1.5 kV DC of Vierzon—Bourges (32 km), allowing elimination of the traction change on trains from Paris.

The go-ahead was given in 1996 for the electrification of the 42 km Persan-Beaumont to Beauvais line north of Paris. The project includes resignalling, track remodelling and station improvements and is costed at FFr637.5 million including FFr202 million for rolling stock. Half of the cost will come from central government, the Picardie and Ile de France Regions and the Oise département. Completion is expected in 2000.

Other electrification schemes under study include Rennes to St Malo in Brittany. Electrification of branches from Nancy to Remiremont and St Dié is included in the TGV-Est project.

Track
Rails: 60 kg/m where traffic exceeds 30,000 tonnes/day; 50 kg/m elsewhere
Sleepers: Wood (oak or tropical wood) 150 mm thick; concrete (mono- or duo-block) 220 mm thick
Spacing: 1,600-1,722/km
Fastenings: Wooden sleepers; rigid or screw or elastic (Types NR and NABLA); Concrete sleepers: elastic or NR or NABLA type.
Min curve radius: 150 m (in depots)
Max gradient: 4%
Max axleloading: (on selected routes): 22.5 tonnes

NEW ENTRY

French National Railways (SNCF)

Société Nationale des Chemins de Fer Français
88 rue Saint-Lazare, F-75436 Paris Cedex 09
Tel: +33 1 42 85 60 00   Fax: +33 1 42 85 60 30

Key personnel
President: Louis Gallois
Director (Strategy): Dominique Maillard
Director (European Affairs): Hervé de Tregoldé
Director (Research): Jacques Pellegrin
Director (President's Cabinet): Olivier Marembaud
Secretary, Council of Administration: Jean-Claude Lala

Directors
Freight: Armand Toubol
Finance: Jean-Pierre Leclerc
Human Resources: Pierre Vieu
Operating: Francis Taillanter
Secretary General: Pierre Fa
Business Directors
Main Line Passenger: Thierry Mignauw
Press Service: Pascal Bourgue/Maryse Archambault
Tel: +33 1 42 85 94 50
Ile-de-France Passenger: Jean Boutanquoi
Press Service: Patrick Audran
Tel: +33 1 42 85 98 15
Regional Activities: Jacques Chauvineau
Freight: Armand Toubol

Press Service: Marianne Burtin
Tel: +33 1 42 85 96 57
Outer Suburban and Paris Basin:
Bruno Baufine-Ducrocq
Sernam: Guy Moynot
Directors of Support Services
Infrastructure: Francis Taillanter
Traction and Rolling Stock: François Lacôte
Fixed Installations: Jacques Couvert
Delegate — TGV-Méditerranée: Gilles Cartier
Delegate — TVG Est: Pierre Cerisier
Head of Press Service: Michel Torres

Political background
SNCF is a 'Public Establishment of an Industrial and Commercial Character' or EPIC, being entirely state-owned but with a legally autonomous status. Apart from the rail core, SNCF has full or part ownership of 357 other companies connected with transport, including road hauliers, hotels, travel agencies and ferry operators.

Relations between SNCF and the state have been governed in the past by five-year contracts (Contrats de Plan) from which SNCF derived five-year development plans (Plans d'Entreprise). SNCF came to the end of the 1990-94 contract but a new contract was delayed by the presidential elections in May 1995. In June 1996, the government decided to abandon this arrangement in favour of a looser state-SNCF relationship which was sealed by a 'modernisation pact' in July 1996.

Under the new arrangements, the government accepted future responsibility for infrastructure finance and proposed to write off FFr 134 billion of SNCF's debt, the part linked to infrastructure investment and past infrastructure losses, leaving FFr70-81 billion which corresponds to other investment, such as that in traction and rolling stock. The infrastructure debt has been transferred to a new EPIC, known as Réseau Ferré de France (RFF, qv), which was established on 1 April 1997. RFF now owns all SNCF rail infrastructure as defined by European Union rules. SNCF remains sole manager of the network, having responsibility for allocating train paths and approving new operators. SNCF's own trains will receive first priority for train paths.

Another features of the new arrangements is the transfer of greater organisational powers to regional government.

Following the striking of the new deal with government, SNCF was putting together a new strategy in the second half of 1996 under a new president, Louis Gallois. Aims included the elimination of losses by 2000. Gains in productivity would be shared with staff.

Organisation
A major restructure of top management in 1991 divided SNCF into five businesses each of which has its own budget and bottom-line responsibility: Long-Distance Passenger (Grandes Lignes); Regional Passenger (Transport Expres Régional); Paris Region Passenger

(Ile-de-France); Freight (Fret SNCF); and Sernam (the intermodal small freight consignment subsidiary). Each Business Director contracts with the other departments for the means of production and back-up services.

An early decision taken by Louis Gallois after his appointment to the SNCF presidency was to move out of the historic railway headquarters near Paris St Lazare and to reduce the number of managers considerably. Staff in the Paris HQ number 10,900 out of 177,000 staff — around 6 per cent of SNCF staff compared with 1-2 per cent in comparable industries. The eventual aim will be to move more staff to regional headquarters and to bring more management in contact with the customers.

Finance

After good results in 1994 and rising traffic in the first half of 1995, which caused shortages of traction and personnel, traffic was affected by terrorism on the Paris RER system during summer and a strike at the end of 1995. As a result the year end saw a record deficit of FFr16.6 billion.

The budget for 1996 forecast a FFr12.1 billion deficit. Losses were expected to be concentrated in regional passenger (FFr1.73 billion), freight (FFr410 million), Sernam (FFr500 million) and infrastructure (FFr 9.90 billion). Passenger traffic outside Paris was expected to grow by 3.3 per cent, leading to an increase in revenue of 13.8 per cent, mainly thanks to Thalys and Eurostar. Freight traffic was expected to remain stable although revenue would fall by 3.2 per cent. SNCF was to reduce investment from the FFr20.4 billion initially foreseen to FFr18.9 billion.

SNCF started 1996 badly with long-distance passenger revenue down 2.4 per cent, Paris region revenue down 7 per cent and freight traffic falling by 1.4 per cent. Provisonal results for 11 months showed passenger-km on target for a slight increase over 1995.

Finances (FFr million)

Operating Revenue	1993	1994	1995
Passenger traffic	31,356	31,421	30,565
Freight traffic	11,094	11,946	11,313
Sernam	4,352	4,410	4,129
Postal services	472	426	273
Other activities	5,674	5,849	5,655
Own work capitalised	7,058	6,019	6,582
Turnover subtotal	60,006	60,072	58,517
State/local authority support	17,277	18,202	20,165
Reversal of provisions	1,536	1,691	1,284
Total operating revenue	78,819	79,962	79,963
Expenditure			
Materials, supplies and services	24,859	24,634	26,240
Staff costs	44,100	43,887	43,847
Taxes and similar charges	2,508	2,763	3,218
Depreciation and amortisation	8,899	9,771	12,064
Total	80,366	81,045	85,369
Revenue			
Total operating revenue	78,818	79,966	79,963
Total financial income	5,137	4,299	3,698
Extraordinary income	5,292	5,745	3,650
Total	89,247	90,007	87,314
Expenditure			
Total operating costs	80,366	81,045	85,369
Total financial charges	12,574	12,765	14,972
Extraordinary charges	4,014	4,381	3,556
Total	96,954	98,191	103,897
Result	−7,707	−8,184	−16,583

Passenger operations

SNCF's passenger operations are divided into three sectors:
Grandes Lignes for long-distance services including TGV;
Régional for local semi-fast and stopping trains;
Ile de France for Paris region suburban trains.

Grandes Lignes and Ile de France have their own directors but responsibility for regional services has now been delegated to local managers who negotiate directly with regional councils, albeit with co-ordination by the Regional Affairs support service. SNCF has reorganised

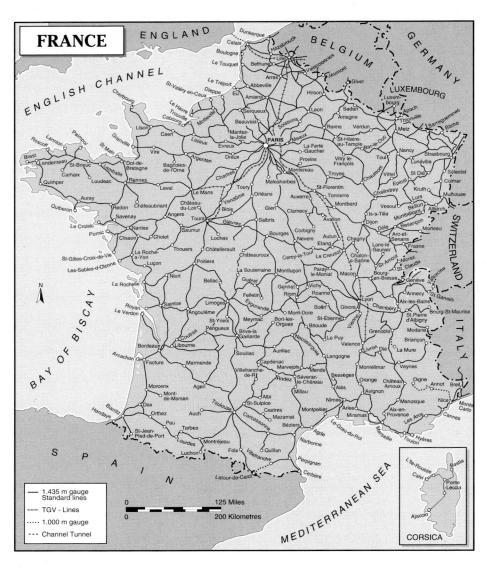

the boundaries of several of its regions to correspond more closely to the territory of regional government.

Long-distance services

Grandes Lignes (GL) is SNCF's main activity, in terms of turnover and the contribution made to infrastructure from the surplus of revenue over direct costs. This surplus has exceeded FFr3 billion in most recent years. In 1995, Grandes Lignes traffic was 40.4 billion passenger-km, down 4 per cent on 1994 whilst turnover fell by 3 per cent. TGV services, which now extend well beyond the limits of the new infrastructure, produce a growing proportion of GL revenue — reaching 53 per cent in 1995 due to the opening of new high-speed lines, increases in services and the decline in patronage on non-TGV services. Passenger-km on TGV services rose from 10.49 billion in 1988 to 20.51 billion in 1994 (+ 96 per cent) but fell on 'classic' services from 37.31 billion to 21.70 billion (−42 per cent).

In 1992, SNCF presented a plan for the revival of non-TGV services. Renamed *Trains Rapides Nationaux*, they are split into three market segments:
— journeys under 90 minutes, typically by commuters into Paris or provincial cities;
— journeys of 90 minutes to three hours, typically by business people and families and
— long journeys over three hours, where journeys for leisure purposes dominate.

A major part of the plan is the modernisation of 830 of SNCF's 3,300 Corail day coaches, 16 years old on average. Series refurbishment, at a cost of FFr330,000 per coach, started in 1995 and scheduled for 1997 completion. The first modernised vehicles were introduced on services from Paris to Cherbourg, Limoges, Nancy and Metz in 1996.

Over medium distances, SNCF will introduce more 'Euraffaires' services. This is a first-class, supplementary fare facility using rebuilt ex-Trans Europ Express 'Grand

Confort' locomotive-hauled cars, and backed up by exclusive Euraffaires lounges in principal stations.

On longer routes, pricing will be made more flexible, in order to compete with airlines (see below). At the same time, poorly used services will continue to be pruned. Cross-country services such as Bordeaux—Lyon have been drastically reduced in recent years, for example.

As well as participating in the EuroNight network, SNCF has improved its internal overnight services. In general, trains have been accelerated, with fewer stops and better departure and arrival times. All vehicles are now air conditioned and seated coaches are all fitted with reclining seats. Trains on some shorter routes, such as Paris—Brittany and Paris—La Rochelle, were withdrawn.

Developments in TGV services are shown in the accompanying table.

International services

To improve management of international passenger services and to stem the general decline in their use, SNCF has moved to create joint ventures (Groupement d'Intérêt Economique or GIE) with other national operators. The aim of these agreements is to help counter competition from airlines and prepare for competition under European Union open access rules. GL aims to increase the proportion of revenue from international services from 14 per cent today to 24 per cent by 2000.

Apart from the joint management of Eurostar and Channel Tunnel night services, the first joint venture, concerning Paris—Lausanne/Bern TGV services, was created in 1993 with Swiss Federal Railways. The first fruits of this agreement was the extension, from December 1995, of one Paris—Lausanne service to Brig in order to tap the winter sports market. In the longer term, the GIE is studying extending the Bern service to Zürich and the refurbishment of the nine three-voltage TGV sets capable of operation into Switzerland.

Principal developments in TGV services
Sud-Est Line

27 September 1981	**Opening of Sud-Est line St Florentin—Aisy/Lyon.**
	Maximum speed on high-speed line 260 km/h.
	Paris—Lyon in 2 hours 40 minutes.
	Services Paris—Lyon, Dijon, Besançon, Geneva and St Etienne.
25 September 1983	**Opening of Sud-Est line Lieusaint—St Florentin.**
	Maximum speed lifted to 270 km/h.
	Paris—Lyon in 2 hours.
	Services extended Paris to Marseille, Montpellier, Chalons-sur-Saône, Annecy and Chambéry.
December 1983	First ski-special 'TGV-Neige' services to Evian, Modane and St Gervais.
January 1984	Start of Paris—Lausanne services with tri-voltage TGV sets.
May 1984	Extension of Paris—Marseille service to Toulon.
25 September 1984	Start of Lille—Lyon service, avoiding Paris via the Grande Ceinture freight route.
1 October 1984	First postal TGV services Paris—Lyon.
4 March 1985	Paris—Grenoble services begin after electrification of Lyon—Grenoble.
May 1986	All 109 TGV-Sud-Est rakes in service.
	A second Lille—Lyon service begins.
20 September 1986	Start of Rouen—Lyon service avoiding Paris.
April 1987	Start of Paris—Nice service.
May 1987	Start of Paris—Berne service.
December 1988	Ski-season Paris—Bourg St Maurice service begins after completion of electrification.
	One Paris—Montpellier extended to Béziers.
September 1991	Start of Lyon—Nantes/Rennes via Massy using Atlantique sets.
January 1992	**Lyon bypass opened Satolas—St Quentin Fallavier.**
	Used only by trains serving the Winter Olympics at Albertville.
May 1992	Start of Lyon—Tours via Massy.
September 1992	One Paris—Besançon extended to Belfort (taken off in July 1993).
13 December 1992	**Lyon bypass, Montanay—Satolas opened.**
	New line used daily by Paris—Grenoble, gaining 20 minutes, plus some Paris—Chambéry/Annecy and in season by ski trains to Alps.
29 May 1994	Lille—Lyon services diverted via 'Jonction' line.
	TGV Haute—Picardie and Marne—la-Vallée—Chessy (for EuroDisney) stations opened.
	Lille—Avignon and Lille—Marseille services introduced.
3 July 1994	**Rhône—Alpes line, St Quentin Fallavier—St Marcel lès Valence, opened.**
	Lyon—Satolas station opened.
	Services Paris—Valence and beyond accelerated by around 30 minutes.
	Lille—south of France services increased. Lille—Nice service introduced.
2 June 1996	Paris services diverted via Jonction Sud line.
	One Paris—Béziers extended to Perpignan.
	One Paris—Toulon extended to Hyères.

Atlantique Line

24 September 1989	**TGV Atlantique western arm opened Paris (Bagneux)—Connerré.**
	Maximum speed 300 km/h.
	Services Paris—Rennes, Brest, Nantes and Le Croisic.
18 May 1990	TGV-A set 325 reached 515.3 km/h, a world record which still stands.
30 September 1990	**TGV-A southern arm opened Courtalain—St Pierre des Corps and Tours avoiding line.**
	Services Paris—Tours, Poitiers, Bordeaux, Toulouse, Irun and Tarbes.
29 September 1991	Start of Rennes/Nantes—Lyon services (see above).
	Massy station opens.
	Start of Paris—Lorient services after electrification of Rennes—Lorient.
May 1992	Start of Tours—Lyon service (see above).
September 1992	Start of Paris—Quimper services after electrification of Lorient—Quimper.
May 1993	Tours—Lyon extended back to Poitiers.
July 1993	Start of Paris—La Rochelle services after electrification of Poitiers—La Rochelle.
July 1994	Experimental Lille—Bordeaux service Saturdays only in 5 hours 45 minutes.

Nord Europe Line

23 May 1993	**TGV Nord Europe line opened from Gonesse to Arras.**
	Paris—Lille in 80 minutes.
	Services Paris—Lille, Tourcoing, Valenciennes and Dunkerque.
26 September 1993	**TGV Nord Europe line opened from Croisilles to Lille and Lille—Calais Fréthun.**
	Paris—Lille in one hour.
	Services extended Paris—Cambrai and Calais Ville.
23 January 1994	Services extended Paris—St Omer.
29 May 1994	Services extended Paris—Boulogne via Calais—Fréthun after electrification Calais—Boulogne.
	Lille Europe station opened for Jonction services.
	TGV Haute Picardie and Calais—Fréthun stations opened.
November 1994	Paris—London Eurostar services introduced over LGV Nord Europe Paris to Channel Tunnel.
2 June 1996	Paris—Brussels TGV service introduced over LGV Nord Europe and LGV Belge.

Jonction
(Interconnexion) Line

29 May 1994	**Jonction line from Vémars to Moisenay opened.**
	Marne—la-Vallée—Chessy station (serving EuroDisney) opened.
November 1994	Charles de Gaulle Airport TGV station opened.
2nd June 1996	**Jonction Sud line from Coubert triangle to Pompadour opened.**
	Services Lille—Nantes, Lille—Rennes introduced. Lille—Bordeaux, Lyon—Tours, Lyon—Nantes/Rennes and Lyon—Rouen diverted and accelerated.

In 1994, SNCF and Italian Railways (FS) signed an agreement to create a GIE known as 'Alpetunnel', a company which will study the future TGV Lyon—Turin. At the same time, SNCF and FS agreed on interim measures to improve France—Italy services. The result was a direct daytime service from September 1996 between Paris and Milan via Turin operated by three-voltage TGV-Réseau trainsets. In addition FS ETR460 'Pendolino' tilting trainsets took over the Milan—Turin—Lyon service at the same time. These measures were designed to boost passenger figures by 50 per cent.

In 1994, SNCF and Belgian Railways signed a similar agreement with the aim of developing Paris—Brussels services, as well as possible extensions to Antwerp and Liège. A doubling of traffic from just over one to three million passengers annually was targeted on this route. In 1996, it was decided to inaugurate Paris—Brussels service via the LGV-NE and over the first section of the Belgian high-speed line to be completed, from the French border to Antoing, then over classic lines via Mons. Although indirect, this cut Paris—Brussels times by around 30 minutes to just over two hours. From the June 1996 timetable, all Paris—Brussels services were replaced by TGVs operating this way. Paris—Brussels—Amsterdam trains are operated by TGV-Réseau PBA sets in Thalys colours (see 'Traction and rolling stock' section). From December 1997, the new Belgian high-speed line would be used in its entirety (see Belgium entry for details), and four-voltage PBKA Thalys TGVs would be introduced on the route in late 1997.

In 1995, SNCF agreed the creation of two GIEs in conjunction with Spanish Railways (RENFE). The first group is charged with studying the proposed TGV Languedoc—Roussillon line between Narbonne and Barcelona. The second aims to develop night services between Paris and Madrid/Barcelona, on which passenger numbers fell by 22 per cent from 1990 to 1993. The first measure to be agreed was the creation of a new service operated with Spanish 'Talgo' stock which replaced the Paris—Madrid 'Puerta del Sol' in June 1996. As part of the agreement, SNCF will buy four Talgo rakes, although they will continue to be maintained in Spain. In addition, SNCF and RENFE will refurbish Talgo night stock for Paris services to 'hotel train' standards.

Loss-making services
The recession has highlighted the problem of uneconomic transversal express services, such as Caen—Rennes, which receive no specific subsidy and lose around FFr4 billion per year. In better times these were cross-subsidised from other express services. SNCF has now identified these trains as EIR (Regional Expresses) and is looking to Regional government to provide subsidy. The first Region to do this was Midi—Pyrénées where 22 daily trains were losing FFr13 million annually. However, this exercise is complicated as most services cross regional boundaries and local government is not ready to assume financial responsibility for what it considers strategic national services.

Ticketing
SNCF introduced the Socrate electronic reservation system, based on American Airlines' Sabre system, in 1992-93 (see earlier editions of *JWR* for details). Socrate has allowed SNCF to introduce a flexible market pricing system, with fares no longer linked to the number of kilometres travelled. Socrate is also allowing abolition, in stages, its red, white and blue 'travel calendar' which restricted reduced fares at peak travelling times, but which had become too inflexible.

In order to maximise the effect of Socrate, SNCF had intended to introduce compulsory reservation on all GL trains. However, this met with public opposition and was dropped. In addition, SNCF has relaxed access rules to TGV-Nord Europe services at the request of passengers and is considering abolishing compulsory reservation on the frequent Paris—Lille route. This was followed by the abolition of compulsory reservation on 200 off-peak 'green trains' in 1996.

Paris Region (Ile de France) suburban services
SNCF services in the Paris region carried about 10 billion passenger-km from 1991 to 1993. This fell to 9.48 billion in 1994 and was down more than 10 per cent to 8.48 billion in 1995, mainly due to the effects of terrorist bombs and a strike.

Transport provision in the Paris region is governed by five-year contracts (*contrats de plan*) between the Ile de France region and the state. The 1994-98 plan budgets for spending of FFr34.414 billion over the period, of which FFr11.575 billion goes to public transport; 68 per cent of the total is financed by the region and 32 per cent by the state. Specific projects are outlined in the 'Improvements to existing lines' section.

Major developments of the Paris network centre on the RER (Regional Express) network, started in 1969, which links suburban lines across the centre of the city. The network consists of four lines, A, B, C and D, to which line E (see EOLE under 'New lines' section) is being added at present. The RER is operated by the SNCF, in the case of Lines A and B jointly with the Paris transport authority RATP; SNCF now has 1,282 route-km of

'Sybic' locomotive hauling Lille—Marseille 160km/h freight (David Haydock)   **1996**

suburban operation in the region. All but 15 km are electrified.

Three-quarters of the traffic is with discounted fares. Operating costs are met 40 per cent by fares (but employers pay half the cost of their employees' annual tickets or Orange Card monthly/weekly tickets); 40 per cent by the *Versement Transport*, the payroll tax levied from employers; and 20 per cent by public authorities (the state, 70 per cent; departmental authorities 30 per cent).

Regional services
Regional services (Train Express Régional — TER) carried 6.59 billion passenger-km in 1995, down 10.7 per cent on 1994, mainly because of the effect of the strike at the end of 1995.

Central government provides basic financial support for local transport services throughout the country, but regional councils have the power and resources to supplement that, in developing passenger transport systems within their respective Regions as they judge will best suit local social and economic development need. All but one of the 20 regions have completed contracts with SNCF. For background to regional services, see *JWR 1996-97*.

Following an inquiry by the government Haenel commission, new powers over public transport are to be transferred to regional government. Regions will establish public transport plans, then negotiate five-year contracts for train services with SNCF, which will retain the monopoly over operations. Regions will take over complete responsibility for financing all train services rather than simply for newly created services as has been the case until now.

To finance regional service deficits, the state will transfer a portion of the national subsidy of FFr4 billion per year to each Region. The Haenel commission estimated that an additional FFr1 billion would have to be added to this sum and the pilot Regions are holding out for the higher sum.

The new organisation is to be tested in six Regions — Alsace, Centre, Nord-Pas-de-Calais, Pays-de-la-Loire, Provence—Alpes—Côte d'Azur and Rhône—Alpes. A trial period of two to three years began in 1997, after which the new organisation will be reviewed before being applied to other regions.

Other plans include the reopening to passengers in 1998 of the 20 km freight line from Sucé-sur-Erdre to Rézé-Pont Rousseau in the suburbs of Nantes. Rolling stock for TER services is now being developed in consultation with the Regions (see 'Traction and Rolling Stock' section). A new type of unmanned but fully equipped station for TER stations serving less-populated localities is being tested at three locations.

Freight operations
Fret SNCF registered 47.4 billion tonne-km in 1995 compared with 49.7 billion in 1994, the loss being mainly down to a strike which took place in late 1995. Revenue fell by 6.5 per cent. Despite the strike, intermodal traffic rose by 6.2 per cent but there was a 3.9 per cent fall in block trains and 3.8 per cent in wagonload traffic.

In commercial terms, the freight business is divided into business sectors: coal and steel; oil, chemicals and metals; manufactured goods; agricultural products; automobile, exceptional loads and military; and wood, paper and building materials.

Freight traffic has consistently fallen short of the 1990-94 plan's target of 53 billion tonne-km at the end of its term, which would have allowed the sector to break even. Freight rates are depressed by over-capacity in road transport. Rail's share of the French freight market has fallen from 46 to 25 per cent since 1974, but is still the highest in the European Union. To resolve its difficulties in the freight sector, SNCF is increasingly calling on the state to enforce road transport laws effectively.

In 1993 SNCF created a subsidiary, France Wagons (FW), charged with management of its fleet of 85,000 wagons. The wagon fleet, worth FFr5 billion, plus the accompanying FFr1.4 billion debt, was transferred to the wholly owned subsidiary which rents back the wagons to SNCF.

SNCF hopes to improve its wagon productivity, which is much lower than that of French private wagons. SNCF wagons made an average of only 15 loaded journeys carrying 501 tonnes over a total of 5,500 km in 1993. Wagon numbers are expected to fall to 54,000 by 2000. By 1995, the figure was down to 67,900. FW had a turnover of FFr941 million and produced a surplus of FFr23.3 million.

Wagonload traffic
The wagonload network has been rationalised considerably. Although its traffic declined from 31.8 billion tonne-km in 1980 to 15.9 billion in 1993, it accounts for 28 per cent of all freight and almost half total freight revenue. However, the number of terminals served has been halved to 1,250, and service to some 2,800 private sidings was withdrawn between 1989 and 1993. In addition, in 1993-94, the number of marshalling yards handling general traffic was cut from 27 to 19. Only some 239 principal terminals (Gare Principal Fret, or GPF) generating at least 10 wagonloads daily now have direct connection with a marshalling yard. Some GPFs are linked by through trains avoiding the main marshalling yards. The plan has obtained Day-A-Day-B transits for 70 per cent of wagonload traffic. All freight trains now run at a top speed of at least 100 km/h where track alignment permits. All SNCF main lines are passed for axleloads of 22.5 tonnes, so that four-axle wagons can gross up to 90 tonnes, which means payloads can reach at least 60 tonnes.

Given the continued losses by wagonload services, SNCF is considering cutting back further to 12 marshalling yards and abandoning one-third of traffic. This would leave most of the west and centre of France without wagonload service.

Block trains
This traffic is relatively stable. Despite a general downward trend in movement of heavy products, SNCF is aiming for a 5 to 10 per cent increase in traffic, mainly through better service. To improve productivity, the carriage of wood was concentrated on 250 to 300 terminals, served by a dedicated network of trains, in the early 1990s. This will now be cut by around half as 50 per cent of stations generate 90 per cent of traffic. Aggregates traffic is to be rationalised in a similar way.

In 1995, Fret SNCF began an experiment aimed at improving utilisation of traction, known as TENOR, which involves operating block trains over the Dunkerque—Thionville heavy freight route with a fleet of locomotives and team of drivers dedicated solely to this traffic and controlled from a single office. The experiment involves 42 Class BB 16500 electric locomotives which have been equipped with a satellite tracking system. If successful, traction and staff specialisation will be extended throughout the SNCF to both freight and passenger services.

Automatic Vehicle Identification
SNCF has been carrying out a field trial of an AVI system on some 400 wagons on the 160 km/h Lille—Avignon—Marseille freight service. The system employs vehicle-mounted transponders and trackside interrogators. SNCF has now decided to adopt a UIC standard AVI system for the tracing of locomotives and for TGV sets and RER

Transfer yard for road freight trailers travelling by piggyback over the rail system   **1997**

Balance sheet

Assets (DM million)			Liabilities (DM million)		
	31.12.1995	*31.12.1996*		*31.12.1995*	*31.12.1996*
A. Fixed Assets			A. Capital		
intangible assets	524	514	subscribed capital	4,200	4,200
tangible assets	40,584	44,765	reserves	7,300	7,300
financial assets	1,435	2,300	profit reserves	0	616
			operating surplus	361	978
	42,543	47,579		11,861	13,094
B. Circulating Assets			B. Provisions for liabilities and charges	20,640	22,352
stocks	962	766			
amounts receivable and other assets	5,410	6,811	C. Amounts payable	17,007	20,288
cheques, cash, bank etc accounts	654	705			
	7,026	8,282			
C. Deferrals and Accruals	79	46	D. Deferrals and Accruals	140	173
TOTAL	**49,648**	**55,907**		**49,678**	**55,907**

Local services

The Local Passenger Traffic Business, like its Long Distance counterpart, is investing very heavily in new rolling stock. A 10-year programme will bring about the elimination of hauled trains on local services. Since, as noted above, the long-distance passenger business is also moving to unit operation, the hauled passenger train is scheduled to disappear from the German scene.

Local services are branded as Regional Express (RE), RegionalBahn (RB), StadtExpress (SE) and S-Bahn.

RE trains running at a maximum speed of 160 km/h improve rail's competitiveness by limiting stops to railheads from which co-operating bus operators cater for smaller communities. There are also upgraded station facilities, improved passenger information, higher line speeds, and a market-orientated regular-interval timetable. In the future it is likely that certain routes at present marketed as IR will move to the RE branding.

RB services tend to have a maximum speed of 100 or 120 km/h and an average route-length of about 30 km.

An interesting development shows the way in which European frontiers are ceasing to be barriers even for stopping services. Local cross-border services between Germany and France, from Winden to Wissembourg (Weissenburg) began in March 1997 after completion of upgrading work on the line and stations. At Wissembourg there is a German ticket vending machine accepting only German currency.

Purchase of local passenger services by the *Länder* (qv) raises questions about the future of services running across *Land* boundaries. Bavaria, Baden-Wurttemberg, and the Rhein-Main-Verkehrsverbund in Hessen have already made an agreement providing for the improvement of existing patterns in their area covering long-distance Regional Express (RE) lines.

S-Bahnen

Provided no increase in subsidised operating costs is involved, the federal government has an obligation to grant-aid the capital cost of S-Bahn work. Under the 1967 Municipal Transport Finance Act *(Gemeindeverkehrs-finanzierunggesetz (GVFG))* the state dedicates part — currently DM0.054 per litre — of its oil tax revenues to meeting 60 per cent of the cost of urban transport infrastructure improvements approved and financially supported locally.

Berlin: The Vekehrsverbund Berlin-Brandenburg (VBB) came into existence on 1 January 1997. Covering four cities and 14 rural areas with a total area of 30,000 km², it is Germany's largest Verkehrsverbund (regional public transport agency) in area terms, though second to Rhein-Ruhr in terms of inhabitants. By the beginning of 1998 at the latest the 1,230 bus and rail routes are due to have been co-ordinated and there will be a single timetable for the user instead of the former 25 books from 30 undertakings. Already 600,000 Brandenburgers and 1.8 million Berliners use public transport daily. The aim is to double or treble this number.

Since 1 January 1995 the Berlin S-Bahn has been run by a wholly owned DB AG subsidiary, S-Bahn Berlin GmbH. Restoration of the S-Bahn network to its 1930s extent continues under a specially financed programme. Broken cross-border links have already been restored between Wannsee and Potsdam, Frohnau and Hohen Neuendorf, and Lichtenrade and Blankenfelde. Schönholz to Tegel, and Priesterweg to Lichterfelde Ost have been reopened. Restoration of the first section of the West Berlin part of the (Inner) Ring, southeastwards from Westend, was completed in late 1993, including its cross-border connection to Baumschulenweg on the Görlitzer Bahn. Westend to Jungfernheide was reopened in April 1997, and work on closing the gap in the southeast corner between Neukölln and Treptower Park was due to be completed by the end of 1997. The Lichterfelde Ost line is being extended to Lichterfelde Süd (still within the borders of the former West Berlin), and the Tegel line is being extended first across the former border to Hennigsdorf and then back to its former terminus at Velten. The Westkreuz-Spandau line was due to be reopened as far as Pichelsberg by the end of 1997.

Rolling stock on the Berlin S-Bahn is being replaced; 500 new trains will be needed eventually. The first vehicles of a new design, Class 481, began test running in public service in 1997. However, since it will be a number of years before all the 548 prewar units have been replaced, as a safety measure these have been modified so that it is no longer possible to open their doors whilst the train is in motion.

A radio network covering the whole S-Bahn system has been commissioned.

Cologne: To segregate S-Bahn traffic between Cologne and Aachen following that line's upgrading, two extra tracks are being provided from Cologne to Horrem and one thence to Düren.

Cologne/Bonn Airport is to be linked to the S-Bahn network.

In 1994 the Nordrhein-Westfalen government funded the purchase of two four-car bilevel sets to avoid increasing train lengths and thus incurring the expense of platform-lengthening on two busy S-Bahn routes in the Cologne—Dortmund area.

Dresden: Four tracks are being restored over the 17 km between Dresden Hbf and Pirna under a DM326 million five-year project to allow the segregation of S-Bahn services from main line traffic on the international route to the Czech Republic. The cost of the work is being shared between the federal government, the *Land* government and DB AG, under a contract signed on 26 April 1996. Ten stations will be modernised and equipped for disabled travellers. New stopping points are to be provided at Dresden-Dobritz and Dresden-Zschachwitz. A 15 minute headway will be worked at first, a 7½ minute headway later. Two stations on Line 5, Freital-Deuben and Freital-Hainsberg, are to be rebuilt and modernised. Further measures are planned, including widening of the lines to Arnsdorf and Meissen — work on the latter being dependent on progress on the *Deutsche Einheit* scheme for the rebuilding of the Dresden—Leipzig main line.

Halle (Saale): The former DR (East German railways) and the bus and tram company HAVAG in Halle formed a transport and tariff union in 1992. In 1993 and 1994 bilevel rolling stock of a new design was introduced by the railway, liveried in violet-turquoise and pastel-turquoise. A major programme of renovation and improved access is now under way. Lift access is being provided at Halle (Saale) Hbf and Halle-Neustadt. Plans are being developed for S-Bahn segregation between Halle Hbf and Halle-Neustadt, a separation also justified by the planned S-Bahn connection between Leipzig and Halle and the linking of the two cities' S-Bahn systems. Preparations are being developed for a Verkehrsverbund (regional public transport agency) for the Leipzig/Halle region.

The five-year on/off saga of the Halle-Leipzig S-Bahn line came to an end on 18 December 1996 when the financial contract for its development was finally signed. The line will cost DM450 million and the two *Länder*, Sachsen and Sachsen-Anhalt, will pay 20 per cent each. At 32 km it will be 6 km shorter than the existing route, mainly because of a different approach to Leipzig. Some 26 km of new construction are required. There will be 10 intermediate stops. The planned 114 trains a day are expected to convey about 35,000 passengers.

Hamburg: On 1 January 1997 the Hamburg S-Bahn followed the Berlin S-Bahn by becoming a separate company. More than DM900 million are to be invested in the next few years. A link to join Fulsbüttel Airport to the S-Bahn at Hamburg-Ohlsdorf is being planned.

Trials with the first of the new Class 474 trains began at the end of 1996; 45 of these three-car emus have been ordered from a consortium of Adtranz and Linke-Hofmann-Busch; the end-cars in each set are powered by Adtranz equipment with four water-cooled 125 kW asynchronous AC motors under GTO inverter control. DB AG has exercised an option to buy a further 58 units for delivery from 1999 from a consortium of Adtranz and LHB at a cost of some DM350 million — Adtranz will supply the entire electrical equipment, with a value of DM160 million.

Hannover: EXPO 2000 has been the spur to the development in Hannover of a substantial S-Bahn network. There are to be five lines: S1 Stadthagen—Wunstorf—Hannover Hbf—Weetzen—Haste (that is forming a loop), S2 Nienburg—Wunstorf—Hannover Hbf—Weetzen—Haste, S3 Hannover Hbf—Lehrte—Celle, S4 Bennemühlen—Hannover Hbf—Hameln, and S5 Flughafen Langenhagen—Hannover Hbf—Hameln. S1 and S2 running hourly will give a 30 minute service between Wunstorf and Haste via Hannover Hbf, as will S4 and S5 between Langenhagen and Weetzen. The arrangements will be different at first in order to provide maximum capacity to the exhibition site for the year 2000. Total cost of the north-south S-Bahn is put at DM690 million. Work on two additional tracks from Seelze to Hannover began in October 1993 at a total cost of DM375 million and they were bought into use in June 1997. Work on the proposed third line (and on some sections of the fourth line as well) between Hannover and Lehrte has not yet begun.

Leipzig, Magdeburg, Rostock: There are S-Bahn services in these three cities in the 'new federal states'.

Rhine-Main: The *Land,* city, and other local authorities involved are financing Frankfurt am Main—Langen—Darmstadt and Frankfurt—Offenbach—Hanau extensions of the S-Bahn. The line from Mühlberg to Offenbach was completed in May 1995 and work on extensions beyond Offenbach is now in progress. The state of Hessen provided half the cost of 60 Görlitz-type bilevel cars to relieve overcrowding of commuter services from Giessen, Fulda, and Limburg to Frankfurt.

In early 1996 construction of the 'Messe' S-Bahn station began. The city of Frankfurt is providing DM50 million, the Messe AG another DM35 million for an access to the station.

Rhine-Neckar: An agreement for the construction and financing of the new DM340 million Rhine-Neckar S-Bahn was signed on 20 March 1996. MVV (Mannheimer Versorgungs- und Verkehrsgesellschaft) and DB were originally competitors as potential operators of the forthcoming Rhine—Neckar S-Bahn, but at the end of October 1996 they came together and put forward a joint proposal for working not only the proposed Neustadt–Speyer–Ludwigshafen–Mannheim–Heidelberg–Biberach–Bruchsal regional line but also all local traffic between the Palatinate and Odenwald.

The Neustadt/Speyer–Ludwigshafen–Mannheim–Heidelberg–Bruchsal/Eberbach route is to be modernised throughout, quadrupled between Ludwigshafen and Mannheim (with a new Rhine bridge), and electrified between Speyer and Schifferstadt. A half-hourly service will be run, with trains dividing in Schifferstadt for Neustadt and Speyer and in Heidelberg for Bruchsal and Eberbach.

Extensions to Mosbach (Baden), Karlsruhe, and Kaiserslautern are envisaged later, and further lines are proposed to follow the initial east-west route. A cost-benefit analysis has given positive forecasts for a Worms–Frankenthal–Ludwigshafen–Mannheim route with a connection to the BASF works station. The possibility of an S-Bahn service on the Main-Neckar-Bahn from Darmstadt to Mannheim and Heidelberg via Bensheim and Weinheim (Bergstrasse) is being investigated, and also under discussion is a route from the South Hessen towns of Biblis, Bürstadt, and Lampertheim through Mannheim and on over the Rheintalbahn via Schwetzingen/Hockenheim to Karlsruhe.

Rhine-Ruhr-Wupper: An extension of S-Bahn operations from Dortmund to Hagen is due to be introduced, and other extensions in the Dortmund area are being planned.

Rhine-Ruhr RE services such as Aachen–Hagen and Aachen–Cologne–Essen–Bielefeld are likely to receive a share of the 250 bilevel car order placed with the DWA Görlitz works in 1994.

In 1993 Nordrhein-Westfalen signed a contract for creation of a new north–south S-Bahn route, S9, between Haltern, Essen, and Wuppertal-Vohwinkel. The project, due to be completed at the turn of the century, involves electrification, track upgrading for 120 km/h, five new stations, and the elimination of level crossings.

Munich: Munich Airport is already one of the most heavily used stations in the city's S-Bahn network, with 12,000 passengers a day — virtually capacity. A second S-Bahn connection to the airport is to be opened by the end of 1998. Whereas the existing S8 comes in from the south, a 19 km line from Ismanning, the new 6.7 km line — the so-called Neufahrner Spange — will come in from the west, leaving the S1 Munich–Freising line at Neufahrn station and reaching the existing line at Besucherpark station. The work will cost DM277 million and the *Land* of Bavaria sees it as the first step towards a main line connection for the airport. On completion, the total airport service will be six trains an hour.

Separation of local traffic is required on the Munich–Ingolstadt route, to be upgraded as an ABS, and the federal government has requested DB AG to start planning a DM200 million quadrupling between Obermenzing and Dachau, for expansion of the Munich–Dachau S-Bahn service.

Impending track capacity saturation in Munich's city-centre S-Bahn tunnel, where six S-Bahn routes converge, causes mounting concern. The cost of construction of a second double-track tunnel is estimated at more than DM1.2 billion. A project group has recommended the alternative of four-tracking the city's southern S-Bahn ring from the Hauptbahnhof to Munich Ost at a cost of DM450 million. This could be achieved by 2005. Meanwhile it is planned to equip the core tunnel tracks with LZB (the German automatic train protection equipment) to lift peak-period operating capacity from 24 to 33 trains per hour on each track. Some immediate alleviation of the capacity problem has been obtained through the introduction of bilevel rolling stock.

Nuremberg: Construction work on the 26 km section from Nuremberg to Roth currently being modernised is expected to be completed within three years. Planning is now focused on the Nuremberg–Fürth–Forchheim axis.

Stuttgart: Agreements were concluded with the Baden-Württemberg government and other local authorities in 1993 for financing an S-Bahn extension beyond the airport to Bernhausen, involving a 3 km tunnel under the airport runway. Also planned is extension of the route from Plochingen to Kirchheim/Teck.

Mixed running
DB AG trains and trams of the Albtal Railway (qv) share tracks in the Karlsruhe area. The aim was to establish a

Income and expenditure

Deutsche Bahn AG Income	1995		1996	
	Income	Sub-totals	Income	Sub-totals
Turnover (DM million)				
Long-distance passenger traffic	5,171		5,350	
Local passenger traffic	10,597		10,829	
Total passenger traffic		15,768		16,179
Freight	6,799		6,606	
Parcel service	792		577	
Total freight transport		7,591		7,183
Other activities	296		1,039	
Total turnover		23,655		24,401
Other operating income (DM million)		3,204		—
Net participation income (DM million)		97		—
Income from interest		37		—
	Expenditure		*Expenditure*	
Materials (DM million)				
Raw materials, consumables, goods purchased	3,033		2,936	
Charges for services	2,182		3,613	
Charges for maintenance	5,484		5,243	
		10,699		11,792
Contribution from the state		−2,310		−2,030
Total materials		8,389		9,762
Renumeration (DM million)				
Employees of DB AG	12,009		10,488	
Transferred civil servants				
(a) payment to BEV	4,670		4,356	
(b) directly paid to additional benefits	280		265	
		16,959		15,109
Social Security Charges and Pensions				
(a) employees of DB AG	1,887		1,898	
(b) to BEV for transferred civil servants	1,067		974	
		2,954		2,872
Less BEV refund of personnel costs		−3,404		−2,993
Total renumeration		16,509		14,998
Other operating expenditure (DM million)		3,659		3,980

Dual-voltage low-floor light rail vehicle for Saarbrücken; this system includes inter-running on the DB AG network
1997

large regional network at low cost by laying connecting tracks between light rail routes and DB AG, allowing trams to travel out into the surrounding areas on DB AG tracks shared with ordinary trains. By the end of 1994 a fleet of 36 dual-system light rail cars was available, able to operate on both 750 V DC and 15 kV AC.

The initial route, opened in 1992, was from Karlsruhe to Bretten. May 1994 saw the extension of 'Stadtbahn' services to four more DB AG routes: Karlsruhe to Bruchsal, Bruchsal to Bretten, Karlsruhe to Rastatt and Baden-Baden, and Karlsruhe to Wörth. There have been further extensions over SWEG tracks from Bruchsal to Menzingen and Odenheim. The Karlsruhe operation is proving enormously successful.

A similar operation is planned for Saarbrücken, where construction work began in 1995. The *Saarbahn* opened in 1997 between Saarbrücken and Saargemünd (France), and by 2000 it will extend northwards via Riegelsberg and Heusweiler to Lebach, giving a total length of 44 km. Of this, 19 km will be new construction and the remainder will be existing DB AG or SNCF tracks. Future connections to the University of the Saarland and to Forbach are planned. Total cost will be some DM540 million, with the federal government providing DM214 million through the GVFG and the *Land* Saarland DM224 million. The first 15 trains have been built by Bombardier, with an option to purchase more on the same terms. An eight-axle three-section unit is 37 m long and 2.65 m wide with a weight of about 54 tonnes and installed power of 960 kW. About half of each unit is low-floored and each offers 108 seats and carries about 240 passengers altogether. There is air conditioning but no toilets and the upholstery is vandal-proof. Maximum speed is 80/100 km/h. Up to three units can run coupled.

Customer Care

By mid-1998 all 10,000 local-train guards are to become customer-care staff in a new grade *Kundenbetreuer im Nahvekehr* (KiN). Teams of about 20 KiN wil look after 'their' lines and 'their' trains. Each group will always have an experienced team-leader, generally someone from the *Zugführer* or *Fahrmeister* grades. Each group will have its own base-room with fax and PC. All will have mobile telephones (known as 'handys' in German). They will regulate their duties themselves, look after their own service and leave planning, and aim to bring about improvements in the services for which they are responsible.

DB is running a trial in Berlin/Brandenburg of a new *Regionale Ansprechpartner Nahverkehr* (RAN) scheme. Five staff man an office to deal with all queries and complaints about local passenger traffic. If the scheme proved successful, it was to be extended nationwide before the end of 1997.

After a successful trial, the first 210 portable terminals for onboard ticket-sale came into use on long-distance trains in September 1995 and by April 1996, 5,850 terminals were in service on 80 per cent of all long-distance trains. The aim is to equip all conductors. A simple terminal, with a battery good for 150 printings and 96 hours between charges, replaces the price and distance tables hitherto carried. All DB AG fares, including Verbünde fares, can be handled. The ticket is cancelled as it is issued. All accounting is dealt with in the machine and the data can be read directly into the main accounting system. In the reverse direction, the portable machines can be downloaded with the latest tariff information. The terminals are capable of extension, so that, for example, the option of payment by credit cards is now being added. They are also suitable for 'fixed' use at smaller stations on the network. They free on-train staff to spend more time on other customer-service matters.

A four-month experiment began in April 1996 in Dresden, Frankfurt am Main, Hamburg, Munich, and Stuttgart, with a new PayCard on a joint DB AG, Telekom, and Verband Deutscher Verkehrsunternehmen (VDV) project. The chip-card allows cash-free travel in local transport services and use of the public telephone system. The aim is to speed things up for the customer, especially at peak times. There are two versions of the card, one personal which can be charged up at Telekom card-phones and one impersonal which can be charged by using cash at special machines.

In late 1996, DB began to experiment with a BahnTaxi system similar to NS's Treintaxi service. First locations are Hamburg, Hannover, Frankfurt/Main, Nuremberg, Munich, and Cologne. As in Holland, the taxi is shared, its driver making several calls. Prices, valid within the city boundaries, are DM12 in Nuremberg and Frankfurt, DM15 in Hannover and Munich, and DM17 in Hamburg and Cologne. Money does not change hands; the customer gives the driver a voucher. These can be bought not only in the normal fashion at ticket offices or through DB's remote booking facilities but also from the conductors in all trains worked by the Long Distance Passenger Business. The taxis use a clearly marked waiting point at stations.

'RoLa' intermodal train bound for Munich from Brennero. The lorry drivers ride in the coach behind the locomotive (David Haydock)
1996

Freight operations

DB AG's freight sector is divided into five profit centres: Coal & Steel, Building Materials & Waste Disposal, Oil & Chemical Products, Industrial Goods, and Commercial Goods, Agriculture & Forestry.

For the premium end of the market, DB AG has developed a service known as InterCargo-Express: this offers guaranteed overnight service. The network has 133 nightly trains interconnecting 17 centres. The international counterpart of InterCargo is the EurailCargo network, which targets second-morning delivery over distances up to 1,500 km.

DB AG aims to increase its freight traffic with Eastern Europe by some 20 to 25 per cent over the next few years. It carried more than 23 million tonnes in 1995 and now aims through better co-operation and the provision of new rail and logistical services to raise this to some 30 million tonnes. Poland and the Czech Republic, with an annual growth rate of about 10 per cent in international goods traffic, are seen as particularly strong potential partners. Rail's share of freight traffic with Poland is currently about 38 per cent, more than 40 per cent with the Czech Republic and Slovakia, the principal traffics being building materials, iron and steel products, coal and oil, as well as machinery, metals, chemical goods, and foodstuffs.

The 'Moravia Express' has run three times a week since May 1995 between Ostrava, Czech Republic, and the Ruhr. The experience gained is being applied to Polish traffic: from June 1996 the 'Silesia Express' has run four to six times a week between the Katowice area and Hamburg, carrying principally steel, chemical products, and finished goods. The million tonnes a year exchanged between DB AG and Russia is principally served by the 'Ostwind' between Berlin and Moscow.

On 1 January 1995 the Freight Sector's Parcels Division passed to a new company, Bahntrans GmbH, set up as a subsidiary with Thyssen Haniel Logistik.

Driverless freight trains

Following the success of trials with a driverless freight train over a 3-km stretch of line near Aachen in which two Class 364 shunting locomotives were equipped to take instructions via the LZB automatic train protection system, the system is being brought into commercial use to transport products for Volkswagen. That company produces some 8,000 transmissions daily in Salzgitter and some 3,400 of these go to Wolfsburg. Radio-controlled Class 365 small diesels hauling two or three slide-wall wagons operate over distances and with quantities which up to now DB AG has considered uneconomic. There are two round trips a day, which can rise to five if required, at first between Salzgitter and Braunschweig and later (when track upgrading work is completed) on to Wolfsburg. Transit is completely automatic, with supervision from the controlling signalboxes and speed information conveyed to the locomotive through Euroloop installations in the tracks. The system is fail-safe: the locomotive stops at each signal if it does not receive explicit information to proceed.

Intermodal operations

DB AG's KLV (*Kombinierter Ladungsverkehr*) intermodal unit operates trains carrying containers, swapbodies, and piggyback unaccompanied road trailers. The KLV portfolio also includes both domestic and international (Austria, the Czech Republic and North Italy) *Rollende Landstrasse (RoLa)*, or 'Rolling Highway', trains using ultra-low-floor well-wagons on small-wheeled bogies to form a continuous roadway for the drive-on/drive-off conveyance of accompanied truck and truck-and-trailer rigs.

Railway traffic figures

Rail Traffic	DB AG 1994	DB AG 1995
Passenger journeys (million)	1,507.8	1,334.2
Passenger-km (million)	60,119	60,513.5
Freight tonnes (million)	315.5	309.2
Freight tariff-tonne-km (million)	71,399.1	70,536.0
Average journey distances		
overall average (km)	39.9	45.4
long-distance journeys (km)	237.3	222.3
local journeys (km)	21.9	24.7
Average goods distances		
express freight	300	300
parcels	355	357
mass transport	227	229
freight transport	228	230
in-company	132	153
Containers conveyed		
loaded	1,024,169	—
empty	502,492	—
tonnes transported (million)	14	—
RoRo traffic		
consignments carried	1,296,708	—
tonnes transported (million)	18	—

At the start of 1994 the KLV network served 120 terminals with over 400 trains daily in a system based on the overnight delivery of containers and semi-trailers by dedicated trains running between a few main centres. Some rationalisation of the service was envisaged, with the aim of cutting marshalling costs.

To cater for the top end of the market, at the start of 1995 DB AG introduced *InterKombiExpress*. Some 22 Monday-to-Friday trains conveying containers, swap-bodies, and trailers run overnight at speeds of 120 km/h between principal centres, offering evening consignment and early morning unloading. A further 28 trains were introduced in 1995, so that all economic centres 400 km or more apart are linked in a dense network.

RoadRailer bimodal vehicles operated by Bayerische Trailerzug AG (qv) entered commercial service in mid-1995 between Munich and Verona.

To maximise block train opportunities, DB AG aims over the next five years to secure co-operation from road hauliers in developing strategically sited Railfreight Centres (GVZ) offering good road access and intermodal transfer and groupage facilities. They will accommodate forwarding agents and offer a range of value-adding services such as refrigerated stores, tank storage areas, and container maintenance. Some 46 potential sites have been defined.

The first of a new generation of major interchanges for *Kombinierter Verkehr* is being built at Hannover-Lehrte at a cost of DM150 million. Alongside the traditional road/rail facilities for the transfer of containers and swap-bodies there will be facilities for rail/rail transfer.

The *RoLa* service between Germany and Lovosice in the Czech Republic, up the Elbe Valley from Dresden, introduced in 1994, has been very successful and Saxon and Czech negotiators have agreed that it will be maintained through to the start of the next century.

New lines
Neubaustrecken — NBS
Under an Action Plan published in early 1994, DB AG submitted all outstanding new line projects to economic reappraisal following mounting concern that financial strains might force a rephasing of the promised federal investment in new infrastructure. The reappraisal was also associated with an intention to pursue a wide-scale deployment of tilting stock. The aim now is to maintain the investment level, but a significant element of the money will come from the sale of surplus lands rather than from the state and there will also be a greater involvement of private finance.

Hannover—Würzburg and Mannheim—Stuttgart
The first two NBS were brought into use for the 1991 timetable. Engineered as mixed traffic lines, both pass through geographically difficult countryside. The west of Germany is also (by comparison with France) a densely populated country. For these reasons the lines were very expensive, with a substantial proportion of the cost (some 10 per cent, or DM1.5 billion) attributable to environmentally necessitated measures. The final section of the Hannover—Würzburg project, the Nantenbach Curve, was not opened until 1994.

Berlin—Oebisfelde NBS
From the outskirts of Berlin an NBS is being built parallel to the existing Lehrter Bahn to Oebisfelde, whence the upgraded Lehrter Bahn will be used to Hannover. Completion — now delayed from the 1997 target because of problems with the Brandenburg authorities, especially over the question of a breeding site of great bustards recognised as of world importance — will slash the current Berlin—Hannover journey time of about 3 hours to 1¾ hours.

The high-speed line from Berlin to Hannover will have a connection to Braunschweig by means of the Weddeler Schleife. Work began on this 160 km/h single line (12 km of new railway and 7 km upgrading of an existing line) in the spring of 1997 and it will come into use in 1999. The cost will be DM242 million.

Cologne—Frankfurt NBS
Fixed-price contracts to a value of DM4 billion were let during 1996 for the construction of this 300 km/h line. Work has begun, both in the Frankfurt Airport station area and elsewhere, and completion is due at the end of the century.

The line takes a direct course through the hills to the east of the Rhine and for a third of its length will be in tunnel. Much of the route parallels the A3 motorway. Because this line will be for passenger trains only and because the terrain it crosses is very difficult, the design parameters have been relaxed, so that the ruling gradients will be 4 per cent, minimum curve radius will be 3,500 m, and the use of slab track throughout will allow cant of up to 180 mm.

In Cologne trains will either use the Hauptbahnhof (with a time-penalty of about ten minutes) and cross the Rhine by the hitherto freight-only Südbrücke or will run through the low-level platforms at Deutz station on the right bank of the river. There will be two additional tracks beside the present Right Rhine main line to Siegburg where the new line will turn away to follow the motorway through Montaubaur and Limbaur.

Cologne—Bonn Airport will be served by a loop, the cost being shared between the federal treasury, the Nordrhein-Westfalen government, and the airport authority. Near Breckenheim the NBS will throw off a branch paralleling the A66 motorway to Wiesbaden, and then at Eddersheim it will split, one branch heading to a junction with the Wiesbaden—Frankfurt line, the other to the new, north station to be built at Frankfurt Airport.

Maglev on the Transrapid test track. A Berlin-Hamburg route is planned **1995**

In order to obtain official approval for the routine use of slab track, DB AG has commisioned a test section between Mannheim and Karlsruhe where 3 km of track due for renewal have been replaced by seven different types of slab track laid by seven different firms. (Although some 130 km of slab track are already in use in various places, these have all required special permission.)

Erfurt—Ebensfeld NBS
Work on this line began in April 1996 near Erfurt, on the so-called 'bundled' section where the railway and the new autobahn (A71/73) will run parallel. Of the total DM4.3 billion required for the 107 km, DM1.56 billion of funding is already in place. The total cost of the NBS/ABS link between Erfurt and Nuremberg will be DM8.5 billion. The ruling gradient of the line will be 1.25 per cent, which will permit use by freight traffic as well as passenger services.

Halle/Leipzig—Erfurt NBS
The outline planning process was completed in mid-1993 and a year later the Ministry of Transport agreed to the route and authorised construction of the 110 kV overhead supply line. Contruction work began in late 1996. This 123 km line will cost DM4.5 billion and will cut Leipzig—Erfurt journey times in half.

Leipzig—Dresden NBS/ABS
Work began in late 1993 on what was then a DM12.4 billion scheme to create 106 km of new high-speed infrastructure between Leipzig and Dresden, partly by the complete rebuilding of the existing line and partly by long sections of new construction such as a Riesa avoiding line costing some DM2.68 billion. Shortage of money has forced a simplification of the plans and the Riesa avoiding line no longer figures in them. Completion of the work is scheduled for 1999, when the journey time between the two cities will be roughly halved. The first section of the rebuilt railway, between Wurzen and Oschatz, came into full use for 160 km/h running in the June 1996 timetable and is expected to be raised to 200 km/h in 1998.

Nuremberg—Ingolstadt NBS
This line is the northern part of the NBS/ABS between Nuremberg and Munich. It will leave Nuremberg Hbf at the east end and have 80 km of new line (31 km in tunnel) from the outskirts of Nuremberg to Ingolstadt. The formal agreement between DB AG and government for the financing of this line, which on completion will bring the two cities within an hour of each other, was signed in December 1996. The improvement of 40 minutes on today's timings will be a major contribution to the project to cut the Berlin—Munich time from 9½ hours to 3¾ hours, making rail a real alternative to air and road. This is so far the only major rail construction project to be privately financed, the federal government having taken the necessary powers in the 1996 Finance Act. Optimisation in planning and construction and exploitation of all possibilities in awarding contracts has made it possible to reduce the originally envisaged investment costs so that the total burden on the state sinks to DM622 million a year over 15 years, or roughly DM9 billion — well beneath the

permitted level of DM622 million a year for 25 years (DM15.6 billion). DB AG hoped to award the first contracts during 1997. The strategic planning process for the whole route has been completed, as have the first of the local planning enquiries.

Rastatt—Offenburg NBS
In 1987 a start on the part-NBS, part-ABS improvement of the 193 km Karlsruhe—Offenburg—Basel main line was approved. One of Europe's foremost international arteries, the route unites at Rastatt the main lines from Mannheim and Heidelberg and channels into Switzerland traffic from the whole of northwest Europe. In the Offenburg area the Black Forest line to the Lake Constance region and the connection to Strasbourg and France drain off some traffic.

An NBS due for completion in 1999 is being built over the 49 km between Rastatt and Offenburg, generally parallel to the existing line. Between Offenburg and Basel DB AG was at first content, in an ABS project, to add a third track to the existing pair and to realign the latter for 200-km/h operation. However, an extra pair of tracks will now be provided because of the additional traffic expected to be generated by Swiss schemes to increase trans-Alpine rail freight capacity.

Stuttgart—Günzburg NBS
A costly project that began its progress through the planning procedures in 1994 is a continuation of high-speed infrastructure beyond the extremity of the Mannheim—Stuttgart NBS to Munich, to bypass the severe grades and sinuous alignment of the present route between the outskirts of Stuttgart and the Ulm area. The first section will be NBS (much of it in tunnel under the uplands) from Plochingen, 40 km out of Stuttgart, to Günzburg, 9 km beyond Ulm, largely following the course of the A8 motorway.

'Transrapid' Magnetbahn
The federal government decided in March 1993 to back the construction of a 'Transrapid' maglev route between Berlin and Hamburg by a Thyssen-led consortium. In early 1997 there were still question marks over the financing of the project and it was not certain to proceed. However, at the end of April the federal government decided that the scheme would proceed, even after the withdrawal of three construction firms from the consortium, and that DB AG would be the risk-bearing operator.

Improvements to existing lines
Ausbaustrecken — ABS
ABS projects involve the major upgrading of existing routes including, where necessary, realignments and the provision of additional tracks, to maximise the scope for 200 km/h running (which may become 230 km/h, at least for ICEs on the ABS). LZB automatic train protection is required, and no level crossings are permitted where speeds of above 160 km/h are operated.

Reunification in 1990 brought about a shift in priorities: during the 1980s DB sought to strengthen north-south links, but the emphasis is now on east-west routes. In 1991 a programme of 17 major transport works, nine of them rail, was agreed under the title of the *Deutsche Einheit* programme. One of the railway works is the Berlin—Oebisfelde NBS mentioned above, and one is the part Ausbau part Neubau Leipzig—Dresden line, but the others are Ausbaustrecken (ABS).

The nine *Deutsche Einheit* railway routes are: Lübeck/Hagenow Länd—Stralsund; Hamburg—Büchen—Wittenberge—Berlin; Uelzen—Salzwedel—Stendal; Hannover—Stendal—Berlin; Helmstedt—Magdeburg—Berlin; (Kassel—)Eichenburg—Halle; (Frankfurt/Main—)Bebra—Erfurt; Nuremberg—Erfurt—Halle/Leipzig—Berlin; and Leipzig—Dresden.

Work on the most northerly project, the 262 km between the Hansa ports of Stralsund and Lübeck, was formally launched in February 1993, for completion in 1997, but restricted flows of money have brought a substantial slow down in progress. Maximum speeds of 160 km/h will cut journey time between Hamburg and Stralsund from the present 4 hours to 2½ hours.

The Berlin—Wittenberge—Büchen—Hamburg scheme has involved restoration of double track throughout, segregation of the S-Bahn services at the Hamburg end, upgrading for 160 km/h operation, and completion of electrification. The original aim was a line-speed of 200 km/h, but DB AG considered that this could not be justified if 'Transrapid' is to be built.

Where possible, DB AG attempts to segregate flows of traffic moving at different speeds on to different routes. If the two-track Hamburg main line were upgraded to 200 km/h, it would be desirable to use a different line for freight traffic. This was an important aspect of the proposal for upgrading of the Stendal—Salzwedel—Uelzen line. The timescale for this project has now been greatly extended.

An NBS/ABS route is being created between Berlin and Hannover. As part of the major remodelling and upgrading of the Berlin railway system, the routes between the city centre and Spandau are being rebuilt for higher speeds. Near Staaken trains will join an NBS line through to Oebisfelde (qv), whence the existing railway becomes an ABS as far as Lehrte. Work on the ABS section is complete, though a planned major improvement at Lehrte has been dropped.

As part of the same scheme the existing singled Lehrter Bahn between Wustermark and Oebisfelde is being upgraded, redoubled over some sections east of Stendal, and in part electrified, to serve local and regional traffic and freight.

Total route modernisation between Helmstedt and Potsdam was completed in December 1995, save for the gap between Biederitz and Magdeburg (both inclusive). There is the prospect of further work between Werder (Havel) and Biederitz to allow speeds of 200 km/h in place of the 160 km/h now possible throughout that section.

The Halle—Eichenberg—Kassel project was completed in 1994. The route is now electrified double track throughout, with a line speed of 120 km/h.

Total route modernisation, involving redoubling where necessary, upgrading for 160 km/h in the first instance, electrification, and resignalling are also components of the Erfurt—Bebra(—Frankfurt) project, completed save for the resignalling in 1995. Restoration of the so-called Berliner Kurve at Bebra eliminates the need for reversal of through trains between Erfurt and Frankfurt am Main and delivers a saving of some 15 minutes on through journeys. Civil engineering work between Erfurt and Bebra allows for future speeds of 200 km/h wherever possible, but such speeds wait on resignalling work.

On the Berlin—Halle/Leipzig—Nuremberg line restoration of the second track and electrification between Camburg and Hochstadt-Marktzeuln were completed (save for a short section of second track near Ludwigstadt) in 1995 and there was a significant acceleration of services. Work is forging ahead on what is effectively a rebuilding of the Berlin—Halle/Leipzig line between the Berlin Outer Ring and Leipzig for speeds of 200 km/h (after resignalling and elimination of all level crossings). Similar upgrading is planned westwards from Leipzig. The line between Bitterfeld and Halle was closed completely for 10 months in 1994-95 for rebuilding rather than modernised under traffic over the space of 30 months.

The DM12.4 billion Leipzig—Dresden scheme involves substantial stretches of new line (NBS) as well as upgrading (ABS).

A severed-link-restoration scheme that is not part of the *Deutsche Einheit* programme is the 1996 completion of a route between Goslar and Bad Harzburg in the west and

Ilsenburg and Wernigerode in the east. This not only serves tourist traffic but also handles a heavy freight flow between two factories in the Preussag Group, the Peine-Salzgitter steelworks and the Ilsenburg rolling mills. Two routes actually crossed the border in this area, and the new line is a combination of both, 36 km long against 23 km by the direct line, but better graded and aligned and more suitable for the heavy freight flows proposed. This line is now to be further upgraded for 160 km/h running by NeiTec trains.

DB has agreed with the *Länder* of Saxony and Bavaria on the investment of some DM900 million up to 1999. Focus of the improvement is the so-called *Sachsen-magistrale* which forms a part of the ABS across South Germany from Karlsruhe through Stuttgart and Nuremberg to Leipzig and Dresden. A new route through the Vogtland is also to be surveyed to assess the possibility of achieving significant accelerations between Plauen and Hof. Saxony will meet part of the cost of this investigation. From 1999 the new diesel IC-NeiTec trains, already on order, will be deployed, reducing the Dresden—Hof timing from 3 hours 21 minutes to 2½ hours and Dresden—Nürnberg from 5 hours to about 4 hours. Bayreuth will acquire a much-improved link with Hof by the construction of the Schlomener Kurve, which will cut at least 10 minutes off local train timings between the two cities and also allow Bayreuth to be linked into DB's long-distance network.

The Rendsburg high bridge across the Kiel Canal has now been opened to six-axle electric locomotives. Class 155s work on freight trains, and Class 103s are seen on passenger services. Completion of DSB's fixed crossing of the Great Belt will lead to a considerable increase in freight traffic on this route.

A new southern curve into the Duisburg-Ruhrort harbour area has been brought into use. This not only saves trains 30 minutes by eliminating a reversal but also permits a significant rationalisation of traffic. New lines for freight traffic in Hamburg, including a new curve across the Upper Harbour to allow direct running for goods trains between the Berlin main line and Maschen Yard, have also been commissioned.

The city of Berlin
Work began in late 1995 on a DM10 billion north-south tunnel through the heart of Berlin. There is to be a new central station at the Lehrter Stadtbahnhof, where the planned tunnel is crossed by the Stadtbahn west-east main line and S-Bahn route across the city. The old direct routes from the south, from Halle/Leipzig and Dresden, will be restored, but instead of leading, as previously, into a terminal station, they will be rerouted at Papestrasse into the tunnel. At its northern end the tunnel will fork to connect westwards and eastwards with the (Inner) Ring, currently under restoration, enabling trains from the west and north to reach the new low-level Lehrter Bahnhof platforms. Work on the 'Nordkreuz' junctions for main line and S-Bahn trains is now well advanced, and in early 1996 the complete redevelopment of Gesundbrunnen station began.

The plan to run a new S-Bahn line parallel to the north-south main lines has been put on hold to save money, but the alignment is being protected.

Eastwards from Zoologischer Garten the 114-year-old Berlin Stadtbahn which runs for 9 km to the Hauptbahnhof over 530 brick arches and 50 bridges last received major attention in the 1920s. A DM1.5 billion maintenance project is now in progress which includes the laying of modern slab track, electrification of the main lines, and full resignalling. Meanwhile, the Stadtbahn is closed to main line trains. S-Bahn trains, diverted to the former main lines in September 1994, reverted to their own rebuilt tracks in late 1996, allowing rebuilding of the main lines to begin. It had been hoped to complete the work for May 1997, but delays caused by the identification of additional work to be done and the discovery that the Spree bridge at Friedrichstrasse would have to be replaced, have meant the postponement of this date by at least a year. All stations will be modernised, Friedrichstrasse and Alexanderplatz being equipped to serve IR services and the Hauptbahnhof having its main line platforms lengthened to the west to be able to accommodate full-length ICEs. (Long-distance services will serve only the new Lehrter Bahnhof between Zoo and Hauptbahnhof.) To allow work to proceed unhindered, the Hauptbahnhof is closed to all main line traffic for the 1997-98 timetable year.

Work has begun on construction of the completely new

Spandau station (the first new platform came into use in May 1997) and on the rebuilding on a much larger scale of Gesundbrunnen. It was expected that work would soon begin on the new Lehrter Bahnhof itself.

Aachen to Cologne ABS
The line from the Belgian frontier near Aachen to Cologne is the crucial link between the Paris—Brussels high-speed line with its eastern extension through Belgium and the future Cologne—Frankfurt NBS. It is being upgraded for 250 km/h between Cologne and Düren, where the existing tracks are to be appropriated for a new S13 S-Bahn route and new double track installed for other traffic. Elsewhere the route will be upgraded for 220 km/h wherever feasible. Once scheduled for completion in 1996, it was only early in that year that the necessary funding was secured by agreement between DB AG and the Nordrhein-Westfalen Transport Ministry. Construction began in 1997.

Berlin—Dresden ABS
The German and Czech railways have agreed on a one-hour acceleration between Berlin and Prague for 1998, to 3 hours 45 minutes, to be achieved by short-term renovation and modernisation of the existing infrastructure coupled with the introduction of tilting trains, and they aim for a 3 hour 10 minute timing in the year 2000. The Berlin—Prague—Vienna/Bratislava—Budapest corridor is to be integrated into the European high-speed network. The German share involves the upgrading of the 160 km/h Dresden line (which was the first former DR line to become a 160 km/h railway for most of its length) for 200 km/h operation. This means the elimination of the many level crossings and the installation of LZB automatic train protection equipment. The railway is generally very well aligned, so not much in the way of curve-rebuilding will be required.

Dortmund to the Ruhr ABS
The biggest ABS scheme in western Germany covers the 215 km line from Dortmund via Hamm and Paderborn to a junction with the Hannover—Würzburg NBS at Kassel. With the aid of several major curve realignments DB AG aimed originally to create 250 km/h capability over almost 90 per cent of the distance from Dortmund to Kassel, but financial considerations have watered the scheme down to the creation of 200 km/h capability over 98 km between Dortmund and Paderborn and 160 km/h wherever possible over the topographically unfavourable stretch onwards to Kassel. Work began in 1989 but was not expected to be finished until mid-1997 at the earliest. A one-year complete closure of the Paderborn—Soest section was involved. On completion, at a cost of DM1.63 billion, the Dortmund—Kassel journey time will be cut from 2½ hours to 110 minutes.

Ebensfeld—Nuremberg ABS
Instead of continuing the NBS coming south from Erfurt through to Nuremberg there will be an ABS from Ebensfeld southwards, involving the laying of two additional tracks alongside the well-aligned existing railway at a cost of DM3.3 billion.

Günzburg—Augsburg(—Munich) ABS
This is the continuation of the new line proposed between Stuttgart and Günzburg to form a high-speed line between Stuttgart and Munich. Beyond Augsburg the main line is already 200 km/h territory to Munich, since this section was West Germany's first 200 km/h railway.

Ingolstadt—Munich ABS
This is the continuation from the outskirts of Ingolstadt to Munich of the new high-speed line coming southwards from Nuremberg . The total distance between Nuremberg and Munich will be cut to 171 km.

Karlsruhe—Basel
In 1987 a start was approved on the part-NBS, part-ABS improvement of the 193 km Karlsruhe—Offenburg—Basel main line. The amount of the line to be NBS and the amount to be ABS has changed, with much more now to be new construction.

Mannheim—Frankfurt am Main—Fulda ABS
The ABS upgrading of the 103 km main line between the Hannover—Würzburg NBS at Fulda and Frankfurt am Main, and of the 79 km 'Riedbahn' line between Frankfurt and Mannheim, continues. The Fulda—Frankfurt line

passes through difficult country to gain the Rhine—Main plain and over the first 25 km or so speeds have been limited to 110 km/h. The ABS works will make 200 km/h possible over 55 km of the rest of the route.

The 'Riedbahn' works have included the laying of a third track to allow overtaking at eight locations, the elimination of 27 level crossings, and realignments at 11 points to permit 200 km/h over 62 km of its length.

Associated with this scheme is a major enlargement of facilities at Frankfurt Airport; and, east of the present airport station, construction of a new triangular junction with the 'Riedbahn' so that trains from the airport can run direct to Mannheim without reversal in Frankfurt Hbf. The original plan was to provide a fourth platform line in the existing Airport station, but by 1990 forecast traffic growth had dictated the construction of a second station exclusively for IC traffic, leaving the present station for exclusive S-Bahn use. The new station, served by three ICE routes, will not be on the same site as the present one but will be a distinct entity located on a branch of the Cologne—Frankfurt NBS.

Munich—Markt Schwaben—Mühldorf—Freilassing ABS
Prospective European Union single-market growth of north-south freight traffic, Austria's accession to the EU, and that country's restrictions on lorry transit-traffic demand an increase in cross-border capacity. An ABS scheme, including electrification, has been developed for the 120 km route from Munich to Freilassing through Markt Schwaben, to create a high-quality relief route for the heavily taxed main line from Munich to Freilassing via Rosenheim. Cost of the project is estimated at some DM1 billion. Mühldorf's considerable commuter traffic to Munich will also benefit from the electrification.

Strasbourg—Appenweier and Saarbrücken—Mannheim ABS
To connect DB AG's ICE network with the recently authorised French TGV Est from Paris to Strasbourg, ABS schemes have been tabled for the lines between Strasbourg and Appenweier and between Saarbrücken and Mannheim. The lines will be upgraded for 200 km/h where feasible.

Level crossings
DB AG, working together with federal, *Land,* and local authorities, is engaged in a major programme to improve safety at 30,000 level crossings. New lines and ICE routes are free of crossings. The current aim is to eliminate all existing crossings on heavily trafficked routes by the end of the decade. Those remaining will be renewed with up-to-date safety technology. These measures will cost roughly DM630 million a year. It is a requirement of the Eisenbahn Bau- und Betriebsordnung that there should be no level crossings on lines where speeds of above 160 km/h are run. Because the elimination work is not complete, it has been necessary to reduce speeds on certain lines, such as that between Dortmund and Hannover.

Major new stations
'Station 21' projects have already been announced for Stuttgart, Ulm, Saarbrücken, Frankfurt, Munich and Mannheim. Planning is most advanced at Stuttgart, where a subsidiary has been formed to realise the project. Additionally, DM110 million is being spent on a thorough modernisation of Hannover Hbf in time for the Expo 2000 and DM130 million is being spent on similar work at Cologne. These modernisation projects follow in the footsteps on the now-well-advanced work at Leipzig where a total redevelopment within the old structure of Europe's largest terminal station is taking place.

Stuttgart Hauptbahnhof
Stuttgart's main station is to be replaced by an eight-platform through station with its tracks parallel to the existing listed main building of the present terminal and at a lower level than at present. Completion is scheduled for 2008 at a cost of DM4.9 billion. A hundred hectares of railway land in and near the present station will be released for rebuilding, increasing the size of the inner city by no less than 40 per cent and thus helping to defend Stuttgart's green edges from further encroachment. A conservative estimate is that the sale of this land will raise DM2.175 billion towards the rebuilding costs. A further DM886 million will come from the federal government in connection with the Stuttgart-Ulm NBS project. The funds provided by central government, *Land,* regional and local authorities for local transport will provide DM850 million, and the *Land* of Baden-Württemberg will also make

Thirty Class 218 diesel locomotives have been fitted with exhaust gas-optimised 12V956 engines from MTU
1997

available DM200 million. The balance is due to come from DB AG, but the railway foresees no problem: it predicts an annual gain of DM176 million from a more customer-friendly station with much lower operating costs and increases in rentals from traders. Four tunnels are required for the approach lines to the station, the longest of them 8.2 km, and there will be three major new bridges, over the river Neckar, in the Körschtal, and in Untertürkheim.

Düsseldorf Airport station
Contracts for the new Düsseldorf Airport station on the main line between Düsseldorf and Duisburg were signed in December 1995. The station will be linked to the airport by a people mover running on a 3 minute headway and capable of conveying about 2,000 people per hour in each direction. Total cost of the project is about DM350 million. All trains (except S1 at first) will call at the station, which will add 4 minutes to the running time of all long-distance services (though connections in Cologne and Dortmund are to be maintained). Completion is envisaged for spring 1999.

Neuwiederitzsch — Leipziger Messe
This station, replacing the old Neuwiederitzsch station, was built to serve the Leipzig Trade Fairs; it opened on 16 March 1996. The Leipzig Trade Fairs have moved to a new DM1.3 billion development north of the city opened by the President of the Republic on 12 April 1996 and very well located for public transport. DB AG put a total of DM60 million into the connection, DM23 million into the new fair-station alone, including the provision of a new bus-tram interchange (Line 16) with full facilities for disabled passengers. Passengers wanting to use the tram for the 400 m from station to the fair have a very easy interchange. The station is served by a 20 minute shuttle-service from Leipzig at exhibition times, with a 6 minute journey time, in addition to its ordinary services, and at peak times 30,000 passengers a day are expected. Some IC and IR trains also call during exhibitions.

Mukran
Grants of DM21 million made available to the town of Sassnitz, on the Baltic near the Polish border, in September 1995, have ensured the realisation of the planned DM27 million development of the ferry port of Mukran, giving it a long-term future and preserving a large number of jobs. A three-year building programme will see completion of all facilities necessary for a high-capacity port by the end of 1998. Mukran will be able to handle cars, lorries, passengers, and broad- and standard-gauge trains. In addition to the two ferry berths for the Russian traffic already there, a new berth will be provided for Swedish traffic, to which the Trelleborg ferries will be diverted in 1997. The Russians plan a terminal on their own territory — Kleipeda (once Memel) being now on Lithuanian soil. The German, Danish, and Swedish railways have worked up a strategy for rail traffic between Scandinavia and the mainland in which Mukran will play a key role. A German-Finnish working party is at present engaged on planning a Ro-Ro operation between Hamina and Sassnitz/Mukran.

Puttgarden
The future of the 'Bird's Flight Line' between Germany and Copenhagen via the Rødby-Puttgarden train ferry appears to be secure even after the opening of a through rail route via the Great Belt Bridge. Two new ferries are being built for the route and the Puttgarden terminal is being modernised and adapted to the needs of today's traffic at a total cost of some DM230 million. This will secure the long-term future of the route and its economic operation. The present joint DFO/DSB operation uses six ships to provide a 30 minute-interval service. The two new German ships and two new ships being provided by Denmark are double-ended ferries with twice the capacity of the previous vessels. They are able to maintain the 30 minute service.

Traction and rolling stock
At the end of 1995 DB AG stock stood at 66 steam locomotives, 3,562 electric locomotives, 2,984 diesel locomotives, and 2,373 shunting locomotives. There were 1,915 electric multiple-units, 702 diesel multiple-units, and 157 rail-buses. The ICE fleet was 60 trains. Total coaching stock was 15,202, including 694 ICE trailers, 2,231 EC/IC cars, 2,651 IR cars, 204 sleepers, and 512 couchette cars. There were 181,178 freight wagons and 77,487 privately owned freight wagons. Of the locomotives, Classes 101, 103, 112, 120, 181 and 184 are assigned to the Long-Distance Passenger Business, Classes 110, 111, 113, 141, 143, 202, 211, 213, 215, 218, 219, 228, 229, and 234 to the local Passenger Traffic Business, and all remaining classes to Freight.

The InterCity Express (ICE) family
The ICE1 entered squadron service in June 1991. The fleet comprises 694 trailers and 120 power cars, and trains are made up with 12 or 14 trailers. Two new fleets are under construction, ICE2 (which are half-length ICE1s) and ICE3 (previously ICE2-2) (a new design of ICE with distributed traction rather than power cars).

In early 1994 a DM2.2 billion contract was finalised with a Siemens/AEG consortium for construction of an ICE2 fleet of 44 trains. Deliveries of power cars and trailers began in 1996. The ICE2 is half the length of the ICE1: each comprises a Class 402 5,000 kW power car, six intermediate trailers, and a driving control trailer, and sets can work singly or in pairs. The intermediate trailers, wholly of open saloon layout, resemble those of ICE1 but are around five tonnes lighter and are mounted on a new design of bogie developed by SGP Verkehrstechnik of Austria, with air secondary suspension and that manufacturer's semi-active wheelset guidance system, described as Radial-Hydraulic-Controlled (RHC).

In August 1994, DB AG ordered 50 eight-car ICE2-2s (now ICE3s) from Siemens/AEG, with the first two units due into service at the end of 1997 and the remaining 48 by the end of the century. The design aims to reduce weight further, cut fuel consumption and costs, and produce a train suitable for pan-European operation. The ICE3 will be a genuine unit-train: traction will be distributed throughout the entire train with roughly every second axle powered. Advantages include better transmission of tractive effort to rail, reduction of slipping, more seats for the same train length, and a more favourable weight distribution. Axleload will be below 17 tonnes. Maximum speed will be 330 km/h and the train will be suitable for use on inclines of up to 4 per cent. Four trains will be three-voltage (15 kV 16⅔ Hz AC, 1.5 kV DC, and 25 kV 50 Hz AC) and nine will be four-voltage (adding the Belgian 3 kV DC) for cross-border workings; the remaining 37 trains will be equipped only for the German/Austrian/Swiss 15 kV 16⅔ Hz AC.

A new experimental train, designated the ICE21, is to be built, in which components for the next generation of ICEs will be tried. It is hoped to bring this into service in the year 2000.

Developments in ICE maintenance

Major ICE examinations now take place in Hamburg-Eidelstedt as well as in Nuremberg — the only location for such work until early 1996. The arrangement is a first for DB AG, in that the work is carried out in two stages, each running from a Monday to a Friday, with the set being returned to service for the intervening weekend when need for ICEs is especially great. Such split maintenance procedures are established practice in the airline industry.

A new ICE maintenance depot in Munich was brought fully into use and formally opened on 15 December 1995, two tracks having been in use since May 1993. Built at a cost of DM320 million and employing 860 people, the depot has six roads 450 m long. Work on the stationary trains can proceed simultaneously on four levels. Through a glass wall passengers passing by can see work in progress. A new maintenance depot is currently under construction at Berlin-Rummelsburg.

In mid-1996 a DM4 million driver-training ICE simulator was brought into use. Of DB's 30,000 drivers, roughly 800 had been trained to drive the 60 ICEs. Every year about 50 newcomers will receive a two-week course, at 'speeds' of up to 300 km/h, and the simulator will also be used for regular follow-up courses for existing ICE drivers. The simulator offers improved quality training with more flexibility and more uniformity. It saves energy and takes training runs off the track. Ten more are planned by 1998. The suppliers are Krauss-Maffei and Daimler-Benz Aerospace Dornier, and the CBT (Computer Based Training) software comes from IAS (*Interaktive-Computer-Ausbildungs-Systeme*).

Tilting trains

DB AG is already using VT610 tilting dmus in Bavaria. Three new types of tilting train have been ordered.

At the top of the range are 40 new electric express tilting units, which have been designated ICT and externally will resemble other members of the IC(E) family. They will share internal design and equipment with the ICE3 trains. The ICT trains will use the latest Fiat tilt technology, which is entirely underfloor. The trains will have a top speed of 230 km/h and will comprise five or seven vehicles, the majority being seven. Because the

ICE2s feature a power car at one end and one of these driving trailers at the other   **1997**

Principal outstanding orders for DB AG

Vehicle	Class	Maker	Number	DM price from (millions)	Options	Delivery begins
ICE3, 8-car	403/405/406	Siemens/AEG/DWA	50	1,600	50	1998
ICT (Neitec), 7-car	411/412/415/416	DWA/Siemens/Fiat	40	900	40	1997
IC diesel Neitec, 4-car	605	DWA/Siemens	20	280		1999
VT611, 2-car		AEG/DWA	50	220	50	1996
Eco 2000 locos	101	ABB-Henschel	145	800		1996
Eurosprinter	152	Siemens/Krauss-Maffei	195	1,000	100	1996
12 × locos	145	AEG	80	400	400	1999
4-car S-Bahn	ET 423	ABB/LHB	100	580	200	1998
4-car S-Bahn	ET 425	Siemens-Duewag/AEG/DWA	196	1,300		1997
4-car S-Bahn	ET 426	Siemens-Duewag/AEG/DWA	43			1997
2-car S-Bahn	ET 481/2	DWA/AEG	100			1995
Regiosprinter, 2-car		Siemens/Duewag	8			1996
Cargo-Sprinter, 5-car		Bombardier/Windhoff	6			1997
Cargoloc DH 440		Allrad	3			1997

profile of the trains will be a little smaller than the ICE's, on account of the need to allow for the tilt, there will be a slight reduction in comfort. The motors will be positioned lengthways under the floors and will have a performance similar to that of the ICE3. The seven-car sets will include a restaurant, the shorter sets will have a bistro.

Twenty diesel four-car high-speed tilting trains (ICTs) have been ordered in a DM280 million contract with Siemens (with its Duewag AG subsidiary) and Deutsche Waggonbau AG; delivery to begin in early 1999. The four-car 200 km/h trains, designated Class 605, will have 193 seats (41 first, 143 second, 6 in a mother-and-child

compartment, 3 in the bistro area). Addition of a fifth car for strengthening will be possible, and the sets will be able to run in multiple. This class, designed to bring modern standards to non-electrified lines, will complete DB's family of modern high-speed units.

Meanwhile, delivery of 50 Class 611 tilt-equipped 'Neitec' diesel units has begun. These are being built by AEG (now Adtranz) with the participation of DWA; they use military tilting technology, from the Leopard tank, and Voith hydraulic transmission. Each train offers 141 seats, and a closed toilet system is used. A further order for 50 units, with an option on another 100, has been placed, these later units will be known as Class 612. After a problematical introduction to service in September 1996 the Class 611s were withdrawn for further work. They came back into service in June 1997 on the same timings as conventional trains. The aim was to restore accelerated timings with tilt in September 1997.

New electric locomotives

In 1994 DB AG placed equipment orders to the value of DM4 billion. In addition to the ICE3, ICT, and Class 611 trains mentioned above, 420 locomotives (of the three types described below) and 339 S-Bahn units were ordered, with options for a further 500 locomotives and 200 S-Bahn units to a value of DM3.5 billion. The first new locomotives were delivered by the end of 1996 and by the end of the century a large part of the obsolete equipment from the 1960s and 1970s, now unreliable and expensive to maintain, will be scrapped. The urgent need for the replacement of locomotives is proved by the fact that 20 per cent of all daily perturbations in traffic are currently caused by locomotive faults and failures.

By 1998 the Class 103 will have largely gone, replaced by the new Class 101 from ABB-Henschel (now Adtranz). In total 145 of these three-phase, AC drive 6 MW locomotives are being built. With 220 km/h top speed, the Class 101s will initially be used on the IC network, but as more ICEs come on stream they will gravitate towards freight traffic. By mid-1997 these machines were being delivered at a rate of one per week.

There will be 195 representatives of the new Class 152 from Krauss-Maffei/Siemens. This class, based on the

VT611 dmu from Adtranz with electric tilting system   **1997**

Adtranz is building 145 Class 101 locomotives for DB; this example is at Hamburg-Altona (Joachim Kemnitz)   *1997*

EuroSprinter supplied to Spain and Portugal, is a heavy freight locomotive, with a 6,000 kW rating and a 140 km/h maximum speed. These will be delivered from 1997 to the end of the century and, along with the 101s, will replace the 30 year-old Class 150s. DB AG holds an option on a further 100 of these 6 MW locomotives.

In 1999 and 2000 the 32-year-old Class 110 and the Class 141 will be replaced by a first delivery of 80 of Adtranz's new Hennigsdorf-built Class 145, of 4 MW power and a 140 km/h maximum (light freight and passenger work). There is an option for a further 400 of these machines.

Multiple-unit fleet renewal
By 2000, the Local Passenger Traffic Business will have spent almost DM6 billion in the greatest-ever investment programme in new trains for local traffic, designed to fit services for the new century. Included in the orders are 440 S-Bahn sets and electric units for regional traffic as well as the Neitec diesel sets discussed in the 'Tilting trains' section above. Additionally, more lightweight and double-deck units are to be bought. A further DM1 billion will go on the modernisation of existing stock.

Delivery of a second and third series of Class VT628/928 diesel railcar twin-sets, totalling 189 sets and begun in late 1992, has now been completed. To accelerate the

elimination of obsolescent rolling stock on shorter-haul services in the east, in early 1994 DB AG placed a further order for 120 Class 628.4 dmus and at the same time called for accelerated delivery of the remainder of the then-current order.

In December 1994 DB AG ordered 339 new S-Bahn sets. These are to be more economical by some 25 per cent in their use of energy than existing designs.

From 1997 the Munich, Stuttgart, and Frankfurt/Main S-Bahn systems will receive 100 units of a new Class 423 design, built by ABB (now Adtranz) with the participation of Linke-Hofmann-Busch and having a floor-height of 998 mm, to replace the Class 420/421 equipment dating from 1972. There is an option for a further 200 sets.

A consortium of AEG (now Adtranz), Siemens, and DWA received an order for 60 units of a new Class 424, with a 760 mm floor-height and the electronics largely underfloor. Of the 60, 45 were for the new Hannover Expo 2000 S-Bahn, Dresden, and Leipzig, and the remainder for deployment in the Mannheim area.

The same consortium received an order for a further 136 units designated Class 425, a variant of the Class 424 design with more seats, fewer doors, and a 160 km/h maximum speed, for Express S-Bahn work in longer routes, together with 43 two-car units designated Class 426 and essentially shortened Class 425s. Classes 425 and 426 were to be provided with entry steps to allow

them to work on lines without high station platforms. All three classes were to have Jakob's bogies.

It was announced in early 1996 that the Class 424 design will not now be built, 60 additional Class 425s being acquired instead, provided that automatic entry-steps can be provided to deal with platform heights of 380, 560, and 760 mm.

The new class ET 474 units for Hamburg's S-Bahn have begun to enter service. Floor-level in the new units is 100 mm lower than in their predecessors, which will help all passengers and especially the disabled. Glass dividing walls allow a good view through the whole unit, and each vestibule has facilities for voice connection to the driver, thus contributing to greater passenger safety. DB's 2005 energy-saving programme is taken into account, and the braking systems return energy to the overhead line. The total DM800 million order is for 103 trains.

Coaching stock
Bilevel cars now feature significantly in local operations all over Germany. DWA has been promised orders totalling at least 250 cars for these services, notably those of the Rhine-Ruhr region.

DWA has been engaged in a comprehensive modernisation of the former DR's bilevel passenger car fleet. Besides new seating, improvements to the provision of facilities include WCs for the handicapped, spaces for cycles and prams, and reconstructed vestibules with entrances that are wider and at 550 mm platform-height level. DWA's Görlitz factory has built 200 new control trailers for the refurbished bilevel sets. The first refurbished sets were applied to the regional Wunsdorf—Blankenfelde route in the Berlin area, and to the Rostock and Halle S-Bahn services.

Görlitz Works has produced a new design of double-deck driving trailer, DBbfz Class 761, for use on local trains. Essentially these vehicles have a similar design to the IR driving trailers (see above), but their maximum speed is 140 km/h only; they have a simpler form of Indusi train control equipment, and, although all are prepared for it, only seven, destined for use in the CIR-ELKE experiments, are fitted with LZB automatic train protection equipment.

DB AG's own workshops are also modernising large numbers of old coaches, including 200 double-deckers at Wittenberge and 103 driving trailer conversions for IR and IC stock at Halberstadt. All DB passenger vehicles will have retention toilets by 2002 as another step in the railway's general environmental programme.

Experimental freight vehicles
The prototype CargoSprinter, a freight dmu, appeared on 9 October 1996. The train is 91 metres in length and consists of two air-sprung air conditioned driving positions integrated into end-wagons, and three intermediate wagons. It offers space for up to 10 swap-bodies. Weight is 120 tonnes and maximum load is 160 tonnes. The unit has automatic couplings, disc brakes, low-noise running-gear, modern underfloor low-emission diesel engines (diesel power being required because most sidings are not electrified), and electronic braking control. Maximum speed is 120 km/h with up to 112 tonnes load, 100 km/h above that. The unit consumes up to a third less diesel fuel per 100 km than five loaded lorries.

In conjunction with the railways of Austria and Italy, DB AG has been developing a 'quiet' freight train for the Brenner route. An experimental train of 30 wagons features disc brakes, bogie shrouds and special wheels to minimise transmissions of vibrations.

Signalling and telecommunications
DBKom, the new DB AG telecommunications subsidiary, chose a Mannesmann-led consortium as its future strategic partner. Partners with Mannesmann are AT&T and Unisource (made up of the national tele-communications companies of Holland, Spain, Sweden, and Switzerland). DB AG holds 50.2 per cent of the company now called Arcor and based in Frankfurt am Main. Arcor has at its disposal a national ISDN network of 40,000 km and aims to be Germany's second telecommunications operator.

Following reunification of Germany, a DB/DR working party drew up the specification for a new signals system which is now standard. Under what is known as the Ks-System, signals are either home or distant colourlights, though both can be mounted on the same post. Block indications are given for two sections ahead, and speeds can be signalled in multiples of 10 km/h. With the

Bombardier's Talent lightweight dmu for local services   *1997*

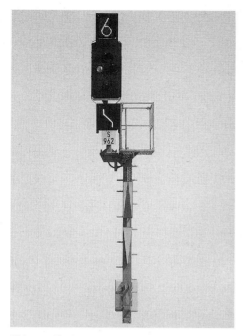

This new Ks-signal displays a 'proceed at 60 km/h' aspect and indicates that the train is to take a route diverging to the left **1996**

Driving trailers converted from conventional saloons by DB's workshops began appearing in 1997. This is a Dresden—Basel train at Mainz; the new vehicle facilitates the reversals necessary at Leipzig and Magdeburg on this route (Joachim Kemnitz) **1997**

exception of the Biederitz to Magdeburg section, the line between Berlin Zoologischer Garten and Helmstedt is entirely signalled by the new system and substantial installations are beginning to appear on other lines too. For example, the new Eisenach box controlling the line between Neudietendorf and Gerstungen was fully commissioned on 19 May 1996.

Traditional German colourlight signalling practice has not favoured large control areas. Even a very large installation such as that at Frankfurt am Main does not control very far beyond the immediate station area. There have always been some exceptions, such as the centralised control of the Neustrelitz to Rostock main line of the former DR. Only in the last two or three years and with the development of electronic control has there been a shift, and the first major installation is that at Magdeburg.

DB AG's aim is eventually to have a 17,000 km network on which 90 per cent of the traffic is controlled from just seven Traffic Centres like the new one in Magdeburg. Following completion of the first stage of development in December 1995, this now controls trains between Werder (on the outskirts of Berlin) and Marienborn on the east-west main line and between Stendal and Güterglück on the north-south line. Its final stage was due to be completed in 1997.

The new electronic signalling installation at Hannover, formally handed over to DB by Siemens Transportation Systems in August 1996, is the world's largest, controlling 5,100 interlocking and shunting routes and operating more than 800 signals and pairs of points. Its commissioning marks another stage in the spread of modern electronic signalling through the DB AG system.

A serious accident to the 'Gläserner Zug' in late 1995 dramatically illustrated the risks when a train leaves a platform against a red signal. To prevent such accidents in future, the Indusi (PZB) is to be modified, the new form being designated PZB 90. Additional monitoring beyond the signal and additional stop monitoring are provided, so that if any train does start against the signal it will be braked at a speed as low as 25 km/h. DB AG is to introduce the new equipment throughout its system by the end of 1999 at a cost of about DM110 million. Every stop signal must be equipped with a 500 Hz track magnet and all motive power (including private owner machines and historic locomotives in running order) must be converted, at a cost of about DM17,000 to DM20,000 per unit.

Computer-aided control

Nuremberg was the first hub on the historic system to commission a computer-aided traffic control centre (RZu). Similar installations are being completed at Frankfurt and Karlsruhe by SEL, which supplied the Nuremberg apparatus, and at Cologne and Hannover by

Electric locomotives

Class	Origin	Line voltage	Wheel arrangement	Power kW	Speed km/h	Weight tonnes	No in service	First built	Builders Mechanical	Electrical
103	DB	15 kV	Co-Co	5,950/6,420 [1]	200	110 [2] }	139	1965 [2]	Henschel	Siemens
	DB	15 kV	Co-Co	7,440/7,780	250 [3]	114 }		1970	Henschel	Siemens
109	DR	15 kV	Bo-Bo	4,200	120	82	4	1962	LEW	LEW
110	DB	15 kV	Bo-Bo		140	86.4 }	374	1956	Krauss-Maffei	Siemens
	DB	15 kV	Bo-Bo	3,620/3,700	140	86 [4] }		1963	Henschel/Krupp	AEG/BBC
111	DB	15 kV	Bo-Bo	3,620/3,700	160	83	226	1974	Krauss-Maffei	Siemens
112	DR	15 kV	Bo-Bo	4,200	160	83	128	1991	LEW	LEW
113	DB	15 kV	Bo-Bo	3,620/3,700	120	86	11	1962	Krauss-Maffei/ Henschel	Siemens
120	DB	15 kV	Bo-Bo	4,400/5,600	160/200 [5]	84	64	1979	Krauss-Maffei/ Krupp/	BBC
										Thyssen, Henschel
127	—	15 kV	Bo-Bo	6,400	230		1	1993		Siemens
128	—	15 kV	Bo-Bo	6,400	220/250		1	1994		AEG
139 [6]	DB	15 kV	Bo-Bo	3,620/3,700	110	86	47	1957 }	Krauss-Maffei/ Krupp/	AEG, BBC
140	DB	15 kV	Bo-Bo	3,620/3,700	110	83	795	1957 }	Thyssen/ Henschel	Siemens
141	DB	15 kV	Bo-Bo	2,310/2,400	120	67	393	1956	Henschel	BBC
142	DR	15 kV	Bo-Bo	2,920	100	82	103	1962	LEW	LEW
143	DR	15 kV	Bo-Bo	3,720	120	82.8	636	1984	LEW	LEW
150	DB	15 kV	Co-Co	4,410/4,500	100	126/128	168		Krupp/Henschel/ Krauss-Maffei	AEG, BBC, Siemens
151	DB	15 kV	Co-Co	5,982/6,288	120	118	170	1973	Krupp/ Krauss-Maffei	AEG/BBC/ Siemens
155	DR	15 kV	Co-Co	5,400	120	123	270	1974	LEW	LEW
156	DR	15 kV	Co-Co	5,880	125		4	1991		
171	DR	25 kV	Co-Co	3,660	80		11	1965		
180	DR	15/3 kV	Bo-Bo	3,080	120	84	20	1988	Skoda	Skoda
181	DB	15/25 kV	Bo-Bo	3,000/3,240	150	84 }	26	1968	Krupp	AEG
181.2	DB	15/25 kV	Bo-Bo	3,200/3,300	160	83 }		1975	Krupp	AEG
184	DB	1.5/3/ 15/25 kV	Bo-Bo	3,240	150		1	1967		

Notes:
[1] Nos 103.001-4 and 103.101-215
[2] Nos 103.001-4 only
[3] No 103.118 only
[4] Nos 110.288 onwards, which are Class 110.3; remainder are Class 110.1
[5] Nos 120.001-4 only
[6] The principal difference between Classes 139 and 140 is that the former has rheostatic braking for heavily graded routes

CargoSprinter freight dmu from Bombardier Eurorail, delivered in early 1997 **1997**

Deutsche Philips. Total cost of these projects is DM126 million.

In an RZu train movements are monitored by train describer apparatus and visual display units (VDUs) in the control centre depict graphically train performance against schedule. In the light of real-time progress the computer will propose individual train priorities for optimal adherence to the timetable.

CIR-ELKE (Computer Integrated Railroading : Erhöhung der Leistungsfähigkeit im Kernnetz)

DB AG aims to use modern technology to increase capacity on main lines by up to 40 per cent. The key is CIR-ELKE, which began trials on the 124 km Offenbach—Basel route in 1995.

CIR-ELKE is a development of the LZB (Linien-zugbeeinflussung) form of automatic train protection based on the old fixed block sections which has been in use in Germany since 1965. The NBS (new high-speed lines) were equipped with a development of LZB which uses shorter sections and retains the traditional lineside signals only to a limited extent (at passing loops, junctions, and diversion points) where it is necessary for trains with locomotives not equipped with LZB to work.

CIR-ELKE combines a high-capacity block scheme with LZB. To avoid delay to following trains, block sections are made very much shorter at places where speeds are low. This involves adjusting the block length to suit alignment, line speed, and train loads, shortening the block sections through the use of LZB, and thus raising the productivity of the line. For each train the computer calculates individually the necessary safe distance from speed and braking distance related to its precise location on the track. The driver of a following train does not watch fixed signals but receives a display over the LZB equipment in the cab. Because sections are not demarcated by lineside signals, all traction units require cab displays.

Offenbach to Basel is an ideal test section, partly because its lack of connections with other main lines and the limited number of locomotives in use make it possible to limit the amount of equipment needed and the numbers of staff to be trained: some 320 units will have to be fitted in addition to those that have already been equipped for service over NBS and 200 km/h ABS infrastructure.

The eventual aim is to extend the new system to the whole of the principal network. High on the list for its installation are the Rhine Valley, Stuttgart—Ulm, Würzburg—Nuremberg, the Oebisfelde and Halle/Leipzig routes to Berlin, and the Gerstungen—Dresden line. The LZB already in place on ABS 200 km/h sections will be modified to accommodate the new system, but the existing system will be retained on the NBS.

Electrification

Hamburg-Altona to Kiel via Neumünster and Neumünster to Nortorf (on the Flensburg line) went live on 2 August 1995 and electric services to Kiel began with the September 1995 timetable change. Electric working reached Flensburg in March 1996. Infrastructure and signalling have been upgraded to raise maximum speed from 140 to 160 km/h where possible. The work was supported by the federal and *Land* governments; of the total cost of DM550 million DB AG contributed DM285 million, including rolling stock, and the *Land* Schleswig-Holstein contributed DM150 million.

Electric operation of the 79 km Murrbahn (Crailsheim to Backnang, with the Backnang—Marbach branch) began on 31 May 1996. The DM101 million programme (costs shared with the *Land* of Baden—Württemberg and including purchase of 10 new electric units) raised maximum speed from 120 to 140 km/h and included preparatory work for future ICT operation, since Stuttgart—Dresden InterCity trains will eventually run this way.

The *Land* of Baden—Württemberg is negotiating with DB AG a further programme totalling 432 route-km and covering the following sections: Heilbronn—Schwäbisch Hall—Hessental; Ulm—Friedrichshafen; Basel—Schaffhausen; Radolfzell—Lindau; Breisach—Freiburg; Neustadt—Donaueschingen; and Villingen—Rottweil.

There is now electric operation throughout on the Berlin—Hamburg main line after the provision of separate S-Bahn lines and the commissioning of a new main line layout in the Hamburg area and completion of the work between Charlottenburg and Nauen in the Berlin area.

Electrification between Oldenburg and Wilhelmshaven was due to start in 1997 for completion in May 2000. There will be a new centralised signalling control centre at Sande.

Significant further extensions to the wiring of the ex-DR system continue. 1995 saw the restoration of through electric working between Leipzig and Nuremberg and the inauguration of electric working between Erfurt and Bebra and between Werder and Biederitz (the Berlin—Magdeburg main line). The first link-up of the former DB

Diesel locomotives

Class	Origin	Wheel arrangement	Power kW	Speed km/h	Weight tonnes	No in service	First built	Mechanical	Builders Engine	Transmission
201	DR	B-B	735	100	66	79	1966	LEW	12 KVD 18/21 A II	H Pirna
202	DR	B-B	900	100	65	496	1969	LEW	12 KVD 21 AL-3	H Pirna
204	DR	B-B	1,100	100	65	65	1969	LEW	12 KVD 21 AL-4	H Pirna
211	DB	B-B	760	90/100	62	69	1961		MTU MD 12 V 538 TZ MTU MB 12 V 493 TZ	H
212	DB	B-B	930	100	63	308	1962		MTU MB 12 V 652 TA	H
213	DB	B-B	930	100	63	10	1962		MTU MB 12 V 652 TA	H
215	DB	B-B	1,430/ 1,849	140	77.5	133	1968		MTU MB 16 V 652 TB MTU 12 V 956 TB 10	H
216	DB	B-B	1,300	120	77.5-77	176	1964		MTU MB 16 V 652 TB	H
217	DB	B-B	1,430	140	77	13	1965		MTU MD 16V 652 TB	H
218	DB	B-B	1,840/ 2,060	140	80	417	1968		MTU MA 12 V 956 TB MTU 12 V 956 TB 11 Pielstick 16 PA 4 V 200	H
218.2-4	DR	C-C	1,470	120	95		1966	Babelsberg	2 × 12 KVD 18/21 A II	H Pirna
218.9	DR	B-B	1,840	90/140			1979			H
219	DR	C-C	1,980/ 2,200	120	99	167	1962	Bucharest	2 × M820 SR	H
220	DR	C-C	1,470	100	115	34	1966	Voroshilovgrad	14 D 40	E Voroshilovgrad
228.1	DR	B-B	1,470	120	79		1965	Babelsberg	2 × 12 KVD 18/21 A II	H Pirna
228.5	DR	B-B	1,472	120			1962			H
228.6	DR	C-C	1,766	120			1966			H
229	DR	C-C	2,760	140		20	1992			H
231	DR	C-C	2,200	100	116	1	1973	Voroshilovgrad	5 D 49	E Voroshilovgrad
232	DR	C-C	2,200	120	112.4	577	1973	Voroshilovgrad	5 D 49	E Voroshilovgrad
234	DR	C-C	2,200	140		59	1992			E
290	DB	B-B	810	70/80 [7]	77/77.8	407	1964		MTU MU 12 V 652 TA	H
291	DB	B-B	810	80	76-90	103	1965		Mak 8 M 282 AK	H
293	DR	B-B	735	65	64	2	1981	LEW	12 KVD 18/21 A3	H Pirna
298		B-B	750	80		80				

[7] Nos 290.001-20 only

Electric railcars or multiple-units (excluding Berlin S-Bahn stock)

Class	Cars per unit	Line voltage	Motor cars per unit	Motored axles/car	Power kW	Speed km/h	Weight tonnes	No in service	First built	Builders Mechanical	Electrical
401					4,800	280		120	1989		
410					4,200	350		2	1985		
420	3		3	4	2,400	120	138	1,473	1971	MBB/MAN/ Duewag/ABB/WV	AEG/BBC/SSW
450	3	15 kV/750 V			560	100		4	1994		
470/87**	3	DC	2	4	1,280	100	107	90	1959	MAN/Wegmann	BBC/SSW
471/87**	3	DC	2	4	1,160	80	131.2	124	1940	LHW/Wegmann/ MAN	BBC
472/47**	3	DC	3	4	1,500	100	114	124	1974	LHB/MBB	BBC/SSW
515/81	1		1	2	200	100	49/56	26	1957	Rathgeber/O & K/ Waggon Union/ Wegmann/AFA	SSW

** Hamburg—S-Bahn third-rail DC

Diesel railcars or multiple-units

Class	Cars per unit	Motor cars per unit	Motored axles/car	Power kW	Speed km/h	Weight tonnes	No in service	First built	Mechanical	Builders Engine	Transmission
610	2			970	160		40	1992			E
614	3	2	2	370	140	124.5	84	1972			H
624/634 [8]	3	2	2	330	120	115.5-118.1	60	1961	MAN/Uerdingen		H
627	1	1	2	285/287	120	36	13	1974			H
628	2	1	2	2 × 210/ 1 × 375	120	64	393	1974	Duewag/KGB MBB		H
628.2	2	1	2	410	120			1987	Duewag/KGB/ MBB		H
771/172	Max 2	2	1	132	90	22	70	1960	Bautzen	6 kVD 18	M Bautzen
772/172	Max 2	2	1	132	90	22	89	1964	Bautzen	6 kVD 18	M Bautzen
798 [9]	1	1	2	110	90	20.9	329	1953	MAN/Uerdingen/ WMD		M

[8] Type 624 rebuilt with air suspension bogies
[9] Two-axle railbus: works as required with non-powered trailers, but not in permanent set formations

and DR power supply systems came in 1995 as the former DR area moves over to a centralised supply system in place of its former decentralised system.

Track

Standard rail: Type S49, weighing 49.5 kg/m; Type S54, 54.5 kg/m; Type S64, 64.9 kg/m. Lengths generally 30-120 m

Type of rail joints: 4- and 6-hole fishplates

Sleepers (crossties): Wood; steel; reinforced concrete. Wood sleepers impregnated beech, fir or oak, 2,600 × 260 × 160 mm

Steel, 2,600 × 9 mm weighing 86.3 kg

The latest type of RC sleeper (Spannbetonschwelle B58) weighs 235 kg, is 2,400 mm long, 190 mm thick under rails, 280 mm wide at bottom and 136 mm at top

Spacing: 650-800 mm

Rail fastenings: Baseplates and bolts, clips and spring washers with thin rubber or wood (poplar) pad between rail and plate; resilient rail spikes with wood and concrete sleepers and resilient rail clips with steel sleepers.

Max gradient: Main lines: 2.5%

Secondary lines: 6.6%

Max curvature:

Main lines: 9.7° = min radius 180 m

Secondary lines: 17.5° = min radius 100 m

Maximum superelevation: 150 mm on curves of 300 m and under

Rate of slope of superelevation: Generally 1:10 V (V = speed in mph). On occasion this may be increased to 1:8 V up to 1 in 400. On reverse curves the permissible limit is 1:4 V up to 1 in 400

Max altitude: Main line: 967 m between Klais and Mittenwald. Highest station Klais, 933 m

Secondary line: 969 m between Bärenthal and Aha on the Titisee—Seebrugg line

Max axleloading: 22.5 tonnes

UPDATED

Other German Railways (arranged alphabetically by location)

Name (Alphabetically by place of business)	Chief Executive	Route-km owned	Route-km worked	Motive power	Tonnes freight	Passengers carried
Ahaus-Alstätter Eisenbahn GmbH (AAE) 48683 Ahaus-Alstätte, Gronauer Str. 26 Tel: +49 25267 4 66/36 32 Fax: +49 25267 35 34	Dipl-Kfm Markus Vaerst	9.3	9.5	1	6,000	
Ankum-Bersenbrücker Eisenbahn GmbH (ABE) 49577 Ankum, Bersenbrücker Str. 6 Tel: +49 5462 2 53 Fax: +49 5462 89 85	Helmut Zimmermann	5.3	5.3		8,000	
Augsburger Lokalbahn GmbH (AL) 86161 Augsburg, Frudberger Str. 43 Tel: +49 821 5 60 97-0 Fax: +49 821 5 60 97-45	Dipl-Ing (FH) Dietrich Neumann	26.8	40.4	5	430,000	
Bentheimer Eisenbahn AG (BE) 48422 Bad Bentheim, Postfach 1153 Tel: +49 5922 75-0 Fax: +49 5922 75-55	Dipl-Betriebsw Peter Hoffmann	75.7	75.7	15	541,000	
Mecklenburgische Bäderbahn Molli GmbH u. Co, KG i. G. (MBB Molli) 18209 Bad Doberan, Am Bahnhof Tel: +49 38203 2400 Fax: +49 38203 2126/2400	Dr jur Horst Metz	15.8	15.8		—	600,000
Hersfelder Eisenbahn-Gesellschaft mbH (HEG) 36251 Bad Hersfeld, Heinrich-Börner-Str. 10 Tel: +49 6621 7 40 34	Dipl-Ing Peter Berking		244.2			1,100,000
BEHALA Berliner Hafen- und Lagerhaus-betriebe 13302 Berlin, Postfach 65 02 05 Tel: +49 30 3 90 95-0 Fax: +49 30 3 90 95-139	Dipl-Ing Horst Aulig	43.7	54.6	8		
Osthavelländische Eisenbahn Berlin-Spandau AG 13587 Berlin, Schönwalder Allee 51 Tel: +49 30 37 59 81-0 Fax: +49 30 3 75 60 35	Dipl-Ing Klaus Vollberg	14.5	22.5	4	370,000	
Neukölln-Mittenwalder Eisenbahn-Gesellschaft AG in Berlin (NME) 12099 Berlin, Gottlieb-Dunkel-Str. 47/48 Tel: +49 30 70 09 03-50 Fax: +49 30 7 03 30 78	Rudi Hahn	8.9	17.2	7	1,300,000	
Industriebahn-Gesellschaft Berlin mbH (IGB) 13302 Berlin, Postfach 65 02 05 Tel: +49 30 39 60 11-0 Fax: +49 30 39 60 11-70	Dipl-Ing Horst Aulig	27.7	14.6	3	640,000	
Niederbarnimer Eisenbahn Aktiengesellschaft (NEB) 13353 Berlin, Westhafenstr. 1 Tel: +49 30 39 60 11-11 Fax: +49 30 39 60 11-70	Dipl-Ing Klaus Duscha	72.7	72.7			
Regiobahn Bitterfeld GmbH (RBB) 06749 Bitterfeld, Zörbiger Str. Tel: +49 3493 7 70 58 Fax: +49 3493 7 61 27	Max Bräutigam	107	92	8	870,000	
Borkumer Kleinbahn und Dampfschiffahrt Gesellschaft mbH (Kleinbahn Borkum) 26738 Borkum, Postfach 12 66 Tel: +49 4922 3 09-0 Fax: +49 4922 3 09-34	Dr rer pol Bernhard Brons	7.3	7.3	6		
Industrietransportgesellschaft mbH Brandenburg (ITB) 14746 Brandenburg, Postfach 19 19 Tel: +49 3381 34 04-11 Fax: +49 3381 34 04-32	Dipl-Ing (FH) Joachim Meissner	23.6	19.4	3	270,000	
Wendelsteinbahn GmbH 83094 Brannenburg, Postfach 11 61 Tel: +49 8034 3 08-0 Fax: +49 8034 3 08-106	Dipl-Ing Manfred Thoma	8.4	7.7	3	400	
Farge-Vegesacker Eisenbahn-Gesellschaft mbH (FVE) 28777 Bremen, Farger Str. 128 Tel: +49 421 6 86 46 Fax: +49 421 68 35 60	Dipl-Ing Volkmar Köhler Heinz Wolfgramm	10.4	10.4	4	420,000	
Butzbach-Licher Eisenbahn AG (BLE) 35510 Butzbach, Griedeler Str. 64 Tel: +49 6033 61 55/56	Dipl-Ing Peter Berking	24.5	24.5	2	61,000	
Osthannoversche Eisenbahnen AG (OHE) 29206 Celle, Postfach 16 63 Tel: +49 5141 2 76-0 Fax: +49 5141 2 76-258	Dr rer pol Jens Jahnke	326.2	326.2	30	800,000	
Rinteln-Stadthagener Verkehrs GmbH (RStV) 29206 Celle, Postfach 16 63 Tel: +49 5141 2 76-0 Fax: +49 5141 2 76-258	Dipl-Ing Wolfgang Joseph Heinrich Lindhorst	20.0	20.4	1	159,900	
Verkehrsgesellschaft Dormagen mbH (VGD) mit Industriebahn Zons-Nievenheim 41542 Dormagen, Kirschfeld 8 Tel: +49 2133 27 26-25 Fax: +49 2133 7 29 82	Dipl-Volkswirt Ulrich Pfister Jürgen Alef	9.6	9.6	3	590,000	
Dortmunder Eisenbahn GmbH 44010 Dortmund, Postfach 10 10 41 Tel: +49 231 9 83 95 Fax: +49 231 9 83 96 02	Dipl-Ing Heinrich Brod (Techn) Reiner Woermann (Kfm)	20.3	20.3	45	48,400,000	
Dürener Kreisbahn GmbH (DKB) 52304 Düren, Postfach 10 04 62 Tel: +49 2421 39 01-0 Fax: +49 2421 39 01-88	Dipl-Ing Reinhold Alfter	44.7	44.7	16/2		700,000

Name (Alphabetically by place of business)	Chief Executive	Route-km owned	Route-km worked	Motive power	Tonnes freight	Passengers carried
Industriebahn Düsseldorf-Reisholz AG (IDR) 40554 Düsseldorf, Postfach 13 04 67 Tel: +49 211 7 48 36-0 Fax: +49 211 74 79 59	Dipl-Ing Eberhard Kiesner	7.9	7.9	5	1,410,000	
Eisenbahn und Hafen GmbH (EH) 47142 Duisburg, Postfach 11 02 63 Tel: +49 203 51-1 Fax: +49 203 52-2 42 67	Dr-Ing E.h. Karl-Heinz Jesberg Baldur Tauer	611.9		127	71,900,000	
Duisburg-Ruhrorter Häfen AG 47102 Duisburg, Postfach 13 02 51 Tel: +49 203 80 3-1 Fax: +49 203 80 3-2 32	Klaus van Lith Prof Dr-Ing Jochen Müller	99.3	76.5	2	373,000	
Ilmebahn GmbH (ILM) 37554 Einbeck, Postfach 13 33 Tel: +49 5561 93 25-0 Fax: +49 5561 93 25-44	Dipl-Verw-Wirt Bernd Amelung	13.1	13.3	2	20,000	
Hörseltalbahn GmbH (HTB) 99817 Eisenach, Adam-Opel-Str. 100 Tel: +49 3691 66 31 60/66 31 50 Fax: +49 3691 66 31 62	Dipl-Ing (FH) Peter Stockhausen Dipl-Ing Volkmar Köhler	8.4	1.0	3	260,000	
Niedersächsisches Hafenamt Emden 26700 Emden, Postfach 20 44 Tel: +49 4921 8 97-150 Fax: +49 4921 8 97-137	Dipl-Ing Hinrich Romaneessen	63.4	63.4	5	—	
Erfurter Industriebahn GmbH (EIB) 99086 Erfurt, Paul-Schäfer-Str. 35 Tel: +49 361 71 13 34 Fax: +49 361 64 33 905	Heidemarie Mähler	15	45	6		
Stadtwerke Essen AG — Hafenbetrieb 45117 Essen (Postadresse) Tel: +49 201 8 00-29 01 Fax: +49 201 8 00-29 09	Manfred Arenz (Kfm) Gerhard Höper (Techn)	15.0	20.0	4	327,000	
Verkehrsbetriebe Extertal — Extertalbahn GmbH (vbe) 32696 Extertal, Postfach 12 54 Tel: +49 5262 4 09-0 Fax: +49 5262 4 09 35	Dipl-Ing Bernd Rehm	23.8	23.8	2	38,000	
Hafenbetriebe der Stadt Frankfurt a. M. 60327 Frankfurt, Westhafen, Bau 9 Tel: +49 69 2 12-3 36 89 Fax: +49 69 23 19 19	Witsch-Ing (grad) Michael Schrey	10.6	10.6	4	670,000	
Bodensee-Oberschwaben-Bahn GmbH 88046 Freidrichshafen, Kornblumenstr. 7/1 Tel: +49 7541 5 05-5 Fax: +49 7541 5 05-221	Dipl-Betriebsw Peter Turkowski	19	19			500,000
Stadt Fürth — Hafenverwaltung 90744 Fürth, Postfach 25 37 Tel: +49 911 9 74-12 84 Fax: +49 911 9 74-10 12	Dr Peter Iblher	3.9	3.9	[DB]	150,000	
Kreiswerke Heinsberg GmbH 52501 Geilenkirchen, Postfach 11 91 Tel: +49 2451 6 24-0 Fax: +49 2451 6 70 15	Dr-Ing Peter Grünberg Ass Jur Andreas Schwarberg	0.5	0.5	[DB]	18,000	
Gelsenkirchener Hafenbetriebsgesellschaft mbH (GHG) 45809 Gelsenkirchen, Postfach 10 09 33 Tel: +49 209 4 40 34 Fax: +49 209 4 31 79	Helmut Kowallek	14.8	3.6	3	900,000	
Georgsmarienhütten-Eisenbahn (GME) 49110 Georgsmarienhütte, Postfach 12 80 Tel: +49 5401 39-43 60 Fax: +49 5401 39-43 73	Dr Stephan Rolfes	7.3	7.3	6	670,000	
Gross-Bieberau-Rheinheimer Eisenbahn GmbH 64398 Gross-Bieberau, Postfach 40 Tel: +49 6162 62 31	Günter Plaumann Herbert Zunk	3.7	3.7	1	200,000	
Teutoburger Wald-Eisenbahn-AG (TWE) 33330 Gütersloh, Am Grubenhof 2 Tel: + 49 5241 1 60 67/68 Fax: +49 5241 2 52 45	Dipl-Ing Volkmar Köhler (OBL) Karl Gottwald	103.2	103.2	7	200,000	
AKN Eisenbahn AG 20043 Hamburg, Postfach 10 63 22 Tel: +49 40 32 88-0 Fax: +49 4191 9 33-309	Dr-Ing Armin Wirsching	128.8	103.6 (P) 135.4 (G)	68 (P) 10 (G)	441,000	6,500,000
Hafenbahn Hamburg 20457 Hamburg, Dalmannstr. 3 Tel: +49 40 32 85/25 41 Fax: +49 32 85-25 46	Dipl-Ing Reinhard Höfer Dipl-Ing Michael Röfer	25.5	25.5	6	20,400,000	
Bahnbetriebsgesellschaft Lägerdorf mbH 20423 Hamburg, Postfach 11 23 07 Tel: +49 40 3 60 02-0 Fax: +49 40 36 24 50	Rainer Naudiet	7.7	7.7	—	203,000	
Hafen Hamm GmbH 59014 Hamm, Postfach 24 67 Tel: +49 2381 2 74-0 Fax: +49 2381 2 74-367	Dipl-Oec Walter Oppenheim Dr-Ing Kurt Hunsänger	3.4	3.9	4	575,000	
Stadtwerke Hanau GmbH — Abteilung Mainhafen 63411 Hanau, Postfach 21 53 Tel: +49 6181 3 65-201 Fax: +49 6181 3 65-307	Wilhelm Baumann	8.8	11.5	1	837,000	
Städtische Häfen Hannover — Hafen- und Anschlussbetriebe 30430 Hannover, Postfach 91 10 14 Tel: +49 511 1 68 25 26 Fax: +49 511 1 68-5082	Jürgen Schulz	72.4	72.4	8	1,700,000	
Brinker Hafengesellschaft mbH — Hafenbahn 30179 Hannover, Am Brinker Hafen 5 Tel: +49 511 63 30 33 Fax: +49 511 63 95 04	Dipl-Ing Richard Hecke	2.2	16.3	2	260,000	
Delmenhorst-Harpstedter Eisenbahn GmbH (DHE) 27240 Harpstedt, Postfach 11 61 Tel: +49 4244 10 11 Fax: +49 4244 85 40	Werner Mahlendorf	27.1	31.6	1 (P) 2 (G)	77,000	
Hohenzollerische Landesbahn AG (HzL) 72372 Hechingen, Postfach 12 37 Tel: +49 7471 18 06-0 Fax: +49 7471 18 06-12	Dipl-Kfm Günter Zeiger Dipl-Ing Bernhard Strobel	107.4	107.4	9 (P) 11 (G)	400,000	10,000,000
Stadt Heilbronn — Hafenamt 74024 Heilbronn, Postfach 34 40 Tel: +49 7131 56-2260 Fax: +49 7131 56-2655	Hans Betz Werner Dietz	19.2	24.1		600,000	
Wanne-Herner Eisenbahn und Hafen GmbH (WHE) 44634 Herne, Postfach 20 04 63 Tel: +49 2325 7 88-0 Fax: +49 2325 7 88-430	Dipl-Kfm Richard Görl	12.4	13.7		5,806,000	

GREECE

Ministry of Transport & Communications

Xenofontos Street 13, GR-10191 Athens
Tel: +30 1 325 1211-19   Fax: +30 1 323 9039

Key personnel
Minister: H Kastanidis
Secretary-General, Transport: K Stefanakos
Director-General, Transport: D Bekiaris
International Affairs Director: G Ratsiavos

UPDATED

Hellenic Railways Organisation (OSE)

Organismos Sidirodromon Ellados
1-3 Karolou Street, GR-10437 Athens
Tel: +30 1 524 8395   Fax: +30 1 524 3290/524 6239

Key personnel
President: C Papageorgiou
Director-General: A Lazazis
Deputy Director-General: I Rigas
Directors
    Personnel: S Xirakis
    Finance: B Siamos
    Operation: D Hondromitros
    Traction: A Giannissis
    Track: S Bobotas
    Organisation, Design and Planning: E Lalakakis
    Modernisation and Development: G Arkondis
    Commercial: E Manolas
    Electrification, Signalling, Telecommunications:
    D Pavlopoulos
Regional Management
    Athens: K Kallianos
    Thessaloníki: G Ninos
    Peloponnese: A Chatzinikolas
Manager, International Relations: E Kosteas
Manager, Public Relations: C Karaboikis

Gauge: 1,435 mm; 1,000 mm; dual-gauge, 1,435 mm and 1,000 mm; 750 mm
Route length: 1,565 km; 961 km; 23 km; 22 km
The railway from Athens to the Peloponnese, serving Patras and southern Greece, is metre-gauge.

Passenger operations

OSE operates passenger services on two main lines from the capital, Athens. To the north, a standard-gauge line runs to Thessaloníki, with services beyond to Alexandrúpolis and the former Yugoslavia; to the south, a metre-gauge line runs to the Peloponnese, serving Patras and southern Greece.

Passenger journeys in 1995 amounted to 11.5 million, with passenger-km at 1.568 billion.

Freight operations

OSE carried 1.3 million tonnes of freight in 1995, for 292 million tonne-km. One of the most important lines for freight is that from Thessaloníki to Idomeni, on the border with the former Yugoslavia.

A new freight facilities complex for the Athens region is planned at Thriassio Pedio.

New lines

A new line to serve the port of Kavala is planned. This would link in with the Thesssaloníki—Alexandrúpolis line.

Improvements to existing lines

The principal project, in hand since 1978, has been electrification, doubling and realignment of sections of the Athens—Thessaloníki—Idomeni main line, together with track renewal employing UIC54 continuously welded rail on two-block concrete sleepers, with minimum curve radius of 2,000 m. This axis carries more than half the railway's total traffic.

In December 1996, OSE appointed a 170-strong team to oversee the DR500 billion EU-backed modernisation work, including both its own personnel and engineering specialists from a consortium of consultants. The consortium comprises Halcrow of the UK (30 per cent); Metrotech of Greece (30 per cent); Obermeyer of

A200 class General Electric-built locomotive at Thessaloniki (Michal Málek)   **1997**

German-built dmus are the mainstay of intercity services in Greece   **1996**

Germany (25 per cent) and ILF Consulting Engineers of Austria (15 per cent).

Amongst other work, the team will supervise doubling of the track on the difficult mountain section between Evangelismos and Leptocarya (35 km). By 2000, travel time on the 510 km between Athens and Thessaloniki should be reduced from the 6 hours it takes today to 4 hours 20 minutes. Except between Larissa and Plati (134 km), electric signalling will be operative and a modern telecommunications system will cover the whole axis from Athens to Idomeni. There will be double track over the whole route between Athens and Thessaloniki except for Lianokladi-Domokos (65 km).

A subsidiary project would see the 80 km metre-gauge Paleofarsalos—Kalambaka line converted to standard-gauge. The line connects with the Athens—Thessaloníki route.

Athens—Patras upgrading

Conversion of the 220 km metre-gauge line from Athens to Patras to an electrified 1,435 mm gauge line with modern signalling, engineered for speeds of up to 200 km/h, is a goal of OSE. Work began in late 1990 on some upgrading of the existing metre-gauge track and modernisation of the route's telecommunications. This would help to achieve accelerated schedules for the new metre-gauge trainsets introduced between Athens and Patras in 1992.

The international team of consultants working on the north-south line will also oversee dual gauging of the eastern section of this route, so that standard-gauge trains will be able to reach Corinth. Funding has also been obtained for the first phase of a new depot at Thiarsion-Pedion.

Traction and rolling stock

	1,435 mm gauge	metre-gauge
Diesel locomotives	156	42
Diesel railcars	62	44
Trailers	52	39
Passenger cars	280	14
Baggage cars	18	23
Freight wagons	7,664	959

For the Athens—Thessaloníki and Thessaloníki—Alexandrúpolis routes, German industry manufactured 12 four-car intercity dmus in 1989. In 1994, a further eight five-car trains were ordered from AEG Bahnsysteme (now Adtranz) for these lines, and in 1995, 12 extra trailer cars were ordered from DWA's Bautzen factory so that the original units could be made into five-car sets.

The former AEG's Hennigsdorf works has had responsibility for the eight new trains; the first was due to be delivered in 1995. Each train has two power cars, each fitted with an MTU 12-cylinder V-shaped 396 engine generating 1,000 kW at 1,800 rpm. These drive Siemens synchronous alternators which supply the AEG traction motors. The trains have a top speed of 160 km/h.

Adtranz is building a new fleet of 25 diesel-electrics for delivery by January 1998, while Siemens/Krauss-Maffei is supplying six Eurosprinter-based 5,000 kW electrics for hauling express passenger and freight trains over the newly electrified section from Thessaloníki to the Yugoslav border.

For the metre-gauge system, a total of 10 air conditioned three-car trainsets for intercity operation have been built by Hellenic Shipyards. Two of the cars in each unit have each bogie powered by a 398 kW 2,100 rpm engine. They entered service in 1992.

Electrification

Two electrification projects are planned. Priority is being given to the 25 kV 50 Hz AC electrification of the 587 km Athens—Thessaloníki—Idomeni main line, which has the backing of the European Union. First section to be tackled is the 76 km of single line from Thessaloníki to the former Yugoslav border at Idomeni, where track is being renewed and curvature eased. This route carries three times the freight of the Athens—Thessaloníki line. Wiring is in place; commissioning was scheduled to take place in 1997. In 1996 a consortium led by ABB and including Adtranz won a US$ 145 million contract to electrify the Athens—Thessaloniki route by 2001.

For the longer term, OSE aspires to convert to standard gauge and electrify the metre-gauge line to Patras (see 'Improvements to existing lines' section).

Coupler in standard use: 1,435 mm gauge, UIC 520-521
Brake in standard use: Air, mostly Knorr

Diesel locomotives

Class	Wheel arrangement	Power kW	Speed km/h	Weight tonnes	No in service	First built	Builders Mechanical	Engine	Transmission
1,000 mm gauge									
A9100	Co-Co	1,200	90	80	10	1967	Alsthom	P PA4-185/V12	E GE Canada
A9000	Co-Co	1,005	96	80.3	12	1965	Alco	Alco 6-251D	E GE 761 A3
A9400	B-B	2 × 240	90	48	20	1966	Mitsubishi	GM V8-71N	H Niigata
1,435 mm gauge									
A250	B-B	1,345	103	66	11	1982	G-M	G-M H 182-11	H G-M
A550	Co-Co	2,935	145	123	9	1980	E	Alco V16 R 251	E E
A450	Co-Co	2,650	149	124	8	1974	MLW	Alco V16-251 F	E GE Canada
A430	Co-Co	2,015	149	120	20	1973	MLW	Alco V12-251 F	E GE Canada
A500	Co-Co	1,790	105	89.4	24	1967	Alsthom	P V16 PA 4 185	E Alsthom
A320	Co-Co	1,490	120	107	6	1966	Alco	Alco V12-251 C	E GT
—	Co-Co	1,345	120	107	8	1963	Alco	Alco V12-251 B	E GE
A200	Bo-Bo	795	109	63.5	13	1973	GE	C D398B-V12	E GE
A360	Bo-Bo	785	105	64.6	7	1962	Alco	Alco 251 B	E GE
A150	B-B	520	70	48	12	1973	Faur	M-MB820Bb	H Voith
—	B-B	560	70	48	7	1978	Faur	M V12MB820Bb	H Voith
A100	C	485	60	51	30	1962	Krupp	M GT06A-V12	H Voith L27 zub
A420	B-B	1,005	140	81	20	1962	Krupp	MTU 12V652TA10	H Mek K184U

Abbreviations: C: Caterpillar; E: Electroputere; G-M: Ganz-Mávag; M: Maybach; Mek: Mekydro; P: Pielstick

Diesel railcars or multiple-units

Class (running numbers)	Car per unit	Motor cars per unit	Motored axles/car	Power/car kW	Speed km/h	No in service	First built	Builders Mechanical	Engine	Transmission
1,435 mm gauge										
601-624, 1601-1624	4	2	4	1,180	160	12	1989	LEW	MTU 396 TC13	E S
11-26, 27-36	2	2	2 2	335 417	95	13 8	1949 1957	Fiat	Fiat 700110/1/6 and 8217-32	M Fiat
71-90	1	1	2	600	105	16	1960	Ferrostaal	M GTO 6AV 12	HM Mek 1045
91-101	3	2	2	895	140	9	1973	G-M	GM-SEMT	HD Voith L520-RO
4201-4204	2	2	2	155	100	1	1936	MAN	MAN W6V 17.5/22	H
701-725	1	1	4	305	120	25	1990	MAN	MAN D2842/ME	H Voith T320RZ
6521-6530, 5521-5530	2	2	2	305	100	10	1990	MAN	MAN D2842/ME	H Voith T320RE
1,000 mm gauge										
6451-6454	4	1	2	895	100	4	1973	G-M	P PA4-155/V8	HD Voith 520 R02
6461-6471	3	1	4	850	100	11	1983	G-M	P 8PA4-185V	HD Voith KB380/1
6001-6007	3	2	2	375	100	6	1957	Esslingen	Mer MB 836 BB/6	HD Voith T24Z
6401-6413	3	2	2	240	90	4	1952	DD	Saurer BZDS/V12	M DD
1-14	1	1	2	145	75	3	1952	Breda	Breda D20/6	M Wilson DA12
n/a	3	2	4	398	—	10	1992	HS		
750 mm gauge										
3001-3003	2	1	2	260	40	3	1959	Billard	Mer Y15-536	E
3004-3006	2	1	2	375		3	1967	Decauville	Mer MB836-B/L	E

Abbreviations: DD: De Dietrich; G-M: Ganz-Mávag; HS: Hellenic Shipyards; M: Maybach; Mek: Mekydro; Mer: Mercedes; P: Pielstick; S: Siemens

Alsthom-built Co-Co locomotive at Mesonisi (Klonos Artemis)   *1997*

Traffic	1992	1993	1994
Passenger journeys (thousands)	12,233	11,747	11,726
Passenger-km (thousands)	2,045,606	1,725,647	1,599,035
Freight tonnes	3,397	3,417	1,375
Freight tonne-km	564,410	523,770	324,439

Track

Rail: 1,435 mm gauge, UIC 50, 54; narrow-gauge, 31.6 kg/m
Sleepers: 1,435 mm gauge, reinforced concrete twin-block (Vagneaux type) 680 x 290 mm; steel 2,550 x 260 mm; timber 2,600 x 250 mm. Narrow-gauge, steel and timber
Fastenings: 1,435 mm gauge, RN and Nabla for concrete sleepers; K direct fastenings for wood or steel
Min curve radius: 1,435 mm gauge, 300 m; narrow-gauge, 110 m
Max gradient: 1,435 mm gauge, 2.8%; narrow-gauge, 2.5%
Max permissible axleload: 1,435 mm gauge, 20 tonnes; narrow-gauge, 14 tonnes
Max permissible speed: 90-100 km/h; 120 km/h parts of Athens—Thessaloníki main line

UPDATED

GUATEMALA

Ministry of Communications and Public Works

Edificio Aeronautica Civil, Zona 13, Guatemala City
Tel: +502 2 512769   Fax: +502 2 81613

Key personnel
Transport Minister: Fritz Garcia

UPDATED

Guatemala Railways (FEGUA)

Ferrocarriles de Guatemala
9a Avenida 18-03, Zona 1, 01001 Guatemala City
Tel: +502 2 382661/2 327720   Fax: +502 2 383039

Key personnel
General Manager: Andrés Castillo
Directors
   Operations: Hector Herrera
   Finance: José M Carrillo
Managers
   Engineering: Carlos A Moino González
   Finance: Sorgio Lenin Reyna
   Legal: Jaimo Osorio

Gauge: 914 mm
Route length: 782 km

Traffic	1994	1995	1996
Freight tonnes (000)	146	106	106
Freight tonne-km (million)	25.3	14.2	NA
Passenger-km (million)	0.99	—	—

Finance (Q million)	1994	1995	1996
Revenue	19.12	14.66	10.1
Expenditure	22.4	15.33	10.1

Political background
Guatemala's railway was nationalised in 1968. At this time, the railway had significant flows of passengers,

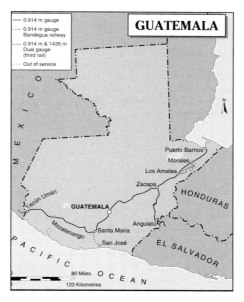

coffee and bananas, although a severe lack of investment in the ensuing 20 years effectively eroded this traffic base. From a 1980s yearly average in excess of 500,000 tonnes of freight carried, FEGUA was down to little more than 100,000 tonnes per year by the mid-1990s and the government decided to privatise the railway.

In 1997, US-based Railroad Development Corporation beat out one other firm to win a 50-year concession to run the system, paying the government US$10 million, plus 5 per cent of revenues for the first two years of operation and 10 per cent annually thereafter. A further US$10 million will need to be spent on upgrading the main Guatemala City—Puerto Barrios line.

New lines
FEGUA has studied the creation of a 28 km commuter line in Guatemala City. The scheme involved construction of a

10 km cross-town link between existing sections of the railway. Service by railbuses was proposed, and the cost of the scheme was estimated to be US$70 million. FEGUA trackage in Guatemala City was subsequently proposed for conversion into an east-west surface metro, under a scheme promoted in 1995 by the Guatemalan company Metroguat.

Improvements to existing lines
Little track maintenance has been carried out in recent years; from a derailment every 36 hours in 1986, one was occurring every 24 hours by 1989, even though less freight was being carried. The 1982 purchase of locomotives from Bombardier proved to be a costly mistake, since these were too heavy and caused excessive damage to the track. In 1989, 300,000 wooden sleepers and lengths of second-hand rail were acquired from Canada, but were sufficient only to upgrade 109 km of track.

Traction and rolling stock
The company owns 28 diesel and two steam locomotives, 68 passenger coaches and 1,523 wagons. Recent additions are 10 Type MX620 1,492 kW locomotives from Bombardier; only these machines and two General Electric-built locomotives are believed to have been in use recently.

Track
Rail: 30 kg/m
Sleepers: Timber, spaced 1,800/km in plain track, 1,000/km in curves
Max curvature: 6°
Max gradient: 3.3%
Max permissible axleload: 20 tonnes

UPDATED

Bandegua Railway

Cia de Desarrollo Bananero de Guatemala Ltd
Edificio La Galeria 5° Nivel, 7 Avenue 1444, Zone 9, Guatemala City
Tel: +502 2 340378   Fax: +502 2 322152

Key personnel
General Manager: G K Brunelle
Director of Engineering: E Casado
Railroad Superintendent: G Aguirre
Mechanical Superintendent: M Pérez

Gauge: 914 mm
Route length: 102 km

Traction and rolling stock
The company operates 11 diesel locomotives, 17 diesel railcars, seven passenger coaches and 101 freight wagons.

VERIFIED

GUINEA

Ministry of Trade, Transport & Tourism

PO Box 715, Conakry

Key personnel
Minister: I Sylla

UPDATED

Chemin de Fer de la Guinée (ONCFG)

PO Box 581, Conakry

Key personnel
Director: M K Fofana

Gauge: 1,000 mm
Route length: 662 km

Organisation
The railway links Kankan and the limit of navigability of the Upper Niger at Kouroussa with the port of Conakry. Crossing the Fouta Djalon mountains on gradients as steep as 2.9 per cent, and with curves of 100 to 150 m radius, it was lightly laid, without ballast, and has

consequently deteriorated badly with rising axleloads. Some renovation of track and rolling stock has been carried out under foreign aid programmes.

New lines
Construction of a US$200 million, 350 km line linking bauxite deposits at Dabola with the port of Conakry was due to start in 1998, with the line slated for opening in 2000. ZSR of Slovakia has a letter of intent to supply reconditioned track materials and rolling stock.

Traction and rolling stock
At last report the motive power fleet included 30 main line diesel locomotives and 16 diesel railcars. Rolling stock numbered about 20 passenger coaches and 500 freight wagons. However, no recent figures are obtainable and much equipment is reported unserviceable.

Industrial railways
There are three other lines in operation, all serving bauxite deposits. Guinea is the world's second largest exporter of the mineral, with 16 million tonnes mined in 1992.

The CF de Friguia, opened in 1960, carries the products of the bauxite mine and aluminium plant at Friguia to the port of Conakry. It is of metre-gauge, 145 km single-track, laid with 46 kg/m continuous welded rail on

metal sleepers. Three Alsthom 820 kW diesel-electric locomotives hauling 50-tonne load wagons transported one million tonnes in 1993. Freight stock totals 61 wagons.

The Boké Railway of the Compagnie des Bauxites de Guinée is a mineral ore line, running 134 km from mines at Boké and Sangaredi to Port Kamsar on the northern coast of Guinea. Built by a consortium of European contractors, the line was inaugurated in 1973. It is owned and operated by the Office d'Aménagement de Boké.

The first half of the line runs through the coastal sea plain while the upper half reaches into the foothills of the Fouta Djalon mountains. The line is standard-gauge with 60 kg/m continuously welded UIC profile rail laid entirely on steel sleepers. The line moves some 12 million tonnes annually. Rolling stock comprises 17 US-built diesel locomotives, 460 ore wagons, 39 other wagons and three passenger cars.

In 1974, with technical and financial assistance from the USSR, the Kindia Bauxite company built a 1,435 mm gauge line from Débélé to Conakry, running almost parallel to ONCFG's Kankan line. With a fleet of 13 diesel locomotives, in 1994 the line carried three million tonnes to a mineral quay at Conakry.

UPDATED

HONDURAS

Ministry of Communications, Public Works and Transport

Barrio La Bolsa, Comayaguela
Tel: +504 337690 Fax: +504 339227

Key personnel
Minister: G Aparicio

VERIFIED

Honduras National Railway (FNH)

Ferrocarril Nacional de Honduras
PO Box 496, San Pedro Sula
Tel: +504 534080/531879 Fax: +504 528001

Key personnel
General Manager: N Torres Rivera
Directors
   Administration and Finance: J O Garcia
   Commercial and Marketing Services:
   A Ramos Carrazco
   Mechanical: F Maury Martell
   Operations: J Manuel Benegas

Gauge: 1,067 mm; 1,057 mm; 914 mm
Length: 190 km; 128 km; 277 km

Organisation
The 914 mm Vaccaro system was formerly run by the Standard Fruit Company; FNH took control in 1983. The 1,067 mm gauge network comprises the Tela Railroad, operated by the United Brands Company. Rail installed on the Tela system is ASCE 25, 30, 35, 38 kg/m, minimum curve radius 3°, maximum gradient 0.62 per cent and maximum axleloading 6.82 tonnes.

Passenger operations
At the start of 1996, passenger operations were reported to comprise a San Pedro Sula–Puerto Cortés railcar service and a tourist train from Tela.

Freight operations
Principal traffic is fruit.

New lines
In 1983 the Honduran government agreed to a major enlargement of the 1,067 mm gauge system, likely to cost US$100 million. Its central features would be new lines from Puerto Castilla on the Caribbean to Sonaguera and from Arenal to Bonito Oriental on the Pacific, a total of

some 350 route-km. The existing line between Sonaguera and Arenal was to be upgraded to match the extensions.
   There has been no subsequent report of a start to implement this plan. However, construction of a new line of 97 km, from the banana traffic centre of San Pedro Sula to Yoro, on the route of the projected new Arenal–Bonito Oriental line, was begun.

Traction and rolling stock
The 1,057 mm system is operated with two steam and 34 diesel locomotives, 37 passenger coaches, 22 diesel railcars and 1,960 wagons. The 914 mm fleet comprises eight diesel-electric and two diesel-mechanical locomotives, 17 diesel railcars, 16 passenger coaches and 530 wagons. Operations on the 1,067 mm Tela system are conducted with 28 diesel locomotives, 18 railcars, 70 passenger coaches and 1,324 freight wagons.

VERIFIED

HUNGARY

Ministry of Transport, Communication & Water Management

PO Box 87, H-1400 Budapest (Dob utca 75-81)
Tel: +36 1 322 0220 Fax: +36 1 322 8695

Key personnel
Minister of Transport: Dr Károly Lotz
International Affairs: A Hardy
Railways: L Horváth

VERIFIED

Hungarian State Railways Ltd (MÁV)

Magyar Államvasutak Rt
Andrássy út 73-75, H-1062 Budapest
Tel: +36 1 322 0660/342 9399/9500
Fax: +36 1 342 8596

Key personnel
President: István Tompe
Acting General Manager: István Sipos
First Assistant General Manager: Dr Gyòrgy Magos
Assistant General Managers:
   Economics: Annamaria Benczédi
   Infrastructure: József Pál
Chief of International Affairs Bureau: József Lovas
Departmental Managers
   Passenger: Csaba Szilvási
   Commercial: Márton Kukely

Gauge: 1,524 mm; 1,435 mm; 760 mm
Route length: 36 km; 7,394 km; 176 km
Electrification: 2,207 km at 25 kV 50 Hz AC

Political background
Like all railways of the former Communist East European countries, MÁV has steadily lost traffic since 1989 in the face of political and industrial change. Freight traffic more than halved in the 1989-94 period, from 104 to 44.2 million tonnes; in 1995, there was a modest rise, to 46.4 million tonnes. Passenger traffic, stagnant since the mid-1980s, dropped 30 per cent as unemployment rose and public and private road transport competition intensified. By 1994, MÁV was carrying 159 million passengers, compared to 225 million in 1989, but by 1995 the steep drop appeared to be over and carryings stabilised. MÁV expects a loss of 2 or 3 per cent over the next few years as

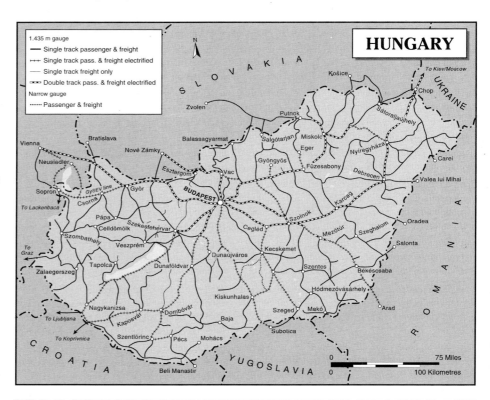

Suburban emu built by Ganz-Hunslet

1996

increasing motorisation of Hungarian society takes hold. Levels of car ownership already exceed 200 vehicles per 1,000 inhabitants.

State subsidies have been drastically falling since 1986. In response to the financial crisis, the payroll was cut to 70,000 in 1995 from its earlier level of 127,000, and track and rolling stock maintenance has been delayed. To save money, in mid-1997 the government decreed that 180 of MÁV's 5,000+ services (mostly early morning and late evening trains) should be cut. Ancillary businesses such as engineering departments have been transferred to separate companies.

From 1 January 1994 new legislation divorced the passenger and freight operations of MÁV from its infrastructure, accounting each separately. Main lines will continue to be owned by the central government, while branch lines may be handed over to local authorities. Private sector firms will be able to apply to run railway services, subject to government licence.

Under the Act, on 1 February 1995 a two-year contract was agreed between the state and MÁV Ltd. It defined which infrastructure elements would remain exclusively in state (treasury) ownership, the fee to be paid for their use and public service obligations whose deficits would be covered by the state. This contract contributes to the consolidation of MÁV's finances; at the beginning of 1996, the contract was extended to run through to 1998.

Efforts are being made to reduce operating costs, particularly on 3,900 km of rural branch lines. The World Bank has recommended closure of these lines. MÁV drew up a list of 25 lines totalling 900 km (including 165 km of narrow-gauge lines) for closure in 1995, mostly in the poorer eastern part of the country, but after strong protests the plan was put on hold. In 1996, MÁV identified three branch lines which it was prepared to close despite protests.

Another strand of the financial restructuring is to reduce holdings in subsidiary companies and to sell off property that is no longer needed for railway operational purposes. In January 1996, MÁV sold a 39 per cent stake in its Dunakeszi workshops to Adtranz.

Passenger operations

MÁV joined the western European EuroCity system with the 1988 conferring of EC status on the Vienna—Budapest 'Lehar'. EC links later added are the Dortmund—Budapest 'Franz Liszt', the Frankfurt—Stuttgart—Munich—Budapest—Debrecen 'Béla Bartók', the Berlin—Budapest 'Hungaria' and the Hamburg—Budapest 'Comenius'. These use new MÁV Spanish-built cars.

An international night train, the 'Kálmán Imre', links Munich with Budapest, and runs on to Bucharest in Romania during the day. A EuroNight service introduced in 1996, the 'Ister', gives a night connection to Bucharest. Another EuroNight service (the 'Zürichsee') runs to Zurich via Wiener Neustadt, the Semmering Pass and Innsbruck. Other overnight services are the 'Orient Express' to Paris and 'Venezia' to Zagreb, Ljubljana and Venice.

International trains used to run lightly loaded down Line 1 from Budapest to Györ on their way to Vienna and the West. They were generally not open to domestic travel, and international tickets cost twice as much per kilometre as inland ones. From 1 June 1997 these trains have been open to domestic travellers to and from Györ with inland tickets plus a simple intercity supplement. This has almost doubled the intercity frequency with Györ and inludes one through service to Debrecen. MÁV hopes the revenue from new travellers will offset the loss from some international journeys being partly made with cheaper inland tickets.

Domestically, MÁV runs a number of supplementary-fare intercity services radiating from Budapest: 182 km non-stop to Miskolc (introduced in 1991), 270 km to the eastern cities of Debrecen and Nyíregyháza (1992), 228 km non-stop to Pécs (1994) and 191 km to Kecskemét and Szeged (1994).

Since May 1995, the latter service has been operated by three new intercity emus made by Ganz-Hunslet (see 'Traction and rolling stock') which freed up loco-hauled stock for new intercity services. A four times daily Budapest—Györ—Csorna—Szombathely service was introduced, which runs diesel-hauled over the final 72 km from Csorna. Sopron is now served three times daily: twice with portions off the Szombathely service adding and detaching at Csorna, and once with a portion on the 'Zürichsee' EuroNight service.

Freight operations

Freight traffic has been badly affected by the political and economic changes in Hungary since 1989, with some

BV 160 km/h intercity emu built by Ganz-Hunslet

1996

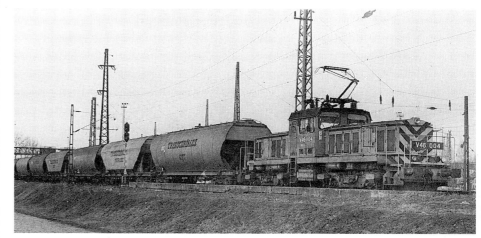

Class V46 Bo-Bo electric locomotive hump shunting at Budapest's main marshalling yard at Ferencváros (David Haydock)

1997

Diesel locomotives

Class	Builder's type	Wheel arrangement	Power kW	Speed km/h	Weight tonnes	No in service	First built	Builders Mechanical	Engine	Transmission
M28	Rába M033	B	100	30	20	23	1955	Rába	Ganz	*M* Rába
M31	DHM2	C	330	60	45	6	1958	Mávag	Ganz	*H* Voith
M32	DHM6	C	260	60	36	20	1973	Mávag	Ganz	*H* Ganz
M40	DVM6	Bo-Bo	440	100	75.6	54	1966	Mávag	Ganz	*E* Ganz Electric
M41	DHM7	B-B	1,320	100	66	113	1973	Mávag	Pielstick/Ganz	*H* Voith/Ganz
M43	LDH45	B-B	330	60	48	127	1974	Aug 23	Aug 23	*H* Brasso Hydrom
M44	DVM2	Bo-Bo	440	80	62	136	1956	Mávag	Ganz	*E* Ganz Elec
M47	LDH70	B-B	520	70	48	88	1974	Aug 23	Aug 23	*H* Brasso Hydrom
M61	M60	Co-Co	1,430	100	108	9	1963	Nohab	GM	*E* GM
M62	M62	Co-Co	1,470	100	120	130	1965	Lugansk	Kolomna	*E* Charkov
M42	DVM14	Bo-Bo	640	80	68	1	1994	Ganz-Hunslet	MM	*E* Ganz Ansaldo

Diesel railcars or multiple-units

Class	Builder's type	Cars per unit	Motor cars per unit	Motored axles/car	Power/motor kW	Speed km/h	Units in service	First built	Builders Mechanical	Engine	Transmission
Bzmot	Bzmot	2	1	1	140	70	228	1977	Studenka	Rába/MAN	*HM* Praha
MDmot†	MDa	5	1	4	590	100	40	1969	Ganz-Mávag	Ganz	*HM* Ganz

† Power units of *Piroska* sets

Electric locomotives

Class	Builder's type	Wheel arrangement	Speed km/h	Weight tonnes	No in service	First built	Builders Mechanical	Engine
V43	VM14	B-B	130	80	359	1964	Mávag	Ganz Electric
V46	VM16	Bo-Bo	80	80	60	1983	Mávag	Ganz Electric
V63	VM15	Co-Co	120/160	116	53	1975	Mávag	Ganz Electric

Electric railcars or multiple-units

Class	Cars per unit	Motor cars per unit	Motored axles/car	Output kW	Speed km/h	No in service	First built	Builders Mechanical	Electrical
BDv	4	1	4	1,444	120	19	1988	Ganz-Hunslet	Ganz Electric
BV	4	1	4	1,755	160	3	1995	Ganz-Hunslet	ABB/Ganz Ansaldo
BVh	4	1	4	1,755	120	2	1996	Ganz-Hunslet	ABB/Ganz Ansaldo

plants which generated heavy traffic having closed and new private sector road operators having taken other freight. Freight traffic more than halved in the 1989-94 period, from 104 to 44.2 million tonnes, but then stabilised, with 46.4 million tonnes in 1995. As Hungary is a landlocked country, international traffic is very important, with over half of MÁV's freight tonnage crossing the border.

MÁV's wagon fleet has been drastically reduced to reflect the reduced tonnage being carried, from a fleet of around 70,000 vehicles in the 1980s to 30,000 today.

Intermodal operations

To offset the drop in heavy industrial traffic such as coal and steel, MÁV is promoting container and piggyback transport transport.

The railway-owned international container company Intercontainer-Interfrigo (ICF), along with several business partners, established Pannoncont, a Budapest-based company, in mid-1992. An Intercontainer service, the 'Adria Express', runs daily between Budapest and Trieste in northern Italy, transiting Slovenia. Transit times are 24 hours. Other such services operate from Sopron to Hamburg (the 'Hansa Hungaria') and to Rotterdam (the 'Hungaria Express'). In conjunction with MÁV, Hungarokombi, the Hungarian member of UIRR (the international piggyback organisation), operates RoLa ('rolling motorway') services for trucks accompanied by their drivers. RoLa services were first introduced on a twice-daily basis between Wels (Austria) and Budapest in 1992. Since August 1993 services have operated three times daily between Wels and Kiskundorozsma, on the southeastern border of Hungary. A daily service started in 1994 between Sopron and Wels and in 1995 between Budapest and Ljubljana, Slovenia. Hungarokombi doubled its shipments in 1995 and in 1996 Ganz-Hunslet was building more RoLa wagons for MÁV.

New lines

A rail link to Budapest's Ferihegy airport, financed by private capital, has been proposed, but there are no firm dates for construction of this link.

Improvements to existing lines

In 1991 the General Managers of MÁV and the Austrian federal railways (ÖBB) agreed a plan for upgrading of the Budapest–Vienna trunk route. This was due to be finished in 1997.

Track and catenary were being renewed to raise the line's permissible top speed to 160 km/h. This, in conjunction with provision by the ÖBB of 18 Class 1014 dual-voltage electric locomotives to eliminate frontier traction changes, would cut the intercity journey time by a third to 2 hours when the project was complete. New German-built coaching stock is being purchased for the route by MÁV.

When funds and political conditions in the former Yugoslavia permit, the next project to follow the Vienna–Budapest line will be upgrading of the Budapest–Kelebia line leading to Belgrade and Athens. This is a bigger job than the Vienna line as the Belgrade route is only single-

MÁV's most powerful electric locomotive type is the Co-Co Class V63; this example is at Budapest Nyugati (David Haydock)   **1997**

track and in worse physical condition. Double-tracking and alignment for 200 km/h is planned.

Traction and rolling stock

At the start of 1997 MÁV was operating 472 electric locomotives, 704 diesel locomotives, 23 emus, 268 dmus, 3,427 hauled passenger cars (including 89 buffet/dining and 93 sleeper/couchette cars) and 30,000 wagons.

In 1990-91 delivery was taken of 20 type BDvmot emus derived from two prototypes delivered by Ganz-Mávag in 1988. Each unit consists of a 25 kV AC power car with a 1,520 kW rating, two intermediate trailers and a control trailer; maximum speed is 120 km/h, total weight 191 tonnes and seating capacity 356. The power car has two body-mounted asynchronous three-phase motors with thyristor control driving one bogie via a cardan shaft transmission, and has regenerative braking.

In 1994-95, MÁV took delivery of five type BV emus from Ganz-Hunslet. Three four-car intercity and two four-car surburban emus were in the initial order. The units have three-phase asynchronous drive and a continuous power rating of 1,755 kW; electrical equipment was supplied by Adtranz and Ganz Ansaldo.

In 1992 a contract worth US$95 million was awarded to CAF of Spain for 76 UIC type Z1 cars of various configurations, from sleeping and couchette to compartment, saloon and restaurant, capable of operation in EuroCity service at up to 200 km/h. Delivery was completed in 1995.

In 1995, DWA started supplying 72 new coaches of UIC Type Z2. Being built chiefly at the Bautzen and Ammendorf plants in Germany, some local assembly is taking place at the MÁV/Adtranz Dunakeszi workshops. These vehicles are being mounted on Type GH250 high-speed bogies supplied by Ganz-Hunslet.

In 1996, Ganz-Hunslet was tendering to build 18 motor cars (with electrics from Adtranz) and 18 driving trailers

for MÁV. These would be mated with trailers MÁV already owns to form four-car suburban emus.

Signalling and telecommunications

Nearly half of the system is equipped with automatic colourlight signalling and modern integral signalling centres have been installed at two-thirds of all stations. Track-to-train radio is operational on 1,400 km of the radial routes from Budapest. CTC (Centralised Traffic Control) is operative over 700 route-km.

In the southeast of the network three main line sections totalling some 300 km have been brought under the control of one centre at Szeged. Forward plans include development of this centre and resignalling at Budapest Ferencváros.

In consortium with Austria's Alcatel, MÁV is developing and installing a train control system on the Vienna–Budapest main line which will be compatible with the European Train Control System currently under development.

Some World Bank aid has contributed to development of a computerised traffic management information system. This provides real-time data on traction and vehicle movements, marshalling yard operation and wagon distribution as well as fulfilling client information functions. Some 800 terminals throughout the railway will be linked to it; it was brought into operation in 1996.

Electrification

Electrification of a 30 km section from Somogyszob to Gyékényes was completed in 1994, closing a gap to the Croatian system, speeding freight transit and allowing Croatian locomotives to work 'IC Kvarner' right through to Budapest.

In 1997, Siemens was awarded a DM280 million contract to electrify the following routes: Székesfehérvar–Szombathely; Újpest–Vácrátót; and Balatonszentgyërgy–Murakeresztúr. On the latter line, Croatian diesels currently work some services from Zagreb over the 41 km non-electrified section in Hungary to limit the number of locomotive changes needed.

MÁV is electrifying the line from Miskolc northwards to the border with Slovakia.

Rail: 60, 54 or 48 kg/m, in some places lighter
Sleepers: Concrete and timber. Length, 2,420 mm; height, 190 mm; width, base, 280 mm; width, top, 200 mm
Min curve radius: 1,300 m for 140 km/h top speed; 1,800 m for 160 km/h top speed
Max gradient: 2.5%
Max permissible axleload: 22.5 tonnes

All new rail is 54.3 kg/m laid on prestressed concrete sleepers with a ballast depth of 500 mm. Minimum curve radius is 1,300 m and normal top speed is 140 km/h.

Under the Communist regime, five-year plans saw programmed upgrading of track for heavier axleloads and higher speeds. Due to lack of funding, this upgrading fell into abeyance for a few years, but restarted in 1994. The aim is to eliminate most speed limitations related to the condition of track on the international main lines by 1998.

The 'Lehar' EuroCity service from Vienna enters Budapest hauled by a dual-voltage Austrian Class 1014 locomotive (Stefan MacGill)   **1996**

Györ-Sopron-Ebenfurt Railway (GySEV/ROeEE)

Györ–Sopron–Ebenfurti-Vasút
Raab-Oedenburg-Ebenfurter Eisenbahn AG
Szilágyi Dezsö-tér 1, H-1011 1 Budapest
Tel: +36 1 201 4988   Fax: +36 1 201 9197

Key personnel

General Manager: Dr János Berényi
Deputy General Managers:
    Dr László Fehérvári, Csaba Siklos
Director — Sopron: Dr Tibor Jozan
Director — Wulkaprodersdorf: Csaba Székely
Personnel Director: György Tabori
Commercial Director: Tibor Varga
Finance Director: Eszter Menich

Gauge: 1,435 mm
Route length: 101 km (Hungary), 65 km (Austria)
Electrification: 156 km at 25 kV 50 Hz AC

Organisation

The Austrian and Hungarian components of this international link are under separate operational management. The railway owns 12 electric and 19 diesel locomotives, 44 passenger cars and 226 wagons. In 1994, Ganz-Hunslet built 20 sliding side wagons for GySEV.

Passenger operations

In 1995, GySEV carried 2.4 million passengers for 104 million passenger-km.

V43 class electric locomotives at Sopron (Stefan MacGill)   **1996**

Freight operations

In 1995, GySEV handled 3.9 million tonnes of freight for 265 million tonne-km.

Intermodal operations

In March 1996, Intercontainer-Interfrigo launched a new intermodal service between the Dutch port of Rotterdam and Sopron entitled 'Rotterdam-Hungaria-Container-Express' (RHCE). The RHCE shuttle trains operate twice weekly and have a capacity of 60 TEU. At GySEV's Sopron terminal, containers are either transhipped to feeder trains for Hungary, the Balkan countries and Turkey or to road vehicles.

UPDATED

INDIA

Indian Railway Board (IR)

Rail Bhavan, Raisina Road, New Delhi 110 001
Tel: +91 11 338 8931-41   Fax: +91 11 338 4481
Telex: 3166061 rail in

Key personnel

Minister for Railways: Ram Vilar Paswan
Minister of State for Railways: Satpal Maharaj
Chairman: M Ravindra
Railway Board Members
    Engineering: M Ravindra
    Electrical: S K Khanna
    Traffic: Shanti Narain
    Staff: V K Agarwal
    Mechanical: L K Sinha
Financial Commissioner: V Siva Kumaran
Secretary: D P Tripathi
Additional Members
    Staff: G Ramakrishnan
    Management Services:
    Mechanical: Jasbir Pal Singh
    Mechanical, Production Units: R Subramanyam
    Civil Engineering: N C Binalish
    Works: U R Chopra
    Traffic: S K Gupta
    Projects M M Goyal
    Finance: P V Vasudevan
    Budget: N P Srivastava
    Telecommunications: V P Chandan
    Signalling: Chandrika Prasad
    Electrical: K S Sharma
    Stores: K P Varma
    Planning: S Suryanarayan
    Commercial: K K Chakraborty
    Vigilance: Kanwarjit Singh
    Computer & Information Systems: A Mukerjee
    Tourism & Catering: Dr A J Kumar
Director General, Railway Protection Force:
    A P Durai
Director General, Health Services: Dr Phani Dhar
Executive Directors
    Coaching: K C Jena
    Safety: Indra Ghosh
    Statistics & Economics: H G Sharma
    Accounts: P Rajgopalan
    Efficiency & Research: A K Gupta
    Land Management: V K Agarwal
    Railway Electrification: S L Bhargava
    Track: R P Gupta

General Managers, Manufacturing and other units
    Chittaranjan Locomotive Works: S Dharni
    Varanasi Diesel Locomotive Works: R K Jain
    Integral Coach Factory: A K Malhotra
    Wheel and Axle Plant: G K Malhotra
    Rail Coach Factory: V P Ojha
    Railway Electrification, CORE:
    Metro Railway, Calcutta:
    NF Railway Construction: R L Malik
Research, Design and Standards Organisation:
    P C Verma
Principal, Railway Staff College: J M Ovasdi
Director, IR Centre for Advanced Management and
    Technology: Jose Phillip
Chief Administrative Officers
    Diesel Component Works: Hari Mohan
    Central Organisation for Modernisation of Workshops:
    O P Gupta
Chairman, Konkan Railway Corporation: E Sreedharan

Gauge: 1,676 mm; 1,000 mm; 762 mm and 610 mm
Route length: 40,620 km; 18,501 km; 3,794 km
Electrification: on 1,676 mm gauge 11,713 km at 25 kV 50 Hz AC, 429 km at 1.5 kV DC; 165 km of 1,000 mm gauge at 25 kV 50 Hz AC

Organisation

Indian Railways, organised as a central government undertaking, is Asia's largest and the world's second largest state-owned railway system under unitary management. The railway is made up of nine zonal systems: Central, Eastern, Northern, North Eastern, Northeast Frontier, Southern, South Central, South Eastern and Western. Due to the changing traffic patterns caused by large-scale gauge conversion and opening of the Konkan Railway (qv), IR is creating a further six zones. These are the East Coast, East Central, North Central, North Western, South Western and West Central railways, with headquarters respectively at Bhubaneswar, Hajipur, Allahabad, Jaipur, Bangalore and Jabalpur. Work started in late 1996 on creation of the necessary administrative infrastructure.

IR confronts serious problems of adjustment to rising demand for efficient rail transport, undertaking just over two-thirds of all freight movement. The crux is that its cash and physical resources cannot cope with the need for capacity expansion throughout its network and in its ancillary services, such as workshops.

Electrification, track doubling, gauge conversion and resignalling on key routes are priorities to augment operating capacity. Since 1950 doubling has been carried out over almost 10,000 route-km. Since 1990, however, IR has not been immune to global economic factors. For the first time for some years traffic volumes did not reach budgeted levels in 1990. A new constraint on passenger traffic has been some draconian fare increases (see Finance), though during 1994-95 this trend was reversed when passenger earnings increased from Rs51.38 billion to Rs54.1 billion. The budgeted figure for FY97-98 is Rs71.06 billion.

The cost of the eighth five-year plan (1992-97) was fixed at Rs272 billion, including federal budgetary support of Rs53.7 billion. The objectives were an annual growth rate of 5 per cent in passenger traffic and attainment of 443 million tonnes (for 318.3 billion tonne-km) in the final year (1996-97) of the plan. Against this, the revised estimate for 1996-97 is 410 million tonnes and 281 billion tonne-km. Main areas of investment are in renewal and replacement of worn-out assets, gauge conversion (6,000-7,000 route-km), electrification (2,500-3,000 route-km), rolling stock acquisition, replacement and renewal of track and other assets, improved passenger services, development of greater terminal capacity and intermodal transport. In addition, considerable importance is being given to development of the rail network in inaccessible and backward regions of the country, especially in the northeast and Jammu & Kashmir.

Finance

In the budget for FY1997-98, the first year of the ninth national five-year plan, IR's annual planned outlay is Rs83 billion, that is the same level as for FY1996-97. This is to be financed through budget support of Rs18.31 billion, IR internally generated funds of Rs34.19 billion, investment through the Indian Railway Finance Corporation of Rs20.5 billion, and private sector investment under BOLT (Build, Own, Lease, Transfer) and 'own your wagon' schemes amounting to Rs9 billion.

Budgetary support to IR from central government is being reduced over the years, mainly due to severe shortage of resources. On the other hand, there is a steady increase in working expenditure. For example, in FY1995-96, expenses inclusive of depreciation were higher by Rs19.57 billion than those in FY1994-95. These factors have forced IR to mobilise additional resources internally, necessitating further fare and rates rises.

In the budget for 1996-97 there was a 10 per cent increase in all fares for air conditioned and first class mail/ express travel, and 5 per cent in second class sleepers. On freight tariffs, there was a 12 per cent rise for all

New Delhi–Howrah 'Rajdhani Express' hauled by Adtranz WAP5 three-phase electric locomotive **1997**

commodities except those for mass consumption. IR's estimates for 1997-98 are for gross traffic receipts of Rs278.55 billion, an increase of Rs34.05 billion over the revised estimate for 1996-97.

The Railway Fare & Freight Committee set up to examine the whole structure of fares and freight rates has made several recommendations for attracting more traffic, raising additional revenue and reducing costs. Many of its recommendations have been accepted by IR, but implementation will be in stages. However, the government has yet to solve overmanning in the public sector, and the tradition that a public sector post is effectively a job for life. IR's staff, for example, totalled 1.586 million in 1995-96 for a wage bill of Rs93.78 billion, an increase of Rs13 billion over 1994-95.

Gauge conversion

To boost the country's transport infrastructure and speed up development of the areas served by metre-gauge routes, IR had planned conversion of 6,000 km of busy metre-gauge routes to 1,676 mm gauge at a cost of Rs39 billion during the 1992-97 five-year plan. The so-called Project Unigauge has been carried out successfully, with conversion of 1,350 km, 1,619 km, 1,805 km and 758 km being completed in the years 1992 to 1996. In 1996-97, Rs6 billion was provided for conversion of a further 1,200 km, completion of which would see the 6,000 km target exceeded by over 900 km. Conversion of the 934 km Delhi–Ahmedabad route was completed in 1997 at a cost of Rs7.85 billion. In FY1997-98, IT has budgeted Rs9.10 billion for conversion of a further 900 km of metre- and narrow-gauge routes.

Revenue (Rs million)	1994-95	1995-96
Passengers	54,636.6	61,244.9
Freight	136,696.7	152,904.0
Other income	13,715.6	10,796.0
Total	205,048.9	224,944.9

Expenditure	1994-95	1995-96
Working expenditure	127,001.2	143,749.0
Reserve Funds	38,900.0	41,500.0
Financial charges	13,617.1	
Total	179,518.3	185,249.0

Traffic (million)	1994-95	1995-96
Freight tonnes	381	405
Freight tonne-km	252,967	273,516
Passenger journeys	3,915	4,018
Passenger-km	319,363	341,999

Passenger operations

Since 1950 IR's passenger traffic, measured in journeys, has risen by 213 per cent. Assessed in passenger-km of non-suburban rail travel, growth during the same period has been as much as 414 per cent. The rise in passenger-km has been due mainly to the increase in average journey length from 68.8 km in 1950 to 175.2 km in 1995-96.

There is continuous demand for introduction of new trains and increased frequency of existing service, especially 'Rajdhani Expresses'. In 1995-96, IR introduced 175 new trains, including five pairs of 'Shatabdi Expresses', and extended runs of 130 existing

services. During 1996-97, 82 trains were added to the timetable and 62 extended. Additional main line emu and dmu services were introduced over several sections to segregate short- and long-distance traffic. Railbus service was introduced on the Mankapur–Katra section.

Introduction of three-tier air conditioned sleeper cars is providing affordable sleeping accommodation for those who would have used chair cars. These cars have 67 berths against the 46 available in existing two-tier stock; all 'Rajdhani Expresses' are now so equipped. The computerised reservation system, now installed at 271 locations, has brought considerable improvement in passenger amenity, and its operations are being extended to a further 29 locations.

New passenger terminals have been commissioned at Kurla and Bandra in Bombay, Shalimar in Calcutta and Nizamuddin in Delhi, all locations where operations are severely constrained by shortage of platforms. Remodelling of suburban platforms is being carried out at Howrah to provide for double-discharge of commuter trains, and an additional platform is being built for double-discharge at Sealdah.

Freight operations

In FY95-96 revenue-earning freight grossed 391 million tonnes, some 26 million tonnes more than in the previous year and an improvement on the revised estimates.

The chief measures taken to enlarge freight operating capacity (and also to enhance productivity and efficiency) are recourse to more unit train working, block train segregation of high-capacity, roller bearing-equipped wagons, pursuit of as many 4,500 tonne trainloads as are feasible within existing passing loop parameters, and raising train speeds to a maximum of 80 km/h. Between 90 and 100 per cent of all coal, ore and petroleum product

traffic moves in unit trains. Point-to-point fast freights known as 'Speed Link Express', introduced for movement of general goods between Delhi, Calcutta, Bombay and Madras, brought encouraging results and are to be extended to other corridors.

One challenging feature now visible in freight operations is the 'peaking pattern' of traffic on offer. During the first eight months of the year, capacity is generally under-utilised, while the excess of traffic in the remaining four months leads to unsatisfied demand. Since capacity generation is capital intensive, IR has taken two initiatives to remedy the situation. One is to offer greater encouragement to purchase private-owner wagons ('Own your own wagon'), the other is to lease infrastructure and rolling stock under Build/Own/Lease/ Transfer schemes. Initially, response to these schemes had not been very encouraging, but IR has taken measures to make the offer more attractive and expects investment of Rs9 billion in BOLT/OYW schemes during 1997-98.

IR is developing a computerised freight operations information and control system (FOIS), which will improve efficiency and productivity. The system has been on trial at 22 locations in and around Delhi on the Northern Railway. If the exhaustive tests prove successful, FOIS will be extended to all railways.

Intermodal operations

The Container Corporation of India (Concor) was set up in 1988 under the administrative jurisdiction of the Ministry of Railways (qv). Its remit is to market freight movement in containers and to develop the necessary infrastructure for multimodal operations. At present, Concor operates 35 domestic and international container-handling terminals. Traffic has risen from 66,187 TEU in FY90-91 to over 594,000 in 1995-96. Package deals have been agreed with several major industries for through carriage of raw materials to production sites plus movement of finished products to destination.

A recent innovation was the introduction of tank containers for domestic movement of petroleum products. New container handling facilities opened recently include CFSS at New Muland, Sabarmati (Ahmedabad) and Tuticorin. New facilities are under construction at Nagpur and Gwalior. Through the operations of Concor, IR is now firmly involved in multimodal transport. Concor handles international traffic at the ports of Bombay, Nhava Sheva, Madras, Calcutta, Haldia, Kandla, Tuticorin, Cochin and Vizag.

Electrification

DC traction is confined to the 425 km suburban network on the Central and Western railways in the Bombay area. All recent electrification has been at 25 kV 50 Hz, which was adopted as standard in 1957. Recently the focus has been on electrifying the trunk routes linking Bombay, Delhi, Calcutta and Madras; and five of the seven major routes between these cities are energised. Electrification of the Madras–Calcutta route is in progress, with energisation also planned for the high-density routes in and around the mineral-rich areas of Bihar, West Bengal and Orissa.

Typical block train of coal diesel-hauled on the South Eastern Railway **1996**

By March 1996, electrification extended to 12,875 route-km. This was 20 per cent of total route-km, but electric traction was handling 42 per cent of passenger train-km and 59 per cent of gross tonne-km on broad-gauge.

In 1991 the Asian Development Bank approved a loan worth US$225 million towards the US$617 million expansion of operating capacity between New Delhi and Calcutta. This focuses on creation of a second electrified route with modern signalling between the two cities. In 1992 IR consequently started electrification work on the 218 km from Patratu to Sonenagar, and to add a third electrified track between Sonenagar and Mughalsarai, as well as various ancillary works including bidirectional signalling.

IR assigns high priority to electrification of the remaining high-density routes operated by diesel traction in a move to reduce dependence on imported petroleum products. In FY96-97, electrification of 642 route-km was completed, and a 2 × 25 kV autotransformer system is now in operation on the heavy haul route Bina—Katni—Anuppur—Bishrampur/Chirimiri.

During FY97-98, IR plans to complete electrification of nearly 500 km of missing links and densely trafficked sections, for which Rs3.50 billion has been allocated. Among the sections proposed for energisation are: Ambala—Saharanpur, Sonenagar—Patratu—Gomoh, and Sitarampur—Mughalsarai.

Track

Extension of mechanised track maintenance remains a priority. The World Bank has financed substantial purchases of equipment. Besides using its own resources, IR is also resorting to funding from the Asian Development Bank and recourse to leasing and contracting of mechanised maintenance. During 1995-96, 38,900 km of mechanised tamping was completed, and 1,080 km of track renewal carried out. High-output tampers are being used for straight track, and Unimat machines for turnouts. Timber sleepers are no longer installed.

In FY95-96 renewal was completed over 2,893 track-km, and 2,564 km was targeted for 1996-97. With rapid progress being made on gauge-conversion, the aim is to liquidate all arrears of track renewal on the busiest broad-gauge sections. Ultrasonic rail testing has been introduced on all major routes.

Signalling and telecommunications

Following an accident at Firozabad in 1995, IR is urgently pressing ahead with installation of track circuiting at block posts on all important main lines. Otherwise, the main emphasis is on replacement of mechanical interlockings at main line wayside stations by panel interlockings on an age/condition basis, and in busy yards by route-relay interlockings. At the end of FY95-96, IR had 1,494 panel and 170 route-relay systems, having added 98 and 4 respectively during the year. By March 1996, six solid state interlockings were in operation. Now that indigenous SSI equipment is available, IR plans an increasing number of installations.

Other areas of investment currently enjoying attention are increasing line capacity and improved safety, by provision of tokenless block, track circuiting, block-proving by axle counters, and interlocking of level crossings. The Bombay suburban networks of the Central and Western railways are to be equipped with train management systems.

On the telecommunications side, IR is replacing analogue microwave by digital systems, installing electronic telephone exchanges in place of electro-mechanical, and providing UHF radio links over busy sections. During 1995-96, 404 route-km of long-haul digital microwave was installed. On the other hand, progress wih fibre optic communications has been slow, the network remaining static at 953 km for two or three years.

Commercial Inmarsat mobile telephone service has been provided on Delhi-Bombay 'Rajdhani Express' services, using a satellite located in the Indian Ocean. All 'Rajdhanis' are to be so equipped.

Research and development

Some recent projects undertaken by IR's Research Standards & Development Organisation (RDSO) include: design and development of the WCAM3 and WAP6 electric passenger locomotives; conversion of a metre-gauge coach to a railbus; development of the IR-31 bogie for operation at 160 km/h and the IRF-101 freight bogie for 100 km/h; and 25 tonne axleload hopper wagons. Three-phase drive has been developed for AC emus, along with universal emergency communications. In addition, RDSO undertook oscillation trials on WDP1, WCAM2 and WDG2 locomotives, and braking trials on chopper-controlled emu rakes.

It has been proposed to redefine the role of RDSO and make it fully autonomous. It is felt that the organisation should concentrate on research and design, handing peripheral activities like inspection over to workshops and production units.

Traction and rolling stock

During 1996-97, Adtranz completed delivery of 30 three-phase 6,000 hp locomotives under an order placed in 1993 for 20 six-axle freight locomotives with top speed of 100 km/h, and 10 for 160 km/h passenger service. The contract also involves transfer of technology to CLW. After precommissioning tests, the freight units are being used on the Northern and Eastern railways, while the passenger locos are employed on Delhi-Howrah and Delhi-Kanpur 'Rajdhani' and 'Shatabdi' expresses.

With these locomotives, India is the first country in Asia to have three-phase drive locomotive technology, incorporating gate turn-off inverters and thyristor control.

On the diesel side, in 1996 IR ordered 20 4,000 hp diesel-electrics with AC traction motors from General Motors USA.

With a view to developing export business in complete locomotives, a design and development centre has been created at Chittaranjan Locomotive Works. During 1995-96, IR production units manufactured 138 diesel and 135 electric locomotives, and 1,580 coaches including 236 suburban emu cars, 24 dmu cars and 164 main line emu cars.

The Railways Ministry 1996-98 budget provided for local supply to IR of 150 diesel and 178 electric locomotives, 420 emu and 90 dmu cars, 1,550 coaches and 26,000 wagons.

In 1996 IR's fleet comprised 209 steam, 4,313 diesel and 2,387 electric locomotives, 3,692 emu cars, 24 diesel railcars, 29,758 coaches and 5,654 other passenger cars, and 280,791 wagons.

Type of coupler in standard use: Passenger cars, screw and automatic buffer coupling; freight wagons, Alliance II and centre buffer.

Type of brake in standard use: Most broad-gauge freight stock built after 1982 is airbraked; others vacuum, as is all passenger stock except that for the 'Rajdhani' and 'Shatabdi' expresses which are airbraked. Phased programme under way for conversion of broad-gauge passenger stock to airbrakes.

UPDATED

Konkan Railway Corporation Ltd

Belapur Bhavan, Sector 11, CBD Belapur, Navi Bombay (New Bombay) 400 614
Tel: +91 22 757 2015/2016/2017/2018
Fax: +91 22 757 2420

Key personnel

Chairman: E Sreedharan
Director, Technical: A K Somanathan
Director, Project: B Rajaram
Director, Finance: U V Acharya
Chief Engineer, Co-ordination: S D Limaye
Chief Mechanical Engineer: R S Chugh
Chief Electrical Engineer: I D Chopra
Chief Signal and Telecommunications Engineer: S G Royadhyaksha
Chief Operating Superintendent: H S Duggal

Gauge: 1,676 mm
Route length: 760 km

Organisation

This major railway opened in 1997. It extends from Roha, south of Bombay, down the coast to Mangalore. It provides a much shorter route than the historic Bombay—Mangalore line, which also entailed a break of gauge. The new line, in addition, opens up remote areas of Maharashtra, Goa and Karnataka states.

Though construction started in 1978, by the end of the 1980s less than 100 km had been completed, as far as Roha. In 1990 the Konkan Railway Corporation was formed to take over construction of the 760 km route and operate it on completion. Initially the line is be a single 1,676 mm gauge track with 53 intermediate stations, built through difficult country even by Indian standards. There

A dmu crosses Savrita bridge on the Konkan Railway **1996**

are 171 major bridges, the longest of 2,065 m and the highest 64 m, and a further 1,670 minor structures. The 92 tunnels total 83.6 km, with the longest extending to 6.5 km and using incrementally launched concrete box girder construction for the first time in India. Engineered for 160 km/h top speed, ruling gradient is 0.67 per cent and minimum curve radius 1,250 m. Track is 52 kg/m rail on prestressed concrete sleepers. The entire route is equipped with specially designed points and crossings with thick-web switches and laid on concrete sleepers.

Stations have panel interlockings and colourlight signals; communication is by fibre optic link. Computerisation of operations is being implemented.

By January 1997, the 364 km northern section and the 100 km southern portion were open for revenue service, but unforeseen geological problems have delayed opening throughout.

UPDATED

Container Corporation of India Ltd

Kanishka Office Plaza (4th Floor), Ashoka Road, New Delhi 110001
Tel: +91 11 371 0895/5421   Fax: +91 11 371 5424
Telex: 3162309 Cont IN

Key personnel
Managing Director: S K Sharma
Director, Marketing & Operations Karan Ahuja
Director, Projects & Services: A K Kohli
Group General Manager, Operations: P Uniyal
Group General Manager, Planning & Development:
S B Roy
Group General Manager, Marketing: S C Misra

UPDATED

The new container terminal at Mulund (Bombay),
opened in 1996
1997

Central Railway

400000 Chatrapati Shivaji Terminus, Bombay
Tel: +91 22 262 1551   Fax: +91 22 262 4555
Telex: 011 73819 crst in

Key personnel
General Manager: N C Sinha
Additional General Manager: S Seth
Senior Deputy General Manager: B S Kushwah
Chief Administrative Officer, Construction:
   Arvind Kumar
Chief Electrical Engineer: M M Adiga
Chief Commercial Manager: B M S Bisht
Chief Operating Manager: P K Dixit
Chief Engineer: G R Madan
Chief Mechanical Engineer: B S Kushwah
Financial Adviser and Chief Accounts Officer:
   S N Trevedi
Chief Signal and Telecommunication Engineer:
   R C Tripathi
Controller of Stores: T V Ramakrishnan
Chief Personnel Officer: S K Aggarwal
Chief Security Officer: S P Srivastav
Chief Public Relations Officer: R Saxena

Gauge: 1,676 mm; 762 mm; 610 mm
Route length: 6,051 km; 693 km; 303 km
Electrification: 2,620 km at 25 kV 50 Hz AC; 369 km at 1.5 kV DC

Intercity emu of Central Railway   *1997*

Organisation
CR serves six states: Maharashtra, Madhya Pradesh, Uttar Pradesh, parts of Rajasthan, Haryana and Karnataka, and has divisional headquarters at Bombay, Bhusawal, Nagpur, Jabalpur, Solapur, Jhansi and Bhopal.
   By virtue of its central location, CR is of pivotal importance to the IR network, connecting North and South India and East and West India. Besides carrying heavy transit traffic, it has a high loading potential of its own.

Passenger operations
CR transports over 3 million passengers on about 1,600 passenger trains every day. In 1995-96, passenger-km constituted 25 per cent of the IR total and are the highest amongst the nine zonal railways.
   The Bombay area suburban services account for 82.4 per cent of the total originating passengers and 31.8 per cent of total passenger-km, with an average trip length in 1995-96 of 25.6 km. Suburban traffic has grown from 452 million originating passengers to 876 million since 1970. CR runs 1,116 suburban trains a day. The network has also been extended by a double-track line across Thane Creek to a satellite city, New Bombay, on the mainland to absorb population from the overcrowded Bombay island.
   In 1995-96 originating passenger journeys totalled 1,067 million, compared to the previous year's total of 1,040 million, of which suburban traffic accounted for 876 million and non-suburban for 185.9 million on the broad-gauge system. The balance of 5.3 million passengers was carried on narrow-gauge lines. Total passenger-km was 86,956 million.
   Future planning is based on an annual growth rate of 4 per cent for suburban and 3 per cent non-suburban

The Bombay–Pune 'Shatabdi Express' on the DC-electrified section out of Bombay   *1996*

traffic. To cater for the rise in suburban traffic, the network in the Bombay area is being expanded, and a further extension of the double-track line in New Bombay is under construction from Belapur to Panvel. Additional emu rakes are being introduced and signalling works are under way. It is also planned to reduce progressively the headway of suburban services during peak hours initially from 5 to 4 minutes, and later 3 minutes. The pace of

track renewal is being stepped up, and passenger information systems are being made more efficient.
   In 1995, CR commissioned one of the two new terminal stations in Bombay, at Kurla on the city's outskirts. Its five platforms can accommodate the 26-car trains which IR plans to introduce. This terminal is already being expanded to cater for three additional pairs of trains. A new station is also being built at Habibganj (Bhopal).

CR runs IR's fastest train, the air conditioned 'Shatabdi Express' which, with licence to run at up to 140 km/h on parts of the New Delhi—Bhopal route and the benefit of a route equipped with AWS, averages 101 km/h over the 195 km from Delhi to Agra and Bhopal, in 7 hours 45 minutes for the 701 km.

Traffic (million)	1994-95	1995-96
Freight tonnes*	95.7	98.5
Freight tonne-km	38,736	40,889
Passenger journeys	1,296	1,345
Passenger-km	81,171	86,956

* includes non-revenue traffic

Revenue (Rs million)	1994-95	1995-96
Passengers	10,973	11,920
Freight	19,899	21,426
Other income	1,934	2,264
Total	32,806	35,610

Expenditure (Rs million)	1994-95	1995-96
Staff/personnel	n/a	n/a
Materials and services	n/a	n/a
Depreciation	2,898	2,879
Financial changes*	n/a	n/a
Total	25,577	28,827

* Pension fund and payment to general revenue

Freight operations

Freight consists chiefly of bulk commodities such as coal, cement, fertiliser, petroleum products, food grains and raw material to steel plants. Total originating revenue traffic was 38.5 million tonnes in 1995-96.

Until 1992-93, annual growth of originating and total traffic had been almost 4 per cent since the mid-1980s. To meet the increased demand, extensive electrification, doubling of tracks, track renewals and improved signalling are in various stages of completion. Higher capacity electric locomotives are also coming into service. Freight trains with trailing loads of 4,700 tonnes are already running and their number is being increased.

A rapid increase in ISO container traffic followed the 1989 opening of Jawaharlal Nehru Port at Nhava Sheva in New Bombay. This is served by an offshoot of the new suburban line across Thane Creek.

Improvements to existing lines

Double-tracking of three sections — Diva—Vasai Road, Diva—Panvel and Daund—Bhigwan — is in progress at a cost of Rs1.75 billion. Gauge conversion of 52 km of narrow-gauge between Pandhar and Kurduwadi was also under way during 1995-96, while conversion of Chindwara—Parasia was completed.

Electrification

A considerable electrification programme has been implemented. In 1992 the Delhi—Madras route and the Bombay—Delhi (via Bhusawal) routes were energised throughout. During 1994-95, 89 route-km was electrified and in 1995-96 electrification of the Bina—Katni east-west collieries route (263 km) was completed. IR's first 220/2×25 kV traction substation was commissioned on this section in 1993.

New lines

Following opening of the 78 km Deeg—Alwar line in 1994, four major new line construction projects are in progress: Panvel—Karjat; Guna—Etwah via Shiapur, Gwalior and Bhind (348 km); Amravati—Narkhed (138 km); and Satna—Rewa (50 km). Construction of the 250 km Amednagar—Parli Vaijnath line in the underdeveloped area of Marathwada, approved in 1995-96, is also being taken up. In the 1997-98 works programme, a further Rs10.32 billion has been allocated for new works.

Signalling and telecommunications

The present emphasis is on rehabilitation of ageing assets, along with enhancement of safety, reliability and application of modern technology. Safety aids are being installed like block-proving by axlecounter, track circuiting of whole station areas, provision of two distant signals and introduction of route-relay and solid-state interlocking. In 1997-98, new works costing Rs300 million have been approved.

Traction and rolling stock

At the start of 1996 the railway was operating on broad-gauge 596 electric and 621 diesel locomotives, 336 emu motor cars and 657 trailers, 2,794 passenger coaches (including 1,081 sleeping and 12 dining cars), and 74,547 freight wagons (four-wheel equivalent).

Coupler in standard use

Passenger cars: Screw, Schaltbau (emus)
Wagons: CBC AAR-type screw; CBC Alliance II

Braking in standard use

Locomotive-hauled stock: Vacuum and air
Emus: Air

Track (BG)

Rail: 60, 52 and 44 kg/m FF
Crossties (sleepers): Monobloc concrete, 2,750 × 270 × 230 or 151 mm; wooden, 2,750 × 250 × 130 mm; steel, of various sizes
Sleeper spacing: 1,660/km on A routes; 1,540/km on B, C and D routes; 1,310/km on E routes
Fastenings: Keys, elastic fastenings such as Pandrol clip
Max gradient: 2.9% (1 in 34)
Max permissible axleload: 22.5 tonnes

UPDATED

Eastern Railway

17 Netaji Subhash Road, Calcutta 700 001
Tel: +91 33 220 6811

Key personnel

General Manager: A P Murugesam
Additional General Manager: A Chatto Padhya (Acting)
Senior Deputy General Manager: A K Roy
Financial Adviser and Chief Accounts Officer:
  A Ghosh
Chief Operating Manager: M C Srivastav
Chief Commercial Manager: R N Bhattacharyya
Chief Electrical Engineer: N K Chidambaram
Chief Personnel Officer: A S Gupta
Chief Engineer: K P Singh
Chief Mechanical Engineer: R N Aga
Chief Signal and Telecommunications Engineer:
  Subur Basu
Controller of Stores: N K Sahu
Chief Public Relations Officer: A S Upadhyay

Gauge: 1,676 mm; 762 mm
Route length: 4,184 km; 132 km
Electrification: 1,559 km at 25 kV 50 Hz AC

Organisation

ER is described as the 'Black Diamond' railway on account of its prime task of supplying coal to power stations. It runs mainly in the states of West Bengal and Bihar, and also in parts of Uttar Pradesh.

Freight operations

In 1995-96 ER originated 62.8 million tonnes of coal, which accounted for 85.6 per cent of freight traffic emanating from its territory. Freight as a whole aggregated 73 million tonnes and 28,824 million tonne-km.

Passenger operations

Originating passenger journeys amounted to 552 million in 1995-96, for 36,275 million passenger-km. Of the total, some 1.1 million daily journeys were made on the Calcutta suburban network. Almost all main line passenger services are electrically operated, while Calcutta emu trains have been increased from eight to nine cars, with 10-car trains running on the Howrah and Sealdah divisions.

Following introduction of dmus in 1990, ER's first main line emu services were introduced in 1994 between

Diesel multiple-unit on Sealdah—Hasanabad service of Eastern Railway

Asansol and Bardhaman. These multiple-unit services have proved very popular, and in 1997-98 were to be extended to the Purulia—Bardhaman, Asansol—Jhajha and Dhanbad—Gaya—Mughalsarai sections.

At Calcutta's Howrah station, work is in progress remodelling platforms to provide double-discharge facilities for crowded suburban trains. At Sealdah, which deals with 580 trains a day, another 22-coach platform is under constuction and double-discharge is to be provided. Computerised reservation is now available at most locations handling more than 300 reservations a day.

Improvements to existing lines

It is estimated that the freight and passenger traffic task will rise to 101 million tonnes and 731 million passenger journeys annually by 2000. Accordingly, several development works are in progress or planned to improve the infrastructure. Important projects include construction of the remaining portion of new route between Lakshmikantpur and Namkhana; double-tracking of three key sections; provision of a third electrified line on the Sonenagar—Mughalsarai and Bandel—Howrah sections; and completion of microwave communications between Howrah and Mughalsarai. During 1995-96 double-tracking of 35 km was completed.

Electrification

During 1995-96, electrification was completed of 81 route-km, including Bandel—Katwa (53 km) and Sitarampur—Mughalsarai (16 km), and a further 196 route-km was energised in 1996-97. In the budget for 1997-98, electrification of the 23 km Kusunda—Jarnuniatand branch has been approved.

Traction and rolling stock

At the start of 1996 the railway operated 381 electric and 519 diesel locomotives, 352 emu motor cars and 753 trailers, 3,426 passenger coaches, and 86,594 freight wagons (four-wheel equivalent).

Signalling and telecommunications
Apart from signalling works to improve line capacity on busy sections, ER is at present concentrating on replacement of old electromechanical installations by route-relay and panel interlockings. Route-relay interlocking is being installed at five stations, panel interlocking at 28, and solid-state equipment at eight. Electronic telephone exchanges are being provided at three stations.

Coupler in standard use
Passenger cars: Drawbar with screw coupling
Freight cars: Centre buffer coupler; CBC with transition coupling; drawbar with screw coupling
Braking in standard use
Locomotive-hauled stock: Air and vacuum brake

Track (BG)
Rail: 52 and 60 kg/m

Crossties (sleepers): CST-9; thickness: M + 4 to M + 7; spacing 1,562/km; PRC, wooden
Fastenings: Key
Min curvature: 8°
Max gradient: 1.25%
Max permissible axleload: 22.5 tonnes

UPDATED

North Eastern Railway

Gorakhpur 273012, Uttar Pradesh
Tel: +91 551 333041

Key personnel
General Manager: S N Pandey
Chief Personnel Officer: A K Misra
Financial Adviser and Chief Accounts Officer:
    Sushma Pandey
Chief Commercial Manager: V M Pandey
Chief Engineer: G R Madan
Chief Administration Officer, Construction: R N Sachan
Chief Operations Manager: R A Pandey
Chief Electrical Engineer: Vinod Prasad
Chief Signals and Telecommunications Engineer:
    S K Chopra
Chief Mechanical Engineer: Mahesh Chandra
Controller of Stores: R N Sahu
Chief Medical Officer: Dr V K Sanadaya

Gauge: 1,676 mm; 1,000 mm
Route length: 1,593 km; 3,513 km

Organisation
Increases of population and economic development now exert extreme pressure on the predominantly metre-gauge network of the NER. It covers Bihar and Uttar Pradesh from Achnera in the west to Katihar in the east, and moves traffic for Nepal.

Passenger and freight operations
In 1995-96 originating passenger journeys totalled 120 million, of which 37 per cent were on broad-gauge, for 270,796 million passenger-km. Originating freight amounted to 3.03 million tonnes, for 5,158 million tonne-km.

Improvements to existing lines
Conversion to 1,676 mm gauge of NER's entire trunk route from Lucknow to Katihar was completed before the current programme. This had greatly improved rail access to Assam, while regauging of the Bhatni—Varanasi line simplified interchange of freight with the Central, Eastern and Northern railways.
    Under the current programme, conversion of Burhwal—Sitapur (98 km), Varanasi—Allahabad (125 km) and Mankapur—Katra (90 km) has been completed. In

addition, the Ranpur—Kathgoclam conversion/construction project enabled introduction of direct broad-gauge trains between Kathgoclam and Delhi/Calcutta. Conversion of the Muzaffarpur—Raxaul section in 1994-95 has provided a direct broad-gauge route from several Indian ports to Nepal. During 1995-96, 208 km of metre-gauge route was converted, and conversion of the Mau—Shahganj and Sagauli—Narkatiaganj sections was completed in 1996-97. Rs6.90 billion has been allocated for further conversions in FY1997-98.
    Another major project is restoration of the line to Bagala (29 km), completion of which will facilitate economic development in the area. The work has involved construction of an 896 m road/rail bridge over the Gandak river.

Traction and rolling stock
In March 1996 NER operated, on metre-gauge, 55 steam and 112 diesel locomotives, 1,300 passenger cars and 9,433 wagons; and on broad-gauge, 109 diesel locomotives, 1,197 passenger cars and 2,662 wagons.

UPDATED

Northeast Frontier Railway (NFR)

Maligaon, Guwahati 781 011, Assam
Tel: +91 361 70422/40338/70530
Telex: 031 0235 336

Key personnel
General Manager:
General Manager, Construction: R L Malik
Additional General Manager: S D Gupta
Financial Adviser and Chief Accounts Officer:
    R Shadab
Senior Deputy General Manager: M K Dev Varma
Chief Commercial Manager: C Murry
Chief Operating Manager: R A Pandey
Chief Engineer: V Ramaswami
Chief Electrical Engineer: R P Bhatnagar
Chief Mechanical Engineer: S C Das
Chief Signal and Telecommunications Engineer:
    Ravindra Nath
Controller of Stores: S Paul
Chief Personnel Officer: K Laloo
Chief Public Relations Officer: J D Goswami

Gauge: 1,676 mm; 1,000 mm; 610 mm
Route length: 1,044 km; 2,685 km; 87 km

Organisation
NFR serves the whole of Assam and North Bengal, parts of North Bihar, the states of Arunachal, Manipur, Meghalaya, Mizoram, Nagaland, and Tripura. Its 610 mm gauge component is the world-famous Darjeeling—Himalaya Railway.
    Besides playing a vital role in the transport of people and essential commodities, NFR is also of strategic importance, since the region is practically enveloped by international borders. NFR covers one of the most picturesque regions, overlooked by the Himalayas. Apart from serving well-known tourist centres like Darjeeling, Shillong and the wildlife sanctuaries of Kaziranga, Manas and Jaldapara, it also covers the vast tea-garden belts of

North Bengal and Assam. From Darjeeling to Dibrugarh, several stretches of NFR are prone to damage by floods or landslides during monsoons. To maintain this vital communication link with the least interruption has always been a challenging task.

Passenger and freight operations
Direct mail/express trains link Guwahati with Delhi, Bombay, Bangalore, Calcutta, Madras, Patna, Lucknow, Kanpur, Varanasi, Allahabad, Cochin and Trivandrum. In FY95-96 originating passenger traffic totalled 22 million journeys, for 7,260 million passenger-km.
    Inward freight traffic consists mainly of essential commodities such as food grains, salt, sugar, cement and steel. Outward traffic, which is smaller in volume, comprises petroleum products, coal, bamboo, timber, jute, tea, and dolomite. In FY95-96 revenue-earning traffic totalled 7.2 million tonnes and 6,039 million tonne-km.

New lines
Since 1979 NFR has had an independent construction organisation which has given a boost to the development of the railway network in the region. Present policy is to build rail links between the capitals of the region, and accordingly construction of a 119 km line from Kumarghat to Agartala was included in the 1996-97 budget.
    An important project is construction of the rail/road bridge across the Brahmaputra river at Jogighopa, along with 142 km of broad-gauge line thence to Guwahati. Now, yet another crossing of the Brahmaputra is planned, with link lines between Dibrugarh and the north bank of the river, at a cost of Rs10 billion.

Improvements to existing lines
In 1995-96, double-tracking of 9 km and gauge-conversion of 115 km was completed, along with conversion of Dimapur—Dibrugarh and Tinsukia—Lekhapani in the following year. Conversion of New Jalpaiguri—Siliguri—New Bongaigaon is budgeted for in the 1997-98 plan at a cost of Rs3.8 billion.

Signalling and telecommunications
Major telecommunications works are in progress throughout the region. Work is in progress on provision of UHF links over the 340 km between Lumding and Tinsukia, Maligaon and Guwahati, and Lumding—Badarpur—Bharmanagar.

Traction and rolling stock
At the start of 1996 NFR was operating on 1,676 mm gauge, 84 diesel locomotives, 714 passenger cars and 3,744 wagons (four-wheel equivalent); on 1,000 mm gauge, 37 steam and 142 diesel locomotives, 651 passenger cars and 6,884 wagons (four-wheel equivalent); and on 610 mm gauge, 17 steam locomotives, 43 passenger cars and 4 wagons.

Type of coupler in standard use: Passenger cars, screw; freight cars, CBC/screw type
Type of braking in standard use: Vacuum

Track
Rail: Flat-bottom 52, 44.61, 37.13, 29.76, 24.8 kg/m
Crossties (sleepers): Wood, steel trough, cast iron
Thickness: Wood: BG, 127 mm
 MG, 114 mm
 NG, 114 mm
Spacing
Main lines: BG, 1,540/km
 MG, 1,596/km
 NG, 1,230/km
Branch lines: BG, 1,309/km
 MG, 1,344/km
Fastenings: Wooden sleepers: CI/MS bearing plates and rail screws; steel trough sleepers: loose jaws with keys; cast-iron sleepers: keys
Max gradient: BG 0.64%; MG 2.7%; NG 4.344%
Max permissible axleload: BG 22.9 tonnes; MG 12.7 tonnes; NG 7.6 tonnes

UPDATED

Northern Railway

Baroda House, Kasturba Ghandi Marg, New Delhi 110 001
Tel: +91 11 387227   Fax: +91 11 384503
Telex: 3166329

Key personnel
General Manager: S P Mehta
Senior Deputy General Manager: S K Mahajan
Additional General Manager: S A A Zaidi

Financial Adviser and Chief Accounts Officer:
    Indu Chopra
Chief Commercial Manager: Aslan Mahmud
Chief Engineer: S D Sharma

Chief Mechanical Engineer: Ajit Kishore
Chief Electrical Engineer: A J Gupta
Chief Operations Manager: Govind Ballabh
Chief Signal and Telecommunications Engineer:
  R C Vatra
Chief Administrative Officer, Construction:
  K R Mehra
Controller of Stores: B K Singh
Chief Personnel Officer: N N S Rana
Chief Public Relations Officer: Arun Arora

Gauge: 1,676 mm; 1,000 mm; 762 mm
Route length: 8,669 km; 2,076 km; 259.6 km
Electrification: 1,024 km of 1,676 mm gauge at 25 kV
50 Hz AC

Organisation
NR's territory extends from Delhi through Punjab, Haryana Delhi, Himachal Pradesh, parts of Jammu & Kashmir, Rajasthan and Uttar Pradesh states.

Passenger and freight operations
In 1995-96, the railway recorded 389 million originating passenger journeys, 48,789 million passenger-km, 25.9 million tonnes of originating freight and 41,681 million tonne-km.

NR has introduced four new 'Shatabdi' expresses, linking New Delhi with Jaipur, Dehradun, Amritsar and Kalka, along with 'Rajdhanis' to Bhubaneshwar, Guwahati and Jammu. The frequency of 'Rajdhani' expresses is being increased between Delhi and Bangalore, Bubaneshwar and Madras. In addition, dmu services, main line emus and the first broad-gauge railbuses have been introduced, along with dmu service in the Amritsar area.

NR carries food grains from the Punjab and Haryana to almost all parts of the country, and loads 1,400 to 1,500 wagons daily during harvest.

Traction and rolling stock
At the start of 1996 the railway operated 253 electric, 654 diesel and four steam locomotives; 47 three-car emus, five diesel railcars; 6,283 passenger cars; and 37,231 freight wagons.

Signalling and telecommunications
Besides fitting of track circuits, major works in progress on NR include installation of train-to-control mobile communications on important trains on the Delhi–Mughalsarai route, replacement of analogue by digital microwave, the Delhi Main and Gaziabad route-relay interlockings, and provision of electronic telephone exchanges.

Tenders for installation of solid-state interlocking at 11 stations in the Allahabad division are yet to be finalised. In the meantime, approval has been granted for installation of optical fibre cables, route-relay interlocking, digital microwave and provision of track circuits at a number of locations.

New lines
Work on the new broad-gauge line from Jammu to Udhampur (53 km) is in full swing. The project, which has high embankments, deep cuttings and a 2.5 km tunnel, is progressing well. Now it has been decided to extend this

Class WAU4 25kV AC emu at Tilak Bridge Station on Northern Railway (K K Gupta)   **1995**

Dmu on Northern Railway   **1995**

line from Udhampur to Srinagar and Baramula via Katra as a national project.

Improvements to existing lines
During 1995-96, double-tracking of the Rampur–Bareilly section was completed, along with electrification of the Delhi–Ambala route (200 km). In 1995-96, electrification was extended over a 14.6 km section of the Ambala–Ludhiana route. The wires are being extended a further 113 km through to Ludhiana during 1996-97.

As regards gauge-conversion, by March 1996 NR had completed 1,347 km — 24 per cent of the entire IR task over the past four years. Work was in progress on conversion of a further 292 km during 1996-97. In the 1997-98 works programme, conversion of further sections has been approved at a cost of Rs3.97 million.

UPDATED

South Central Railway

Rail Nilayam, Secunderabad 500 371, Andhra Pradesh
Tel: +91 842 73583

Key personnel
General Manager: K M Rao
Senior Deputy General Manager: G C Sande
Financial Adviser and Chief Accounts Officer:
  J C Jaganadhan
Chief Commercial Manager: M M Farooqui
Chief Engineer: G V Ratnam
Chief Electrical Engineer: V Nagrajan
Chief Mechanical Engineer: V P Ozha
Chief Signal and Telecommunications Engineer:
  M L Gambhir
Chief Operating Manager: Vacant
Controller of Stores: S Sathyamurthy
Chief Personnel Officer: R S Pagar
Chief Public Relations Officer: P Krishnaiya

Gauge: 1,676 mm, 1,000 mm
Route length: 5,084 km, 2,118 km

Electrification: 1,156 km of 1,676 mm gauge at 25 kV
50 Hz AC

Organisation
SCR was set up in 1966 from portions of the Southern and Central railways. It covers the states of Andhra Pradesh and Goa, northwest Karnataka and southwest Maharashtra.

Passenger and freight operations
The principal raw material moved is coal, which in 1995-96 accounted for 36.8 per cent of revenue freight. Other major bulk freight flow is iron ore from the Hospet–Bellary region to Madras for export, which the railway moves in 4,500-tonne unit trains. Many new industries are arising in SCR territory, including steelworks, cement plants and a fertiliser plant at Kakinada, which promise considerable traffic growth. In the six years from 1988 cement traffic more than doubled to 10.6 million tonnes annually.

In FY95-96 revenue freight traffic grossed 65.3 million tonnes and 28,669 million tonne-km.

SCR has no considerable suburban traffic, relying mainly for passenger growth on improved intercity services. In FY95-96 originating traffic totalled 125.6 million journeys and 24,238 million passenger-km.

New lines
Construction is in progress of a 177 km route between Peddupalli, Karimpur and Nizamabad, at a cost of Rs1.9 billion, designed to open up an undeveloped region. In the works programme for 1997-98, approval has been given for construction of a 222 km line between Munirabad and Mehboudnager costing Rs3.8 billion.

Improvements to existing lines
Double-tracking of 157 km is in progress, and a further 83 km between Gudu and Renigunta has been approved in the 1997-98 works programme at a cost of Rs1.4 billiion. Gauge conversion work is in progress on eight sections totalling 2,118 km, with Muraj–Hubli (279 km) and Dinakonda–Giddalur (84 km) completed in 1994-95. In 1995-96, conversion of sections totalling 244 km were completed. When regauged throughout, the Goa–

Hospet—Guntur line will provide a direct broad-gauge route between the east and west coasts.

Electrification

In 1995-96, electrification of 166 route-km was completed. The major projects in hand are the 366 km Vijayawada—Vishakhapatnam portion of the Howrah—Madras main line along the east coast, at a cost of Rs1,960 million, and the 466 km Hospet—Renigunta line. During 1996-97, electrification of the 189 km Vijaywada—Vishakapatnam routre was ccompleted. A new depot with capacity for 100 electric locomotives was opened in Lallaguda during 1995-96.

Traction and rolling stock

At the start of 1996 the railway operated on 1,676 mm gauge 208 electric and 371 diesel locomotives, 2,261 coaches and 20,818 wagons; and on metre-gauge 70 diesel locomotives, 601 coaches and 3,067 wagons.

UPDATED

South Eastern Railway

11 Garden Reach Road, Kidderpore, Calcutta 700 043
Tel: +91 33 451 741
Telex: 021 2417 cosy

Key personnel

General Manager: S Ramanathan
Additional General Manager: V Narayanan
Senior Deputy General Manager:
  V Balasubramanian
Financial Adviser and Chief Accounts Officer:
  K K Mitra
Chief Operating Manager: Swastik Misra
Chief Commercial Manager: R M Das
Chief Mechanical Engineer: N C Sinha
Chief Engineer: S S Kapoor
Chief Electrical Engineer: V K Agarwal
Chief Signals and Telecommunications Engineer:
  R N Kumar
Controller of Stores: A K Mukhopadhaya

Gauge: 1,676 mm; 762 mm
Route length: 6,010 km; 1,340 km
Electrification: 2,886 km at 25 kV 50 Hz AC

Organisation

SER was created in a 1955 partition of the Eastern Railway and comprises the lines of the former Bengal—Nagpur Railway centred on Calcutta.

Passenger and freight operations

In 1995-96, originating passenger traffic totalled 172.2 million journeys, of which 34 per cent was suburban, for 20,722 million passenger-km.

SER originates over one-third of Indian Railways' total freight; 85 per cent of the railway's earnings come from freight traffic, which amounted to 155.5 million tonnes originating in 1995-96. It is known as the 'blue chip' railway; in 1995-96 its operating ratio was 63.93 per cent — the lowest of all Indian railways — and it achieved a surplus of Rs15.45 billion. Principal traffic is steel, coal and cement, and movement of export ore to Vishakhapatnam and Paradip ports.

A new station in Calcutta for SER trains is being built at Shalimar, and the city is also gaining a new freight terminal at Sankrail.

New lines

Several major construction schemes are in progress. To serve the new Vishakhapatnam steelworks, a 164 km line from Koraput to Rayagada was commissioned in 1995 at a cost of Rs4.42 billion. Access to Paradip port is being improved by a bypass between Sambalpur and Talcher (174 km), of which the Talcher—Angul section (18 km) was completed in 1992-93 and Sambalpur—Maneswar the following year. The remaining section is nearing completion. Construction work between Daitari and Banspani (155 km) is also making steady progress.

Development of the tribal area of Orissa is the objective of a major new route approved in the 1994-95 budget at a cost of Rs3.5 billion. This will link Khurda Road with Bolangir, 289 km distant. An 87 km line for Tamluk to the coast at Digha will benefit the tourist trade in West Bengal.

It was also proposed in the 1995-96 budget to start construction of a new line between Dallijahara and Jagdalpur (235 km) for transport of iron ore to Bhillai steelworks. It will be built on a shared-cost basis, with SER's portion being Rs1.28 billion.

Improvements to existing lines

Double-tracking of 111 km was completed in 1995-96, and work is in progress on doubling or tripling a further 200 km. In the 1997-98 budget, further double-tracking works were approved at a total cost of Rs5.16 billion. Gauge conversion is in progress on the Gondia—Chandafort narrow-gauge line (242 km), of which the 104 km between Gondia and Wadasa was opened in

Nimpura Freight Yard   *1995*

Express freight at Kharagpur, SER   *1996*

1994 and Wadasa—Nagbir in 1997. Completion is scheduled for 1997-98. Conversion of Rupsa—Bangaposi (89 km) has also been approved.

Electrification

During 1995-96 and 1996-97 respectively, 29 km and 73 km were energised. Electrification of Adra—Midnapur (155 km) is currently under way, and a further Rs6.85 billion of work has been approved for 1997-98.

Traction and rolling stock

In March 1996 SER was operating on 1,676 mm gauge 491 electric and 549 diesel locomotives, 86 emu power cars and 182 trailers, 2,762 coaches and 117,206 wagons

(four-wheel equivalent); and on its 762 mm gauge lines 70 diesel and four steam locomotives, 351 coaches and 1,100 wagons.

Track (BG)
Rail: 60, 52, 44.6 kg/m
Crossties (sleepers): Steel 106 mm thick; CST/9 122 mm thick; concrete 210 mm thick; timber 125 mm thick
Spacing
On straight track: 1,660/km, 1,540/km
On curves (438 m); 1,660/km, 1,540/km
Fastening: Elastic on cwr, conventional elsewhere
Max gradient: 2%
Max axleload: 22.86 tonnes

UPDATED

Open gondola wagon for iron and manganese ore
1995

Southern Railway

Park Town, Madras 600 003
Tel: +91 44 535 4141

Key personnel
General Manager: V K Agnihotri
Additional General Manager: S Setharaman
Financial Adviser and Chief Accounts Officer:
 R S Narayanan
Chief Operating Manager: A S Krishnamoorthy
Chief Engineer: L C Jain
Chief Mechanical Engineer: S Dasarathy
Chief Commericial Manager: N Rajankutty
Chief Personnel Officer: P P Kunnikrishna
Chief Electrical Engineer: Arvind Sharma
Chief Signals and Telecommunications Engineer:
 V Jayaraman
Controller of Stores: Harjivan Alva
Chief Public Relations Officer: S Sridhar
Chief Administrative Officer, Construction:
 B S S Sudhirchandra

Gauge: 1,676 mm; 1,000 mm; 762 mm
Length: 3,677 km; 3,270 km; 102 km
Electrification: 951 km of 1,676 mm gauge at 25 kV 50 Hz AC; 166 km of 1,000 mm gauge at 25 kV 50 Hz AC

Organisation
SR extends from Mangalore on the west coast and Kanya

Kumari in the south to Renigunta in the northwest and Gudur in the northeast.

Passenger and freight operations
Revenue freight traffic in FY95-96 amounted to 21 million originating tonnes. Container traffic is expanding fast.
 Passenger traffic in FY95-96 grossed 365 million journeys and 29,880 million passenger-km.

Improvements to existing lines
As part of the gauge conversion project between Madras Beach and Tiruchchirapalli, a parallel broad-gauge line has opened between Beach and Tambaram (29 km). Conversion is in progress between Villupuram and Tiruchchirapalli (176 km) and onwards to Dindigul (93 km). These works are targeted for completion in March and December 1998 respectively.
 The 43 km Yelahanka—Chikballapur narrow-gauge line has been converted to broad-gauge; other sections under conversion are Hassan—Mangalore (189 km) and Mysore—Hassan (118 km). Track-doubling of Bangalore—Kengary (12 km), Kuppam—Whitefield (81 km), and Karunagapalli—Quilon—Trivandrum Central is also in progress, while work starts shortly on Guruvayur—Kuttipuram (36 km) and Kuttipuram—Mangalore (277 km).
 SR is making rapid progress in track modernisation, with some 2,976 km already laid with concrete sleepers. A computerised track management system is being introduced on high-speed routes.

New lines
The surface/elevated rapid transit between Madras Beach and Chepauk is now operational, with the section onward to Luz being completed in the first half of 1997.

Electrification
A total of 1,116 route-km has so far been energised; electrification of Erode—Palghat—Ernakulam is in progress, with 89 km of this line being completed during 1996-97. Another ongoing project is the Madras Beach—Luz rapid transit route.

Traction and rolling stock
At March 1996 the railway operated on 1,676 mm gauge 130 electric and 302 diesel locomotives, 74 emu power cars and 173 trailers, 3,504 coaches and 12,986 wagons (four-wheel equivalent); and on metre-gauge 10 steam, 132 diesel and 20 electric locomotives, 69 emu power cars and 161 trailers, four diesel railcars, 1,217 coaches and 3,294 wagons (four-wheel equivalent).
 In 1994-95, the railway introduced diesel push-pull trains to provide suburban-style services in non-electrified areas between Bangalore, Tumkar, Whitefield and Mysore, and on the Guruvayur—Ernakulam—Alleppey—Kottayam—Quilon route.

UPDATED

Western Railway (WR)

Churchgate, Bombay 400 020
Tel: +91 22 203 8016   Fax: +91 22 201 7630

Key personnel
General Manager: N Krithivasan
Additional General Manager: V Vankateswaran
Senior Deputy General Manager: Arvind Sharma
Chief Engineer: P K Wahi
Chief Administrative Officer, Survey and Construction:
 Rajendra Nath
Chief Commercial Manager: S K Pande
Chief Electrical Engineer: M Rangachari
Chief Mechanical Engineer: S C Sengupta
Chief Signal and Telecommunications Engineer:
 A K Chopra
Financial Adviser and Chief Accounts Officer:
 S M Singru
Controller of Stores: C G Bijlani
Chief Operating Manager: Vijay Kapoor
Chief Public Relations Officer: R K Tandon

Gauge: 1,676 mm; 1,000 mm; 762 mm
Route length: 4,305 km; 4,841 km; 874 km
Electrification: 1,730 km at 25 kV 50 Hz AC; 63 km at 1.5 kV DC

Organisation
Formed in 1951, WR is India's second-largest railway. It

serves the whole of Gujarat state, most of Rajasthan and parts of Maharashtra, Madhya Pradesh, Haryana and Uttar Pradesh.

Passenger operations
The railway is IR's busiest passenger carrier and its most profitable component, with an operating ratio of 64.7 per cent in FY95-96. WR covers the commuter network of Bombay, running over 900 emu commuter trains daily and bringing a morning peak flow of almost 450,000 passengers into the city's Churchgate terminal, where trains arrive at 1.8 minute intervals.
 Since 1960 greater Bombay's population has trebled and WR's suburban passenger journeys soared from 236 million to 990 million a year. But it has not been possible to raise the number of trains operated in proportion. Consequently, some peak-hour trains, with a seating capacity of only 900 or so, carry 3,000 to 3,500 commuters each. Some relief has been provided by raising the standard train formation from nine to 12 cars, and 70 such sets are now in operation.
 The railway's daily total of 60 Mail and Express trains on the broad-gauge includes IR's prestigious 'Rajdhani Express'. In 1994 WR introduced another crack train — the 'Shatabdi Express' linking Bombay and Ahmedabad on a record 6 hour 30 min timing for the 500 km with five stops. In 1995-96, originating passenger journeys totalled 1,209 million, for 61,079 million passenger-km. Computerised reservation has now been extended to almost all major stations.

Freight operations
WR was the first of the Indian railways to cater for container traffic in 1966, and current services include dedicated trains from Bombay to the New Delhi dry port at Tughlakabad. WR also operates a guaranteed transit Bombay—New Delhi wagonload service under the title 'Speed-Link Express'. Most of WR's bulk commodity unit trains, like three of the country's other major bulk-hauling railways, are now made up to 4,500-tonne formations of BOX-N wagons with double-headed locomotive power. In 1995-96, originating freight traffic amounted to 29.4 million tonnes, for 39,723 million tonne-km.

Electrification
During 1993-94, electrification was completed of 23 km between Sabarmati and Gandhinagar.

Improvements to existing lines
During 1994, a fifth track was completed between Bombay Central and Santacruz to raise capacity for commuter trains. Extension of a fifth track from Santacruz to Borivali, and quadrupling between Borivali and Virar is being undertaken under the same scheme. Doubling of Anas bridge on the Ratlam—Godhra section is complete, and similar work on Chambal bridge near Kota is in progress.
 Conversion of the important metre-gauge route between Delhi and Ahmedabad (934 km), the major portion of which is in WR's zone, was completed in April 1997. In addition, gauge conversion is in progress over

12-car emu at Bombay Churchgate **1996**

several sections in Rajasthan and Gujerat, while Agra Fort—Bandikul (152 km) and Bhildi—Viramgram have been approved in the 1997-98 works programme.

Traction and rolling stock

In March 1996 the railway was operating on 1,676 mm gauge, 308 electric and 279 diesel locomotives, 241 emu power cars and 467 trailers, 2,820 coaches and 35,835 wagons (four-wheel equivalent); on metre-gauge, 233 diesel and 74 steam locomotives, 1,431 coaches and 11,412 wagons; and on 762 mm gauge, 22 diesel and five steam locomotives, 178 coaches and 102 wagons.

Signalling and telecommunications

IR's first fibre optic communications system was commissioned between Bombay Churchgate and Virar in 1989. An automatic switching system has been installed more recently, connecting all points on the route through a microprocessor at Churchgate.

Digital microwave was installed between Ahmedabad and Jaipur on the Delhi—Ahmedabad trunk route during 1994-95. In addition to replacement of electromechanical signalling by panel interlocking, block-proving by means of axle counters is being installed on all main lines to raise safety standards. Bids for provision of train describers and train management on the heavily used approaches to Bombay Churchgate from Borivali were being finalised in mid-1997. Solar power plants have been commissioned at three microwave/UHF repeater stations located on hilly terrain.

Coupler in standard use

Passenger cars: Screw
Freight cars: Centre buffer couplers and screw coupling

Braking in standard use

Loco-hauled stock: Vacuum and air; emu: air

Indian Railways track

Rail, types and weight

Broad-gauge	*Type/specification*
Flat bottom	
65 kg steel rails	Gost 8160 & 8161.56
Wear-resistant rails	
60 kg/m	UIC 860/0 grade 'C'
Wear-resistant rails	
52 kg/m	UIC 860/0 grade 'B'
Medium manganese	
flat bottom 60, 52 and 44.6 kg/m	IRS speen T12
Metre-gauge	
Medium manganese	
44.6, 37.1 and 29.7 kg/m	IRS speen T12

Sleepers: Wooden, cast-iron, concrete and steel sleepers. The standard now adopted for high-speed trunk routes is concrete or steel trough.

Concrete: Monobloc, thickness at centre 180 mm, thickness at rail level 210 mm, length 2,750 mm. With elastic rail clips

Wooden

1,676 mm gauge 2,750 × 250 × 130 mm
1,000 mm gauge 1,800 × 200 × 115 mm
762 mm gauge 1,500 × 180 × 115 mm

Steel/cast-iron: CST-9 for 1,676 and 1,000 mm gauge

Electric multiple-units

Class	Cars per unit	Motor cars per unit	Motored axles/car	Output/motor kW	Speed km/h	First built	Builders Mechanical	Builders Electrical
1.5 kV DC BG								
WCU14	3	1	4	139/187	105/80	1970	ICF	TDK/BHEL/Japan
WCU15	3	1	4	139/187	105/80	1970	Jessop/BEML	BHEL
25 kV AC BG								
WAU-4	3/4	1	4	167.3	80/90	1967	ICF	BHEL/Hitachi
25 kV AC MG								
YAU-	4	1	4	126.5	65	1966	ICF	Hitachi
YAU- (Thyristor)	4	1	4	90	65	1991	ICF	GEC Alsthom/UK BHEL
MEMU	4	1	4	163.3	100	1994	ICF	BHEL

Electric locomotives

Class	Wheel arrangement	Output kW continuous/ one hour	Speed km/h	Weight tonnes	No in service	First built	Builders Mechanical	Builders Electrical
Broad-gauge 1.5 kV DC								
WCM1	Co-Co	2,365/2,760	120	124	7	1955	Vulcan Foundry	EEC
WCM2	Co-Co	2,095/2,305	120	112.8	10	1957	Vulcan Foundry	EEC
WCM4	Co-Co	2,390/2,985	120	125	6	1961	Hitachi	Hitachi
WCM5	Co-Co	2,365/2,760	120	124	20	1961	CLW	CLW
WCM6	Co-Co	3,430	105	120	1	1996	CLW	CLW
WCG2	Co-Co	3,130/1,220	80	132	57	1971	CLW	CLW
Broad-gauge 25 kV AC								
WAM1	Bo-Bo	2,140/1,385	112	74.0	6	1960	50 c/s Group	50 c/s Group
WAM2	Bo-Bo	2,080/2,170	112	76.0	28	1961	Mitsubishi	Mitsubishi
WAM3	Bo-Bo	2,080/2,170	112	76.0	2	1964	Mitsubishi	Mitsubishi
WAM4	Co-Co	2,715/2,450	120	112.8	478	1971	CLW	CLW
WAP1/3	Co-Co	2,800/2,910	130/140	107	74	1980	CLW	CLW
WAP4/6	Co-Co	3,730/3,990	140	107	16	1995	CLW	CLW
WAP5	Bo-Bo	2,985/4,000	160	78	10	1996	ABB	ABB (3 phase loco)
WAG1	B-B	2,160/2,185	80	85.2	92	1963	50 c/s Group/CLW	50 c/s Group/CLW
WAG2	B-B	2,370/2,575	80	85.2	35	1964	Hitachi	Hitachi
WAG3	B-B	2,350/2,680	80	87.32	9	1965	50 c/s Group	50 c/s Group
WAG4	B-B	2,350/2,680	80	87.6	159	1971	CLW	CLW
WAG5	Co-Co	2,870/3,250	80	118.8	1,178	1978	CLW	CLW/BHEL
WAG7	Co-Co	3,730/3,990	100	123	162	1992	CLW	CLW
WAG6A	Bo-Bo-Bo	4,475/4,560	100	123	6	1988	ASEA	ASEA
WAG6B	Bo-Bo-Bo	4,475/4,560	100	123	6	1988	Hitachi	Hitachi
WAG6C	Co-Co	4,475/4,560	100	123	6	1988	Hitachi	Hitachi
WAG9	Co-Co	4,565	100	123	*7	1996	Adtranz	Adtranz
Broad-gauge dual-voltage 25 kV AC/1.5 kV DC								
WCAM1	Co-Co	2,715/2,870 2,185	120/80	113	52	1975	CLW	CLW
WCAM2	Co-Co	3,505 2,160	120/80	113	20	1995	BHEL	BHEL
Metre-gauge 25 kV AC								
YAM1	Co-Co	1,215/1,300	80	52	20	1965	Mitsubishi	Mitsubishi

*Under service trials

Diesel locomotives

Class	Wheel arrangement	Power kW	Speed km/h	Weight tonnes	First built	Builders Mechanical	Builders Engine	Transmission
Broad-gauge								
WDM1	Co-Co	1,340	104	112	1958	Alco	Alco/V251B	E GE
WDM2	Co-Co	1,790	120	112.8	1962	DLW	Alco/V251B	E BHEL
WDM2C	Co-Co	2,310	120	112.8	1994	DLW	Alco/V-251B/upgraded	E BHEL
WDG2	Co-Co	2,310		123	1996	DLW	Alco	E BHEL
WDP1	Bo-Bo	1,715	120	80	1995	DLW	Alco	E BHEL
WDM4	Co-Co	1,965	120	113	1962	GM	GM567D3	E GM
WDM6	Bo-Bo	895	75	70	1981	DLW	DLW/251D	E BHEL
WDM7	Co-Co	1,475	105	96	1987	DLW	DLW-Alco/251-B 12 Eye	E BHEL
WDS2	C	330	54	51	1945	Krauss-Maffei	MAN/W 8V-17-5/ 22A	H Voith
WDS3	C	460	65	57	1961	MaK	Maybach/MD-435	H MaK
WDS4	C	520	65/27	60	1969	MaK/CLW	MaK/CLW/6M282A(k)	H/HM KPC Voith L4v2U2
WDS4A	C	490						H
WDS4B		520						H
WDS4D		450	65	60	1968 1969 1988	CLW	MaK/6M282A(k)	H Voith L4r2u
WDS5	Co-Co	795	109	126	1967		Alco/251-B	E GE
WDS6	Co-Co	1,045	62.5	126	1977	DLW	Alco/DLW/251D	E BHEL
Metre-gauge								
YDM1	B-B	472	88	44	1955	MaK/CLW	MaK/CLW/6M282A	H Voith
YDM-2	B-B	520	75	48	1986	CLW	CLW/MaK/6M282A(k)	H Voith
YDM3	1B-B1	1,055	80	58.5	1961	GM	GM 12 567c	E GM
YDM4	Co-Co	1,045	96	72	1961	Alco/DLW	Alco 251-D	E BHEL
YDM4A	Co-Co	1,045	96	67	1964	MLW Canada	MLW/251-D	E GE Canada
YDM5	C-C	1,035	80	69	1964	GM	GM 12 567c	E GM
Narrow-gauge								
NDM1	B'-B'	110	33	29	1955	Arn Jung	MWM TRHS/518 S	H Voith L33 U
NDM5	B-B	365	50	22	1987	CLW	Cummins/KTA 1150L	H Voith L2r2zu2
ZDM2	B'-B'	520	50	32	1964	MaK	Maybach/MD 435	HM MaK
ZDM3	B'-B'	520	32	35	1971	CLW	CLW/MaK/6M282A(k)	HM Kirloskar
ZDM4A	1B-B1	520	50	38.5	1984	CLW	CLW/MaK/6M282A(k)	H Voith L4r 22

Spacing: 1,660/km high-speed routes; 1,310 to 1,540/km other routes

Max curvature: 10° (175 m radius) on 1,676 mm gauge (BG)

Max gradient: 2.9% on BG

Max axleload: 22.9 tonnes on 1,676 mm gauge

VERIFIED

INDONESIA

Department of Communications

Departement Perhubungan, 8 Medan Merdeka Barat, 10110 Jakarta Pusat
Tel: +62 21 351596/361308   Fax: +62 21 361305

Key personnel
Minister: Haryanto Danudirto
Secretary-General: S Kramadibrata

UPDATED

Indonesian Railway Public Corporation (Perumka)

Perusahaan Umum Kerata Api
Jalan Perintis Kemerdekaan, 1, Bandung 40113, Java
Tel: +62 22 430031/43039/43054
Fax: +62 22 430062/50342

Key personnel
Chief Director: Dr Anwar Suprijadi
Corporate Secretary: S Sonny
Director, Personnel: A S Harsono
Director of Finance: E Haryoto
Director of Marketing: T B Padmadiwirja
Director of Operations: Adi Witjaksono
Director, Technical: S E Saputro
Chief of Planning and Development: S Siregar
  Accounting: Hadijono
  Development: Soegeng G
  Way and Works: P J Sujatno
  Signalling and Telecommunications: M Iyad
  Workshops: Soeparman
  Traction: Soekamto
  Rolling Stock: N Sumarna

Gauge: 1,067 mm; 750 mm
Route length: 5,961 km; 497 km (partly undergoing gauge conversion)
Electrification: 125 km at 1.5 kV DC

Organisation
The railway network in Indonesia is confined to two islands: Java, where the main system of some 4,967 km is located, and Sumatra.

Political background
Perumka's current concern is to overtake past shortfalls in investment so as to satisfy rising demand for its services. It has been helped by a government decision in 1992 to accept responsibility for maintenance of the railway infrastructure.

This followed liberalisation in 1991, when Perumka was released from full government control to become a public corporation, a move that was completed in 1992. It has commercial freedom in all but fixing third-class passenger fares; those remained under government control and at levels unvaried since 1984. Perumka also gained freedom to borrow in the domestic banking market.

Starting in 1992, Perumka planned to make some of its more intensively used lines in Java accessible to private passenger and freight service operators. The railway would continue to run its own services in competition with any private sector entrepreneurs. The primary aim of the move was to satisfy rising demand for transport without straining Perumka's own resources. The first such private service started in late 1995.

Passenger operations
Perumka draws almost two-thirds of its income from a passenger business that has steadily increased since the 1970s. In 1991 this sector recorded 66 million journeys and 10,417 million passenger-km, rising spectacularly to 95.4 million journeys and 12,224 million passenger-km in 1993. But with more than one-third of total volume represented by third-class travel at government-controlled fares in the Jakarta area, the growth has not been matched by a commensurate increase in revenue.

A through-ticketing deal agreed in 1992 with the Indonesian national airline Garuda is seen as one way of helping Perumka regain the business travellers lost to internal air services. Some upgrading of 'Eksekutif' class coaches has been undertaken and a few new vehicles ordered, but major purchases must await the fruits of Perumka's new flexibility to charge market fares for better-quality accommodation.

A start was made during 1995 with introduction of a new faster service between Jakarta and Surabaya, christened JS950 in commemoration of the 50th anniversary of the national railway. Cutting four hours off current timings, the trains are formed of GE locomotives and a new fleet of coaches built locally by PT Inka.

The first private passenger service was due to start in late 1995 under a 25-year profit-sharing deal agreed with PT Arion, a bus operator, which purchased its own rolling stock fleet of three diesel locomotives and 30 coaches. Perumka will operate the trains — initially two daily returns between Jakarta and Solo — while PT Arion markets the service.

Freight operations
Annual freight carryings have soared even more strikingly, from 800 million tonne-km in 1982-83 to almost 4 billion in 1993, when freight tonnage reached 15.7 million. This reflects the rapid advance of the country's liberalised economy, which has generated a 26 per cent rise of non-oil exports and a 12 per cent growth of non-oil manufacturing since 1983. Long-term estimates show an even more substantial rise than that envisaged for passenger traffic, with 18 million tonnes forecast for 1996 and 35 million by 2005.

Intermodal operations
A recent feature in the freight sector has been intermodal development, which since 1987 has increased ninefold to over 24,000 TEU a year. The government plans creation of five rail-connected inland container terminals to serve maritime container traffic. To maximise potential, however, more track improvement is required and also some work on clearances, which in at least one area restrict the railway to movement of standard ISO container sizes.

Over its 180 km main line between Bandung and Jakarta Perumka runs, to American President Lines' charter, a weekly unit train for maritime containers. For domestic traffic Perumka's four 17-wagon container trains run daily each way between the port of Tangjungpriok, near Jakarta, and the Gedebage terminal near Bandung. Another container train plies between Cigading port and Bekasi, on the outskirts of Jakarta. A 17 km line has been built from Tangjungpriok to Cakung for the benefit of container traffic.

Improvements to existing lines
The country has substantial coal reserves, which the government sees as a major source of exports, as well as fuel for much-needed additions to electricity-generating capacity and for cement manufacture. For 1995 the country's coal production was expected to gross 29 million tonnes, with half of it being shipped abroad.

The first major investment in Perumka's bulk freight capability was a US$1.3 billion project to upgrade the 410 km 1,067 mm gauge route in Sumatra for 40-wagon unit train movement of 2.5 to 3 million tonnes of coal a year from the Bukit Asam field to a new south coast port of Tarahan, for shipment thence to an electricity-generating station near Merak in West Java. Parts of the route are also used by other bulk freight flows. The works raised maximum permissible axleloadings from 13 to 18 tonnes and line speed to 60 km/h for freight and 90 km/h for passenger trains. Mechanical signalling was retained, but traffic control by single-line token has been superseded by radio control through a new UHF/VHF radio network.

The Bukit Asam—Tarahan port coal haul could eventually gross 12 million tonnes a year. The investment needed and the operational economics of quadrupling the scheme's present design capacity have been studied by a Canadian consultancy.

The Sumatran coal railway from Pandang to Solok has been upgraded, as has the 120 km line from the port of Merak, west of Jakarta, to Serpong (needed for coal destined for a cement works at Cibinong in West Java).

A 240 km stretch of 750 mm gauge line in Sumatra between Besitang and Banda Aceh has been regauged to 1,067 mm. The objective was to capture for rail agricultural and timber products then moving by road or water.

There are also plans to rebuild some 1,330 route-km on Java and Sumatra through to the end of the century, and for doubling of 492 km to raise capacity and cut journey times.

Jakarta—Merak upgrade
In late 1996, Davy British Rail International Ltd (DBRI) completed the rehabilitation of the 120 km rail link between Jakarta and Merak, in a £45 million contract for Perumka.

The project involved the design of a new 30 km spur linking with the Jakarta—Merak line, and complete rerailing with 140 km of new R42 continuously welded rail, to give a traffic speed of 80 km/h. Other tasks included

rehabilitating 14 existing stations and creating three new ones, with associated trackwork, and uprating 70 bridges — including masonry substructures and steel superstructures — to take increased axleloads.

In addition, the project team installed a new colourlight signalling system (based on centralised traffic control — CTC), a VHF utility radio system and a lineside telephone system; and provided a signalling and tele-communications training centre. Civil works comprised improvements to the track alignment, drainage and earthworks; and reballasting.

Traction and rolling stock

In 1992 Perumka was operating 563 diesel locomotives, 30 four-car emus, 147 diesel railcars, 1,262 passenger cars and 12,683 freight wagons.

PT Inka, the BN Division of Bombardier Eurorail of Belgium and Holec of the Netherlands agreed joint production of seven four-car emus for the Jakarta suburban network, delivered in 1993. The first three trains were assembled by BN in Belgium, the remainder locally by PT Inka. A further 25 sets were being built by BN in 1996.

Meanwhile, Hyundai of Korea supplied two prototype four-car emus, of which the asychronous motors, GTO thyristors and Micas S power control system were provided by ABB.

Passenger car needs, to cope with severe overcrowding in third class and satisfy government requests for more business travel capacity, comprised 420 economy class, 55 executive class and 245 business class cars. These were supplemented by delivery in 1993 of 96 economy class coaches from PT Inka at a cost of Rp13 million funded from the government's approved transport project list. A further 69 executive class cars were refurbished for 1994 delivery. Bogies for 30 coaches for the Jakarta—Surabaya run are being supplied by GEC Alsthom.

Over half of the 105-strong fleet of Class D301 diesel shunters is being remanufactured with Mercedes 250 kW engines and Voith turbo transmissions. An initial programme was in 1991 refitting 28 Class D301. Voith turbo transmissions were also being fitted to 64 Nippon Sharyo-built dmu power cars under a refurbishment programme scheduled for late 1995 completion. A further 24 diesel railcars were on order from Mitsubishi/Hitachi.

Signalling and telecommunications

Over 2,580 route-km is equipped with Siemens & Halske mechanical tokenless block, located at some 300 centres in Java and 45 in Sumatra. All-relay interlockings are operational at numerous traffic centres.

Under an A$115 million contract, Westinghouse Brake & Signal of Australia has been installing new colourlight signalling controlled by the Westrace system on the 300 km route between Cirebon on the north coast and Yogyakarta in the southeast. Computerised signalling master control and communication centres are being established at Cirebon, Yogyakarta and Purwokerto; all 43 stations on the route have local control centres. One problem has been what to do about the many unofficial crossings on the line; under the old mechanical system, cans of stones suspended from the signal wires rattled when the signal changed, warning crossing keepers to drop bamboo barriers over crossings. This system will not be feasible with colourlights and how these crossings will be controlled, or if they will be allowed to continue in existence, has yet to be established.

Westrace signalling is also being installed on 130 km between Tasikmalaya and Kroya in central Java.

The railway's first solid-state interlocking has been installed by GEC Alsthom, along with Sigview ATC, to control a critical 20 km section of the Tanggerang line in suburban Jakarta.

Electrification

The 1.5kV DC electrified system in Java covers the line between Jakarta and Bogor (55 km) and some sections around the city of Jakarta. It is being expanded under the Jabotabek scheme into a regional network of nine lines and some 220 km embracing the satellite cities of Bekasi and Tanggerang.

So far work has chiefly concerned track renewal, double-tracking and installation of some new halts and signalling improvements, for example GEC Alsthom Signalling was in 1992 contracted to modernise signalling on the 25 km Tanah Abang—Serpong line. Electrification proceeds — but slowly — on the Tanggerang line and also on the western line from Jakarta to Manggarai, where it is now operational over the new elevated alignment opened

New station on the Jakarta—Merak line, on which upgrading was completed in 1996   **1997**

BN emu for Jakarta suburban services

Diesel locomotives

Class	Wheel arrangement	Power kW	Speed km/h	Weight tons	First built	Engine	Builders Transmission	Repowering
CC 200	Co-Co	1,200	90	96	1951	GE 12V 244E	E	Alco 12V 250 (4 locos)
CC 201	Co-Co	1,450	100	82	1976	GE 7 FDL 8	E	
BB 200	A1A-A1A	650	120	74.8	1956	GM 8567CR	E	
BB 201	A1A-A1A	1,000	120	78	1964	GM G12 567C	E	
BB 202	A1A-A1A	745	100	65	1968	GM GL8 645E	E	
BB 203	A1A-A1A	1,290	100	78	1978	GE 7 FDL 8	E	
BB 204	B-2-B	745	60	55	1982	MTU 12V 396 TC 12	H Voith hydrostatic	
BB 300	B-B	500	75	36	1956	MB 820 B	H	
BB 301	B-B	1,120	120	52	1962	MTU 12V 652 TR 11	H L630 r U2	MB 12V 652 TB11 (23 locos)
BB 302	B-B	820	80	44	1969	MTU 12V 493	H L520 r U2	
BB 303	B-B	860	90	44	1971	MTU MB12V 493	H L52 r U2	
BB 304	B-B	1,120	120	52	1974	MTU 12V 652	H L720 r U2	
BB 306	B-B	640	75	40	1983	MTU 8V 396TC 12	H L4 r 42 U2	
C 300	C	260	30	30	1964	MB 836 B	H L203 U	
D 300	D	250	50	34	1956	MB 836 B	H 2WIL1.15	GM 8V92 (40 locos)
D 301	D	250	50	28	1960	MB 836 B/2	H 2WIL1.5	GM 8V71 (6 locos) GM 12V 71 (6 locos) MWM TD 232V12 (13 locos)

Electric railcars or multiple-units

Class	Cars per unit	Motor cars per unit	Motored axles/car	Output/motor kW	Speed km/h	First built
MCW 5	4	2	4	230	120	1976
VCW 8		2	4	230	120	1978
BN-Holec	4	2	4	180		1993
Hyundai-ABB	4	2	4	180		1993

Diesel railcars or multiple-units

Class	Cars per unit	Motor cars per unit	Motored axles/car	Power/motor kW	Speed km/h	First built	Builders Engine	Transmission
MCDW 300/ MCW 300	1	1	4	160	90	1964	8V 71	H Diwabus
MCW 301	2	2	2	135	90	1976	DMH17H	H TC 2A
MCW 302	2	2	2	215	90	1978	DMH17SA	H TCR 2-5

in 1992. Rolling stock shortages prevented immediate utilisation of this route for a 12 minute interval service between Jakarta and Gongondia.

Two further phases of the scheme were authorised in 1995, including rebuilding more track on elevated alignment.

Track
Standard rail
R54 54-43 kg/m; R50 50.4 kg/m; R14A 42.59 kg/m; R14 41.52 kg/m; R3 33.4 kg/m; R2 25.75 kg/m
750 mm gauge: R10 16.4 kg/m
600 mm gauge: ID 12.38 kg/m
Crossties (sleepers): Wood 130 mm thick; concrete 195 mm thick; steel 100 mm thick
Spacings: 1,666/km plain track, 1,700/km curves
Rail fastening: Rigid: dog or screw spike for R2 rail; Klem plate KI/KK for R42 rail; Klem plate KE/KF for R2 rail; Dorken spike; double elastic spring clip F type with rubber pad; double elastic Pandrol clip and rubber pad; single elastic Pandrol clip
Max gradient: 2.5%; 7% (rack sections)
Min curvature radius
Main line: 300 m
Max altitude: 1,246 m near Garut, Java
Max axleload
Main line: 14 tons

UPDATED   *Class BB303 745 kW diesel-hydraulic B-B by Thyssen-Henschel*   *1996*

IRAN

Ministry of Roads & Transportation

49 Taleghani Avenue, Tehran
Tel: +98 21 646 4157   Fax: +98 21 641 7218

Key personnel
Minister: Abbas Torkan
Deputy Minister of Roads and Transportation:
Eng Sadeqh Afshar

VERIFIED

Islamic Iranian Republic Railways (RAI)

Rahahane Djjomhouriye Eslami Iran
Shahid Kalantari Building, Railway Square, Tehran 13185 - 1498
Tel: +98 21 5641600   Fax: +98 21 5650532

Key personnel
President: Eng Sadeq Afshar
Deputy President: Nasser Pour Mirza
Vice-Presidents
Administration and Finance: Alireza Mahfouzi
Operations: Hormoz Qotbi
Technical: Farrokh Moadeli
Rolling Stock: Eng Mohsen Pour Seyed Aghaie

Gauge: 1,435 mm; 1,676 mm
Route length: 5,241 km; 94 km
Electrification: 143 km at 25 kV 50 Hz AC

Inauguration ceremony for the international Silk Road railway in 1996; at right is one of RAI's GM-EMD Type GT26-CW diesel locomotives   *1997*

Political background
In 1988 RAI became a government company, with greater freedom for management. Restructuring has been based on decentralisation to regional managements, with a split also effected between infrastructure and operations. Eventually, it is aimed to allow access to RAI tracks for private operators.

Market orientation was another key principle of the restructure. In the freight sector this has been marked by capacity increases to fit the railway for its role as a carrier of transit traffic, and development of door-to-door arrangements with improved intermodal transhipment.

Other priorities include improved facilities for staff training, adoption of computer-based data transmission systems for strict vehicle control, and investment in mechanised track maintenance equipment.

Both passenger fares and freight rates were increased substantially in 1993 to help offset increased costs, and the railway now runs without operating subsidy.

Organisation
RAI's key routes run from the ports of Bandar Khomayni and Khorramshar on the Persian Gulf to Tehran; from the capital northwest to Razi on the Turkish border and Djolfa on the Azerbaijan border. Tehran also radiates lines northeastward to Bandar Turkhman, Mashhad and Sarakhs on the Turkmenistan border, and southeast to Bafq, Kerman and Bandar Abbas. Further to the southeast is an isolated 94 km 1,676 mm gauge line from Zahedan to the Pakistan border at Mirjaveh.

The electrified part is the final 143 km of the route to Azerbaijan, from Tabriz to Djolfa. The electrification was undertaken by Technoexport and the traction is furnished by eight 3,600 kW locomotives based on Swedish Railways' Rc4. Built by SGP of Austria, the units have ABB electrical equipment.

Some 32,260 staff were employed by RAI at the end of 1996.

New bridge on the border with Turkmenistan on the Silk Road route opened in 1996   *1997*

Traffic	1995	1996
Freight tonnes	21,401,070	19,127,707
Freight tonne-km	11,865,231,722	11,628,184,687
Passenger journeys	9,663,730	7,000,000
Passenger-km	7,294,143,722	5,305,236,784

Passenger operations

Passenger journeys rose from 9.2 million in 1993 to 9.7 million in 1995, but slipped back to around seven million the following year. Thanks to track upgrading, the maximum speed for the Turbotrains has been raised to 170 km/h. Ticket sales and accounting procedures have been computerised, following contracting-out to a private sector company.

There is a service between the isolated Iranian border station of Zahedan and Quetta in Pakistan, and also a daily service between Razi in Iran and Kapiköy in Turkey.

Freight operations

In 1996, over 19 million tonnes were carried, up from 12.5 million tonnes in FY1988-89. Minerals generate 50 per cent of RAI's freight tonnage, oil products 16 per cent. Transit traffic to and from the Central Asian republics is of rapidly increasing importance, and completion of the line from Mashhad into Turkmenistan in 1996 places Iran astride major routes to Europe and the Persian Gulf.

New lines

Bandar Abbas railway

Construction of a 635 km line from Bafq to Bandar Abbas, to connect the port of Shahid Rajai and the copper and iron ore mines of Golegohar to the existing railway network, begun in 1982, was completed in 1995. Initially laid as single track, the line will eventually be double track, electrified and CTC-controlled. These works are to be carried out by 1998. The line is engineered to a high standard, with 160 km/h the design speed for passenger trains. The signalling contract was awarded to Siemens.

A fleet of 1,200 four-axle wagons of large capacity has been delivered by Wagon Pars for use on this line which, apart from transit traffic to and from Bandar Abbas, will also be used for movement of iron ore from the inland mines to the steel complex of Mobarekeh in Isfahan. Light axleload freight will be able to run at 120 km/h, with 70 km/h permitted for the bulk ore trains.

Silk Road railway

An important new international route opened in May 1996. This is the 180 km connection from Mashhad to Sarakhs on the Turkmenian frontier, where it meets the 130 km line built simultaneously from the Central Asian main line at Tajan. Together with the new line to Bandar Abbas, this connection will give the Central Asian republics an important new outlet to the Persian Gulf and Europe. Some half-million passengers and three million tonnes of freight a year are expected initially.

Other projects

Construction is reported to have started in May 1996 on a 450 km line from Isfahan to the southern city of Shiraz. With very difficult terrain to surmount, the line is expected to take eight years to build.

Provision of a still shorter route to the Persian Gulf is the aim of a direct Mashhad—Bafq line (768 km). This would reduce the distance from the Central Asian republics to Bandar Abbas by several hundred kilometres. A start on this line was reported in early 1997.

A start on another major new line, for which agreement was reached with Pakistan Railways in 1991, was also reported in early 1997. The two countries are undertaking joint construction of a 545 km line from Kerman to Zahedan, which is at present the terminal railhead of the 1,676 mm gauge cross-border line from Pakistan. Whilst a

change of gauge will be necessary at Zahedan, this line will complete a through rail connection between Europe and the Indian subcontinent.

Improvements to existing lines

Doubling of track continues on lines where limits of capacity have been reached. Of late this has concerned the Tehran—Ghom (180 km), Ahwaz—Bandar Khomayni (120 km) and Tehran—Mashhad lines.

With the increase of the length of trains and of their tonnage the loops of all stations on the Tehran—Ghom, Tehran—Mashhad, Andimeshk—Ahwaz and Tehran—Tabriz lines have been lengthened.

A further 600 km of route is scheduled for complete rebuilding under the 1994-99 five-year plan, and some 1,000 km will be upgraded.

Traction and rolling stock

In 1996 RAI's motive power fleet consisted of 300 diesel-electric and eight electric locomotives, plus two emus and the three Turbotrains bought from ANF-Frangeco in 1982. The wagon fleet totalled 14,200, and there were 776 passenger cars, including 60 restaurant and 140 couchette cars.

In 1995, 39 new SD70MAC 3,000 kW Co-Co diesel locomotives were ordered from General Motors in the United States, while in 1996, 12 new Class SS5 Bo-Bo 180km/h electric locomotives were ordered from Chinese builder Zhu Zhou Electric Locomotive Works in Guangxi Province.

In the early 1990s, 125 passenger cars, including 30 couchette cars, were acquired second-hand from the German Federal Railway, while 400 new coaches were acquired in a technology transfer agreement with SGP of Austria.

Two five-coach prototype Intercity diesel trains have been bought by Iran from DSB of Denmark; built in 1982, they were the forerunners of the successful Danish IC/3 Class. The two prototypes were refurbished at DSB's workshops in Århus before delivery to Iran in 1995; they have been put into service on the Tehran—Mashhad line.

Local builder Wagon Pars constructs about 800 wagons each year for RAI.

Signalling and telecommunications

Ericsson Telekomunikayson, the Turkish subsidiary of the Ericsson company, has been contracted to install an optic fibre-based communications system along 860 km of RAI between Qazvin and Rezayeh on the Turkish frontier.

To increase the reliability of the signalling and communications system, a project for replacement of overhead cables by coaxial cables has been implemented on the 330 km Ghom—Sistan line. Radio communication with trains is being introduced.

India's Ircon is signalling the Central Asian line between Mashhad and Sarakhs, and is resignalling the 110 km Arwaz—Bandar Khomayni branch of the Khorramshar line.

CTC now extends to 1,645 route-km, radio-based signalling is installed over 1,074 km, and semaphores control 328 km. Other routes are operated on the automatic block system.

Standard rail

Type U33 46.3 kg/m
Type IIA, 38.4 kg/m in 12.5 m lengths
Type IIIA, 33.5 kg/m in 12 m lengths
UIC 50 kg/m in 12.5 m lengths
UIC 60 kg/m in 18 m lengths (Zahedan—Mirjaveh)
Rail joints: 4- and 6-hole fishplates; and welding
Crossties (sleepers): Creosote-impregnated hard wood, steel and mono- or twin-block concrete. Wood 2,600 × 250 × 150 mm. Steel 2,400 × 300 × 70 mm. Concrete sleepers under welded rail
Spacing: 1,680/km
Rail fastenings
Wood sleepers: sole plates, screws and bolts
Steel sleepers: clips and bolts
Filling: Part broken stone, and part river ballast; minimum 200 mm under sleepers
Max curvature: 7.9° = min radius 220 m
Longest continuous gradient: 16 km of 2.8% (1 in 36) grade between Firouzkouh and Gadouk
Max altitude: 2,177 m near Nourabad station
Max axleloading: 20 tonnes (25 tonnes Bafq—Bandar Abbas)
Max permitted speed
Freight trains: 55 km/h
Passenger trains: 80 km/h

UPDATED

Diesel locomotives

Builder's type	Wheel arrangement	Power kW	Speed km/h	Weight tonnes	No in service	First built	Builders Mechanical	Engine	Transmission
G8	Bo-Bo	715	84	68.4	12	1957	GM-EMD	567C	E
G12	Bo-Bo	980	105	72.7	57	1956	GM-EMD	567C	E
G18	Bo-Bo	746	105	64.8	2	1968	GM-EMD	567C	E
G22W	Bo-Bo	1,118	105	77.2	25	1975	GM-EMD	645E	E
GT26-CW	Co-Co	2,235	120	119.6	74	1971	GM-EMD	645E3	E
GT26-CW2	Co-Co	2,235	120	119.6	31	1983	GM Canada	645E3B	E
HD10C	Bo-Bo	798	100	69	17	1971	Hitachi	0398TA	E
LDE626	Co-Co		100	120	4	1986	Romania	Asea	E
U30C	Co-Co	2,250	105	119.7	26	1992	GE Canada	7FDL	E
C3071	Co-Co	2,250	110	132.1	26	1993	GE Canada	7FDL	E

Electric locomotives

Class	Wheel arrangement	Output kW	Speed km/h	Weight tonnes	No in service	First built	Builders Mechanical	Electrical
40-700RCH	Bo-Bo	3,600	100	80	7	1982	Asea	Asea

IRAQ

Ministry of Transport & Communications

Kanat Street, Baghdad

Key personnel
Minister: A M Khalil

UPDATED

Iraqi Republic Railways (IRR)

Damascus Interlock, Baghdad
Tel: +964 1 884 0450
Telex: 212272 railway ik

Key personnel
Director-General: A Y Al Safi
Directors
Traffic and Operations: Najim Shattee
Mechanical and Electrical Engineering:
Eng Alla Aldin Sadk
Managers
Civil Engineering: Eng Feuad Habib
Planning: Eng Mohammad Abdul Ghafour
Stores and Purchasing: Eng Adnan Al Mula
Signalling and Telecommunications:
Eng Hussain Abas Hindi
Personnel: Muder Mohammad Ali
Foreign Relations: Adiel Abdul Amir
Financial: Nouri Al Jumaili

Operations: Salam Yousif
Legal: Fareed Abas Hindi

Gauge: 1,435 mm
Route length: 2,422 km

Organisation

Since closure of the metre-gauge network in 1988, IRR's network consists principally of a 1,435 mm gauge main line linking the Persian Gulf port of Um Qasr and Basra with Baghdad, there splitting to form routes to the Syrian border at Husaiba (opened in 1987) and El Yaroubieh. Branches to Kirkuk and Akashat to exploit mineral deposits are also of recent construction.

Passenger operations

Iraqi railways suffered serious disruption in the 1991 Gulf War and the subsequent international sanctions against the country. Passenger traffic has recovered to some extent, up from 434 million passenger-km in 1991 to 2.198 billion in 1995 (7.4 million passenger journeys).

Freight operations

In 1992 freight tonne-km amounted to no more than 115 million. The figure for 1995 was 1.139 billion (3.4 million tonnes).

New lines

The first of several new line projects, completed in the 1980s, was a 404 km line from Baghdad via Radi and Haditha to the Syrian border at Husaiba, with a 115 km

branch from Al Qaim to the phosphate mines at Akashat in the west, so as to link the latter with a fertiliser plant at Al Qaim, in the Euphrates valley. Like all new IRR lines, the Baghdad—Husaiba was engineered for 250 km/h, partly for ease of maintenance in the forseeable future, when speeds would be limited to 140 km/h for passenger and 100 km/h for freight.

From Haditha on this route a 252 km transversal, built initially as single track with provision for later doubling, was completed via Baiji to Kirkuk in 1987. This project involved bridging the Euphrates, Tigris and Therthar rivers. The line is CTC-controlled with the complement of track-to-train radio and hot box detectors.

Improvements to existing lines

The situation caused by the imposition of economic

sanctions led IRR to seek assistance from India. Under an agreement signed in April 1996, India will assist in rehabilitation of Iraq's railways and in execution of new projects. Amongst those cited is upgrading of the Baghdad—Basra route between Baghdad and Samawa.

Traction and rolling stock

In 1995, the railway was operating 382 diesel-electric locomotives, 434 passenger cars and 12,445 freight wagons.

UPDATED

IRELAND

Department of Public Enterprise

44 Kildare Street, Dublin 2
Tel: +353 1 670 7444   Fax: +353 1 670 9633

Key personnel
Minister: Mary O'Rourke
Secretary: John Loughrey

UPDATED

Iarnród Éireann (IE)

Connolly Station, Amiens Street, Dublin 1
Tel: + 353 1 836 3333   Fax: +353 1 836 4760

Key personnel
Chairman: Michael McDonnell
Directors: Patrick Lynch, Brendan Murtagh,
   A J O'Brien
Chief Executive: Joe Meagher
General Manager, Engineering: Gerry Dalton
General Manager, Freight: L Kirwan
Tel: +353 1 7034682   Fax: +353 1 8364470
Manager, New Business (Freight):
   Donie Horan
Manager, InterCity: J P Walsh
Manager, Safety: Ted Corcoran
Manager, Human Resources: J Keenan
Manager, Finance and Administration: Richard O'Farrell
Chief Engineer, Infrastructure: Brian Garvey
Chief Mechanical Engineer: J McCarthy
Manager, Strategic Planning: Tom Finn
Manager, Resources and Central Traffic Control: O Doyle
Manager, Media and PR: Cyril Ferris

New De Dietrich driving van trailer for upgraded Dublin—Belfast service introduced in 1997   **1997**

Manager, Network Catering: Tom Mythen
Manager, Suburban Rail: Michael Murphy
Manager, Quality and Customer Standards: Ray Kelly
Manager, Passenger Services (South/West): Willie O'Connor
Manager, Passenger Services (North/East): Bertie Corbet
Manager, Combined Transport: Steve Aherne
Manager, Navigator Freight Agency: Shay Hart
Manager, National Accounts: Patsy Mee
District Manager, Connolly: Tom Devoy

District Manager, Galway: Gerry Glynn
District Manager, Cork: Sean Cullinane
District Manager, Limerick: Brian Kelly
District Manager, Waterford: Paul Cheevers
Manager, Rosslare Harbour: Walter Morrissey

Gauge: 1,600 mm
Route length (open to traffic): 1,947 km
Electrification: 38 km at 1.5 kV DC

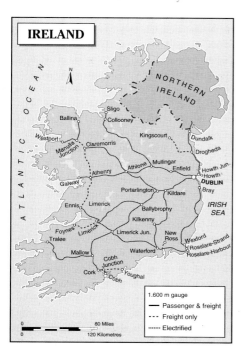

IRELAND

1.600 m gauge
— Passenger & freight
- - - Freight only
······ Electrified

Arrow dmu at Kildare   **1996**

Organisation

Iarnród Éireann is responsible for all rail services in the state including the Dublin Area Rapid Transit system. It is also responsible for rail freight and the company's own road freight services, for catering services, and for the operation of Rosslare Harbour, which caters for sailings to the UK and the Continent.

Passenger operations

IE offers a nationwide service of diesel-hauled passenger trains, while in the Dublin area it operates an electrified suburban system, known as Dublin Area Rapid Transit (DART). The DART system operates over 38 route-km electrified at 1.5 kV DC from Bray, south of Dublin Connolly Station, to Howth, in the north, with a fleet of 40 two-car emus. A 7.5 km single-track extension of the electric service to Greystones in the south is going ahead; operations were due to begin in 1997. A further extension to Malahide in the north is proposed.

Freight operations

IE's major freight customers are the brewing, construction and fertiliser industries. The railway also hauls maritime containers and offers a parcels service known as 'Fastrack'.

Revenue from freight in 1996 was on a par with the previous year's income, despite the withdrawal of IE from groupage service in the later part of the year. Fertiliser and Bell Lines container revenue was down, while cement, Fastrack, non-Bell Lines container and Guinness (stout beer) traffics were all up on 1995.

Intermodal operations

Containers form an important part of IE's freight traffic, with around 150,000 TEU carried each year. IE provides daily (Monday to Friday) domestic common-user services between Dublin and Ballina, Dundalk, Galway, Limerick, Sligo, Waterford and Westport. Three common-user services run each day (Mondays to Fridays) between Dublin and Cork and daily private-user services are operated for Bell Lines (Dublin–Waterford and Limerick–Cork/Waterford).

A number of infrastructure improvements are being made to accommodate intermodal traffic. A new curve, costing I£1.2 million, has been built to allow container trains to bypass Kilkenny and avoid a time-consuming reversal. In the upgrading of the Dublin–Belfast line, bridges are being raised to accommodate 9 ft 6 in high containers. There is a strong flow of traffic from the Republic of Ireland to Belfast's Adelaide container yard.

Improvements to existing lines

A major upgrading project on the Dublin–Belfast line with European Union grant assistance was finished in June 1997. The I£110 million project involved relaying trackwork, new signalling, and new rolling stock (see 'Traction and rolling stock' section below). Top speed on the improved line is 145km/h.

The Dublin–Cork line maximum speed is now generally 145 km/h, with some stretches passed for 160 km/h.

On the remainder of the system, maximum speed is being increased to 130 km/h (with a few stretches at 145 km/h). EU funding is helping to upgrade the main intercity routes.

201 Class locomotive with Mk III InterCity stock   **1996**

DART electric commuter train   **1996**

Recent rolling stock acquisitions include 32 2,219 kW Co-Co JT42HCW diesel-electric locomotives of 201 Class built by GM Canada at London, Ontario, in 1994-95. Two JT42HCWs were purchased by Northern Ireland Railways (see United Kingdom entry) to operate cross-border passenger services in conjunction with a pair of IE units.

IE and Northern Ireland Railways also collaborated on an order for 28 new coaches (14 for each railway) for cross-border Dublin-Belfast services placed with De Dietrich of France in September 1994. The new coaches will operate as push-pull sets with the recently delivered JT42HCW locomotives. Delivery of this order was completed in February 1997.

In 1995, IE acquired from British Rail the 'International' train built in Derby, UK, in the early 1980s. The train was built speculatively by the state-owned manufacturer BREL (since bought by Adtranz) but never attracted series orders; it languished in sidings until acquired by IE and refurbished in its Inchicore works. The train comprises seven saloons, a buffet and a driving trailer.

In June 1996 Irish Rail ordered 27 diesel-hydraulic railcars from GEC Alsthom Transporte in Spain, with delivery due to begin at the end of 1997; the majority of these vehicles are for forming as pairs, but there are two single railcars in the order.

IE went out to tender in 1997 for extra electric trains for the Dublin suburban system.

In 1996, IE took delivery of three anhydrous ammonia wagons (tare 32.6 tonnes) from Bombardier Prorail in Wakefield, UK.

Traffic	1994	1995	1996
Freight tonnes (000)	3,015	3,179	3,188 est.
Freight tonne-km (million)	569.3	602.5	604.0 est.
Passenger journeys (000)	25,813	27,124	
Passenger-km (million)	1,260.3	1,291.2	

Finances (I£000)		
Revenue	1994	1995
Passenger	60,473	65,387
Freight	21,913	20,985
Total	82,386	86,372

Expenditure		
Staff/Personnel	88,385	87,373
Materials and services	70,017	86,049
Depreciation	12,826	15,934
Financial charges	11,444	13,161
Total	182,672	202,517

Traction and rolling stock

IE's motive power fleet at the start of 1996 consisted of 114 diesel locomotives, 17 dmu vehicles and 40 two-car DART emus. Freight wagons totalled some 1,831, and there were 287 passenger coaches (of which 50 are luggage vans and 26 buffet/dining cars).

Diesel locomotives

Class	Wheel arrangement	Power kW	Speed km/h	Weight tonnes	No in service	First built	Mechanical	Builders Engine	Transmission
071	Co-Co	1,800	145	102	18	1976	GM	GM12-645 E2C	E
121	Bo-Bo	700	120	65	15	1961	GM	GM 8-645CR	E
141	Bo-Bo	700	120	68	37	1962	GM	GM 8-645 CR	E
181	Bo-Bo	820	120	68	12	1966	GM	GM 8-645 E	E
201	Co-Co	2,219	165	112	32	1994	GM	GM 12-710G3 B	E

Electric multiple-units

Class	Cars per unit	Motor cars per unit	Motored axles/car	Output/motor kW	Speed km/h	Cars in service	First built	Builders Mechanical	Electrical
8101	2	1	4	130	100	80	1983	LHB	GEC Traction

Diesel multiple-units

Class	Cars per unit	Motor cars per unit	Motored axles/car	Speed km/h	Cars in service	First built	Mechanical	Builders Electrical	Transmission
2601	2	2	2	110	17	1993	Tokyu Car	Cummins NTA-855-R1	H Niigata DW14G

Signalling and telecommunications

The Dublin suburban line is controlled from a computer-based VDU console at Connolly station. The system utilises automatic route-setting and optimisation of public road level crossing closures, the latter being supervised by closed-circuit television. The CTC building also houses a similar console for control of 458 route-km of main line railway. The system permits operation of cab signalling equipment fitted to all locomotives, as well as train radio, and is being extended to cover further lines. In 1997 coverage was extended on the Belfast route to reach the border with Northern Ireland.

DART electric trains in the Dublin suburban area are fitted with Automatic Train Protection (ATP) equipment, activated by coded currents passed through the running rails, detected by coils on the emus and processed on board. Lineside signalling has been retained for diesel-hauled trains on the route.

Locomotives are fitted with a Continuous Automatic Warning System (cab signalling). Both emus and locomotives are fitted with AEG-Telefunken train radio allowing two-way transmission of fixed-message telegrams and voice communication with the controlling signalman at the appropriate CTC centre (suburban or main line). The equipment also permits voice communication between train drivers and on-train staff using hand-held portable radios.

Type of coupler in standard use: Passenger cars, buckeye or screw; emus, Scharfenberg and Dellner automatic; freight cars, screw or Instanter

Type of braking: Locomotive-hauled stock, vacuum or air

Track

Standard rail: Flat bottom 113, 95, 92 and 85 lb/yd, 54 kg/m, 50 kg/m; bullhead 95, 90, 87 and 85 lb/yd

Crossties (sleepers): Timber 2,590 × 255 × 125 mm; concrete 2,475 × 220 × 180 mm

Spacing: Concrete 1,144/km straight, 1,556/km curved track; timber, 1,313/km straight, 1,422/km curved track

Rail fastenings: Timber sleepers: CI chairs and sole plates; concrete sleepers: H-M (Vossloh) fastenings, Pandrol and H-M (Vossloh) on crossings

Min curvature radius
Running lines: 115 m
Sidings: 80 m

Max gradient: 1 in 40

Longest continuous gradient: 8.45 km, with 1% ruling gradient

Max altitude: 165 m at Stagmount, Co Kerry

Max axleloads: 18.8 tonnes for locomotives; 15.75 tonnes for wagons; 18.8 tonnes for specific traffics on bogie wagons

UPDATED

ISRAEL

Ministry of Transport

97 Jaffa Road, Jerusalem
Tel: +972 2 319211   Fax: +972 2 319203

Key personnel
Minister: Y Levy
Director-General: Dorron S Horrer

VERIFIED

Ports & Railways Authority

74 Petach Tikva Road, Tel Aviv
Tel: +972 3 565 7905   Fax: +972 3 561 7142

Key personnel
Chairman: Artur Israelovici
Director-General: Shoresh Lerer

VERIFIED

Israel Railways (IR)

Central Station, PO Box 18085, Tel Aviv 61180
Tel: +972 3 693 7401   Fax: +972 3 693 7480

Key personnel
General Manager: Amos Uzani
Deputy General Managers
   Technical: Nachman Levinger
   Operation: Doron Yzraeli
   Finance & Economics: David Haim
   Personnel & Administration: Isaac Siri
Managers
   Northern Region: Yossi Mor
   Southern Region: Eli Tilas
   Traffic: Yaacob Abutbul
   Traction and Rolling Stock: Bobi Solonicv
   Signalling and Telecommunications: Pinhas Katz
   Infrastructure and Civil Engineering: Doron Rubin
Purchase and Supply: Yoel Hoffmann
Public Relations and Spokesman: Benny Naor

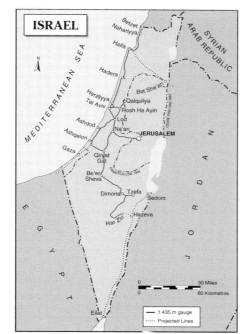

Gauge: 1,435 mm
Route length: 610 km

Political background

IR was long operated as a separate economic enterprise by the Ministry of Transport, but in 1988 the system became part of a new public enterprise, the Ports & Railways Authority. One objective was to reallocate some of the former Ports Authority's accumulated funds to railway investment; government policy for the past few years has been to renovate the railway, principally its passenger operations, as an attractive alternative to the rising volume of motor transport. Another aim of the change was to allow the railway more commercial freedom to react to changing market conditions.

The new government installed in May 1996 immediately announced that stronger emphasis would be placed on upgrading and expanding the rail system by

tapping private finance. In March 1997, IR was separated from the Ports & Railway Authority and the intention was to split it in two to form an operations company and an infrastructure authority. The government intended to sell the operations company, and might sell a minority stake in the infrastructure authority.

Traffic (million)	1993	1994	1995
Passenger journeys	3.8	4.2	4.85
Passenger-km	214	231.2	266.80
Freight tonnes	8.7	8.9	9.4
Freight tonne-km	1,072	1,089.4	1,175.7

Passenger operations

In 1991 the Transport Minister approved investment in passenger services totalling NIS500 million. The railway's development plan, recently updated for the next decade, includes extension of passenger service to new routes and raising train frequency on existing lines.

The 4.5 km Ayalon corridor linking Tel Aviv's South and Central stations opened in 1993, permitting introduction of through Haifa—Jerusalem trains in February 1996, though in the southerly direction only at first. At the same time, a new station opened at Hashalom, 1.6 km south of Tel Aviv Central. There are now 59 trains in each direction over the corridor, many running through to destinations north and south of the city.

The Rehovot—Tel Aviv service introduced in 1991 has proved very attractive, and now offers 19 trains each way daily. Again, some run through to Netanya or Haifa and Nahariyya. A further increase in frequency awaited 1997 completion of track doubling between Tel Aviv and Lod (15 km).

Plans exist to reintroduce service to Dimona and Beer Sheva, initially to the existing station at Beer Sheva but later right into the city centre. Two suburban services proposed around Tel Aviv, to the satellite towns of Kefar Sava and Petach Tikva, have been postponed on financial grounds. On the other hand, the new Hof Hacarmel station opening in 1997 will become the southern terminus of Haifa suburban trains until the proposed extension to Tirat Hacarmel comes to fruition. It will also be an outer-suburban stop for main line trains.

Freight operations

In 1995 the volume of freight hauled was the highest ever, at 9.4 million tonnes a 5 per cent increase over 1994. Rail's current market share is about 20 per cent of the total land transport task in terms of tonne-km, and this should rise as volume is expected to reach 15 million tonnes annually during the next decade.

About 40 per cent of the tonnage and 70 per cent of tonne-km is potash from the Dead Sea and phosphates from Oron and Har Zin, which are conveyed to the port of Ashdod in unit trains of up to 4,000 tonnes (west of Dimona) hauled by two GM Type G26CW 1,640 kW Co-Co diesel-electrics in multiple. Some goes to chemical plants on Haifa Bay, 310 km from Har Zin. For the rest, IR's freight is chiefly bulk movement of containers, grain and oil.

In 1987 a new rail terminal was completed at Tzefa, to which a conveyor belt of 18 km length delivers increased quantities of potash from Sedom on the Dead Sea. The potash is carried by rail from Tzefa mainly to the port of Ashdod (155 km), but some for domestic purposes is taken to the industrial area north of Haifa (270 km).

Unit train of imported coal bound for the Ashkelon power station leaves Ashdod port behind EMD GT26CW-2 Co-Co

1996

In 1990 a new power station located at Ashqelon, 42 km south of Ashdod, was completed. IR is moving 2.5 m tonnes of coal per annum from the port of Ashdod to the power station on the merry-go-round unit train principle. The coal is conveyed in five daily trains each of 30 self-discharging hopper wagons (60 tonnes payload) hauled by a 2,200 kW diesel-electric locomotive, the most powerful operated by IR, equipped with slow-speed control for moving train discharge.

Finances (NIS million)

Revenue	1993	1994	1995
Passenger	23.6	30.1	39.4
Freight	99.3	101.2	116.6
Other income	8.2	13.0	14.7
Total	131.1	144.3	170.7
Expenditure			
Staff	123.5	144.9	160.0
Materials & services	70.7	80.2	92.1
Capital charges	21.6	82.8	98.8
Total	215.8	307.9	350.9

New lines

The long-awaited project for a railway to Eilat has once more been postponed on financial grounds, but a variant of the scheme is under discussion. The plans call for a line from the Red Sea ports of Eilat and Aqaba to the Jordanian potash works on the eastern coast of the Dead Sea and Israel's Sedom works at the southern end. Under this proposal, Jordanian potash might also be exported through the port of Ashdod, while Israeli potash and phosphates might flow to the Red Sea ports.

In early 1995 an accord was signed between the Israeli and Jordanian governments approving in principle construction of a line extending some 90 km from the port of Haifa to Irbid in northern Jordan, designed to provide access to the Mediterranean for Jordanian import/export traffic. The first section of the route would utilise the derelict alignment of the former Hedjaz Railway branch from Deraa to Haifa, which was closed when Israel was created in 1948.

In late 1996, Israel reached agreement with the autonomous Palestinian authority to restore the long-disused 18 km rail link between Ashkelon and Gaza.

Traction and rolling stock

Diesel locomotive stock in early 1996 comprised 45 main line units and three shunters. Coaching stock totalled 90, including eight buffet cars and eight diesel generator cars. Freight stock totals 1,400 wagons, including 500 privately owned.

The most recent locomotive acquisitions are two GM-EMD 2,200 kW GT26CW2 for the Ashdod port—Ashkelon power station coal haul; and a 1,230 kW Type T44 Bo-Bo from Kalmar, originally planned for freight use, but found on delivery to be apt for mixed traffic employment. Four GM G12 diesel locomotives, formerly 1,040 kW, have been rebuilt with new 1,230 kW engines. An order for 18 3200 CV diesel locomotives was placed with GEC Alsthom Transporte of Spain in July 1996, with delivery scheduled to begin in March 1998.

Recent wagon purchases include 82 bogie container flats from Poprad of Slovakia and MTR of Israel, and 53 bogie potash hoppers from CAF Spain with local

Diesel locomotives

Class	Wheel arrangement	Power kW	Speed km/h	Weight tonnes	No in service	First built	Mechanical	Builders Engine	Transmission
AFB	Bo-Bo	840	105	84	3	1952	Société Franco-Anglo-Belge	GM 567B	E GM
G12	Bo-Bo	1,040	105	76	22	1954-66	GM	GM 12-567C	E GM
G16	Co-Co	1,450	107	124	3	1960-61	GM	GM 16-567C	
G26CW	Co-Co	1,640	124	99	9	1971-79	GM	GM 16-645E	E GM
G26CW-2	Co-Co	1,640	124	116	6	1982-86	GM	GM 16-645E	E GM
GT26CW-2	Co-Co	2,200	124	119	1	1989	GM	GM 16-645E3	E GM
T44	Bo-Bo	1,230	105	76	1	1989	Kalmar	GM 645E3	E GM
G8	Bo-Bo	635	105	70	1	1956	GM	GM 8-567C	E GM
V60 Shunting	0-6-0	485	65	54	1	1956-58	Esslingen	MTU 8 V 331 TC10	H Voith-Gmeinder

Diesel railcars or multiple-units

Class	Cars per unit	Motor cars per unit	Motored axles/car	Rated power kW	Speed km/h	Units in service	First built	Mechanical	Builders Engine	Transmission
IC3	3	3	4	300	160	10	1992	ABB-Scania	Deutz	H ZF
IC3-2	3	3	4	300	160	7	1996	Adtranz Sweden	Deutz	H ZF

A peak-hour Haifa—Tel Aviv—Rehovot train of four IC3 sets on the Ayalon corridor   **1996**

company Vulcan Industries. There is also an option for 24 grain hoppers from Bradken of Australia, with local input from Kibbutz Netzer Sereni Metal Works.

New stock on order includes a further 10 IC3 trainsets from Adtranz to complement the fleet of 17 delivered in 1992 and 1996. GEC Alsthom is building 20 loco-hauled coaches, including three with driving cabs and auxiliary diesel engines for push-pull operation. In 1996 an option was placed with GEC Alsthom Transporte, Spain, for a further 17.

In late 1996, IR announced plans to borrow four double-deck coaches from France to test them on Tel Aviv commuter services. The railway intended to invite tenders for five dmus and two double-deck trains, probably push-pull diesel worked.

Type of coupler in standard use: Screw
Type of brake in standard use: Air

Track
Rail: 54 kg/m
Crossties (sleepers): Concrete monobloc 300 kg and timber
Spacing: 1,670/km, concrete; 1,720/km, timber
Fastenings: Tension clamp
Min curvature radius: 140 m; 600 m min, new projects
Max gradient: 2.2% (compensated)
Max permissible axleload: 22.5 tonnes

UPDATED

ITALY

Ministry of Transport and Navigation

Piazza della Croce Rossa 1, I-00100 Rome
Tel: +39 6 841 6944   Fax: +39 6 855 9192

Key personnel
Minister: Claudio Burlando

VERIFIED

Alifana Railway

Gestione Governata Ferrovie Alifana e Benevento-Napoli
Piazza Carlo III, Naples
Tel: +39 81 293815   Fax: +39 81 459752

Key personnel
Government Commissioner: F Giovanni
Director-General: P Ruggiero

Gauge: 1,435 mm
Route length: 42 km

The Alifana Railway is managed in conjunction with the 48 km Benevento-Naples Railway (qv). In 1996 the government agreed to fund 50 per cent (Lit96 billion) of the cost of a new route from Piscinola to Capodichino.

The railway operates 16 diesel railcars, eight trailers, three diesel locomotives and 22 freight wagons.

VERIFIED

Arezzo Railways (LFI)

La Ferroviaria Italiana
Via Concino 2, Arezzo
Tel: +39 575 21607   Fax: +39 575 300939

Key personnel
General Manager: Marcello Grillo

Gauge: 1,435 mm
Route length: 85 km
Electrification: 85 km at 3 kV DC

The railway operates nine electric and three diesel locomotives, 12 electric railcars, 18 trailers and 60 wagons.

VERIFIED

Bari-Nord Railway

Ferrotramviaria SpA-Ferrovia Bari-Nord
Piazza Moro 50B, I-70122 Bari
Tel: +39 80 521 3577   Fax: +39 80 523 5480/524 3641

Key personnel
President: Dr Oscar Pasquini
Managing Director: Dr Ing Nicola Nitti
Operations Manager: Dr Ing Cesare Soria
Administration Manager: Dr Giambattista Angiuli

Gauge: 1,435 mm
Route length: 70 km
Electrification: 70 km at 3 kV DC

In 1993, passenger journeys totalled 4.46 million, with
108.3 million passenger-km recorded.
   The railway operates two electric and two diesel
locomotives, one diesel shunter, 15 electric railcars and
11 control trailers, four coaches and 16 wagons.

VERIFIED

Benevento—Naples Railway

Gestione Governata Ferrovie Alifana e Benevento—Napoli
Piazza Carlo III, Naples
Tel: +39 81 293815   Fax: +39 81 459752

Key personnel
Government Commissioner: F Giovanni
Director General: P Ruggiero

Gauge: 1,435 mm
Route length: 48 km
Electrification: 48 km at 3 kV DC

The Benevento—Naples Railway is managed in conjunction with the Alifana Railway (qv).
   The railway operates one diesel and one electric
locomotive, five electric railcars, one two-car emus, three
three-car emus and seven wagons.

VERIFIED

Calabria/Apulo—Lucane Railways

Ferrovie della Calabria
Ferrovie Apulo—Lucane
Managed by Government Commission, Rome
Viale del Caravaggio 105, Rome

Key personnel
Government Commissioner: Ing U Quaranta
Director-General: Dr Ing V De Luca

Gauge: 950 mm
Route length: 414 km

These two railways were formed in 1991 by splitting the
former Ferrovie Calabro—Lucane into separate operations based on the Bari and Cosenza networks. The
174 km Bari network connects Bari with Avigliano and
Matera. The 240 km Cosenza network connects Cosenza
with San Giovanni in Fiore and Catanzaro.
   The lines are operated with 14 diesel locomotives and
70 diesel railcars.

VERIFIED

Casalecchio—Savignano—Vignola Railway

Azienda Trasporti Consorziali, Bologna
Via Saliceto 3a, I-40128 Bologna
Tel: +39 51 350117/350123 Fax: +39 51 350177/
350106

Key personnel
General Manager: A Cocuccioni

Gauge: 1,435 mm
Route length: 32.5 km
Electrification: 30 km at 3 kV DC

The railway operates six electric and five diesel
locomotives, and seven wagons.

VERIFIED

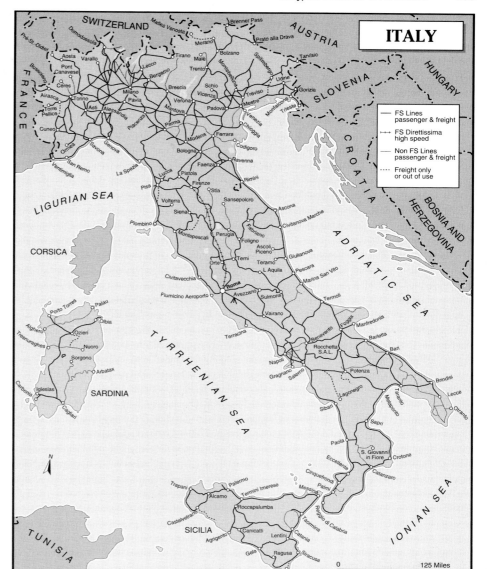

Railcar and trailer at Bari Central (David Haydock)   **1996**

Apulo—Lucane diesel railcars at Bari Central (David Haydock)   **1996**

Central Umbria Railway (FCU)

Ferrovia Centrale Umbria
Managed by Government Commission, Rome
Largo Cacciatori delle Alpi 8, I-06121 Perugia
Tel: +39 75 572 3947   Fax: +39 75 576 5257

Key personnel
Government Commissioner: Dr G Buffa
General Manager: M Mazzi

Gauge: 1,435 mm
Route length: 152 km
Electrification: 152 km at 3 kV DC

In 1996 government funding of Lit131 billion was allocated to projects on the Central Umbria network.

The railway operates two electric and seven diesel locomotives, four electric railcars, 33 diesel railcars and 65 wagons. Very little use of the electric stock has been made recently.

VERIFIED

Circumetnea Railway (FCE)

Ferrovia Circumetnea
Via Caronda 352A, I-95128 Catania
Tel: +39 95 545111   Fax: +39 95 431022

Key personnel
Manager: F Abbadessa
Deputy Manager: A Lollobatista

Gauge: 950 mm
Route length: 113 km

In 1996 the government allocated Lit270 billion to the Circumetnea system for improvements. It was intended to convert the Catania—Randazzo section to 1,435 mm gauge and electrify it at 3 kV DC.

The railway operates 25 diesel railcars, 11 coaches and 41 wagons. Four 1,435 mm gauge two-car emus are on order from Firema for delivery in 1998.

VERIFIED

Circumvesuviana Railway

Gestione Governativa Della Circumvesuviana
Corso Garibaldi 387, I-80142 Naples
Tel: +39 81 779 2111   Fax: +39 81 779 2450

Key personnel
Government Commissioner: Dr Ing Gaetano Danese
General Manager: Dr Fernando Origo
General Secretary: Dr Domenico Sica
Rail Operations Director: Dr Ing Michele di Matteo

Gauge: 950 mm
Route length: 144 km
Electrification: 144 km at 1.5 kV DC

The Circumvesuviana serves an extensive territory to the east of Naples stretching to Baiano, in the province of Avellino, and to Sarno in the province of Salerno, and also skirts the Bay of Naples to a terminus in Sorrento. The Sorrento branch is largely in tunnel, one of which under Monte Faito is 4.8 km long with a station inside the bore.

Passenger journeys in 1995 amounted to 111,950 and passenger-km 410 million.

The railway has a heavy continuing programme of engineering works to increase operating capacity and improve operation, see earlier editions of *JWR* for details. Plans include: double-tracking of the Sorrento branch between Torre Annunziata and Castellamare di Stabia; double-tracking and realignment of the Sarno branch east of Scafati, a total of 14.5 km; and construction of a new

Circumvesuviana emu approaching Naples (David Haydock)   *1996*

30 km double-track branch from the Baiano line at Nola to Avellino. Further extensions, double-tracking and realignments have been statutorily authorised, including a new line from Alfa Sud to Acerra. In 1996 Circumvesuviana was allocated government funding of Lit229 billion for improvements.

The company operates 118 articulated three-car emus, three diesel shunting locomotives, four Bo-Bo electric locomotives and 33 wagons.

VERIFIED

Cumana & Circumflegrea Railways (SEPSA)

Società per l'Esercizio di Pubblici Servizi
Via Cisternia dell'Olio 44, Naples
Tel: +39 81 552 5121

Key personnel
General Manager: R Bianco

Gauge: 1,435 mm
Route length: 45 km
Electrification: 45 km at 3 kV DC

The Cumana (19 km) and Circumflegrea (26 km) railways connect Naples with Torregaveta, serving a densely populated area. Passenger journeys totalled 13.7 million in 1992, and 13.9 million in 1993.

In 1996 the government allocated SEPSA Lit145 billion towards the Lit209 billion cost of the Mostra—Soccavo section of a new line to serve a university at Monte Angelo.

The railway operates 31 two-car emus, one diesel locomotive and 10 wagons.

VERIFIED

Domodossola—Locarno Railway

Società Subalpina Imprese Ferroviarie
PO Box 60, Via Mizzoccola 9, I-28037 Domodossola
Tel: +39 324 242055   Fax: +39 324 45242

Key personnel
General Manager: Ing Daniele Corti

Gauge: 1,000 mm
Route length: 32 km (and 20 km in Switzerland)
Electrification: 32 km at 1.35 kV DC

The railway operates 11 electric railcars, 11 coaches and 27 wagons.

VERIFIED

Genoa—Casella Railway (FGC)

Ferrovia Genova—Casella
Piazza Manin, Via alla Stazione per Casella 15,
I-16122 Genoa
Tel: +39 10 839 3285   Fax: +39 10 891433

Key personnel
Manager: G Bertoldi
Assistant Manager: P Gassani

Gauge: 1,000 mm
Route length: 24.3 km
Electrification: 24.3 km at 3 kV DC

Future plans include the construction of a new cut-off 4.5 km in length and of a new terminus in Genoa to connect with the upper station of the Granarolo funicular.

The railway operates nine electric railcars, one electric and one diesel locomotive.

VERIFIED

Italian Railways (FS)

FS SpA
Piazza della Croce Rossa 1, I-00100 Rome
Tel: +39 6 84901   Fax: +39 6 883 1108

Key personnel
President: Giancarlo Cimoli
General Secretary: Stefano Spinelli
Finance Director: Roberto Paolo Rossi
Director, Central Administration: Luigi di Giovanni
Directors of Central Departments
    Quality Control: Dr Carlo Gregoretti
    Organisation and Human Resources: Giovanni Satta
    Strategy: Francesco Pantile
    Public Relations: Mario Fortunato
    International Affairs: Francesco Pellegrini
    Legal Services: Mario Cevaro
Divisional Directors
    Intercity and Inter-regional Passenger:
        Giuseppe Sciarrone
    Suburban and Regional Passenger: Cesare Vaciago
    Freight: Antonio Lorenzo Necci, Giuseppe Pinna
    Traction: Mario Moretti
    Infrastructure: Silvio Rizzotti
    Engineering: Emilio Maraini
    Property: Daniel Buarron
Regional Managers
    Ancona: C Cingolani
    Bari: Ing Alessandro Natale
    Bologna: Ing Gian Pietro Monfardini
    Cagliari: Ing Errico Laneri
    Florence: Dr Ing Giovanni Bonora
    Genoa: Ing Carlo Rebagliati
    Milan: Dr Ing Paolo Enrico de Barbieri
    Naples: Ing Riccardo Augelli
    Palermo: Ing Mario La Rocca
    Reggio Calabria: G Biava
    Rome: Ing Giovannino Caprio
    Trieste: C Lo Vecchio
    Turin: Dr Luca Barbera
    Venice: Ing Giovanni Stabile
    Verona: C Abbadessa

Gauge: 1,435 mm
Route length: 15,941.7 km
Electrification: 10,030.2 km at 3 kV DC

Political background
The 1995-2000 contract plan agreed by FS and the government in 1995 tied public funding of Lit55,000 billion over the five years to performance-related targets. Performance was to be monitored by a government committee also responsible for fare levels, safety and other regulatory matters, the precursor of a proposed national transport authority to oversee FS privatisation.

It was expected that FS infrastructure functions would be established as a separate company by the end of 1999, with the gradual privatisation of operating divisions to follow.

In 1997, government attempts to cut Lit2,800 billion from the FS budget sparked a crisis, with the railway potentially unable to pay its staff and creditors; the crisis passed when the government backed down.

The government is seeking to cut FS's annual subsidy from Lit14,500 billion to Lit10,000 billion, but FS says it will be unable to make progress towards this target while political meddling with fares and refusal to allow closure of uneconomic branch lines persists.

Organisation
In 1992 Italian State Railways was formally reconstructed as a joint stock company (SpA), though at present its entire capital is held by the state. With capital totalling Lit42,418 billion, FS SpA has become the country's wealthiest joint stock company.

Within FS SpA, management and accounting of infrastructure and operations have been separated. At the head of the new structure is a holding company with responsibility for matters such as strategic planning and labour relations.

Since April 1996 there have been seven autonomous divisions or business units with profit-centre obligations within FS SpA. Long-distance and local passenger services have been divided between two divisions, with others responsible for freight, traction, infrastructure (Rete), engineering (Italferr) and property (Metropolis).

Subsidiary companies have been or are being created

E454 locomotive at Pisa Airport (Wolfram Veith)   *1995*

for development of activities apt for joint ventures with the private sector. These are:

Treno SpA: Formed with the Wagons-Lits Co (CIWLT) in 1993 to take over rolling stock management and marketing of overnight services. Other private sector involvement was to be enlisted. A comprehensive upgrade of existing sleeping cars and purchase of at least 120 new 'hotel train' cars by 1999 is an objective.

Data-Sint: To develop computerised data systems within the country's transport systems. The FS holding is 60 per cent; the remainder is held equally by Olivetti Information Services and Fionsiel of the state-owned IRI group.

TAV SpA: To organise finance for construction of the high-speed network (see below). The FS holding is 40 per cent; the remainder is shared by major banks, insurance companies and foreign financial bodies.

TAV CO SpA: To operate and market passenger services on the high-speed network, paying track rental to TAV.

Fintral: A financial organisation to work with local transport undertakings for rationalisation of local services and for their co-ordination for more effective and economical coverage of individual territories. The objective was to bring FS local services under the management of new regional, multimodal transport authorities.

Finance
In 1996, FS ended with a deficit of Lit2,800 billion, compared to a Lit5,000 billion deficit in 1995. Despite the scale of the losses, the state is determined to push on with FS modernisation, including construction of the high-speed network.

To help FS towards financial self-sufficiency, the state has taken over its accumulated debt and has met the costs of a programme begun in 1990 to reduce staff numbers through voluntary retirement. Between 1989 and 1997 the workforce was cut from 209,000 to 120,000 and productivity (measured in traffic units per employee) rose by 55 per cent. The target workforce for 2000 is 90,000 employees.

Loss-making routes to close
In the 1993-95 period a core network of some 5,200 route-km was defined, where FS would have freedom of commercial judgement and operate without subsidy. Over the rest of the system it was anticipated that some 2,000 route-km of heavily loss-making regional lines would close in order to eliminate up to 80 per cent of historic government cash support of the railway's revenue.

In 1993 FS purchased a 55 per cent holding in Italy's largest bus company, Sogin. A system of bus feeders to rail hubs has been proposed to replace loss-making regional train services. On what was retained of the non-commercial network, FS would furnish service under contract to the state and/or regional administrations. In early 1997, the government had yet to grant approval for any line closure programme, but some 2,000 trains were expected to be cut from lightly used routes on financial grounds.

Spending cutbacks
Creation of FS SpA was accompanied by publication of a 1993-1995 business plan featuring some severe economics. Due to Italy's deteriorating financial state, the government sharply cut planned railway investment over the 1993-1997 period from Lit79,000 billion to Lit40,000

billion. FS operational subsidy was also drastically cut in 1993, with many local trains replaced by buses on Sundays and public holidays and workshop and depot closures ordered.

Standard fare levels were frozen in 1993 and increased by 3 per cent in 1994. The 8 per cent rise scheduled for 1995 was not approved by the government. From the start of 1996 FS was to be free to set its own tariff levels, although subsequent government plans for a transport authority included fares in the latter's remit. The introduction of market-based pricing for passenger services was also planned for 1996 (initially on long-distance services), pending governmental approval and the results of studies into the projected effects on traffic and revenue. In the event, a fares rise for 1997 was not approved by the government, and more service cuts were planned for February 1997.

Investment
Under the terms of a 1995-2000 contract plan agreed with the government in 1995, FS was to receive public funding of Lit55,000 billion over the five-year period. It was hoped that the contract plan would allow Lit15,275 billion of private funding to be invested in the high-speed (AV) line construction programme. Investment projected for 1996 amounted to Lit9,561.1 billion, with Lit1,444.2 billion to be spent on new rolling stock. Other major areas of projected expenditure included Lit6,000 billion for construction of new lines, Lit323 billion for major track improvements and Lit1,384 billion for signalling.

Passenger operations
In long- and medium-haul passenger traffic, FS SpA has been set a target of lifting the 1992 gross of 20.4 billion passenger-km to 23 billion by 1995, and to 34 billion by the end of the decade. That would raise the railway's 1992 market share of 5 per cent to 6.5 per cent by 2000. In the course of the decade investment in new rolling stock for this sector has been forecast to total Lit5,660 billion, of which Lit1,140 billion was to come from private sector involvement in development of the high-speed network.

In 1994, total FS passenger traffic grew by 3.9 per cent when compared with 1993, with 48.9 billion passenger-km recorded. In 1995 50 billion passenger-km (462.5 million passenger journeys) were recorded, despite delays and train cancellations caused by unexpected staff shortages.

In 1995 FS unveiled its plans for a three-tier network of long-distance regular-interval services to be introduced by 1999. Services operated between Italy's principal cities and to France and Switzerland with tilting and non-tilting high-speed rolling stock were to be marketed as Eurostar Italia, connecting with Intercity trains serving regional centres and provincial capitals. The third tier was to be formed by Interregionali trains radiating from principal nodes.

FS and SNCF of France have formed joint ventures to market and develop high-speed and overnight services between Italy and France. Handling some 1 million passengers a year by the start of 1995, overnight services linking Paris with Milan, Florence, Venice and Rome were restructured in 1995 with improved timetables and new fares. New or refurbished rolling stock was to be provided in 1996-97.

September 1996 saw introduction of two daily return services worked by SNCF TGV Réseau high-speed trainsets on the Paris—Turin—Milan route, with a journey time of 6 hours 35 minutes for Paris—Milan. At the same time, FS ETR 460 trainsets began working one return Milan—Lyon and two return Turin—Lyon services.

Suburban operations are managed by 21 local business units which are structured to facilitate their eventual privatisation or separation from FS proper. In 1995 Rome suburban services came under a common fares scheme also adopted by the city's bus, tram and metro networks. A similar scheme was introduced in Naples, leading to a 25 per cent increase in patronage at certain FS stations.

A long-term aim is to increase rail's share of the commuter market from 15 per cent to 40 per cent, with the present 7 billion suburban passenger-km a year climbing to 15 billion through introduction of regional metro networks with regular-interval services. These networks would be based on existing suburban routes in 10 cities.

Freight operations

In the freight sector, FS is mandated to lift its market share from 12.4 per cent in 1992 to 19.6 per cent by 2000. A rise of tonne-km to 26.7 billion by 1995 and to 42.5 billion by 2000 has been targeted. In the event a total of 22.2 billion tonne-km on the year before were recorded in 1995, an increase of 8.6 per cent (73.5 million tonnes), but provisional results for January to October 1996 showed a fall of 5.8 per cent in total tonne-km, dashing hopes of financial break-even by the freight sector in that year. A cost-cutting programme includes the transfer of freight wagons to a separate FS subsidiary, running fewer trains, reducing the workforce by 25 per cent, bringing the present 50:50 ratio of wagonload to trainload traffic to 40:60 and reducing the number of terminals to around 200 (there were 600 at the end of 1993).

Investment totalling Lit3,965 billion is to take place during the period up to 2000. Strategy centres on moulding FS as a door-to-door carrier and priorities include provision of more specialised wagons and the ability to run top-rate merchandise and intermodal trains at 140 to 160 km/h. New private sidings are to be encouraged with incentives; joint ventures with foreign partners have been sought, to foster cross-border traffic; and EDI development will be energetic. The FS freight division is involved with the private sector in joint-venture companies which specialise in the management, operation and retailing of intermodal operations and terminals, road collection and delivery, warehousing, information technology for freight services and the carriage of dangerous goods by rail.

Controllo Centralizzato Rotabili (CCR), a central real-time and computer-based data transmission system, now monitors freight operation through input via 400 terminals of activity at all 2,800 freight-generating and reception points.

Almost two-thirds of FS freight is international. There have been considerable gains in traffic with Germany as a result of the extra trains scheduled following new Austrian restrictions on transit road freight (for details see Austria entry). Despite fierce competition, rail holds 40 per cent of the Italo-German market, carrying 13 million tonnes in 1994. Traffic conveyed by block trains includes Italian cars for the German market, and fresh fruit and vegetables carried in temperature-controlled wagons to Cologne and Munich. In 1995 FS and DB AG agreed to set up a business unit to manage all Italo-German traffic, except cars and intermodal business. SBB and BLS of

Class E636 locomotive, dating from the 1940s, hauling a 'rolling motorway' service. Lorry drivers ride in the coach immediately behind the locomotive (John C Baker)   **1997**

Switzerland and ÖBB of Austria were expected to join the organisation at a later date.

In 1996, direct VIALP services for wagonload traffic to and from France were in operation on the Udine—Dijon, Verona—Brescia—Lyon, Bologna—Dijon, Naples—Pisa—Lyon and Turin—Lille routes, with the Lille service connecting with Channel Tunnel services to and from the UK. A daily train conveying Rover cars produced in the UK for the Italian market was in operation between Longbridge and Arluno via the Channel Tunnel, with a weekly train carrying Italian cars from Turin to Avonmouth.

Intermodal operations

Intermodal freight is managed by Italcontainer, of which a 65 per cent share is held by the wholly owned FS subsidiary Nuova INT, 25 per cent by Intercontainer-Interfrigo, and 10 per cent by CEMAT, the Italian piggyback company. In intermodal business FS itself is essentially a wholesaler of track space and train operation.

Intermodal traffic now constitutes 25 per cent of FS freight. Recent improvements have included a move from 100 to 120 km/h operation of intermodal trains on the north-south trunk route from Milan and a 3 per cent advance in the commercial speed of such services. In 1995, intermodal traffic grew by 11.4 per cent, with container traffic growing by 5.9 per cent, growth that was sustained in 1996 despite falls elsewhere.

Grants for equipment and terminals

Legislation of 1990 provided financial inducements for companies to invest in rail-based intermodal transport. A 20 per cent contribution to capital cost is on offer for purchase of containers or swapbodies and other apparatus needed for intermodal operation, and a 10 per cent rebate of the cost of rail movement.

Legislation of 1990 put up almost ECU500 million towards the creation in key commercial areas of multifunction 'freight villages', or Interporti, equipped to deal in both conventional rail and intermodal freight, and where the rail installations are surrounded by

warehousing and other value-adding activities that combine to offer a full logistics service. FS is supported in this programme by CEMAT, and further finance for most of the Interporti has come from local authorities, banks and other private sector bodies. The nine 'first level' Interporti are members of Assointerporti, a European Economic Interest Group set up to associate similar enterprises throughout the EU.

New lines

Rome—Florence Direttissima

Italy's first high-speed line, the Rome—Florence Direttissima, became fully operational in 1992 with the opening of its final 44 km section from Arezzo South to Figline. It is electrified on the 3 kV DC system. The final stretch was made traversable at 300 km/h to allow for testing of new ETR 500 rolling stock. ETR 450 tilt-body trainsets have been limited to 250 km/h in commercial service over the Direttissima.

A total of Lit460 billion is to be spent on upgrading the Direttissima for 300 km/h operation throughout, to be completed for the projected opening of the Rome—Naples high-speed route in 1999. At its northern end, the Direttissima is to be linked to the planned Florence—Bologna high-speed line by an orbital line around Florence running mostly on the surface.

High-speed routes: network plan

In 1991 a mixed holding company, Treno Alta Velocita (TAV), was formed to carry forward plans for a high-speed (Alta Velocita, or AV) network approved in 1986 by the FS board. The network was to be T-shaped, running south-north from Battipaglia (south of Salerno) to Milan via the Rome—Florence Direttissima, and west-east from Turin to Venice via Milan.

TAV is owned by FS (45 per cent) and by a dozen banks, nine of them Italian, two French and one German, which together put up 60 per cent of the company's starting capital of Lit100 billion. The latter was to be increased to Lit1,000 billion by the end of 1995. TAV was granted a 50-year concession to design, construct and market the high-speed network in 1991. Train operation and rolling stock and infrastructure maintenance will be the responsibility of FS.

In 1993 the government made available the funds for a start of the high-speed project, having agreed to provide 40 per cent of the total cost of the infrastructure. The components authorised were: Rome—Naples; Florence—Bologna; Bologna—Milan; and Milan—Turin. Some 70 per cent of the state funding for these sections was provided in the 1993 and 1994 national budgets, with the remainder in the 1995 spending round. The government later authorised Milan—Venice and Genoa—Milan high-speed routes. The total cost of building the approved high-speed infrastructure (964.7 km) has been put at Lit28,870 billion.

Delays to the high-speed programme have been caused by the vetting of construction contracts following allegations of corruption and by opposition on environmental grounds, although the new routes have been designed to follow existing motorway corridors where possible. At mid-1995 it was anticipated that the first route would enter service in 1999 with the network completed by 2005.

The new high-speed routes are to be electrified at 25 kV 50 Hz AC rather than 3 kV DC, and have a minimum curve

Class E444 locomotive with an intercity train on the 'Direttissima' near Florence (David Haydock)   **1997**

radius of 5,450 m and a maximum gradient of 1.8 per cent. Maximum axleload is to be 18 tonnes. Signalling and train control will be derived from the French TVM 430 system, supplied by CS Transport of France and Ansaldo Trasporti. Although the new lines are to be engineered for a maximum speed of 300 km/h, in 1995 it was announced that high-speed services would not operate above 250 km/h for an indeterminate period, in response to environmental concerns. Passenger services over the new routes will be provided by high-speed trainsets and locomotive-hauled trains operating at up to 220 km/h. The high-speed network will also be used by freight trains (principally intermodal services) operating at up to 160 km/h.

High-speed routes: Rome—Naples

Work began on the Rome—Naples high-speed line at 11 sites in 1994. Completion is expected by mid-1999, at a cost of Lit5,300 billion, excluding environmental protection measures. The route follows the A1 motorway for most of its length and comprises 204.5 km of new construction and 15.5 km of upgraded infrastructure to gain access to Rome and Naples. Other connections with existing routes are to be provided at Frosinone and Cassino.

High-speed routes: Florence—Bologna

The final alignment of the 78.3 km Florence—Bologna high-speed line was approved in 1995. In May 1996 Italferr-SIS TAV signed a contract valued at Lit3,900 billion with a consortium led by Fiat and construction company Impregio to build the major part (71.5 km) of the route the outskirts of Florence. It is expected that construction will be completed by the end of 2002. Crossing the Apennine range, 66.8 km of the principal 71.5 km section will be in tunnel.

High-speed routes: Bologna—Milan

The existing route between Bologna and Milan is one of the most congested on the FS network. The new route would take 62 months to build, at a cost of Lit4,480 billion, excluding connections with existing lines.

The high-speed route comprises 180 km of new infrastructure starting at Melegnano, 21 km south of Milan Central. The subject of controversy during the early planning stages, it runs parallel to the A1 motorway as far as Bologna's outskirts. The new line is to pass below Bologna in tunnel, with a station below the existing FS facility. Connections to existing routes are to be provided at Piacenza, Fidenza and Modena.

With future high-speed services in mind, two extra tracks were commissioned in 1996 on the Milan—Melegnano route between Milan Rogoredo and San Giuliano Milanese (7 km).

High-speed routes: Milan—Turin

Costed at Lit2,700 billion (excluding connections to existing lines), construction would take 60 months. The alignment of the 127 km route has caused controversy, particularly in the Novara area, and is planned to follow the A2 motorway. New infrastructure is to begin at Certosa, 9 km from Milan Central, and run to Settimo Torinese, 8 km from Torino Porta Nuova. Connections with existing lines are to be provided at Novara.

High-speed routes: Milan—Venice

Construction has been costed at Lit5,400 billion, excluding connections to existing lines. The route comprises 212 km of new line, starting 20 km from Milan Central at Melzo. It follows the SS1 motorway to Brescia (where connections with the existing network are to be provided), and then the A4 motorway to south of Verona where it rejoins the existing FS system. The remainder of the high-speed route links Verona and Padua, with a connection to the existing network at Vicenza. High-speed services will reach Venice over the existing Padua—Mestre route, upgraded and expanded.

High-speed routes: Genoa—Milan

Genoa—Milan (126 km) has been costed at Lit3,690 billion, including connections to existing lines. New infrastructure is to begin at Milan Rogoredo and will follow the A7 motorway as far as Novi Ligure, where a connection with the existing network will be provided. Between Novi Ligure and Genoa (entered over existing infrastructure), the high-speed line crosses the Apennine range by a 16 km tunnel.

High-speed routes: Lyon—Turin

This project comprises 235 km of new infrastructure for 300 km/h operation between Turin and the TGV-Rhône-

E402 locomotive at Milan Central (M Tolini) **1996**

Alpes high-speed line west of Lyon. Its centrepiece is a new 54 km base tunnel between St-Jean-de-Maurienne in France and Susa in Italy, with twin bores large enough to accommodate 'rolling highway' services of lorries riding on flat wagons. In 1994 FS and SNCF of France formed the Alpetunnel joint venture to undertake technical and economic studies for the base tunnel.

In 1996 the French and Italian governments announced creation of an international commission that was to draw up a treaty for the project, defining its characteristics and how it was to be built, financed and operated. The commission was also to supervise technical, legal and financial appraisals undertaken before the treaty had been signed. FS hoped to attract private investment for the project, which would cost an estimated Lit150,000 billion and take some seven years to survey and build. In late 1995 it was reported that Eximbank of Japan was to invest Lit4,000 billion.

Cross-city routes: Milan

In 1982 construction started of a new cross-Milan line, known as the Passante, as the first step toward creation of an integrated public transport system for the conurbation. The 18.4 km Passante extends from Rogoredo, south of the city on the FS Bologna main line, to Certosa, on the line to Turin. The centrepiece is a 5.9 km double-track tunnel between Lancetti and Porta Vittoria, with six new stations below ground.

Diesel locomotives

Class	Wheel arrangement	Power kW	Speed km/h	Weight tonnes	No in service	First built	Mechanical	Builders Engine	Transmission
D343	B-B	995/ 1,015	130	60	74	1967	Fiat/OM/Sofer Omeca/Breda	Fiat 218 SSF/ Breda-Paxman 12YJCL	E TIBB/OCREN
D443	B-B	1,400	130	72	49	1966	Fiat/OM/ Sofer/IMAM/ Reggiane	Fiat 2312 SSF/ Breda-Paxman 12YLCL	E ASG/OCREN
D345	B-B	995	130	61	145	1974	Breda/Sofer/ Savigliano	Fiat 218SSF	E TIBB/Marelli/ Italtrofo
D445	B-B	1,560	130	72	149	1974	Fiat/Omeca	Fiat 2112SSF	E Ansaldo
D141	Bo-Bo	515	80	64	29	1962	TIBB/Reggiane	Fiat MB 820B	E TIBB
D143	Bo-Bo	420	70	65	49	1942	TIBB/OM	OM	E TIBB
D145	Bo-Bo	850	100	72	100	1982	Fiat/TIBB	BRIF ID 36 SS12V Fiat 8,297.22 × 2	E TIBB/Parizzi
235	C	160	50	34	17	1957	Badoni	BRIF 1D36 N8V	H Voith
225	B	129	50	32	125	1955	Breda/Jenbach/ Greco/Sofer/ IMAM	Breda/Jenbach/ Deutz	H Breda/Voith
245	C	258	65	48	407	1962	Reggiane/OM/ Breda/IMAM/ Ferraro/Greco	MB820-Fiat D26N12V BRIF JW 600 CNTR OM-SEV	H BRIF-Voith Llt24
214	B	95	35	22	494	1964	Badoni/Greco	Fiat 8217-02,001	H BRIF-Voith Llt33
255	C	500	53.5	53	30	1991	Badoni/Greco	BRIF ID 3658V	H Voith

Diesel railcars

Class	Motored axles/car	Power/motor kW	Speed km/h	No in service	First built	Mechanical	Builders Engine	Transmission
ALn668	2	110-170	110-130	738	1956	Omeca/Breda/ Fiat Savigliano	Fiat	M
ALn663	2	170 × 2	120/130	120	1983	Fiat Savigliano	Fiat 8217.32	M

Electric trainsets

Class	Cars per unit	Line voltage	Motor cars per unit	Motored axles/car	Output/motor kW	Speed km/h	No in service	First built	Builders Mechanical	Electrical
ETR 220/240	4	3 kV	2	4	250	160	11	1936	Breda	Breda
ETR 250	4	3 kV	2	4*	250	180	4	1960	Breda	Breda
ETR 300	7	3 kV	3	4	262	180	1	1952	Breda	Breda
ETR 401	4	3 kV	2	4	260	250	1	1976	Fiat	Fiat
ETR 450	11	3 kV	10	2	315	250	11	1987	Fiat	Marelli
ETR 460	9	3 kV	6	4	500	250	(40)†	1988	Fiat	Parizzi
ETR 500	13	3/25 kV	2	4	1,100	300	(60)†	1992	Trevi	Trevi

* Plus two further motored axles on trailers
† On order

Electric multiple-units: power cars

Class	Cars per unit	Line voltage	Motor cars per unit	Motored axles/car	Output/motor kW	Speed km/h	No in service	First built	Builders Mechanical	Electrical
ALe 540	1	3 kV	1	4	180	150	25	1957	OCREN/Stanga	OCREN/Stanga/ Sacfem
ALe 582	2/4	3 kV	1/2	4	280	140	90	1987	Breda	Marelli/Ansaldo
ALe 601	1	3 kV	1	4	250	200	65	1961	Casaralta	Casaralta/OCREN
ALe 660	1	3 kV	1	4	180	150	15	1955	OCREN	OCREN
ALe 803	3*	3 kV	1	4	250	130	53	1961	Stanga/ Savigliano/ IMAM	Savigliano/ Sofer
ALe 840	1	3 kV	1	4	180	130	49	1950	OCREN/OM/ OTO	OCREN/OM
ALe 801 ALe 940	4† 4† }	3 kV	2	4	250	140	62	1976	Stanga/Fiore/ Aetal/Lucana Sofer	Marelli/Stanga/ Fiore/Lucana/ Sofer
ALe 644	2	3 kV	1	4	280	140	6	1980	Breda	Breda
ALe 724	3/4	3 kV	1 .	4	280	140	89	1982	Breda	Marelli/Ansaldo
ALe 804‡	4	3 kV	2	4	250	140	6	1980	Breda	TIBB

* Including two Type Le 803 trailers
† Including two Type Le 108 trailers
‡ Including Type Le 884 trailer

Besides connecting main lines to and from the south (Genoa and Bologna), east (Bergamo, Cremona and Treviglio, by a 3.1 km branch from Porta Vittoria) and northwest (Turin and Domodossola), the link will throw off a connection between Lancetti and Villa Pizzone to the North Milan Railway (FNME) system at Bovisa, enabling integration of FNME and FS services.

It is expected that the entire Passante route would be open to traffic by the end of 2000, used by services operating every 20 minutes at peak periods and hourly at other times on five routes — Novara—Lodi, Gallarate—Codogno, Malpensa—Brescia, Saronno—Treviglio and Seveso—Pavia.

Further FS investment associated with the scheme has included four-tracking from Piotello to Treviglio (22 km), approved in 1995 for completion around 2000 at an estimated cost of Lit700 billion. Two extra tracks were commissioned in 1996 between Rogoredo and San Giuliano Milanese (7 km), on the route to Lodi and Codogno. The upgrading of the Milan orbital route connecting Certosa, Lambrate, Porta Vittoria, Rogoredo and Porta Romana has also been proposed; it was expected that four-tracking between Piotello and Lambrate would be completed in 1996.

In 1995 FS, FNME and the Lombardy region signed an agreement to create Servizio Ferroviario Regionale (SFR), which from January 1997 became responsible for regional and suburban railway services within Lombardy. As part of the formation of SFR, FS was to acquire a 50 per cent shareholding in FNME and staff from both operators were to transfer to the new undertaking.

Cross-city routes: Turin
In 1983 FS signed an agreement with the Turin city authorities aiming to establish a regional rail system similar to Milan's. This featured construction of a 3.3 km cross-city tunnel, through Zappata, to create a through axis between Lingotto, Porta Susa, Dora and Stura. The scheme involved the quadrupling of 15 to 20 route-km between Porta Susa and Dura. Porta Susa was to be the starting point of a putative link with Caselle airport, 15 km from the city centre, over the independent Turin—Ceres Railway. That was to be connected to the cross-city line at Dora. But disagreements arose in the mid-1980s and the project came to a standstill. At the end of 1994, it was hoped that Turin's cross-city tunnel would open to traffic in 2000.

Improvements to existing lines
Brenner route
In 1991 the Transport Ministers of Italy, Austria and Germany agreed on a new initiative to advance construction of a Brenner Pass base tunnel (for details see Austrian Railways entry). In the meantime, Lit1,250 billion was to be invested in the Verona—Brennero portion of the existing route, with funding provided in part by loans from the European Investment Bank. Four new tunnels were to be bored, partly to bypass speed-restricting curvature and partly to protect areas vulnerable to rock falls. Heading northward from Verona, the tunnels would replace existing alignments on the Domegliara-Dolcé, Bolzano—Prato Tires, Prato Tires—Ponte Gardena and Colle Isaro—Brennero sections.

The 13 km Prato Tires—Ponte Gardena tunnel opened in 1994, with the remaining three tunnels (totalling 17 km) due to open by the end of 1997. FS is also undertaking some realignments for 160 km/h between Bolzano and Colle Isaro. Associated with these improvements is double-tracking between Verona and Bologna. For piggyback traffic the route will satisfy C loading-gauge parameters after completion of the new tunnels.

Pontebbana route
The Pontebbana route between Villach, Austria, and Trieste/Venice via the Tarvisio Pass and Udine already carries 11 per cent of FS international traffic, almost the same as the Brenner, and is heading for major growth of its freight traffic. Its single line and outdated electrification have consequently become more of a burden year by year, prompting FS to launch a programme of double-tracking, track rebuilding for heavier axleloads, realignment and grade easement, re-electrification and resignalling with automatic block for reversible working. New tunnelling is involved in obtaining an alignment for the second track over 85 per cent of the route. The first 19 km of renewal were completed in 1985, and the final 32 km to Tarvisio, involving nine viaducts and five tunnels with a total length of 25 km, was expected to be completed in 1997.

Power cars for ETR 500, the non-tilting Italian high-speed train, lined up outside the Breda factory   **1997**

Type ETR 450 tilt-body trainset

ETR 460 tilt-body trainset at Milan Central (M Tolini)   **1996**

Rome
Major projects in the Rome area have included a new orbital link from St Peters via Vigna Clara to the Rome—Florence route north of Tiburtina. The link includes a 4.6 km tunnel under Rome's northern suburbs. Other ugrading projects include the double-tracking of the Tiburtina—Guidonia route, quadrupling between Casilina and Ciampino and double-tracking and electrification of the St Peters—Cesano di Roma route. In 1995 tenders were invited for double-tracking and electrification between St Peters and La Storta. It was estimated that the work, under way in 1996, would cost around Lit250 billion.

These projects form the basis of a scheme to dramatically increase suburban rail provision in Rome by 2000. Cross-city services would be provided between Fiumicino and Fara Sabina and between La Storta and Ciampino, sharing the southern Trastevere—Ostiense—Tuscolana orbital route and operating in conjunction with St Peters—Vigna Clara—Tiburtina and Tiburtina—Guidonia services. Investment totalling Lit4,000 billion would be required for the scheme, which also includes

refurbishment work at Rome's Termini, Tiburtina, St Peters, Ostiense and Trastevere stations.

Traction and rolling stock
Total FS rolling stock resources in 1995 comprised 2,058 electric locomotives, 1,160 diesel locomotives, 33 electric trainsets, 603 electric railcars, 911 diesel railcars, 1,380 shunting locomotives, 12,493 hauled passenger coaches and 80,088 freight wagons.

ETR 460
FS ordered 40 ETR 460 tilt-body trainsets from Fiat, capable of 250 km/h. The new units are nine-car, like the earlier ETR 450, but with only six cars motored, due to use of more powerful three-phase asynchronous motors with GTO inverter control. Body width is 2.8 m, and improved sound insulation and full pressure sealing have been applied to the aluminium alloy bodies. The first ETR 460s entered service in 1995. Three trainsets configured for operation at the Italian and French DC voltages (3 kV and 1.5 kV respectively) entered service between Milan and Lyon in 1996.

It has been proposed to equip 15 sets for 15 kV 16⅔ Hz AC operation in Austria or Switzerland. Production of a batch of 15 dual-voltage ETR 480 trainsets equipped for 25 kV 50 Hz AC operation on Italian high-speed routes was due to begin in 1996. Trials of a prototype tilting two-car diesel-electric trainset, developed by Fiat from the ETR 460, were due to start in 1997. The prototype was to have a three-phase drive and a maximum speed of 160 km/h, and it was reported that FS was to order 16 such trainsets.

ETR 470

Nine dual-voltage electric trainsets with the Fiat active body-tilt system were to enter service on the Geneva–Milan route in June 1996 and on the Basle/Berne–Milan and Zurich–Milan routes in September. Introduction of the first two trainsets to the Geneva–Milan route was in the event postponed until September 1996 due to technical problems, with the other routes coming on stream in subsequent months.

A joint venture company, Cisalpino AG, has been set up to manage operation of the ETR 470s. This is based in Berne, Switzerland (see Switzerland entry for details), but FS is a major partner, with a 50 per cent holding; the Swiss Federal (SBB) share is 33 per cent, that of the Berne–Lötschberg–Simplon (BLS) 7 per cent, and the remaining 10 per cent is held jointly by certain Swiss Cantons.

ETR 500

Track parameters for Italy's planned high-speed (AV) network, dictated by need to make the new lines usable by fast freight as well as passenger trains, obviated need of body-tilt in the Type ETR 500 train for dedicated AV operation at 300 km/h. Design of a prototype was entrusted to a Breda-led consortium known as TREVI and background to its development is covered in past editions of *JWR*.

The decision taken in 1993 to electrify the new AV routes at 25 kV 50 Hz AC has resulted in design changes to the ETR 500. The initial batch of 30 ETR 500 trainsets was ordered before this decision was taken, and thus has been delivered configured for DC only (although AC equipment is expected to be retrofitted at a later date). The second batch of 30 ETR 500 trainsets is being equipped with both AC and DC traction equipment. Both batches will be able to operate from a 1.5 kV DC supply (the norm in the French regions) at half power. Other modifications by comparison with the prototypes include reduction of maximum axleloading from 19 to 17 tonnes, which would permit operation over the French high-speed network.

By the June 1997 timetable change, 36 ETR 500 sets were in use.

Electric locomotives

Preproduction prototypes of the 3,600 kW Class E453 freight locomotive and Class E454 passenger locomotive (both single-cab 79-tonne Bo-Bo designs) emerged in 1989-90, with FS later ordering both types in a combined batch of 50. The E454 is intended to work medium-distance trains with a unit at each end at up to 160 km/h. The E453 is to operate in back-to-back pairs, at a maximum of 120 km/h. Pininfarina was commissioned to style the E453/4 outline and construction of the first examples (two Class E453 and three Class E454) was undertaken by Breda.

Five Class E402 prototypes were built by a consortium including Ansaldo, Fiat and Breda. Equipped with a three-phase drive, the E402 is an 84-tonne, 5,600-kW, Bo-Bo locomotive designed for 250 km/h, with a tractive effort of 180 kN at 102 km/h and of 92 kN at 200 km/h. Since 1992, FS has ordered a total of 40 E402A (3 kV DC only) and 80 E402B (3 kV DC and 25 kV 50 Hz AC) locomotives, with deliveries scheduled for completion in 1996.

In mid-1997, FS took delivery of the first of 20 Class E412 locomotives from Adtranz. Designed for international services to Austria and Germany, this 200 km/h design can run under both 3 kV DC and 15 kV AC 16.66 Hz catenary, and at reduced performance under 1.5 kV DC.

In 1996 FS placed an order valued at Lit170 billion with Adtranz for 50 lightweight E464 electric locomotives. The locomotives were to be used on regional and suburban push-pull passenger services.

Passante emus

FS and FNME have ordered 50 four-car double-deck electric multiple-units for the Passante line under construction in Milan. Each trainset will comprise two motor and two trailer cars, have a maximum speed of

Electric locomotives

Class	Wheel arrangement	Line voltage	Output kW continuous/ one hour	Speed km/h	Weight tonnes	No in service	First built	Builders Mechanical	Electrical
E626	Bo-Bo-Bo	3 kV	1,890/ 2,100	95	93	105	1928	Savigliano/CGE/ Brown Boveri/ Saronno/Breda/ OM/Ansaldo/ CEMSA Saronno/ Reggiane/Fiat	Marelli/Savigliano CGE/Brown Boveri/Saronno/ Breda/OM/Ansaldo/ CEMSA Saronno
E412	Bo-Bo	3/15 kV	6,000	200	87	20	1997	Adtranz	Adtranz
E402	Bo-Bo	3 kV	5,000	220	86	6	1988	Reggiane	Ansaldo
E424	Bo-Bo	3 kV	1,500/ 1,660	100/ 120	73	141	1943	Breda/Savigliano/ Ansaldo/Reggiane/ Brown Boveri/OM	Breda/Savigliano/ Brown Boveri/CGE
E444	Bo-Bo	3 kV	4,000/ 4,440	200	83	113	1967	Savigliano/Breda/ Casaralta/Fiat	OCREN/Asgen/ Savigliano
E636	Bo-Bo-Bo	3 kV	1,890/ 2,100	110	101	459	1941	Breda/Brown Boveri/ Savigliano/OM/ Reggiane/Pistoiesi	Breda/Brown Boveri/Savigliano/ CGE/Ansaldo
E645	Bo-Bo-Bo	3 kV	3,780/ 4,320	120	110	98	1958	Breda/Brown Boveri/ Savigliano/OM/ Reggiane/Pistoiesi/ IMAM	Breda/Brown Boveri/Savigliano/ CGE/Marelli/ Ansaldo/OCREN
E646	Bo-Bo-Bo	3 kV	3,780/ 4,320	140	110	198	1961	Breda/Brown Boveri/ Savigliano/OM/ Reggiane/Pistoiesi/ IMAM	Breda/Brown Boveri/Savigliano/ CGE/Marelli/ Ansaldo/OCREN
E652	B-B-B	3 kV	4,950	160	106	130	1989	ABB/Sofer/ Casertane	ABB/Ansaldo/ Marelli
E656	Bo-Bo-Bo	3 kV	4,200/ 4,800	150	120	459	1975	TIBB/Sofer/Casaralta Reggiane/Casertane	TIBB/Italfrafo/Asgen Marelli/Ansaldo/ Retam
E632	B-B-B	3 kV	4,350/ 4,900	160	103	65	1982	Fiat/TIBB/Sofer	Ansaldo/Marelli/ TIBB
E633	B-B-B	3 kV	4,350/ 4,900	130	103	150	1979	Fiat/TIBB/Sofer	Ansaldo/Marelli/ TIBB
E321	C	3 kV	190	50	36	33	1960	FS	
E322	C	3 kV	190	50	36	18	1961	FS	TIBB
E323	C	3 kV	190	32/60	46	130	1966	TIBB	TIBB
E324	C	3 kV	190	32/60	45	10	1966	TIBB	TIBB

Class E412 is designed for hauling international expresses to Austria and Germany (M Tolini) **1997**

140 km/h and accommodate 700 passengers (with seats for 475). A consortium of Ansaldo, Adtranz, Breda and Firema was to deliver the new trainsets, beginning in 1997.

Passenger coaches and freight wagons

Other recent orders have included 100 air conditioned Type Z1/b IC/EC passenger coaches and 1,100 sliding-wall freight wagons from Keller Meccanica. An order for 1,377 freight wagons has been shared by Breda, ITIN, OMS, Casertane and Fiore.

In mid-1996, work was under way in FS workshops to convert 650 first class passenger coaches to couchette coaches, with delivery of the first 200 conversions expected by the end of 1997. Firema had begun conversion of 20 self-service restaurant cars to cars with a snack counter and table service. In 1996, Costamasnaga was building 20 luxury sleeping cars, for a hotel train joint venture with Wagon-Lits.

Purchasing programme for 2000

A rolling stock acquisition programme to meet FS needs as far as 2000 was approved by the Ministry of Transport in 1994 and costed at Lit9,000 billion. In addition to orders

mentioned above, it included a further 105 E402 and 190 E453/4 electric locomotives, 160 two-car dmus, 270 emus, 164 diesel railcars, 620 coaches for medium-distance services and 35 driving trailers. Some 3,000 wagons are required under the programme, which also includes rebuilding of 850 coaches and of 120 ALe 601 emus for regional services between 1994 and 1999.

Signalling and telecommunications

For speeds above 150 km/h, automatic block with coded current cab repetition is being adopted. Cab repetition is integrated with automatic speed control. For speeds up to 250 km/h on the Rome–Florence Direttissima the following speeds are encoded (km/h): 250-230-200-150-100-60-30.

In 1996 Ansaldo completed the first phase of the Lit190 billion Naples–Reggio di Calabria route modernisation project, comprising the 200 km between Battipaglia and Paola. This section, controlled by a new CTC installation with 22 interlockings at Sapri, received automatic block signalling with coded current cab repetition, a centralised hotbox detection system and improved public address and wayside telephone systems.

Electrification

The historic network in Italy, and the Rome–Florence high-speed line, is electrified at 3 kV DC; however, future high-speed lines will be energised at 25 kV 50 Hz AC.

FS had plans to electrify routes in Sardinia at 25 kV 50 Hz AC but these have been abandoned. It has been suggested that the E491 and E492 locomotives built for this project might be sold, or rebuilt for operation at 3 kV DC. The conversion of the 25 E492 locomotives for operation at both voltages and over Italy's future high-speed network has also been proposed.

Electric working of the 150 km Bari–Lecce route was inaugurated in 1996, following three years of work at a cost of Lit100 billion. It was reported that Lit320 billion had been allocated for subsequently double-tracking and electifying the 115 km Bari–Taranto route. In 1996 FS also completed electrification of the Verona–Mantova–Suzzara–Modena route.

Track

Monoblock prestressed concrete sleepers are being used almost exclusively in current track upgrading and doubling projects (though a test installation of slab track was recently completed). Length of sleeper is 2.3 m but for new track, where speeds may exceed 160 km/h, a new design with a length of 2.6 m is being adopted. For rail renewals, and all new lines, UIC 60 (60 kg/m) rails are being used, fastened with K-type clips. FS replaces about 850 km of track each year.

UPDATED

North Milan Railway (FNME)

Ferrovie Nord Milano Esercizio SpA
Piazzale Cadorna 14, I-20123 Milan
Tel: +39 2 85111   Fax: +39 2 851 1551

Key personnel

General Manager: Ing Arnaldo Siena
Production and Operations Manager, North Milan:
  Ing Luigi Legnani
Operations Manager, Brescia-Edolo:
  Ing Federico Bonafini
Assistant Operations Manager and Director, Studies and
  Quality: Ing Angelo Colzani
Director, Marketing: Gasparino De Servi
Director, Rolling Stock: Ing Vincenzo Celentano
Director, Purchasing: Dr Massimo Stoppini
Director, Fixed Installations: Ing Sergio Ceriani
Director, Personnel: Dr Felice Orsi
Director, Operating Department: Ing Giorgio Zuliani
Director, Administration: Dr Gianfranco Fusetti

Gauge: 1,435 mm
Route length: 326.8 km, of which 308.6 km in use
Electrification: 200.3 km at 3 kV DC

Political background

In 1995 FS, FNME and the Lombardy region signed an agreement to create Servizio Ferroviario Regionale (SFR), which from January 1997 became responsible for regional and suburban railway services within Lombardy. As part of the formation of SFR, FS was to acquire a 50 per cent shareholding in FNME and staff from both operators were to transfer to the new undertaking.

Organisation

FNME serves the north Milan suburbs with a main route to Saronno, where it forks to Como and to Laveno on Lake Maggiore. The latter is single track beyond Malnate. Also from Saronno a single track branch heads west to Novara, and a freight-only branch east to Seregno. A further double-track route runs from Bovisa to Seveso, beyond which single track extends to Canzo-Asso. In 1993 FNME took over operation of the 108 km non-electrified Brescia North Railway, linking Edolo with Rovato and Brescia.

Finance

In 1994 it was announced that FNME intended to increase its capital base to Lit220 billion from Lit35.9 billion by means of a share issue. The funds were to be earmarked for purchase of new rolling stock. FNME's projected investment budget for 1996 amounted to Lit18.8 billion, with Lit8 billion to be spent on bridges and structures. Other major items of expenditure included Lit3.5 billion for electrification, Lit4 billion for signalling and Lit2 billion for telecommunications.

Improvements to existing lines

In 1984 the government approved execution of a Lit260 billion modernisation plan. The main item is 17 km of further four-tracking on FNME's Como main line between Bovisa and Saronno, accompanied by level crossing elimination and station reconstruction, plus two new stations. The first 10 km of this project were finished in 1991. Completion will halve Milan–Como journey time to 30 minutes. This development is germane to the integration of FNME and FS as SFR, operating a regional rail system based on the new Passante cross-city line (for details see under FS).

The 4 km from FNME's present Milan terminus to Bovisa, which is common to all FNME services, carries over 300 trains a day, two-thirds of which continue to Saronno. Quadrupling beyond Bovisa will enable separation of fast and slow services.

The first phase of a Lit460 billion scheme to serve Milan's Malpensa airport, by doubling 20.5 km of the Saronno–Novara branch and constructing from it an

Former SNCB coach now in service on the North Milan Railway (M Tolini)   *1997*

Class 500 diesel locomotive arriving at Saronno on the North Milan Railway with a freight train from Seveso (John C Baker)   *1997*

Electric locomotives

Class	Wheel arrangement	Line voltage	Output kW	Speed km/h	Weight tonnes	No in service	First built	Builders Mechanical	Electrical
600	Bo + Bo	3 kV	1,030	75	63	5	1928	OM	CGE
610	Bo + Bo	3 kV	1,030	80	61	4	1949	Breda	CGE
620	Bo + Bo	3 kV	2,250	130	72	6	1985	TIBB	Ansaldo
630	Bo + Bo	3 kV	3,650	120	80	9	1991	Škoda	Škoda

Electric railcars

Class	Line voltage	Motored axles/car	Output/motor kW	Speed km/h	No in service	First built	Builders Mechanical	Electrical
700	3 kV	4	183	80	22	1929	OM	TIBB
730	3 kV	4	272	80	3	1932	Tallero	TIBB
740	3 kV	4	272	80	7	1929	Tallero	CGE
740	3 kV	4	272	90	9	1953	Breda	CGE
740	3 kV	4	272	90	8	1957	Breda	CGE
750	3 kV	4	280	130	24	1982	Breda	Ansaldo/Marelli

Diesel locomotives

Class	Wheel arrangement	Power kW	Speed km/h	Weight tonnes	No in service	First built	Builders Mechanical	Engine	Transmission
500	Bo-Bo	383	75	47	5	1971	TIBB	Fiat	E
510	A-A	103	30	18	2	1966	TIBB	Fiat	E

airport link, was begun in 1990 with double-tracking and realignment between Saronno, Busto Arsizio and Vanzaghello. In 1996 it was reported that the Malpensa scheme was to receive Lit100 billion of government funding.

Completion of these projects, including the Passante, is forecast to boost FNME daily train working to almost 500 services. It is expected that the entire Passante route will be open to traffic by the end of 2000.

Traction and rolling stock

Rolling stock in service at the start of 1996 comprised 24 electric locomotives, 19 diesel locomotives, 79 emu power cars, 17 diesel railcars, 252 trailer vehicles and passenger coaches and 96 freight wagons. The fleet includes many double-deck coaches, which often operate in with Class E750 single-deck railcars.

In 1994 FS and FNME ordered 50 four-car double-deck electric multiple-units for Passante services (see FS entry); FNME's share of the order amounts to 10. Deliveries are scheduled for 1997-98.

FNME purchased nine 3,290 kW Bo-Bo electric locomotives built (but never delivered) by Škoda for Czechoslovakian State Railways and 19 coaches from SNCB, Belgium.

Signalling and telecommunications

Automatic block controls 89.8 route-km, of which 63.8 km is double-track and 17 km quadruple-track. FS-type semi-automatic block controls 4 km. There are 287 signal-protected level crossings on the system. FNME has been testing an experimental track-to-train radio installation between Milan and Saronno.

Track

Rail (km installed): RA 36 kg/m (42.4); FS 46 kg/m (4.9); UNI 50 kg/m (427.5); UNI 60 kg/m (2.1)

Sleepers (km installed): Timber (124.5), FS concrete monobloc (94.4) and bibloc (254.3)

Size: Timber 2,600 × 260 × 150 mm

Monobloc 2,300 × 300 × 190 mm

Bibloc 2,300 × 263 × 217 mm

Spacing: 1,500 per km

Fastenings: Direct for RA 36; Type K for FS 46; Direct UNI 50 for monobloc sleepers; Type RN and Nabla for bibloc sleepers

Min curve radius: 250 m

Max gradient: 3%

Max permissible axleload: 20 tonnes

Traffic	1994	1995
Freight tonnes	227,558	291,222
Freight tonne-km (million)	4.596	15.861
Passenger journeys (million)	42.421	42.213
Passenger-km (million)	878.348	884.867

Finance (Lit million)		
Revenues	1994	1995
Passengers	53,680	57,933
Freight	1,221	1,503
Other	7,022	7,000*
Total	61,924	66,436*

Expenditure	1994	1995
Staff/personnel	210,174	215,000*
Materials and services	87,918	90,000*
Depreciation	4,985	5,000*
Total	302,059	310,000*

*estimate

Škoda electric locomotives at Novate Milanese (M Tolini) **1996**

UPDATED

Padane Railways

Ferrovie Padane
Via Foro Boario 27, I-44100 Ferrara
Tel: +39 532 94178/9   Fax: +39 532 903416

Key personnel

Government Commissioner: P Gattuso
Manager: Gino Zarotti

Gauge: 1,435 mm
Route length: 52 km

In 1991 the railway recorded 564,000 passenger journeys and 19.5 million passenger-km, while freight traffic amounted to 30,600 tonnes and 1.3 million tonne-km.

In 1990 the railway obtained a government grant of Lit50 billion for modernisation. Principal objectives were replacement of 36 kg rail with 50 kg/m, resignalling with solid-state interlockings, elimination of level crossings and acquisition of six Fiat ALn663 diesel railcars. Three such railcars were delivered in 1993. In 1996 the city of Ferrara was awarded Lit31 billion of government grant towards a track upgrading scheme for suburban services.

The railway operates three diesel locomotives and 15 diesel railcars and trailers. The locomotive fleet comprises three diesel-hydraulic locomotives and 11 passenger cars.

VERIFIED

Reggiane Railways

Azienda Consorziale Trasporti
Viale Trento Trieste 11, I-42100 Reggio Emilia
Tel: +39 522 514422   Fax: +39 522 515046

Key personnel

General Manager: S Cavaliere

Gauge: 1,435 mm
Route length: 77 km

The railway operates 12 diesel locomotives and 15 diesel railcars.

VERIFIED

Rome Public Transport Authority (ATAC-COTRAL)

Azienda Tramvie e Autobus del Comune di Roma — Consorzio Trasporti Pubblici Laziali
Via Volturno 65, I-00185 Rome
Tel: +39 6 4695 2027   Fax: +39 6 4695 2284

Key personnel

Chairman: C Vaciago
General Manager: D Mazzamurro
Deputy General Manager: E Sciarra
Manager, Commuter Railways Concession: A Curci

Gauge: 1,435 mm, 950 mm
Route length: 131 km, 18.5 km
Electrification: 102 km of 1,435 mm gauge at 3 kV DC, 29 km of 1,435 mm gauge at 1.5 kV DC, 18.5 km of 950 mm gauge at 1.5 kV DC

Political background

In 1995 Rome bus and tram operator ATAC merged with COTRAL, which operated three suburban rail routes, the Rome metro and regional bus services. An integrated

Firema Type E84A emu on the Viterbo route (David Haydock) **1996**

fares structure including FS suburban services was introduced following the merger.

Passenger operations

The COTRAL suburban passenger network comprises three electrified routes – Rome–Viterbo (102 km, 1,435 mm gauge); Rome–Lido di Ostia (29 km, 1,435 mm gauge); and Rome–Pantano Borghese (18.5 km, 950 mm gauge). Passenger journeys totalled 30.5 million in 1995.

Improvements to existing lines

The Rome Piazzale Flamino–Prima Porta section of the Viterbo route (Line F) has been upgraded. The Pantano Borghese route is being rebuilt to light rail standards on its inner section to become semi-metro Line G, connecting with metro Lines A and B at Termini via a new city-centre tunnel. Further out, the Pantano Borghese line is to be rebuilt to metro standards with segregated tracks.

The inner section of the Lido di Ostia route (Line E) is being rebuilt between Piramide and Magliana, with a new station at San Paolo. In 1996 the government agreed to provide 50 per cent of the Lit242 billion cost of building a new Mezzocamino–Spinaceto–Tor de Cenci section. A project to extend the COTRAL network to Osteria del Curato is also under development.

Traction and rolling stock

COTRAL's electric multiple-unit fleet comprises 47 cars for the Viterbo route, 81 cars for the Pantano Borghese route and 162 cars for the Lido di Ostia route. A fleet of 16 electric locomotives is also in operation.

Recent deliveries include two E84A two-car emus for the Viterbo route from Firema, with a further seven emus due to follow. Six double-articulated trainsets were ordered from the same manufacturer for the Pantano route.

VERIFIED

San Severo—Peschici Railway

Ferrovie del Gargano Srl
Strada Communale 82 S Ricciardi, I-71016 San Severo
Tel: +39 882 321414   Fax: +39 882 247645

Key personnel
Director General: V Scarcia
Operating Manager: A Oliva

Gauge: 1,435 mm
Route length: 79 km
Electrification: 79 km at 3 kV DC

The railway operates four electric locomotives, six electric railcars, nine passenger cars and 28 freight wagons.

VERIFIED

Sangritana Railway

Gestione Governativa Ferrovia Adriatica-Sangritana
Via Dalmazia 9, Piazzale della Stazione, I-66034 Lanciano
Tel: +39 872 7081   Fax: +39 872 708500

Key personnel
Managing Director: Dr Ing Antonio Bianco

Technical Manager: T Iubatti
Personnel and General Affairs Manager: A Tonini

Gauge: 1,435 mm
Route length: 156 km
Electrification: 147 km at 3.2 kV DC

The railway records annually about 900,000 passenger journeys and 18 million passenger-km, with freight traffic amounting to 50,000 tonnes and 1 million tonne-km a year.

The railway operates four electric and five diesel locomotives, 11 electric railcars, six coaches and 28 wagons.

VERIFIED

Sardinian Railways (FDS)

Ferrovie della Sardegna
Via Cugia 1, I-09129 Cagliari
Tel: +39 70 306221   Fax: +39 70 340780

Key personnel
Director General: Dr D Cauli
Deputy Director General: E Porceddu
Manager, Cagliari: P Pezzuoli
Manager, Macomer: F Castori
Manager, Sassari: R Pocci

Gauge: 950 mm
Route length: 631 km

FDS was formed in 1989 with the merger of Strade Ferrate Sardegna and Ferrovie Complementari della Sardegna. Routes operated are Cagliari—Sorgono/Arbatax, Tresnuraghes—Macomer—Nuoro and Alghero—Sassari—Palau Marina.

In 1996 the city of Cagliari was awarded a goverment grant of Lit39 billion towards the Lit69 billion cost of completing a link between Monserrato and San Paulo.

The railway operates four steam locomotives, 19 diesel locomotives, 34 diesel railcars, 96 coaches and 549 wagons. The diesel-electric ADe91 railcar, one of eight delivered in 1995-96, can also operate on electric power, and it is anticipated that the route to Sorgono and Arbatax may be electrified for Cagliari suburban services.

VERIFIED

Sassuolo—Modena Railway (ACTM)

Azienda Trasporti Consorziale de Modena
Piazza Manzoni 21, I-41100 Modena
Tel: +39 59 308011   Fax: +39 59 304299

Key personnel
President: Liliana Albertini
General Manager: Dr Ing Giancarlo Della Casa

Gauge: 1,435 mm
Route length: 16 km
Electrification: 16 km at 3 kV DC

The railway operates two electric locomotives, five emus, six coaches and 10 wagons.

VERIFIED

South Eastern Railway (FSE)

Ferrovie del Sud-Est
Via G Amendola 136, I-70126 Bari
Tel: +39 80 583222   Fax: +39 80 339844

Key personnel
Government Commissioner: E Incalza
Director-General: Dr Carlo Bombrini
Operations Director: Ing Armando Pastore

Gauge: 1,435 mm
Route length: 473 km

The railway recorded 142 million passenger-km in 1992, and 6 million passenger journeys, while 84,044 tonnes of freight were carried and 4 million tonne-km recorded.

In 1996 FSE was allocated government funding of Lit125 billion for improvement projects.

The railway operates 28 diesel locomotives, 50 diesel railcars and 29 trailers, 44 coaches and 206 wagons.

VERIFIED

FSE train at Bari Sud-Est (David Haydock)

1996

Suzzara—Ferrara Railway

Ferrovia Suzzara—Ferrara SpA
Corso Piave 60, I-44100 Ferrara
Tel: +39 532 52152   Fax: +39 532 56737

Key personnel
General Manager: Dr Ing Mauro Mattioli
Manager, Administration: A Carani

Gauge: 1,435 mm
Route length: 82 km

With the benefit of a 1990 government grant of Lit260 billion, the railway aimed to electrify, relay with 50 kg/m rail and realign curves to raise maximum permissible speed from 90 to 150 km/h.

The railway operates five diesel locomotives, 14 diesel railcars, 14 control trailers, 12 coaches and 13 wagons.

VERIFIED

Trento—Malè Railway

Ferrovia Trento—Malè SpA
Via Secondo da Trento 7, PO Box 530, I-38100 Trento
Tel: +39 461 431111   Fax: +39 461 820256

Key personnel
Chairman: Guido Ghirardini
General Manager: Dr Ing Daniele Cozzini
Operating Manager: Dr Ing Agostino Alessandri

Gauge: 1,000 mm
Route length: 56 km
Electrification: 56 km at 3 kV DC

Principally a passenger operator (1.895 million journeys in 1995), the railway also moves 1,435 mm gauge freight wagons using a fleet of 12 transporter bogies and four transporter wagons. There is a 2.3 km dual-gauge section connecting the FS network at Trento with a factory at Gardolo.

Construction of a 10 km, four-station extension from Malè to Mezzana was expected to start in 1997. A 500 m single-track extension from the railway's former Trento terminus to the town's FS rail and local bus stations opened to traffic in 1995.

Various other infrastructure improvements have been undertaken as part of a three-year programme funded by the state (Lit60 billion) and Trento province. Begun in

1992, the programme has included catenary renewal, upgrading of substations and replacement of existing 27 kg/m rail with 50 kg/m.

The rolling stock fleet comprises one electric locomotive, five electric railcars and two trailers, and nine three-car articulated emus.

VERIFIED

Turin Local Railways (SATTI)

SpA Torinese Trasporti Intercomunali
Corso Turati 19/6, I-10128 Turin
Tel: +39 11 57641   Fax: +39 11 576 4340

Key personnel
President: M Boidi
General Manager: R Notaro

Gauge: 1,435 mm
Route length: 71 km
Electrification: 41 km at 3 kV DC

SATTI operates local services over two routes, Turin—Ceres (electrified as far as Germagnano) and Turin—Pont Canavese. A total of 2.85 million passenger journeys and 62.1 million passenger-km were recorded in 1995.

Funds were recently made available by the government for repair of flood damage to the system, part of a Lit10 billion grant shared with other minor railways.

In the long term, the Turin—Ceres route is to be upgraded to regional metro standards and connected to the cross-city route currently under construction for FS (see above). It is hoped to run through services from FS to the Turin—Ceres route, to serve such destinations as Caselle airport.

SATTI operates four diesel and five electric locomotives, 21 diesel railcars, four emus, 31 coaches and 15 wagons. Seven two-car low-floor emus were ordered from Fiat in 1996.

VERIFIED

Venete Railways

Gestione Commissariale Governativa Ferrovie Venete
Largo Europe 16, I-35130 Padua
Tel: +39 49 875 9544   Fax: +39 49 875 4246

Key personnel
Government Commissioner: O Bifaretti
Operating Manager: F Dalla Serra

Gauge: 1,435 mm
Route length: 117 km

The Venete Railways group comprises three routes, the Ferrovia Parma—Suzzara (44 km), the Ferrovia Adria—Mestre (57 km) and the Ferrovia Udine—Cividale (16 km).

Rolling stock comprises:
Parma—Suzzara: three diesel locomotives, eight diesel railcars, five coaches and four wagons.

Adria—Mestre: three diesel locomotives, 10 diesel railcars, three coaches and six wagons.
Udine—Cividale: two diesel locomotives, five diesel railcars, four coaches and 10 wagons.

VERIFIED

IVORY COAST

Ministry of Public Works Transport and Communications

PO Box V6, Abidjan 01, Ivory Coast
Tel: +225 347315   Fax: +225 211 7329

Key personnel
Minister: Ezan Akele
Director of Land Transport: Y B Quattara

VERIFIED

Ivory Coast Railway - SIPF

Société Ivoirienne de gestion du Patrimoine Ferroviaire
1 rue du chemin de fer, PO Box 1415, Abidjan 16
Tel: +225 21 96 24 Fax: +225 21 39 62

Key personnel
President: Youssouf Bakayoko
Director-General: Bernard Tra Bi

Political background
SIPF is the shell corporation administering railway assets, both infrastructure and rolling stock. Operations are now run by Sitarail (qv), which leases the assets from SIPF.

NEW ENTRY

Sitarail

Transport Ferroviaire de Personnel et de Marchandises
PO Box 1216, Abidjan 16, Ivory Coast
Tel: +225 210636   Fax: +225 224847

Key personnel
Director-General: A A Thiam

Gauge: 1,000 mm
Route length: 660 km

Political background
The railway is the Ivory Coast portion of the former Abidjan-Niger Railway that was jointly owned and managed by Ivory Coast and Burkina Faso (formerly Upper Volta). In 1986 the partnership broke up. In 1988 the countries seemed to settle their differences, but this rapprochement was short-lived, and each country managed its part of the railway separately until 1993.

The former operator SICF, created in 1989, was immediately in serious financial difficulty, unable to meet its costs from revenue. Local analysis estimated that the railway was in urgent need of CFAFr1.2 billion to keep going, and of at least CFAFr14 billion for rehabilitation. Services to Burkina Faso continued to run, but operating difficulties on both sides of the border persuaded the two governments that a common management was perhaps the better option after all. At the end of 1992 it was

GM of Canada Type GT22LC 1,680 kW diesel locomotive (Wilhelm Pflug)

decided to call tenders for private-sector operation of the railway.

Two groups put forward proposals, and those of the Sitarail joint venture consortium were preferred. Sitarail comprises various local industrial groups including Saga, SDV and Société Ivoirienne de Café et Cacao working with French consultants Systra (Sofrerail), Transurb Consult and others. These hold 67 per cent of the capital, the remainder being held by the two countries' governments (15 per cent each) and Sitarail staff (3 per cent). Two state-owned companies, SIPF and Sopafer, retain ownership of railway assets, including infrastructure, property and rolling stock.

After a long period of negotiation, Sitarail took over operation of the railway as a single entity in August 1995 with some 1,800 of the original staff complement of 3,600. The World Bank and Caisse Française de Développement provided funding to pay off the redundant workforce.

The concession was let for 15 years, but after seven years Sitarail must be prepared to grant track access to third party operators.

Passenger operations
Sitarail abandoned unprofitable local services when it took over the concession, but retained a vestigial long-distance passenger service. The company was expecting to carry some 0.4 million passengers in 1996. Service provision was severely limited by the amount of rolling stock available, with no more than a thrice-weekly Abidjan—Ouagadougou express being operated in early 1996.

Freight operations
Despite a good network of permanent roads the railway is a vital link with Burkina Faso, which particularly relies on it for transport of freight to and from the coast.

Under the nationalised operator, the railway declined in importance, reaching a low point of 250 million tonne-km in 1994, down from over 600 million in the early 1980s. Prospects for recapturing freight lost during the years of decline are thought to be favourable: indications were that freight traffic was rising rapidly in the first year of the Sitarail concession. Two potential traffic flows are manganese and zinc from mines in Burkina Faso for export from Abidjan.

Improvements to existing lines
The new operator immediately sought bids for rail and other track components to inaugurate an upgrading programme over the entire route in both countries. CFAFr17.6 billion has been allocated to infrastructure improvements in the period 1996-2000.

Traction and rolling stock
At the start of Sitarail operations there were available for traffic 20 diesel locomotives, 17 shunting locotractors, 18 coaches and 600 wagons. In late 1995, priority was being given to obtaining spare parts for rehabilitation of the remaining five GM diesel-electrics out of the original fleet of 25. In the company's five-year plan, some CFAFr13.7 billion will be spent on overhauling rolling stock; in late 1996, Sitarail went out to tender for 20 bogie hopper wagons.

Signalling and telecommunications
A total of 21 stations have been equipped with colourlight signalling and power point operation based on SNCF's NSI relay system. Installation was by a French subsidiary of ABB. Sitarail plans to spend CFAFr1 billion on upgrading the telecommunications system.

Track
Rail: 30 and 36 kg/m
Ballast: Granite, 800-1,200 litres/m, hard sandstone, 700 l/m
Sleepers: Metal, 1,550/km; concrete monobloc (Blochet), 1,357/km
Min curvature radius: 500 m, being raised to 800 m
Ruling gradient: 10%
Max axleload: 17 tonnes

UPDATED

JAMAICA

Ministry of Water and Transport

PO Box 9000, 36 Trafalgar Road, Kingston 10
Tel: +1 809 926 9170   Fax: +1 809 926 2835

Key personnel
Minister: R Pickersgill

UPDATED

Jamaica Railway Corporation (JRC)

PO Box 489, 142 Barry Street, Kingston
Tel: +1 809 922 6620/1531   Fax: +1 809 922 4539

Gauge: 1,435 mm
Route length: 207 km

Political background
In 1994 potential buyers of the largely defunct state-owned JRC system were invited to submit expressions of interest to the National Investment Bank of Jamaica. Interested parties were reported to include a Jamaican consortium comprising J Wray and Nephew, Desnoes and Geddes, Grace Kennedy and the Caribbean Cement Company. In 1996 no trains were running and all rolling stock was mothballed.

VERIFIED

The mothballed terminus at Kingston in 1996 (Alan Williams)   **1996**

Alcoa Railroads

Alcoa Minerals of Jamaica Inc
May Pen PO
Tel: +1 809 986 2561   Fax: +1 809 986 2026/2752/2753

Key personnel
Manager, Railroad Operations: J Shim You
Superintendent, Maintenance: J R Graham

Gauge: 1,435 mm
Length: 40 km

Traction and rolling stock
The railway operates three diesel locomotives and 90 freight wagons.

VERIFIED

Kaiser Bauxite Railway

Kaiser Jamaica Bauxite Co
Discovery Bay PO, St Ann
Tel: +1 809 973 2221

Key personnel
General Manager: R D Honiball
Chief Engineer: A H Gordon

Gauge: 1,435 mm
Length: 25 km

Traction and rolling stock
The railway operates four diesel locomotives and 88 freight wagons.

UPDATED

JAPAN

Ministry of Transport

1-3, 2-chome, Kasumigaseki, Chiyoda-ku, Tokyo
Tel: +81 3 3580 3111

Key personnel
Minister: Makoto Koga
Parliamentary Vice-Minister: Sei-ichi Eto
Administrative Vice-Minister: Minoru Toyoda

UPDATED

Japan Railway Construction Public Corporation (JRCC)

Sanno Grand Building, 2-14-2, Nagata-cho, Chiyoda-ku, Tokyo
Tel: +81 3 3506 1894   Fax: +81 3 3506 1890

Key personnel
President: Sumio Shiota

Organisation
The Corporation was set up in 1964 to construct railways on behalf of the government for subsequent leasing or transfer to railway operating companies. It is responsible for the construction of all new Shinkansen lines and has taken over much other new construction work from the JR Group and other railways.

UPDATED

Japan Railways Group (JR)

Political background
Privatisation
Japanese National Railways (JNR) was statutorily disbanded in 1987 and its assets, operations and liabilities were distributed among a number of new companies, known as the Japan Railways Group. The dismemberment legislation provided that JNR's passenger business, its infrastructure and its assets, on JNR's 1,067 mm gauge network be distributed geographically between six companies, three on Honshu island and one each on Hokkaido, Shikoku and Kyushu.

Initially, all remained in the public domain. Only the Hokkaido, Shikoku and Kyushu companies started free of any inherited debt liabilities, but all three required subsidy for their current operations, which was provided through government-established Management Stabilising Funds.

Privatisation of the new companies was the ultimate objective of JNR's dismemberment. At the start of 1991 the Transport Ministry announced that two million shares in each of the three biggest companies, JR East, JR Central and JR West, would be put on the market in 1992, but, with the subsequent serious downturn of the Tokyo stock market, the placing was postponed. The sale of half the JNR Settlement Corporation's holding of four million JR East shares eventually took place in October 1993 and was heavily oversubscribed. JR Central and JR West flotations were scheduled for 1994-95 but the adverse effects of the Kobe earthquake on revenue and profitability led to postponement; sales of JR West shares have, however, now taken place. The proceeds from the sales are intended to be used to reduce the ¥26,200 billion debt inherited from JNR.

Since 1984 over 35 local companies have been established to take over loss-making JNR/JR rural lines. The new operators are known as third-sector companies, because they are a hybrid of private and local community finance.

Previously, Japanese railway business was governed by two sets of statutes, one to regulate JNR and one

covering other railways. This has been superseded by new legislation covering all railway business. It has reduced the degree of regulation, with provisos that railway safety and customer services are not impaired. A licence is required to run a railway business and railway facilities are subject to inspection. Furthermore, fares and charges must be approved in advance by the Minister of Transport, although written notice is considered adequate for discounted fares and charges. Finally, train schedules must be submitted to the Ministry in advance of implementation.

Shinkansen network
The 1,435 mm gauge Shinkansen network was at first vested in a Shinkansen Property Corporation, which

leased the infrastructure to the new companies for train operation. The companies were responsible for upkeep of the infrastructure. After protracted negotiations, terms were agreed in 1991 for sale of the network later in the year to the three companies operating it.

The proceeds were applied in part to the financing of Shinkansen network extensions begun in 1992, and also to clearing by the JNR Accounts Settlement Corporation of more of the accumulated debt left from the JNR regime.

UPDATED

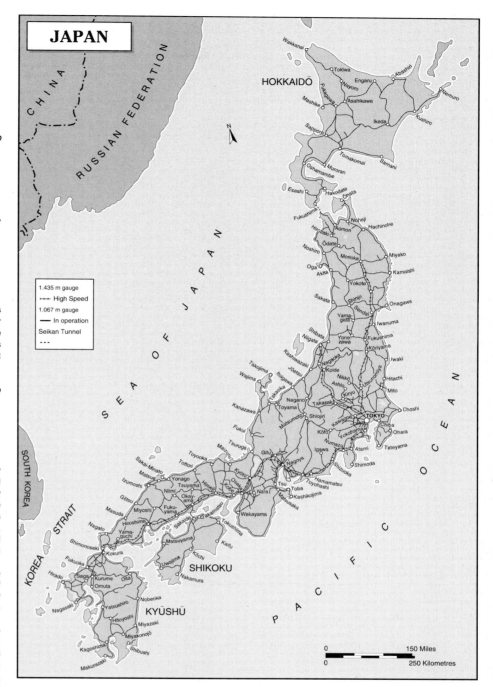

East Japan Railway Co (JR East)

6-5, Marunouchi 1-chome, Chiyoda-ku, Tokyo 100
Tel: +81 3 3215 9648   Fax: +81 3 3213 5291

Key personnel
Chairman: Shoji Sumita
Vice-Chairman: Shuichiro Yamanouchi

President: Masatake Matsuda
Executive Vice-Presidents
  Corporate Planning Headquarters: Kozo Yoshida
  Affiliated Enterprises Headquarters, Construction Department: Yoshiharu Takamatsu
  Railway Operations Headquarters: Kiyomi Harayama

Managing Directors
  Health & Welfare and Finance Departments:
  Eiji Hosoya
  Affiliated Enterprises Headquarters: Kazuhiko Suzuki
  Administration and Public Relations Departments:
  Kikuo Kojima

Inquiry and Audit, Corporate Planning, Personnel and Human Resources and Development Departments: Mutsutake Otsuka
Tohoku District Head Office: Yukio Fukunishi
Tokyo District Head Office: Shuichiro Rikimura
Business Development Headquarters:
Takuro Yamamoto
Marketing and Credit Card Departments, Railway Operations Headquarters: Yoshio Hanazaki

Gauge: 1,067 mm; 1,435 mm (Shinkansen)
Route length: 6,663 km; 839 km
Electrification: 2,760.9 km at 1.5 kV DC (1,067 mm); 1,888.1 km (1,067 mm) at 20 kV 50 Hz AC and 838.9 km (1,435 mm) at 20 kV 50 Hz AC

Organisation
The railway runs rail passenger transport and related activities in the Tohoku region and the Tokyo metropolitan region, including the Tohoku and Joetsu Shinkansen. Some 239 Shinkansen and 11,849 conventional trains were operated daily from March 1997. In April 1997, 80,020 staff were employed.

Finance (million yen) Non-consolidated

Operating revenue	1995-96	1996-97
Railway	1,875,518	1,895,671
Other	81,880	72,264
Total	1,957,398	1,967,935

Operating expenditure	1995-96	1996-97
Railway	1,485,149	1,508,337
Other	75,718	63,376
Total	1,560,867	1,571,713
Operating income	396,531	396,222

In FY96-97, revenues from railway operations rose 1.1 per cent to ¥1,895.7 billion ($15,287 million), and accounted for 96.3 per cent of total operating revenues.

Shinkansen network revenues increased 1.1 per cent to ¥462.2 billion ($3,436 million), as revenues from Shinkansen commuter passes was up 10.0 per cent to ¥16.0 billion ($128 million) and other revenues climbed 0.7 per cent to ¥410.2 billion ($3,308 million). Commuter travel again posted a substantial increase as the scope of Shinkansen commuting continued to expand. Growth in non-commuter revenues mainly reflects a rebound in demand for business and pleasure travel in the first half of the fiscal year.

Tokyo metropolitan area network revenues increased 1.6 per cent to ¥860.6 billion ($6,940 million). Revenues from commuter passes advanced 0.6 per cent to ¥359.7 billion ($2,901 million). Results were supported by a temporary rise in purchases of commuter passes shortly before the April 1997 increase in Japan's consumption tax. In FY94-95 and FY95-96, Tokyo metropolitan area network commuter pass revenues declined 0.2 per cent and 0.1 per cent respectively. Non-commuter revenues were up 2.4 per cent to ¥500.9 billion ($4,039 million) due to a rebound in demand for non-commuter travel, mainly in the first half of the fiscal year.

Intercity and regional networks revenues declined 0.9 per cent to ¥438.4 billion ($3,536 million). Commuter pass revenues decreased 0.8 per cent to ¥125.4 billion ($1,012 million) and non-commuter revenues were down 0.9 per cent to ¥313.0 billion ($2,524 million).

Revenues from other railway business activities are derived from fee-based operations such as advertising, retail businesses within train stations, travel-agency services and fees from Japan Freight Railway Company for the use of JR East lines. In FY96-97 revenues increased 3.5 per cent to ¥170.5 billion ($1,375 million), primarily due to growth in travel-agent revenues.

Traffic (million)

	1993-94	1994-95	1995-96
Passenger journeys	6,080	6,059	6,067
Passenger-km	128,910	128,144	128,599

Passenger operations
Tokyo metropolitan area network
The Tokyo metropolitan area network consists of 1,096.5 km of lines operating within a radius of approximately 100 km from Tokyo station, an area with a population of over 32 million. This network accounts for 60.1 per cent of JR East's total passenger-km and 43.3 per cent of its total operating revenues. Demand for commuter rail services is immense and the metropolitan area is the focus of considerable investment, aimed at reducing the serious overcrowding and lack of capacity. The company's Tokyo New Network 21 project involves

Principal JR East diesel locomotives

Class	Wheel arrangement	Power kW	Speed km/h	Weight tonnes	No in service	First built	Mechanical	Builders Engine	Transmission
DD51	B-2-B	2,200	95	84	21	1966	H/Me/K	2 × 745 kW DML61Z	H 2 × DWZA
DD14	B-B	1,000	70	58	16	1966	K	2 × 373 kW DMF31SB-R	H 2 × DS1.2/1.35
DD15	B-B	1,000	70	55	7	1961	N	2 × 373 kW DMF31SB	H 2 × DS1.2/1.35
DE10	AAA-B	1,350	85	65	57	1969	K/N/H	DML61ZB	H DW6
DE11	AAA-B	1,350	85	70	10	1970	K/N	DML61ZA, B	H DW6
DE15	AAA-B	1,350	85	65	30	1970	N	DML61ZB	H DW6

Principal JR East electric railcars or multiple-units

Class	Cars per unit	Motor cars per unit	Motored axles/car	Output/motor kW	Speed km/h	Cars in service	First built	Builders Mechanical	Electrical
1.5 kV DC									
103	10	6	4	110	100	1,640	1964	N/T/H/K/Kn	H/T/Me/Fe/To
105	2	1	4	110	100	4	1980	T	H/T/Me/Fe/To
107	2	1	—	—	100	54	—	1988	
201	10	6	4	150	100	783	1979	N/T/H/K/Kn	H/T/Me/Fe/To
203	10	6	4	150	100	170	1982	N/T/H/K/Kn	H/T/Me/Fe/To
205	10	6	4	150	100	1,413	1984	N/T/H/K/Kn	H/T/Me/Fe/To
207	10	6	4	150	100	10	1986		
209	10	4	4	95	110	718	1993	R/T	M/T/To
113	4	2	4	120	100	1,292	1963	N/T/H/K/Kn	H/T/Me/Te/To
115	4	2	4	120	100	1,063	1966	N/T/H/K/Kn	H/T/Me/Fe/To
211	10	4	4	120	110	575	1985	N/T/H/K/Kn	H/T/Me/Fe/To
215	10	4	4	120	120	40	1992	N/N	To/Se
165	3	2	4	120	110	96	1962	N/T/H/K/N	H/T/Me/Fe/To
167	4	2	4	120	110	35	1965		
169	3	2	4	120	110	72	1968		
251	10	6	4	120	120	40	1990	R/S	To/Se/M
253	3	2	4	120	130	99	1991	T/S	H/M/Se/To
301	10	8	4	110	100	56	1966		
E127	2	1	4	120	110	26	1994	K	To/Me
E217	11	4	4	95	120	315	1994	K/Tk	Me/To
255	9	4	4	95	130	45	1993	Kn/Tk	T/To
E351	8	4	4	150	130	60	1993	H/N	H/To
Dual-voltage 1.5 kV/20 kV									
417	3	2	4	120	100	15	1978		
403	4	2	4	120	100	53	1966		
415	4	2	4	120	100	303	1971	N/K/Kn	H/T/Me/Te/To
455	3	2	4	120	110	134	1962	N/T/H/K/Kn	H/T/Me/Fe/To
183	4	2	4	120	120	285	1972	N/T/K/Kn	H/T/Me/Fe/To
185	4	2	4	120	110	227	1980	N/T/K/H/Kn	H/T/Me/Fe/To
189	9	3	4	120	120	166	1974		
485	4	2	4	120	120	361	1968	N/T/H/K	H/T/Me/Fe/To
489	9	6	4	120	120	29	1971		
583	4	2	4	120	120	87	1968	N/T/H/K/Kn	
651	17	4	4	120	130	99	1988	K	
E501	10	4	4	120	120	60	1994	Tk	Si/H/T
20 kV AC									
715	4	2	4	120	100	36	1983		
717	3	2	—	—	110	30	1985		
719	3	1	—	—	110	108	1990		
200*	12	12	4	230	240	700	1980	N/T/H/K	H/T/Me/Fe/To/Se
400*	6	6	4	210	240	84	1990	T/H/K	H/T/M/Fe To
701	2	1	4	125	110	214	1992	K	Me/T/Fe
25 kV AC									
E1*	12	6	4	410	240	72	1993	H/K	H/T/Me/To
E2*	8	6	4	300	275	64	1995	H/K/N	H/Me/T/To
E3*	5	4	4	300	275	80	1995	K/TK	H/T/Me/To

* Shinkansen
Abbreviations: D: Daihatsu Motor; F: Fuji Heavy Industries Ltd; Fe: Fuji Electric; H: Hitachi; K: Kawasaki Heavy Industries; Kn: Kinki Sharyo; Me: Mitsubishi Electric; Mh: Mitsubishi Heavy Industries; N: Nippon Sharyo Seizo; NC: Niigata Converter; NT: Niigata Engineering; S: Shinko Engineering; Se: Shinko Electric; T: Toshiba; To: Toyo Denki Seizo; TK: Tokyu Sharyo; Si: Siemens
Note: JR East leases Series 400 and Series E3 trains from Yamagata JR through Superexpress Holding Co and Akita Shinkansen Trains Holding Co respectively.

Series E501 suburban emu   1996

lengthening trains, increasing train services and running faster trains on existing lines, together with infrastructure improvements — such as the electrification of the outer suburban Hachiko line which was completed in 1996.

On the Yamanote line orbiting central Tokyo, where the peak service operates at 2½ minute headways, standard train formations have been extended by one car to 11. The line's latest emu cars have six pairs of double doors in

Series 209 'disposable' emu **1997**

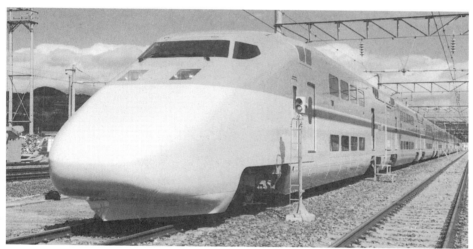

JR East Series E1 double-deck Shinkansen trainset

each bodyside to accelerate passenger loading and detraining, and foldaway seats to increase peak standing space. Similar cars were introduced on the Yokohama line in 1994, allowing an increase in train length from seven to eight cars, and on the Keihin-Tohoku line in May 1995. Extra capacity is also provided by bilevel cars inserted in Series 211 electric trains operating west of Tokyo on the Tokaido line. In 1992 a new Series 215 design of 10-car emu formed exclusively of bilevel cars was introduced between Tokyo and Odawara. A further capacity increase has been provided by opening up freight tracks for new passenger services, notably the extension of the Saikyo Line to Ebisu.

Following trials with three Series 901 prototypes, the first production Series 209 10-car 'disposable' commuter emus entered service on the Keihin—Tohoku line in Tokyo in April 1993, with 624 cars in service by September 1996, including a six-car set operating on the Nambu line in Kawasaki. These lightweight trains have a planned service life of around 13 years but cost only two-thirds of a conventional unit designed for a life of 30 years. An extended maintenance cycle produces a further reduction in costs. JR East needs to introduce some 400 cars each year to replace existing commuter stock, around 200 of which have been manufactured at the company's own Niitsu facility, supplemented by deliveries from traditional suppliers. The short life concept has also been employed in the development of 15-car Series E217 outer suburban emus which now operate many services on the Sobu/Yokosuka lines. These units include two double-deck green class cars and 13 ordinary class cars, 10 of which have only longitudinal seats to maximise capacity. The Series E501 emu built for Tokyo area commuter services incorporates converter-inverters made in Germany by Siemens. This Series E501 features 50 Hz AC/DC dual mode and inverter control.

Intercity and regional networks

The intercity and regional networks operate on 5,566.6 km of rail lines serving areas throughout eastern Honshu, and include all non-Shinkansen lines outside the Tokyo metropolitan area, generating 27.3 per cent of the company's passenger-km and 22.6 per cent of total operating revenue.

Intercity services are being upgraded through the provision of improved connections with Shinkansen lines, increased frequencies, faster speeds, and through the introduction of newly designed trains tailored to the requirements of specific services. The Series 255 'Boso View Express' emus which were introduced in 1993 for limited express 'Super View Sazanami' and 'Super View Wakashio' services between Tokyo and the Boso Peninsula are designed for business and leisure travel, featuring both individual and group seating arrangements and compartments for stacking surfboards and golf bags.

Series E351 emus began running on 'Super Azusa' limited express services between Tokyo and Nagano prefecture in December 1993. This series features an innovative suspension system for a smoother ride, longer trainsets giving 30 per cent more seating capacity and large windows for panoramic views.

On electrified regional lines Series 701 emu cars have been introduced to reduce travel times and increase operational efficiency. Modelled on commuter emus used in Tokyo, the trains incorporate lightweight, stainless steel bodies and motors that realise energy and maintenance savings. The Series 701 has a maximum speed of 110 km/h and is operated as a two-car or three-car set. The latest variant is the two-car 701-5000, 10 sets of which have provided local services on the Tazawako Line (Akita Shinkansen) since March 1997. On non-electrified regional lines new one-person-operated diesel railcars have been introduced.

In late 1994 a three-year programme of tests commenced on the Joban line with a three-car Series E991 high-speed experimental train designed to assess the technical and environmental acceptability of speeds over 160 km/h on the 1,067 mm gauge network. Known as 'TRY-Z', the dual-voltage AC/DC set features two driving motor cars with different style noses, lightweight aluminium carbodies, hydraulic brakes, a carbody control device to improve performance on curves and an active suspension system.

Tohoku and Joetsu Shinkansen

Maximum speed on the Tohoku Shinkansen was lifted to 240 km/h in 1985. Its fastest trains are timed to cover the 171.1 km between Sendai and Morioka in 48 minutes at a start-to-stop average of 213.9 km/h.

In 1990 permissible speed on a section of the Joetsu Shinkansen was lifted to 275 km/h. The section selected

Principal JR East electric locomotives

Class	Wheel arrangement	Line voltage	Output kW	Speed km/h	Weight tonnes	No in service	First built	Builders
ED75	B-B	20 kV	1,900	100	67.2	30	1968	Me/H/T
ED78	B-2-B	20 kV	1,900	100	81.5	12	1968	H
EF 63	B-B-B	1.5 kV	2,550	100	108	21	1962	T/Me/K
EF64	B-B-B	1.5 kV	2,550	115	96	14	1964	T/K/To
EF65	B-B-B	1.5 kV	2,550	115	96	36	1965	T/To/N
EF81	B-B-B	1.5 k kV 20 kV	2,550 2,370	115	100.8	73	1968	H/Me

Principal JR East diesel railcars

Class	Cars per unit	Motor cars per unit	Motored axles/car	Power/motor kW	Speed km/h	Weight tonnes	Cars in service	First built	Builders Mechanical	Engine	Transmission
28	1	1	1	135	95	34.1	31	1961	F/NT	DMH17H D/S/NT	TC2A S/NC
58	1	1	2	135 × 2	95	39.4	83	1961	F/NT	DMH17H D/S/NT	TC2A S/NC
23	1	1	1	135	95	34.2	11	1966	F/NT/N	DMH17H D/S/NC	TC2A S/NC
30	1	1	1	135	95	32.4	7	1962	F/NT/N	DMH17H D/S/NC	TC2A S/NC
35	1	1	1	135	95	32.0	3	1961	F/NT/N	DMH17H D/S/NC	TC2A S/NC
52	1	1	2	135 × 2	95	36.6	27	1962	F/NT/N	DMH17H D/S/NC	TZ2A S/NC
40	1	1	1	165	95	37.3	117	1977	F/NT	DMF15HSA D/S/NT	DW10 S/NC
47	1	1	1	165	95	35.9	28	1977	F/NT	DMF15HSA D/S/NT	TC2A S/NC
48	1	1	1	165	95	36.2	74	1979	F/NT	DMF15HSA D/S/NT	TC2A S/NC
100/101	1	1	1	245	100	24.9	64	1990	F/NT	DMF11HZ DMF14HZT	DW14B NC
110	1	1	1	313	100	29.4/29.9	80	1990	F/NT	DMF13HZA DMF14HZA	DW14A Voith
111	1	1	1	313	100	28.9/29.4	38	1991	F/NT	DMF13HZA DMF14HZA	DW14A-B NC
112	1	1	1	313	100	28.4/28.9	38	1991	F/NT	DMF13HZA DMF14HZA	DW14A-B NC

Abbreviations: D: Daihatsu Motor; F: Fuji Heavy Industries Ltd; Fe: Fuji Electric; H: Hitachi; K: Kawasaki Heavy Industries; Kn: Kinki Sharyo; Me: Mitsubishi Electric; Mh: Mitsubishi Heavy Industries; N: Nippon Sharyo Seizo; NC: Niigata Converter; NT: Niigata Engineering; S: Shinko Engineering; Se: Shinko Electric; T: Toshiba; To: Toyo Denki Seizo

was largely in tunnel, to avoid environmental problems from increased noise. JR East has been working to increase speeds on both the Tohoku and Joetsu lines through its STAR 21 project (see 'Shinkansen rolling stock' section), which has been addressing the technological and environmental issues arising from high-speed running. Having set a Japanese speed record of 425 km/h in December 1993, STAR 21 is expected to lead to the development of trains that can run commercially on existing tracks at 300 km/h, whilst maintaining low levels of noise, vibration and energy consumption. In May 1997, new Shinkansen trainsets (Series E2), making use of the results of technical development in the STAR 21 project, were introduced on the Tohoku Shinkansen line. Maximum speed on some sections of this line was lifted to 275 km/h.

JR East has been energeticaly promoting sales of Shinkansen season tickets for regular travel of 200 km or so to and from the city. In 1991 JR East launched specific commuter train services known as 'Toki' on the Joetsu, and at the same time some Series 200 trainsets on both this and the Tohoku were expanded from their original 12 to 16 cars. In July 1994, two Series E1 double-deck 'MAX' Shinkansen trainsets were introduced into service on the Tohoku and Joetsu lines to meet increased demand, with 40 per cent more seating capacity than a conventional Series 200 Shinkansen trainset. The number in service was increased to six sets in December 1995. A new E4 double-deck design for this traffic has been developed, with three 16-car E4 trains due to enter service in late 1997.

Yamagata Mini-Shinkansen

In 1992 conversion to 1,435 mm gauge of most of the 1,067 mm gauge line running 88 km from the Tohoku Shinkansen at Fukushima to Yamagata was completed. The final 12 km into Yamagata is mixed-gauge. To minimise loading-gauge problems, the dual-gauge line's trains are the Series 400, a lower-slung and narrower version of the standard Shinkansen design. On the Tohoku Shinkansen a seven-car Series 400 runs coupled to a standard Series 200 unit at the maximum 275 km/h, but it is limited to 130 km/h on the regauged line beyond Fukushima. A prototype Series 400 was, in March 1991, tested up to a new Shinkansen speed record of 336 km/h on the Joetsu line. In the following September the same unit achieved up to 345 km/h on the same route.

Akita Mini-Shinkansen

Following the Yamagata Shinkansen, Akita Shinkansen 'Komachi' trains, using new Series E3 cars, inaugurated services from Tokyo to Akita in March 1997. The Akita Shinkansen trains operate through on the Tohoku Shinkansen and converted conventional lines. The conversion involved widening from the current gauge of 1,067 mm to standard gauge (1,435 mm) on the section between Morioka and Omagari on the Tazawako line. The section beyond Omagari on the Ou line accommodates both standard- and narrow-gauge trains.

On the Tohoku Shinkansen section, the Akita Shinkansen trains are coupled to the new Series E2 cars on the Series 200 Shinkansen cars. The Akita Shinkansen is supported by technology that includes the coupling and uncoupling system developed for the Yamagata Shinkansen, anti-noise and anti-vibration measures and improvements to the train control system (COSMOS) and electrical equipment introduced in 1996.

New lines

Tohoku Shinkansen extension

The Tohoku Shinkansen is being extended from Morioka to Aomori. For details see 'Shinkansen network development' section.

Hokuriku Shinkansen

Trial running began on the Takasaki to Karuizawa section of the Hokuriku Shinkansen in October 1996, with trials between Karuizawa and Nagano following in early 1997. 'Asama' services will begin between Tokyo and Nagano in October 1997 with a top speed of 260 km/h and a fastest journey time of 80 minutes. The initial service will be operated by eight-car Series E2 sets. Construction work to provide additional capacity at Tokyo station has included the building of new high-level platforms for Chuo line suburban services to free up space for the new Hokuriku Shinkansen platforms.

Traction and rolling stock

As of March 1997 the railway was operating one steam, 194 electric and 153 diesel locomotives, 10,890

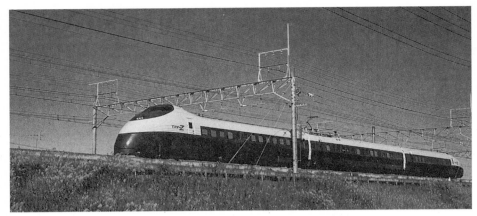

Series E991 TRY-Z experimental trainset, used for studying the feasibility of speeds in excess of 160 km/h on the JR East 1,067 mm gauge network   *1995*

Series E2 Shinkansen trainset   *1996*

Prototype Series E3 train for the Akita Mini-Shinkansen   *1995*

Shinkansen amd emu cars, 623 dmu cars, and 636 hauled passenger coaches.

JR East has converted its maintenance works at Niitsu, Niigata prefecture, into a full-scale manufacturing plant for the production of a proportion of its own rolling stock. Production began in 1993, and in May 1994 a 10-car trainset was completed. Annual output since 1994 has been 200 cars and initial production has comprised Series 209 emus.

Signalling and telecommunications

The principal signalling systems comprise:

CTC (Centralised Traffic Control): 5,581.1 km
ATS-P (Automatic Train Stop-Pattern): 842.1 km
ATC (Automatic Train Control): 904.8 km.

The ATS-P automatic train protection system is being installed in the Tokyo metropolitan area, along with ATOS (Autonomous Decentralised Transport Operation Control System). Special features of ATOS, which is being fitted to 16 lines totalling 846.5 route-km in the metropolitan area, include a new type of electric interlocking equipment making use of general purpose computers, computerised support for control operations and functions to ensure safe intervals for maintenance work and to set routes automatically from portable terminals. ATOS also provides passenger information, with each station terminal linked by FDDI-LAN to the control centre.

At the end of 1995, CTC installation was in progress on the Kobuchizawa-Shiojiri (62 km) and Iwama-Iwaki (118 km) routes and 17 lines in the Tokyo metropolitan area totalling 980 km. Fibre optic cable has been laid along routes in the Tokyo area to provide a self-supporting digital communications network.

Track
Rail type and weight: 50 kg N rail; 60 kg N rail
Sleepers
PC (concrete) sleepers:
Shinkansen: 2,400 × 254.6 × 330 mm
Conventional lines: 2,000 × 174 × 240 mm

Wood sleepers:
Conventional lines: 2,100 × 140 × 200 mm
Fastenings
Shinkansen: direct fastening 8-type for slab track; 102-type for PC sleeper ballasted track
Conventional lines: 5-type
Min curve radius: Shinkansen: 4,000 m
Max gradient: Tohoku and Joetsu Shinkansen 2.5%, Yamagata and Akita Shinkansen 3.8%; conventional lines 3.5%
Max permissible axleload: 17 tonnes

Sleeper spacing per km
1st grade line, PC (prestressed concrete): 1,760; wood: 1,920
2nd grade line, PC: 1,560; wood: 1,640

3rd grade line, PC: 1,560; wood: 1,560
4th grade line, PC: 1,480; wood: 1,480
On sharp curves and sharp gradient sections, the number of wood sleepers shown is increased by 2/25 m.
Shinkansen lines: 1,720

Min curvature radius on trunk lines:
300 m-800 m, depending on train speed and tonnage carried as well as on the numbers of sleepers used.

UPDATED

Central Japan Railway Co (JR Central/JR Tokai)

Head office: 2-14-19/Meieki-minami Nakamura-ku, Nagoya 450
Tel: +81 52 564 2317   Fax: +81 52 587 1300

Tokyo office, International section: Yaesu Center Building, 1-6-6 Yaesu, Chuo-ku, Tokyo 103
Tel: +81 3 3274 9727   Fax: +81 3 5255 6780

Key personnel
Chairman: Hiroshi Suda
President: Yoshiyuki Kasai
Vice-Presideint: Shigeru Saito
Senior Executive Directors:
    Technical Research and Development: Tomosada Shinji
    Shinkansen Operations: Horomasa Tanaka
Executive Directors:
    Affiliated Enterprises: Ryosuke Baba
    Conventional Lines Operations: Hajime Imamura
    Corporate Planning: Kazuhisa Matsuda
    Finance: Takeshi Shida
    Kansai Branch Office: Takao Watanabe
    Linear Express Development: Katsutoshi Isoura
    Personnel, Public Relations: Masataka Ishizuka
    Secretariat, Administration: Masayuki Matsumoto
Counsellor: Seiichi Tanaka

Gauge: 1,067 mm; 1,435 mm (Tokaido Shinkansen)
Route length: 1,431 km; 553 km
Electrification: 939 km at 1.5 kV DC (1,067 mm); 553 km at 25 kV 60 Hz (1,435 mm)

Organisation
The company runs rail passenger transport and related activities in Nagoya and surrounding areas including the Tokaido Shinkansen. It operated 283 Shinkansen and 1,960 conventional trains daily from March 1997. It has diversified into 35 subsidiary companies forming the Central Japan Railway Group, and engaged chiefly in non-rail transport services (including a helicopter company which, amongst other activities, assists in inspections of the rail system), restaurants and retail shops, commercial development of stations, hotels, a theme park, construction, advertising and publishing.

Traffic (million)	1994-95	1995-96	1996-97
Passenger journeys	521	526	n/a
Passenger-km	48,909	49,508	50,705

Finance (million yen)	1994-95	1995-96	1996-97
Operating revenues (non-consolidated)			
Railway	1,075,775	1,105,677	1,136,343
Other	8,157	7,028	9,903
Total	1,083,932	1,112,705	1,146,246
Operating expenses (non-consolidated)			
Railway	729,264	721,733	749,230
Other	5,507	3,982	7,039
Total	734,771	725,715	756,269

Total non-consolidated operating revenues expanded 3.0 per cent during FY96-97 to ¥1,146.2 billion. The principal reason for this rise was a 2.8 per cent increase, to ¥1,136.3 billion, of revenues from railway operations, due mainly to an increase in transportation volume and sales promotion strategies aimed at boosting ticket sales for the *Nozomi* Shinkansen trains. Revenue from the Tokaido Shinkansen accounted for 83.1 per cent of JR Central's

Series 300 (foreground) and Series 100 Shinkansen trains   *1997*

Series 383 'Shinano' trainset   *1995*

Maglev test track in Yamanashi prefecture   *1997*

turnover in FY96-97. Revenues from railway operations accounted for 99.1 per cent of JR Central's total operating revenues. An increase in revenues from real estate sales led to revenues from other operations jumping 40.9 per cent to ¥9.9 billion. Non-railway operations are a comparatively new business field for the company and are expected to develop further in the future.

In FY96-97, total operating costs and expenses expanded 4.2 per cent from the previous fiscal year, to

¥756.3 billion. By sector, railway operating expenses increased 3.8 per cent to ¥749.2 billion. During FY96-97, the company returned to budgeting at normal levels after limiting spending subsequent to the Great Hanshin Earthquake in January 1995. Consequently, costs associated with the repair and upgrading of facilities climbed 16.2 per cent to ¥152.2 billion, contributing to higher railway operating expenses. Administrative expenses advanced 7.8 per cent to ¥160.2 billion. Other operating costs surged 76.8 per cent to ¥7.0 billion, due to an increase in expenses associated with the sale of real estate. As a result of these factors, operating income increased 0.8 per cent, to ¥390.0 billion. Flotation of shares in the company was scheduled to take place during 1997-98.

Passenger operations

Tokaido Shinkansen

Centrepiece of the railway's operations is the inaugural 552.6 km Tokaido Shinkansen, which celebrated its 30th anniversary on 1 October 1994. With 283 trains daily, the maximum business peak service out of Tokyo in a single hour is now 11 departures: one super-express 'Nozomi', seven limited-stop 'Hikari' trains and three all-stations 'Kodama' trains. To cope with the rising number of Shinkansen commuters a 16-car formation is now standard on all 'Kodama' as well as 'Hikari' and 'Nozomi' services. Load factors of the 'Nozomi' and 'Hikari' services averaged 72 per cent in 1995-96, slightly up on the previous year.

An increase of the single-hour total of train departures to 15 in the medium to long term is planned. To achieve this a second terminal at Shinagawa in Tokyo is to be built, as the six-platform Tokyo station has reached the limit of its capacity and is the major obstacle to a lift of service frequency. Preparatory work on the new ¥100 billion Shinagawa station has commenced. It is due to open in 2003. In the meantime, JR Central is modifying its 'Kodama' trainsets for enhanced acceleration from station stops to achieve some increase of line operating capacity.

The decline in ridership on the Tokaido Shinkansen due to the Hanshin earthquake was reversed with a 3.6 per cent increase in ridership during 1995-96 to 133 million passengers and a 2.3 per cent rise in passenger-km to 39.8 billion. The company is working to improve performance by introducing measures to combat the effects of earthquakes and other disasters and by continuing to replace Series 0 trains with Series 300 models.

'Nozomi' services

The Series 300's lower-slung profile, greatly reduced maximum axleloading and much higher seat-to-weight ratio, plus enhanced traction equipment, has made a top speed of 270 km/h possible despite the Tokaido line's tighter curves and their less favourable superelevation than those of later Shinkansen. For other types of trainset the maximum permissible speed is 220 km/h. In February 1991 the prototype Series 300 was tested to a Tokaido record speed of 325.7 km/h.

In March 1992, with three sets available, the Series 300 entered public service branded 'Nozomi' ('Hope') between Tokyo and Osaka, making two return trips daily. Its 270 km/h maximum speed allowed the end-to-end journey time to be cut from the 'Hikari' standard of 2 hours 52 minutes to 2 hours 30 minutes, with an average end-to-end speed of 206.2 km/h.

Air competition has been increasing following expansion of Tokyo's Narita and Haneda airports and the opening of Osaka's Kansai International Airport. To counter the impact of these developments, additional Series 300 units were delivered to JR Central and JR West to provide hourly 'Nozomi' services between Tokyo and Hiroshima/Hakata from March 1993. The Tokyo—Hakata journey time was cut by 40 minutes to 5 hours 4 minutes.

The 1,067 mm gauge network

To boost ridership on the 12 1,067 mm gauge lines radiating from Nagoya, JR Central is taking steps to increase the speed and comfort of its services. In December 1994 the company introduced new schedules aimed at reducing transfer times between the 'Nozomi' Shinkansen and conventional lines. However, lower demand due to poor economic conditions and the effects of the Hanshin earthquake led to a 0.8 per cent decline in ridership on conventional lines from 396 million in 1993-94 to 393 million in 1994-95. A 0.1 per cent increase followed in 1995-96.

Tests begun in August 1994 with the Series 383 'Shinano Express' proved positive and from 1 December 1996 the type was introduced to regular service along the Chuo line. The 130 km/h Series 383 emu features computerised active body-tilt, self-steering bogies and VVVF control and has replaced most existing Series 381 emus used on the Nagoya—Nagano route, reducing the journey time for the 250 km trip by 10 minutes. The 'Fujikawa Express' on the Minobu line was upgraded to special express service with the introduction of the new

Diesel locomotives

Class	Wheel arrangement	Power kW	Speed km/h	Weight tonnes	No in service	First built	Builders Engine	Transmission
DE10	AAA-B	1,000	85	65	6	1969	DML61ZB	H DW6
DE15	AAA-B	1,000	85	65	2	1970	DML61ZB	H DW6
DD51	B-2-B	1,640	95	81	4	1966	2 × DML61Z	H 2 × DW2A

Electric locomotives

Class	Wheel arrangement	Output kW	Speed km/h	Weight tonnes	No in service	First built
1.5 kV DC						
EF58	2C + 2C	1,900	120	113	2	1946
EF64	B-B-B	2,550	115	96	3	1964
EF65	B-B-B	2,550	115	96	5	1965
ED18	A1A-A1A	915	70	66	1	1924

Diesel railcars or multiple-units

Class	Cars per unit	Motor cars per unit	Motored axles/car	Power/motor kW	Speed km/h	No in service	First built	Bodies	Builders Engine	Transmission
11	1	1	1	225	95	35	1989	Nt	C-DMF14HZA DMH17H	H C-DW15 H Niigata
28	2	2	1	135	95	17	1961		DMH17H	H TC2A, DF115A
40	1	1	1	165 260 260	95	40	1977		DMF15HSA C-DMF14HZ C-DMF14HZB	H DW10 C-DW14A C-DW14A
47	2	2	1	165 260	95	5	1977		DMF15HSA C-DMF14HZB	H DW10 C-DW14A
48	2	2	1	165 260 260	95	14	1979		DMF15HSA C-DMF14HZ C-DMF14HZB	H DW10 C-DW14 C-DW14A
58	2	2	2	135 × 2 260 × 2	95 110	25	1961		DMH17H C-DMF14HZB	H TC2A, DF115A C-DW14A
65	2	2	1	375	95	8	1969		DML30HSD	H DW4F
85	4	4	2	260 × 2	120	79	1988	N/F/Nt	C-DMF14HZ	H C-DW14A
75	2	2	2	260 × 2	120	12	1993	N	C-DMF14HZB	H C-DW14A

Abbreviations: N: Nippon Sharyo Seizo Ltd; F: Fuji Juko; Nt: Niigata Tekko

Electric railcars or multiple-units

Class	Cars per unit	Motor cars per unit	Motored axles/car	Output/motor kW	Speed km/h	Cars in service	First built
1.5 kV DC							
103	3, 7	2, 4	4	110	100	50	1964
113	3, 4, 6	2, 4	4	120	100	322	1963
115	3	2	4	120	100	72	1966
117	4	2	4	120	110	72	1977
119	1, 2	1	4	110	100	57	1982
123	1	1	4	100	100	7	1986
165	3, 4	2	4	120	110	39	1962
211-0	4	2	4	120	110	8	1985
211-5000	2, 3, 4	1, 2	4	120	110	242	1988
213	2	1	4	120	110	28	1989
311	4	2	4	120	120	60	1989
371	7	5	4	120	120	7	1991
373	3	1	4	185	120	42	1995
381	4, 6	2, 4	4	120	120	40	1973
383	2, 4, 6	1, 2, 3	4	155	130	76	1994
303	3	1	4	185	120	42	1995

Shinkansen trainsets (1,435 mm gauge)

Class	Cars per unit	Motor cars per unit	Motored axles/car	Output/motor kW	Speed km/h	Weight tonnes	Cars in service	First built
25 kV 50 Hz								
0	16	16	4	185	220	60.6	368	1963
100	16	12	4	230	220	57.8	848	1985
300	16	10	4	300	270	44.4	728	1990

Series 373 emu in 1996. Series 373 stock is also used on the new limited express 'Tokai' between Tokyo and Shizuoka and the overnight 'Moonlight Nagara' between Tokyo and Ogaki.

At 14 of its stations JR Central has opened travel centres that cover all transport modes, foreign as well as domestic travel and hotel and restaurant reservations. Rail tickets are also sold in over 1,000 stores in the Tokyo metropolitan area. The company's Planet computer system, accessible in 115 stations and travel centres, handles reservations for 7,600 hotels, over 2,700 restaurants and other leisure activities, and numerous bus and car-rental operations.

New lines

Chuo high-speed project: maglev or bullet train

A second high-speed route between Tokyo and Osaka, envisaged for several years, has become a more pressing need to cope with rising travel demand. At the start of the 1990s choice of mode seemed to be favouring a maglev system employing the Japanese technology in this field and known as the Chuo Shinkansen. In 1990 construction began of a new 42.8 km maglev test track from the western outskirts of Tokyo through the mountainous

tracts of Yamanashi prefecture to near Kofu, on a course which could serve as the start of the projected Tokyo—Osaka route. The operating speed of the proposed intercity maglev line would be 500 km/h, at which Tokyo—Osaka travel time could be cut to a flat hour. Despite delays, construction is proceeding on the test track and experiments are scheduled for 1997-99 on the first 18.4 km section; they began on 30 May 1997. Prototype train MLX-01, delivered in July 1995, is designed for maximum test speeds of 550 km/h with a three-car unit configuration and two different nose designs to test aerodynamic efficiency. A second five-car unit is to be built for tests involving two trains in operation at the same time.

By 1992, however, a second bullet train line was again in the running because of delays in maglev development. For this possibility JR Central has developed a 300X derivative of the Series 300 which is designed for a maximum service speed of 350 km/h and is to be tested at up to 400 km/h (see 'Shinkansen rolling stock' section). A decision on the type of technology to be used is likely to be made around 2000 following the completion of the maglev and Series 300X trials, with construction taking place in the early years of the 21st century.

Traction and rolling stock

As at 31 March 1997 JR Central operated on 1,067 mm gauge 10 electric and 12 diesel locomotives, 46 hauled passenger cars, 316 electric trainsets, 60 diesel trainsets, 19 other electric and 82 other diesel railcars. Shinkansen rolling stock (1,435 mm gauge) comprised 121 16-car trainsets.

In 1991 JR Central began remotoring its diesel railcars with Cummins engines. The initial programme embraced 33 Kiha 11, five Kiha 40 and 48 Kiha 85 cars. Over 200 JR Central railcars are now powered by Cummins NTA855R1 engines including the Kiha 75 and Kiha 85 dmus.

Signalling and telecommunications

The revision of the Tokaido Shinkansen's ATC (Automatic Train Control) system for introduction of 270 km/h operation with the Series 300 trainset (see above) was completed in early 1992. The coded track circuit frequencies and the signalling have been adjusted to provide for staged reduction from top speed to 255, 230, 220, 170, 120, 70 and 30 km/h to dead stop. Cost of the changes was ¥3 billion.

A major priority for 1,067 mm gauge operations is the installation of CTC (Centralised Traffic Control) equipment to reduce manpower and enhance safety. CTC installation is now in progress on the Tokaido line.

A new automatic train stop system known as ATS-ST is now standardised throughout the 1,067 mm gauge network.

Track (1,067 mm gauge lines)
Rail: 30.1 to 60.8 kg/m
Sleepers: Prestressed concrete 2,000 x 240 x 174 mm or timber, spaced 1,480 to 1,920/km according to grade of route, increased in curves on lower grade routes
Fastenings: elastic or rigid
Min curve radius: 800 m
Max gradient: 4%
Max axleloading: 18 tonnes

Track (Tokaido Shinkansen)
Rail type: 60.8 kg/m
Sleepers: Prestressed concrete 2,400 x 330 x 255 mm, or 2,400 x 300 x 219 mm, spaced 1,720/km
Fastenings: Elastic
Min curve radius: 2,500 m
Max gradient: 2%
Max axleloading: 18 tonnes

UPDATED

Series 300X Shinkansen experimental train, JR Central's 350 km/h answer to maglev proposals; the aerodynamic cusp shape includes pantograph covers
1995

In April 1997, JR Central introduced a dmu on its 1,067 mm gauge lines that can simultaneously assess track and overhead wire; a similar inspection train is already in use on the company's Shinkansen lines
1997

West Japan Railway Co (JR West)

4-24, Shibata 2-chome, Kita-ku, Osaka, 530
Tel: +81 6 375 8939   Fax: +81 6 375 8862

Key personnel
Chairman: Masatake Ide
President: Shojiro Nanya

Gauge: 1,067 mm; 1,435 mm (Sanyo Shinkansen)
Route length: 4,435 km; 645 km
Electrification: 3,217 km at 1.5 kV DC (1,067 mm);

645 km (1,435 mm) and 320 km (1,067 mm) at 20 kV AC 60 Hz

Organisation
The railway runs passenger transport and related activities in the Hokuriku region and western Honshu including the Sanyo Shinkansen. The network totals 50 lines, with 245 Shinkansen and 7,711 conventional trains operated daily from March 1997. The company has steadily diversified into activities such as the travel trade, restaurants and retail shops, but rail operations still account for 97.8 per cent of operating revenues.

Shinkansen services generate 40 per cent of passenger fare revenue and 26 per cent of passenger-km.

Finance
During 1995-96 the company's financial performance recovered from the severe effects of the Hanshin earthquake. Passenger journeys grew 4.4 per cent from the previous year and passenger-km rose 6.7 per cent to nearly 55.5 billion passenger-km, the highest figure since JR West's establishment. Revenues from railway operations were up 7.2 per cent at ¥917,252 million, including a record contribution of ¥10 billion from JR West's travel business. A number of cost-reducing measures were introduced, including the introduction of a new retirement benefit scheme and renewed efforts to reduce long-term debt. Public listing of 1.7 million of the company's 2 million shares took place on major Japanese stock exchanges on 8 October 1996.

Finance (million yen)	1993-94	1994-95	1995-96
Operating revenue			
Railway	914,309	855,410	917,252
Other	23,296	18,761	18,999
Total	937,606	874,172	936,252
Operating expenses			
Railway	779,024	763,041	778,884
Other	14,791	9,735	8,513
Total	793,817	772,777	787,398
Operating income	143,789	101,395	148,853
Pre-tax profit	63,161	9,190	64,549
Profit after tax	29,851	7,564	25,837

Passenger operations			
Traffic (million)	1993-94	1994-95	1995-96
Passenger journeys			
(rail only)	1,805	1,805	1,884
Passenger-km	54,647	51,987	55,484

Series 223-1000 emu
1996

JR West diesel locomotives

Class	Wheel arrangement	Output kW	Speed km/h	Weight tonnes	No in service	First built	Mechanical	Builders Engine	Transmission
DD14	B-B	745	70	58	3	1965	K D S	DMF31SB-R	H DS1.2/1.35
DD15	B-B	745	70	55	11	1961	N D S	DMF31SB	H DS1.1/1.35
DD16	B-B	600	75	48	1	1971	K S/D	DML61Z H/K	H DW2A
DD51	B-2-B	1,640	95	84	30	1966	H/Mh/K S/D	DML61Z H/K	H DW2A
DE10	AAA-B	1,000	85	65	31	1969	K/N/H S/D	DML61ZB H/K	H DW6
DE15	AAA-B	1,000	85	65	12	1970	N/K S/D	DML61DZB H/K	H DW6

JR West diesel railcars

Class	Cars per unit	Motor cars per unit	Motored axles/car	Output/motor kW	Speed km/h	Weight tonnes	Cars in service	First built	Mechanical	Builders Engine	Transmission
191	2	2	2	330	120	46.7	2	1968	F	DML30HSF D/S/NC	H DW4F S/NC
181	3	3	2	370	120	44.6	94	1968	F/NT/N	DML30HSE D/S/NC	H DW4E S/NC
28	2	2	1	135	95	34.3	124	1961	F/NT/N	DMH17H D/S/NC	H TC2A/DF115A S/NC
23	1	1	1	135	95	34.2	16	1966	F/NT/N	DMH17H D/S/NC	H TC2A/DF115A S/NC
33	1	1	1	185	95	34	2	1988	GW	DMF13HS D/S/NC	H DF115A NT/S
35	2	2	1	135	95	32	8	1961	F/NT/N	DMH17H D/S/NC	H TC2A/DF115A S/NC
37	2	2	1	155	95	31.6	2	1982	NT	DMF13S D/S/NC	H TC2A/DF115A S/NC
40	1	1	1	160	95	36.4	63	1979	F/NT	DMF15HSA D/S/NC	H DW10 S/NC
47	2	2	1	160	95	35.5	189	1976	F/NT	DMF15HSA D/S/NC	H DW10 S/NC
48	2	2	1	160	95	35.9	5	1971	F/NT	DMF15HSA D/S/NC	H DW10 S/NC
52	1	1	1	135 × 2	95	36	7	1962	F/NT/N	DMH17H D/S/NC	H TC2A/DF115A S/NC
53	1	1	2	135 × 2	95	39.7	6	1966	F/NT/N	DMH17H D/S/NC	H TC2A/DF115A S/NC
58	2	2	2	135 × 2	95	39.4	138	1961	F/NT/N	DMH17H D/S/NC	H TC2A/DF115 S/NC
65	2	2	2	375	95	42.9	23	1969	F/NT/N	DML30HSD D/S/NC	H DW4F S/NC
120	1	1	1	225	95	26.7	82	1992	NT	SA6D125H-1 D/S/NC	H TACN-22-1605 S/NC

JR West electric locomotives

Class	Wheel arrangement	Output kW	Speed km/h	Weight tonnes	No in service	First built	Builders Mechanical	Electrical
1.5 kV DC								
EF15	1-C-C-1	1,900	75	102	1	1947	H	H/T/Mh/F/To
EF58	2-C-C-2	1,900	100	115	1	1946	T	H/T/Mh/F/To
EF59	2-C-C-2	1,350	90	106.6	1	1963	H	H/T/Mh/F/To
EF60	B-B-B	2,550	100	96	1	1962	To	H/T/Mh/F/To
EF64	B-B-B	2,550	100	96	2	1964	T/K/To	H/T/Mh/F/To
EF65	B-B-B	2,550	110	96	23	1969	K/To/T/N	H/T/Mh/F/To
EF66	B-B-B	3,900	110	100.8	15	1973	K/To	H/T/Mh/F/To
EF81*	B-B-B	2,550/2,370	110	100.8	16	1968	H/Mh	H/T/Mh/F/To

Abbreviations: D: Daihatsu; F: Fuji Heavy Industries; GW: Goto Workshop; H: Hitachi; K: Kawasaki Heavy Industries; Ki: Kinki Sharyo; Mh: Mitsubishi Heavy Industries; Me: Mitsubishi Electric; MW: Matto Workshop; N: Nippon Sharyo Seizo; NC: Niigata Converter; NT: Niigata Engineering; S: Shinko Engineering; T: Toshiba; Tk: Tokyu Haryo; To: Toyo Denki Seizo; Ty: Toyo Electric
*Dual-voltage 1.5 kV/20 kV

Principal JR West electric railcars or multiple-units (1,067 mm gauge)

Class	Cars per unit	Motor cars per unit	Motored axles/car	Output/motor kW	Speed km/h	Cars in service	First built	Builders Mechanical	Electrical
1.5 kV DC									
103	7	4	4	110	100	795	1964	K/Ki/H/N/Tk	H/T/Me/F/Ty
105	2	1	4	110	100	121	1980	Ki/H/Tk	H/T/Me/F/Ty
113	4	2/4	4	120	110	535	1963	K/Ki/H/N/Tk	H/T/Me/F/Ty
115	4	2/4	4	120	110	484	1962	K/Ki/H/N/Tk	H/T/Me/F/Ty
117	6	2/4/6	4	120	115	122	1979	K/Ki/N/Tk	H/T/Me/F/Ty
165	3	2	4	120	110	41	1962	K/Ki/N/Tk	H/T/Me/F/Ty
167	4	2	4	120	110	16	1965		
183	4	2	4	120	120	78	1990	K/Ki/H/N	H/T/Me/F/Ty
201	7	4	4	120	100	224	1981	K/Ki/H/N/Tk	H/T/Me/F/Ty
205	7	4	4	120	110	48	1986	Ki/H	H/T/Me/F/Ty
207	3/4/7	1/2/3	4	155	120	151	1991	K/Ki/H	H/T/Me/F/Ty
207-1000	2/6	1/3	4	200	120	193	1994	K/Ki,H	H/T/Me/F/Ty
211	2	1	4	120	120	2	1988	Ki	H/T/Me/Ty
213	3	1	4	120	110	37	1986	K/Ki/H/N/Tk	H/T/Me/F/Ty
221	2/4/6/8	1/2/3	4	120	120	474	1988	K/Ki/H/N	H/Ts/Me/Ty
223	2/6	1/3	4	180	120	68	1994	K/Ki	H/Mh/Mh/Me/T/Ty
223-1000	4/8	2/3	4	220	130	48	1995	K/Ki/H	H/Mh/Me/T/Ty
281	5	2	4	180	130	63	1994	K/Ki	H/Mh/Me/T/Ty
381	7	4	4	120	120	189	1978	K/Ki/H/N	H/T/Me/F/Ty
283	3/6	1/2	4	220	130	18	1996	K/Ki/H	
1.5 kV DC/20 kV AC									
413	3	2	4	120	110	31	1975	MW	H/T/Me/F/Ty
415	3	2	4	120	100	33	1990	K/Ki/H/N/Tk	H/T/N/F/Ty
419	3	2	4	120	100	45	1975	MW	H/T/Me/F/Ty
457	3	2	4	120	110	80	1969	H	H/T/Me/F/Ty
485	10	6	4	120	130	250	1968	K/Ki/H/N/Tk	H/T/Me/F/Ty
489	9	6	4	120	130	94	1971		H/T/Me/F/Ty
583	10	6	4	120	120	60	1968	K/Ki/H/N	H/T/Me/F/Ty
681	9	3	4	190	160	66	1992	K/Ki/H	T/M/Ty

Services on 1,067 mm gauge

JR West's conventional lines comprise the Urban Network of 12 commuter lines (600 km) serving the metropolitan areas of Kyoto, Osaka and Kobe; major regional lines (1,100 km); and local lines (2,800 km). In 1994-95, despite the earthquake-related suspension of service on sections of the Kobe line, transportation volume on Urban Network rose 0.1 per cent to 25.89 billion passenger-km. This was due mainly to the company's new line to Kansai International Airport and an increase in the frequency and number of cars per train on Urban Network services. A larger increase, to 27.95 billion passenger-km took place in 1995-96.

The company foresees potential for further growth in Urban Network revenue due to the continuing population shift to suburban areas, and through development of new lines to serve major growth points such as Kansai International Airport and Kansai Science City. A recent major Urban Network improvement has been the opening of the 12.5 km Tozai (East-West) line linking Kyobashi and Amagasaki on 8 March 1997; 10.2 km of the line is underground and it has seven intermediate stations. Off peak, eight trains an hour in each direction now run through from the Takarazuka and Kobe lines to the line serving Kansai Science City, with 13 an hour during the morning peak period.

Services on the Kisei line have been enhanced since 31 July 1996 with the introduction of Series 283 'Ocean Arrow' emus on 'Super Kuroshio' limited expresses between Kyoto and Shingu. Five out of six through services between Osaka and Tottori via the third-sector Chizu Express Railway are now operated by modern stock as the 'Super Hakuto' limited express service.

The dual-voltage inverter-controlled Series 681 emu has been developed to increase the maximum speed on major regional lines from 130 km/h to 160 km/h. JR West is also developing a 'West 21' emu, designed to raise average speeds on secondary regional lines from the current 80 km/h to 100 km/h. 'West 21' would, for example, reduce the journey time between Shin-Osaka and Shingu (Kisei line) by 1 hour, and help to improve the competitiveness of rail compared to road. Lighter materials and an active suspension system based on technology from the WIN350 Shinkansen test train will be employed in the prototype which is due to be launched in 1997. Commercial running is planned for 2000.

Local lines account for about 30 per cent of the total network but only 3 per cent of passenger-km. Some lines have been transferred to third-sector companies, and JR West has established 27 regional operating units aimed at upgrading service and enhancing the profitability of the remaining lines on an individual basis.

Higher Shinkansen speed

From March 1993 through 'Nozomi' services were introduced over the Tokaido-Sanyo Shinkansen between Tokyo and Hakata, cutting journey time by 40 minutes to 5 hours 4 minutes. These services are operated by Series 300 trainsets running at a maximum speed of 270 km/h.

Following completion of trials with the WIN350 six-car experimental train, a 16-car Series 500 prototype was delivered in January 1996. Following trials, the 500 entered service on 22 March 1997. It currently operates a daily return service on the Sanyo Shinkansen between Shin-Osaka and Hakata. The journey time is 2 hours 17 minutes, 15 minutes faster than other 'Nozomi' services. Operating at a maximum speed of 300 km/h, the fastest station-to-station speed is 242.5 km/h for the section between Hiroshima and Kokura. The company is also considering raising the permitted line speed to 310 km/h to further reduce journey times (see 'Shinkansen rolling stock' section).

Following the 81-day interruption of service between Shin-Osaka and Himeji following the Hanshin earthquake, earthquake countermeasures are being introduced on the Shinkansen, including UrEDAS (Urgent Earthquake Detection and Alarm System) which allows the early detection of vibration and automatically stops trains.

The 'Family Hikari', which was introduced in 1995 and which features a car with a playroom for children, continues in operation.

New lines

A new 11-km spur connecting JR West's Hanwa line and the Nankai Electric Railway main line with the new offshore Kansai International Airport opened in 1994. The new line incorporates a 3.75 km bridge to reach the airport island and one intermediate station. The 12.3 km underground Tozai line, opened in March 1997, links the existing JR Takarazuka and Gakkentoshi commuter lines, providing improved access to central Osaka. JR West is a partner with Osaka city and prefecture in a third-sector venture to rebuild and introduce passenger services on a 20.4 km orbital freight line running from Shin-Osaka around the eastern suburbs of the city. The project could be completed by 2005.

Traction and rolling stock
In September 1996 the company operated on 1,067 mm gauge five steam, 60 electric and 92 diesel locomotives, 4,415 emu cars, 775 dmu cars, 526 hauled passenger coaches and 334 wagons. Shinkansen rolling stock comprised 813 emu cars.

Deliveries in the period April 1995 to March 1996 consisted of 42 Series 207-1000 emu cars, 48 Series 223-1000 emu cars, 18 Series 281 emu cars, six Series 618 emu cars, 25 Kiha 120 diesel railcars and the first 16 Series 500 Shinkansen cars. Additionally, 24 series 207-1000 emu cars, the first 18 Series 283 emu cars and a further six Kiha 120 diesel railcars were delivered between April and September 1996.

Signalling and telecommunications
In 1993 the company completed a further CTC (Centralised Traffic Control) installation over 61.3 km between Tennoji and Wakayama on the Hanwa line and electronic interlockings were installed at 13 stations. ATS-P (Automatic Train Stop) is being introduced over 26.2 km of the Katamachi line between Shigino and Matsu-Yamate.

Electrification
A 42 km segment of JR West's San-in main line from Sonobe to Ayabe was electrified in 1996 enabling the 158 km Kyoto—Kinosaki limited express service to be converted to emu operation, with a 38 minute reduction in journey time to 2 hours 12 minutes. Electrification of a 29.6 km section of the Bantan line between Himeji and Teramae is due for completion in 1998.

Track (1,067 mm gauge lines)
Rail: 30 to 60.8 kg/m
Sleepers: Wood 140 x 200 x 2,100 mm; and concrete 174 x 156-240 x 2,000 mm
Sleeper spacing: Wood 1,480-1,920/km depending on class of route; concrete 1,480-1,760/km. On Class 2, 3 and 4 track with wooden sleepers, increased by 80 through curves of 600 m radius or less

Sanyo Shinkansen electric multiple-unit cars

Class	Cars per unit	Motor cars per unit	Motored axles/car	Output/motor kW	Speed km/h	Cars in service	First built	Builders Mechanical	Builders Electrical
25 kV 60 Hz									
0	16	16	4	185	220	502	1969	K/Ki/H/N/Tk	
	12	12	4						
	6	6	4						
922	7	6	4	185	210	7	1979	K/Ki/N/Tk	F/H/M/S/T/Ty
100	16	12	4	230	230	144	1987	K/Ki/H/N/Tk	F/T/M/H/Ty
300	16	10	4	300	270	144	1992	K/Ki/N/Tk	T/Ty/N
500	16	16	4	300	350	16	1995	K	

Abbreviations: D: Daihatsu; F: Fuji Heavy Industries; GW: Goto Workshop; H: Hitachi; K: Kawasaki Heavy Industries; Ki: Kinki Sharyo; Mh: Mitsubishi Heavy Industries; Me: Mitsubishi Electric; MW: Matto Workshop; N: Nippon Sharyo Seizo; NC: Niigata Converter; NT: Niigata Engineering; S: Shinko Engineering; T: Toshiba; Tk: Tokyu Haryo; To: Toyo Denki Seizo; Ty: Toyo Electric

Series 500 Shinkansen prototype

1996

Fastenings: Wooden sleepers, spike or spring clip with plate and pad; concrete sleepers, spring clip with pad
Min curve radius: 800, 600, 400 and 300 m for maximum speeds respectively of 110 km/h or over, 90-110 km/h, 70-90 km/h and 70 km/h
Max permissible axleload: 19 tonnes

Track (Shinkansen lines)
Rail: 60.8 kg/m

Sleepers: Concrete 255 x 172-300 x 2,400 mm
Sleeper spacing: 1,720/km in plain track
Fastenings: Spring clip with pad
Min curve radius (main line): 4,000 m
Max permissible axleload: 17 tonnes

UPDATED

Hokkaido Railway Co (JR Hokkaido)

1-1 Nishi 15-chome, Kita 11-jo, Chuo-ku, Sapporo 060
Tel: +81 11 700 5717   Fax: +81 11 700 5719

Key personnel
Chairman: Yoshihiro Omori
President: Shin-ichi Sakamoto
Executive Director, Manager of Railway Operations: Koichi Fujita
Managing Director, Planning: Akio Koike
Managing Director: Takashi Nagano

Gauge: 1,067 mm
Route length: 2,628 km
Electrification: 431 km at 20 kV 50 Hz AC

Organisation
The company is responsible for rail passenger transport and related activities in Hokkaido, the northernmost Japanese island which has a low population density. It operated 1,267 trains daily from March 1997. Approximately 1,450 route-km of loss-making rural lines were closed by JNR before the formation of JR Hokkaido but some very unremunerative lines are still operated; only one line has been transferred to third-sector operation, the 140 km Chihoku line. The most recent closure was the rural 120 km Shinmei line between Fukagawa and Nayoro which was replaced by a bus service in September 1995.

Finance (million yen)	1993-94	1994-95	1995-96
Operating income	106,000	102,000	101,864
Operating expenses	151,000	144,000	142,520
Non-operating profit	46,000	42,000	39,247
Pre-tax profit	700	400	-2,247

Series ED79 AC electric locomotive of JR Hokkaido in the undersea Seikan tunnel

JR Hokkaido diesel locomotives

Class	Wheel arrangement	Power kW	Speed km/h	Weight tonnes	No in service	First built	Mechanical	Builders Engine	Transmission
DD51	B-2-B	1,618	95	84	15	1967	H/M/K	DML61Z S/NT/D	H DW2A H/K
DE10	AAA-B	993	85	65	12	1973	K/N	DML61ZB S/NT/D	H DW6 H/K
DE15	AAA-B	993	85	65	24	1969	N	DML61ZB S/NT/D	H DW6 H/K

Passenger operations

In 1995-96 JR Hokkaido recorded 129 million passenger journeys and 4,795 million passenger-km.

JR Hokkaido is responsible for operation through the Seikan Tunnel, where in 1991 the maximum permissible speed for 1,067 mm gauge trains was raised to 140 km/h.

Since it took over the Hokkaido system from JNR, the company has been concerned to develop more attractive services within the island, both interurban for the island's own population and to its tourist areas for visitors. This has involved introduction of new types of diesel train that are more competitive against road transport, in terms both of passenger amenities and speed.

The company has introduced a small number of individually styled dmus for use on a network of tourist services to ski resorts including the four-car 'Crystal Express' set, which incorporates a double-deck car, and the 'North Rainbow Express' set, which features panoramic windows. Modern conventional stock has also been introduced on some local lines in the form of Kiha 130 railbuses and Series 150 dmus. Journey time reductions have been achieved on longer distance services with the introduction of Series 785 emus on the 'Super White Arrow' and 'Lilac' limited expresses between Sapporo and Asahikawa and with the use of rebuilt Series 183 'Super Tokachi' sets between Sapporo and Obihiro.

JR Hokkaido has developed a 130 km/h diesel trainset with active automatic body-tilting, which is activated by a computer preprogrammed with data on the characteristics of the route to be travelled. Titled 'HEAT 281' (Hokkaido Experimental Advanced Train), a prototype, consisting of two motored cars, was completed to the railway's own designs by Nippon Sharyo in 1992; the body-tilt system is by Fuji Heavy Industries. A third car was added before HEAT 281 was submitted to 1992-93 testing in Hokkaido's severe winter conditions, when temperatures can drop to −30°C. To prepare for that, the prototype was provided with comprehensive protection of vulnerable assemblies, the body-tilting apparatus in particular. Production seven-car Series 281 trainsets entered service in 1994 cutting the fastest journey time between Sapporo and Hakodate to three hours.

Following tests with a prototype Series 283, developed from the earlier Series 281, operational use has begun on the Sapporo—Kushiro route. The Series 283 'Furico' sets operating these 'Super Oozora' limited expresses have independent wheel bogies and a four-speed gear system. In spite of difficult operating conditions, including sharp curves and heavy winter snowfall, the three return services in each direction take 3 hours 45 minutes, about 50 minutes less than older stock.

In contrast to the rest of Hokkaido, suburban services in the Sapporo area are seeing growth of 3 to 10 per cent a year. Four new three-car Series 731 emus able to carry 435 passengers (152 seated) entered service in December 1996. Additionally, four new three-car Series 201 dmus allow an increase in capacity on services operating into Sapporo from the unelectrified section of the Hakodate main line west of Otaru.

Traction and rolling stock

In April 1996 the railway operated 35 electric and 51 diesel locomotives, 511 diesel railcars and 306 emu cars.

Loco-hauled passenger trains are no longer operated, apart from through trains from Honshu via the Seikan tunnel.

Electric locomotives

Class	Wheel arrangement	Output kW	Speed km/h	Weight tonnes	No in service	First built	Builders Mechanical	Electrical
ED76	B-2-B	1,900	100	90.5	1	1968	M/T	H/M/T
ED79	B-B	1,900	100	68	34	1971	H/M/T	H/M/T

Principal JR Hokkaido diesel railcars or multiple-units

Class	Motored axles/car	Power/motor kW	Speed km/h	Weight tonnes	No in service	First built	Mechanical	Builders Engine	Transmission
27	1	132	95	35	8	1962	T/NT/N	DMH17H S/NT/D/JNR	H TC2A/DF115A S/NC
56	2	132	95	38.9	17	1986	NT	DMH17H S/NT/D/JNR	H TC2A/DF115A S/NC
29	1	132	95	33.8/38.3	3	1966	T	DMH17H S/NT/D/JNR	H DF115A NC
59	2	132	95	41.4	2	1983	NT	DMH17H S/NT/D/JNR	H TC2A/DF115A S/NC
40	1	162	95	36.4/37.6	141	1976	F/NT	DMF15HSA S/NT/D	H DW10 S/NC
48-300	1	162	95	36.6	3	1982	NT	DMF15HSA S/NT/D	H DW10 S/NC
480-1300	1	162	95	36.3	4	1982	NT	DMF15HSA S/NT/D	H DW10 S/NC
182	2	324	100	42.6/45.2	65	1978	F/NT	DML30HSI D/S/NT	H DW9A S/NC
182-500	2	405	110	38.8	38	1986	F/NT	DML30HSJ	H DW12
183	1	162	100	47.4	24	1979	F/NT	DMF15HSA D/S/NT	DW10 S/NC
183-100	1	162	100	43.8	4	1981	F/NT	DMF15HSA D/S/NT	H DW10 S/NC
183-500	2	405	110	40.9	7	1986	F/NT	DML30HSJ D/S	H DW12 S/NC
183-1500	1	184	110	40.3	23	1986	F/NT	DMF13HS NT	H DW12 NC
184	1	162	100	44.2	8	1981	F/NT	DMF15HSA D/S/NT	H DW10 S/NC
	1	162	100	46.6	1	1979	F	DMF15HSA D/S/NT	H DW10 S/NC
80	2	132	100	41.2/43	2	1964	F/NT	DMH17H S/NT/D/JNR	H TC2A/DF115A S/NC
83	1	132	100	41.2	3	1986	NT	DMH17H S/NT/D/JNR	H DF1125A NC
84	2	132	100	41.2	4	1986	NT/F	DMH17H S/NT/D/JNR	H DF115A NC
54	2	184	95	38.7/39.3	29	1986	F/NT	DMF13HS NT	H TC2A/DF115A NC
130			95	27.5	10	1988		DMF13HS	H N-DW130
400	1		95	40.9	9	1988		DMF13HZ-B	H DW14B
480			95	37.6	4	1988		DMF 13HZ-B	H DW14B
141			95	34.5	14	1989		DMF13HS	H DF115A
142			95	40.1	15	1989		DMF13HS	H DF115A
281	3		130	41.0	27	1992		DMF11HZ	H N-DW15
283	2	355	130	43.6	3	1995	F	DMF11HZ	H N-DW18

Abbreviations: D: Daihatsu; F: Fuji Heavy Industries; H: Hitachi Ltd; K: Kawasaki Heavy Industries Ltd; M: Mitsubishi Heavy Industries; NC: Niigata Converter Co Ltd; NT: Niigata Engineering Co Ltd; S: Shinko Engineering Co Ltd; T: Toshiba Corp; To: Toyo Denki Seizo KK

JR Hokkaido electric railcars or multiple-units

Class	Cars per unit	Motor cars per unit	Motored axles/car	Output/motor kW	Speed km/h	Cars in service	First built	Builders Mechanical	Electrical
711	3	1	4	150	110	Mo 38 Tr 76	1966	H/T/K	H/T/M/Fe/To
781	4	2	4	150	120	Mo 24 Tr 24	1978	H/K	H/T/M/Fe/To
721	3/6	2/4		150	130	Mo 67 To 47	1988		
785	2/4	1/2		190	130	Mo 15 Tr 15	1990	H	

Abbreviations: D: Daihatsu; F: Fuji Heavy Industries; H: Hitachi Ltd; K: Kawasaki Heavy Industries Ltd; M: Mitsubishi Heavy Industries; NC: Niigata Converter Co Ltd; NT: Niigata Engineering Co Ltd; S: Shinko Engineering Co Ltd; T: Toshiba Corp; To: Toyo Denki Seizo KK Mo: motor car; Tr: trailer car

UPDATED

Shikoku Railway Co (JR Shikoku)

1-10, Hamano-cho, Takamatsu 760
Tel: +81 878 51 1880   Fax: +81 878 51 0497

Key personnel

Chairman: Hiroshi Yamamoto
President: Hiroatsu Ito
Senior Managing Directors: Toshiyuki Umehara
    Hachiya Hirono
Managing Directors: Minoru Sasago, Shozo Nakayama

Gauge: 1,067 mm
Route length: 856 km
Electrification: 236 km at 1.5 kV DC

Organisation

The company runs passenger transport and related

Series 8000 express emu and Series 121 local emu at Takamatsu (Anthony Robins)   *1995*

activities in the Shikoku region. It operated 945 trains daily from March 1997.

Finance (million yen)	1993-94	1994-95	1995-96
Operating income	50,000	47,000	48,368
Operating expenses	61,000	60,000	60,198
Non-operating profit	14,000	13,000	11,040
Pre-tax profit/loss	2,000	-300	-408

Passenger operations

Traffic has risen significantly since the introduction of through trains from Honshu island over the Seto bridges opened in 1988. In 1994-95 the railway recorded 64 million passenger journeys and 1,959 million passenger-km. 1995-96 saw the same number of pasenger journeys but a small decline to 1,950 million passenger-km.

The service of 34 rapid trains each way daily to Shikoku connects with the Sanyo Shinkansen at Okayama. There is also an overnight Tokyo—Shikoku sleeper service.

Traction and rolling stock

In 1996 the railway operated 9 diesel locomotives, 280 dmu and 144 emu cars.

Equipment includes three Type TSE-2000 diesel trainsets with a top speed of 120 km/h. Employed on cross-island services between Okayama/Takamatsu and Kochi, they are the world's first diesel-powered vehicles to be equipped with an active body-tilt system, which is designed to raise acceptable curving speed by 20 to 30 per cent depending on curve radius.

Each bolsterless, air-sprung bogie is driven by a body-mounted 245 kW 2,000 rpm Komatsu engine via a ball-bearing-type spline shaft transmission. Track-mounted transponders at the approach to curves are detected by microprocessors on the leading car of the set and convey data on which the train's control progressively activates and measures the degree of tilt to be applied to each carbody. An upgraded version, the N2000 Special Express, with a top speed of 130 km/h was introduced in 1995. This two-car unit features 260 kW engines to improve acceleration, calliper disk brakes and automatic wheelslip prevention.

The Series 8000 emus used on the electrified Okayama/Takamatsu—Matsuyama routes also feature active body-tilting. These units have VVVF three-phase drive motors, a maximum speed of 160 km/h and carbodies carried on pendulum roller bolsters. An onboard memory checks the train location through the ATS system and issues tilting signals. The pantographs are mounted on an independent carriage on guiderails, with linkages to the bogies to ensure correct positioning of the pantographs when body-tilt is activated.

JR Shikoku has also recently introduced the new three-car Series 6000 suburban emu with inverter control for use on the Seto-Ohashi line.

Signalling and telecommunications

A new centralised traffic control centre and headquarters in Takamatsu was under construction in 1996 for 1997 opening.

Electrification

Electrification was begun to tie-in with completion of the Seto bridge complex. Catenary between Takamatsu and Iyo on the Yosan line (206.3 km) was completed in early 1993, with Okayama—Matsuyama services in the hands of Series 8000 tilting emus from March of that year.

JR Shikoku diesel locomotives

Class	Wheel arrangement	Power kW	Speed km/h	Weight tonnes	No in service	First built	Mechanical	Builders Engine	Transmission
DE10	AAA-A	1,250	85	65	8	1966	K/N/H	DML61ZB NT/S/D	H DW6 KH

JR Shikoku diesel railcars or multiple-units

Class	Motored axles/car	Power/motor kW	Speed km/h	No in service	First built	Mechanical	Builders Engine	Transmission
1000	1	300	110	50	1989	NT	SA6D125-HD-1	NT DW14
TSE-2000	2	245 × 2	120	3	1989	F	SA6D125-H	NT TACN 22-1600
2000	2	245 × 2	120	11	1989	F	SA6D125-H	NT TACN 22-1600
2100	2	245 × 2	120	23	1989	F	SA6D125-H	NT TACN 22-1600
2150	2	245 × 2	120	7	1989	F	SA6D125-H	NT TACN 22-1600
2200	2	245 × 2	120	19	1989	F	SA6D125-H	NT TACN 22-1600
185	1	185 × 2	110	32	1986	NT/F/N	DMF13HS NT	S/NC TC2A DF115A
65	2	375	95	14	1969	NT/F/N	DML30HSD NT/S/D	S/NC DW4F
58	1	135 × 2	95	23	1962	NT/F/N	NT/S/D	S/NC TC2A DF115A
54	1	185 × 2	95	12	1987	NT/F	DMF13HS NT	S/NC TC2A DF115A
47	1	165	95	42	1980	NT/F	DMF15HSA NT/S/D	S/NC DW10
40	1	165	95	11	1981	NT/F	DMF15HSA NT/S/D	S/NC DW10
32	1	165	95	21	1987	NT/F	DMF13HS NT DMH17H	S/NC TC2A DF115A
28	1	135	95	9	1961	NT/F/N	NT/S/D	S/NC TC2A DF115A

Abbreviations: NT: Niigata Tekko; F: Fuji Juko; N: Nippon Sharyo Seizo Ltd; S: Shinko Zouki; D: Daihatsu; NC: Niigata Converter; K: Komatsu Seisakusyo

JR Shikoku electric railcars or multiple-units

Class	Cars per unit	Motor cars per unit	Motored axles/car	Output/motor kW	Speed km/h	No in service	First built	Builders Mechanical	Electrical
111	4	2	1	100	100	20	1962	N/K	H/T/M/To/Se
121	2	1 *	1	110	100	38	1986	H/K/Kn/Tk	H/T/M/To
7000	1	1 *	4	120	110	36	1990	K	Fuji
8000	3/4/5	2 *	4	185	140	44	1992	N/H	To/T

* VVVF Inverter control
Abbreviations: H: Hitachi Ltd; K: Kawasaki Heavy Industries; Kn: Kinki Sharyo; M: Mitsubishi; N: Nippon Sharyo; Se: Shinko Electric; T: Toshiba; To: Toyo Denki Seizo

JR Shikoku's TSE-2000 dmu with active body-tilting (A W Phipps)

Track
Rail: 40 and 50 kg/m
Sleepers: Wood or prestressed concrete spaced 1,560/km in plain track, 1,640/km in curves
Fastenings: Spike (wood sleeper) or double elastic

Min curve radius: 200 m
Max gradient: 3.3%
Max axleload: 17 tonnes

UPDATED

Kyushu Railway Co (JR Kyushu)

1-1, Chuogai, Hakataeki, Hakata-ku, Fukuoka 801
Tel: +81 92 474 2501   Fax: +81 92 474 4805

Key personnel

Chairman: Toshiaki Yamashita
President: Yoshitaka Ishii
Vice-President: Koji Tanaka
Senior Managing Director: Tadayoshi Ishitani
Managing Directors: Tomoyuki Maruyama, Yoshiteru Choami, Koji Kaminagayoshi

Gauge: 1,067 mm
Route length: 2,101 km
Electrification: 1,092 km at 20 kV 60 Hz AC; 42.6 km at 1.5 kV DC

Organisation

The company runs rail passenger transport and related activities in the Kyushu region. It operated 2,675 trains daily from March 1997. Since formation of JR Kyushu, several local lines have been transferred to third-sector undertakings.

Finance (million yen)	1993-94	1994-95	1995-96
Operating income	173,000	170,000	176,614
Operating expenses	199,000	196,000	199,757
Non-operating profit	28,000	26,000	23,896
Pre-tax profit/loss	900	-200	1,324

Passenger operations

In 1995-96 traffic totalled 322 million passenger journeys and 8.676 billion passenger-km.

JR Kyushu has introduced several new types of rolling stock over recent years to upgrade its services. Refurbished Series 485 emus predominate on intercity services, but these are now supplemented by Series 783 'Hyper Saloon' emus introduced since 1990 and by nine-car Series 787 emus. The latter were introduced on 'Tsubame' services between Hakata and Kagoshima in 1992 to counter competition from parallel expressway bus services and short-distance air routes. Since March 1994, Series 787 units have also operated daily 'Kamone' return services between Hakata and Nagasaki.

March 1995 saw the introduction of a new 'Wonderland Express' service between Hakata and Oita operated by four seven-car Sonic 883 VVVF emus with active body-tilt. These units feature a distinctive exterior design and a colourful interior based on an amusement park theme; they have a variety of seating patterns and a panoramic section.

Series 811 commuter emus have been introduced on the Town Shuttle network of routes linking the main urban areas in northern Kyushu.

On non-electrified lines, new Kiha 200- and 220-type dmus have been introduced on local services. Since 1992, Kiha 185 express dmus have been running on the

Trans-Kyushu Highland Express routes linking Hakata with the Mount Yofu area and Kumamoto with the Mount Aso region.

New lines

Construction began in 1991 of JR Kyushu's first Shinkansen. As described the 'Shinkansen Network Development' section, the 128 km Kyushu Shinkansen from Yatushiro to Kagoshima is being built with infrastructure suitable for 1,435 mm gauge, but initially it is to be laid with 1,067 mm gauge track.

It will be worked by a new design of 1,067 mm gauge trainset designed for operation at a maximum speed of at least 200 km/h. The design may emerge from development work being carried out by the Japanese Railway Technical Research Institute on a design known as 250X, with the aim of attaining 250 km/h on 1,067 mm gauge. This envisages short and low-slung 14 m lightweight bodies equipped with automatic body-tilt and active suspension that are articulated over single-axle bogies with independent wheels.

Improvements to existing lines

Recent developments include the opening of a short (1.4 km) branch linking Tayoshi on the Nichinan line with Miyazaki Airport on 18 July 1996. Services are operated by refurbished two-car Series 713-900 emus as well as limited expresses. The 22.6 km section of the Hohi line between Kumamoto and Higo-Ozu is to be electrified, with funding by JR Kyushu and local government (Kumamoto Prefecture) as a third-sector project.

Traction and rolling stock

In 1996 the company operated 19 electric and 18 diesel locomotives, 1,172 emu cars and 438 dmu cars, 225 other passenger coaches and 71 freight wagons.

Signalling and telecommunications

CTC (centralised traffic control) controls 67 per cent of the system; automatic block signalling covers 81 per cent of the system.

Track

Rail: 50.4 and 60 kg/m
Sleepers: Prestressed concrete or timber 2,100 x 200 x 140 mm spaced 1,480, 1,560 or 1,760/km according to class of route
Fastenings: Elastic
Max axleload: 18 tonnes

UPDATED

JR Kyushu electric locomotives

Class	Wheel arrangement	Output kW	Speed km/h	Weight tonnes	No in service	First built	Builders
EF81	B-B-B	2,550	100	100.8	4	1968	H
ED76	B-2-B	1,990	100	90.5	15	1965	T/M/H

Abbreviations: T: Toshiba; M: Mitsubishi; H: Hitachi

JR Kyushu diesel locomotives

Class	Wheel arrangement	Power kW	Speed km/h	Weight tonnes	No in service	First built	Mechanical	Builders Engine	Transmission
DD51	B-2-B	2,200	95	84	1	1966	M	2 × DML61Z	H DW2A
DD16	B-B	800	75	48	2	1971	K	DML61Z	H DW2A
DE10	AAA-B	1,350	85	65	15	1969	K/N	DML61ZB	H DW6

Abbreviations: K: Kawasaki; M: Mitsubishi; N: Nippon Sharyo

JR Kyushu diesel railcars or multiple-units

Class	Cars per unit	Motor cars per unit	Motored axles/car	Power/motor kW	Speed km/h	No in service	First built	Mechanical	Builders Engine	Transmission
65	1	1	1	500	95	31	1969	N, F	DML30HSD	N DW4D
58	1	1	2	360	95	86	1961	Nt, F, N, TE	DMH17H N	N TC2A DF115A
28	1	1	1	180	95	41	1961	Nt, F	DMH17H N	N TC2A DF115A
66	2	2	1	440	95	15	1975	Nt, F	DML30HSH	N DW9
67	2	2	1	440	95	15	1975	Nt, F	DML30HSH	N DW9
40	1	1	1	220	95	25	1978	Nt, F	DMF15HSA	N DW10
47	1	1	1	220	95	76	1979	Nt, F	DMF15HSA	N DW10
52	1	1	2	360	95	3	1961	Nt	DMH17HSN	N TC2A DF115A
31	1	1	1	250	95	23	1987	F, N	DMF13HS	N, F TC2A DF115A
185			1	250	110	20	1986	Nt, F, N	DMF13HS	N TC2A DF115A
200	2	2	1	420	110	30	1990		DMF13HZA	R-DW4

Abbreviations: Nt: Niigata; F: Fuji; N: Nippon Sharyo; TE: Teikoku; Tk: Tokyu

JR Kyushu electric railcars or multiple-units

Class	Cars per unit	Motor cars per unit	Motored axles/car	Output/motor kW	Speed km/h	No in service	First built	Builders
20 kV AC								
421	4	2	4	100	100	} 115	1961	H/Tk/Ki/TE/R
423	4	2	4	120	100		1961	H/Tk/Ki/TE/R
415	4	2	4	120	100	184	1971	H/N/S/Tk/R
713	2	1	4	150	100	8	1982	H/Tk
715	4	2	4	120	100	36	1985	H/N/S/R
717	2	2	4	120	100	8	1985	R/S/H
475/457	2	2	4	120	100	111	1965	R/S/Tk
485	4	2	4	120	120	212	1969	Ki/Tk/N/R/S
811	4	2	4	150	120	112	1989	H/S
783	4/7/9	2/4/5	4	135/150	120	90	1987	H/J/S
787	9	6	4	150	130	120	1992	H/J/S
883	7	3	4	190	130	35	1994	H
1.5 kV DC								
103	3	4	4	110	100	54	1964	H/R

Abbreviations: Ki: Kisha; H: Hitachi; TE: Teikoku; S: Kinki Sharyo; R: Kawasaki; N: Nippon Sharyo; Tk: Tokyu; J; JR (Kokura)

Japan Freight Railway Co

6-5, Marunouchi 1-chome, Chiyoda-ku, Tokyo 100
Tel: +81 3 3285 0071   Fax: +81 3 3212 6992

Key personnel
Chairman: Masashi Hashimoto
President: Yasushi Tanahashi
Vice-President: Hisashi Ueda

Vice-Chairman: Yoshio Kaneda
General Managers: Naohiko Itoh, Shigeho Nimori, Hiroshi Hatanaka

Organisation

Freight service is managed and marketed by JR Freight nationwide on the 1,067 mm gauge network. This concern owns its locomotives, wagons and terminals, but hires its track space from the six passenger railway companies. It has no marshalling yards and dedicates itself to bulk commodity and container traffic in trains using rolling stock modified to permit operation at up to 130 km/h. Some maintenance is subcontracted to the passenger railways.

Finance

JR Freight is a drastically slimmed-down enterprise compared with the freight activity of JNR at its death, when wage costs alone exceeded freight revenue by 25 per cent. The company has withdrawn from a third of the route-km served by JNR and is running 40 per cent fewer daily trains. It has also discarded most individual wagonload traffic in favour of complete trainloads from one terminal to another and increased labour productivity.

As a result of these measures JR Freight was operating profitably, but the continuing Japanese recession, combined with the high value of the yen and a poor harvest, has taken its toll, with the company recording its first annual loss in 1993-94. Operating revenues fell slightly to ¥196.3 billion in 1995-96. However, a pre-tax profit of ¥1.7 billion was achieved, mainly through the sale of surplus land.

To counter deteriorating performance the company adopted 'Freight 21', a 10-year management plan, in November 1994 with the aim of enhancing marketing, improving cost competitiveness, promoting planned capital investment and expanding non-railway business. Measures are in hand to restructure container services (into high-speed direct services between major terminal cities, express services between medium-size cities and local feeder services), to reduce terminal transfer times, to improve timetable efficiency by co-ordinating the speed of freight and passenger trains and to transfer more paper, tobacco and chemical products to containers. In

'Super Piggyback' wagon accommodating three purpose-built road vehicles   *1995*

the longer term, the company also intends to increase the number of wagons per train on the Tokaido line, to introduce new locomotives to speed up services and to reduce railway employee numbers from 11,000 to 7,000 by 2003 through expansion of its early retirement scheme.

Finance

(million yen)	1993-94	1994-95	1995-96
Operating revenues			
Railway	180,684	171,700	
Other	25,160	25,200	
Total	205,844	196,900	196,293
Operating expenses			
Total	203,954	201,000	199,294
Pretax profit/loss	−3,800	−7,000	1,698
Profit/loss after tax	−2,700	−8,000	701

Traffic (million)	1993-94	1994-95	1995-96
Freight tonnes	54.0	53.5	52.5
Freight tonne-km	25,100	25,500	26,300

Freight operations

A further decline in traffic levels occurred in 1995-96 with total freight tonnes down 1.8 per cent to 52.5 million; but tonne-km increased 0.3 per cent to 26.3 billion. Bulk commodities fell by 7.2 per cent to 31.52 million tonnes while container traffic rose 5.4 per cent to 20.58 million tonnes, the first rise in four years. The most significant bulk commodities by weight are petroleum (34 per cent of total carryings), cement (19 per cent), limestone (14 per cent), paper and pulp (6 per cent), chemicals (4 per cent) and coal (2 per cent).

Containers are the biggest single traffic component, however, travelling 900 km on average compared to 200 km or so for other traffic, and yielding 60 per cent of JR Freight's total revenue. The company's total number of daily scheduled trains stood at 844 in 1993 compared to 906 in 1992.

Intermodal operations

In 1994, 329 container trains were running daily over trunk routes extending from Asahikawa and Kushiro in Hokkaido down to Fukuoka, Nagasaki and Kagoshima in Kyushu. One service runs throughout from Fukuoka to Sapporo, a distance of 2,130 km. 'Superliner' container trains connecting the main cities such as Tokyo, Osaka, Hiroshima and Fukuoka are permitted a top speed of 110 km/h. In all, 148 terminals are served by the container train system.

Most container traffic moves in JR Freight's own stock of 76,400 distinctively sized containers, but some 17,600 privately owned containers are also employed in rail transport. Width is the difficult dimension rather than height; since 1987 JR Freight has raised the latter from 8 ft (2.4 m) to 2.5 m in its own stock. Length was at first a standard 20 ft, but now JR Freight has available numerous 30 ft containers with 47 m³ capacity; that approximates to the cube available in the Japanese trucking industry's most widely used vehicles. JR Freight also deploys refrigerated and live fish containers, as well as boxes, tanks, hoppers and open tops.

JR Freight has now accumulated a stock of new low-floor flatcars that can carry 40 ft, 8 ft 6 in high ISO containers of 30 tonnes gross weight, or two 20 ft boxes with a total gross weight of 40 tonnes.

Because of its inherited scant terminal cranage, JR Freight partnered lorry manufacturer Izuku to develop a craneless transhipment technique for swapbody business. Known as 'Slide Vanbody', this uses a system of electrically powered winches and rollers with which the move from rail to road vehicle can be effected by one person.

From early 1995 JR Freight introduced a daily car transporter service between Nagoya and Niigata using new fully enclosed 'Car Rack' wagons. The sides and roof of the rail wagons lift upwards to accommodate a total of eight cars carried on two levels. These wagons can accommodate ordinary containers as return cargo.

JR Freight diesel locomotives

Class	Wheel arrangement	Power kW	Speed km/h	Weight tonnes	No in service	First built	Mechanical	Builders Engine	Transmission
DE10	AAA-B	1,000	85	65	143	1967	K/N/H	DML6ZB	H DW6 (2000 series)
DE11	AAA-B	1,000	85	70	4	1979	K/N	DML61ZA/B	H DW6
DD51	B-2-B	1,650	95	84	140	1966	H/M/K	2 × DML61Z	H 2 × DW2A
DF200	B-B-B	2,500	110	96	7	1992	K/T	MTU 12V396TE14	E

JR Freight electric locomotives

Class	Wheel arrangement	Output kW	Speed km/h	Weight tonnes	No in service	First built	Builders
1.5 kV DC							
ED62	B-1-B	1,560	90		7		
EF64	B-B-B	2,550	100	96	113	1964	T/K/To
EF65	B-B-B	2,550	100	96	184	1964	K/To/T/N
EF66	B-B-B	3,900	110	100.8	73	1968	K/To
EF67	B-B-B	2,850	100	99.6	8	1981	To
EF200	B-B-B	6,000	120	100.8	21	1990	H
20 kV AC							
ED75	B-B	1,900	100	67.2	89	1963	M/H/T
ED76	B-2-B	1,900	100	87	24	1967	H/M/T
ED79	B-B	1,900	110	68	10	1989	T
Dual-voltage 1.5 kV/20 kV							
EF81	B-B-B	2,550/2,370	110	100.8	64	1968	H/M
EF500	B-B-B	6,000	120	100.8	1	1990	M/K

Abbreviations: K: Kawasaki; H: Hitachi; M: Mitsubishi; N: Nippon Sharyo Seizo; T: Toshiba; To: Toyo Denki Seizo

Class EF200 electric locomotive hauling an intermodal service through Nagoya (Anthony Robins) **1997**

Piggyback services

Recently perfected, too, is a low-floor flatcar with wheels of 610 mm diameter. That has enabled JR Freight to pursue ro-ro piggyback train service for the smaller size of road freight vans in common Japanese use. Over 300 truck movements a day are now made on 18 daily piggyback services. The wagon can also take 9 ft 6 in high containers.

Test running of a new concept known as 'Super Piggyback' began in 1993, with regular services introduced in 1994. Super Piggyback wagons accommodate three 6.5 m 'Freight Liner' road vans, each designed to carry 30 m³ compared to conventional piggyback wagons which carry two 8.5 m vans with a capacity of 28.5 m³ each.

Traction and rolling stock

In September 1996, JR Freight operated 594 electric and 293 diesel locomotives and 11,647 wagons.

Recent deliveries include Hitachi-built Class EF200 1.5 kV DC Bo-Bo-Bos with inverter-controlled asynchronous motors and a dual-voltage EF500 prototype built by Mitsubishi/Kawasaki which is being evaluated for hauling container trains from Tokyo to Hokkaido via the Seikan tunnel. Following a one-year trial with a prototype DF200 diesel-electric 'Inverter Hi-Tech Loco' built by Kawasaki, JR Freight has taken delivery of a further six production versions for use on timber trains in Hokkaido. The DF200 has a maximum speed of 120 km/h, with power supplied by two MTU 12V396 engines (total output 2,500 kW at 1,800 rpm), each of which drives an alternator.

In 1996 trials commenced with a prototype Class EF210 1.5 kV DC 4,000 kW output electric locomotive designed for 110 km/h container services on the main Tokaido/Sanyo trunk route. Construction costs have been reduced by the use of inverters to control pairs of traction motors. From 1997 onwards, JR Freight plans to take delivery of 100 production Class EF210 locomotives to replace Class EF65 locomotives which have seen over 25 years service.

UPDATED

Shinkansen network development

The network in operation at the start of 1996 and its owning and operating railways comprised:

JR East:
Tohoku Shinkansen	Tokyo to Morioka
Joetsu Shinkansen	Omiya to Niigata
Yamagata Mini-Shinkansen	Fukushima to Yamagata

JR Central:
Tokaido Shinkansen	Tokyo to Shin-Osaka

JR West:
Sanyo Shinkansen	Shin-Osaka to Hakata

The Shinkansen programme agreed in 1988 specified three types of extension:

Type 1. To full Shinkansen 1,435 mm gauge standard, engineered for 260 km/h by present equipment, 300 km/h by the next generation equipment in design.

Type 2. Addition of a third rail to existing 1,067 mm gauge, possibly with some realignment, with the use of small-profile trainsets restricted to 130 km/h on mixed-gauge.

Type 3. Infrastructure to full Shinkansen 1,435 mm gauge standard, but initially laid with 1,067 mm gauge track, engineered for 160 to 200 km/h.

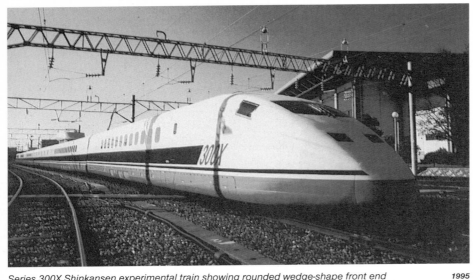

Series 300X Shinkansen experimental train showing rounded wedge-shape front end   **1995**

Three generations of Shinkansen rolling stock: (left to right) Series 300, Series 100 and Series 0   **1995**

Application of these concepts to the extensions approved in 1990 was as follows:

Hokuriku Shinkansen

Type 1: Takasaki—Karuizawa (41 km)

Type 1: Karuizawa—Nagano (75 km)

Type 3: Nagano—Kanazawa (89 km)

Tohoku Shinkansen

Type 2: Morioka—Aomori (125 km)

Type 1: Numakunai—Hachinohe (but dual-gauged for use also by freight trains)

Kyushu Shinkansen

Type 3: Yatushiro—Kagoshima (128 km)

Construction work began on the Karuizawa—Nagano section of the Hokuriku, the Morioka—Aomori extension of the Tohoku, and the Yatushiro—Kagoshima section of JR Kyushu's first Shinkansen in September 1991. Construction commenced in October 1993 on the Itoigawa Uozu section of the Hokuriku Shinkansen. All are being built by the Japan Railway Construction Corporation (see above). Construction costs will be shared between central government (40 per cent) and the JR companies which will pay their share out of receipts from the Shinkansen lines they now own.

The outcome of a government review of the Shinkansen programme was announced at the beginning of 1994. The previously authorised sections of the Hokuriku, Tohoku and Kyushu lines retained priority. Environmental assessment studies of the Takefu—Osaka section of the Hokuriku line, the Nagasaki branch of the Kyushu line and the Hokkaido branch of the Kyushu line and the Hokkaido line from Aomori to Sapporo were to commence in 1994-95, although work on these sections was not to start before the next programme review in 1997.

A recent change in government policy has, however, seen a 25 per cent increase in funding for Shinkansen construction which is enabling work to progress on some additional sections of the network. About 90 per cent of

the ¥228 billion budget is allocated to the Takasaki—Nagano section of the Hokuriku Shinkansen, but work is also in progress on the Toyama section of the Hokuriku line, the Kumamoto section of the Kyushu line and the Morioka—Numakunai section of the Tohoku line which will now be built to Type 1 rather than Type 2 standard.

Shinkansen rolling stock

Series 0

During the first 20 years after the opening of the Tokaido-Sanyo Shinkansen, rolling stock of essentially the same performance and accommodation was employed. The original cars of this Series 0 have now all been replaced.

Series 100

Series 0 is now complemented on the Tokaido-Sanyo Shinkansen by the Series 100, which combines pursuit of better aerodynamics, more effective noise control and economy in energy consumption with improvement of passenger comfort and amenities. Earlier Shinkansen types had all cars powered, but in the Series 100 four of a set's 16 cars are trailers. The powered cars, which are paired, each have a 230 kW motor of lighter (828 kg) and more compact design on each axle. A Series 100 set is lighter than a Series 0 set, even though two (or in some sets all) of a Series 100's four trailers are bilevels (the other two are the end cars with driving cabs): the comparison is 922 tonnes as against 967 tonnes for 16 cars with a full complement of 1,277 passengers. Maximum axleloading, at 15 tonnes, is one tonne below that of a Series 0.

Aerodynamic improvements in the Series 100 include a longer and reshaped nose and closer attention to smooth exterior surfaces, in particular by avoiding recessed windows. The effect has been to reduce drag coefficient by 20 per cent, compared with Series 0, and also noise emission. Moreover, even though the total installed power of a Series 100 (11,040 kW) is less than that of a Series 0

16-car unit, the Series 100 has proved 17 per cent more economical in power consumption on a Tokyo—Sanyo 'Hikari' schedule. The 1.6 km/h/s acceleration rate of a Series 100 compares with the 1.0 km/h/s of a Series 0. Nose shaping is a factor in noise control as well as reduction of drag, since the noise emanating from an accelerating train's front end rises by a factor of between the fifth and sixth power of its speed.

With eddy current brakes on its non-motored trailers to complement the regenerative braking of the powered cars, the Series 100 has a superior braking performance to its predecessors.

Series 200

Advances in Shinkansen speed resulted from an exhaustive programme of research and high-speed tests begun in the late 1970s. It proved possible to limit lineside noise at 240 km/h to 79 dB(A), the figure previously achieved at 210 km/h to respect the statutory limit of 80 dB(A), largely by increasing the frequency of rail grinding to eliminate surface defects, and by pantograph alterations.

As built for the Joetsu and Tohoku lines, the Series 200 trainsets were formed of two-car units; each of the latter had to run with a pantograph operative. The normal 12-car formation now runs with only three pantographs raised and a 25 kV bus-line laid along the tops of the cars distributes the current. Noise has been further curbed by adoption of three-stage pantograph springing to sustain contact with the overhead wire and to minimise the intermittent arcing that has been a perennial cause for environmentalist complaints; and by surrounding the pantograph with shielding, which limits transmission of noise to the lineside.

A programme of replacement of Series 200 units is likely to commence after the opening of the Hokuriku and Akita Shinkansen projects in 1997. Two new types of train are envisaged; a high-capacity version based on Series E1 and a high-speed version based on Series E2.

Series 300

Test programmes demonstrated that speeds up to 300 km/h were feasible on the present track of all Shinkansen, but not with existing sets, which at that speed would break both the 80 dB(A) noise limit and also generate unacceptable vibration. Also, aerodynamic drag in tunnels would be too high. Consequently a new Series 300 train was designed and, as described above, was put into public service by JR Central on the Tokaido Shinkansen in 1992.

The Series 300 is distinguished externally by a dramatically reshaped nose-end and low-slung body. Floor level is 1.15 m and roof crown 3.6 m above rail, compared with 1.3 m and 4 m respectively for the Series 100. A considerable reduction of weight results from adoption of aluminium alloy body construction and more powerful traction motors. With six of a set's 16 cars non-motored, total weight is 691 tonnes, compared with the 922 tonnes of a Series 100. Maximum axleloading in the bolsterless bogies is 14 tonnes. Like the Series 100, the 300 adds eddy current to its braking systems; a change is that the 300 has regenerative instead of dynamic braking.

Traction is provided by three-phase AC 300 kW motors, four per motor car, supplied by a 3,000 kW pulse-width modulation converter with 4,500 V, 2,000 A GTO thyristors feeding 1,760 kVA VVVF inverters. Power:weight ratio is 17.37 kW/tonne. Designed top speed is 300 km/h.

Series 300X

In 1994 JR Central took delivery of a six-car series 300X experimental trainset, designed for commercial speeds of 350 km/h, and is undertaking a two-year programme of high-speed trials on an upgraded section of track between Kyoto and Maibara. The 300X achieved a record speed for Japan of 443 km/h in July 1996. The train features two different nose configurations (cusp shape — pictured in the JR Central description, above — and rounded-wedge shape — pictured here) to test air resistance and noise, reduced cross-section smooth-sided aluminium-bodied cars with coupling bellows and undercarriage skirts, pantograph covers, dampers between cars, tilting system and active control system. Individual cars have been constructed by four different manufacturers using different body fabrication techniques in order to assess the scope for further weight reductions.

The Series 300X forms the basis for trains that may be required for the Chuo Shinkansen between Tokyo and Osaka via Kofu if the proposed maglev line does not proceed.

Series 400

For its Yamagata Mini-Shinkansen, as described above, JR East acquired 12 small-profile six-car Series 400 sets. All axles are powered by thyristor-controlled 220 kW motors. The cars are of the same height as those of the Series 200, to which the sets are coupled when running over the Tohoku Shinkansen and run at up to 240 km/h between Tokyo and the divergence of the Mini-Shinkansen at Fukushima. But the bodies are significantly narrower, so that each seating bay has one seat less per row than in a Series 200. A seventh car was subsequently added to each set.

In September 1991 a Series 400 was run at up to 345 km/h on the Tohoku Shinkansen.

Series E1

To meet rising demand for commuter services on its Tohoku and Joetsu lines, JR East launched the all double-deck 12-car Series E1 'MAX' (Multi Amenity Express) in March 1994, and commercial services commenced in July 1994. Because the car height has been increased, the front cars have been given an ultra-streamlined shape to improve their appearance. Doors have been widened to prevent congestion around the entrances and wheelchair lifts are installed in two cars. Cars are equipped with electronic information displays and FM radio receivers. Vending machines are available in some cars in place of restaurant or buffet facilities. Half the cars are motored, with 24 traction motors providing a total continuous rating of 9,840 kW. Maximum speed is 240 km/h.

Series E2

Services on the Hokuriku Shinkansen are to be operated by eight-car Series E2 trainsets designed to achieve 260 km/h and climb 3.5 per cent gradients. Performance trials began following the delivery of a prototype set in May 1995. The train features a low-profile cross-section as on the Series 300 and a streamlined nose to reduce pressure when entering tunnels. To reduce aerodynamic noise, underfloor equipment is enclosed, plug doors are fitted flush with body sides and pantographs are surrounded by shields. VVVF-controlled 300kW motors are fitted to six power cars and accept power supply at 50 or 60 Hz. The Series E2 and E3 units are designed so that noise and vibration levels at 275 km/h do not exceed those of existing 240 km/h trains.

Series E3

A prototype five-car Series E3 unit was delivered in April 1995 for test running prior to commercial operation on the Akita Shinkansen from 1997. Series E2 and E3 share main electrical components and bogies to reduce construction and maintenance costs but the E3 has a smaller cross-section to meet clearances on the Akita line. The unit features asynchronous motors and a maximum speed of 270 km/h, though speed is limited to 130 km/h on the regauged line between Morioka and Akita. Power is supplied at 25 kV 50 Hz AC on the Shinkansen and 20 kV 50 Hz AC on the converted line. Due to limited underfloor space, some equipment is roof-mounted under an aerodynamically designed cover. Series E3 sets are coupled to Series 200 or E2 trains for the run between Tokyo and Morioka.

Series E4

JR East was due to introduce the new double-deck Series E4 from December 1997 on the Tohoku Shinkansen to alleviate rush-hour congestion, particularly in the Omiya to Oyama section. The newly designed 16-car trainset, consisting of two eight-car units, will have total seating capacity of 1,634 and run at 240 km/h. This will make it the highest capacity high-speed train in the world.

STAR 21

A prototype nine-car train was completed for JR East by Kawasaki in 1992. Tagged STAR 21 (Superior Train for the Advanced 21st Century Railway), it is designed to prove various components and technologies with a view to future operation at 300 to 400 km/h. Consequently, it features some alternative concepts, a peculiarity most apparent in the differing outlines of its two end cars. Of the latter, one is designated Series 952, the other Series 953.

The unit features three types of body in which aerospace techniques and materials have been employed for weight saving, which has been so effective that the maximum axleloading is 10.5 tonnes. For the first time in Shinkansen rolling stock development, five of the cars are articulated. Eight different designs of bolsterless bogie have been applied to the unit. Hollow axles and aluminium axleboxes are features.

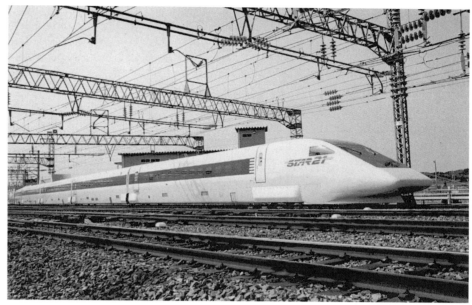

JR East's STAR 21 prototype trainset

Four of the cars are motored for a continuous rating of 2,640 kW to serve a total train weight of 256 tonnes. The motors are three-phase AC under VVVF control, and draw their current from pantographs on the third and seventh cars.

In November 1992 STAR 21 set a Japanese speed record of 358 km/h and in December 1993 reached 425 km/h, at that time second only to the French TGV-A's 515 km/h. Further work is now in progress to reduce noise levels associated with high-speed running.

Series 500

In 1992 JR West unveiled a six-car prototype variously designated Series 500 and WIN 350, the latter to mark its objective of commercial operating speed. As with JR East's STAR 21, the unit featured differently styled end cars for investigation of aerodynamics and noise suppression at high speed. Test running of the WIN 350 train enabled the development of measures to respond to environmental concerns and to ensure passenger comfort at operational speeds of 300 km/h.

In January 1996 JR West took delivery of a 16-car Series 500 preproduction train, based on the results of the WIN 350 research. The 500 entered commercial service at a maximum speed of 300 km/h between Shin-Osaka and Hakata in March 1997 and was scheduled to operate through to Tokyo in late 1997. This new train features a reduced cross-section lightweight aluminium body, 'smooth' surfacing technology with plug doors and enclosed underfloor equipment modules, a distinctive 15 m long aerodynamic pointed nose, a wing-shaped pantograph to reduce aerodynamic and wire contact noise and active suspension to allow curves to be negotiated up to 20 km/h faster than other trains. All axles are motored and bolsterless bogies reduce vibration. The passenger capacity of 1,323 is the same as the 'Nozomi' trainsets. A total of nine Series 500 trainsets are expected to be in service by the end of 1998.

Series 700

Rolling stock engineers from JR Central and JR West have been working on a joint project known as Series 700. A 16-car prototype train, N300, was due to be rolled out in September 1997. Drawing on experience with JR West's WIN 350 and JR Central's 300X, N300 will be a low-noise, low-maintenance design.

ATLAS

Japan's Railway Technical Research Institute is also working up designs for a 350 km/h Shinkansen train, in a project dubbed ATLAS (Advanced Technology for Low Noise and Attractive Shinkansen).

UPDATED

The rump of JNR

What remains of JNR was reorganised as the Japanese National Railways Accounts Settlement Corporation, which retains all the assets and liabilities that are not transferred to successor companies (including the Japan Railway Construction Corporation). Its tasks are:
Reimbursement of long-term liabilities and payment of interest;
Disposal of real estate and other assets in order to raise the necessary money;
Execution of necessary business activities to utilise the rights and meet the obligations transferred to the company from JNR;
Action to achieve re-employment of personnel made surplus by the Reform. Some 93,000 JNR personnel were surplus to the needs of the new companies at the latter's formation.

JNR Settlement Corporation

6-5, Marunouchi 1-chome, Chiyoda-ku, Tokyo 100
Tel: +81 3 3214 7959   Fax: +81 3 3240 5586

Key personnel
Chairman: Yasuo Nishimura

The corporation's function is disposal of the assets and long-term liabilities not transferred to new companies during the restructuring of 1987, and promotion of the re-employment of surplus employees. JNRSC took on most of the JNR debt in order to facilitate the privatisation of the ex-JNR companies, but 10 years after the JNR break-up the continued existence of ¥28,100 billion of debt (equivalent to nearly 6 per cent of gross domestic product) was a political embarrassment. Reduction of the inherited JNR debt is proving difficult because of lower than expected proceeds from railway privatisation and land sales due to the sluggish economy and collapse in property values. A proposal put forward in early 1997 was that the government should assume ¥13,800 billion of the outstanding debt; land sales might cover a further ¥8,000 billion. The balance of ¥6,300 billion required to enable the winding up of JNRSC might be financed by a surcharge on rail fares, an idea which is being strongly resisted by the ex-JNR companies.

Japan Telecom Co

1-7-4 Kudan-kita, Chiyoda-ku, Tokyo 102
Tel: +81 3 3222 6651   Fax: +81 3 3222 6660

Key personnel
Chairman: Kazumasa Mawatari
President: Koichi Sakata

Maintenance of railway telecommunication equipment and provision of general telecommunication services.

Railway Information Systems Co Ltd

6-5, Marunouchi 1-chome, Chiyoda-ku, Tokyo 100
Tel: +81 3 3214 4695   Fax: +81 3 3240 5593

Key personnel
Chairman: Yoshisuke Mutoh
President: Hiroyuki Hayashi

Information processing for railway companies, and related computerised information services.

Railway Technical Research Institute

2-8-38, Hikari-cho, Kokubunji-shi, Tokyo 185
Tel: +81 425 73 7219   Fax: +81 425 73 7255

Tokyo Office
Tel: +81 3 3240 9672

Miyazaki Maglev Centre
Tel: +81 982 58 1303

Key personnel
Chairman: Yoshinosuke Yasoshima
President: Hiromi Soejima
Executive Directors: Nobuhisa Izumi, Toshiaki Sasaki

Organisation
Research and development activities to meet the requirements of the railway companies.

High-speed 1,067 mm gauge design
The Institute has developed a preliminary design for a 12-car lightweight train with active tilt-body apparatus for high-speed operation on the country's 1,067 mm gauge routes, with the objective of completion of a 250 km/h trainset by 1997.

ATLAS Shinkansen project
As noted above, the Institute is developing a 350 km/h Shinkansen train design under the title of ATLAS.

Maglev system
The Institute continues to pursue development of maglev vehicle technology employing opposed, liquid helium-cooled superconductor magnets and linear synchronous motors. Previously, the track for vehicle tests was one of 7 km near Miyazaki, on which unmanned test vehicle ML 500 reached a record speed of 517 km/h in 1979.

The inverted T-shaped guideway was then modified into a U-shaped configuration, and tests were run with a new vehicle, MLU-001, as a single car, two-car and, from 1982, a three-car unit. With the two-car unit manned, a speed of 400.8 km/h was recorded in 1987.

In parallel with these field tests, studies were directed toward development of operational concepts for a maglev system and toward technologies for vehicle control at turnouts, power supply, onboard power sources and emergency aerodynamic braking. Research was also surveying vehicle-guideway dynamics and precise measurement of guideway irregularities, reduction of reactive power, performance of associated equipment, and human body reactions to magnetic effects and to high-speed running.

From 1987 trials progressed with a 44-seat MLU-002 vehicle. In mid-1991 testing began of a sidewall levitation system.

In October 1991 operation of the Miyazaki test guideway was brought to a halt when the MLU-002 vehicle was destroyed by fire. Trials recommenced in April 1993 with MLU-002N, rebuilt from an earlier test car, which in 1994 recorded a speed of 431 km/h in unmanned tests and 411 km/h in manned mode in January 1995.

Maglev is being considered as an option for the second Tokyo—Osaka high-speed route (see JR Central entry

above). The objective is to operate at 500 km/h so as to cover the Tokyo—Osaka distance in 1 hour. To further this aim, the government authorised construction of a 43 km test track as a national project, and construction of this has progressed in Yamanashi Prefecture, roughly 100 km from Tokyo. The test track is to be used to study vehicle behaviour in tunnels and when passing another car running in the opposite direction, operation and control of a full train service, permissible gradient and curvature parameters, and turnout performance. Progress with construction of the test track has been held up due to lack of government finance and land acquisition difficulties, but the Japan Railway Construction Corporation and JR Central have now completed an 18.4 km priority section (16 km in tunnel) between Sakaigawa and Akiyama. Test running in superconducting mode, but without levitation, began in February 1997. Test running in levitation mode was scheduled to follow in April 1997.

A three-car test train known as MLX-01 was delivered in July 1995. MLX-01 comprises a 'double cusp' end car built by Mitsubishi, an 'aero wedge' end car by Kawasaki and a Nippon Sharyo middle car. The cars are linked by articulated levitation bogies which incorporate superconducting magnets and retractable take-off and landing wheels for use at low speeds. Aircraft technology has been used for the ultra-lightweight bodyshells which are constructed in a semi-monocoque style to a slightly smaller cross-section than Series 300 Shinkansen trains. A second five-car train is to be built for trials with two trains in operation at the same time. It is hoped to achieve a maximum speed of 550 km/h in the main test programme.

UPDATED

MAJOR PRIVATE AND THIRD SECTOR RAILWAYS

In addition to the JR Group Companies there are over 125 private and third sector railways in Japan, excluding

metros, tramways and new transit systems. These range from major private interuban networks to individual rural lines, many of which were former loss-making JNR/JR lines that have been taken over by third sector companies.

Chichibu Railway

Chichibu Tetsudo
1-1, Akebono-cho, Kumagaya-shi 360
Tel: +81 485 23 3311   Fax: +81 485 26 0551

Key personnel
President: K Kakihara

Gauge: 1,067 mm
Route length: 79.3 km
Electrification: 79.3 km at 1.5 kV DC

Organisation
The railway operates passenger services on two lines which connect at Kumagaya in Saitama prefecture; the 14.9 km Hanyu line and 56.8 km Chichibu line. The latter serves a mountainous area northwest of Tokyo which attracts sightseers and provides limestone for cement, an important source of freight traffic for the railway. Interchange is available with JR, Tobu and Seibu lines and some Seibu services run through between Tokyo and Chichibu line destinations, mainly on Sundays and holidays; a steam-hauled tourist service also operates on

the Chichibu line. A 7.6 km freight connection provides for the transfer of freight traffic to and from the JR network. Rolling stock comprises 22 electric locomotives, 67 emu cars and 168 wagons.

UPDATED

Hankyu Corporation

Hankyu Dentetsu
16-1, Shibata 1-chome, Kita-ku, Osaka 530
Tel: +81 6 373 5092   Fax: +81 6 373 5670

Key personnel
Chairman: Kohei Kobayashi
President: Motohiro Sugai

Senior Managing Directors: Yoshihito Utahashi, Norikazu Matsubara

Gauge: 1,435 mm
Route length: 146.8 km
Electrification: 146.8 km at 1.5 kV DC

Organisation
The Corporation was set up in 1907 to construct an interurban railway to develop suburban Osaka, and is now a diversified enterprise. The railway remains the

cornerstone of the group, but other activities range from bus and taxi companies to real estate development, department stores, recreation centres and audio-visual entertainment.

Finance
Revenue from railway operations constitutes approximately 54 per cent of total operating revenue.

Passenger operations
The railway serves nine lines with 84 stations and runs over 1,000 eight-car trains daily on its Kobe line and to Kyoto, and over 700 a day to Takarazuka. The terminal in Osaka, built in the 1970s, has 10 platforms and is located in a complex including a 17-storey office building and an underground shopping mall; the rail exit from the terminal is six-track. The company is currently implementing a programme to replace existing Automatic Train Stop (ATS), Total Train Control (TTC) and other safety equipment with more advanced systems. Elevated tracks are under construction at six locations to eliminate level crossings.

Passenger journeys declined from 789 million in 1993-94 to 758 million in 1994-95 due largely to Japan's economic downturn and the effects of the Hanshin earthquake of January 1995. The railway experienced severe damage in the earthquake with services suspended on the main line between Nishinomiya and Kobe and on the Itami and Koyoen branch lines. Reconstruction works costed at ¥85.2 billion were completed by June 1995.

Hankyu electric multiple-units

Class	Cars per unit	Motor cars per unit	Motored axles/car	Output/motor kW	Speed km/h	Cars in service	First built	Builders Mechanical	Electrical
2000					110	38	1960	Alna Koki	
2300	4/7	2/4	4	150	110	78	1960	Alna Koki	Toshiba/Toyo Denki
2800	4/7	2/4	4	150	110	28	1964	Alna Koki	Toyo Denki
3000	3/4/6/8	2/4	4	170	110	114	1964	Alna Koki	Toshiba
3100	3/4/8	2/4	4	120	110	40	1964	Alna Koki	Toshiba
3300	6/8	4/6	4	130	110	126	1967	Alna Koki	Toshiba/Toyo Denki
5000	8	4	4	170	110	47	1968	Alna Koki	Toshiba
5100	8/10	4/6	4	140	110	90	1971	Alna Koki	Toshiba
5200	4/6	2/4	4	170	110	12	1970	Alna Koki	Toshiba
5300	6/7/8	4/6	4	140	110	105	1972	Alna Koki	Toshiba/Toyo Denki
2200	4	2	4	150*	110	10	1975	Alna Koki	Toshiba
6000	6/8/10	4/6/8	4	140	110	130	1976	Alna Koki	Toshiba
6300	8	4	4	140/150	110	72	1975	Alna Koki	Toshiba/Toyo Denki
7000	6/8/10	4/5/6	4	150	110	210	1980	Alna Koki	Toshiba
7300	6/8/10	3/4/5/6	4	150/180*	110	83	1982	Alna Koki	Toshiba/Toyo Denki
8000	6/8/10	3/4/5	4	170*	110	90	1988	Alna Koki	Toshiba
8300	6/7/8	3/4	4	170*	110	61	1989	Alna Koki	Toshiba/Toyo Denki
8200	2	1	4	200	110	4	1995	Alna Koki	

* VVVF inverter control

Rolling stock

The railway owns 1,343 emu cars, all air conditioned. The most recent motored cars have VVVF inverter control and the new Series 8200 units feature seats which fold away during the rush hour to increase passenger capacity.

Track

Rail: 50.4 or 60.8 kg/m
Sleepers: Wood: 230 × 2,400 mm; prestressed concrete: 300 × 2,400 × 170 mm
Fastenings: Double elastic

Spacing: 1,760/km
Min curvature radius: 100 m
Max gradient: 3.5%
Max permissible axleload: 17.78 tonnes

UPDATED

Hanshin Electric Railway

Hanshin Denki Tetsudo
1-24 Ebie 1-chome, Fukushima-ku, Osaka 533
Tel: +81 6 457 2123

Key personnel
Chairman: Shunjiro Kuma
President: Masatoshi Tezuka

Gauge: 1,435 mm
Route length: 40 km
Electrification: 40 km at 1.5 kV DC

Organisation

The Hanshin Electric Railway is at the centre of the Hanshin Group of approximately 60 affiliated companies extending into transport, retailing, real estate, sports, leisure, construction and computer-related business. Rail operations account for 41 per cent of group turnover.

Passenger operations

The railway operates a main line between Osaka and Kobe with two branches. In 1993-94 the railway recorded 240 million passenger journeys and 2,249 million passenger-km. The Hanshin earthquake of January 1995 affected performance in 1994-95 with passenger journeys down to 229 million and passenger-km down to 2,187 million.

Services extend via the underground Kobe Rapid Railway on to the Sanyo Electric Railway to the west of Kobe; reciprocal through running services are operated, providing a metro-style service across central Kobe.

All cars and underground stations are equipped with air conditioning. Programmed Traffic Control (PTC) and Automatic Train Stop (ATS) systems have been introduced. The proportion of main line in tunnel or elevated is due to rise to 87 per cent within 10 years through elimination of level crossings.

The railway was severely damaged in the January 1995 earthquake, with buses replacing trains between central Kobe and the eastern suburbs and all through-running services via the Kobe Rapid Railway suspended. Full service was restored, however, by June 1995. From the total fleet of 314 cars, 41 were written off as a result of earthquake damage. New replacement vehicles comprised two 4-car Series 5500 units, three Series 8000 cars and five 6-car Series 9000 units delivered during 1995-96.

UPDATED

Iyo Railway

Iyo Tetsudo
4-1, Minatomachi 4-chome, Matsuyama-shi 790
Tel: +81 899 48 3321

Key personnel
President: H Nagano

Gauge: 1,067 mm
Route length: 33.9 km
Electrification: 24.5 km at 750 V DC and 9.4 km at 600 V DC

Passenger operations

The railway operates 53 electric multiple-unit cars on two lines serving Matsuyama, on the island of Shikoku. Apart from its 33.9 km railway, it operates a 6.9 km urban tramway system in Matsuyama with 36 cars. There were 24 million passenger journeys and 99.4 million journeys in 1994-95.

UPDATED

Izu Express

Izu Kyuko (Izukyu)
1-21-6 Dogenzaka, Shibuya-ku, Tokyo 150
Tel: +81 3 3496 7155

Key personnel
President: Shunichi Ohki

Gauge: 1,067 mm
Route length: 45.7 km
Electrification: 45.7 km at 1.5 kV DC

Passenger operations

The railway, opened in 1961, serves the eastern coastline of the Izu peninsula from Ito to Izukyu-Shimoda. For the most part this is territory of the Fuji Hakone Izu national park, not far from Tokyo, and at Ito the railway connects with the JR East branch from Atami. Most local services operate through to Atami and JR 'Odori-Ko' limited expresses run through from Tokyo to Izukyu destinations. The railway operates 68 emu cars and its operations account for 37 per cent of the company's revenue.

UPDATED

Izu Hakone Railway

Izu Hakone Tetsudo
300, Daiba, Mishima-shi 411
Tel: +81 559 77 1200

Key personnel
Chairman: Yoshiaki Tsutsumi
President: Kakuro Kato

Gauge: 1,067 mm
Route length: 29.4 km
Electrification: 29.4 km at 1.5 kV DC

Passenger operations

The railway operates two electric locomotives and 60 emu cars on the 9.6 km Daiyousan line in Kanagawa prefecture and the 19.8 km Sunzu line in Shizuoka prefecture. JR East limited express 'Odori-Ko' trains run through from Tokyo to the Sunzu line. The company also operates two funiculars. Railway operations account for 15 per cent of the company's revenue.

UPDATED

Keifuku Electric Railway

Keifuku Denki Tetsudo
3-20, Mibu-kayo-goshomachi, Nakagyo-ku, Kyoto 604
Tel: +81 75 841 9381

Key personnel
Chairman: Minoru Miyashita
President: Seiya Yamakami

Gauge: 1,067 mm
Route length: 59.2 km
Electrification: 59.2 km at 600 V DC

Passenger operations

The railway operates 30 emu cars and two electric locomotives on three 1,067 mm gauge lines totalling 59.2 km at Fukui. It also operates a separate 11 km 1,435 mm gauge tramway system in Kyoto with a fleet of 28 cars. Railway operations account for 27 per cent of the company's revenue.

UPDATED

Keihan Electric Railway Co Ltd

Keihan Denki Tetsudo
2-27, Shiromi 1-chome, Chuo-ku, Osaka 540
Tel: +81 6 944 2521   Fax: +81 6 944 2501

Key personnel
Chairman: Minoru Miyashita
President: Akio Kinba
Executive Vice-President, Accounts, Finance, Purchases, Subsidiaries: Yutaka Ogura
Senior Managing Director, Railway Operation, Electrical Engineering, Rolling Stock: Rikuro Kimura
Chief Manager, New Business Planning and Development: Hiroshi Yoshida
Managing Director, Personnel, Audit, Information Systems: Junzo Takai
Deputy Chief Manager, Business Planning and Developments: Toru Nakanishi
    Otsu Branch: Kazuyuki Hasegawa
Director, New Line Construction: Kihachiro Nakaichi
Railway Operation: Kimio Nishimura
Accounting and Finance: Hiroichi Shimizu

Gauge: 1,435 mm
Route length: 91.5 km
Electrification: 66.3 km at 1.5 kV (Keihan line); 25.2 km at 600 V DC (Otsu line)

Passenger operations

The railway's main Keihan line runs 51.6 km from its Yodoyabashi station in Osaka to the underground Demachi Yanagi station in Kyoto City, with two branches, the Uji and Katano lines. The 11.5 km of continuously elevated quadruple-track between Temmabashi and Kayashima stations is the longest on any Japanese private railway. The Otsu line is light rail extending 25.2 km from Kyoto Sanjo to Hamaotsu, Ishiyama-dera and Sakamoto.

Serving 89 stations, the railway recorded 401 million

passenger journeys and 5,319 million passenger-km in 1994-95.

The railway generates 58 per cent of the company's income. The rest is derived from 65 subsidiary and affiliated companies covering activities ranging from bus, taxi and leisure boat services to hotels, retail stores and construction.

Future developments include through operation from Otsu to Kyoto City's new Tozai underground line with new Series 8000 four-car emus being delivered in readiness for this and construction of a Nakanoshima line westward through Osaka City to connect with a new line serving the Kansai International Airport.

Traction and rolling stock

Series 8000 stock is for limited express services and features onboard television and a telephone booth. Five double-deck cars have been ordered for delivery in 1997 and another five in 1998. They are based on the double-deck car incorporated into an older Series 3000 unit in December 1995 and will eventually see all limited express units including a double-deck car. The latest emu type is the eight-car Series 9000.

Signalling and telecommunications

Autonomous decentralised traffic control system (ADEC) is installed throughout the Keihan line. It links central control's mainframe computer and local processors by fibre optic cable, and allows overall traffic control to proceed simultaneously with independent control of an area's operation where that has become irregular.

Coupler in standard use: Tightlock automatic couplers; rotary key-block Tightlock automatic couplers; rod couplers

Braking in standard use: Electric command digital and electric pneumatic brake

Track

Rail: Keihan line: 50 kg/m (144.2 km) and 60 kg/m; Otsu line 40 kg/m (47.8 km) and 50 kg/m
Crossties (sleepers): Keihan: concrete, thickness 170 mm; spacing 1,760/km; Otsu: wood, thickness 150-170 mm; spacing 1,520/km
Fastenings: Elastic (spring clip or F type)
Min curvature radius: Keihan line: 200 m; Otsu line:45 m
Max gradient: Keihan: 3.3%; Otsu: 6.7%
Max permissible axleload: Keihan: 15 tonnes; Otsu: 8-15 tonnes

UPDATED

Keihan electric railcars or multiple-units

Class	Cars per unit	Motor cars per unit	Motored axles/car	Output/motor kW	Speed km/h	Cars in service	First built	Builders Mechanical	Electrical
Keihan line 1.5 kV DC									
9000	8						1995		
8000	7	4	4	175	110	70	1989	K/S/N	To/T/M
7000	7	3	4	200	110	28	1989	K/S/N	To/T/M
6000	8	4	4	155	110	112	1983	K/S/N	To/T/M
5000	7	4	4	155	110	49	1970	K/S/N	To/T/M
3000	7	4	4	175	110	9	1971	K/S/N	To/M
2600	4/5/6	2/3	4	155	110	131	1978	K/S/N	To/T/M
	7	4							
2200	7/8	4	4	155	110	100	1964	K/S/N	To/T/M
2400	7	4	4	155	110	42	1969	K/S/N	To/M
1000	7	4	4	155	110	42	1977	K/S/N	T/M
1900	5	4	4	108	110	45	1956	S/N	T/M
7200	1/3/4	1/2	4	200	110	16	1995	K/S	
Otsu line 600 V DC									
700	2	2	2	70	70	10	1992	Ke/S/N	To/T
600	2	2	4	53	70	20	1984	Ke/S/N	To/T
80	2	2	4	45	65	16	1961	Ki/N	To/T
260	2	2	4	45	65	8	1957	Ki/N	To
350	2	2	2	85	65	7	1966	Ki/N	To

Abbreviations: K: Kawasaki; Ke: Keihan; Ki: Kinki; M: Mitusbishi; N: Nabco; T: Toshiba; To: Toyo Denki Seizo; S: Sumitomo

Double-deck car added to existing Series 3000 set (Anthony Robins)   *1997*

Keihin Express Electric Railway

Keihin Kyuko Dentetsu
20-20, Takanawa 2-chome, Minato-ku, Tokyo 108
Tel: +81 3 3280 9123   Fax: +81 3 3280 9193

Key personnel
President: I Hiramatsu
Vice-Presidents: K Koyama, S Kotani
Senior Managing Directors: M Takano, T Yabe
Managing Directors: K Tomita, H Fujima

Gauge: 1,435 mm
Route length: 83.8 km
Electrification: 1.5 kV DC

Finance
In FY95-96, the company posted operating revenues of ¥138.3 billion, a gain of 4.5 per cent from the previous year. Profits grew 0.6 per cent to stand at ¥3.2 billion. The railway's share of turnover was ¥64.4 billion; most of the residue comes from buses, real estate and hotel and leisure operations.

Passenger operations
The railway extends from Shinagawa in Tokyo southward to Yokohama and the Miura peninsula, and exercises through-running over the Asakusa line of the Tokyo metro. The railway recorded some 435.9 million passenger journeys and 6,275 million passenger-km in 1994-95.

In 1993 through services commenced between Keihin Kyuko's Haneda branch line, serving Haneda airport, and central Tokyo via the Asakusa line metro. At present passengers transfer to the newly extended Tokyo Monorail for final access to the airport, pending completion of a planned underground extension of the Haneda line to the new airport terminal building.

The railway owns 738 emu cars. Its track is laid with 50 kg/m rail on 165 mm-thick prestressed concrete sleepers with elastic fastenings, with a minimum curvature of 60 m radius. Maximum axleloading is 13.7 tonnes.

UPDATED

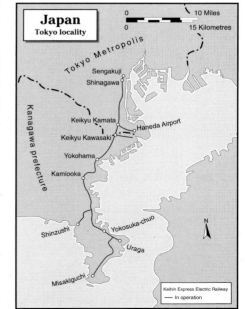

Keihin electric railcars or multiple-units

Class	Cars per unit	Motor cars per unit	Motored axles/car	Output/motor kW	Speed km/h	Cars in service	First built	Builders Mechanical	Electrical
1000	2	2	4	75.9	105	268	1958	K/Tk/S	M/To/Ko
	4	4							
	6	6							
	8	8							
800	3	3	4	100	100	132	1978	K/Tk/S	M/To/Ko
	6	6							
2000	8	6	4	120	105	72	1982	K/Tk/S	M/To/Ko
700	4	2		150	120	84	1967		
1500	6-8	6		150	100/120	166	1988		
	4	2			120/130				
600	8	6				16	1993		

Abbreviations: K: Kawasaki; Ko: Koito; M: Mitusbishi; S: Sumitomo; Tk: Tokyu; To: Toyo Denki Seizo

Keio Teito Electric Railway

Keio Teito Dentetsu
9-1, Sekido 1-chome, Tama City, Tokyo 206
Tel: +81 423 373141

Key personnel
Chairman: K Kuwayama
President: H Nishiyama

Gauge: 1,372 mm; 1,067 mm
Route length: 72 km; 12.8 km
Electrification: 84.8 km at 1.5 kV DC

Organisation
The railway runs northwest from Shibuya in Tokyo and southwest from Shinjuku, exercising through running over the Shinjuku line of the Tokyo metro. The railway, one of 46 companies in the group, generates 64 per cent of the group's income. It operates 833 emu cars, and records some 587.5 million passenger journeys and 6,935.7 million passenger-km annually. New Series 1000 emus with 20 m long cars have been introduced to increase capacity on the narrow-gauge Inokashira line.

UPDATED

VVVF/inverter-controlled Series 1000 narrow-gauge emu   *1997*

Keisei Electric Railway

Keisei Dentetsu
1-10-3 Oshiage 1-chome, Sumida-ku, Tokyo 131
Tel: +81 3 3621 2231

Key personnel
President: Hiroto Senoo

Gauge: 1,435 mm
Route length: 91.6 km
Electrification: 1.5 kV DC

Organisation
The railway stretches eastward from Ueno in Tokyo to Chiba and to the station in the international airport of Narita, to which it operates its 'Skyliner' expresses at half-hour frequency. It has a reciprocal through service with the Asakusa line of the Tokyo metro and with the Chiba Express Electric Railway. Passenger journeys in 1994-95 totalled some 280.4 million, passenger-km 3.860 billion. Rail revenues form 62 per cent of the company's gross, the remainder coming from buses and real estate. The

company has a half-share in Tokyo's Disneyland, but has no rail connection with the site. The railway operates 496 emu cars.

Track
Rail type and weight: 50N 50 kg/m
Crossties (sleepers): Type K2

Thickness: 172 mm
Spacing: In plain track 1,560/km; in curves 1,680/km
Fastenings: Dogspike (double elastic fastening)
Min curvature radius: 160 m
Max gradient: 3.5%
Max axleload: 14.75 tonnes

UPDATED

Keisei electric railcars

Class	Cars per unit	Motored axles/car	Output/motor kW	Speed km/h	First built	Builders Mechanical	Electrical
AE 100	6 Mo 2 Tr				1990	Tk/N	
AE	6 Mo 2 Tr	4	140	120	1972	Tk/N	T/To/M
3600	4 Mo 2 Tr	4	140	120	1981	Tk/N	T/To/M
3500	4 Mo	3	100	120	1972	Tk/N/K	T/To/M
3050	4 Mo	4	75	120	1959	N/Ki/Te	T/To/M
3100	4 Mo	4	75	120	1960	N/Ki/Te	T/To/M
3150	4 Mo	4	75	120	1963	N/Ki/Te	T/To/M
3200	4 Mo/6 Mo	3	100	120	1964	N/Ki/Tk	T/To/M
3300	4 Mo/6 Mo	3	100	120	1968	N/Ki/Te	T/To/M
3700	6 Mo 2 Tr				1991	N	
3400	6 Mo 2 Tr				1993		

Abbreviations: Ki: Kisha; M: Mitsubishi; N: Nippon; T: Toshiba; Te: Teikoku; Tk: Tokyu; To: Toyo
Mo: motor; Tr: trailer

Kinki Nippon Railway

Kinki Nippon Tetsudo (Kintetsu)
6-1-55, Uehommachi, Tennoji-ku 6-chome, Osaka 543
Tel: +81 6 775 3444   Fax: +81 6 775 3468

Key personnel
President: Wa Tashiro
Chairman: Shigeichiro Kanamori

Gauge: 1,435 mm; 1,067 mm; 762 mm
Route length: 404.4 km; 162.4 km; 27.4 km
Electrification: 1.5 kV DC: (394.2 km of 1,435 mm gauge; 159.1 km of 1,067 mm gauge)
750 V DC: (10.2 km of 1,435 mm gauge; 27.4 km of 762 mm gauge)

Organisation
The Kinki Nippon Railway is part of the Kintetsu group of about 150 associated companies, ranging from hotels and construction concerns to bus and taxi companies, and including Japan's largest railway rolling stock manufacturer, Kinki Sharyo.

The Kinki Nippon has the most extensive route-km of any of Japan's private railways and lies third in the table of passenger movement, carrying two million daily. Extending eastward from Namba and Abenobashi termini in Osaka to Kyoto, Nara, Nagoya and Ise Bay, the railway runs limited expresses throughout the Kinki and Tokai areas. Its main line is intercity, running 186 km from

Osaka to Nagoya, and it also serves Nara, Kyoto and the Ise-Shima National Park (136 km from Osaka). A 10.2 km extension, 4.7 km of it in tunnel, was opened from Ikoma to Nagata in 1986; at Nagata it makes a junction with the Osaka metro, over which through service is run to central Osaka.

The railway has its own research laboratory and generates 79 per cent of the income of its parent company.

Passenger operations
In 1995-96 the Kinki Nippon recorded 825 million journeys and 15,251 million passenger-km. It introduced computer-based seat reservation as early as 1960 and has since computerised its timetabling.

Traction and rolling stock
Rolling stock comprises two electric locomotives and 2,071 emu cars, including bilevel and vista-dome vehicles.

The company operates a fleet of luxury six- and eight-car emus known as 'Urban Liner' on its non-stop service between Nagoya and Osaka. These trains were built by Kinki Sharyo.

Recent deliveries include Series 16400 'ACE' two-car sets for the 1,067 mm gauge Minami—Osaka system introduced from June 1996 and the 'Vista Ex', a Series 30000 remodelled with two new intermediate double-deck cars and operated between Vehonmachi (Osaka) and Kashikojima.

Kinki Nippon Railway electric express multiple-units

Class	Cars per unit	Motor cars per unit	Motored axles/car	Output/motor kW	Speed km/h	Cars in service	First built	Builders
21000 (Urban Liner)	6	6	4	125	130	24	1988	Kinki Sharyo
22000 (ACE)	2 4	2 4	4	135	130	96	1992	Kinki Sharyo
2300 (Ise-Shima Liner)	6	4	4	200	130		1994	Kinki Sharyo

UPDATED

Kobe Electric Railway

Kobe Dentetsu
1-1, Daikai-dori 1-chome, Hyogo-ku, Kobe 652
Tel: +81 78 575 2236   Fax: +81 78 577 2467

Key personnel
President: Yasuo Ipponmatsu

Gauge: 1,067 mm
Route length: 64.4 km
Electrification: 1.5 kV DC

Organisation
This Hankyu subsidiary operates to Ao, Sanda and the hot-spring resort of Arima-Onsen via a steeply graded route through the Rokko mountain range north of Kobe. Within Kobe trains operate over 0.4 km of Kobe Rapid Railway tracks to an underground terminus at Shin-Kaichi where interchange is available with Hankyu, Hanshin and Sanyo services. A 5.5 km branch to serve a new town at Kobe-Sanda Garden City was completed in March 1996. Rolling stock comprises one electric locomotive and 167 emu cars. Railway operations represent 68 per cent of the company's revenue.

The Kobe earthquake of January 1995 caused damage estimated at ¥14.9 billion and resulted in the suspension of services between central Kobe and Suzurandai, a distance of 7.5 km, for approximately six months.

UPDATED

Konan Railway

Konan Tetsudo
23-5, Kita-Yanagida, Hommachi, Hiraka-machi, Minami-Tsugaru-gun, Aomori 036-01
Tel: +81 172 44 3136

Key personnel
President: T Tarusawa

Gauge: 1,067 mm
Route length: 36.9 km
Electrification: 30.7 km at 1.5 kV DC

Organisation
The railway operates two unconnected electrified lines and a non-electrified former JNR line in and around Hirosaki, Aomori prefecture. Rolling stock comprises

three electric locomotives, three diesel railcars and 43 emu cars.

UPDATED

Nagoya Railroad

Nagoya Tetsudo (Meitetsu)
1-2-4, Meikei, Nakamura-ku, Nagoya 450
Tel: +81 52 571 2111   Fax: +81 52 581 6060

Key personnel
Chairman: Seitaro Taniguchi
President: Sokichi Minora

Gauge: 1,067 mm
Route length: 539 km
Electrification: 479 km at 1.5 kV DC; 59 km at 600 V DC

Organisation
Between 1941 and 1944 the private urban railways of the Nagoya region were knitted into a coherent regional network by the conversion of city-centre tram tracks into an inter-system connection focused on a new underground Shin-Nagoya station alongside the Japan Rail station. Since then the system has been rationalised by some closures, but new lines have been laid to cater for fresh suburban development, such as the Chita line in 1980. The network includes 59.4 km of 600 V DC tramway and light rail in Gifu prefecture and a 1.2 km monorail line

operating six cars. Besides the Nagoya Railroad, the diversified Meitetsu Corporation also runs bus, taxi, road freight, sea ferry and air-taxi services, hotels, restaurants and travel agencies, but the railway produces 59 per cent of total revenue.

Passenger operations
Shin-Nagoya station handles over 800 trains a day, with 25 trains hourly each way on the main route between Shin Gifu/Inuyama and Toyohashi/Toko-name/Kowa. Reciprocal through-running services operate between the Toyota and Inuyama lines and the Tsurumai line of the Nagoya metro. Electrification was progressively standardised at 1.5 kV DC after the unification of the system, but 600 V DC survives on tramway and light rail lines in Gifu and to the north of that city. Passenger traffic amounted to 399 million journeys a year and over 7.313 billion passenger-km.

Traction and rolling stock
Rolling stock comprises 1,023 emu cars, 42 tramcars, six monorail cars, 16 diesel railbuses, 13 electric locomotives and 28 wagons. The fleet includes three types of distinctively styled limited express units: 'Panorama Car' (introduced 1961); 'Panorama DX' (1984) and 'Panorama

Super' (1988). New stock entering service for the April 1997 timetable revision comprised eight further 1000 Series 'Panorama Cars', 28 cars of the new 3100 Series (two-car emu) and 3700 Series (four-car emu) plus four new 780 Series cars for the 600 V DC system.

Coupler in standard use: Passenger cars: Tightlock automatic; freight cars: automatic
Braking in standard use: Electromagnetic

Track
Rail: 50 kg/m; 37 kg/m
Crossties (sleepers): Prestressed concrete: 200 × 160 × 2,000 mm; wood: 200 × 140 × 2,100 mm
Spacing: 1,640/km
Fastenings: Tie plate, dogspike
Min curvature radius: 160 m
Max gradient: 3.5%

Principal Nagoya Railroad electric railcars or multiple-units

Class	Cars per unit	Motor cars per unit	Motored axles/car	Output/motor kW	Speed km/h	Cars in service	First built	Builders Mechanical	Builders Electrical
1000	4	2	4	150	120	92	1988	N	T
1200	6	4	4	150	120	64	1991	N	T
7000	4	4	4	75	110	106	1961	N	T
7500	6	6	4	75	110	42	1963	N	To
6500	4	2	4	150	110	96	1984	N	T
6800	2	1	4	150	110	78	1987	N	M
3500	4	2	4	170	120	136	1993	N	To

Abbreviations: M: Mitsubishi; N: Nippon; T: Toshiba; To: Toyo

Principal Nagoya Railroad diesel railcars or multiple-units

Class	Cars per unit	Motor cars per unit	Motored axles/car	Power/motor kW	Speed km/h	Cars in service	First built	Mechanical	Builders Engine	Transmission
20	1	1	2	187.5	80	5	1987	Fuji	Nissan	Shinko
30	1	1	2	187.5	80	4	1995	Fuji	Nissan	Niigata
8500	2/3	2/3	2	262.5	120	5	1991	Nippon	NTA-855-R	Niigata

UPDATED

Series 3100 two-car emu introduced in 1997 (Anthony Robins)   *1997*

Nankai Electric Railway

Nankai Denki Tetsudo
1-60 Namba 5-chome, Minami-ku, Osaka 542
Tel: +81 6 644 7120

Key personnel
Chairman: Shigeo Yoshimura
President: Taiji Kawakatsu

Gauge: 1,067 mm
Route length: 171.7 km

Electrification: 157.4 km at 1.5 kV DC; 14.3 km at 600 V DC

Passenger operations
The railway operates 724 emu cars, and in 1995-96 recorded 302.6 million passenger journeys. The main line runs from Namba in Osaka to Wakayama (64.2 km), with five branches, and the Koya line links Osaka with the pilgrimage and resort destination of Koya-San. Reciprocal through-running services operate over the Semboku Rapid Railway, built to serve new town development to

the south of Osaka. The company also operates a 14.3 km 600 V DC line at Wakayama and a 0.8 km funicular. Railway operations represent 63 per cent of the company's revenue.

New lines
A new 8.8 km spur connecting Nankai's main line with the new offshore Kansai International Airport opened in September 1994, with Nankai's 'Rapi:t' airport service operated by new Series 50000 stock. These distinctively styled five-car units have porthole-shaped side windows

Class 87 light axleload locomotives (technically similar to the fleet of Class 37 locomotives in the UK), some of which date back to 1960; these machines are expensive to maintain but equally would be costly to replace. Remanufacture, put at US$28 million, would be some US$12 million cheaper than buying new.

KR's Class 47 shunting locomotives have been receiving new Cummins power packs.

To help alleviate the shortage of motive power, 10 Class 34-400 locomotives were hired from Spoornet in 1994 for an initial period of four years. Similarly, a small number of URC Class 73 diesel-hydraulic locomotives is also on hire.

Type of coupler in standard use: PH/DA

Brake system: Graduated automatic air

Track
Rail: 50, 60, 80 and 95 lb FB
Crossties (sleepers): Steel
Spacing: 1,485/km (1,568/km in curves)
Fastenings: 'K' type (Pandrol)
Max gradient: 3.5%
Max axleload: 18 tonnes

UPDATED

KIRGHIZIA

Kirghiz Railways

Kirghizia Zhelezni Darogy (KZD)
ul L'va Tolstogo 83, 720009 Bishkek
Tel: +7 3312 253054

Gauge: 1,520 mm
Length: 424 km

Political background
This state system emerged from the collapse of the USSR in 1991.

Organisation
The main railway, formerly part of the USSR's Alma-Atinskaya Railway, is a 323 km branch from the Trans-Kazakhstan line to the capital, Bishkek (formerly Frunze),

and its terminus at Issyk Kule (Rybachie) on the shores of Lake Issyk Kule. There are also several short branches in the south linking such cities and towns as Tashkumir, Djalal-Abad, Osh and Kyzylkia with the eastern Uzbekistan system.

Passenger operations
In 1995, there were 30 million passenger-km travelled.

Freight operations
In 1995, there were 2.5 million tonnes travelling for 403 million tonne-km; virtually all freight crosses the border. Major commodities are coal (932,000 tonnes) and petroleum products (862,000 tonnes).

New lines
Japanese interests have studied a proposed Trans-Kirghizia Railway of about 400 km which would give access to coal and non-ferrous ore deposits and link the existing southern and northern lines. However, the high cost of such a mountainous route seems likely to discourage immediate investment.

Freight traffic could benefit from the agreement signed in late 1994 with six other countries promoting the so-called Eurasian Railway route to China via the Alatau Pass.

Traction and rolling stock
The railway is entirely diesel worked. There are 34 main line locomotives of classes 3TE10 and 2TE10, and 23 shunting locomotives of classes TEM2 and ChME3.

The rolling stock fleet comprises 520 coaches (of which 79 were out of use in 1996) and 2,616 wagons (727 not in use).

Class 2TE10 diesel locomotive hauling a passenger train in the Bishkek region   **1997**

UPDATED

KOREA, NORTH

Korean State Railway (ZČi)

Zosun Tchul Zosun Mindzuzui Inminhoagug
Pyongyang

Key personnel
Minister of Railways: Pak Yong Sok

Gauge: Almost entirely 1,435 mm, but some narrow-gauge
Route length: 8,000 km
Electrification: 3,940 km at 3 kV DC

Organisation
Little reliable data is available, but it is known that the railway handles much of the country's freight traffic. Despite the poor economic situation, there are plans for several new routes to strengthen links with neighbouring China and Russian Federation.

Passenger operations
At last report, annual passenger journeys totalled some 35 million, passenger-km 3,400 million.

Freight operations
At last report, freight carryings totalled some 38.5 million tonnes and 9,100 million tonne-km.

New lines
Recent completions include an 80 km railway from Jukchon to Onchon, for more direct access to the port of Nampo, and a 252 km line from Hyesan to Kanggye and Manpo. An 80 km extension of the Onchon—Nampo line to Namdong was expected to open for traffic in 1994.

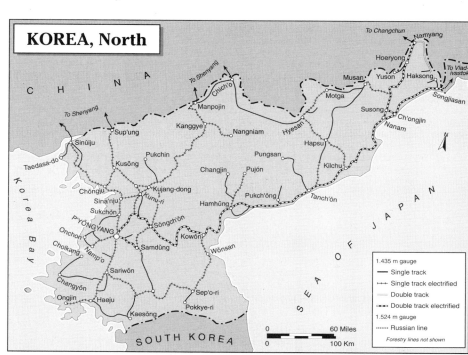

A new double-track route is planned for the Russian Federation border crossing, between Tumangang and Hassan near Rajin.

Improvements to existing lines
The year 1992 was marked by launching of a programme of modernisation of the country's rail infrastructure and

industry. The first sign of action was production of a plan for reconstructing the strategic northern main line parallel to the Chinese border between Haksong and Komusan, on which capacity is to be raised to 50 million tonnes a year. Double-tracking of the 337 km route started in 1993 and is being carried out in two stages.

Traction and rolling stock

No details are known of the numbers of locomotives, coaches and freight wagons, but a fleet of more than 300 electrics is believed to be available. With just over 80 per cent of the network now under wires, 90 per cent of all freight is reported as hauled by electric traction. The latter began with importation of 10 2,030 kW Škoda Bo-Bos similar to the Type E449.0 of CSD, and of some USSR-built locomotives. Since the early 1980s locomotives as well as rolling stock have been produced by the country's Kim Jong Tae factory at Pyongyang. In 1992 this plant was reported to be building bilevel passenger cars.

Local production of rolling stock has been supplemented by delivery of seven French-built 3,600 hp diesel-electric Co-Cos similar to those delivered to Iraq. A first batch of seven was supplemented in 1987 by five more, built by De Dietrich with Alsthom electrical equipment.

In December 1996, six ex-DR Class 220 diesel locomotives built at the Voroshilovgrad locomotive works arrived in North Korea from Germany.

Electrification

In 1992 electrification was reported complete on the Singhung—Hamjiwan stretch of the Lake Pujon line in the northeast; this line is to be wired throughout. By the close of 1992 electrification was completed from Haeju to Ongjin, completing the wiring from Pyongyang to the southwest extremity of the country.

Electrification is continuous throughout the 780 km from Pyongyang northeast to Vladivostok, and through passenger service (involving a bogie change at Tumangang, near Rajin in Korea) between Pyongyang and Moscow was launched in 1987.

Electrification of the link to China via Hoeryong was completed in 1995, and upgrading to carry heavier traffic is in progress. Another partially built cross-border route in the region is being completed to cope with the increasing traffic with China.

UPDATED

KOREA, SOUTH

Ministry of Construction and Transport

1 Joongang-Dong, Kwacheon-shi, Kyungki-Do, 100162 Seoul
Tel: +82 2 504 9024   Fax: +82 2 504 9199

Key personnel
Minister: Choo, Kyung Suk
Vice Minister: Koo, Bohn-Young

UPDATED

Korea High Speed Rail Construction Authority

20th Floor, Kumhwa Building, 949-1 Togok-Dong, Kangnam-Gu, 135270 Seoul
Tel: +82 2 569 3137   Fax: +822 554 8224

Key personnel
President: Kim, Jong-han
Executive Vice President: Yoon, Joo-soo

Political background

KHRC is the government body set up to plan and build high-speed railways, first from Seoul to Pusan and later on other axes.

New lines

In 1989 the country's President announced his support for construction of both the Seoul—Pusan, or Kyongbu, high-speed line and of new electrified lines from Seoul to the east coast at Kangnung and Bukpyong, and from Taejon on the Seoul—Pusan line southwest to Mokpo.

The 431 km Seoul—Pusan line is to be built first and construction work started on the Chonan—Taejon test section in 1992, with a view to completion by the end of 2001. However, by 1997, it appeared that completion of the Seoul—Pusan line would be at least two years after the target date, resulting in cost over-runs due to the extension of the construction period and for other reasons. The project was originally costed at US$13.4 billion at 1993 prices, of which 45 per cent would come from the government with the rest raised through bonds, overseas loans (including suppliers' credits for provision of rolling stock), and private-sector participation.

The performance objective is 300 km/h top speed to achieve a two hour Seoul—Pusan non-stop timing. There will be four intermediate stations. Those at Chonan, Taejon (population 1.2 million), Taegu (population 2.1 million) have been uncontroversial. The fourth, planned for the ancient city of Kyongju (population 1.1 million), ran into problems on environmental grounds; in 1997 a decision was taken to relocate it at nearby Hwachon-ri. This is necessitating replanning the southern section of the line, from Hwachon-ri to Pusan, and this is a prime cause of delays to the high-speed project.

To mollify the city of Ulsan, whose residents will now have to travel further to reach the high-speed station, a promise has been made that the line from Kyongju to Ulsan will be electrified.

The mountainous character of the country will require about 38 per cent of the high-speed route to be in tunnel. Ruling gradient will be generally 1.5 per cent, but could in places be 2.5 per cent, and minimum curve radius will be 7,000 m. Tunnels will be of 100 m² cross-sectional area, and within them distance between track centres will be 5 m.

Track capacity will be 240 movements a day, with trains running at four-minute intervals during peak periods. The prospective rolling stock fleet will total 46 trains, each with 1,000 seating capacity.

French TGV, German ICE and Japanese high-speed technologies keenly contested for the project, and, following an opportunity for all three to lower their bids, GEC Alsthom was selected in 1993 as preferred bidder for the US$2.4 billion contract. In 1997, the contract was being renegotiated in an atmosphere of strained Franco-Korean relations following the French government's cancellation of the sale of Thomson SA to Daewoo Electronics.

For trainsets GEC Alsthom proposed a derivative of the London—Paris—Brussels Eurostar design, with two power cars enclosing 18 trailers; the outer bogies of a set's end-trailers would also be motored. The first completed train was handed over the KHSRCA at a ceremony in France in May 1997, and would undertake 20 months of high-speed tests before being shipped out to Korea. The second train to be completed would be the first to reach Korea, in late 1997. In all 46 trains will be built, with about half the content coming from Korean companies. The first trains should be running on the Seoul—Taejon section at the beginning of 2000.

Associated engineering from other French companies was included in the GEC Alsthom bid. Cegelec will supply

GEC Alsthom completed the first train for the Korean TGV line in May 1997   *1997*

KOREA, South

0   80 Miles
0   120 Kilometres

1.435 m gauge
— Single track
╍ Single track electrified
═ Double track
═ Double track electrified
— Single track freight only
••• High speed line projected or under construction
762 mm gauge
ıɪɪɪ In operation

the catenary and be responsible for its assembly and commissioning, while CSEE Transport will install the TVM 430 track-to-train signalling system, and an automatic train speed control system. About 50 per cent of the equipment will be made in Korea.

Several other high-speed lines are envisaged in the long term, including the Honam (about 270 km from Chonan to Mokpo via Nonsan), the East-West (240 km from Seoul to Kangneung), the Kyongjeon (about 315 km from Kwangju to Pusan), and the East Coast (about 388 km from Kyongju to Kangneung).

NEW ENTRY

Korean National Railroad (KNR)

122, 2ka Pongnae-dong, Chung-ku, Seoul 100-162
Tel: +82 2 392 1322   Fax: +82 2 392 0430

Key personnel
Administrator: Kim, Kyung-hoi
Deputy Administrator: Min, Churk-kee
Directors-General
  Planning and Management: Rhi, Jeong-goo
  Transportation: Kim, Si-won
  Rolling Stock: Kim, Jin-sung
  Engineering: Kwon, Young-dae
  Electrical: Kim, Jeong-koo
  Finance and Accounting: Jung, Yun-sup
Director, International Co-operation: Sim, Kwang-bo

Gauge: 1,435 mm
Route length: 3,101 km
Electrification: 644 km at 25 kV 60 Hz AC; 19.2 km at 1.5 kV DC

Organisation
The backbone of the railway system is the 444 km double-track Kyongbu line, running between the nation's two principal cities, Pusan on the southeast coast and the capital city of Seoul in the northwest. Principal intermediate cities reached by this route include Taegu and Taejon. While it constitutes less than 15 per cent of total route-km, the line accounts for nearly half of the system's operating revenues.

Diverging to the southwest from the Kyongbu line at Taejon, the Honam line reaches into the rich agricultural plain of North and South Cholla provinces and to the important southwestern port of Mokpo. Branching from the Honam line at Iri is the Cholla line, which extends southward to Yosu, an important southern port and the site of a major oil refinery.

Linking these two lines across the south coast with the Kyongbu line near Pusan is the Kyongchon line. The Yongdong line, which links the east coast with the Chungang line at Yongju, extends northward to the major east coast city of Kangnung. KNR's second route to the east coast was completed through the heart of the Taebaek mountain range in 1973.

The solitary 762 mm branch, opened in 1937 from Suweon to Songdo, was closed in 1995.

Total number of staff employed on 31 December 1996 was 35,365.

Passenger operations
Passenger traffic, which has been rising steadily in recent years, is KNR's principal source of income. No less than 64 per cent of South Korea's population lives astride the Seoul—Pusan axis. Both forms of land passenger transport in the corridor are approaching saturation; the motorway is carrying 50 per cent more traffic than its theoretical capacity, and the double-track railway now logs 77 million journeys annually, as well as carrying considerable freight. Train travel is often impossible unless accommodation is reserved several days in advance.

Diesel locomotives

Class	Wheel arrangement	Power kW	Speed km/h	Weight tonnes	No in service	First built	Mechanical	Builders Engine	Transmission
2000	Bo-Bo	596	105	95.5	12	1955	GMC	GMC	E GMC D27
2100	Bo-Bo	746	105	87	28	1961	GMC	GMC	E GMC D75D
3000	Bo-Bo	653	105	75	44	1956	GMC	GMC	E GMC D47B
3100	Bo-Bo	709	105	71	2	1966	Alco	Alco	E Alco GE761
3200	Bo-Bo	653	105	73	34	1966	Alco	GMC	E GMC GE761
4000	Bo-Bo	977	105	78.5	8	1963	GMC	GMC	E GMC D57B1
4100	Bo-Bo	977	105	88.5	10	1966	GMC	GMC	E GMC D77B
4200	Bo-Bo	977	105	88	22	1967	GMC	GMC	E GMC D75B
4300	Bo-Bo	1,119	105	78.5	5	1963	GMC	GMC	E GMC D77B
5000	Co-Co	1,305	105	141	5	1957	GMC	GMC	E GMC D37B
6000	Co-Co	1,343	105	147	3	1963	GMC	GMC	E GMC D57B1
6100	Co-Co	1,343	105	147	2	1966	GMC	GMC	E GMC D77B
6200	Co-Co	1,343	105	132	21	1967	GMC	GMC	E GMC D57B
6300	Co-Co	1,492	105	99	2	1969	GMC	GMC	E GMC D75B
7000	Co-Co	2,238	150	113	15	1986	Hyundai	GMC	E Hyundai D77B
7100	Co-Co	2,238	150	132	87	1975	GMC/Hyundai	GMC	E GMC/Hyundai D77B
7200	Co-Co	2,238	150	132	39	1971	GMC/Hyundai	GMC	E GMC/Hyundai D77B
7300	Co-Co	2,238	150	124	63	1989	Hyundai	GMC	E Hyundai D77B
7500	Co-Co	2,238	105	132	66	1971	GMC/Hyundai	GMC	E GMC/Hyundai D77B

Electric locomotives

KNR series	Wheel arrangement	Output kW	Speed km/h	Weight tonnes	No in service	First built	Builders Mechanical	Electrical
8000	Bo-Bo-Bo	3,900	85	132	90	1972	BN/Alsthom	Alsthom/AEG/ABB
8000	Bo-Bo-Bo	3,900	85	132	4	1986	Daewoo	Daewoo/Woojin

Diesel railcars or multiple-units

Class	Cars per unit	Motor cars per unit	Motored axles/car	Power/car kW	Speed km/h	No in service	First built	Mechanical	Builders Engine	Transmission
DHC	6	2	4	1,469	150	4	1987	Daewoo/Hyundai	MTU 12V396TC13	H Voith L520RU
	8	2	4	1,469	150	51	1988	Daewoo/Hyundai/Hanjin	MTU 16V396TC13	H Voith L520 RZU2
DEC	5	2	4	723	110	2	1980	Daewoo	Cummins KTA 2 300L	
NDC	4	2	4	231	120	9	1984	Daewoo	Cummins NT835R4	H NT855R4 T211R
CDC	3	2	3	231	120	7	1996	Daewoo	Cummins NT835R4	H Voith T211YZ

Electric railcars or multiple-units

Class	Cars per unit	Motor cars per unit	Motored axles/car	Power/motor kW	Speed km/h	Units in service	First built	Builders Mechanical	Electrical
Dual-voltage 25 kV/1.5 kV									
1000	4/10	4/6	4	120	110	70	1974	Hy/D/H	D/Hy/W/C/T/M
2000	10	5	4	200	110	18	1994	Hy/D/H	D/Hy/W/C/T/M
25 kV									
2000	6	3	4	200	110	25	1994	Hy/D/H	D/Hy/W/C/T/M
1.5 kV									
3000	10	5	4	200	110	13	1996	Hy	Hy/M

Abbreviations: C: Chung Gye, D: Daewoo, H: Hanjin, Hy: Hyundai, M: Mitsubishi, T: Toshiba, W: Woojin

Freight operations
Freight traffic has been in gentle decline in recent years, falling from 60 million tonnes in 1993 to 53.5 million in 1996. Freight revenue is little more than a third that derived by KNR from passengers.

Traffic (million)	1994	1995	1996
Freight tonnes	58	57	53.5
Freight tonne-km	14,070	13,838	12,947
Passenger journeys	729	791	820
Passenger-km	28,859	29,335	29,580

Revenue (million US$)	1996
Passenger	1,120
Freight, parcels and mail	465
Other income	449
Total	**2,034**

Expenditure (million US$)	
Staff	838
Materials and services	1,078
Depreciation	183
Total	**2,099**

New lines
For information on the Seoul-Pusan high-speed line see Korea High Speed Rail Construction Authority entry.

Improvements to existing lines
KNR is working on a 10-year upgrading of the 199 km Cholla line between Iri and Yosu. Realignment to eliminate the most severe curvature will cut journey time

Push-pull trainset powered by MTU 16V396 diesel engine   *1997*

by 45 minutes, and with other works will raise capacity from 27 to 53 trains daily.

Expansion of the Seoul metro is being complemented by major works on KNR, where suburban traffic is growing by up to 12 per cent annually. In 1994 KNR opened the 18.5 km Bundang line linking with Line 3 of the metro at Suso, and another Line 3 connection, the 21 km Ilsan line, opened in January 1996.

Doubling and electrification is under way between Kuro in southwestern Seoul and Inchon to relieve saturation on this suburban route. It was due to be finished in 1997; capacity would be doubled to 576 trains daily.

Traction and rolling stock
At the end of 1996 the fleet comprised 1 steam, 488 diesel and 94 electric locomotives, 1,168 emu cars, 502 dmu cars and nine single-unit diesel railcars. Other passenger stock in operation totalled 2,117 locomotive-hauled cars, including 88 dining and 17 sleeping cars, and there were 14,048 wagons.

Recent orders include nine 2,200 kW Co-Co diesel-electrics ordered from Hyundai in 1996 following on from earlier orders for 55 of this type; 238 emu cars ordered from Hyundai in 1995; 250 emu cars ordered from Hyundai in 1996; and 34 dmu cars ordered from Daewoo in 1996. In 1996, 76 hauled coaches were ordered from Hanjin and 470 freight wagons from Hyundai.

Signalling and telecommunications
On the Seoul—Pusan trunk, CTC (centralised traffic control) is installed throughout the 403 km from Pusan to the periphery of the Seoul suburban electric system at Suweon. CTC is also installed over the heavily used Seoul—Chechon line and throughout the Seoul suburban area. In total, 857 route-km are so controlled.

At the end of 1996, two resignalling schemes were under way: centralised traffic control was being installed on the 126.9 km between Chechon and Choram, while automatic block signalling was being installed on the 129.5 km between Yongju and Choram.

Electrification
Electrification in progress at the beginning of 1997 amounted to 126.3 km being electrified on the 25 kV 60 Hz AC.

Track
Main lines are mostly laid with 50 kg/m rail, but since 1981 KNR has laid continuously welded 60 kg/m rail to heavily trafficked sections and 180 route-km is now installed. Some secondary lines have 50 kg/m rail, others 37 kg/m. Sleepers on main lines are now mostly of locally manufactured concrete, with Pandrol fastenings securing long-welded rail. On branch lines, timber sleepers prevail.

Rail: flat-bottom 37, 50 and 60 kg/m
Crossties/sleepers
Material: Wooden or prestressed concrete ties
Dimensions
Common tie: 15 × 24 × 250 cm;
Switch tie: 15 × 25 × 280-460 cm or 23 × 23 × 250-300 cm
Total number installed
in plain track: 1,700 per km
in curves: 1,700 or a few more per km
Fastenings type
Wooden tie: elastic fastening type
PC tie: Pandroll fastening type
Min curvation radius: 200 m
Max gradient: 3.5% (3°)
Max permissible axleload: 25 tonnes

Rolling stock technical data
Type of coupler in standard use: passenger cars — tight lock type; freight cars — Shibada (E-Type)
Type of braking in standard use, locomotive-hauled stock: air brake

UPDATED

LAOS

Ministry of Transport

Vientiane

Key personnel
Spokesman: Songkane Luangmuninthorne

New lines
Laos has been without railway lines until now, but a rail

link is to be laid across the recently completed Friendship Bridge across the Mekong river, which is the border with Thailand (see Thailand entry for details). A 20 km line is now under construction linking Vientiane, the Laotian capital, with the bridge; it is due to open in late 1998. The line is being funded by a joint venture of the Shaviriya Group of Thailand (75 per cent) and the Laotian government (25 per cent). The company will have a 60-year operating concession, property development and

telecommunications rights along the route and tax breaks on the first 18 years of operating revenues.

Under discussion by the joint venture partners are construction of a west-east new line from Vientiane to the Vietnamese capital Hanoi, and a line striking northwards from Vientiane to the Chinese border.

NEW ENTRY

LATVIA

Ministry of Transport

Gogola iela 3, Riga LV-1743
Tel: +371 7 226922   Fax: +371 7 217180

Key personnel
Minister: A Gutmanis
Director, Railway Transport: Janis Petersons
Deputy Director, Railway Transport: J Mukans

UPDATED

Latvian Railway

Latvijas Dzelzcels (LDZ)
Gogola iela 3, Riga LV-1547
Tel: +371 2 234449   Fax: +371 7 820231/229556

Key personnel
Director-General: Andris Zorgevics
First Deputy Director-General: Stanislav Baiko
Deputy Director-General: Rihards Peders
Directors
Commercial: Janis Racko
Technical: Janis Vevers
Financial: Igor Nikolayev
Personnel: Edgars Elksnis
Economic: Vladimir Gryaznov
Technical Inspection: Arijs Sinats
Infrastructure: Mikhail Yagodkin
Rolling Stock: Janis Petersons
Real Estate: Andris Burtnieks
Department Heads
Passenger: Vasily Khristin
Operating: Mikhail Mikhailov
Locomotives: Vitolds Kulins

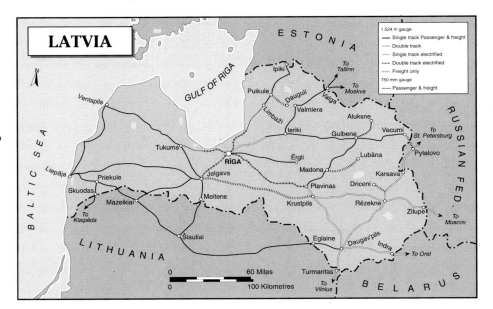

Rolling Stock: Sergei Cherkovsky
Permanent Way: Vladimir Yunovich
Electrotechnical: Pavel Lapchinsky
Legal: Valdi Vismanis
Scientific and Technical Centre: Gennady Burak
Computer Centre: Valentins Vevers
Stores: Nikolai Vasilyev
External Relations: Valery Turko

Gauge: 1,520 mm; 750 mm
Route length: 2,380 km; 33.2 km
Electrification: 270.7 km of 1,520 mm gauge at 3 kV DC

Political background
The rail system of this Baltic state became legally established in August 1991 and started independent operations in January 1992 with a workforce of around 24,000; by December 1996, the number of employees was down to 19,000.

LDZ has been struggling to adapt to a market economy, with the background of an overall economy which has been taking longer to adapt than those of the former Comecon countries of central Europe. In 1995, Latvia was also outperformed by the other Baltic states, Estonia and Lithuania, due to a severe crisis in the Latvian banking sector which prompted a 1.6 per cent fall in gross domestic product (GDP). In 1995, the Baltic states' GDP was over 50 per cent below the 1989 level.

In November 1995 the government invited expressions of interest in the privatisation of the Riga Carriage-building Works (RVR) — once by far the biggest supplier of emu vehicles in the USSR. Also, two passenger operating companies have been created. However, there have been no moves so far to follow neighbouring Estonia by seeking complete privatisation of the railway system.

Finance
The railways made a loss of some 18 million lats on passenger traffic in 1994 and were able to collect only about half the revenue due on freight traffic as of early 1995. Such losses are causing the withdrawal of services, bus substitution and reductions in train frequency and size. Tariff increases have been frequent. Riga suburban ticket prices were raised by 75 per cent in January 1996, and similar rises were to follow in other cities.

Passenger operations
International services link Riga, the Latvian capital, with Russia: among others, there are two overnight services to Moscow (the 'Latvia Express' and the 'Jurmala') and one to St Petersburg (the 'Baltiya'). the overnight service to Kaliningrad (the Russian enclave on the Baltic coast) has been reintroduced. Vilnius in Lithuania is served by one night and three day trains. Since 1993 the 'Baltic Express' has connected Latvia with Warsaw and Western Europe.

The main domestic lines link the capital Riga with Daugavpils, 217 km away in the southeast of the country, and Ventspils, a major port 207 km away. Suburban lines around Riga are operated by 3 kV emus.

Passenger traffic has declined steeply since 1991 from over 130 million passenger journeys annually to little more than 35 million in 1996, as a result of changed travel patterns and the rise of private sector buses; in 1994 some 187 million passengers were carried by bus.

Freight operations
The decline of heavy industry since the break-up of the Soviet Union and the rise of road-based freight transport have seen freight tonnages on LDZ decline from around 50 million tonnes annually two decades ago to 28.8 million tonnes in 1995, although volumes recovered somewhat in 1996 to reach 35.3 million tonnes. Over 20 million tonnes of that was international transit traffic, including block ammonia, potash and container trains. Domestically, construction materials, timber and grain are the most important commodities.

Improvements to existing lines
In June 1995 LDZ signed up to Baltrail-2000, aiming to upgrade its trunk routes to Estonia and Lithuania as part of a Scandinavia—Germany rail corridor; the Council of Europe is sponsoring the project, provided that the cost does not exceed ECU500 million.

Reconstruction of Riga station was scheduled to begin in 1997. A Norwegian group, Varner-Halzow Invest, plans to develop a US$6 million commercial and shopping centre complex there. The renovation of Liepaja, Jelgava, Daugavpils, Rezekne and Ventspils stations was also planned. The rail network of Ventspils port is to be developed if funding can be found.

Traction and rolling stock
Outside the Riga suburban system, trains are diesel hauled. The decline in traffic has prompted withdrawal of older locomotives, with all remaining steam locomotives scrapped or sent to museums and many diesel locomotives taken out of service.

At the start of 1997 the broad-gauge fleet comprised 300 diesel locomotives, 26 dmu sets and 37 emu sets. There were 391 passenger coaches (including five buffet, 17 dining, 165 sleeper and 163 couchette cars) and 9,755 freight wagons (1,629 box wagons, 1,795 gondolas, 627 cement hoppers, 1,096 flat wagons, 1,833 tank wagons, 232 container flats, 499 special flats, 993 grain-carrying box wagons, 451 refrigerated wagons, 600 other). No new stock was on order but new lightweight multiple units were being developed for LDZ at RVR.

Some emus have been exchanged with LG of Lithuania with the aim of achieving standardised fleets on the two railways. No electrification work is in progress.

Signalling and telecommunications
Automatic block signalling has increased from 522 km of LDZ's network in 1994 to 1,081.2 km; the 'Neva' centralised traffic control (CTC) system now covers

Class ER2 suburban emu at Riga main station (Michal Málek) **1997**

Class M62 diesel-electric locomotive in freight service in the Riga area (Michal Málek) **1997**

Diesel railcars or multiple-units

Class	Cars per unit	Motor cars per unit	Motored axles/car	Power/motor kW	Speed km/h	No in service	First built	Mechanical	Builders Engine	Transmission
DR1A	3/6	1	2	756	120	8	1973	Riga	Zvezda	H Kalugamash
DR1P	3/6	1	2	756	120	38	1973	Riga	Zvezda	H Kalugamash

Diesel locomotives

Class	Wheel arrangement	Power kW	Speed km/h	Weight tonnes	No in service	First built	Mechanical	Builders Engine	Transmission
1,520 mm gauge									
TEP60	Co-Co	2,206	160	126	17	1960	Kolomna	11D45	E Kharkov
2TEP60	2 × Co-Co	2 × 2,206	160	2 × 126	8	1960	Kolomna	11D45	E Kharkov
TEP70	Co-Co	2,942	160	129	24	1981	Kolomna	2A-5049	E Kharkov
2TE10M	2 × Co-Co	2 × 2,206	100	2 × 138	10	1981	Lugansk	10D100	E Kharkov
2TE10U	2 × Co-Co	2 × 2,206	100	2 × 138	14	1990	Lugansk	14D40	E Kharkov
2M62	2 × Co-Co	2 × 1,471	100	2 × 120	78	1976	Lugansk	14D40	E Kharkov
2M62U	2 × Co-Co	2 × 1,471	100	2 × 126	30	1988	Lugansk	14D40	E Kharkov
M62	Co-Co	1,471	100	118.5	40	1965	Lugansk	14D40	E Kharkov
ChME3	Co-Co	993	95	123	66	1964	Bryansk		E Czech
TEM2	Co-Co	882	100	120	3	1976	Bryansk	PD1M	E Czech
TGM3	Bo-Bo	550	30	68	3	1959	Murom	M753B	H Murom
TGM23	C	294	30	44	2	1973	Murom	1D12	H Murom
750 mm gauge									
TU2	—	—	—	—	3	1973	Kambarka	—	H Kaluga
TU7	Bo-Bo	294	50	24	2	1972	Kambarka	1D12	H Kaluga

Electric railcars or multiple-units

Class	Cars per unit	Motor cars per unit	Motored axles/car	Output/motor kW	Speed km/h	Units in service	First built	Mechanical	Builders Electrical
ER2	4/6	2/3	4	200	130	31	1962	Riga	Riga
ER2T	6	3	4	435	130	6	1988	Riga	Riga

400 km, the 'Minsk' CTC 81 km and the semi-automatic block system 1,115.4 km.

In 1997, resignalling schemes under way were Gulbene-Ranka (34 km, semi-automatic block), Krace-Pupoli (12 km, upgrading Neva CTC) and Zasulauks-Priedaine (13 km, upgrading coded block).

Track
Rails: 75, 65, 50, 43 kg/m; 65 kg/m is the most common, covering 1,534 km
Sleepers: Wood (2,750 x 180 x 250 mm), concrete (2,700 x 300 x 219 mm)
Spacing: 1,840/km in plain track, 2,000/km on curves
Fastenings: Soviet screw types: KB, KD, D-2
Min curve radius: 200 m

Max gradient: 1.5%
Max axleloading: 23.5 tonnes

Traffic	1994	1995	1996
Freight tonnes (000)	27,796	28,840	35,264
Freight tonne-km (million)	9,520	9,757	12,413
Passenger journeys (000)	55,669	44,532	35,140
Passenger-km (million)	1,794	1,373	1,182

Finance (000 lats)
Revenue

	1994	1995	1996
Passengers, baggage and mail	12,155	15,147	NA
Freight parcels	55,822	58,156	NA

	1994	1995	1996
Other income	1,486	1,369	NA
Total	69,463	74,672	NA

Expenditure

	1994	1995	1996
Staff/personnel	19,417	22,591	—
Materials and services	42,232	39,827	69,988*
Depreciation	7,001	12,370	12,318
Total	68,650	74,788	82,306

*includes staff and personnel costs for 1996

UPDATED

LEBANON

Chemins de Fer de l'Etat Libanais (CEL)

Transport en commun de Beyrouth et de sa Banlieue (CEL/TCB)
PO Box 109, Beirut
Tel: +961 447007

Key personnel
President: R Ammache
Director-General: Dr E Choueiri
Chief of Traffic and Operation: N Borgi
Chief of Traction: H Koudayes
Chief of Track and Structures: Sayed Aouad
Chief of Finance: B Raad
Chief of Stores: B Abdallah
Chief of Personnel: R Chedid

Gauge: 1,435 mm
Route length: 222 km

Organisation
The hostilities that ravaged the country during the 1980s affected the railway very severely and major parts of the system became unusable. The only service now operative is a short suburban service in Beirut operated with railbuses.

UPDATED

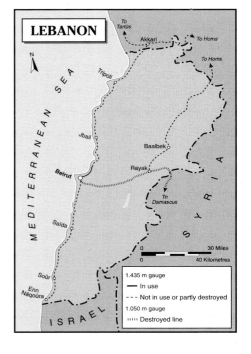

LIBERIA

There are three railways in Liberia, all originally constructed for iron ore transport. After several years of civil war, there is no report that any of the three are in operation.
VERIFIED

Bong Mining Company

PO Box 538, Monrovia

Gauge: 1,435 mm
Length: 78 km

At the start of the 1990s, before the onset of civil war, annual freight traffic grossed 6.7 million tonnes and 860 million tonne-km.

VERIFIED

Lamco Railroad

Roberts International Airport

Gauge: 1,435 mm
Route length: 267 km

Organisation
Lamco, the Liberian American-Swedish Minerals Company, is an iron ore mining company which mined at Nimba and Tokadeh. The railway served principally to move ore, latterly amounting to some 6.5 million tonnes annually, from these mines to the deep water port in Buchanan. There were 24 diesel-electric locomotives and 545 wagons. Operations ceased in 1989.

VERIFIED

National Iron Ore Company Ltd

PO Box 548, Monrovia

Gauge: 1,067 mm
Length: 145 km

Organisation
The railway was opened in 1951. It operated 12 diesel locomotives, 253 ore and 28 other wagons. Annual traffic before the civil war totalled approximately 1 million tonnes.

VERIFIED

LIBYA

Department of Communications

PO Box 14527, Bab Ben Ghashir, Tripoli
Tel: +218 21 49932   Fax: +218 21 40106

Key personnel
Director-General: Izz Al-din Al-Hinshiri
Director, Railways: Eng Alaeddin Al Weyfati

Political background
With the dismantling of the British projection of 1,435 mm gauge from Egypt to Tobruk laid in the Second World War, no railways have run in Libya since 1965. Also discarded is the 950 mm system built around Tripoli and Benghazi on the eve of the First World War.

The present government, however, has ambitions to build a new 1,435 mm gauge system from the Tunisian frontier to Tripoli and Misratah, then inland to Sebha, the country's third city, in the heart of a mineral-resource area. In 1983 an agreement was signed for Chinese construction of the line for 170 km from Ras Jedir, on the

Expenditure	1995	1996
Staff/personnel	986,157	972,937
Materials and services	1,597,690	2,007,415
Depreciation	364,886	361,437
Total	2,948,733	3,341,789

Passenger operations
The most important routes run south from the capital Skopje to Gevgelija (206 km) on the Belgrade—Thessaloniki—Athens route (three pairs of trains a day) and Bitola (229 km, six trains a day).

Traffic (million)	1995	1996
Passenger journeys	1.073	1.550
Passenger-km	65.59	119.87
Freight tonnes	1.590	1.554
Freight tonne-km	168.74	263.69

New lines
The main line through Macedonia runs from the Greek border in the south to the Yugoslav border in the north. A new east—west line is under construction in the north of the country to complement this north—south line. This route, 56 km in length, will run from Kumanovo to the Bulgarian border. It is eventually intended to form part of an Adriatic to Black Sea through link, from Durrës in Albania to Burgas in Bulgaria; in Macedonia, this will require construction of another new line from Kičevo to the Albanian border.

Traction and rolling stock
At the end of 1995 MŽ was operating 13 electric and 54 diesel locomotives, four electric and 16 diesel multiple-units, and five diesel railcars. Coaching stock amounted to 138 passenger cars, 18 sleeping cars and 21 couchette cars; there were 2,431 freight wagons.

Type of coupler in standard use: U-85t

Signalling and telecommunications
Automatic block signalling is being installed on 55 km from Dubrovo to Gevgelija; it is already in place on a further 200 km. Centralised traffic control is being installed on 247 km from Tabanovci to Gevgelija.

Track
Rail: 30-54 kg/m; 49 kg/m rail is the most common, being installed on 483 km
Sleepers: Wooden (1,030,900 installed), concrete (6,300), metal (16,500)
Sleeper spacing: 1,660 per km, in plain and curved track
Fastening type: K system
Minimum curve radius: 250 m
Max gradient: 2.6%
Max permissible axleload: 22.5 tonnes

UPDATED

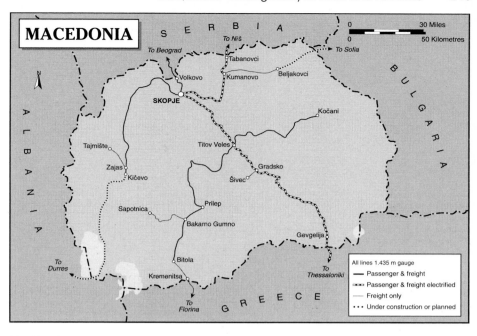

MACEDONIA

All lines 1.435 m gauge
— Passenger & freight
═══ Passenger & freight electrified
— Freight only
••• Under construction or planned

Diesel locomotives

Class	Wheel arrangement	Power kW	Speed km/h	Weight tonnes	No in service	First built	Builders Mechanical	Builders Engine	Transmission
661	Co-Co	1,434	124	108	29	1961	GM	GM	E EMD
643	Bo-Bo	680	80	65	3	1967	B & L	MGO	E B & L
643	Bo-Bo	606	80	63	8	1961	Duro Daković	MGO	E Končar
734	C-C	440	60	48	8	1960	MAK	Maybach GT06	H Voith
732	C-C	397	60	43.5	4	1965	Duro Daković	Jenbacher 600	H Voith
667	Co-Co	882	100	120	2	1981	BMZ SSSR	BMZ	E BMZ SSSR

Electric locomotives

Class	Wheel arrangement	Output kW continuous/ one hour	Speed km/h	Weight tonnes	No in service	First built	Builders Mechanical	Builders Electrical
441	Bo-Bo	3,400/4,080	120/140	78/82	8	1973	ASEA/Končar	ASEA/Končar
461	Co-Co	5,100/5,400	120	120	5	1978	Electroputere	Electroputere

Diesel railcars and multiple-units

Class	Cars per unit	Motor cars per unit	Motored axles/car	Power/motor kW	Speed km/h	Units in service	First built	Builders Mechanical	Builders Engine	Transmission
712	3	1	4	103	120	16	1975	MACOSA/ Duro Daković	MAN	H Voith

Electric railcars and multiple-units

Class	Cars per unit	Motor cars per unit	Motored axles/car	Output/motor kW	Speed km/h	Units in service	First built	Builders Mechanical	Builders Electrical
412	4	2	4	170	120	4	1980	Riga	Riga

MADAGASCAR

Ministry of Transport & Meteorology

PO Box 4139, Anosy, Antananarivo
Tel: +261 2 24604   Fax: +261 2 24001

Key personnel
Minister: Aimé Rakotondrainibe

VERIFIED

Société d'État Réseau National des Chemins de Fer Malagasy (RNCFM)

PO Box 259, 1 Avenue de l'Indépendance, Antananarivo 101
Tel: +261 2 20521   Fax: +261 22288

Key personnel
Director-General: R Andriantsoavina

Director of Finance: J C Rajemialisoa
Director of Technical Services: J P Andriantsilavo
Heads of Department
  Human Resources: E Rakotomavo
  Transport: M Rakotomanga
  Studies: J C Rafanomezantsoa
  Engineering: J Rakotondrainibe
  Finance and Accounting: J C Randrianarivelo
  Manpower: S Rakotondravao
  Track and Infrastructure: A B Rabarijoely
  Toamasina Region: P Razafimahatratra
  Timber Impregnation: E Randriantsilany
  Quarry Production: M Rakotomalala
  Inspection: C E Ramaroson

Gauge: 1,000 mm
Route length: 883 km

Organisation
The system lies mostly in the central-eastern region of the country. Its northern system comprises three main lines: the TCE (Antananarivo—Eastern Coast) 380 km, connecting Antananarivo in the inland with the port of Tamatave; the MLA (Moramanga—Ambatosoratra), connected to the TCE, which runs between Moramanga and Lake Alaotra, the rice-producing region (180 km); and the TA (Antananarivo—Antsirabé) serving the far southern region of Antananarivo (154 km).

The southern system consists of one main line, the FCE (Fianarantsoa—Eastern Coast). This 163 km route serves the Fianarantsoa semi-industrial region from Manakara harbour.

Political background
Since 1982, the railway has been established as a state-owned society operating under the country's laws governing limited companies, which allow some independence in commercial policy-making.

Neglect of the infrastructure has left the railway poorly equipped, and there is no foreign exchange available for essential spare parts. Election of a new government on a liberalisation ticket in 1993 led to moves to open railway operations to private contractors, and in 1996 US consultant Hickling Transcom was assisting the government in awarding concessions to operate the northern network.

Passenger operations

Passenger traffic has declined since 1989 from already insubstantial levels on account of the poor state of the national economy. In 1992 passenger journeys, at 1 million, were less than half their 1990 level, and there was a further substantial drop to 0.7 million in 1993.

Freight operations

Freight tonnage, which had dipped below the half-million mark for the first time in 1992, reached 506,000 tonnes in 1993. Provisional figures for 1994 showed ever poorer results.

Rice production was being developed at the northern end of the MLA. In the rainy season road traffic is severely handicapped, so a 35 km rail extension from Ambatosoratra around Lake Alaotra to Imerimandroso was built in 1986, to facilitate shipment of rice from the territory.

The busiest line is that from Antananarivo to Toamasina, which bears about 85 per cent of RNCFM's traffic but which is now in competition with a recently completed macadamised road and its encouragement of higher capacity road freight vehicles. Freight traffic includes a rising component of containers; a terminal at the Indian Ocean port of Toamasina has been complemented by one on the outskirts of Antananarivo at Soanierana.

New lines

In the south of the country the mountainous territory has extraordinarily rich and very diverse mineral deposits. RNCFM has built a 27 km extension of the TA to a new cement works 1,800 m above sea level in the Ibity mountain massif. The previous government had ordered a feasibility study of an extension of almost 900 km from Antsirabé and Ibity south to Tuléar, through almost uninhabited terrain, to exploit the barely tapped mineral resources of the area. At last report, 10 km of new line was in place as far as Vinaninkarena. An 8 km stretch of the projected Imerimandroso route is in place to Ambohidava but no work is believed to have taken place on either project since 1987.

Signalling and telecommunications

With World Bank aid under the Third Railway Project, the MLA line has been equipped with a radio telecommunications system that should greatly improve the efficiency of traffic control and train use in the chrome ore export flow to Toamasina, and in rice movement.

Traction and rolling stock

At the start of 1994 the railway was operating 19 diesel

Principal diesel locomotives

Class	Wheel arrangement	Power kW	Speed km/h	Weight tonnes	No in service	First built	Builders Mechanical	Builders Engine	Transmission
BB 220	Bo-Bo	1,200	70	58	18	1973	Alsthom/SACM	UD 30 V12R5	E
BB 250	Bo-Bo	1,600	70	64	5	1986	Alsthom/SACM	UD 30 V16R5	E

Diesel railcars

Class	Cars per unit	Motor cars per unit	Motored axles/car	Power/car kW	Speed km/h	No in service	First built	Builders Mechanical	Builders Engine	Transmission
ZE 800	3	1	2	500	70	3	1958	De Dietrich	MGO V8	E Alsthom
ZE 700	4	1	2	900	70	1	1983	Soulé	MGO V12	E Alsthom

Alsthom-built BB250 Class diesel locomotive at Toamasina depot (Marcel Vleugels)   **1996**

locomotives, three diesel railcars, 40 passenger coaches and 644 freight wagons.

Type of coupler in standard use: Freight cars, Willison automatic, Madagascar type; passenger cars, De Dietrich, Soulé

Type of brake in standard use, locomotive-hauled stock: Automatic air; direct air; and vacuum

Track
Rails: S25, 26, 30, 36, 30 US, 30 East, 37 English
Sleepers: Wood 1,920 × 220 × 150 mm; steel 1,900 × 294 × 147 mm

Spacing: 1,666/km wood; 1,500/km steel
Fastenings: Screw (wood sleepers); frog (steel sleepers)
Min curvature radius: 80 m
Max gradient: 3.5%
Max axleload: 20 tonnes

Traffic	1994-95	1995-96
Freight tonnes	473,249	254,264
Freight tonne-km (million)	78.340	43.431
Passenger-km (million)	21.272	18.048
Passenger journeys	536,624	338,942

VERIFIED

MALAWI

Ministry of Transport and Civil Aviation

Private Bag 322, Capital City, Lilongwe 3
Tel: +265 730122   Fax: +265 733826

Key personnel
Minister: Harry Thomson
Principal Secretary: J L Kalemera   ***UPDATED***

Malawi Railways (1994) Ltd

PO Box 5144, Limbe
Tel: +265 640844   Fax: +265 640683

Key personnel
Chairman: Dean Lungu
General Manager: E R Limbe
Assistant General Managers
   H T Thindwa, K S J Chenjerani, J A Kazembe
Chief Accountant: M Ndenya
Company Secretary: Vacant
Chief Marketing Manager: T Nnensa
Chief Traffic Manager: M F Mlenga
Chief Mechanical Engineer: H Chimwaza
Chief Engineer (Telecoms and Electrical): M F Kuntiya
Supplies Manager: H P Nyasalu

Gauge: 1,067 mm
Route length: 763 km

Passenger train on MR   **1996**

Diesel locomotives

Wheel arrangement	Power kW	Speed km/h	Weight tonnes	No in service	First built	Builders Mechanical	Builders Engine	Transmission
Co-Co	1,120	116	86	13	1980	Bombardier	Alco 8-251-E	E Canada GE
0-6-0	380	56	43.5	5	1993	CMI	Cummins KTA 19L	H Twin Disc

Organisation

A single-track line runs from Mchinji near the Zambian border through Lilongwe and Blantyre to the southern border with Mozambique. This line connects with the Mozambique port of Beira. A line from Nkaya to Nayuci on the eastern border with Mozambique connects with the port of Nacala.

Following restructuring passenger and cargo services on Lake Malawi are now run by a separate company, Malawi Lake Services. These connect with the rail system at Chipoka at the south end of the water.

A major restructuring of the railway was carried out in 1995 under the auspices of the World Bank, and in 1996 the Malawi government invited consultants to advise of strategies for possible privatisation. During 1997, the Hickling Transcom consultancy was undertaking a study of the feasibility of privatisation; it was due to be finished in August 1997.

Improvements to existing lines

Rehabilitation of the Nkaya—Nayuci line to the border of Mozambique (44 km) is going ahead following agreement in mid-1995 of World Bank and USAID credits totalling US$28.6 million. Of the total, US$9.53 million is being spent on track rehabilitation, which includes bridge and structure strengthening, points and crossing work, production of 17,000 sleepers, rental of a track tamper and purchase of gang and inspection trolleys.

Traction and rolling stock

The locomotive fleet at the start of 1997 comprised 13 main line diesel-electrics (all now refurbished under a USAID programme), one diesel-hydraulic unit for light traffic, and four diesel-hydraulic shunters. The five diesel hydraulics were supplied in 1993 by Cockerill Mechanical Industries of Belgium. The rolling stock fleet consisted of 400 freight wagons, 47 engineering service wagons, 29 passenger coaches and one special coach, and 10 diesel railcars.

Type of coupler in standard use: AAR 10 Automatic profile

Type of brake in standard use: Vacuum

Track

Standard rail: BSR 30 kg/m, length 12.2 m; BSA 30 kg/m, length 48.8 m; BSA 40 kg/m, length 48.8 m and cwr

Sleepers: Timber, steel and concrete

	Spacing in plain track	Spacing in curved track
Timber	1,310/km	1,476/km
Steel (30 kg)	1,310/km	1,476/km
Concrete	1,460/km	1,640/km

Fastenings: Pandrol clips on concrete sleepers, clip and steel key, elastic rail spikes

Min curve radius: 111 m

Max gradient: 2.27%

Max axleload: 15 tonnes (old track) 18 tonnes (new track)

Traffic (000)	1994-95	1995-96
Freight tonnes	473	254
Freight tonne-km	78,340	43,431
Passenger journeys	537	339
Passenger-km	21,272	18,048

Finance (MK 000)	1994-95	1995-96
Revenue		
Passengers	4,209	4,424
Freight	50,362	43,851
Miscellaneous	78,283	10,856
Total	132,854	59,131

Expenditure	1994-95	1995-96
Staff/personnel	78,939	19,791
Materials and services	100,199	15,671
Depreciation	6,199	17,422
Financial charges	7,912	3,378
Total	193,249	56,262

MR's most modern motive power is a fleet of five diesel-hydraulic shunters from Cockerill Mechanical Industries of Belgium

1996

UPDATED

MALAYSIA

Ministry of Transport

Wisma Perdana, Tingkat 3-9, Jalan Dungun, 50616 Kuala Lumpur

Tel: +60 3 254 8122   Fax: +60 3 255 7041

Key personnel

Minister: Dato'Seri Dr Ling Liong Sik
Secretary-General: Othman Rijal

VERIFIED

Malayan Railway (KTMB)

Keretapi Tanah Melayu Berhad
Jalan Sultan Hishamuddin, 50621 Kuala Lumpur
Tel: +60 3 274 9422   Fax: +60 3 272 3936

Key personnel

Executive Chairman: Tan Sri C Selvarajah
Managing Director: Abdul Rahim Osman
Directors
  Operations and Customer Service: Mohd Zin Yusop
  Special Projects: P Satyamoorthy
  Finance: K Sinnappu
  Corporate Services: Dr Ismail Rejab
  Human Resources: Md Fauzi Hj Said
  Engineering: Haji Mazlan Waad
General Managers
  Permanent Way: Z A Salleh
  Fleet Engineering: Madzin Majid
  Signalling and Communications: R Paranchothi
  Human Resources (Services): Abdul Mokti Zakaria
  Safety Operations: S Apputhurai
  Corporate Communications: Hamdan Ahammu
  Training and Development: K Sudharmin
  Traffic Operations: Sarbini Tijan
  Electrification: Dzulkifli Mohd Ali
  Freight Services: Abd Radzek Abd Malek

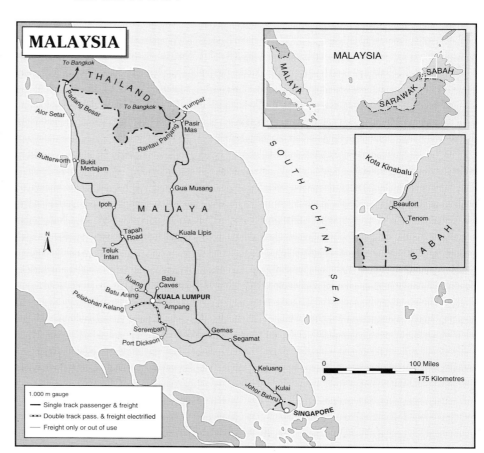

Passenger Services: Zainab Hashim
Commuter Services: Azhar Darus

Property Management: Mahmud Hashim
Corporate Planning: Hilmi Mohamad

Information Technology: Shafiin Yunus
Finance: Azman Ahmad Shaharbi
Operation Safety: S Apputharai
Company Secretary: Nor Aida Othman

Gauge: 1,000 mm
Route length: 1,798 km
Electrification: 148 km at 25 kV 50 Hz AC

Political background

The government has long been seeking to privatise KTM. A new Railway Asset Corporation takes interim responsibility for all railway infrastructure and facilities, while KTM acts as the operator of rail service. Government financial support continues, both for capital works and some unremunerative services, but KTM bears the costs of rolling stock and infrastructure maintenance. Rolling stock maintenance is now in the hands of a private-sector company, Rail Tech Industries, in which KTM has a 26 per cent holding.

Organisation

The railway's prime route is the 787 km main line from Singapore north through the capital, Kuala Lumpur, to Butterworth, one of Malaysia's principal sea ports on the west coast of the peninsula. Short branches reach sea ports at Port Klang, Pasir Gudang and Port Dickson. The other major route is the 528 km East Coast line running northwards from a junction with the Singapore—Butterworth line at Gemas to Kota Bharu and Tumpat. Both lines link with the State Railway of Thailand.

Passenger operations

KTM operates both electric commuter services around the capital, Kuala Lumpur, and long-distance trains.

Long-distance travel soared spectacularly in the 20 years to 1991, lifting the total of annual passenger-km from 620 million to 1,850 million; thereafter patronage began to fall. Following opening of the North-South Expressway (NSE) road in 1994, passenger-km declined to 1,348 million; in 1995, there was a further fall, to 1,270 million.

The stiff competition focused attention on the long-term need to reduce journey times between Kuala Lumpur and Singapore. This will be achieved by the introduction of tilting trains, which were ordered in November 1996 from Fiat Ferroviaria of Italy.

In addition to ordinary train services, KTM operates day and night Singapore—Kuala Lumpur and Kuala Lumpur—Butterworth express trains, and a single daily express between Gemas and Tumpat on the East Coast line. In conjunction with the State Railway of Thailand, KTM runs a daily International Express between Butterworth and Bangkok. All express and night trains on the north-south main line are air conditioned.

Orient-Express Hotels of the UK, operators of the Venice Simplon-Orient Express in Europe, runs a weekly luxury cruise train service, the Eastern & Oriental Express, between Singapore, Kuala Lumpur and Bangkok.

Traffic	1993	1994	1995
Passenger journeys (000)	-	-	-
Passenger-km (million)	1,763	1,348	1,270
Freight tonnes (000)	—	5.2	5.2
Freight tonne-km (million)	—	1,463	1,416

Freight operations

Traffic has remained stable in recent years. Cement is one of the most important commodities carried.

In 1997, Bradford Kendal of Australia was building 500 wagons for KTM, with axles coming from SWASAP in South Africa.

KTM has developed in-house and begun to implement a computerised rolling stock control known as SPOT.

Intermodal operations

Container traffic is a fast-growing business. Begun in 1974, this has become KTM's second biggest freight earner, surpassed only by cement, traditionally KTM's major freight traffic. A significant component of the growth has been containers from southern Thailand, which have a quicker haul across the border at Padang Besar to a Malaysian port than to Bangkok. Around a quarter of southern Thailand's rubber exports are shipped through Butterworth. The government is promoting intermodal transport, and KTM has formed a wholly owned subsidiary, the Multimodal Freight Company, which has acquired 20 highway tractors and 100 trailers so as to offer door-to-door-service. This operates from the inland container depots at Kuala Lumpur, Ipoh, Prai, Port Klang and Padang Besar.

KTM diesel locomotives

Class	Wheel arrangement	Power kW	Speed km/h	Weight tonnes	No in service	First built	Mechanical	Builders Engine	Transmission
17	C	305	56	35.6	10	1964	KSK	GM 12V-71	H Niigata
18	0-6-0	450	24	46.25	10	1979	Brush	MTU 6V 396 TC 12	E Brush
19	Bo-Bo	480	78	58.4	10	1983	Hitachi	MTU 6V 396 TC 12	E Hitachi
22	Co-Co	1,275	96.5	84	38	1979	EE-AEI	EE8CSVT-MK 111	E EE
23	Co-Co	1,610	110	90	15	1983	Hitachi	SEMT/ SP12 PA4V	E Hitachi
24	Co-Co	1,790	120	90	26	1987	Toshiba	SEMT/16V-PA4	E Toshiba
25	C-C	1,120	107	89.6	12	1990	GM	EMD 8-645E 3C	E GM

Electric railcars or multiple-units

Class	Cars per unit	Motor cars per unit	Motored axles/car	Output/motor kW	Speed km/h	Units in service	First built	Builders Mechanical	Electrical
EMU	3	2	4	190	120	18	1994	Jenbacher	Holec

Electric trains are now serving suburban Kuala Lumpur   **1995**

Improvement and expansion of rolling stock is one of KTM's current priorities. A further 1,000 TEU of flatcar capacity was added in 1995-96, bringing the total to 3,200 TEU. Structures are being modified to gain clearance for 9 ft 6 in cube containers. A major bridge study was commissioned in 1992 with a view to strengthening structures for a lift of maximum permissible axleloads from 16 to 20 tonnes.

New lines

A line to the new Kuala Lumpur International Airport is proposed.

Improvements to existing lines

The 785 km Butterworth—Kuala Lumpur—Singapore line is to be upgraded for the introduction of tilting trains. In 1997 KTM was due to select a consortium to undertake the work, which will involve doubling the track, resignalling and electrification of the route. Sasib (electrification and signalling) and Impregilo (civil works) of Italy in consortium with local partner Diversified Resources Berhad were bidding against a Japanese group led by Mitsui. The aim is a 4 hour Singapore—Kuala Lumpur timing.

Traction and rolling stock

In 1995 KTM's traction fleet comprised 114 diesel locomotives. The passenger stock totalled 345, including 25 buffet/dining and 37 sleeping/couchette cars, plus 18 three-car emu trains. Freight stock totalled 4,325 vehicles.

For the Butterworth—Kuala Lumpur—Singapore line improvement project (see 'Improvements to existing lines' section above) in November 1996 KTM ordered seven tilting trains of six cars each from Fiat Ferroviaria of Italy, with an option for a further 15 trains. The trains on option could have as many as 10 cars. The first trains are due to be in service in 1999.

To supplement the 18 emus supplied by Hunslet Transportation Projects/Jenbacher, two further batches of 22 sets each were ordered in late 1995 from Mitsubishi/Hyundai and GEC Alsthom/Union Carriage for delivery by early 1997.

Motive power shortages have been alleviated by delivery of 30 Indian Railways' Class YDM4 Co-Cos, hired

on a power-by-the-hour basis from Ircon which is also maintaining the locos with its own staff. There are also four MKA-2000 Co-Cos remanufactured and regauged by Morrison Knudsen Australia; they are English Electric units surplus to Australian National's requirements in Tasmania which in 1995 were leased to the Malaysian firm Rail Tech Services for use by KTM as required. MKA retains another three such locomotives which are available to be sent to Malaysia if needed.

Coupler in standard use: Hook and knuckle. Hook couplers are being progressively replaced by the automatic knuckle-type on all wagons; this should permit increases of up to 50 per cent in gross freight train weights.

Braking in standard use: Air and vacuum

Signalling and telecommunications

KTM is modernising signalling and communications on the south main line between Seremban and Johor Baru. Route relay interlockings at stations and automatic block signalling, when completed, will have the entire distance from Singapore to Ipoh controlled by colour light signals.

Electrification

Operation of the country's first electric trains started in 1995 with commissioning of the Kuala Lumpur suburban network. With 25,000 passengers daily being recorded within six months, capacity of the 18 three-car emus very quickly became strained, and a further 44 sets were ordered (see 'Traction and rolling stock' section for details).

Completion of the scheme saw the launch of an air conditioned commuter emu service on the routes from Kuala Lumpur to Port Klang, Seremban and Rawang. The new emus have cut Kuala Lumpur—Port Klang journey time from 70 to 30 minutes and Kuala Lumpur—Seremban time from 90 to 45 minutes. Especially within the Klang Valley area operating capacity for freight as well as passenger traffic is markedly improved.

The main line from Butterworth to Singapore via Kuala Lumpur is now being electrified. As a preliminary, the first 60 km of the route from Singapore to Kulai will be

Hitachi-built Class 23 locomotive hauling bulk cement　　　**1996**

energised in a separate project to create an electrified network around the city of Johor Baru in the far south of the country. This was due to be running by 1998.

Track
Standard rail: Flat bottom in 12.2 m (40 ft) lengths
Main line: 40 and 60 kg/m
Rail fastening: Elastic spikes
Crossties (sleepers): Malayan hardwoods 242 × 127 × 2,000 mm
Spacing: 1,666/km
Filling: 6 cm (2½ in) limestone ballast to a depth of 15 cm (6 in) under sleepers
Max curvature: 12.25° = radius of 142 m
Ruling gradient: 1%; except Taiping Pass 1.25%
Longest continuous gradient: 8.2 km on Prai—Singapore main line, with 1.25% grade, sharpest curve 142 m radius for a length of 320 m
Max altitude: 137 m near Taiping
Max axleload: 16 tons

UPDATED

Sabah Ministry of Transport and Communications

88999 Kota Kinabalu, Sabah
Fax: +60 88 239852

Key personnel
Minister: W M Bumburing
Assistant Secretary, Railways: H Gunggut

VERIFIED

Sabah State Railways

Jabatan Keretapi Negeri Sabah
Karung Berkunci 2047, 88200 Kota Kinabalu, Sabah
Tel: +60 88 54611　Fax: +60 88 236395

Key personnel
General Manager: M T Jaafar

Gauge: 1,000 mm
Route length: 134 km

Organisation
The railway links Tanjong Aru with Beaufort, running along the coastal strip before climbing inland along the Padas river to Tenom.

Freight and passenger operations
In 1992 the railway carried 0.4 million passengers and some 2.2 million tonnes of freight, mainly rice, rubber and timber products.

There is a daily return mixed train and several short workings by ancient diesel railcars.

Traction and rolling stock
In 1992 the fleet comprised 15 diesel locomotives, 21 coaches, 3 diesel railcars and 215 wagons.

VERIFIED

MALI

Ministry of Public Works and Transport

PO Box 260, rue Baba Diarra, Bamako
Tel: +223 225967/8　Fax: +223 228388

Key personnel
Minister: Mohammed Ag Erlaf
Director of Cabinet: M Sidibe
Technical Adviser, Railways: M Traore

VERIFIED

Chemins de Fer du Mali (RCFM)

PO Box 260, rue Baba Diarra, Bamako
Tel: +223 225968　Fax: +223 225967

Key personnel
Director-General: Lassana Kone
Deputy Director-General: Hamadoun Assouman Cisse
Directors
　Traffic: Daouda Diane
　Finance: Djibril Nama Keita

Technical: Tounko Danioko
Planning: Mady Konate
Purchasing: Mohamed Traore
Personnel: Fodé Traore

Gauge: 1,000 mm
Route length: 641 km

Organisation
The former Dakar—Niger Railway starts at Dakar in Senegal and runs inland via Kayes to the River Niger. The present CF du Mali is that portion of the line inside its territory, the remainder being the CF du Sénégal. A new line linking Bamako, capital of Mali, with Conakry, capital of Guinea, is planned to give Mali an alternative outlet to the Atlantic with a route length of 800 km, of which 600 km will be in Guinea.

Passenger operations
In 1994, the Senegal—Mali railway recorded 346 million passenger-km (figure excludes traffic domestic to Mali only).

Freight operations
In 1994, the Senegal—Mali railway recorded 752 million

tonne-km of freight (figure excludes traffic domestic to Mali only).

Recovery of a major international traffic role is a prime management objective and this has been recognised in the railway's contract with the government. The latter has proclaimed RCFM to be its main means for spurring development in the west of the country.

In 1992 a new freight terminal, including container transhipment facilities, was opened at Korofina, 6 km east of the capital, Bamako.

Traction and rolling stock
RCFM owns 30 line-haul diesel locomotives, two diesel shunters, four diesel-electric railcars, 19 trailers, 19 passenger coaches and 545 freight wagons. The locomotive fleet includes 11 Alsthom Type BB1100, 12 GM Canada CC2200 and seven Alsthom CC2400 machines.

In common with RCFS of Senegal (qv), RCFM has recently acquired and adapted for metre-gauge 20 redundant French Railways Type B10t passenger cars of the 'Bruhat' type.

UPDATED

MAURITANIA

Ministry of Transport

Centre Administratif, Nouakchott

Key personnel
Minister: S M Deina

NEW ENTRY

Mauritanian National Railways (TFM-SNIM)

PO Box 42, Nouadhibou
Tel: +222 2 45174　Fax: +222 2 45396

Key personnel
Minister of Mining and Industry: N'Gaide Lamine

Director-General: Mohamed Saleck Ould Heyine
Director of Railway and Port:
　Mohamed Khalifa Ould Beyah
Head of Rolling Stock: Mohamed El Moctar
Head of Permanent Way:
　Dah Ould Mohamed Mahmoud

Gauge: 1,435 mm
Route length: 704 km

Organisation

The line, completed in 1963, runs from Nouadhibou to Tazadit for the transport of iron ore from the mines at F'Derik. Built and originally operated by Miferma, the line was nationalised in 1974 and is now operated by Société Nationale Industrielle et Minière (SNIM).

Freight operations

Principal traffic is iron ore, carried in trainloads of 230 wagons grossing around 23,000 tonnes and hauled by three or four locomotives. Three return trips are made daily. Passenger traffic, carried on a daily service between Nouadhibou and Zouerate, is negligible.

Traffic (million)	1993	1994	1995
Freight tonnes	9.2	11.4	11.3
Freight tonne-km	1,480	2,280	2,230

Traction and rolling stock

Equipment at the beginning of 1997 consisted of 31 main line diesel-electric locomotives, eight shunting diesel-electrics of 635 kW, 1,200 freight wagons and eight passenger coaches. General Motors delivered a batch of five SDL40-2 locomotives in 1997.

Signalling and telecomunications

Operations are controlled by manual dispatching with HF and VHF radio.

Track

Standard rail: 54 kg/m UIC
Welded joints: Practically the whole line was laid with long-welded rails; 8 × 18 m railbars were flash-butt welded at the depot into 144 m lengths, which after laying were Thermit welded into continuous rail. Longest individual length of welded rail is 80 km

Diesel line-haul locomotives

Wheel arrangement	Power kW	Speed km/h	Weight tonnes	No in service	First built	Mechanical	Builders Engine	Transmission
Co-Co	1,865	60	138	10	1961	Alsthom	SACM MGO V16 BSHR	E Alsthom
Co-Co	2,460	60	145	10	1982	EMD	EMD 645 E3	E EMD
Bo-Bo	630	70	73	8	1961	B&L	SACM MGO V12 ASHR	E B&L
Co-Co	2,240	60	145	6	1994	EMD	EMD	E EMD
Co-Co	2,240	60	145	5	1997	EMD	EMD	E EMD

Crossties (sleepers): Type U28 steel and timber, weight 75 kg
Spacing: 600 mm
Rail fastening: Clips and bolts to metal sleepers, Nabla ties to timber sleepers
Max curvature: 1.75° = min radius of 1,000 m
Max gradient: 0.63% against loaded trains
1.3% against empty trains
Max altitude: 400 m
Max axleload: 26 tonnes
Max speed: Loaded trains 50 km/h; empty 60 km/h
Type of signalling: Radio control

UPDATED

MEXICO

Secretariat of Communications & Transport

Avenida Universidad y Xola, Col Narvarte, 03028 Mexico City 12, DF
Tel: +52 5 519 7456/9203   Fax: +52 5 519 0692

Key personnel

Secretary: Carlos Ruiz Sacristán
Under-Secretary: Aaron Dychter

Organisation

Overseeing the privatisation of the state railway industry is the Railway System Restructuring Committee, which is chaired by Carlos Ruiz Sacristán. The committee forms part of the overall Inter-Ministerial Divestiture Commission, tasked with disposing of state assets. Representatives from both Mexican railways and the government sit on the committee, with CS First Boston and Banca Serfin active as financial advisors and Mercer Management Consulting co-opted as primary consultant. These private sector organisations have been valuing assets, overseeing the bidding process and facilitating due diligence financial investigations.

UPDATED

Ferrocarril del Noreste

Transportación Ferroviaria Mexicana SA de CV
Av de La Cúspide No 4829, Col Parquest del Pedregal, Mexico, DF, CP 14010
Tel: +52 5 447 5879/447 5836   Fax: +52 5 447 5830

Key personnel

Chief Executive Officer: Chris Aadnesen
General Director: Mario Mohar

Gauge: 1,435 mm
Route length: 3,928 km

For map see Kansas City Southern entry in US section

Political background

On 29 November 1996, three consortia were shortlisted for the 50-year concession on offer for the North East network of FNM (qv), with the award eventually going to a joint venture known as Transportación Ferroviaria Mexicana (TFM) on 5 December 1996. TFM, which assumed control of the railway on 31 January 1997, consists of the Mexican multimodal transport company, Transportaciónes Marítimas Mexicanas (49 per cent), and the US firm Kansas City Southern Industries (51 per cent). It won control of the North East network after having agreed to pay US$1.4 billion. The high level of the bid caused much surprise, being almost three times higher than that of two rival bidders. Financing of the deal almost fell apart, but the Mexican government agreed to help by injecting $200 million in the form of a bridge equity stake, in addition to retaining a 20 per cent interest in the line.

The North East network, serving the US border crossings at Nuevo Laredo and Matamoros and the ports of Veracruz, Tampico and Lázaro Cárdenas, generated some 14 billion tonne-km and peso 1.02 billion of revenue in 1994 and accounts for 40 per cent of Mexico's rail freight movements. The port of Veracruz is an extremely important traffic generator in its own right, handling around a quarter of all maritime cargo.

A total of US$700 million of investment is promised for the first five years of the concession, of which US$200 million was due to be spent in 1997. This is needed for new locomotives, rolling stock and communications systems required to meet projected traffic figures, part of which will be derived from developing intermodal traffic. An 18 to 20 per cent return on investment is being predicted by the new owners.

The company has announced its intention to separate its data centre from that of FNM, with either Monterrey or Mexico City put forward as a possible site. However, the SICOTRA traffic monitoring system (see 'Signalling and telecommunications' section in FNM entry) will be adopted by the company.

NEW ENTRY

Ferrocarril Pacifico Norte

US office
10 Eddy Street, Alamogordo, New Mexico 8831
Tel: +1 915 534 3732   Fax: +1 915 534 3740

Key personnel

Director: Xavier García de Quevedo

Gauge: 1,435 mm
Route length: 6,524 km

Political background

In June 1997, Grupo Ferroviario Mexicano was awarded the second 50-year concession to be offered by the government in its railway privatisation programme, for the Pacific North network. GFM is made up of mining concern

Grupo México, with a 74 per cent stake, Constructoras ICA, part of Mexico's biggest construction group, with 13 per cent, and Union Pacific of the US, with 13 per cent.

Although several other groups expressed interest, in the end GFM was the only bidder for the Pacific North network. It bid peso 4.2 billion (US$528 million) for the system, which exceeded the government's minimum price. The government has agreed to sell 100 per cent of the system despite its original intention to retain a 20 per cent stake.

GFM agreed to invest peso 3.4 billion in the network. Priorities would be upgrading of track and purchase of new locomotives and rolling stock. Some of the 6,000-strong workforce would be made redundant.

Ferrocarril Pacifico Norte comprises routes from Mexico City to Nogales and Mexicali via Guadalajara, to Ciudad Juárez via Torreón, and from Torreón to Piedras Negras, Monterrey and Tampico. In 1994, under FNM ownership, the network generated some 17.2 billion tonne-km of freight and peso 1.23 billion of revenue.

NEW ENTRY

National Railways of Mexico (FNM)

Ferrocarriles Nacionales de México
Avenida Jesús Garcia Corona 140, Col Buenavista, Delegación Cuauhtémoc, 06358 Mexico City, DF
Tel: +52 5 547 9458   Fax: +52 5 547 0623

Key personnel

Director General: Luis de Pablo Serna
Assistant Directors General
    Finance: Juan José Huerta Coria
    Planning and Restructuring: Emilio Sacristan Roy
    Operations: Romualdo Ruiz Castro
    Human Resources and Labour Relations:
    Miguel Angel Pino de la Rosa
Comptroller General: Horacio Medecigo Pérez
Executive Co-ordinator, Marketing and Services:
    Sergio Saggiante García
Executive Co-ordinator, Materials:
    Olga Rosa Romero Ruano
Manager, Public Relations: Miguel Tirado Rasso
Regional Directors
    Valley of Mexico: Carlos Carmona Garduño
    South East: Lorenzo Reyes Retana
    North-Pacific: Francisco J Gorostiza Pérez
    Chihuahua-Pacific: Francisco J Zamarripa Mora

Gauge: 1,435 mm; 914 mm
Route length: 20,506 km; 90 km
Electrification: 246 km at 25 kV 60 Hz

Political background

Legislation for FNM privatisation was passed in 1995 as part of a programme to inject some US$12 billion of foreign capital into the economy following the devaluation of the Mexican peso. The process gathered momentum in November 1995 when potential bidders for 50-year concessions to operate freight services were invited to register their interest. The Mexican government was to retain ownership of railway infrastructure, with concessionaires responsible for maintenance and future investment. FNM rolling stock was to be divided between the concessions, with the new operators free to set their own staff requirements and meet them from any source. The government was to continue to meet the costs of some 55,000 FNM pensions and the company's accumulated debt of US$400 million, as well as retaining responsibility for redundancy payments to FNM employees displaced by privatisation.

Privatisation structure
For the purposes of privatisation, the FNM network has been divided into three regional systems, a terminal company serving the Valley of Mexico (greater Mexico City) area and a series of short lines. The regional systems and the Mexico City terminal operation came into being as FNM divisions on 1 January 1996; a fifth division covered the largest short line, the 1,510 km Chihuahua-Pacific network connecting Topolobampo on the Gulf of California with the US border at Ciudad Juárez and Ojinaga.

FNM's principal routes, which carried over 90 per cent of its total freight traffic in 1994, formed the basis of the three regional systems radiating from Mexico City.

The North East network (3,960 km), serving the US border crossings at Nuevo Laredo and Matamoros and the ports of Veracruz, Tampico and Lázaro Cárdenas, generated some 14 billion tonne-km and peso 1.02 billion of revenue in 1994. This network has now been sold and trades as the Ferrocarril del Noreste (qv).

The North-Pacific network (6,200 km) generated some 17.2 billion tonne-km and peso 1.23 billion of revenue in 1994, comprising routes from Mexico City to Nogales and Mexicali via Guadalajara, to Ciudad Juárez via Torreón, and from Torreón to Piedras Negras, Monterrey and Tampico. This network has now been sold and trades as the Ferrocarril Pacifico Norte (qv).

Some 3.2 billion tonne-km and peso 0.27 billion of revenue were generated in 1994 by the South East network (2,200 km), linking Mexico City with Veracruz, Coatzacoalcos, Salina Cruz, Campeche and Mérida.

In addition to the Chihuahua-Pacific network, short line concessions were to be offered for six routes/clusters: Nogales—Nacozari; Escalón—Ciudad Frontera; Durango—Torreón/Felipe Pescador; Mexico City—Cuernavaca/Puebla; routes in Yucatán east of Mérida; and the line from Ixtepec to the Guatemalan border. In 1994 these routes and the Mexico City terminal operation generated 2.9 billion tonne-km on 8,000 km of track. It was anticipated that the concessionaires of the three major regional systems would each receive a 15 per cent stake in the terminal company.

In 1997, IXE Banco SA was appointed to oversee the sell-off of branches as short lines. Registrations of interest were to be submitted by May for the isolated Tejuana—Tecate branch (71 km) in the northeast, the 320 km Nacozaria short line and the 973 km route crossing the states of Coahuila, Durango, Chihuahua and Zatecas. GFM, the owner of the Pacific North concession, was showing interest in bidding.

Marginal routes excluded from the short line and regional concessions were thought likely to close. FNM's government-subsidised passenger operations faced drastic cutbacks, with service maintained on only those routes where no other means of transport exist. FNM's passenger services cover only 20 per cent of their costs from ticket revenue, with 85 per cent of journeys confined to secondary routes where rail fares are 40 per cent cheaper than the buses; passengers are amongst the poorest section of society. In November 1995 it was suggested that concessions for remaining passenger services would be let after those for freight operations, with concessions awarded to bidders requiring the smallest amount of government subsidy. In early 1997, there was little interest from potential concessionaires in running these services.

An FNM subsidiary company has been set up to run the national railways fibre-optic communications network. This includes the SICOTRA computerised train control system currently being installed. It is thought the concessionaires will buy into this system, although this will not be obligatory.

Privatisation progress
The first concession to be offered was that for the Chihuahua-Pacific short line network and a total of 35 parties had shown interest by the deadline of 10 June 1996. It was reported that the government was expecting minimum bids of the order of US$40 million; in the event a sole bid of US$28 million was received and the sale collapsed. It was eventually decided to re-offer the line, minus the 571 km La Junta—Ciudad Juárez branch, as an option with the Pacifico Norte railway. GFM was awarded this as part of its 50-year concession for that system (see below).

The first main line system was sold to a US-backed consortium in December 1996 and now trades as the Ferrocarril del Noreste (qv).

The Pacifico Norte railway was awarded to the GFM consortium in June 1997 and the Sureste was expected to be in private hands by year end, with FNM to be officially wound up in 1998.

Finance

FNM's planned investment programme for 1996 totalled peso 1.185 billion. Workshops and repair facilities were to receive peso 696.43 million and peso 239.42 million was to be spent on major track improvements. Other minor items of projected expenditure concerned track maintenance machinery, bridges and structures, electrification and signalling.

Finance (peso million)

Operating revenue	1994	1995
Passengers	101.7	138.7
Freight	2,840	4,075
Other	104.4	121
Total	3,047	4,335

Operating expenditure	1994	1995
Staff	2,720	3,413
Materials and services	888.9	1,025
Depreciation	864.4	1,378
Other	737.4	1,457
Total	5,211	7,274

Traffic (million)	1993	1994	1995
Freight tonnes	50.4	52	52.4
Freight tonne-km	35,672	37,314	37,243
Passenger journeys	10.9	7.1	6.6
Passenger-km	3,219	1,855	1,800

Passenger operations

FNM is reckoned to command as little as 1 per cent of the national travel market, and passenger traffic has experienced steady decline since 1983, when 25.6 million passenger journeys and 5,997 million passenger-km were recorded. This trend became more pronounced as passenger and mixed train services were trimmed under an economy programme initiated in the early 1990s. FNM mixed trains accounted for 894 million tonne-km and 2,671 million train-km in 1993.

Freight operations

FNM freight traffic has enjoyed a period of steady growth since 1991 when 46.4 million tonnes were carried and

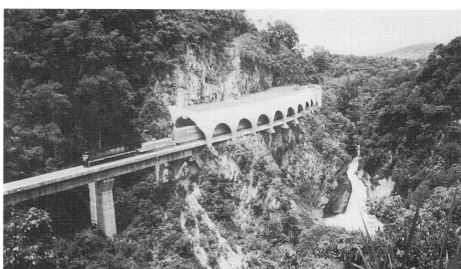

Double-stack container train at Atoyac on the upgraded section of the Mexico City—Veracruz route **1995**

32,698 million tonne-km recorded. In decline between 1984 and 1991, freight traffic grew by 5 per cent in 1992 and 3.4 per cent in 1993. FNM is reckoned to have captured some 13 per cent of the Mexican transport market.

Principal commodities carried include agricultural produce (especially maize, sorghum and wheat), coal, iron ore, petrochemicals, limestone, cement and paper products, concentrated in recent years into block trains. With the aim of lifting maximum trainloads to 5,600 tonnes on some routes, FNM was adopting the Locotrol system of mid-train 'slave' locomotive control. A drastic reduction of the points at which less-than-wagonload freight is handled has been carried out.

International traffic

In 1992, the governments of the United States, Canada and Mexico passed legislation creating the North American Free Trade Area (NAFTA), which came into effect at the beginning of 1994. One of the direct results of the act was to ease cross-border restrictions on road freight vehicles, effectively eradicating the considerable advantages that rail previously enjoyed. This led to dramatic changes in the relationship between the various railway companies in all three countries, with North American involvement in Mexico growing stronger by the day.

The Mexican government has been keen to promote agreements between FNM and both US and Canadian railways for expansion of international unit freight train operation. International freight traffic on FNM grew by 19 per cent in 1992 to reach 17.186 million tonnes, 35 per cent of FNM's total freight traffic. Imports accounted for 13.348 million tonnes, and exports 3.838 million tonnes. Growth of 4.7 per cent was recorded in 1993 with international traffic totalling 17.995 million tonnes (again 35 per cent of total freight traffic). Imports accounted for 13.194 million tonnes, and exports 4.801 million tonnes.

The devaluation of the Mexican peso in January 1995 had serious consequences for the established trade patterns between the NAFTA partners. In April 1995 it was reported that imports into Mexico from the USA and Canada had declined dramatically, with exports of Mexican goods in the reverse direction growing rapidly. As Mexican imports had previously outweighed Mexican exports, this led to an immediate drop in overall cross-border freight volumes and a reduction in freight rates as freight equipment was now running empty southbound.

Automotive business

NAFTA and the opening of Mexican manufacturing facilities by foreign car manufacturers provided a major boost to FNM's automotive business, which in 1993 grew by 30 per cent to reach 1.537 million tonnes. FNM carried 472,000 motor vehicles for export (82 per cent of the market) in 1993, traffic which grew by 600 per cent in the first six months of 1994. By the start of 1996, terminals for automotive (and some intermodal) traffic were being operated by General Motors at Ramos Arizpe and Silao; Ford at Cuautitlán and Hermosillo; Chrysler at Toluca and La Encantada; Nissan at Aguascalientes; and VW at Puebla.

Intermodal operations

NAFTA has especially boosted intermodal traffic on FNM, as US railroads have established through services to Mexico and private companies have become involved in the financing and operation of intermodal terminals. Intermodal services are operated using wagons and containers owned by other railways and shipping

FNM diesel locomotives

Builder's type	Wheel arrangement	Power kW	Speed km/h	Weight tonnes	No in service	First built	Builders Mechanical	Builders Engine	Transmission
S7C30MP	Co-Co	2,250	104	164	34	1994	GE	GE	E GE
S7C30N	Co-Co	2,250	104	164	98	1990	GE	GE	E GE
S7C30R	Co-Co	2,250	104	164	97	1989	GE	GE	E GE
C30-7	Co-Co	2,250	104	169	296	1979	GE	GE	E GE
C36-7	Co-Co	2,700	104	164	25	1979	GE	GE	E GE
U36C	Co-Co	2,250	104	164	17	1973	GE	GE	E GE
B23-7	Bo-Bo	1,680	104	115	79	1980	GE	GE	E GE
U23B	Bo-Bo	1,680	104	112	10	1975	GE	GE	E GE
U18B	Bo-Bo	1,350	104	–	16	1974	GE	GE	E GE
SD40-2	Co-Co	2,250	104	167	179	1972	EMD	EMD	E EMD
SD40	Co-Co	2,250	104	164	61	1968	EMD	EMD	E EMD
SD45	Co-Co	2,700	104	164	1	1978	EMD	EMD	E EMD
GP40-2	Bo-Bo	2,250	104	120	40	1975	EMD	EMD	E EMD
GP40	Bo-Bo	2,250	104	120	5	1967	EMD	EMD	E EMD
GP38-2	Bo-Bo	1,500	104	113	143	1964	EMD	EMD	E EMD
MP15DC	Bo-Bo	1,120	104	112	25	1983	EMD	EMD	E EMD
SW1504	Bo-Bo	1,120	104	100	60	1973	EMD	EMD	E EMD
GP9	Bo-Bo	1,310	104	–	1	1958	EMD	EMD	E EMD
G12	Bo-Bo	980	104	–	30	1956	EMD	EMD	E EMD
GP18	Bo-Bo	1,350	104	–	1	1961	EMD	EMD	E EMD
M424	Bo-Bo	1,800	104	116	60	1980	MLW	Alco	E GE
M630	Co-Co	2,250	104	172	33	1972	MLW	Alco	E GE
C628	Co-Co	2,060	104	156	20	1966	Alco	Alco	E GE
C424	Bo-Bo	1,800	104	117	2	1964	Alco	Alco	E GE
RSD12	Co-Co	1,350	104	155	34	1958	Alco	Alco	E GE
RS11	Bo-Bo	1,350	104	–	18	1958	Alco	Alco	E GE
C420	Bo-Bo	1,500	104	–	1	1966	Alco	Alco	E GE
S6	Bo-Bo	675	104	–	2	1955	Alco	Alco	E GE
DL420	Bo-Bo	1,500	104	–	1	1978	MLW	Alco	E GE
AP1620A	Co-Co	1,500	104	–	8	1979	MLW	Alco	E GE
M420TR	Bo-Bo	1,500	104	124	6	1975	MLW	Alco	E GE
BX620	Co-Co	1,500	104	147	9	1980	MLW	Alco	E GE
M636	Co-Co	2,700	104	191	5	1973	MLW	Alco	E GE

companies. A total of 2.225 million tonnes of intermodal traffic and 36,908 TEU were carried in 1994, and 2.067 million tonnes and 149,050 TEU carried in 1995.

Infrastructure improvements to enable double-stack container trains to operate between Mexico City and the port of Veracruz on the Gulf of Mexico were completed in September 1994. Similar improvements on the route between Mexico City and the Pacific port of Manzanillo were due for completion in 1996. At the start of 1996, FNM was operating regular container services for TMM between Veracruz and Pantaco (Mexico City); Lázaro Cárdenas and Pantaco, Hibueras and Altamira; and Manzanillo and Pantaco, Hermosillo, Guadalajara, Aguascalientes and Miramar. Regular Lázaro Cárdenas–Pantaco services were also being operated for Navemar, with Manzanillo–Pantaco and Guadalajara–Manzanillo services provided for Sea Land/Trafimar and American President Lines.

International services

At the start of 1996, FNM was operating regular intermodal services for American President Lines between Pantaco and Nuevo Laredo (six times a week in each direction), Piedras Negras (four times a week southbound) and Ciudad Juárez (once a week in each direction). A weekly return service from Piedras Negras to Rojas was also in operation. For US railways Southern Pacific and Burlington Northern Santa Fe, FNM was operating a total of four services a week in each direction between Pantaco and Ciudad Juárez.

Through intermodal services between the US and Mexico were launched in 1990 with two double-stack container services from Long Beach, California, to Pantaco. In addition to a Southern Pacific service, FNM combined with Santa Fe and Rail-Bridge Corporation (a subsidiary of the maritime company K Line) in an operation branded 'Azteca' and designed for Far East–Mexican trade, also calling at Monterrey. To reduce risks of delay to key cross-border traffic, Union Pacific (former

Southern Pacific) locomotives work into Mexico on some key services, such as the Long Beach–Mexico City double-stack train and 'just-in-time' services to car assembly plants. Around 20 UP locomotives are involved daily.

In 1991 Union Pacific, American President Lines and FNM combined to launch a 'Double Eagle' double-stack container train service between Mexico City and Chicago. APL provides the stack wagons, containers, drayage in Mexico, and the service's marketing and management; from Chicago, APL's own highway truck services radiate connecting services to other Midwest cities. Besides traction, the railways provide the transhipment terminal facilities. UP also offers through container service to Guadalajara and Monterrey and operates a door-to-door piggyback service between the USA and Mexico. Road haulier J B Hunt initially delivered road trailers to UP at Memphis for onward shipment into Mexico; the service now starts at Chicago. Since early 1991 UP (which has the largest share of USA–Mexico traffic) has operated a Mexican customs preclearance system known as 'Despacho Previo' which has reduced journey times and congestion at the border.

Sunac International of Canada and Transmex of the USA also introduced a door-to-door intermodal service, linking Toronto/Montreal with Mexico City, with transit times in the region of five to seven days. FNM has moved to develop Chicago–Pantaco piggyback service in conjunction with road hauliers Schneider National, and has negotiated contract rates with American President Lines for the movement of intermodal unit trains between Pantaco and border crossings at Nogales, Piedras Negras and Nuevo Laredo.

New lines

Links for satellite towns

In 1990 the government announced its intention to build five or possibly six new electrified double-track lines to cater for 140 km/h electric multiple-units to serve six satellite towns that are being created within a 70 km radius of Mexico City. They were to originate from interchanges with the Mexico City Metro on the periphery of the metropolis. Preliminary work was undertaken in 1991, but construction was swiftly brought to a halt by protests from environmentalists. Little progress has been made since.

In 1992, an agreement was signed between the Mexico state governor and the federal district to permit construction of a series of elevated railways linking Mexico City with its suburbs; concessions would be granted to private sector operators. French, German, Canadian and Japanese companies showed interest, and at the beginning of 1994 a contract was let to a consortium of three local companies and Bombardier of Canada. The contract is for a 20.3 km mainly elevated route between Tlalnepantla and the city centre; a fleet of 93 cars would be required. No recent progress on this project has been reported, there was much local opposition to the proposed elevated structures.

Passenger service on the Chihuahua–Los Mochis route (Stuart King)

1995

Traction and rolling stock

At the start of 1996, FNM's locomotive fleet comprised 1,222 diesel-electric locomotives and 22 electric locomotives. In 1993 FNM operated 38,839 freight wagons (the majority boxcars and gondolas), of which 32,043 were in service. The passenger coach fleet of 1,029 vehicles included 112 sleeping cars, 34 bar/dining cars and 26 diesel railcars.

The most recent additions to the FNM diesel fleet are 34 2,250 kW S7C30P Co-Co locomotives delivered by General Electric, USA, in September 1994.

Signalling and telecommunications

A new train dispatching system known as CDT (*Control Directo de Tráfico* — Direct Traffic Control) was introduced between Nuevo Laredo and Monterrey in 1993 and between Guadalajara and Manzanillo in July 1994. CDT involves the direct transmission of movement authority from dispatcher to train, eliminating written train orders. By the end of 1995, 5,060 km of the FNM network was under CDT control and the system was being installed between Piedras Negras and Rojas (571 km). CTC controlled 1,751 km of the FNM system at the end of 1995.

A programme to modernise FNM's Valley of Mexico marshalling yard outside Mexico City was due for completion around mid-1996. In order to raise maximum potential throughput from 800 to 2,000 freight wagons a day, a new yard control system and electromechanical retarders were being installed by Deco Industries, USA, and GEC Alsthom Signarail of Canada.

SICOTRA

In mid-1991 FNM contracted with Union Pacific and its UP Technologies subsidiary to acquire the US railway's Transportation Control System (TCS). Known to FNM as SICOTRA (Sistema de Control de Tráfico), the system provides computer-based monitoring and management of train and wagon movement and status, yard operations, invoicing, scheduling and planning. The agreement included provision for project management, software development and a four-phase implementation programme.

A total of 50 SICOTRA reporting stations were planned for the FNM system. With the first phase of the programme complete by late 1993, reporting stations were in place at 10 major locations (including Mexico City, Monterrey and San Luis Potosí), four border crossings and the ports of Tampico, Veracruz and Coatzacoalcos. For the benefit of North American customers and railways, wagon movement data is fed into the Association of American Railroads' (AAR) Railinc computer via a datalink which came on stream in December 1993.

Work was under way on the third phase of the programme in 1994, with 26 reporting stations in service on 1 August of that year. However, in March 1995 it was reported that the SICOTRA programme had been suspended in the wake of the devaluation of the Mexican peso at the start of that year.

Electrification

The Mexico City—Querétaro route has been electrified at 25 kV 60 Hz and provided with modern signalling and telecommunications systems.

The first of 39 Type E60C 4,400 kW Co-Co locomotives ordered from General Electric (USA) were completed in 1982, but then lay idle for over 10 years pending completion of the electrification. A fleet of 22 E60C electric locomotives was in service with FNM at the start of 1996.

UPDATED

MOLDOVA

Ministry of Transport

Vlaiku Pirkelab Str 48, 277012 Kishinev
Tel: +373 422 628911

Key personnel
Minister: V Kozlov

VERIFIED

Moldovan Railways (CFM)

Căile Ferate Moldova
Vlaiku Pirkelab Str 48, 2012 Kishinev
Tel: +37 32 23 35 83   Fax+37 32 22 13 80

Key personnel
President: I Curkan
Assistant Director General: Georgui Efrim
Departmental Heads
   International Relations: Grigori Ignakov
   Freight: Victor Garkoucha
   Passengers: Dionisi Semeniouk

Finance: Marina Kniazeva
Traffic: Alexï Kouz
Rolling Stock: Edouard Rastorgouev
Traction: Ivan Vasilaki

Gauge: 1,520 mm
Route length: 1,328 km

Political background

Moldovan Railways was formed in 1992 in the break-up of SZhD (Soviet Railways), and comprises the latter's Moldova section. Two lines traverse the rebellious Dnestr region in the east of the country. Civil war disrupted the fledgling independent railway, meaning that much of it has been out of action — but by 1995 most lines were back in traffic, including those in the Dnestr region.

With peace, the railway has an opportunity to build up transit traffic: the main line bisecting the country from east to west joins the Ukrainian port of Odessa with Romania.

Passenger operations

International passenger trains operate to the Ukraine and several cities in the Russian Federation. There are also international trains, mostly at night, to Romania, operating over the main east—west line via Ungheni. Restoration of passenger service to Romania across two freight-only links over the Prut river, at Prut and Reni, is under discussion.

Most internal day trains are operated by Riga-built diesel multiple-units, at speeds up to 100 km/h. There are plans to increase speeds on the main east—west line to 140 or 160 km/h.

Traffic statistics for 1995 were 11.7 million journeys, 1.02 billion passenger-km.

Freight operations

Most freight traffic is in transit between Romania and countries formerly in the Soviet Union. Agricultural goods make up much of the internally generated traffic. Maximum weight for freight trains is 2,800 tonnes.

As elsewhere in the former Soviet bloc, freight traffic has dropped off rapidly in recent years. Traffic statistics for 1995 were 13.1 million tonnes, 3.0 billion tonne km.

New lines

The Romanian and Moldovan governments have discussed construction of a new line from Nicolina in Romania to the Moldovan capital Kishinev. The new line, to be built at 1,435 mm gauge, would run parallel to the CFM's existing east—west 1,520 mm gauge line, a few kilometres to the south.

Traction and rolling stock

Moldovan Railways inherited from SZhD 112 diesel locomotives (mainly of the 2TE10M, 3TE10M, M62 and ChME3 Classes), dmus of Class D1 and various stored steam locomotives including standard-gauge ex-German Class TE 2-10-0s. There were also about 500 loco-hauled coaches and over 17,000 wagons — with less than 50 per cent of the latter serviceable. Financial problems make acquisition of spare parts difficult.

Track
Rail: 65 kg/m on main lines, 45-55 kg/m on secondary lines
Sleepers: Mostly wooden, spaced at 1,840 per km
Max axleload: 24 tonnes

UPDATED

Type 2TE-10L-798 Co-Co+Co-Co diesel locomotive at Kishinev, with D1 type dmu in the background

MONGOLIA

Ministry of Infrastructure

Ulaanbaatar

Key personnel
Minister: R Sandalhaan

NEW ENTRY

Mongolian Railway (MTZ)

Mongolin Tömör Zam
PO Box 376, Ulaanbaatar
Tel: +976 1 322117   Fax: +976 1 328360

Key personnel
President: Radnaabazaryn Rash
Chief Engineer: J Nyamaa
Deputy Directors-General: N Batmonkh, Y Batsaihan

Gauge: 1,520 mm
Route length: 1,815 km

Organisation
MTZ's core main line, the Transmongolian Railway, extends 1,111 km from the Russian Federation frontier at Sukhbaatar to the Chinese border at Zamyn-Ude, with a line to Erdenet (164 km) and six other branches. There is an isolated 349 km line, the Oriental Railway, in the east of the country which links the Mongolian-Russian Federation border station at Solovyevsk with Choibalsan, and throws off a branch to Erdes.

Freight operations
From a peak of 17.8 million tonnes hauled in 1988, freight traffic has declined inexorably; by 1992 tonnage had halved to 8.5 million and fell further in 1993 and 1994. In that year, due to the continuing political and economic upheaval in neighbouring countries, transit traffic fell to a new low of 0.2 million tonnes — more than 1 million tonnes down on the 1988 figure. As a consequence of the fall-off in movements, many fewer trains are being run and more than 30 passing loops have been taken out of use until business improves.

Internal traffic has fared better, with rail still handling some 80 per cent of total tonne-km. Movements comprise mainly bulk minerals and imported goods.

There was an improvement in this trend in 1995, when tonnage rose 3.5 per cent to 7.3 million tonnes.

Traffic (million)	1994	1995
Freight tonnes	7.077	7.325
Freight tonne-km	2,150.3	2,284.0
Passenger journeys	2.884	2.827
Passenger-km	788.8	681.0

Revenue (tugrik million)	1994	1995
Passengers	4,133.0	4,793.3
Freight	8,875.5	10,741.4
Other income	513.0	840.5
Total	13,521.5	16,375.2

Expenditure	1994	1995
Staff/personnel	1,401.4	2,698.7
Materials and services	507.1	1,068.8
Depreciation	3,895.5	3,973.6
Fuel	4,351.5	4,952.2
Other	1,872.7	2,956.5
Total	12,028.2	15,649.8

Passenger operations
Passenger traffic, on the other hand, declined less dramatically through to 1993. An increase was recorded in 1994, and there was a slight fall again in 1995. The 2.8 million passengers carried in that year represented about 30 per cent of national passenger-km.

Improvements to existing lines
Several capacity improvement projects are under way or planned to cope with transit traffic once the business revives. A major procurement programme agreed in 1994 and funded by OECF Japan loans will see purchases of new passenger coaches and wagons, rail and track accessories, and computers. To be implemented in two phases, starting in 1994-96, the project will raise track

New transhipment facilites at Zamyn-Ude **1996**

The Transmongolian Railway south of Ulaanbaatar (David Rhodes) **1996**

Diesel locomotives

Class	Wheel arrangement	Power kW	Speed km/h	Weight tonnes	No in service	First built	Mechanical	Builders Engine	Transmission
2M62	2 × (Co-Co)	2 × 1,472	100	2 × 120	64	1981	Lugansk	Lugansk	E Lugansk
M62	Co-Co	1,472	100	120	13	1987	Lugansk	Lugansk	E Lugansk
TEM2	Co-Co	883	100	120	28	1972	Briansk	Penza	E Briansk

maintenance standards and ease rolling stock availability at pinch points.

Allied to this plan is establishment of a concrete sleeper manufacturing plant, capable of turning out 200,000 units a year, and raising output of ballast from 60,000 to 400,000 tonnes annually.

Rehabilitation of the existing fleet is addressed in a World Bank scheme which will finance procurement of spare parts and materials. Still awaiting a source of funding is the proposed central workshops at Ulaanbaatar, construction of which would eliminate the need to send locomotives and coaches to other countries for repair.

Japanese funding is also involved in a programme of works at the Chinese border station of Zamyn-Ude, where Mongolian 1,520 mm gauge tracks meet those of 1,435 mm gauge in the People's Republic. Additional and improved transhipment facilities have been provided for transit traffic to and from China, including a new container loading platform.

New lines
Considerable benefits would accrue from linking the isolated Oriental Railway with the main network, feasibility studies for which were carried out in 1986. This remains a long-term goal, but a new shorter route to China from the Oriental Railway at Choibalsan is much favoured as a means of opening up eastern Mongolia and accessing the Tumen river economic zone. Also planned is a line from Erdenet to the Moron region, principally for fertiliser movement.

There are better prospects for a line from Airag to tap the huge reserves of coking coal at Tavantolgoi.

Prefeasibility studies were made in the late 1980s, but construction would depend on availability of foreign funding and technical assistance.

Track
Rail: Type R-43 , 44.65 kg/m; Type R-50, 51.5 kg/m; Type R-65, 64.64 kg/m
Crossties (sleepers): Wood, 200 × 250 × 2750 mm
Fastenings: Conventional, Russian Federation standard
Min curvation radius: 296 m
Max gradient: 1.8%
Max axleload: 23.5 tonnes

Traction and rolling stock
The stock of 105 diesel-electric locomotives is formed chiefly of USSR-built Type 2M62 4,000 hp 2 x Co-Cos and TEM2 1,200 hp Co-Cos. There are also 13 M62M units of 2,000 hp and 10 Type TE2 of 2,000 hp. Passenger cars total 202 and freight wagons 1,981.

At the beginning of 1996 there were two Co-Co diesel-electrics on order, as well as 30 coaches (DWA Ammendorf) and 455 wagons (Roszheldorsnab, Russia). Funding for these purchases was made available by OECF Japan.

Signalling and telecommunications
Semi-automatic block is in operation between Ulaanbaatar and Zamyn-Ude and on several branches, totalling 1,577 km, while the Choibalsan—Eereencav line (237 km) is worked by electric token.

VERIFIED

MOROCCO

Ministry of Transportation

Rabat
Fax: +212 774578

Key personnel
Minister: Said Ameskane
Secretary General: Abdelkader Nouini

UPDATED

Moroccan Railways (ONCFM)

Office National des Chemins de Fer du Maroc
8 bis rue Abderrahmane Al Ghafiki, Rabat-Agdal
Tel: +212 7 774747   Fax: +212 7 774480

Key personnel
General Manager: Mohamed El Alj
Secretary General: Abdellatif Benali
Traffic Manager: Abdesselam El Ghissassi
Transport Manager: Mohamed Smouni
Commercial Manager: Mohamed El Ouerkhaoui
Rolling Stock Manager: Abderrahim Touimy
Fixed Installations Manager: Mohamed Soufi
Track Manager: Moha Khaddour
Electrification, Signalling and Telecommunications
   Manager: Rachid Bouslama
Buildings and Property Manager: Driss Hamri
Human Resources Manager: Moulay El Hassan Rachidi

Management and Finance Manager:
   Mohamed El Gueddari
Data Processing Manager: Mustapha Benmoussa
Supply Manager: Ahmed Raissi
International Relations: Larbi Aidi

Gauge: 1,432 mm
Route length: 1,907 km
Electrification: 1,003 km at 3 kV DC

Political background
ONCFM is a state-owned enterprise with its own legal entity and financial autonomy, working under the administrative umbrella of the Ministry of Transport.

In early 1997, the World Bank and European Investment Bank approved loans of US$195 million towards the US$600 million cost of a restructuring and investment programme.

Organisation
The railway runs about 220 km south from Tangier to the Sidi Kacem junction with the northwest coastal line to Rabat. The latter continues to Marrakech via Sidi-el-Aidi and has a spur to Oued-Zem and east to Oujda, via Fez, to link up with Algerian Railways at the frontier. A line running south from Oujda skirts the Moroccan-Algerian frontier as far as the southeast railhead at Bou-Arfa.

Passenger operations
The 90 km main line between Rabat and Casablanca has been upgraded for 140 to 160 km/h over 76 km and is

exploited by a near-hourly service of emus built in Belgium by BN (now Bombardier Eurorail) and ACEC to a design based on SNCB's Type AM80. But whereas the SNCB AM80 has regenerative braking, the Moroccan units have rheostatic. The Moroccan three-car sets can operate in multipled pairs.

UIC Type X air conditioned cars (see below), designed for 160 km/h operation, equip named trains between Rabat and Marrakech; Casablanca, Tangier, Fez and Oujda; Tangier and Marrakech; and Oujda and Marrakech.

A 13 km electrified branch opened in 1992 connecting the main line out of Casablanca to the south with the King Mohamed V International Airport. Financial assistance for the project came from the African Development Fund.

Traffic (million)	1994	1995
Freight tonnes	28.1	26.7
Freight tonne-km	4,679	4,509
Passenger journeys	9.9	9.6
Passenger-km	1,881	1,564

Freight operations
Phosphates are moved for export shipment in 78 three-axle wagon trains of 3,900 tonnes payload, 4,680 tonnes gross, over the Beni Idir–Khouribga/Sidi Daoui–Casablanca and Sidi Azouz/Youssoufia–Safi electrified routes.

Joint rail-ferry freight service started between Tangier and Muizen in Belgium in conjunction with SNCB in 1994.

Improvements to existing lines
In March 1997, ONCFM announced it would spend US$233 million upgrading the 140 km double-track line between Kenitra (40 km north of Rabat) to the city of Meknes.

Traction and rolling stock
The fleet in 1996 included 40 line-haul and 104 shunting diesel locomotives, 93 electric locomotives, 20 three-car emus and eight diesel railcars.

Under an agreement with De Dietrich, UIC Type X air conditioned cars of side-corridor layout have been built locally for ONCFM. The initial order comprised 79 cars,

Brush-built Bo-Bo diesel-electric locomotive   *1995*

Co-Co electric locomotive hauls Corail stock forming the 'Tour Hassan' Casablanca—Fez service
(Marcel Vleugels)
1996

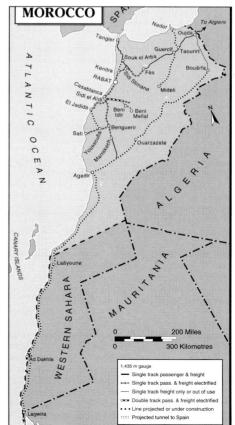

the first five of which were shipped from France part-assembled; the remainder were fully built in Morocco by Société Chérifienne du Matériel Industriel et Ferroviaire (SCIF), though some parts were supplied from France. In addition, 52 cars for local service were acquired second-hand from Belgian Railways (SNCB). A fleet of 80 Corail-type cars, mounted on Y32 bogies supplied by De Dietrich, was assembled locally by SCIF in 1990, and a further 21 coaches were supplied in 1994.

In 1992 ONCFM received 19 820 kW Cummins-engined Bo-Bo diesel-electric shunters from Brush Traction.

In December 1996, seven 4,400 kW electric locomotives were ordered from GEC Alsthom, with an option on two more; they are being built in France. ONCFM has now ordered 27 electric locomotives of this type.

Signalling and telecommunications

Much work remains to be done to improve the signalling. Manual block is being installed under the 1994-98 plan on the principal non-electrified lines from the Algerian border at Oujda to Fez and Tangier to Sidi Kacem. Other works include equipping the main line between Fez and Sidi-el-Aidi with automatic speed control.

Electrification

The 584 km Fez—Marrakech line was electrified in the 1930s by the Paris-Orleans Railway. ONCFM is now undertaking renewal of the catenary using a modern rewiring train from Geismar of France.

Track

Rail: Less than 45 kg/m (657 km); 45-54 kg/m (1,154 km); 54 kg/m over (1,253 km)

Crossties (sleepers) material: Concrete, 1,464 km; steel, 1,541 km; timber, 59 km
Number per km: 1,666 km
Fastenings type: Nabla and rigid fastenings
Min curvation radius (°): 300 m
Max gradient (%): 2.5%
Max permissible axleload: 22 tonnes

UPDATED

MOZAMBIQUE

Ministry of Transport & Communications

PO Box 2158, Maputo
Tel: +258 1 427173   Fax: +258 1 427746

Key personnel
Minister: Paulo Muxanga

UPDATED

Mozambique Ports & Railways (CFM)

PO Box 2158, Maputo
Tel: +258 1 427173   Fax: +258 1 429357

Key personnel
Director-General: Mario A Dimande
Directors
   Engineering: Eng Anibal Laice
   Finance: B M Cherinda
   Commercial: D Gomes
   Computer Services: Avito Jequicene
   Purchases and Stores: Sancho Quipiço
   Personnel: I R Júnior
   Southern Railway: A Manave
   Central Railway: J A Felipe
   North Railway: F J Nhussi
   Zambésia Railway: O J Jaime

Gauge: 1,067 mm; 762 mm
Route length: 2,983 km; 140 km

Political background
In 1990 the Mozambique Railways (CFM) were joined with the country's ports of Maputo, Beira and Nacala in a new state corporation, Mozambique Ports & Railways. This changed the status of both activities from government agency to a financially accountable corporation.

In the following year a new law was enacted to give impetus to plans for revitalisation of CFM, envisaging for the first time the possibility of private sector participation.

Freight traffic performance has been at the mercy of low motive power availability and poor security, both at Maputo port and en route. In an attempt to address the endemic congestion at Maputo in particular, several of the port's facilities have been franchised to private operators. Another long-standing problem demanding attention is the need for dredging at Maputo and Beira to permit larger vessels to call at the ports.

Because of CFM's poor performance, donor governments have been pressing for outright privatisation of the railway as a means of strengthening operational control. World Bank assistance was obtained in 1993 for the Maputo Corridor Revitalisation Technical Assistance Project, designed to review the options for private sector involvement and negotiate its implementation.

In the second half of 1997, six operating concessions in the Maputo Corridor were put up for sale. The six concessions cover the 93 km from Komatipoort to Moamba and Maputo, the 528 km Limpopo line from Chichualacuala to Maputo, the 69 km route from Goba in Swaziland, the harbour at Maputo and CFM's motive power workshops. It was intended to let all six concessions by the end of the year.

Organisation

The railway is made up of five distinct systems linking the coastal ports to the hinterland; managed from four regional headquarters. These are:

CFM-North
Gauge: 1,067 mm
Route length: 919 km

This line runs from the port of Nacala, with a branch (at present closed) to Lumbo westward to Cuamba and Lichinga. A recently built line from Cuamba connects at Entre Lagos, on the border, with Malawi Railways and affords Malawi rail access to the port of Nacala.

CFM-Centre
Gauge: 1,067 mm
Route length: 994 km

From the port of Beira the line runs westwards to connect with Zimbabwe Railways at Machipanda. From Dondo Junction, 29 km from Beira, a line runs northward to connect with Malawi Railways with an extension from Dona Ana to Moatize. A branch line of 83 km links Inhamitanga with Marromeu.

CFM-Zambésia
Gauge: 1,067 mm
Route length: 145 km

An isolated line running from the coastal town of Quelimane to Mocuba.

CFM-South
Gauge: 1,067 mm; 762 mm
Route length: 930 km; 143 km

Three major international routes run from the port of Maputo to the Swaziland border at Goba (64 km); to the South African border at Ressano Garcia (88 km); and the Limpopo line to the Zimbabwe border at Chicualacuala (528 km).

The first joins up at the border of Swaziland with the Swaziland Railway, which connects the Umbovu Ridge iron ore complex at Kadake with the port of Maputo. The second continues into South Africa. The third line goes through Zimbabwe to Zambia, Botswana and the southeast of the Democratic Republic of Congo.

CFM-South also operates the two isolated lines linking Xai-Xai with Mauele and Chicomo (762 mm gauge), and Inhambane with Inharrime (1,067 mm gauge, 90 km).

Passenger operations

Improved passenger services depend on rolling stock availability; currently there are insufficient coaches to run through trains to Swaziland and Zimbabwe, though the Johannesburg—Maputo train resumed thrice-weekly operation in 1994 using Spoornet stock. A local service introduced between Maputo and Manhica proved popular immediately. Some relief was provided by delivery of 25 coaches second-hand from South Africa in 1994, and a batch of new vehicles was ordered from Zimbabwe builders.

Traffic figures for 1995 were 5.5 million journeys, 251 million passenger-km, both of which were dramatically better than the previous year.

Freight operations

In the 1980s operation was severely disrupted by hostilities, with serious consequences for neighbouring railways for which Mozambique's ports provide a shipment outlet. Now that relations are improving, the prospects for rail are similarly reviving. In the short term, close attention is being given to retaining existing freight business, while new export traffic is being sought on the rehabilitated corridors. Closer co-operation with neighbouring railways should see more through running, joint cross-border operations, and streamlined customs and accounting practices.

Traffic figures for 1995 were 3.1 million tonnes, 886 million tonne km.

Improvements to existing lines

Reconstruction of CFM's deteriorated trunk route tracks has been a top priority, first in view of the demands for access to the ports for traffic to and from the country's landlocked neighbours, and latterly in the light of the new political situation following normalisation of relations with South Africa.

Loans from Canadian, French and Portuguese sources helped to fund a US$195 million rebuilding of the 538 km Northern line from Nacala to Cuamba with 40 kg/m long-welded rail on concrete sleepers for 20-tonne axleloadings. Work on the remaining 77 km section from Cuamba to the Malawi border at Nayuci was due to be completed during 1996 after a final Fr20 million tranche of funds was agreed early in the year. There is also a plan to boost passenger service on the route with EU assistance.

Export/import traffic is moving again in the Limpopo corridor northwards from Maputo, over which a partial renovation was completed in 1993. Nevertheless, a further programme of works is necessary before the line can be considered fully operational, and British, Canadian, German, Portuguese and Kuwaiti donors have proffered a further US$65 million towards the US$200 million cost.

Rehabilitation of the Goba line is also being undertaken, with 45 kg/m rail on concrete sleepers and resignalling. Assistance provided by the Italian government funded work on the initial 20 km from Goba to Boane, while a start on the remaining 63 km awaits funding from other sources.

In the Beira corridor to Machipanda, on the Zimbabwe border, there was some encouragement in 1992 from opening of a new container terminal at Beira port, but through running is impossible on the line northwards to Malawi on account of damage to the Zambesi bridge near Dona Ana.

A grant from the UK of US$20 million supported rehabilitation of the Beira corridor line west of Dondo Junction, starting with the severely graded 100 km near the Zimbabwe border, where 30 kg/m rail was replaced by 40 kg/m, curves eased to a minimum radius of 500 m and ruling gradient from 1.2 to 2.4 per cent. The objective is to double-track and resignal the 27 km between Beira and Dondo. Further work planned for this route will benefit from technical assistance provided by the Australian government. All relaying is being carried out with 54 kg/m rail on concrete rather than timber sleepers.

Rehabilitation of the Beira line to Malawi remains to be funded, a difficulty that demands urgent action as international assistance provided under the Beira Corridor Authority programme was to end in 1996. A combined project, involving dredging and other works at Beira with upgrading of the railway, is costed at US$381 million.

South Africa is providing R20 million for rehabilitation of the Maputo—Ressano Garcia line, for which new opportunities are foreseen now that relations between the two countries are improved. Early completion of the route's rehabilitation, along with dredging of the harbour at Maputo, will allow this port once again to fulfil its role as the nearest to Pretoria and Johannesburg. However, the scheme also includes construction with private finance of a toll road to Maputo from Witbank in South Africa.

Traction and rolling stock
In 1995 CFM's fleet comprised 106 locomotives, 17 diesel railcars, 261 passenger cars and 7,267 wagons. Continuing maintenance problems lead to poor availability: in 1993 availability was 73 per cent for main line diesels and only 29 per cent for steam, while more than half the passenger coaches were stopped for repairs. This situation began to improve with staff training assistance from South Africa.

In 1992 GEC Alsthom supplied 15 Type AD26C 1,850 kW diesel locomotives powered by Caterpillar Series 3606 engines, for use in the Limpopo corridor. Finance was provided by France's Economic Co-operation Fund

Diesel locomotives

Class	Power kW	Speed km/h	Weight tonnes	No in service	First built	Mechanical	Builders Engine	Transmission
1a	2,150	103	96	1	1966	GE	7FDL-12B3	E
2a	2,150	103	96	5	1968	GE	7FDL-12B7	E
3a	2,150	103	120	17	1973	GE	7FDL-12D10	E
4a	2,150	108	96	11	1979	GE do Brasil	7FDL-12D29	E
5a	2,150	108	96	17	1980	GE do Brasil	7FDL-12D29	E
6a	2,150	108	96	6	1984	GE	7FDL-12	E
7a	2,150	103	96	5	1990	GE	7FDL-12	E
8a	1,850	103	108	15	1991	GEC Alsthom	3606	E
DH-125	1,250	80	68	28	1980	Faur	6LDA 28B	H Brason
10a	1,100	70	64	6	1991	GE	3508	E
200	1,200	80	82.5	1	1963	AEI	Sulzer-6LDA-28B	E

(CCCE). Also in 1992 General Electric delivered to the Beira Corridor Authority six World Bank financed Caterpillar Series 3512-engined Type U10B 820 kW diesel locomotives.

Signalling and telecommunications
Much of the existing signalling is deficient and the long-term aim is to resignal throughout the network. Rehabilitation of the Goba line includes installation of a new traffic control system, while resignalling and some doubling of the Ressano Garcia line is under study as part of the rehabilitation project mentioned above.

One of the most striking advances has been in the application of computers. A second phase of computerised traffic control was implemented in 1991, bringing on-line a second computer to improve data capture. The system now encompasses wages, traffic and routeing statistics, and movement of ships at the port of Maputo. It will be extended to cover all financial, personnel and commercial matters and stores control.

In an associated project, US Aid has financed computerisation of all clerical activities at the port. The microwave link between Maputo and the South African border at Ressano Garcia is being supplemented by another between Maputo and the Zimbabwe border at Chicualacuala, bringing this route into the data capture system.

Track
Standard rail: 54 kg/m is replacing 30, 40 and 45 kg/m section when rehabilitation takes place
Crossties (sleepers): Timber, 2 × 0.24 × 0.13 m
Concrete and twin-block concrete, 2 × 0.24 × 0.13 m
Spacing: In plain track, 1,500/km
Min curve radius: 100 m
Max gradient: 2.7%
Max axleload: 20 tonnes

UPDATED

MYANMAR (BURMA)

Ministry of Rail Transport

PO Box 118, Yangon

Key personnel
Minister: U Win Sein

VERIFIED

Myanma Railways (MR)

PO Box 118, Bogyoke Aung San Street, Yangon
Tel: +95 1 284455

Key personnel
Managing Director: U Thaung Lwin
General Manager: U Aye Mu
Departmental Heads
  Operating: U Tin Shwe
  Mechanical and Electrical: U Tun Aye
  Civil Engineering: U Kyaw San
  Finance: U Nyan Win
  Commercial: U Myint Wai

Gauge: 1,000 mm
Route length: 3,955 km

Organisation
The most important line connects the two principal cities, Yangon the capital, and Mandalay 619 km to the north. MR has no connections with neighbouring railways. Extension of the Pegu—Martaban line over the Salween river and into Thailand at Phisantouk has been studied, but is not seen as a priority.

Passenger operations
Just over five billion passenger-km were travelled in FY1995-96.

The three daily passenger trains between Yangon and Mandalay include a sleeping-car.

Freight operations
In FY95-96 traffic totalled 926 million tonne-km, almost double what it had been five years before. Principal freight

commodities are timber, rice, sugar cane and aggregates.

New lines
There is a long-standing proposal for a new line to connect the regional capital of Pakkoku with the branch line that currently terminates at Myingyan across the Chindwin river.

Rebuilding of the so-called 'Death Railway' link to Thailand was being discussed by the two governments in 1996.

Improvements to existing lines
Foreign aid has been sought to finance several major projects. One is conversion of Yangon's orbital commuter line to an electrified system operated by 19 locomotives and 105 passenger cars, the total cost of which is put at US$86.7 million. In 1992 bids were invited for resignalling of this line, but satisfactory bids were not forthcoming. The work was readvertised at the start of 1996.

A second aspiration is the first stage of relaying the Yangon—Mandalay main line and equipping it with a VHF communications system.

Traction and rolling stock
In 1995 MR's resources comprised 43 steam and 261 diesel locomotives, 683 passenger cars and 3,852 wagons.

The greater part of MR's diesel fleet is French-built, with Alsthom 900 kW B-B-Bs of 900 kW, 1,200 kW and 1,500 kW prominent. 1980s acquisitions include seven 375 kW diesel-hydraulic locomotives from Kawasaki and Sumitomo of Japan and 19 820 kW diesel-hydraulic locomotives from Krupp of Germany.

In 1993 MR took delivery of six 1,500 kW diesel-electric locomotives from the Dalian rolling stock plant in north-east China's Liaoning province. A further four such locomotives were ordered later, along with two 900 kW units. In 1995 further orders valued at US$40 million were placed with Chinese builders for locomotives, rolling stock and spare parts, including nine MTU-powered diesel-electrics from Quingdao works.

Under a technology transfer arrangement in the 1980s, Daewoo of South Korea set up a factory at Mandalay capable of producing 60 passenger cars and 120 wagons a year.

In 1997, MR awarded a US$11 million order for 400 wagons to Fabrika Vagona Kraljevo of Yugoslavia.

Signalling and telecommunications
Most of the network remains under the control of semaphore signals and wire-based communications. Bids were sought in early 1996 for resignalling of the Yangon suburban network and three other locations.

Track
Standard rail: Flat bottom BS
Main line: 75 and 60 lb/yd (37.2 and 29.8 kg/m) in 39 ft lengths
Main branches: 60 lb/yd (29.8 kg/m)
Other branches and sidings: 50 lb/yd (24.9 kg/m)
Joints: Suspended; joint sleepers 14 in centres. Rails joined by fishplates and bolts
Welded track: 117 ft (35.7 m) lengths. Thermit welded *in situ*
Crossties (sleepers): Hardwood (Xylia Dolabriformis) and creosoted soft wood, 8 in × 4½ in × 6 ft (203 × 115 × 1,829 mm)

Spacing
  Main line: N × 3
  Branch line: N × 2 (N = length of rail in linear yards)
Rail fastening: Dog spikes, elastic rail spikes
Filling (ballast): Broken stone, 70 mm, shingle on branch lines
Thickness under sleeper: 150 mm
Max curvature
  Main line: 6° = radius of 955 ft (291 m)
  Branch line: 17° = radius of 338 ft (103 m)
Max gradient
  Main line: 0.5% = 1 in 200 compensated
  Branch line: 4.0% = 1 in 25 compensated
Max permitted speed
  Main line: 48 km/h
  Branch line: 32 km/h
Max axleload: 12 tons on 75 and 60 lb/yd rail
Bridge loading: Indian Railway Standard ML

UPDATED

NAMIBIA

Ministry of Works, Transport and Communications

Ministry of Works, Transport and Communications
PO Box 13341, 9000 Windhoek
Tel: +264 61 208 2192   Fax: +264 61 228560

Key personnel
Minister: O V Plichta

VERIFIED

TransNamib Rail

TransNamib Ltd
Private Bag 13204, Windhoek 9000
Tel: +264 61 298 1111   Fax: +264 61 227984
email: rail@transnamib.com.na

Key personnel
Chairman, TransNamib Ltd: W Klein
Acting Managing Director, TransNamib Ltd: P Shipo

TransNamib Rail
General Manager: G J J du Preez
Senior Managers
  Rolling Stock: C E F Havemann
  Infrastructure: J J Steyn
  Rail Freight: J du Plessis
Managers
  Finance: M J Smit
  Train Operating: U Hengari
  Technical: A J Stadler

Gauge: 1,065 mm
Route length: 2,382 km

Political background
In 1988 the Namibian rail, road and air services, previously worked by South African Transport Services under contract, were formally handed over to the Namibian body

Windhoek yard   *1997*

that was renamed TransNamib in 1989. This followed a *de facto* transfer in 1985. The government is the principal shareholder. The rail, road and air services are run as separate business units. In 1996, the whole future of TransNamib was being considered by the Independent Task Force to Review TransNamib Ltd, with German consultants DE-Consult looking specifically at the future of the rail operations; complete restructuring of TransNamib Ltd was recommended.

TransNamib Rail has operated without outside funding or subsidy since its inception. At the start of 1997 it had 1,700 employees.

Passenger operations
Business has suffered from the expansion of minibus operations, some actually poaching passengers at stations. TransNamib has responded by offering improved service at lower prices. In order to stem losses, the organisation revamped the whole passenger service by introducing coaches refurbished with airline-type seating and air conditioning attached to timetabled freight trains; these are known as 'StarLine' services and have proved very popular. They have replaced traditional overnight sleeper services, and resulted in an increase in passenger journeys of 20 per cent and a passenger-km increase of 44 per cent in FY94-95.

At the seaside resort of Swakopmund, TransNamib has joined forces with a developer to build a hotel complex incorporating the town's imposing station building. TNR and Air Namibia were planning to introduce a 'Desert Express' for tourists in 1998, to operate between Windhoek and Swakopmund/Walvis Bay.

Through passenger service to South Africa was withdrawn in late 1994.

Freight operations
The main constituents of the freight business are mining products, bulk liquids, building materials and containers.

In 1995, tonnage of local traffic constituted 69.5 per cent of the total, while imports, at 24.7 per cent of total

tonnage, decreased slightly. Exports, amounting to 5.8 per cent of total tonnage, also showed a decrease. This shift in the pattern of movements was due to the increased volumes entering the country through the port of Walvis Bay rather than over the southern border with South Africa. The rail link with South Africa has declined significantly since independence as a result of severe road competition and shorter road distances from the Transvaal area.

Freight traffic is threatened by deregulated road competition. Many customers do not have direct access to rail facilities, therefore road cartage and handling is involved. At present much of this is in the hands of TN's road subsidiary, TransNamib Carriers Ltd. A threat to this traffic is perceived as coming from any future attempt to privatise or hive off TNC from the rail operation. Further competition arises from frequently overloaded road vehicles, reflecting inadequate policing.

New lines
The potential for a northern extension of the railway towards Ovamboland and ultimately Angola is being examined; consideration is also being given to the feasibility of an extension to Zambia using the Caprivi strip.

Traffic	1993-94	1994-95	1995-96
Passenger journeys	91,869	110,462	123,771
Passenger-km (million)	24.2	34.7	48.3
Freight tonnes (million)	1.684	1.733	1.760
Freight tonne-km (million)	1,075	1,077	1,082

Finance
(Namibia Dollars 000)

Revenues	1993-94	1994-95	1995-96
Passengers	2,233	2,113	2,888
Freight	151,641	152,316	161,274
Other income	1,745	2,511	1,575
Total	155,619	156,940	165,737

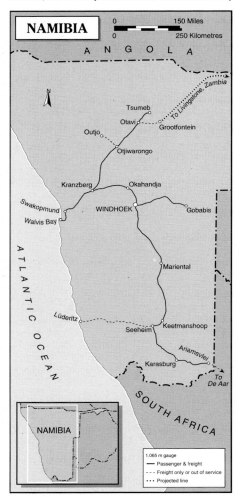

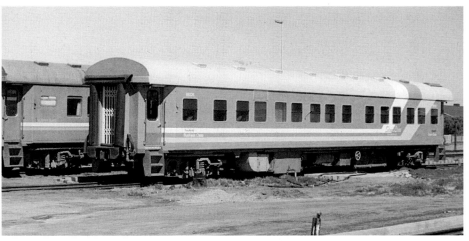

StarLine refurbished coach at Walvis Bay   *1997*

Expenditure	1993-94	1994-95	1995-96
Staff/personnel	48,223	—	—
Materials and services	89,416	—	—
Depreciation	2,130	2,174	2,965
Total	139,778	148,487	153,264

Traction and rolling stock

The railway operates six GE U18C1 1,475/1,340 kW 1-Co-Co-1 and 65 GE Type U20C 1,605/1,490 kW Co-Co diesel-electric locomotives (25 of the diesels are stored). It also has two steam locomotives for special trains. Other rolling stock comprises 113 passenger cars, including two catering, one lounge and 86 sleeping cars; and 1,626 freight wagons.

Signalling and telecommunications

Radio control now covers operation throughout the railway.

Coupler in standard use: SASKOP Type M on passenger cars, and Types M and S on wagons
Braking in standard use: Vacuum; two daily fast trains are air-braked

Track

Rail type and weight: HCOB 22 kg/m (185.4 km), 30 kg/m (1,405.8 km), 48 kg/m (916.5 km), 57 kg/m (78 km)
Crossties (sleepers): Concrete, steel, timber (on bridges and 1:12 pointwork)

Concrete, 2,057 × 230 × 250 mm
Steel, 1,917.7 × 305 × 106 mm
Spacing: In plain track 1,429/km, in curves 1,538/km
Rail fastening: Fist and Pandrol on concrete sleepers, bolt and nut in steel, screw on timber
Min curve radius: 200 m
Max gradient: 1.5%
Max axleload: 16.5 tonnes on 48 and 57 kg/m rail, 15 tonnes on 30 kg/m rail, 11.5 tonnes on 22 kg/m rail

UPDATED

NEPAL

Ministry of Works & Transport

Babar Mahal, Katmandu
Tel: +977 1 226537   Fax:+977 1 225993

Key personnel
Minister: Bijaya Gachhedar

UPDATED

Janakpur Railway (JR)

Jaynagar

Key personnel
Manager: P P K Poudyal
Traffic Officer: K G D Upadhya
Assistant Engineer: D B Khadka

Gauge: 762 mm
Route length: 53 km

Organisation

The Janakpur Railway (JR) runs from Jaynagar in Bihar State, India, across the Nepal border north and west to Janakpur (32 km) and on to Bizulpura (21 km). It is operated by the Nepal Transport Corporation.

The railway was originally built as a timber line designed to open the virgin jungle to the north of Janakpurdam. As the forest has long since been cut, the railway now operates primarily to provide access in an area with few roads. Passengers are the main source of revenue, with pilgrims to the temples of Janakpurdam forming the bulk of traffic. At latest report the railway recorded 1.6 million passenger journeys and 22,000 tonnes of freight.

Improvements to existing lines

In recent years JR has been upgrading track by laying new sleepers and second-hand 16 kg/m rail to replace existing 12.5 kg/m profile. Locomotives (including two Garratts) and wagons released from the Nepal Railway were rebuilt and pressed into service. Recent stock comprised 10 steam locomotives, 25 passenger cars and 52 freight wagons.

In 1991 India undertook to finance upgrading of the line from Bizulpura to Janakpur. In 1994 modernisation came in the form of two ZDM5 diesel locomotives and six coaches supplied by IR. These were operating two return Janakpur—Jaynagar trips daily, while the Bizulpura line was being operated separately by a single diesel. The steam fleet remained in reserve.

VERIFIED

Nepal Government Railway (NR)

Birganj

Key personnel
Manager: Devendra Singh
Traffic Officer: Pratap Bahadur

Gauge: 762 mm
Route length: 6 km

Organisation

There are only two short railways within Nepal, operating in the Terai, a fertile and level strip adjacent to the border with India, the Janakpur Railway (qv) and the Nepal Government Railway (NR).

NR runs a mere 6 km from Raxaul on the North Eastern Railway in India's Bihar State across the Nepal border to Birganj. The line was originally built as a key link in the railway-road-ropeway transport system that supplied the mountain-locked valley of Kathmandu, closed to the outside world until the early 1950s. The line formerly continued north to the base of the Siwalik Hills at Amlekhganj (48 km).

New lines

The government is now undertaking to develop Hetauda into a new industrial centre. As part of the scheme, preliminary feasibility studies have been made for construction of a new rail line from the limit of Indian metre-gauge at Raxaul to Hetauda.

Improvements to existing lines

Plans emerged in 1993 for regauging the cross-border line to eliminate transhipment of freight from metre- to broad-gauge wagons once the NER line to Raxaul is converted to broad-gauge. Rites, the India Railways consultancy, was contracted to carry out a feasibility study, and will supply two diesel locomotives and 12 coaches, as well as technical support, for the project.

Traction and rolling stock

The Nepal Government Railway operates seven steam locomotives, 12 passenger cars and 82 freight wagons.

UPDATED

NETHERLANDS

Ministry of Transport & Waterways

Plesmanweg 1-6, PO Box 20901, NL-2500 EX Den Haag
Tel: +31 70 351 6171   Fax: +31 70 351 7895

Key personnel
Minister: Mrs A Jorritsma-Lebbink
Secretary-General: A B N van der Plas
Director-General of Transport: B Westerduin
Director, Freight Transport: K H van Hout
Head of Railfreight: W A van Zijst
Director, Passenger Transport: J W Oosterwyk

UPDATED

Lovers Rail

Lovers Rail BNV, PO Box 2109, 1000CC Amsterdam
Tel: +31 20 421 2202   Fax: +31 20 421 0997

Key personnel
Managing Director: Pieter Sul

Passenger operations

Lovers Rail is 70 per cent owned by the French CGEA group. The rail subsidiary was set up to take advantage of new opportunities for open access operators on the Dutch railway system. It acquired some second-hand coaches from SNCB in Belgium and began operations on the Amsterdam—IJmuiden line, which is mainly used by tourists, in August 1996. Locomotives come from the NS Cargo fleet.

Lovers Rail has a licence to work as a freight open access operator but in mid-1997 had yet to take advantage of opportunities in this sector.

NEW ENTRY

Netherlands Railways (NS)

NV Nederlandse Spoorwegen
Morelsepark 1, NL - 3511 EP Utrecht
Tel: +31 30 235 9111   Fax: +31 30 233 2458
Web site: http://www.ns.nl

Key personnel

Chairman, NS Holding: E J Verloop
President and Chief Executive: Rob den Besten
Corporate Staff
    Communications: J C B Straatman
    Finance: F A Vermaak
NS Group Passenger Business Unit
    Managing Director: J W Huisinga
    Commercial Director: M M D van Eeghen
    Operations Director: W A G Doebken
    Network North East: P I M Evers
    Fax: +31 38 426 0369
    Network Randstad: H A M Abrahamse
    Fax: +31 10 414 9422
    Network South: W L Walraven
    Fax: +31 40 265 4304
    Long Distance Network: N de Vries
    Fax: +31 30 235 5997
    International Services: F C Marckmann
    Fax: +31 30 235 7068
    Light Rail: Fred Haubrich
    Fax: +31 30 235 5720
Freight Business Unit
    Tel: +31 30 235 4517   Fax: +31 30 235 6713
    Director: E P J Smulders
Stations Business Unit
    Tel: +31 30 235 2508   Fax: +31 30 231 1490
    Directors: P C Stulp, A R A van Engelen
Real Estate
    Tel: +31 30 235 6565   Fax: +31 30 235 6464
    Director: H E Portheine
Rolling Stock
    Tel: +31 30 235 6672   Fax: +31 30 231 4901
    Director: Tj Stelwagen
Government-Commissioned Agencies Railned
    Tel: +31 30 235 8009   Fax: +31 30 235 7400
    Director: P M Ranke
NS Rail Infrastructure
    Tel: +31 30 235 7104   Fax: +31 30 235 9056
    Director: G M F J Hammer
NS Traffic Control
    Tel: +31 30 235 8316   Fax: +31 30 235 3036
    Director: H C Biekart
Infrastructure Maintenance and Construction
    Tel: +31 30 235 7627   Fax: +31 30 235 5766
    Directors: J Schouten, J Jansen, M J L M Rens

Gauge: 1,435 mm
Route length: 2,739 km
Electrification: 1,991 km at 1.5 kV DC

Traffic (million)	1994	1995	1996
Freight tonnes	19.7	20.9	20.8
Freight tonne-km	2,830	3,097	3,123
Passenger journeys	312	305	306
Passenger-km	14,439	13,977	14,091

Revenue (G million)	1994	1995	1996
Passenger traffic	1,848	2,090	2,143
Freight traffic	335	337	316
Other income	n/a	2,526	2,630
Total operating income	n/a	4,953	5,089

Expenditure (G million)	1994	1995	1996
Personnel	2,139	1,929	1,959
Depreciation	491	370	439
Materials	526	609	578
Subcontracts & external costs	968	951	1,041
Other	572	844	848
Total	4,696	4,703	4,865

Political background

NS has been transformed into an independent, commercially oriented business following the 1992 report of the Wijffels select committee, appointed by the Dutch Minister of Transport. Changes centred on separation of rail operations and infrastructure management — completed in 1994 — and the progressive change of NS from a block-subsidised organisation to one of separately accountable business units. NS Cargo has been set up as a freestanding company, with the aim being to sell it off. In

early 1997, negotiations were in hand with four potential partners, with the US company CSX being one of them.

Further changes now being implemented see the advent of limited on-rail competition in a transitional period which will stretch up to 2000. Lovers Rail (qv), a private company, began passenger operations on the tourist line between Amsterdam and IJmuiden in August 1996. In early 1997, the competitive model for rail transport after 2000 had not been decided upon, but franchising out operations on commuter routes in the Randstad urban area along the lines of the British model was a possibility, although it seemed likely that the infrastructure would remain in public hands. NS was lobbying the government to protect the Thalys international high-speed operation from competition until 2012, as it was arguing that this could not stand 'cherry picking' by third party operators.

In 1996, NS drew state financial support of G66 million for operations in respect of unremunerative services and fare reductions deemed socially necessary. An agreement has been reached with the government over the continuation in service until at least mid-1999 of 29 unprofitable lines and the operation of seven new stations. For the period mid-1998 to mid-1999, the government has agreed to pay G155 million for this.

Organisation

NS has been split into four business units: passenger (NS Reizigers), freight (NS Cargo), stations (NS Stations) and real estate (NS Vastgoed) and three service units: traction and rolling stock (NS Materieel), security (NS Beveiliging Services) and support services (NS Facilitaire Bedrijven). NS Cargo, NS Stations and NS Vastgoed became legally independent with effect from 1 January 1995.

Business units

Organisation of NS Reizigers and NS Cargo is described under 'Passenger operations' and 'Freight operations'.

NS Stations was set up as a profit centre in 1993 and intends to charge rental to other NS businesses as well as external concerns. It hopes to lift revenue considerably by improving station environments and encouraging a much wider range of shops into the busiest stations. The number of travellers passing through the 372 stations is put at 900,000 per day with 'other visitors' put at 300,000 per day. In 1995, NS Stations started converting ticket offices to 'Wizzl' shops selling convenience articles as well as tickets. In larger stations, NS Stations is generating commercial space for outlets such as fast food, dry-cleaners, record shops and confectioners. By 2000, the

Class 6400 diesel locomotive for short-distance freight work

The first DM90 dmu was delivered to NS in March 1996 (Quintus Vosman) **1997**

space available for commercial use will have expanded by 30 per cent.

NS Vastgoed, set up in January 1994, is to pursue commercial development of NS property.

Service units

The three service units sell their services to the passenger and freight businesses: NS Materieel comprises rolling stock workshops and depots and manages the railway's traction and rolling stock; NS Beveiliging Services includes police, protection and advisory services; NS Facilitaire Bedrijven includes personnel administration, documentation and research.

Government agencies

Outside the NS Groep (group) are three government-commissioned agencies: Traffic Control (NS Verkeersleiding) which regulates the allocation of train paths on a day-to-day basis between NS businesses and possible private sector operators under the European Union's open access provisions; Railned, a capacity management agency which conducts forward planning of train paths; Rail Infrastructure (NS Railinfrabeheer) which is responsible for the management, upkeep, expansion and development of the system including the commissioning of contractors for the execution of work. These tasks are financed from the government infrastructure fund, Infrafonds. NS Railinfrabeheer contracts outside firms for maintenance, renewal and repair work; these include Strukton Railinfra bv (qv in Permanent Way Equipment and Services section), a joint venture which has taken over the assets of NS Infra Services Materieel. The aim is to have established a completely open market for track construction by 2000.

Finance

NS finished 1996 with a positive result of G105 million, up from G98 million in 1994. Overall, revenue rose by 2.7 per cent.

The average number of full-time employees in the company during 1996 was 28,191, against 28,273 in 1995.

Passenger operations

NS Reizigers passenger business unit has five production-marketing departments: Netwerk International; Netwerk Lange Afstand (Long Distance); Netwerk Randstad (the Amsterdam—The Hague—Rotterdam—Utrecht quadrilateral); Netwerk Noordost (Northeast); and Netwerk Zuid (South).

Since 1995, NS has been free to fix its own fare levels, subject to a 10 per cent ceiling on annual increases. NS is considering market-pricing to reflect demand and average load factors.

Comfort has been improved by the introduction of new rolling stock (see 'Traction and rolling stock' section below) and capacity increases are improving punctuality. An overall increase in the total travel market is expected to bring increased motorway congestion which will favour rail travel.

In June 1996, Thalys TGV-R sets were introduced on the route to Belgium and France, reducing Amsterdam—Paris journey times from 6 hours to 4 hours 45 minutes. In December 1997, the Belgian high-speed line south of Brussels was due to open in its entirety, cutting Amsterdam—Paris timings by a further half-hour. After completion of the HSL-Zuid high-speed line in 2005-07

(see 'New lines' section) this will be cut to 3 hours 5 minutes.

Sleeper services

NS is participating in the European Night Services project, a co-operative effort between German, French, British and Dutch railway companies. This joint venture was set up with the aim of operating luxury 'hotel trains' via the Channel Tunnel, with one of the planned routes being between Amsterdam, The Hague, Rotterdam and London. In 1997, it was uncertain as to whether or not the project would start up due to doubts about its financial viability, but in any case it was unlikely any trains would operate before 1999.

By contributing several renovated sleeping coaches, NS has participated in the improvement of existing night services from Amsterdam to Vienna operating under the EuroNight brandname.

Passenger information services

NS uses the Teletekst system for transmitting real-time information on train running to station screens direct from a transmitter of the national TV service. TV viewers can also receive five pages of NS traffic information.

The Transport Ministry has put up G10 million towards the G25 million cost of running new public transport information centres, the first of which was opened in 1992. These centres supply information for travel planning, through a single national telephone number, based on ICTIS, or Integrated Computerised Travellers Information System, which banks the timetables of all 24 Dutch public transport undertakings. Updated daily, the database covers some 33,500 stations, halts and bus stops, 180,000 street names and 60,000 facilities such as station buffets, bicycle parks, recreation centres, hospitals and museums. Within 30 seconds ICTIS can detail the shortest public transport route between any pair of Dutch locations and to a limited number abroad. The Transport Ministry has also contributed G6 million to development of ICTIS software, which includes *inter alia* a digital topographical map of the country.

Freight operations

The final subsidies from the Dutch government to freight operations were made in 1994. NS Cargo became legally independent from 1 January 1995; in early 1997 partners were being sought in the private sector to take over the company. For its first few years as an independent company, NS Cargo has been given free access to the track and will not start paying Railned for track access until 2000. New operators taking advantage of the new open access rules (for which one or two companies were licensed in early 1997 but which none were actually using) would also get free access to the track in the closing years of the decade.

NS Cargo is reorganising, losing 600 of its 1,650 workforce. However, NS Cargo is taking on some workers: from the end of 1997 the company was to start training 'Cargo drivers' (whose duties will extend further than just driving, to tasks such as coupling and uncoupling of trains), replacing drivers it has been hiring from NS Reizigers. This means the eventual size of the workforce will be around 1,450.

Productivity has improved dramatically: over the 1993-98 period, volume will have been increased by 25 per cent, but with 45 per cent fewer employees, 40 per cent fewer locomotives and 30 per cent fewer wagons.

Unprofitable flows have been abandoned; as a consequence, total volume declined slightly in 1996 (see table). International traffic made up 78 per cent of the total in 1996, considerably more than in previous years. This is part of the trend towards concentrating on more profitable, long-distance flows, but NS Cargo is participating with the government in a study of domestic distribution systems to see if the railways can play a part in reducing motorway congestion.

Wagonload traffic is concentrated, as far as possible, on Kijfhoek yard near Rotterdam, which is now being modernised and automated under a G90 million contract with Siemens Nederland. Work includes installation of a 'mule' wagon-moving system which will eliminate shunting locomotives. A new computer control system to be introduced in 1999 will allow an increase from 120 to 300 in the number of wagons sorted per hour.

Intermodal operations

As Rotterdam is Europe's most important container port, intermodal traffic is extremely important to the Dutch railway system. Two rail terminals serve the port of Rotterdam: Europe Combined Terminals at the Maasvlakte docks on the North Sea (handling about 60 per cent of the traffic), and the Rail Service Centre serving the inner docks on the Maas river. It is anticipated that by 2005, rail will be handling 20 per cent of the five million TEU passing through Rotterdam each year. To do so, a highly automated second terminal is proposed for Maasvlakte, with opening scheduled for 2000. A new line to serve the port is to be built (see Betuwe line in 'New lines' section below) and doubling is proceeding for the single line serving Maasvlakte; this work is involving the first bored tunnel in the Netherlands. The Maasvlakte line will be electrified at 25 kV AC — the first route in the Netherlands at this voltage — and the upgrading should be finished in 2002.

The port is the focus of services run by Intercontainer as well as recently established competitive groups such

The first MDDM vehicle, with seats on the upper floor and power equipment on the lower, was delivered to NS in November 1996. These are replacing Class 1700 locomotives as power units on double-deck trains (Quintus Vosman)
1997

as NDX (see entry in Operators of International Rail Services in Europe section), a company in which NS Cargo has a 25 per cent stake. In early 1997, NS Cargo was still operating all the trains, providing locomotives and crews on behalf of eight firms with operations in Rotterdam, but true open access freight competition under EU directive 91/440 was expected before the end of the decade.

Intermodal accounts for over a third of NS Cargo's tonnage. As well as wholesaling container trains, NS Cargo's wholly owned retailing arm, Holland Rail Container (see entry in Operators of International Rail Services in Europe section), has established its own network of shuttles using fixed-formation wagon sets both for domestic and international services.

Rotterdam generates about 270 container shuttle trains a week. Container shuttles have been introduced to Milan/Melzo, Padua, Basel, Liège, Athus, Duisburg, Neuss, Prague, Donauwörth, Germersheim, Antwerp, Lyon, Poznan and Busto Arsizio. Many services are organised in conjunction with shipping companies. The Milan shuttle was set up with Nedlloyd, Sea-Land, Maersk and P&O - four shipping lines that have come together with NS Cargo as European Rail Shuttle (see entry in Operators of International Rail Services in Europe section).

While international traffic has been growing apace, in recent years NS Cargo has rationalised domestic container services, many of which have been unprofitable.

New lines
Construction of a 300 km/h line from Amsterdam to the Belgian frontier, for access to the Brussels—Paris/London high-speed lines, is proceeding. The route of the northern section of the HSL-Zuid (southern high-speed line), was decided by the Dutch government in May 1996. The line will run from Amsterdam Centraal (later from Amsterdam World Trade Centre) through Schiphol airport. It will depart from the existing alignment at Nieuw Vennep, running east of Zoetermeer to the outskirts of Rotterdam. In order to protect the environment of the 'Green Heart of Holland' the line will run in a 9 km twin-bore tunnel, costing around G900 million, east of Leiden. The southern section will run from Barendrecht to Lage Zwaluwe, parallel with the existing line to Breda Prinsenbeek, then alongside the E19 motorway into Belgium. The cost of the line is put at G7.2 billion. The infrastructure is to be engineered for 300 km/h, which requires electrification at 25 kV 50 Hz AC. Completion of the entire line is planned for June 2005.

NS has plans to build a new route, the HSL-Oost or eastern high-speed line, consisting of rebuilt and new sections of line, all electrified at 25 kV 50 Hz AC, from Amsterdam to Germany. The line will run from Amsterdam via Utrecht and Arnhem to Zevenaar on the German border, trains continuing from there to Cologne and Frankfurt. The new line is likely to consist mainly of sections of new track suitable for 300 km/h laid alongside the existing line. Discussion of the project began in 1996 but a decision on the route is not expected before 2000, with completion scheduled for 2007.

The Betuwe line
In June 1995 the government approved construction of a new west—east freight corridor, the so-called Betuwe line, at a revised cost of G8.4 billion. The cost has risen by 50 per cent since 1992 mainly because of additional environmental measures. The new 121 km line will start from Rotterdam's Kijfhoek yard and will parallel the A15 motorway through the Betuwe area to the north of Dordrecht, serving en route a new intermodal terminal at Valburg. Beyond Geldermalsen the line will closely follow the presently single-track branch to Elst. From Elst, south of Arnhem, it will project a link to Zevenaar near the German frontier station at Emmerich. Work has begun on the route and completion is anticipated in 2005. NS Rail Infrastructure is investigating whether the Betuwe line should be built to allow double-stack transport — one layer of containers on top of another.

The German government has agreed to make the equivalent of ECU1 billion available for supporting improvement of its own routes from Emmerich to the Ruhr and Rhineland.

In addition, the Dutch government started studying in 1996 a possible extension of the Betuwe route in the northeast direction towards Bad Bentheim, with the aim of using the new line for both freight and high-speed trains to Hannover and Berlin. A final decision is not expected before 2000.

The Hanze-lijn
A new line is planned from Lelystad via Dronten to Zwolle — the so-called 'Hanze-lijn' or Hanseatic line. This will open up the Flevoland polder, cut Amsterdam—Zwolle IC journey times by 20 minutes, and will avoid investment in the existing route to the north via Amersfoort, which threads a nature reserve and is also encumbered with level crossings in built-up areas. Studies will continue until 1997-98 and the line is expected to be completed by 2005-07.

Improvements to existing lines
The limit of track capacity was reached in many areas in the 1980s. The international standard for maximum train occupation of double track is normally 60 per cent, 75 per cent in the height of the peak. On the NS the norm is 80 per cent. Use of double-deck passenger cars has given extra capacity, but even so the infrastructure would be unable to cope with anticipated future volumes. As a result, enlargement of eight of the most serious bottlenecks was begun. This is involving building new flyovers, widening of double-track to four tracks, layout expansion at major interchanges, elevation of tracks to eliminate level crossings, and not least, raising waterway overbridge heights, or in one important case replacing a bridge by a tunnel, in places where spans have to be frequently opened to allow shipping passage. Extensive four-tracking of existing trunk route is essential to achieve segregation of the new top-level services from an expanded service of multistop services. In all, some 800 route-km, or 30 per cent of the existing network, is being drastically modified.

Amsterdam, Gouda and Rotterdam works
A 12.5 km double-track Southern Ring route for Amsterdam was completed in May 1993. The line terminating at Amsterdam RAI was extended to Duivendrecht on the Amsterdam—Utrecht line and on to Diemen on the Amsterdam—Amersfoort line. Four trains per hour no longer call at Amsterdam CS station, the environment of which restricts possibilities of capacity enlargement, but use the ring line instead. Future plans include widening the line to four tracks and upgrading Amsterdam Zuid station.

A Western Ring will be four-tracked throughout from Schiphol through Amsterdam Sloterdijk to Zaandam. This will require construction of a second double-track Hem Tunnel under the North Sea Canal.

Amsterdam Centraal, with (left) DD-IRM emu and (right) Thalys-liveried TGV-R bound for Paris (Brian Morrison) **1997**

In 1996 the 'Thalys' Amsterdam—Brussels—Paris TGV service was introduced via Schiphol Airport, which extended operations by opening a second air terminal in the mid-1990s. NS has therefore enlarged its underground Schiphol station from three to six tracks served by three island platforms each long enough to cater for a twin-unit TGV formation. The approach tunnels have been widened to accommodate four tracks, and new buildings erected at ground level.

South of Rotterdam CS, the four-track Willemsspoor tunnel under the Nieuwe Maas river was completed in September 1994. This replaced two double-track bridges, the Koningshaven and Willemsbrug, over the waterway where it flows round the Noorder island. The Konigshaven was a lift bridge that had to be raised for 20 minutes every 2 hours for passage of shipping — a grievous handicap to NS interval timetable planning. The 3 km tunnel is approached on 2.8 per cent gradients, because it must drop to 18 below the level of the former elevated main line. The latter's station of Blaak has been rebuilt inside the tunnel. The elevated track and Willemsbrug have been dismantled to aid local redevelopment.

Other infrastructure projects
Work has been under way at around 25 sites. The major projects planned or already under way, other than those already mentioned, included:
● Extra tracks between Rotterdam and Dordrecht (25 km) with completion planned for 1997-99.
● Installation of four tracks between Boxtel and Eindhoven (20 km), with completion planned for 1998-2001.
● Installation of extra tracks on the Amsterdam—Schiphol—Hoofdorp section of line (10 km) with completion planned for 1998-2001.
● Four-tracking by 2005 of the Vleuten—Utrect—Houten section of line (10 km).

Traction and rolling stock
In 1996, NS completed a long-term G1.3 billion investment programme, involving the acquisition of 290 double-deck carriages. By the end of 1996, total capacity of the NS passenger fleet was around 200,000 seats, compared with 165,000 in 1991. The passenger fleet comprised 1,634 emus, 287 dmus and 767 carriages.

All of NS's 495 locomotives are now owned by NS Cargo, except for Class 1700 electrics, which are owned by NS Reizigers. NS Reizigers hires in use of a proportion of locomotives owned by NS Cargo.

Diesel locomotives

Class	Wheel arrangement	Power kW	Speed km/h	Weight tonnes	No in service	First built	Builders Mechanical	Engine	Transmission
200/300	Bo	64	60	21	120	1934	Schneider	Stork	E Heemaf/ETI
600	C	300	30	41	45	1949	EE	EEC 6KT	E EEC
2200	Bo-Bo	650	100	74	37	1955	Schneider	Stork/ Schneider	E Westinghouse
6400	Bo-Bo	1,180	120	80	120	1988	MaK	MaK	E ABB

Diesel railcars or multiple-units

Class	Cars per unit	Motor cars per unit	Motored axles/car	Power/motor kW	Speed km/h	No in service	First built	Builders Mechanical	Engine	Transmission
DE-II	2	2	2	193	110	24	1953	Allan	Cummins	E Smit
DE-III	3	1	4	182	130	41	1960	Werkspoor	SACM	E Smit
DH-I	1	1	2	212	100	19	1983	Uerdingen	Cummins	H Voith
DH-II	2	2	2	212	110	30	1981	Uerdingen	Cummins	H Voith
DM 90	2	2	2	320	140	53*	1995	Duewag	Cummins	H Holec

* On order or in service

NS is applying distinctive liveries to the rolling stock of each of the passenger service tiers. Long-distance services will have mainly dark blue stock whilst short-distance stock will retain a mainly yellow livery. NS Cargo has adopted a red livery for its locomotives.

NS recently bought 'Gril-Express' cars from SNCF and couchette cars from DB AG and has refurbished them in its own works for operation in international and car-sleeper trains.

High-speed trainsets

NS has ordered high-speed trainsets for services from Amsterdam to Paris and Germany. Amsterdam to Paris services began in June 1996 using 10 SNCF-owned three-voltage Paris—Brussels—Amsterdam or PBA TGV-Réseau sets in Thalys livery. From late 1997, these would be supplemented by 17 four-voltage, second-generation Thalys sets jointly ordered from GEC Alsthom by NS, SNCB, DB AG and SNCF. Of these, two will be owned by NS although they will operate in a pool and be maintained at Paris Le Landy SNCF depot.

In September 1995, NS signed a letter of intent with Siemens Nederland for the supply of six 330 km/h Type ICE2.2 high-speed trainsets seating 400 passengers for services from Amsterdam to Frankfurt and Berlin. The order was later cut back to four trains. Delivery should take place at the end of 1998 and ICE3 sets (as they have since been renamed) will initially go into service over existing tracks at 140 km/h from the 1999 timetable. By 2000, there should be seven Amsterdam—Cologne train pairs, of which three will extend to or from Frankfurt. Two pairs of trains will link Amsterdam with Berlin. By 2003, infrastructure improvements in the Netherlands and Germany will allow Amsterdam—Cologne in 2 hours and Amsterdam—Frankfurt in 3 hours. In the long term, there will be an hourly link with Frankfurt, some trains extending to Munich or Basel.

New double-deck long-distance stock

In 1991 NS placed its largest single rolling stock order ever with Waggonfabrik Talbot of Germany (now part of Bombardier), worth G1,230 million, for 34 three-car and 47 four-car Type DD-IRM double-deck emus. These were all in service by the end of 1996. De Dietrich of France built intermediate trailers for the four-car sets. All sets are air conditioned and have enhanced comfort by comparison with previous types. Seating affords more legroom and there is more baggage space. A lift has been incorporated so that a refreshment trolley can be used on both levels. The first sets took over the Amsterdam—Vlissingen service in January 1995.

Double-deck suburban stock

In early 1994 Waggonfabrik Talbot completed delivery of 118 DDM-2 and 140 DDM-3 double-deck coaches. An accompanying order for 81 Class 1700 electric locomotives from GEC Alsthom was also fulfilled. The Class 1700 is derived from NS's Alsthom-built Class 1600 and is a mixed-traffic unit with a maximum speed of 160 km/h. At one end only it is fitted with an automatic coupler as well as orthodox buffers and drawgear. NS has formed semi-permanent push-pull sets of a Class 1700 and three or four double-deck coaches. Equipped with automatic couplers at each end, such sets can be operated in multiple pairs where required.

From 1997 the Class 1700 locomotives are being replaced by MDDM power cars with an upper floor seating 48. In 1992 an initial order for 50 of these vehicles was placed with De Dietrich, with an option on 29 more; the first was delivered in November 1996. The 2,700 kW power cars are B-B-B, with the central bogie having some lateral play for curve negotiation. The bogies are being supplied by Fiat-SIG. Each bogie is three-phase asynchronous AC-motored; the electrical equipment is being supplied by Adtranz, but fitting out is being supervised by Holec. Class 1700 locomotives no longer required for push-pull service will replace the oldest NS electric locomotives of Classes 1100 and 1200.

SM 90 and DM 90 stopping trains

In its first three-phase AC motor emu venture, NS took delivery from Waggonfabrik Talbot in 1992-93 of nine prototypes of a stopping train emu designated SM 90. These two-car sets have Holec motors and longer and wider bodies than previous emus. This allows NS to evaluate the economy of 3 + 2 seating format instead of the previous 2 + 2 arrangement and also to identify any problems involved in operating longer-bodied trainsets. Other features include a floor 150 mm lower than in existing NS emus, and a built-in power lift to aid the

Class 1700 electric locomotive at Amsterdam Rai (I C Scotchman)   **1997**

Electric locomotives

Class	Wheel arrangement	Output kW	Speed km/h	Weight tonnes	No in service	First built	Builders Mechanical	Electrical
1300	Co-Co	2,885	135	111	15	1952	Alsthom	Alsthom
1200	Co-Co	2,235	130	108	21	1951	Werkspoor-Baldwin	Heemaf-Westinghouse
1100	Bo-Bo	1,925	135	83	24	1950	Alsthom	Alsthom
1600	B-B	4,540	160	83	58	1981	Alsthom	Jeumont-Schneider
1700	B-B	4,540	160	86	81	1991	GEC Alsthom	Schneider

Electric railcars or multiple-units

Class	Cars per unit	Motor cars per unit	Motored axles/car	Output/motor kW	Speed km/h	No in service	First built	Builders Mechanical	Electrical
mP	1	1	4	145	140	32	1965	Werkspoor	Smit
64-II	2	2	2	246	140	242	1964	Werkspoor	Heemaf/Smit
64-IV	4	2	4	246	140	31	1964	Werkspoor	Heemaf/Smit
SGM-II	2	2	4	330	125	30	1975	Talbot/SIG	Oerlikon/Holec
SGM-III	3	2	4	330	125	60	1980	Talbot/SIG	Oerlikon/Holec
ICM-III	3	1	4	312	160	94	1977	Talbot/Wegmann	Heemaf/Smit
ICM-IV	4	2	4	312	160	30	1991	Talbot/Wegmann	TCO Holec
SM 90	2	2	4	300	160	9	1993	Talbot	Holec
DD-IRM-III	3	2	2	200	160	34	1994	Talbot	Holec
DD-IRM-IV	4	2	2	200	160	47	1994	Talbot/De Dietrich	Holec

embarkation of disabled passengers. After initial software problems, the SM 90s started evaluation on the Zwolle—Emmen line in 1995. A production series of the SM 90, which has been tagged the 'Railhopper', is now unlikely, as NS has decided that it should concentrate on double-deck rolling stock for its electrified routes.

The bodyshell of the SM 90 has been adopted for a new design of diesel railcar, the DM 90. For this, a partnership of Talbot and Duewag has been given an initial order for 53 two-car units, with an option for a further 29 single-car units. Each two-car unit will be powered by two 320 W Cummins engines with hydraulic transmission. Maximum speed will be 140 km/h. The units have moquette-covered 2 + 2 seating in second class and in one car, a large compartment with coffee, soft drink and confectionary dispensers, high-level tables and 18 fold-down seats. The first DM 90s went into service on the Arnhem—Winterswijk service in June 1996. Later, DM 90 units will take over Nijmegen—Roermond, Zwolle—Almelo and Groningen—Leeuwarden services. The new units will allow replacement of Type DE II dmus built in 1953-54.

New diesel locomotives

The last of 120 Class 6400 1,180 kW Bo-Bo diesel locomotives, with three-phase AC drive, was delivered to NS Cargo by ABB Henschel (now Adtranz) at the beginning of 1995. The 120 km/h locomotives are used on short distance freight services. The new class has replaced almost all NS's older main line diesels of Classes 2200 and 2400. Around 30 Class 2200 remain for use in the Rotterdam docks complex, shunting freight wagons at Kijfhoek marshalling yard and hauling freight on the

isolated branch to Terneuzen. These will be replaced once the main line serving Rotterdam docks is electrified and Kijfhoek yard is automated.

Signalling and telecommunications

NS is participating in European studies into the possibilities for capacity expansion by introducing new control and safety systems. Part of the research is concentrated on a system for the improved use of infrastructure capacity by means of automatic regulators and recommended speeds.

In September 1994, NS opened a new Siemens SIMIS type microcomputer interlocking signalling centre in Rotterdam, the largest of its type in Europe, to replace the existing relay-based centre. In 1995 a new traffic control centre was opened near Amsterdam Centraal station. Further centres are under construction in Amersfoort and Arnhem.

Electrification

A total of 75 per cent of the NS system is electrified at 1.5 kV DC, including all main routes. The only extension to this in progress at present is the electrification of the Rotterdam dock line. After previously rejecting the idea, NS decided in 1994 to reconsider the gradual conversion of its existing electrification from 1.5 kV DC to 25 kV 50 z AC. This merits consideration in the context of connections with the emergent continental high-speed network and because intensification of passenger traffic will demand traction equipment with enhanced acceleration and braking characteristics. The first applications of 25 kV 50 Hz AC will be on the

Class 1100 locomotives dating from the 1950s (pictured) are being withdrawn as Class 1700s freed up by the arrival of MDDM power cars become available for more duties (Brian Morrison)   **1997**

Amsterdam—Belgium and Amsterdam—Germany high-speed lines and, possibly, the Betuwe freight route. Apart from new traction orders, it is possible that Class 1600 and 1700 locomotives will be converted to dual-voltage operation. The decision on conversion to 25 kV 50 Hz AC will be made by the Dutch government.

Track
Standard rail, weights
Main lines: UIC 54 kg/m (3,025 m installed)
Branch lines: 46 kg/m (3,436 m installed)
Crossties (sleepers): Wood, 250 × 150 × 2,600 mm; twin-block concrete 230 × 300 × 2,250 mm; monobloc concrete 230 × 300 × 2,500 mm
Spacing: 1,667/km; 1,333/km
Fastenings: Wood, bolt or DE-clip; twin-block concrete, DE-clip; monobloc concrete, Vossloh clip
Min curvature radius: 300 m; 500 on track with monobloc sleepers
Max axleload: 22.5 tonnes (20 tonnes on twin-block concrete-sleeper track)

UPDATED

NEW ZEALAND

Ministry of Transport — Land Transport Safety Authority

PO Box 27459, Wellington, New Zealand
Telephone: +64 4 494 8600   Fax: +64 4 494 8601

Key personnel
Minister: M Williamson
Director, LTSA: R A Barrett

Political background
The Land Transport Safety Authority is a regulatory authority responsible to the Minister of Transport; it has responsibility for licensing and audit of safety on the railway.

UPDATED

Tranz Rail

Tranz Rail Ltd (formerly New Zealand Rail Ltd)
Railway Station Building, Bunny Street, Wellington
Tel: +64 4 498 2000   Fax: +64 4 498 3322

Key personnel
Chairman: Edward A Burkhardt
Managing Director: Dr A Francis Small
Group General Managers
  Tranz Link: Roger H Gower
  Passenger: Steven J Voullaire (acting)
  Operations: John L Bradshaw
  Interisland Operations: Paul A Harper
Executive Managers
  Corporate Services: Dr Murray King
  Finance and Business Services: Ron G Russ
  Personnel: Steven J Voullaire
  Quality and Safety: Ray S Ryan
Corporate Managers
  Communications: Helen M Morgan-Banda
  Government Relations: Paul G Spackman
  Strategic Issues: David J Crispin

Gauge: 1,067 mm
Route length: 3,913 km
Electrification: 108 km at 1.5 kV DC, 411 km at 25 kV 50 Hz AC

Political background
For more than a century, railways in New Zealand were run as a government department. In 1982, New Zealand Railways Corporation was established as a statutory corporation with a commercial mandate. In 1986, it became a state-owned enterprise and in October 1990 the New Zealand government established New Zealand Rail Ltd as a limited liability company.

The deregulation of the transport industry and major restructuring were the hallmarks of these years. Staff numbers were reduced from more than 21,000 to around 5,000, productivity improved by nearly 300 per cent and the organisation was transformed from a loss maker into a

An eastbound coal train passes the TranzAlpine tourist service at Otira (Brian Webber)   **1997**

profitable business, trends which have continued through to the present day.

The restructuring culminated in December 1992 when the New Zealand government announced its intention to sell New Zealand Rail. On 20 July 1993, it announced the sale to a consortium comprising local banking interests, with rail expertise coming from the US railroad Wisconsin Central Transportation Corporation. The sale was completed on 30 September 1993 with the company maintaining a lease from the Crown to occupy land for its railway operations. The company changed its name to Tranz Rail Ltd on 18 October 1995, and was floated on the New Zealand stock exchange on 14 June 1996.

Organisation
Tranz Rail operates a nationwide rail network, interisland ferry services and an extensive owner/driver truck network; it is New Zealand's largest freight carrier. The company's vision is to move from being primarily a railway operator to a multimodal transport provider. The company has sold assets that are not essential to its core business.

Tranz Rail's structure comprises: Tranz Link — markets and manages all aspects of freight transport; Tranz Scenic — markets and operates long-distance passenger services; Tranz Metro — operates commuter passenger services in Auckland and Welllington; Interisland Line — manages all interisland ferry operations; Operations — manages the company's infrastructure; Corporate Office — covers such functions as safety, personnel, planning, corporate relations, security, financial and business services.

In early 1997, Tranz Rail had 4,780 employees. About five per cent of company shares are held by management and staff.

Finance
In the year to 30 June 1996, Tranz Rail increased its operating profit to NZ$110.8 million from NZ$105.2 million the previous year. Net profit was NZ$49.2 million. Operating ratio (operating costs as a percentage of revenue) improved to 80.6 per cent from 88.9 per cent at purchase in 1993. Tranz Rail was able to increase its revenue despite a slowdown in the country's economic growth in 1996.

The NZ$175 million raised from the share issue has been used to repay debt, creating a strong balance sheet for future growth.

Passenger operations
Trans Scenic markets eight long-distance passenger services and associated travel packages. The flagship service is the 'TranzAlpine', across the South Island's Southern Alps between Christchurch and Greymouth (231 km), which is regarded as one of the great railway journeys in the world. Other services are: the 'Overlander' and the 'Northerner' between Auckland and Wellington, New Zealand's capital city (681 km); the 'Coastal Pacific' between Christchurch and Picton (348 km); the 'Southerner' between Christchurch and Invercargill (590 km); the 'Bay Express' between Wellington and Napier (317 km); and 'Silver Fern' railcar services between Auckland and Tauranga (236 km) or Rotorua (277 km).

Passenger revenue rose 4.2 per cent to NZ$144 million in FY95-96, accounting for 25.4 per cent of Tranz Rail's revenue. Tranz Scenic achieved growth in spite of international tourism suffering from unfavourable exchange rates and negative perceptions from the spectacular Mt Ruapehu eruption. Passenger numbers, of whom a quarter are international visitors, rose 2.3 per cent. Tranz Scenic is aware that many tourists are committed to road or air travel by travel packages and is aiming to capture more of this market.

An upgrading programme has continued on passenger rolling stock and most services are now worked by refurbished carriages that have wide windows, retention tanks and new catering facilities. Unconverted carriages are attached to some services to provide cheaper 'backpacker' transport.

Tranz Metro, which operates urban commuter services in Wellington (electric multiple-units) and Auckland (diesel railcars), carried 10.6 million passengers in 1995-96. Diesel services also run into Wellington: 'Wairarapa Connection' services link Masterton (91 km) with the capital city and the 'Capital Connection' return service links Palmerston North (136 km) with Wellington. Passenger numbers rose 3.6 per cent while revenue rose 1.4 per cent to NZ$43.6 million.

Tranz Rail purchased 19 second-hand diesel multiple-unit sets from Perth, Western Australia in 1993 for use on commuter services in Auckland, New Zealand's largest city. This was part of a package that resulted in NZ Rail securing a 10-year contract with the Auckland Regional Council for provision of passenger services. Patronage in 1995-96 increased by 300,000 (17.3 per cent) over 1994-95, continuing the growth pattern since the railcars were introduced. It has been proposed that Auckland railway station be moved nearer the city centre to form part of a commuter transport hub, but there is no firm date for such a move to take place.

Freight operations

In FY95-96, freight was Tranz Rail's major revenue earner, generating sales totalling NZ$400.7 million. Some 10.3 million tonnes of freight were carried for 3.26 billion net tonne-km. Each week, about 975 freight trains are scheduled. Average length of haul has been increasing and is now about 340 km. Ten customers account for about 40 per cent of traffic. The Auckland—Wellington (North Island Main Trunk) section carries about 36 per cent of the total amount.

During FY94-95 Tranz Rail acquired full control of RFL Transport Ltd, a company specialising in temperature controlled transport.

Tranz Rail operates three roll-on/roll-off train ferries across Cook Strait between Wellington and Picton. The ferries now operate 24-hour sailings with over 5,000 sailings a year. They connect the 2,500 km of North Island track with the 1,500 km of South Island track. Tranz Rail is investigating building a new open sea port at Clifford Bay (38 km south of Blenheim) to replace Picton, which is reached through a sound. The cost of building the port would be offset by savings in the rail haul. The sea trip would be reduced by 30 minutes and the land trip to Christchurch by 30 minutes. About 80,000 wagons are carried between the islands annually. A freight train from Auckland to Christchurch is run, providing a 24-hour transit time.

Tranz Rail's Tranz Link division provides freight transport by rail, road (emphasised by the development of a network of more than 280 owner/drivers), or sea. It also offers warehousing, distribution and freight management services.

In FY95-96, Tranz Links's Forestry division suffered a drop in its revenue although more tonnage was hauled. Changes within the forestry industry resulted in logs being hauled shorter distances. The company is now considering reopening some closed branch lines to provide better access from forests to logging plants and port. More trains are running from Murupara to Kawerau mill as logging tonnages increase.

Coal hauled from the west coast mines to the port at Lyttelton on the east coast over the South Island's Midland Line now exceeds one million tonnes each year. Tonnages increased in 1995-96 by 9.7 per cent, with two DX class locomotives now hauling 20-wagon trains from Greymouth and Ngakawa. Previously two DC class locomotives could haul only 14 hopper wagons. Seven trains daily have now been replaced by five trains. Future projections indicate coal traffic could treble, although it is possible that a ship-loading facility will be built on the west coast, obviating any need for a rail haul.

Tranz Link has made trial runs hauling livestock, to determine whether it should pursue this traffic some 20 years after the last consignments. The animals were carried in crates which can be transferred to road vehicles when required.

A successful trial was conducted hauling bulk milk in the North Island. Traffic of 1.3 million litres will require the provision of two trains daily. It is believed there is scope to capture more of this traffic.

Two English Electric-built trains dating from the 1940s at Ngaio, on the Wellington suburban system (Brian Webber) **1997**

Diesel locomotives

Class	Wheel arrangement	Power kW	Weight tonnes	No in service	First built	Mechanical	Builders Engine	Transmission
Dbr	A1A-A1A	709	68	10	1980	GM	8-645C	E
Dc	A1A-A1A	1,230	82.75	81	1978	GM	12-645E	E
Df	Co-Co	1,230	86.6	11	1979	GM	12-645E	E
Dft	Co-Co	1,830	87.6	19	1992	GM	12-645E3C	E
Dx	Co-Co	2,050	99	47	1972	GE	7 FDL-12	E
Dxr	Co-Co	2,350	102.5	1	1993	GE	7 FDL-12	E
Dh	Bo-Bo	678	54	6	1978	GE	CAT D398 B	E
Dsc	Bo-Bo	2 × 175	41	47	1962	AEI/NZR	2x Cummins NT855	E
Dsj	Bo-Bo	354	54	5	1987	Toshiba KTA-1150-L	Cummins	E
Dsg	Bo-Bo	2 × 354	56	24	1981	Toshiba KTA-1150-L	2 × Cummins	E
Tr	C (0-6-0)	110-135	20	49	1936-77	Price/Hitachi/ Drewry/Bagnall	Cummins NH/ Gardner GL	H

Electric locomotives

Class	Wheel arrangement	Power kW	Weight tonnes	No in service	First built	Builders Mechanical	Engine
Eo	Bo-Bo	—	55	5	1968	Toshiba	—
Ef	Bo-Bo-Bo	—	106.5	20	1988	Brush	—

Electric multiple-units

Class	Power kW	Weight tonnes	No in service	First built	Builders Mechanical	Engine
DM/D	450	42.4	30/50	1936-47	EE	—
EM/ET	400	72.1	44/44	1982	Ganz-Mávag	—

Diesel railcars

Class	Power kW	Weight tonnes	No in service	First built	Mechanical	Builders Engine	Transmission
Rm	750	111	3	1973	KHI Toshiba	CAT D398	E
ADK/ADB	276	33/16	9/10	1969	Comeng/WAGR	Cummins	HM
ADL/ADC	424	43/36	10	1981	Goninan	Cummins	H

Wagons being shunted on to an interisland ferry at Picton. The locomotive is remotely controlled by radio, with the driver (far right of the picture) walking close by the machine (Brian Webber) **1997**

Tranz Rail has pioneered the use of remotely controlled shunting locomotives. Forty locomotives of three classes are being equipped with the system, which enables safer and more precise shunting to take place. The system has been extensively tested and is fail-safe as the locomotive stops if it does not receive a continuous signal from the shunter's equipment. In the future the equipment may be fitted to certain main line locomotives to enable a single-crewed locomotive to be used for wayside shunting.

Tranz Link has an Amicus 11 computer system connected to all freight terminals to monitor consignments. This has improved revenue collection and billing accuracy and has also allowed paperless documentation. The company has introduced bar-coding technology with the aim of increasing efficiency in freight movements as well as providing real-time management information for the company and its customers.

Freight traffic	1994	1995	1996
Freight tonnes (million)	9.44	9.58	10.31
Freight tonne-km (billion)	2.8	3.2	3.3

Intermodal operations

Tranz Rail has sought to increase carryings of containers and swapbodies, introducing 'Spaceliner' swapbodies in a bid to compete with road transport. Another new design of swapbody, the 'Iceliner', is a refrigerated swapbody that has been specially designed for Tranz Rail's temperature-controlled meat and fish transport market.

Improvements to existing lines

Twelve bridges and about 150 km of track between Stillwater and Ngakawa (South Island west coast) have been upgraded to enable two DX locomotives to be used on export coal trains to Lyttelton, Christchurch's port. These trains work through the 8.6 km Otira tunnel with the assistance of electric locomotives. A new triangular connection near Westport, opened in July 1996, enables coal trains to run directly from Ngakawa to the east coast.

Traction and rolling stock

At 1 January 1996 Tranz Rail operated 319 diesel and 27 electric locomotives, 135 electric units, 38 diesel railcars, 86 passenger cars and 6,949 wagons. The wagon fleet comprises 2,890 container flat wagons, 1,506 hopper wagons, 1,627 box wagons, 536 log wagons and 390 special wagons. In 1995, Tranz Rail purchased eight second-hand Clyde-GM locomotives (now classified as DQ class) from Queensland Rail in Australia.

In 1996, two ex-British Rail InterCity Mark II carriages owned by sister company in the Wisconsin group English, Welsh & Scottish Railway, were imported into New Zealand for trials. When fitted with 1,067 mm gauge bogies and the smaller wheels usual in New Zealand they fit within the loading gauge. The carriages were evaluated to see if the type would be a suitable replacement for existing carriages, which average 44 years of age. In early 1997 a further 16 carriages were shipped from the UK to New Zealand; these will be used on steam-hauled excursion trains. Late 1997 saw yet more shipments, with

One of two ex-British Rail Mk 2 passenger coaches imported into New Zealand in 1996 for trials (John Glover)   **1997**

61 ex-BR carriages to be assigned to surburban Wellington services.

Upgrading work continues on a fleet of insulated wagons for the meat and dairy sectors. A new class of CC coal wagon with a tare of 20 tonnes and designed to carry 70 tonnes has been introduced. Upgrading of track will be required before 22.5 tonne axleload can be accommodated. Twenty used coal hoppers (class CW) were purchased from Australia's Westrail in 1996 for Midland Line traffic.

Tranz Rail has introduced a new class of box wagons, with the marketing name of Spacecharger, equipped with plug-type fibreglass doors. Some 75 of the class, ZH, are being built at Tranz Rail's Hillside workshops. The wagon has two doors on each side which move to open fully their half of the wagon side, making loading by forklift simple.

Overhaul of Wellington's Ganz-Mávag multiple-units commenced in 1995. The 44 two-car units date from 1982 and work most services. The Wellington Regional Council will provide NZ$3.75 million towards the cost of overhaul, enabling about 20 units to be completed by 2000.

Signalling and telecommunications

Most trains operate under either CTC (Centralised Traffic Control) or TWC (Track Warrant Control). Tranz Rail is centralising its train control operations in Wellington.

Electrification

The North Island Main Trunk line between Palmerston North and Hamilton is electrified at 25 kV 50 Hz AC.

The 95 km Wellington suburban passenger network and the 13 km section through the 8.6 km Otira tunnel on the South Island Midland line is electrified at 1.5 kV DC.

Track

In a mountainous country like New Zealand, it is not surprising that the railway includes 149 tunnels (87 km)

and 2,178 bridges (74 km). The three longest tunnels are Kaimai (8.9 km) between Tauranga and Morrinsville; Rimutaka (8.8 km) between Upper Hutt and Featherston; and Otira (8.6 km) between Otira and Arthur's Pass. The longest bridge is over the Rakaia River (Christchurch–Picton) spanning 1,743 m, while the highest is over the Mohaka River (Hawkes Bay) standing 97 m over water height.

Track improvements in 1995-96 included the destressing of 502 km of track and the replacement of 82,000 sleepers and 26 km of rail.

Rail

Main line: 50 kg/m; 91 lb/yd; 85 lb/yd

Provincial lines: 91 lb/yd; 85 lb/yd; 75 lb/yd; 70 lb/yd

Branch lines: 70 lb/yd; 55 lb/yd

Welding method: Flash-butt in depot, Thermit in field. New rails flash-butt welded in depots into 76.8 m lengths and transported to site for laying. Short rail in track may be Thermit-welded into similar lengths. Continuous welded rail is formed by Thermit process with termination joints at extremities and epoxy glue joints, or Benkler encapsulated joints, and anchored. About half of the track (70 per cent of main and provincial lines) comprises continuous welded rail.

Crossties (sleepers)

NZ Pinus radiata (all lines) 69 per cent

Concrete (main lines only) 17 per cent

Hardwood remainder

Spacing

Main line: Timber 600 mm; concrete 700 mm

Fastenings

Main lines: Timber: Pandrol spring fastenings on bedplates; clips, screw spikes, spring washers on double-shoed bedplates. Spring clips and screw spikes without bedplates

Concrete: Pandrol spring fastenings with rubber or plastic pads and nylon insulators

Branch lines: Timber: screw spikes and bedplates and cascaded from higher ranking lines

Laying method: Concrete: by Tranz Rail designed and built sleeper-laying machine or by spot resleepering machinery

Timber: Laid manually either in face or by spot resleepering machinery

Dimensions

Concrete: 254 × 190 × 2,134 mm

Timber: 200 × 150 × 2,134 mm

Maximum gradient: 1 in 33.

Maximum altitude: North Island — 814 m at Waiouru, 290 km north of Wellington on the North Island Main Trunk; South Island — 737 m at Arthur's Pass on the Midland line.

Maximum permitted speed: 100 km/h — passenger trains; 80 km/h — freight trains

Type of coupler in standard use: Passenger cars and coal wagons: Alliance

Freight wagons: 'Norwegian' hook and pin

Type of braking in standard use: Air

The 8.6 km Otira tunnel on the South Island is electrified at 1,500 V DC; these Class Eo locomotives are part of a fleet of five used for ferrying trains through the tunnel (John Glover)   **1997**

UPDATED

NICARAGUA

Ministry of Construction and Transport

PO Box 5, Managua

Key personnel
Minister: P Virgil

New lines
The former Ferrocarril de Nicaragua closed down in 1994, but in 1996 plans emerged for an ambitious new railway linking the Atlantic ocean with the Pacific. The idea was that the 370km line would provide a landbridge alternative to the Panama Canal, shifting containers and other freight from a new port at Monkey Point on the Atlantic seaboard to one of three sites being investigated on the Pacific coast.

A concession to build and operate the line and the two ports was awarded by the Nicaraguan government to the international CINN consortium, but in July 1997 President Arnoldo Aleman said the 'dry canal' project was being scrapped. Prior to this, CINN had hoped to make a start on the US$1.5 billion project in 1998, with a view to completion in 2002.

NEW ENTRY

NIGERIA

Ministry of Transport & Communications

1 Joseph Street, Marina, Lagos
Tel: +234 1 263 7611   Fax: +234 1 263 5010

Key personnel
Administrator: Ibrahim Gumel
Director-General: A T Inuwa
Director, Land Transport: A Abubakar
Deputy Director, Rail Services: S I Sabon-Birni
Assistant Director, Rail Services: F O Ike

VERIFIED

Nigerian Railways (NR)

PMB 1037, Ebute Metta, Lagos
Tel: +234 1 834300

Key personnel
Administrator: Gregory C Ilukwe
Secretary: Tijani Shehu
Directors
   Administration and Finance: A Abubakar
   Operations: L O Oshinubi
   Civil Engineering: D Olabinrin
   Mechanical and Electrical Engineering: C E Okoye
   Internal Audit: S A Ekedebe
Managers
   Signalling and Telecommunications: O Olugbodi
   Legal: I Onyeabor
   Stores: P I Ricketts

Gauge: 1,067 mm; 1,435 mm
Route length: 3,505 km; 52 km

Political background
Political debate raged around the structure of the railway in the early 1990s, but little progress was made with the vital task of rehabilitating the railway's rundown assets until mid-1996. At this time the Nigerian government approved funding for a substantial programme of track and signalling renewals (see 'Improvements to existing lines' section below), and further restructuring of management, costed at N16.8 billion. Two-thirds of that sum has already been made available, reportedly on account of improved government revenues from oil exports.

Passenger operations
The poor state of the infrastructure and rolling stock contributed to a dramatic decline in traffic after 1989, with a nadir reached in 1992 when 1.6 million passengers were carried (451 million passenger-km).

In an attempt to bring some relief to the appalling traffic conditions in Lagos, NRC has been running limited peak-hour passenger services between Ifo and Lagos. These were carrying nearly six million passengers annually in the 1980s. In 1992 the Lagos state government made available N5 million to fund new rolling stock to upgrade these services.

Freight operations
The poor state of the infrastructure and rolling stock contributed to a dramatic decline in traffic after 1989; in 1992 less than 200,000 tonnes were hauled (50 million tonne-km). In 1992 a new marketing strategy was introduced aimed at raising the miserable freight tonnage.

New lines
The 1,435 mm line linking ore deposits at Itakpe with a steelworks at Ajaokuta opened in 1992. Construction of a 270 km link from the steelworks to the sea at Warri is now proceeding.

In 1997, plans were announced for a new line to link Port Harcourt with the Federal Ocean Terminal oil and gas terminal at Onne.

Improvements to existing lines
The greater part of the funds made available in mid-1996 (see 'Political background' section above), N13 billion, will pay for renewal of 720 km of track and realignment at 40 locations where severe curvature imposes operating restraints. Rehabilitation of signalling and telecommunications equipment will absorb a further N2.6 billion.

Traction and rolling stock
At last report in 1992 NR owned 189 main line diesel locomotives, 51 diesel shunters, 13 steam locomotives, 480 passenger cars and 4,653 freight wagons. Of the motive power fleet, only some 40 line-haul locomotives were available for service, plus about 12 shunters.

A grant from the Korean Export-Import Bank was agreed in 1993. This was to provide some N292 million to fund purchase of five diesel locomotives along with technical assistance for rolling stock rehabilitation and track maintenance programmes.

In 1991 traction resources were supplemented by seven ex-Newfoundland GM-EMD Type G12 diesel locomotives bought from Canadian National's CANAC consultancy subsidiary and refurbished by Bombardier before shipment.

In 1993 15 diesels were on order from South Korean builders, funded by Korean Eximbank, along with 36 coaches.

In 1997, Dalian Locomotive Works of China was building 50 1,800 kW CKD8A diesel locomotives for Nigeria for 1997-99 delivery.

In mid-1997, NR began taking delivery of new passenger coaches from China.

Track
As much as 80% of NR track is reported in need of overhaul
Rail: BS60R 29.8 kg/m; BS70A 34.7 kg/m; BS80R, 80A 39.7 kg/m
Crossties (sleepers): Steel, 130 × 7.5 mm
Fastenings: Pandrol: K Type

UPDATED

NORWAY

Ministry of Transport & Communications

Akersgata 59, PO Box 8010 Dep, N-0030 Oslo
Tel: +47 2224 9090   Fax: +47 2224 9570
email: postmottak@sd.dep.telemax.no
Website: http://odin.dep.no/sd/publ/presentasjon

Key personnel
Minister: Ms Sissel Rønbeck
Under-Secretary of State: Torstein Rudihagen
Secretary-General: Ms Karin Bruzelius
Director-General, Rail: Pål Tore Berg

UPDATED

Norwegian National Rail Administration (JBV)

Jernbaneverket
Pilestredet 19, N-0048 Oslo
Tel: +47 2245 5000   Fax: +47 2315 3299

Key personnel
Chairman: Arent M Henriksen
Managing Director: Osmund Ueland
Directors
   Infrastructure: Magne Paulsen
   Regulation and Safety: Åge Lien
   Administration: Ole M Drangsholt
   Personnel: Ms Anne-Kari Bratten

Gauge: 1,435 mm
Route length: 4,012 km
Electrification: 2,422 km at 15 kV 16⅔ Hz AC

Organisation
Established on 1 December 1996 under legislation passed by the Norwegian parliament, Jernbaneverket is responsible for managing and maintaining Norway's rail infrastructure and for the regulation and planning of the rail system in general. The infrastructure function was previously a separate division within Norwegian State Railways (NSB).

The network is divided into four geographical regions for development, maintenance and operations purposes. Jernbaneverket's Directorate in Oslo is responsible for

Class Di6 locomotive from Siemens   *1997*

regulatory functions, comprising planning, operational safety and allocation of track capacity, and for centralised administrative and support functions.

The traffic control function was expected to be transferred to Jernbaneverket on 1 January 1998, but remained with NSB initially for operational convenience.

At its establishment, Jernbaneverket had a total of 3,500 staff. It has the same managing director, chairman and non-executive directors as NSB.

Finance

Parliament fixes annual appropriations for infrastructure maintenance and investment. The budget allocations to Jernbaneverket for 1997 were NKr1,759 million for operations and maintenance, and NKr1,211 million for capital expenditure. In addition, NKr1,690 million was allocated to construction of the Gardermoen airport line (see 'New lines' section).

The charges paid by train operators for use of the infrastructure are also set by parliament. Track charges reflect long-term marginal costs and may therefore differentiate between different types of rail traffic. They also take account of environmental factors and parity with other modes. The rate per tonne-km for 1997 was NKr0.00935, and NKr0.01462 for iron-ore trains on the Narvik—Riksgränsen line.

Jernbaneverket's expenditure is governed by a 10-year plan drawn up by the government and subject to annual review by parliament. The draft Norwegian Railway Plan for the period 1998-2007, published in April 1997, proposes capital investment worth NKr3,744 million over the four years from 1998 to 2001, of which NKr1,320 million will go towards improvements in the Greater Oslo area. Over the same period, the plan proposes to allocate a total of NKr9,010 million to Jernbaneverket's operations and maintenance activities, and NKr599 million to measures aimed at improving the reliability and capacity of the existing network.

New lines

Airport line

In 1992 parliament approved enlargement to international standards of a small airport at Gardermoen, northeast of Oslo. To serve it, a new 48 km double-track line from Oslo, engineered for 200 km/h, is being constructed by NSB Gardermobanen AS and is due to open in October 1998. Journey time from Oslo central station to the airport will be 19 minutes.

The project involves driving a 13.8 km tunnel between Bryn and Lillestrøm, to segregate airport and intercity trains from local services on the existing route, and a new railway from Lillestrøm to Eidsvoll via the airport.

Ringeriksbanen

In 1993 the then NSB infrastructure division began evaluating route options for a new line from Oslo to Hønefoss, which would become the exit from the capital for Bergen. Whereas the present Oslo—Hønefoss distance via Drammen is 90 km, the proposed line, to be built largely in tunnel, would take a direct course and halve the distance. After extensive public consultation, NSB submitted its preferred route to the government in 1995, with the aim of starting construction in 2000 for completion in 2005. However, the draft Norwegian Railway Plan 1998-2007 does not contain any commitment to the line because it cannot be accommodated within the proposed annual investment ceiling of NKr1.2 billion.

Improvements to existing lines

At the end of 1996 the Norwegian rail network had a total of 126 route-km with double track. In recent years priority has been given to extending double-tracking in the Greater Oslo area and on the Østfold (Oslo—Moss) and Vestfold (Drammen—Skien) lines, a policy which the draft Norwegian Railway Plan 1998-2007 proposes to continue.

Double-tracking of the Østfold line between Ski and Sandbukta (north of Moss), completed in 1996, is the start of a prospective 200 km/h route between Oslo and Gothenburg. However, earlier plans to double-track the entire line between Moss and the Swedish border at Kornsjø are likely to be abandoned in favour of a series of dynamic passing loops (long loops in which trains can continue to move while being passed by trains running in the opposite direction), under a review proposed in the draft Norwegian Railway Plan 1998-2007. Double-tracking of the Såstad—Haug section (between Moss and Halden) began in 1997.

Necessary infrastructure modifications to allow the introduction of tilt-body rolling stock on the Oslo—Kristiansand—Stavanger, Oslo—Bergen and Oslo—Trondheim lines are expected to be carried out between 1998 and 2001, at a total cost of NKr1 billion.

Meanwhile, work continues to improve track alignments, reduce the risk of snow blockage and provide additional passing loops on the mountain section of the Oslo—Bergen line. In 1996 work began on a new 5.2 km section at Gråskallen, east of Tunga, to be finished in 1998. The draft Norwegian Railway Plan 1998-2007 includes a commitment to further improvements between Tunga and Finse.

Construction of an enlarged Nationaltheatret station in Oslo's east-west tunnel started in 1996 and is expected to be completed by 1999. The station is the country's second busiest in terms of passenger numbers and has become a major traffic bottleneck. The scheme will create a second station chamber parallel to the existing one, doubling the number of tracks to four.

Track

Rail type: NSB 40 (40 kg/m), S 41 (41 kg/m), S 49 (49 kg/m), S 54 (54 kg/m), UIC-54E (54 kg/m), UIC-60 (60 kg/m)
Sleepers: Concrete 2,400 × 280 × 196 mm; wood 2,500 × 250 × 140 mm
Spacing: 1,667/km
Rail fastenings: Pandrol for concrete sleepers; Hey-Back or Deenik for wooden sleepers
Pads under rails: With Hey-Back fastenings a thin, 1.25 mm rubber pad is inserted between rail and baseplate.
With Pandrol fastenings a 5 mm thick plastic pad is inserted between rail and concrete sleeper.
Min curve radius: 230 m
Max gradient: 2.5%
Max permissible axleload: 22.5 tonnes

NEW ENTRY

Norwegian State Railways (NSB)

Norges Statsbaner BA
Prinsensgate 7-9, N-0048 Oslo
Tel: +47 2315 0000   Fax: +47 2315 3146
Web site: http://www.nsb.no

Key personnel

Chairman: Arent M Henriksen
Managing Director: Osmund Ueland
Directors
 Passenger Services: Leif Øverland
 Freight: Bjørn Kristiansen
 Engineering and Estates: Jan Runesson
Operations: Per Magne Mathisen
Finance: Ms Randi Flesland
Administration: Stein O Nes
Personnel: Morten Buan
Corporate Affairs: Yngve Pedersen
Communications: Svein Horrisland
Regional Managers
 East (Oslo): Einar Evensen
 South (Kristiansand): Oddvar Hodne
 West (Bergen): Ms Anne Gine Hestetun
 North (Trondheim): Tom Ingulstad
NSB Gardermobanen AS
 Managing Director: Ottar Remman
 Traffic Director: Dagfinn Berge

Political background

Under legislation that came into force on 1 December 1996, Norwegian State Railways has been reconstituted as a limited company (NSB BA) with all shares held by the state. From the same date, the operations of the former NSB infrastructure sector have been transferred to the Norwegian National Rail Administration (Jernbaneverket, see Norwegian National Rail Administration (JBV)).

Although NSB has greater commercial freedom than it previously enjoyed, the structure established by the legislation specifically provides for a degree of continuing political control, in the form of public purchasing of services and parliamentary approval for investment plans. The Minister of Transport acts as the sole shareholder, appointing the company's non-executive directors (who are the same as those of Jernbaneverket) and approving major decisions.

Organisation
NSB's railway operations comprise two main businesses, Passenger Services and Freight, while Mechanical Engineering and Estates together form a third unit. At its establishment, NSB BA had 7,400 staff. The bus and travel agency businesses have been established as separate limited companies, wholly owned by NSB.

The Passenger Services business comprises four geographical units: East (Oslo); South (Kristiansand); West (Bergen); and North (Trondheim). The heads of these regional passenger divisions are responsible for NSB's relations with local authorities and other organisations within their area.

NSB Gardermobanen AS, a wholly owned subsidiary of NSB, is responsible for construction of the high-speed line being built to serve Oslo's new international airport (see Norwegian National Rail Administration entry). When the line opens at the end of 1998, the company's role will change to that of train operator.

Finance
In 1995, NSB's operating business recorded a loss of NKr54 million. The company was aiming to be in profit by the end of 1997.

Government revenue support for the operation of passenger services was NKr975 million in 1997. In addition, NSB received a grant of NKr290 million towards the costs of restructuring as a limited company.

In 1996 NSB launched a programme entitled Effekt 600, which aims to improve financial performance by NKr600 million over three years. The strategy includes rationalisation of depot facilities, motive power and rolling stock, as well as investment in freight terminals and new passenger trains.

As a limited company, NSB is now responsible for raising its own investment capital on the private loan market and is no longer subject to government borrowing consents.

Passenger operations
NSB runs commuter services in the Oslo area and long-distance trains throughout the country. Oslo is origin or destination for about a quarter of all rail journeys in Norway. Provisional figures for 1996 show a total of 40 million passenger journeys and 2,326 million passenger-km.

Class BM70 four-car intercity emus, introduced in 1992, operate services from Oslo to Skien and Lillehammer, as well as some journeys to Gothenburg in Sweden. The Class BM70 is designed for 160 km/h operation.

In 1994-96, refurbished locomotive-hauled stock was introduced on daytime intercity services from Oslo to Stavanger, Bergen and Trondheim. The first refurbished sleeping cars entered service between Oslo and Trondheim in 1995.

One of the objectives of the Effekt 600 programme (see 'Finance') is better utilisation of passenger rolling stock. Hauled intercity stock is to operate round the clock in fixed-formation sets, with sleeping cars added on overnight services.

In 1999-2000, NSB will introduce tilt-body electric trainsets on its three main long-distance routes (see 'Traction and rolling stock' section). Following introduction of the new stock, journey times from Oslo will be as follows (current best times in brackets): Stavanger 6 hours 25 minutes (7 hours 30 minutes); Bergen 5 hours 30 minutes (6 hours 30 minutes); Trondheim 5 hours 30 minutes (6 hours 40 minutes).

Freight operations
NSB's freight division was reorganised during 1997 into three sectors covering container, trainload and wagonload operations. These are supported by a business development unit responsible for marketing and relationships with business partners.

Iron ore traffic from Kiruna in Sweden to Narvik, a port in northern Norway, previously accounted for the bulk of NSB's freight tonnage. On 1 July 1996 this operation was transferred to a new Swedish company, Malmtrafik AB (MTAB), in which NSB holds a 24.5 per cent stake. Locomotives, depot facilities and staff connected with ore operations at Narvik were taken over by MTAB's Norwegian subsidiary, Malmtrafikk AS.

As a result of the transfer of the iron ore traffic, statistics for 1995 and 1996 are not comparable. The provisional

Siemens-built Class Di8 locomotive for short-haul freight work   **1997**

Electric locomotives

Class	Wheel arrangement	Output kW	Speed km/h	No in service	First built	Builders Mechanical	Electrical
El11	Bo-Bo	1,676	100	7	1951	Thunes	NEBB
El13	Bo-Bo	2,648	100	18	1957	Thunes	NEBB
El14	Co-Co	5,076	120	31	1968	Thunes	NEBB
El16	Bo-Bo	4,440	140	17	1977	Strømmen/Nohab/Hamjern	ASEA
El17	Bo-Bo	3,400	150	12	1981	Henschel	NEBB/BBC
El18	Bo-Bo	5,880	200	22	1997	Adtranz	Adtranz

Diesel locomotives

Class	Wheel arrangement	Power kW	Speed km/h	Weight tonnes	No in service	First built	Builders Mechanical	Engine	Transmission
Di2	C	441 600	50/80	47	26	1961	Thunes	BMV LT6	H
Di3a	Co-Co	1,305	105	102	24	1954	Nohab	GM 16-567C	E GM-ASEA
Di3b	A1A-A1A	1,305	143	103	3	1958	Nohab	GM 16-567C	E GM-ASEA
Di4	Co-Co	2,430	140	112.8	5	1980	Henschel	GM 16-645E 3B	E GM-BBC
Di5*	C	485	60	47.4/53.0	13	1956	MaK	MTU GTU 6	H Voith
Di6	Co-Co	2,650	160	—	12	1996	Siemens		E
Di8	Bo-Bo	1,570	—	—	20	1997	Siemens	Caterpillar	E

* Acquired from DB in 1985-87

Electric railcars or multiple-units

Class	Cars per unit	Motor cars per unit	Motored axles/car	Output/motor kW	Speed km/h	Units in service	First built	Builders Mechanical	Electrical
BM68A	3	1	4	160	100	21	1956	Skabo	NEBB
BM68B	3	1	4	160	100	9	1960	Skabo	NEBB
BM69A	2	1	4	297	130	13	1970	Strømmen	NEBB
BM69B	2-3	1	4	297	130	19	1973	Strømmen	NEBB
BM69C	3	1	4	297	130	14	1975	Strømmen	NEBB
BM69D	3	1	4	297	130	35	1983	Strømmen	NEBB
BM69E*	3	1	4	297	130	2	1983	Strømmen	NEBB
BM70	4	1	4	430	160	16	1992	ABB Strømmen	ABB

* Rebuilt from BM69D in 1994; (NEBB = Norsk Elektrisk-Brown Boveri)

Diesel railcars or multiple-units

Class	Cars per unit	Motor cars per unit	Motored axles/car	Power/motor kW	Speed km/h	No in service	First built	Builders Mechanical	Engine	Transmission
BM92	2	1	2	2 × 360	140	15	1984	Duewag	2 × Daimler-Benz OM 424A	E BBC

figures for 1996 showed NSB freight traffic standing at 4.5 million tonnes and 1,647 million tonne-km.

A mixed freight service from Oslo to Narvik via Sweden, known as Arctic Rail Express (ARE), was introduced by NSB and Swedish State Railways (SJ) in 1993. The service now runs seven days a week and has markedly increased rail's share of freight transport between Oslo and northern Norway. The 900 tonne train completes the 1,950 km transit in 27 hours. In 1996 a second ARE service was introduced, linking Narvik with Malmö in southern Sweden.

The ARE services paved the way for closer co-operation between NSB and SJ in other areas. In January 1997 a twice-weekly service was introduced under the name Scandinavian Rail Express (SRE), linking Oslo with the Swedish port of Trelleborg, with onward connections to the continent via the train ferry to Germany. One of the main users of this service is Combitrans Combi AS, a joint venture for intermodal transport in which NSB holds 51 per cent of the shares and SJ 49 per cent.

NSB's Effekt 600 programme proposes a reduction in the number of freight wagons from 3,600 to 2,200 by 2002. This is to be achieved through better capacity utilisation, shorter turnround times and standardisation of

wagon types. With a view to making optimum use of rolling stock, an electronic wagon identification system is to be evaluated, initially on timber trains.

New or improved freight terminals at Narvik, Bodø, Fauske, Trondheim, Bergen and Stavanger also form part of the Effekt 600 strategy. Other principal intermodal terminals are located at Mo i Rana, Mosjøen, Åndalsnes, Lillehammer, Hamar, Kristiansand, Skien, Drammen, Alnabru (Oslo) and Fredrikstad.

Finance (NKr million)

Operating income	1994	1995
Passenger	1,825	2,146
Freight	1,260	1,386
Other income	2,093	1,637
Total	5,178	5,169

Operating costs	1994	1995
Personnel	3,002	2,810
Materials and services	1,793	1,775
Track charges	63	61
Depreciation	244	308
Interest	278	319
Total	5,380	5,273

Traffic (million)	1994	1995
Freight tonnage	20.0	20.9
Tonne-km	2,678	2,715
Passenger journeys	37.9	39.6
Passenger-km	2,398*	2,381

*Includes 52 million passenger-km in connection with Winter Olympics

Traction and rolling stock

At 31 December 1995, NSB's motive power fleet consisted of 115 electric locomotives, 70 diesel locomotives, 123 electric multiple-units, 15 diesel multiple-units and seven diesel railcars. Other rolling stock comprised 719 passenger coaches and 3,841 freight wagons.

The 12 Class Di6 diesel-electric Co-Co locomotives ordered from Siemens Schienenfahrzeugtechnik GmbH in 1992, originally due for delivery in 1995, have been plagued by a series of technical problems such as excessive track forces and defective cooling systems. NSB reserved the right to cancel its contract with Siemens if the manufacturer failed to deliver all 12 locomotives in fully operational condition by mid-1997. The 2,650 kW locomotives were intended to replace older members of Class Di3, principally on the Nordland line (Trondheim—Bodø).

Siemens is also supplying 20 diesel-electric Bo-Bo locomotives for short-haul freight and shunting duties. The design is based on the Netherlands Railways Class 6400, but has a 1,570 kW Caterpillar engine. Designated Class Di8 by NSB, delivery of the locomotives began in early 1997.

Also in early 1997, NSB began taking delivery of 22 Class El18 electric locomotives from Adtranz Norway, to a Bo-Bo design based on the Swiss Federal Railways Class 460. The locomotives have an output of 5,880 kW and a top speed of 200 km/h, though initially they are limited to 140 km/h. Although a mixed-traffic design, Class El18 is at present confined to long-haul passenger duties such as Oslo—Bergen.

Under the Effekt 600 strategy, NSB is aiming to have only five main locomotive classes by 2000: Di4, Di6, Di8, El14 and El18.

NSB's new Class El18 electric locomotives are based on the Swiss Loco 2000   **1997**

In 1995 the contract to supply 16 Class BM71 high-speed electric trainsets for the Gardermoen airport line was awarded to Adtranz Norway. The three-car units, fully air conditioned and pressure-sealed, will be designed for 200 km/h operation and will seat at least 170 passengers. The design includes provision for the fitting of tilt equipment, and one set is expected to be delivered with this in place. Delivery should begin in late 1997.

After successful trials with a Swedish X2000 train on the Oslo—Kristiansand route in 1996, NSB placed a follow-on order with Adtranz in March 1997 for 16 tilt-body trainsets based on the airport train design. To be designated Class BM72, the four-car units will feature a revised interior for long-distance services with accommodation for 220 passengers. The trains will progressively enter service on the Oslo—Stavanger, Oslo—Bergen and Oslo—Trondheim routes from June 1999, and the order includes an option on a further five sets.

In late 1996, NSB invited tenders to supply 36 new-generation emus for suburban services, with a view to placing an order in mid-1997 for delivery in 2000. Manufacturers have been asked to include an option to supply 10 of the units as bi-level vehicles.

On the unelectrified Dombås—Åndalsnes and Hamar—Røros lines, NSB's Effekt 600 strategy envisages the introduction of lightweight but fast dmus, possibly with tilt capability. An order for seven sets was expected to be placed during 1997 for delivery in mid-1999.

UPDATED

PAKISTAN

Ministry of Railways

Islamabad
Tel: +92 51 825247   Fax: +92 51 828846

Key personnel
Secretary, and Chairman, Railways Board:
   Muhammad Azhar

VERIFIED

Pakistan Railways (PR)

31 Sheikh Abdul Hameed Bin Badees, Lahore
Tel: +92 42 636 1900   Fax: +92 42 306193

Key personnel
Chairman, Railway Board: Muhammad Azhar
General Manager: Mohammed Afzal Khan
Deputy General Manager: Abdul Wahab Awan
Additional General Managers
   Industrial Relations: —
   Business: Muhammad Aslam
   Engineering: C B Ahmed
   Material Management: C Feroze-ud-Din
Chief Operating Superintendent: Wajihuddin Pervaiz
Chief Mechanical Engines: M Aurangzeb Khan
Chief Marketing Manager: Iqbal Samad Khan
Chief Commercial and Terminals Manager: Kadim
   Hussain Memon

Gauge: 1,676 mm; 1,000 mm
Route length: 7,718 km; 445 km
Electrification: 293 km of 1,676 mm gauge at 25 kV 50 Hz AC

Political background

Some faltering steps were made towards privatisation in the early 1990s. In 1992 it was announced that as a first

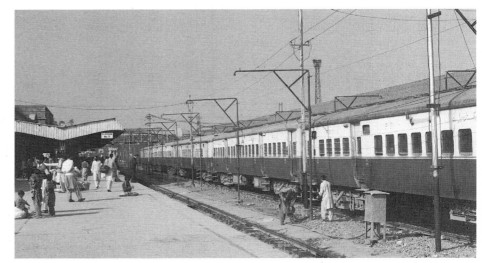

Passengers await an arrival at Rawalpindi (John Bamforth)   **1996**

step the government proposed to franchise out the lines from Lahore to Narowal and Faisalabad, and the Lodhran—Pakpattan route. Initial reports suggested that the franchisees, which took over at the beginning of 1993, had raised income on the routes, but this was due more to tighter security and control of ticketless travel than any immediate improvement to the train services. Both original franchises were later terminated and readvertised, but government approval for new leases was not immediately forthcoming.

In July 1997, disappointed by the lack of progress and the chaotic state of the railways, the government instituted a radical shake-up. World Bank-inspired reforms would see the Railways and Communications Ministries merged into a single transport ministry, a rail regulatory authority set up, and PR divided into three bodies responsible for freight, passengers and infrastructure. Within three years they would be privatised.

The plan also foresaw massive staff cuts at PR and the transfer of schools and hospitals for railway staff and their families to local authorities.

Organisation

PR comprises the whole of the North-Western system of the former British India rail network with the exception of lines in the southwestern Punjab. The main routes connect Karachi with Hyderabad, Multan, Lahore, Rawalpindi, Peshawar, Quetta and Zahedan. It was known as Pakistan Western Railway from 1961 to 1974.

Following a Railways Ministry order that railway operation be divorced from non-railway activity, PR is now structured in several management units. These are: Railway Operations; Production Unit I, which includes the Islamabad coach works and the Moghalpura steel works; Production Unit 2, which includes the new Risalpur locomotive works; Production Unit 3, covering concrete sleeper manufacture and rail welding; Property Management & Development; and PR's Consultancy Service (PRACS).

Finance

PR's financial situation deteriorated rapidly during 1993-94 and, in mid-1994, the outgoing General Manager Syed Zahoor Ahmad warned of impending crisis if the bias in favour of road transport was not reversed and rehabilitation of the rail network begun. Matters declined further during 1995, and it was forecast that PR's deficit would rise from Rs1.3 billion in 1994-95 to Rs2.3 billion in 1995-96. In fact, the deficit for FY95-96 was Rs8 billion, an outcome which brought the railway close to bankruptcy.

Government's response in the eighth five-year plan (1993-98) was to allocate PR a share of some 30 per cent of investment planned for the transport sector, whilst road projects were to receive 57 per cent. But due to poor economic conditions nationally little of this money was forthcoming; by mid-1996 only Rs7.7 billion had been made available for the entire plan period.

Investment
Government release of funds worth US$185 million and World Bank provision of a further US$105 million enabled PR in 1991 to begin an emergency programme of rehabilitation and renewals within the framework of the seventh five-year plan. A special government grant of Rs3 billion was made for the 1992-93 financial year but, in general, insufficient funds have been provided to maintain the momentum of rehabilitation projects.

Principal elements of the eighth five-year plan are works aimed at improving reliability and raising capacity. Almost Rs11 billion are allocated to purchase of new locomotives and rehabilitation of the existing fleet, and Rs8 billion will go on track upgrading projects. A new fleet of 250 passenger coaches (see below) will cost Rs2.5 billion, with a similar sum allocated for purchase of high-capacity wagons. Other objectives of the programme include: improved passenger service quality by increase of air conditioned and economy-class accommodation; equipment of wagons with roller bearings, which will enable faster and heavier freight train operation on the Karachi—Lahore—Rawalpindi main line; air braking of passenger cars to increase train length; and more computerisation of activities, including ticket issue and seat reservation, and a computerised data transmission system for real-time control of rolling stock and freight consignments.

Concerned that almost a third of its diesel locomotives are life-expired, PR plans to remanufacture 101 Alco units, but foreign exchange shortages meant that only six units had been re-engined by the start of 1996. The project was revived after agreement of a further loan of Rs5 billion from Japan in late 1995. PR also needs 30 additional locomotives, as scarcity is costing the railway new freight business, and 18 will be built with Japanese aid at Risalpur shops (see below).

Passenger operations

Passenger journeys reached a record 85 million in 1988-89. By 1993-94, this had fallen to 62 million journeys, for 16,385 million passenger-km.

Prospects were not improved by the poor condition of many coaches, with some services being withdrawn on account of rolling stock shortage. Multan works started a crash programme of light refurbishment to raise comfort standards. More coaches are to be air conditioned, and upholstery will replace hard seating in many second- and third-class cars. Some trains now have video entertainment.

In 1995 there was a move to reduce operating costs by substituting railcars for locomotive-hauled trains, but suitable cars were not available and the cost of construction or conversion was thought too high for the plan to succeed.

In 1993 some 50 passenger trains were withdrawn after it was shown that barely 10 per cent of services were covering their operating costs.

At various times during the 1990s plans were canvassed for introduction of high-speed trains, including construction of a new alignment between Karachi and Hyderabad. While the high cost militated against such schemes, PR nevertheless aims to equip all expresses

Diesel locomotives

Class	Builder's type	Wheel arrangement	Power kW	Speed km/h	Weight tonnes	No in service	First built	Mechanical	Builders Engine	Transmission
HGMU-30	TV6125A2	Co-Co	2,462	120	120	30	1985	Henschel	GM USA 16-645E3C	E GM USA
GMU-30	GTCW-2	Co-Co	2,238	122	114.95	36	1975	GM	GM USA 16-645E3	E GM USA
GMU-15	GL-220	Co-Co	1,119	122	85.44	32	1975	GM	GM USA 12-645E	E GM USA
GMCU-15	G22CU	Co-Co	1,119	122	86.90	30	1979	GM Canada	GM USA 12-645E	E GM Canada
GEU-61	—	Bo-Bo	455	80	67.84	1	1954	GE	Cooper Bessemer USA-FWL-67	E GE USA
GEU-15	U-15-C	Co-Co	1,492	122	83.00	23	1970	GE	GE USA 7FDL-B4	E GE USA
GEU-20	U-20-C	Co-Co	1,119	122	96.00	40	1971	GE	GE USA 7FDL-B11	E GE USA
HAU-10	HFA-10A	Co-Co	746	72	120	4	1980	Hitachi	Alco USA 6-251E	E Hitachi
HAU-20	HFA-22A	Co-Co	1,492	120	102.6	28	1982	Hitachi	Alco USA 12-251GE	E Hitachi
HBU 20	HFA-22B	Co-Co	1,492	125	105	60	1986 1987	Hitachi/ Bombardier	Bombardier 12-251C4	E Hitachi
HPU-20	HFA-24P	Co-Co	1,492	120	101.3	10	1982	Hitachi	Pielstick 12PA4200VG	E Hitachi
ALU-95	DL-531	Co-Co	709	104	73.98	25	1958	Alco	Alco USA 6-251B	E GE
ALU-12	DL-535	Co-Co	895	96	75.00	49	1962	Alco	Alco USA 6-251B	E GE
ALU-18	DL-541	Co-Co	1,343	120	96.00	24	1961	Alco	Alco USA 12-251B	E GE
ALU-20	DL-543	Co-Co	1,492	120	102	52	1962	Alco	Alco USA 12-251C	E GE
ALU-24	DL-560	Co-Co	1,790	120	112.44	21	1967	Alco	Alco USA 16-251B	E GE
ALU-20R	DL-543	Co-Co	1,492	120	102	6	1986*	Alco	Bombardier 12-251G4	E GE
ARP-20	DL-212	AIA-AIA	1,492	120	109.06	23	1977*	Alco	Bombardier 12-251C4	E GE
ARU-20	E-1662	AIA-AIA	1,492	120	111.9	26	1976*	Alco	Bombardier 12-251C4	E GE
ARPW-20	DL-500C	Co-Co	1,492	120	102	42	1982*	Alco	Bombardier 12-251C4	E GE USA/ Canada
FRAU-75	—	Bo-Bo	560	69	68	2	1980*	Alsthom	Pielstick SEMT PA-4	E Alsthom

* Date of rebuilding

Electric locomotives

Class	Wheel arrangement	Output kW	Speed km/h	Weight tonnes	No in service	First built	Builders Mechanical	Electrical
BCU-3DE	Bo-Bo	2,230	120	81.3	29	1966	AEI/Met Cam	English Electric

PR has ordered 30 'Blue Tiger' locomotives from Adtranz/GE   **1997**

with air conditioned coaches in an attempt to improve business prospects. Islamabad works is building 250 air conditioned cars for delivery through to 1998, including 150 economy-class saloons, 50 sleeping cars and 50 generator vans. Of these, 175 are being financed under an agreement with German donors which also covers technology transfer. The first 15 coaches will be built in Germany.

Revival of Karachi's circular railway was being canvassed once again in 1995 as a means of alleviating the city's road traffic problems. This time the project is envisaged as an inexpensive rehabilitation in which refurbished trainsets would run in one direction only on the single line, obviating the need for new track and signalling.

Freight operations

In 1991-92 freight tonnage reached a low point of 7.6 million tonnes, for 5,962 million tonne-km. Loadings improved slightly in 1992-93 to 7.8 million tonnes and 6,180 million tonne-km, and in 1993-94 reached 8 million tonnes (5,939 million tonne-km).

Handling of transfer traffic to and from Afghanistan was much improved following opening in 1993 of purpose-built container facilities at Karachi port, complementing the 'dry port' at Lahore. The terminals are now linked by a daily container train, though 10 or more trains have been run per week on occasions to clear the build-up of goods bound for Afghanistan. Capacity of Lahore's container terminal was stretched even before this latest upsurge in traffic, and private companies were seeking to construct a second terminal under a build-operate-transfer concession.

The first private sector freight operators to run trains over PR tracks are likely to be involved in a scheme to raise three-fold, to 1.8 million tonnes, the amount of oil moved by rail to up-country power stations. Private operators would be permitted to run their own rolling stock over designated routes, and investment of some US$200 million will be required for 48 locomotives and

1,300 tank wagons. Three US companies, General Motors, General Electric and Morrison Knudsen, plus Canadian Pacific and South Africa's Spoornet, expressed interest in running freight trains, but later complained of government lassitude in progressing the scheme. The franchise was readvertised by the government in June 1996.

New lines
Surveying has started on the first new railway to be built with private sector funding. This is a 150 km line into the Thar desert from the Badin terminus of PR's branch from Hyderabad. Designed to tap reserves of coal and other minerals, the line will also facilitate construction of a 1,300 MW power station in the midst of the vast coalfield at Islamkot. The concession to build both railway and power station has been granted to a consortium of Hong-Pak United Power Generation, Tanson Development and American United Corporation.

In 1991 PR and Islamic Iranian Republic Railways signed an agreement to co-operate in development of the two systems. It provided for construction of the long-discussed 375 km connection between PR at Zahedan and IIRR at Kerman. A 40 km branch is to be built from the Zahedan line at Taftan to a copper mining development at Saindak.

Construction of several other lines has been canvassed in recent years, most recently a 650 km direct line from Quetta to Karachi, but the pressure on the investment budget makes it unlikely that a start will be made on any of them.

Improvements to existing lines
A long-planned track-doubling project, from Karachi to Peshawar, was scheduled to get under way in 1993, but no bids had been received for the proposed build-operate-transfer contract. Later, in 1995, doubling of the Lodhran—Peshawar section was reportedly shelved. Allied to this scheme is a proposal for high-speed operations over the route, for which French consultants Sofrerail completed a prefeasibility study in early 1993. An 80 km section of the Multan–Khanewal line was also proposed for doubling in 1995.

Traction and rolling stock
At the start of 1995 there were 79 steam locomotives, 533 diesel-electric locomotives, 29 electric locomotives, five diesel railcars and 132 trailers, 2,574 coaches and 28,525 wagons on the broad-gauge system. Metre-gauge stock comprised 18 steam locomotives, 63 passenger cars and 425 wagons.

In 1996, PR ordered 30 'Blue Tiger' diesel locomotives from a consortium of Adtranz, Germany, and General Electric, USA. The new machines will be delivered in 1998.

In accord with a policy of self-sufficiency in rolling stock manufacture, a diesel-electric locomotive manufacturing works has been constructed near Risalpur at a total cost of Rs1,993 million. The foreign exchange component of that sum was Rs1,237 million. The project has the support of the Japanese government and a technology transfer agreement has been concluded with Hitachi. The first locomotive, a 150 kW shunter, was rolled out at the end of 1993, but the target of 18 locomotives set for 1995 was unlikely to be completed before the end of 1997. Projected output is 25 locomotives per annum.

In early 1995, bids were sought by the Ministry of Railways for contractors to take over maintenance of diesel locomotives at PR workshops. Three US companies — General Electric Transportation Systems, GM and Morrison Knudsen — registered their interest.

Signalling and telecommunications
A major signalling project is under way comprising both conventional and modern signalling works, such as provision of colourlight signals on the double-track main line between Lahore and Raiwind and of tokenless block on other important lines, starting with Lodhran—Khanewal—Faisalbad and Sangla Hill—Wazirabad. Following a call for international tenders, orders for design, supply and installation of the equipment were placed with Siemens.

Signalling over some 2,000 route-km of main lines is to be upgraded in a programme agreed in 1993. Japan's Marubeni Corp will carry out the work, with much equipment to be supplied by Siemens' local subsidiary.

A modern train and traffic control system has been installed on the Rawalpindi—Peshawar Cantt section of main line over a length of 174 km. The equipment was supplied by Aydin Monitor System of the USA.

Further projects, which had been scheduled for 1994-95 completion, provide for UHF communication over 598 km covering the Rawalpindi—Peshawar Cantt and Kot Adu—Attock City sections; and track circuiting of storage sidings at 94 stations on the Hyderabad—Peshawar line.

Type of coupler in standard use: Screw
Type of braking in standard use: Passenger cars (at 2/92): air, 872 cars; vacuum, 1,467 cars.
Freight cars: vacuum all

Electrification
In order to get full benefits of electric traction and to remove operational bottlenecks, extension of electrification from Khanewal to Sama Satta via both Chord and Loop is considered essential. Though planned for more than 20 years, and included in the eighth plan, the project has never been accorded any funds. Estimated cost is Rs1,174 million. Tenders to execute the electrification were called in 1989, but no contracts were let.

At the start of 1994 agreement was reached with Britain's ABB Transportation for overhaul of the 32 traction motors that power the 30-year-old fleet of electric locomotives.

Track
Rail: 50 kg RE, 45 kg R BSS, 37.5 kg R BSS
Crossties (sleepers)

Type	Thickness	Spacing
PSC Monobloc	234 mm	1,640/km
RCC twin-block	231.77 mm	1,562/km
Wooden	125.152 mm	1,562/km
Steel trough	106.36 mm	1,562/km
CST 9 (cast-iron plates joined with tie bar)	133.35 mm	1,562/km

Fastenings
PSC/RCC sleepers: RM Type
Wooden sleepers: WI bearing plates with dog spikes; CI bearing plates with round spikes and keys
Steel trough sleepers: Mills spring loose jaws with keys
CST/9 CI plate sleepers: Keys
Min curvature radius: 10°
Max gradient: 4%
Max permissible axleload: 22.86 tonne

UPDATED

PANAMA

Ministry of Public Works

PO Box 1632, Panama 1
Tel: +507 325505/325572   Fax: +507 325758

Key personnel
Minister: J A Dominguez
Secretary: E Perez Y   *UPDATED*

Chiriquí Land Company Railways

Chiriquí Land Company, Puerto Armuelles, Chiriquí, Apartado 6-2637 or 6-2638, Estafeta El Dorado, Panama City
Tel: +507 70 7641   Fax: +507 70 8064

Chiriquí National Railroad

Ferrocarril Nacional de Chiriquí
PO Box 12B, David City, Chiriquí

Key personnel
General Manager: M Alvarenga

Panama Railroad (FCP)

Ferrocarril de Panamá
PO Box 2023, Estafeta de Balboa, Panama
Tel: +507 326081/326086   Fax: +507 325343

Key personnel
Director-General: Victor M D'Anello

Key personnel
General Manager: Cameron Forsyth
Assistant General Manager: Ricardo Flores
Technical Services Manager: Victor Mirones

Gauge: 914 mm
Route length: 152.5 km

Organisation
The railway, which was formerly divided into the Armuelles (133 km) and Bocas (243 km) Divisions, is dedicated to the transport of bananas. In 1992, the network was reduced to 152 km in length. Track is formed of 30 kg/m rails spiked to wooden sleepers spaced 1,600/km in plain track, 1,700/km in curves. Maximum

Gauge: 914 mm
Route length: 126 km

Organisation
The railway, operated by the government of Panama, consists of a single line linking David City with Puerto Armuelles, in the region of the Costa Rican border.

Gauge: 1,524 mm
Length: 76 km

Political background
National austerity has kept the railway short of investment funds, with the result that both infrastructure and rolling stock are now badly rundown and traffic has declined

permissible axleload is 20 tonnes and the maximum gradient 2 per cent.

Freight operations
Freight traffic in 1993 amounted to 410,670 tonnes.

Traction and rolling stock
The railway operates 17 diesel locomotives, seven diesel railcars and 380 freight wagons. Most powerful traction units are five 700 hp Caterpillar-engined locomotives, one a Whitcomb unit of 1948, the remainder GE of 1959 and 1970. Standard coupler is knuckle-type and braking of vehicles mechanical.

VERIFIED

Traction and rolling stock
The fleet comprises five diesel locomotives, five diesel railcars, five passenger coaches and 24 freight wagons.

VERIFIED

sharply. In 1996, a concession to operate the line was granted to a joint venture consisting of the US firm Kansas City Southern Industries, which owns Kansas City Southern Railway, Mi-Jack Products (equipment supplier and terminal operator) and a Panamanian consortium known as Terminales Portuarios Panamenos. Plans include a complete track upgrade to allow the FCP to offer an alternative to the parallel Panama canal between the coastal ports of Cristóbal and Balboa. A concession was expected to be signed in July 1997.

Improvements to existing lines
Rehabilitation of the system, including the purchase of new diesel locomotives and rolling stock, is considered an urgent priority. Immediate needs have been estimated to cost US$20 million. Modernisation of the single-track route would raise speeds on passenger services to 80 km/h and on freight trains to 60 km/h, although this would require complete reballasting and resleepering throughout, with rerailing of the Mount Hope—Gatún section.

Traction and rolling stock
The railway operates four GM-EMD SW1200 diesel locomotives, some Alco Co-Cos, six passenger cars and 90 freight wagons.

Track
Rail: 40, 45 and 50 kg/m

Sleepers: Wood spaced 2,070/km
Fastenings: Track spike
Min curve radius: 250 m
Max gradient: 1.3%
Max permissible axleload: 20 tonnes

UPDATED

PARAGUAY

Ministry of Public Works & Communications

2° Piso-Gral, Diaz y Alberdi, Asunción

Key personnel
Minister: C Facetti
Under-Secretary: A Gomez Optiz

VERIFIED

Ferrocarril Presidente Carlos Antonio López (FCPCAL)

PO Box 453, Calle Mexico 145, Asunción
Tel: +595 21 443273/445717
Fax: +595 21 447848

Key personnel
President: E A Alvarez
Secretary-General: R del Puerto
Directors
  Technical: J J Servían
  Commercial: H O Guth
  Financial: W C Vallejos O
Managers
  Traffic: J C Torales
  Tariff and Commercial: R V Bareiro
  Materials: C Insfran
  Way and Works: J Adorno
  Traction and Workshops: P M Cantero

Gauge: 1,435 mm
Route length: 441 km

Political background
At the end of 1991, the Paraguayan government passed a law effectively making it possible to privatise all state enterprises. Modernisation work was to be undertaken with a view to privatising the system. In 1997, the government pledged US$150 million to prepare the railway for privatistion.

Organisation
Paraguay's only common carrier railway, the state-owned Ferrocarril Presidente Carlos Antonio López (FCPCAL), extends from Asunción southeast via Villarrica to Encarnación and Pacú-Cuá (375 km) with a branch from San Salvador to Abaí 65 km long. The railway employed some 800 staff as of mid-1995.

Passenger operations
In 1994 FCPCAL recorded 24,000 passenger journeys. In mid-1995, it was reported that passenger services comprised occasional Asunción—Aregua running at weekends, with the reintroduction of daily Asunción—Ypacarai workings tabled for 1997, although new diesel locomotives would have to be acquired, bridges strengthened and some track work carried out.

Freight operations
Freight traffic amounted to 182,000 tonnes in 1994. As of mid-1995, weekly freight services were reported in operation between Asunción and General Artigas, continuing to Encarnación whenever possible. International traffic between Encarnación and Posadas in Argentina comprised exports of Paraguayan soya beans and imported goods moving in containers.

FCPCAL freight and passenger workings cross at San Salvador (Robert Preston) **1995**

New lines
In 1997, plans emerged to build a new line serving Ciudad del Este, which is on the eastern border with Brazil and Argentina.

Improvements to existing lines
Improvements to the decrepit FCPCAL main line are sorely needed. The opening of the fixed link between the Paraguayan and Argentine railway systems was expected to boost traffic, but the poor condition of the Asunción—Encarnación route stands in the way of any sustained system-wide growth. Previous strategies for modernisation have focused on the renewal of track throughout the Villarrica—Encarnación corridor (and the 140 km section between Villarrica and General Artigas in particular) and replacement of the railway's antique rolling stock.

As of mid-1995, FCPCAL operations were hampered by seasonal flooding of the River Paraná severing the main line between Encarnación and General Artigas. The level of the Paraná has risen due to the construction of a dam at Yacyreta and the possibility of relocating the FCPCAL main line appears remote.

Traction and rolling stock
The FCPCAL fleet comprises 24 mainly British-built wood-burning steam locomotives, eight passenger coaches and 195 freight wagons. As of mid-1995, some nine locomotives were reported as serviceable.

Many of the freight and passenger vehicles latterly in use were on loan from Argentine Railways. It was reported in mid-1995 that its successor as FCPCAL's international connection, the private Ferrocarril Mesapotámico General Urquiza SA, was allowing its wagons to proceed no further into Paraguay than Encarnación due to the risk of damage and delay.

UPDATED

PERU

Ministry of Transport, Communications, Housing & Construction

Avenida 28 de Julio 800, Lima
Tel: +51 1 433 1212   Fax: +51 1 433 0427

Key personnel
Minister: Juan Castilla Meza
Secretary General: Dr J J Quelopana Rázuri

VERIFIED

ENAFER-Peru

Empresa Nacional de Ferrocarriles del Perú
PO Box 1379, Jr Ancash 207, Lima 100
Tel: +51 1 428 9440   Fax: +51 1 428 0905

Key personnel
Chairman: Juan B Solari
Managers
    General: Luis Robles Recavarren
    Operations: Roberto Rosell
    Planning and Development: Angel Bottino
    Financial and Administration: Jorge Gagliardo
    Commercial: Jaime Scamarone
Advisors
    Mechanical: Alberto Mori
    Financial: Carlos Reyes
    Legal: Viviano Rodriguez

Gauge: 1,435 mm; 914 mm
Route length: 1,296 km; 314 km

Political background
In 1990 the Peruvian government announced its intention to privatise ENAFER. At the same time it issued a decree permitting the construction of new railways competitive with the state system by private enterprise. In November 1991 President Fujimori confirmed that he intended to end the state regulation of the transport market and abolish the state railway's monopoly. It was proposed that management of infrastructure would be split from day-to-day operation of trains, with private companies invited to run services and paying rent for the use of the track.

In 1997, the Commission for the Promotion of Private Industry was preparing proposals for privatisation; bids were expected to be due by the end of the year. Mercer Consulting of the USA was assisting in the process. It has been decided that the loss-making Huancayo—Huancavelica line will not be privatised; this line provides an essential social service.

A star rating system has been adopted by the Commission. The South Eastern is three-star, Central two-star and Southern one-star. The last will be let as a concession including the port of Matarani and will include the isolated Tacna—Arica line. In the meantime, the workforce has been cut from 5,000 to 1,500 and rolling stock maintenance contracted out to former employees.

Peru has been granted a loan of US$35 million by the World Bank to fund track rehabilitation on the Central and Southern Railways and the purchase of rolling stock spares. Using these funds, bids were invited in 1995 for 5,580 tonnes of rail and rail fastenings, and in 1996 for materials and spare parts to the value of US$2 million for freight wagon refurbishment. It is hoped that the repairs will render ENAFER more attractive to the private sector.

Organisation
ENAFER was formed in 1972 with the nationalisation of The Peruvian Corporation railways, a private company which ran most of Peru's railways and the Lake Titicaca ferry services. The system now comprises the Central, Southern and South Eastern Railways with headquarters in Lima, Arequipa and Cusco respectively.

Passenger operations
Systemwide, ENAFER achieved 1.8 million passenger journeys (216 million passenger-km) in 1995. By mid-1995, passenger services had been suspended on the Central Railway (except for some weekend excursion services to San Bartolomé) but were in operation on the South Oriental Railway between Cusco and Quillabamba, and on the Cusco—Puno and Puno—Arequipa sections of the Southern Railway.

Freight operations
ENAFER carried 1.7 million tonnes of freight and generated 484 million tonne-km in 1994. In 1995, these figures declined to 1.5 million tonnes, 407 million tonne-km.

New lines
A US$1 billion, 1,800 km railway between the port of Bayover and Acre in Brazil has been proposed.

Track
Standard rail: 34.7 and 39.7 kg/m
Crossties (sleepers): Peruvian hardwood
Made-up sleepers consisting of two blocks of reinforced concrete joined by a piece of used rail have been used in sidings and on straight stretches of main line
Spacing
    Main line: 1,600-1,720/km
    Branch line: 1,365-1,700/km
Rail fastenings
Soleplates and ⅞ in coachscrews
Soleplates and ⅝ in dog spikes
Pandrol fastenings are being fitted where new 35 kg/m rail is being laid
Max curvature: 17.5° = min radius 100 m
Max gradient: 4.7% (Central Railway), 4% (Southern Railway)
Max altitude: 4,839 m on Central Railway at La Cima siding on the Ticlio—Morococha branch, 173 km from Callao. On main line 4,782 m inside Galera Tunnel, 172 km from Callao
Max axleloading
    Central Railway: 1,435 mm, 18 t; 914 mm, 14 t
    Southern Railway: 1,435 mm, 17 t; 914 mm, 14 t
    Tacna—Arica: 19.5 t
Bridge loading: Cooper E-40

UPDATED

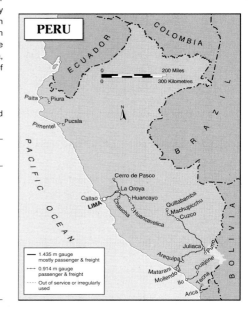

Diesel locomotives

Class	Wheel arrangement	Power kW	Speed km/h	Weight tonnes	First built	Mechanical	Builders Engine	Transmission
	0-6-0	256	30	42	1964	Yorkshire Engine	Rolls-Royce C8TEL	H Rolls-Royce
	0-6-0	140	20	32.6	1950	Hunslet	Gardner 863	M Hunslet
DL-531	Co-Co	671	80	71.6	1958	Alco	Alco 6251B	E GE
DL-532-B	Bo-Bo	708	80	69.4	1974	MLW	Alco 6251B	E GE
DL-535-A	Co-Co	895	80	69.7	1967	Alco	Alco 6251C	E GE
DL-535-B	Co-Co	895	80	81.4	1963	Alco	Alco 6251B	E GE
DL-535B	Co-Co	895	80	80.7	1976	MLW	Alco 6251B	E GE
DL-535D	Co-Co	895	80	80.7	1964	MLW	Alco 6251B	E GE
DL-500-C	Co-Co	1,342	110	104	1956	Alco	Alco 12251C	E GE
DL-543	Co-Co	1,491	110	110	1962-63	Alco	Alco 12551B	E GE
DL-560-D	Co-Co	1,789	105	110	1964-66	Alco	Alco 16251B	E GE
DL-560-D	Co-Co	1,789	105	110	1974	MLW	Alco 16251E	E GE
GT-26CW-2	Co-Co	2,237	105	116	1982	GM	GM 16-645E3B	E GM
GT-26C2-2	Co-Co	2,237	105	116	1983	GM	GM 16-645E3B	E GM

Central Railway

ENAFER-Ferrocarril del Centro
PO Box 1379, Ancash 207, Lima
Tel: +51 1 427 6620   Fax: +51 1 428 1075

Key personnel
Manager: Terry Medina Llerena
Chief of Operations: Raul Liao Rengifo
    Infrastructure: Jorge Vigil Rojas
    Mechanical: Manuel Pinto Podesta
    Commercial: Fernando Tovar Madueño

Gauge: 1,435 mm
Route length: 380 km

Organisation
The standard-gauge main line runs from Callao to Huancayo where it connects with the 914 mm gauge line to Huancavelica, which was privatised in 1996. There are 66 tunnels with aggregate length of 8.9 km, 59 bridges and nine zig-zags (reversing stations).

Freight operations at Galera on the Central Railway of Peru

1997

The main line climbs from sea level to its highest point of 4,782 m in the Galera Tunnel in 171 km from Callao on an average gradient of 4 per cent. The highest point on the system is 4,818 m at a siding at La Cima on the Ticlio—Morococha branch. This makes it the highest standard-gauge line in the world. The steepest gradients occur in the first 222 km from Callao, at sea level, to La Oroya at 3,726 m above sea level.

Traction and rolling stock
The Central Railway operates 25 diesel locomotives, 41 passenger coaches and 972 freight wagons.

UPDATED

South Eastern Railway

ENAFER-Ferrocarril Sur-Oriente
Estación Marko Jara Schenone, Cusco
Tel: +51 84 221931   Fax: +51 84 233551

Key personnel
Manager: Alberto Cruzado

Gauge: 914 mm
Route length: 186 km

Organisation
Formerly managed as part of the Southern Railway, the 914 mm gauge route from Cusco to Quillabamba via Machu Picchu emerged as a separate division in 1993.

Passenger and freight operations
The primary traffic is tourism, from Cusco to Puente Ruinas, the station nearest to the Inca remains of Machu Picchu, for which there is no road access from Cusco. This lack of a parallel road also dictates that most of the available freight traffic travels by rail, with transhipment at Cusco. In 1997 there were two daily trains from Cusco to Puente Ruinas and one mixed train from Cusco to Quillabamba. Trailing load is severely restricted by the zigzags and gradients from Cusco San Pedro terminus up to El Arco.

Traction and rolling stock
The South Eastern Railway operates seven 900 kW diesel locomotives, one Type DL535 and six Type DL535A/B, eight diesel railcars (2 Ferrostaal, 6 Macosa), 36 passenger coaches and 88 freight wagons.

UPDATED

Diesel railcars at Puente Ruinas on Peru's South Eastern Railway
1997

Southern Railway

ENAFER-Ferrocarril del Sur
PO Box 194, Avenida Tacna y Arica 201, Arequipa
Tel: +51 84 238045   Fax: +51 84 231603

Key personnel
Manager: Waldo Olivos Rengifo
Chief of Operations: Henry Vizcarra Turpo
  Mechanical: Percy Gutiérrez
  Infrastructure: Carlos Velasco Loza
  Commercial: Leonel Carpio

Gauge: 1,435 mm
Route length: 915 km

Organisation
The 1,435 mm gauge main line of the Southern Railway runs from the ports of Matarani and Mollendo on the Pacific coast to Juliaca, 476 km, where the line divides to Puno, 47 km, on Lake Titicaca; and to Cusco, 338 km, where it connects with the 914 mm gauge South Oriental Railway to Quillabamba. The main line climbs from sea level to its highest point at Crucero Alto, 4,477 m, in 359 km from Matarani on an average gradient of 3 per cent.

ENAFER's Southern Railway operates shipping services on Lake Titicaca at an altitude of 3,818 m. The highest ferry service in the world runs on a 204 km route from Puno, Peru to Guaqui, Bolivia. The fleet includes one train ferry, three mixed passenger/freight vessels, one dredger and two launches.

Finance
Investment totalling US$22.15 million was planned for the Southern Railway in 1996, with US$12.6 million to be spent on major track improvements. Other major investment items included US$5.43 million to be spent on refurbishing diesel-electric locomotives, US$1.63 million on freight wagons and US$1.22 million on track maintenance machinery.

Traction and rolling stock
The Southern Railway operates 29 diesel locomotives, 36 diesel railcars, 84 passenger coaches and 954 freight wagons.

UPDATED

Empresa Minera del Centro del Perú (Centromin Perú) SA

Railway Division
PO Box 2412, Lima 100
Tel: +51 14 761010   Fax: +51 14 769756

Key personnel
Chairman: J C Barcellos
General Manager: J Merino
Central Manager of Operations: J C Huyhua
Services Manager: L Pérez
Superintendent of Railways: J Chávez
Chief Operations Officer: V Zúñiga
Chief Mechanical Officer: C A Hoyos
Supervising Engineer, Way and Structures: A Chang Way
Accountant, Railways: J Gutiérrez

Gauge: 1,435 mm
Route length: 212.2 km

Political background
In 1997, the government announced that the company would be merged with ENAFER (qv) prior to letting concessions for the operation of that railway. The transfer will be overseen by the Commission for the Promotion of Private Industry.

Organisation
The railway division of the Centromin mining company comprises two lines lying east of Lima branching from ENAFER's Central Railway. These are La Oroya—Cerro de Pasco (132.2 km) and Pachacayo—Chaucha (80 km), operated for the transport of concentrates, ores, raw materials and spare parts. Centromin's railway operations employed a staff of 282 at the end of 1996.

Finance (US$ million)

Revenue	1994	1995	1996
Freight	3.176	3.069	5.812
Other income	1.684	1.242	0.077
Total	4.860	4.311	5.890

Expenditure	1994	1995	1996
Staff/personnel	2.801	3.272	3.197
Materials and services	0.655	0.493	0.552
Depreciation	1.059	0.540	0.482
Total	4.516	4.306	5.955

Traffic (million)	1994	1995	1996
Freight tonnes	0.884	0.885	0.888
Freight tonne-km	103.497	101.347	105.866

Traction and rolling stock
The fleet in 1996 consisted of 10 diesel locomotives and 627 freight wagons.

Coupler in standard use: Sharon 10A
Braking in standard use: Air (valves K, AB, ABD Wabco Westinghouse)

Signalling and telecommunications
The railway uses a combination of mechanical, hand, telegraph, telephone and radio signalling.

Track
Rail type and weight: 9,020 45 kg/m (158 km); 7,040 35 kg/m (112 km)
Crossties (sleepers): Wood; 500,000 installed, spacing 1,850/km
Fastenings: Cut track spikes
Min curvature radius: 15° (La Oroya—Cerro de Pasco); 16° (Pachacayo—Chaucha)
Max gradient: 2.44% (La Oroya—Cerro de Pasco); 4.15% (Pachacayo—Chaucha)
Max permissible axleload: 19.8 tonnes

UPDATED

Diesel locomotives

Class	Wheel arrangement	Power kW	Speed km/h	Weight tonnes	No in service	First built	Mechanical	Builders Engine	Transmission
GR-12	Co-Co	980	105	174	5	1964	GM	GM 12/567C	E GM
GA-8	Bo-Bo	635	70	173	3	1964	GM	GM 8/567C	E GM
G22CW	Co-Co	1,120	105	107	2	1976	GM	GM 12/645E	E GM
G18W	Bo-Bo	745	115	66	1	1976	GM	GM 8/645E	E GM

Ilo—Toquepala Railway

Ferrocarril Ilo—Toquepala
PO Box 2640, Lima
Tel: +51 14 361565   Fax: +51 54 726344

Key personnel
Manager: R D Alley
Resident Engineer: G Pasut
General Foreman: T L Chapman

Operations: D M Krinovich
Maintenance of Way Foreman: R Lungstrom

Gauge: 1,435 mm
Route length: 219 km

Organisation
The railway connects the port of Ilo with copper mines at Toquepala, with a branch serving deposits at Cuajone.

Traction and rolling stock
The railway operates 41 diesel locomotives and 629 freight wagons.

VERIFIED

PHILIPPINES

Department of Transport & Communications

Philcomcen Building, Ortigas Avenue, Pasig, Metro Manila
Tel: +63 2 631 8761   Fax: +63 2 639 9985

Key personnel
Secretary: Arturo Enrile
Under-Secretary, Transport: P C Cal
Under-Secretary, Communications: Josefina T Lichauco
Chief, Railway Planning Division: E C Galvante
Supervising Transportation Development Officer:
    J R Bondoc
Senior Transportation Development Officer:
    J R Magbanua   *UPDATED*

Philippine National Railways (PNR)

Torres Bugallon Street, Kalookan City, Metro Manila
Tel: +63 2 362 2406   Fax: +63 2 362 0824

Key personnel
General Manager: Jose Dado
    Assistant General Management: Rafael Mosura, Jnr
Acting Assistant General Managers
    Maintenance: Erasto Laiz
    Operations: Ramon Jimenez
    Finance and Administration: Francisco Aure
Managers
    Legal Department: Antonio Holgado
    Public Affairs Department: Hilario Rojo
    Performance and Efficiency Board: Lynna Goyma
    OIC, Security and Investigation Services:
        Alexander Josol
    Training Operations Department: Ramon Jimenez
    Station Operations Department: Bonaparte Roque
    Rolling Stock Maintenance Department: Erasto Laiz
    Permanent Ways Maintenance Department:
        Antonio Garcia Jnr
    Materials Management Department: Francisco Aure
    Controllership Department: Edilberto Manalo
    Treasury Department: Stalin Landas
    Personnel Services Department: Salvacion Bundoc
    Hospital Services: Armando Fuentes
    Real Estate Development: Edna Ramos

Gauge: 1,067 mm
Route length: 897 km, of which 492 km in operation

Organisation
Much of the northern part of the network remains closed due to the poor condition of the infrastructure. Operations are currently concentrated on the 478 km Southern line from Manila to Legaspi City, on which major rehabilitation work was completed in 1995. Only the final 41 km from

Reconstruction of the line to Legaspi has seen the previous formation rebuilt with concrete sleepers, fresh ballast and part worn rail   *1997*

Polangui to Legaspi remain closed. Suburban trains run south from Manila on this line as far as Carmona.

Passenger operations
Passenger traffic has suffered from the poor state of the system; the number of journeys declined by more than half between 1990 and 1993. Long-distance passenger figures have continued to languish, but Manila suburban services bounced back sharply in 1993 following commissioning of 10 new diesel locomotives. Passenger journeys doubled to 4.6 million, holding steady for the following two years. Reopening throughout of Main line South (see 'Improvements to existing lines' section below) is expected to improve carryings.

Freight operations
With nearly half the system closed, traffic has been in decline for several years. Tonnage amounted to only 5,000 in 1992 for 0.9 million tonne-km. By 1995 there had been a mild recovery, with 14,000 tonnes moving 3.9 million tonne-km, although the transport of construction materials for the Main line South reconstruction artificially improved the figures.

New lines
In March 1997, a 25-year concession to build a commuter line south from Manila was let by the government to a consortium led by property developer Ayala Land Inc. The US$600 million plan is to reconstruct and electrify the line from Manila to Calamba along the shore of Laguna de Bay. Rolling stock planned is 22 locomotives and 112 coaches. The consortium will own the trains and operate services, but the government has insisted that the track be handed to it upon completion so that other operators can use it.

There are long-term plans for construction of two new lines, once rehabilitation of the existing network is complete. A 153 km line to Sorsogon from Main line South is planned, along with a 281 km route to open up the Cagayan Valley in the north of the country. Reinstatement of the 92 km Balagtas-Cabantuan branch is also planned.

In 1995 a plan to build a railway on the island of Mindanao attracted proposals from Spanish, Czech, French and German companies. There is also a proposal to build a 130 km/h link from Manila to the development area on the former US Clark airbase. This involves reconstruction and electrification of the 25 kV Main line North from Manila to 1,435 mm gauge, with construction of a short branch from Dan to Clark. Construction was expected to get under way in 1997 following granting of a concession to North Rail, a consortium in which RENFE of Spain features.

One other important rail-related project is for construction of toll roads above PNR rights-of-way, allied to development of housing for up to 12,000 families. This is designed to remove the large number of squatters who currently live in shacks alongside the tracks.

Improvements to existing lines
A major project for the total rehabilitation of PNR's 437 km Main line South, from Manila to Polangui (the remaining 42 km to Legaspi have been closed since landslip damage in 1976), got under way in 1992 following the granting of a loan from the OECD, and was largely completed in 1995. In 1996, rehabilitation of the sections from Naga to Legaspi (96 km) was carried out by the Australian contractor John Holland, with consultants TMG International undertaking supervision. PNR's goal is to have 10 trains a day running at speeds of up to 75km/h; the route is expected to carry 2.5 million passengers annually.

Except for a commuter train service from Manila to Malolos (37 km from Manila), the whole of the 266 km

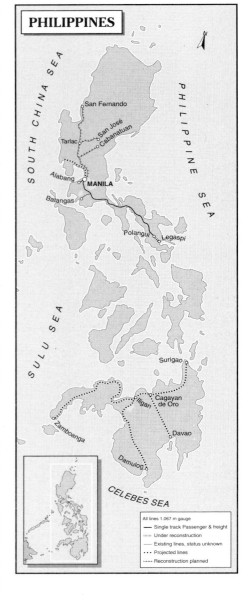

Main line North from Manila to San Fernando La Union and the 55 km branch line from Tarlac to San Jose Nueva Ecija are closed to train operations due to heavy damage caused by storms. Local interests are co-operating with international investors in proposing a US$100 million package of improvements to the Main line North, to serve K-Line's new container port at Subic.

Rehabilitation of the 56 km Calamba-Batangas branch is planned.

Traction and rolling stock
Chronic availability problems have plagued every PNR effort to improve services. In 1995 PNR operated 25 diesel locomotives, 21 diesel railcars, 30 passenger cars and 266 wagons.

In 1992 PNR took delivery from Japanese industry of 16 1,120 kW diesel locomotives for operation on the South line out of Manila. These were immediately utilised on Manila suburban services, where their good availability was responsible for a doubling of traffic in 1993.

Acquisition of six more diesel-electric locomotives, repair of five others and refurbishment of 20 passenger coaches is going ahead under the Main line South improvement project.

Signalling and telecommunications
In the Manila terminal area 13.6 km of double-track line with semaphore signals is controlled from interlocked cabins. On single-track lines elsewhere trains operate on the English 'staff' system or by telegraph or telephone communication and VHF radio from station to station.

Track
Standard rail
Main line: 32.2 kg/m in 30 and 33 ft lengths

37.2 kg/m in 60 and 25 ft lengths
Branch lines: 32.2 kg/m in 30 and 33 ft lengths
Rail joints: Angle bars with slots for spikes
Crossties (sleepers)
Main line: 'Molave' wood, 127 × 203 × 2,133 mm, spaced at 610 mm
Branch line: 'Molave' wood, 127 × 203 × 2,133 mm, spaced at 610 mm
Bridge ties: 'Yacal' wood, 203 × 203 × 2,438 mm, spaced at 406 mm
A limited number of steel ties are also used
Rail fastenings: Track spikes; bolts with square nuts; 'Hipower' nutlock washer, elastic rail spikes

Max curvature
Main line: 9.2° = min radius 190 m
Branch line: 11½° = min radius 150 m
Max gradient: 1.2%
Max axleload: 16 tonnes
Max permitted speed: 60 km/h

UPDATED

POLAND

Ministry of Transport & Shipping

ul Chalubińskiego 4, PL-00-928 Warsaw
Tel: +48 22 624 4300   Fax: +48 22 300261

Key personnel
Minister: Tadeusz Szozda
Director, Railways: K Celinski

UPDATED

Polish State Railways (PKP)

Polskie Koleje Państwowe
ul Chalubińskiego 4-6, PL-00-928 Warsaw
Tel: +48 22 624 4338   Fax: +48 22 624 44 10

Key personnel
PKP Council
President: Adam Wieladek
Vice President: Alexander Janiszewski
Executive
Director-General: Jan Janik
Deputy Director-General: Jerzy Zalewski
Board Members
Motive Power: Jerzy Smialkowski
Personnel: Henryk Pawłowski
Operations and Commercial: Jerzy Zabecki
Directors
Strategic Planning: Marian Łukasiak
Passenger, Commercial: Grzegorz Uklejewski
Freight, Commercial: Jan Tymoszuk
Economic Office: Zbigniew Cieślik
Director General's Office: Jerzy Wiśniewski
Operations: Czeslaw Dudziak
Traction and Rolling Stock: Romuald Keller
Track Maintenance: Bogdan Grzegorzewski
Data Systems: Aleksander Słupczyński
Signalling and Telecommunications: Kazimierz Frak
Research and Development: Radosław Żołnierzak
Personnel: Andrzej Krawczyk
Training Office: Bogdan Ciszewski
Procurement Office: Artur Dudziak
Legal Affairs: Anna Žmuda-Bednarczyk
Investment: Ryszard Sikora

Gauge: 1,524 mm; 1,435 mm; 1,000, 785, 750 and 600 mm
Route length: 652 km; 22,243 km; 1,418 km
Electrification: 11,613 km at 3 kV DC; 35 km at 600 V DC

Political background
Poland's railways have suffered the same difficulties as those of the other former eastern bloc countries in adapting to the closure of heavy industry and other structural changes in the economy following the political changes of 1989. However, Poland has been one of the more successful ex-Comecon countries in acclimatising to change: it is one of the three countries (the Czech Republic and Hungary being the other two) which accounted for over 90 per cent of inward capital flows to the region in 1995. Inflation was around 30 per cent in 1995, in the middle of the range for the region.

An austerity programme in the early 1990s saw the withdrawal of around a thousand little-used passenger trains, and marginal freight terminals have been closed. The government has pushed through other reforms of the

Class EN94 lightweight emu (Andrzej Harassek)

1997

railway system, privatising ancillary operations of PKP and introducing legislation in 1997 to allow open access freight operation.

Of the 412,000 railway staff at the beginning of 1993, some 80,000 were already separated from PKP, as they were employed in maintenance and construction activities that had been or were about to be privatised. It is planned that by the end of the decade PKP's labour force will be down to about 200,000; in 1995 the railway employed a staff of 240,000.

Passenger operations

An intercity passenger network embraces 20 major centres and thereby 50 per cent of the country's urban population. Regular-interval service has been established on several routes.

The network consists of 11 pairs of domestic InterCity (IC) and 27 pairs of Express (Ex) services, supplemented by three pairs of EuroCity (EC) services, two pairs of international IC services and other international services. PKP acquired its first EC service, the Berlin—Warsaw 'Berolina', with the May 1992 timetable change. The train's schedule was improved to 6 hours 17 minutes for the 569 km end-to-end distance, an acceleration of 1 hour 26 minutes over the previous best.

A second EC pair, the 'Varsovia', was installed between Berlin and Warsaw in the 1993 timetable, along with a Warsaw—Vienna EC pair, the 'Sobieski'. Two pairs of international IC services were also introduced, the Warsaw—Prague 'Praha' and the Warsaw—Budapest 'Polonia'.

The domestic intercity network has been steadily expanded. Its trains now consist uniformly of PKP's latest 160 km/h rolling stock and all convey a restaurant car. At the end of 1994, IC and Ex services were running at two-hourly intervals (hourly at peak times) on the Warsaw—Kraków and Warsaw—Katowice routes. In addition to the 'Sobieski' EC service, 11 pairs of Warsaw—Kraków trains and nine pairs of Warsaw—Katowice trains were running at up to 160 km/h on the Central Trunk (CMK) main line. Three pairs of trains consisting exclusively of sleeping cars and couchettes were in operation on the Gdynia—Krynica/Zakopane, Kraków—Szczecin and Warsaw—Szczecin routes.

Passenger traffic has fallen steadily since the collapse of communism. In 1988 there were 984 million passenger journeys; by 1993 this was down to 540 million, and the total for 1995 was 383 million (21 billion passenger-km).

PKP has adopted DB AG's KURS 90 computer-based system of ticket issue, seat reservation and timetable database for dealing with passenger enquiries.

Freight operations

The steep decline of freight traffic that took place after the collapse of communism has bottomed out. Some 214.7 million tonnes were recorded in 1994 and 220.9 million tonnes in 1995. By comparison, 419 million tonnes of freight were carried in 1985.

Principal traffic is coal, which accounts for half the tonnage carried. PKP hauls unit trains of coal from Silesia to power stations, industrial plants and ports, employing rotary tipper or Talbot-system self-discharge hopper wagons. It has signed agreements with other operators allowing them to use its tracks, with these operators handling about 40 million tonnes per year.

Intermodal operations

Intermodal development is a priority; traffic levels in 1995 were about the same as in 1994 due to delays in establishing new services.

A national piggyback company has been formed in partnership with haulage operator Pekaes, forwarding agents C Hartwig and several shipping firms including Polish Ocean Lines. The new organisation operates under the name Polkombi. In March 1995 a test train including a low-floor RoLa ('rolling motorway') wagon ran from Frankfurt an der Oder in Germany to Brest in Belarus via Poznań and Warsaw, confirming the technical feasibility of such a service.

A joint venture container company, Polcont, has been created by PKP, Hartwig and Intercontainer. In addition to domestic services linking a total of 15 terminals, regular container/swapbody services are operated to Germany and Italy (Udine).

New lines

At present Warsaw's airport south of the city at Okecie has only a bus link with Warsaw Central station. PKP has proposed a rail link. As a first step, a dedicated shuttle train service could be run between Warsaw East, Warsaw Central and the existing suburban station of Okecie, on the line to Krakow, whence a bus shuttle would run to the international airport terminal. In a subsequent phase, PKP suggests, a loop serving an airport station could be created by double-tracking and electrifying an existing freight branch to the airport, and extending it to rejoin the Krakow main line.

Improvements to existing lines

In late 1993 the European Investment Bank agreed to loan PKP ECU200 million for upgrading of its sector of the

Class SM31 diesel locomotive (Andrzej Harassek)   **1997**

Diesel locomotives

Class	Wheel arrangement	Power kW	Speed km/h	Weight tonnes	First built	Builders Mechanical	Builders Engine	Transmission
SM 40/41	Bo-Bo	441	80	61.7	1958	Ganz-Mávag	Ganz XVI IV 170/240	E Ganz
SM 03	B	111	45	24	1959	Fablok	Nowotko	M Zastal
SM 30	Bo-Bo	257	58	36	1959	Fablok	Nowotko DVSa-350	E Dolmel
SM 42	Bo-Bo	588	90	72	1963	Fablok	HCP 8 VCD22T	E Dolmel
SP 42	Bo-Bo	588	90	70	1966	Fablok	HCP 8 VCD22T	E Dolmel
ST 43	Co-Co	1,544	100	116	1965	Craiova	Sulzer 12 LDA 28	E BBC
ST 44	Co-Co	1,471	100	116	1966	Voroshilovgrad	Kolomna 14D20	E Charkow
SP 45	Co-Co	1,287	100	96	1967	HCP	HCP Fiat 2112SFF	E Dolmel
SU 46	Co-Co	1,650	120	102	1974	HCP	HCP Fiat 2112SSF	E Dolmel
SM 31	Co-Co	882	80	120	1976	Fablok	HCP	E Dolmel
SM 48	Bo-Bo	882	100	116	1976	PZM-Lugansk	PDG-YM	E Charkow
SP 32	Bo-Bo	1,300	100	74	1985	23 August	23 August M820SR	E Craiova
SP 47	Co-Co	2,200	140	114	1978	HCP	HCP Fiat 2116SSF	E Dolmel

Electric multiple-units

Class	Cars per unit	Motor cars per unit	Motored axles/car	Output/motor kW	Speed km/h	First built	Builders Mechanical	Builders Electrical
3 kV DC								
EW 55	3	1	4	145	110	1959	Pafawag	Dolmel
EN 57	3	1	4	145	110	1961	Pafawag	Dolmel
EN 71	4	2	4	145	110	1974	Pafawag	Dolmel
ED 72	4	2	4	175	110	1994	Pafawag	Dolmel
EW 58	3	2	4	206	120	1975	Pafawag	Dolmel
600 V DC								
EN 94	2	2	2	56.5	80	1969	Pafawag	Dolmel

Electric locomotives

Class	Wheel arrangement	Output kW continuous/one hour	Speed km/h	Weight tonnes	First built	Builders Mechanical	Builders Electrical
ET 21	Co-Co	1,860/2,400	100	112	1957	Pafawag	Dolmel
EU 06/07	Bo-Bo	2,000/2,080	125	80	1963	Pafawag	Dolmel
ET 22	Co-Co	3,000/3,120	125	120	1971	Pafawag	Dolmel
EP 05	Bo-Bo	2,032/2,344	140/160	80	1973	Skoda	Skoda
EP 08	Bo-Bo	2,080/3,000	140	80	1973	Pafawag	Dolmel
ET 40	Bo-Bo + Bo-Bo	4,080/4,680	100	164	1976	Skoda	Skoda
ET 41	Bo-Bo + Bo-Bo	4,000/4,160	125	167	1978	Cegielski	Dolmel
ET 42	Bo-Bo + Bo-Bo	4,480/4,840	100	164	1978	Novocherkassk	Novocherkassk
EP 09	Bo-Bo	2,920/3,230	100	84	1986	Pafawag	Dolmel
EM 10	Bo-Bo	960	80	72	1990	Ciegelski	Dolmel/Elta/IEL

Warsaw—Berlin main line. In August 1996 further funding was obtained, with the European Union's Phare assistance plan for central Europe putting in ECU30 million and the European Bank for Reconstruction and Development ECU50 million; PKP and the Polish government would put in ECU207 million, taking the total funding package to ECU487 million.

The Berlin main line extends 630 km from the Polish capital via Poznań to the frontier at Kunowice. The work includes track and bridge renewal, resignalling and reinforcement of the traction current supply. The British consultancy Gibb was retained to advise on the remodelling of the major junction at Poznan. On completion, the route will be fit for 160 km/h passenger train operation. The target is a Berlin—Warsaw journey time of approximately five hours.

PKP aims to extend the project east of Warsaw to Terespol, the principal point of interchange with the railway system of Belarus.

In May 1997, agreement was reached in principle with neighbouring governments on upgrading of the Gdansk—Vienna/Bratislava north-south corridor. Gibb is to study the needs of the corridor under the EU's Phase programme.

Motive power and rolling stock

At the start of 1994 PKP was operating 13 steam, 1,383 electric and 1,547 diesel locomotives, 1,025 emus, 10 diesel railcars and 63,000 freight wagons (mostly coal hoppers). At the start of 1995, PKP was operating 7,623 passenger coaches (including diesel railcar trailers).

PKP is taking delivery from German manufacturer ABB Henschel Waggon Union (now Adtranz) of 50 Type Z1 air conditioned coaches for operation on EuroCity services at up to 200 km/h. An initial batch of 17 coaches has been built by Adtranz; the first was delivered in May 1996. Subsequent batches are to be built under licence by Cegielski.

Order for new locomotives

In February 1997, a deal was struck which set the foundations for replacement of worn-out locomotives in PKP's fleet and modernisation of the Polish locomotive manufacturing industry. The multinational group Adtranz bought from the Polish state a 75 per cent stake in Pafawag of Wroclaw. Adtranz will invest US$28 million over the next six years in the Wroclaw plant. Pafawag will build for the Polish railways 50 mixed traffic 200 km/h electric locomotives similar to the Italian Type E412, with financing arranged with a 10-year US$209 million loan to PKP from a group of five Polish banks. The first locomotives were scheduled for delivery in 1997.

Tilt-body trainset interest

PKP is interested in the Fiat Pendolino tilt-body system. In May 1994, an ETR 460 trainset visited the country for trials and set a Polish speed record of just over 250 km/h.

The two routes particularly of interest for this technology are Warsaw—Gdansk and Warsaw—Katowice. On the former it is estimated that Fiat tilt-body technology could reduce journey times by 20 to 25 per cent. The latter route includes 226 route-km engineered for 200 to 250 km/h, but never yet operated at more than 160 km/h for lack of suitable rolling stock. Fiat Ferroviaria estimates that trainsets comparable to its Pendolino in Italy could run this route at commercial average speeds of up to 144 km/h.

PKP has also concluded an agreement for collaboration with Spanish industry with a view to acquiring Talgo tilt-body rolling stock. PKP is interested in variable-gauge Talgo trainsets for its services into Belarus, Ukraine and the Baltic states, and also for possible rerouteing of Warsaw—Bucharest services via a shorter route through ex-USSR territory instead of through the Czech Republic. Provided World Bank credits are obtainable, PKP has ambitions to order three 13 to 14 car variable-gauge Talgo trains for Legnica—Wroclaw—Kiev (Ukraine) service.

Signalling and telecommunications

PKP has used part of a World Bank loan worth US$145 million to develop its Katowice signalling works for the production of solid-state interlocking equipment. A contract was let to NKT of Denmark for a pilot scheme embracing installation of optic fibre cabling, fail-safe transmission for signalling and associated equipment over a 40 km section between Gdansk and Tczew.

Bidirectional four-aspect signalling of exclusively Polish manufacture is operative throughout the 224 km Central Trunk Route. PKP had been trying to install this type of equipment at the rate of 300 route-km per annum, but the rate of progress has had to be severely reduced.

PKP's signalling subsidiary, Zwus, has been subsumed in a new PKP-ABB Signal (now Adtranz) joint venture. The new enterprise, in which PKP retains a 70 per cent holding, is titled ABB Zwus Signal. In December 1994 PKP's first solid-state interlocking was commissioned at Ożrów Mazowiecki on the Warsaw—Poznań main line. Ebilock 850 equipment was supplied by ABB Signal via ABB Zwus Signal. A second pilot solid-state interlocking, employing Alcatel SEL ESTW-L90 equipment, was due to be commissioned at Opalencia (west of Poznań) by the end of 1995.

PKP commissioned a pilot installation of UIC-compatible track-to-train radio in late 1993. Five Class EP 08 electric locomotives are using the radio over a 25 km stretch of the Warsaw—Kunowice main line.

Electrification

PKP uses a 3 kV DC system of electrification, except on the 35 km Warsaw—Grodzisk Mazowiecki suburban line electrified at 600 V DC.

Track

On main trunk routes UIC 60 rail is being laid and on other primary lines UIC 60 or S49 rail. With wooden sleepers up to 250 mm ballast depth is prescribed, with concrete sleepers, up to 300 mm.

Rail, type and weight: UIC 60 60.34 kg/m; S49 49.43 kg/m; S42 42.48 kg/m

Crossties (sleepers)

Wooden: Types: IB, IIB, IIO thickness 150 mm; IIB, IIIO, IVO thickness 140 mm

Concrete: Types: BL-3 thickness 210 mm; INBK-3 thickness 202 mm; INBK-4 thickness 180 mm; INBK-7 thickness 190 mm; INBK-8 thickness 183 mm; PBS-1 thickness 180 mm

Spacing

Traditional track: 1,566, 1,600, 1,720, 1,733/km cwr: 1,680 and 1,700/km

Max gradient

Main trunk and primary: 0.6% Secondary: 1% Local: 2%

Min curve radius: 200 m

Max axleload: 20 tonnes, 22.5 tonnes on some sections

UPDATED

PORTUGAL

Ministry of Planning, Transport and Territorial Administration

Praca do Comércio, Ala Oriental, P-1100 Lisbon Codex Tel: +351 1 879541   Fax: +351 1 867622

Key personnel
Minister: João Cravinho

UPDATED

Portuguese Railways (CP)

Caminhos de Ferro Portugueses Calçada do Duque 20, P-1294 Lisbon Codex Tel: +351 1 346 3181   Fax: +351 1 347 6524

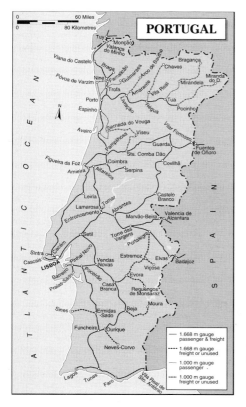

Key personnel
Board of Directors
Chairman: Dr Manuel Frasquilho
Members: Eng Vilaça e Moura, Dr Elsa Roncon Santos, Dr Silva Rodrigues, Dr Moura Calhão, Eng José Espinha, Dr Braancamp Sobral
Directors-General
  Infrastructure: Eng Francisco Carapinha
  Engineering and Investment: Eng Nuno Leandro
  Operations: Dr Oliveira Monteiro
  Sintra Line Business Unit: Eng Martins de Brito
Directors
  Planning: Vacant
  Innovation and Development: Eng Tiago Ferreira
  Data Processing: Eng Guimares da Silva
  Legal Affairs: Dr Almeida Coragem
  Finance: Dr Viegas de Barros
  Audit: Eng Vitor Biscaia
  Human Resources: Dr Maria João Tender Arroja
  Investment Management: Dr Tavares Fernandes
Administration Secretariat: Dr Luis Beato
Public Relations: Dr Américo Ramalho
Regional Managers
  Northern Region: A Villaverde
  Southern Region: Eng Alberto Grossinho
  Cascais Line: Eng João Cunha
  Sintra and Circle Lines: Eng Conceição e Silva

Gauge: 1,668 mm; 1,000 mm
Route length: 2,769 km; 303 km
Electrification: 1,668 mm gauge, 503 km at 25 kV 50 Hz AC; 25 km at 1.5 kV DC

Traffic (million)	1994	1995
Freight tonnes	7.1	8.4
Freight tonne-km	1,635	2,018
Passenger journeys	201.4	190.5
Passenger-km	5,149	4,869

Finances (Esc million)		
Revenues	*1994*	*1995*
Passengers	22,050	21,896
Freight and mail	8,644	10,675
Other	37,147	32,567
Total	67,841	65,138

Expenditure	*1994*	*1995*
Staff/personnel	40,531	43,404
Materials and services	33,359	33,658
Depreciation	8,562	10,198
Total	116,211	124,899

Political background

The government announced a radical restructuring of the Portuguese railway sector in 1996, apparently prompted by CP's worsening financial performance. In 1995 CP recorded a deficit of Esc59.961 billion, following deficits of Esc48.37 billion in 1994 and Esc54.275 billion in 1993. As part of the restructuring, the government agreed to assume Esc500 billion of debt owed by the railways.

A new body, REFER (Rede Ferroviária), will take over responsibility for infrastructure, while the remainder of CP, which will continue to operate the railway, will be known as CP Transport. The bill creating REFER was passed by the parliament in February 1997 and

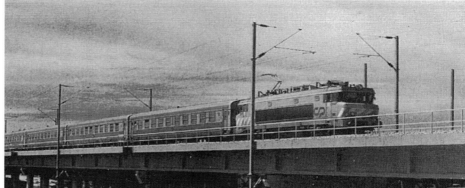

Class 2601 electric locomotive crossing a new bridge on the North line near Cacia

Class LD844C locomotive going through a washer supplied by British company Smith Bros & Webb
1997

infrastructure responsibilities are due to pass gradually to the new body. Signal centres will be the final responsibility assumed by REFER, in January 1999.

Open access rights will encourage new operators to come into the industry, and a regulatory body is to be set up to ensure fair play. Through restructuring, the government hoped to determine which socially necessary services would continue to be subsidised. It was suggested that regional services might be provided under contract by private companies and more public/private partnerships set up, such as the Mirandela Metro venture between CP and local government on the Tua–Mirandela route (see 'Passenger operations' section below). Operation of commuter services over the 25 of April bridge (see 'New lines' section below) is to go out to tender.

Outright privatisation of CP was not on the agenda in early 1997, but at that time the government was concerned that introduction of the other reforms it was proposing was taking much longer than it had anticipated.

Organisation
CP has created over 10 subsidiary companies to manage more peripheral activities. Private companies have a stake in some of these subsidiaries, such as those involved in the movement of containers and cars by rail and the sale of advertising space on railway sites. Recently created subsidiaries include SOFLUSA, managing CP's Lisbon–Barreiro ferry service, door-to-door (using passenger trains) parcel carrier TEX and EMEF. The latter came into being on 9 December 1992 and undertakes work for CP and other operators at four ex-CP heavy-repair sites with a workforce of 1,930. Turnover for 1993 was in the order of Esc8 billion.

CP staff numbers have fallen from 21,037 at the end of 1991 to 13,839 at the end of 1995. This reduction has been achieved in part through early retirement and voluntary redundancy schemes.

Finance
In order to smooth the introduction of the new structure of the industry, the government has pledged investment finance of Esc600 billion in the period up to 2000. Of this, Esc200 billion will go to preparing the Lisbon-Oporto line for tilting train operations, and Esc300 billion for the suburban networks of Lisbon and Oporto.

Passenger operations
CP's passenger traffic has been in steady decline since the early 1990s. Whilst express and interregional services have grown in popularity, this has not been able to compensate for the decline in regional, suburban and international traffic, largely put down to increased car ownership, an improving road network and a higher standard of living for many sectors of the population.

In 1995 suburban services accounted for 58.2 per cent of total CP passenger-km, with interregional and regional traffic making up 27.7 per cent and international and domestic express ('rápido') services 14.1 per cent. Total passenger traffic fell by 5.4 per cent between 1994 and 1995; domestic express traffic grew by 2.3 per cent, regional and interregional traffic fell by 3.7 per cent and suburban traffic fell by some 6 per cent.

In an effort to reverse the decline in international traffic, conventional equipment on the overnight Lisbon–Madrid 'Lusitania Express' was replaced in May 1995 with Talgo Pendular 180 stock marketed as 'Lusitania Hotel Train'. The passive body-tilt Talgo equipment features 'Gran Clase' compartments with showers, as well as more conventional sleeping accommodation and seating. Some 100,000 passengers were carried in the first 12 months of operation, at an average occupancy rate of 70 per cent; the success of the new operation prompted the withdrawal of the daytime 'Luis de Camoens' Talgo service in September 1995. Receipts and expenses from the hotel train operation are shared between CP and RENFE of Spain in the ratio of 36 per cent to 64 per cent.

Exclusive rights to operate from Cachão to Mirandela (14 km) on CP's 1,000 mm gauge Tua–Mirandela route have been granted to Mirandela Metro Co. Owned mostly by the municipality of Mirandela, with CP holding the remaining 10 per cent, the company began operating over an initial 4.1 km section from Mirandela in July 1995. Operations with four LRV 2000 railbuses were to be extended to Cachão in October 1995. Four municipalities commissioned a study of improvement strategies for the 1,000 mm gauge Espinho–Aveiro (Linha do Vouga) route from UK consultancy W S Atkins in 1995.

Freight operations
As measured in tonne-km, CP freight traffic grew by 23.4 per cent between 1994 and 1995, the first upward trend since the 1.763 billion tonne-km carried in 1992. International traffic grew by 4.9 per cent between 1994 and 1995, with a new express service known as CEMI launched on the Lisbon–Barcelona route in conjunction with RENFE of Spain. Specialising in the movement of palletised consumer goods, CEMI offers door-to-door service with collection and onward distribution by road.

Bulk commodities such as coal, cement and fertiliser form the greater part of domestic freight traffic. Of the 2.018 billion tonne-km recorded by CP in 1995, coal formed 26.7 per cent; cement 24.6 per cent; wood and wood pulp 8.8 per cent; fertiliser 8.6 per cent; minerals 4 per cent; cereals and flour 3.4 per cent; and other commodities 23.9 per cent.

Intermodal operations
Three new regular intermodal services to and from Spain were launched in 1995: an Intercontainer service from Lisbon and Leixões (Oporto) to Santurce (Bilbao); an Intercontainer service from Lisbon and Leixões to Algeciras/Cádiz; and a service for Liscont moving refrigerated containers between Lisbon and Vigo. Lisbon's Beirolas container terminal was replaced by a new facility at Bobadela which opened on 24 July 1995. CP eventually hoped to restructure its freight operations around Bobadela and three other principal terminals at Oporto, Aveiro and Setúbal.

New lines
Cross-Tagus link
A 22 km cross-Tagus link has been planned for Lisbon suburban traffic between Chelas on the north bank and Fogueteiro on the south bank. The project involves the installation of a rail deck to carry 700 tonne trains on the 25 of April suspension bridge, opened in 1967 for road

traffic. Between Chelas and Campolide the link will make use of CP's existing Lisbon orbital (Cintura) route, widened to four tracks, but the remainder of the project involves new construction.

Existing stations at Chelas, Areeiro, Entrecampos, Sete Rios and Campolide will be served, and new stations built at Alvito, Pragal, Corroios, Foros de Amora and Fogueteiro. It is hoped eventually to extend the link from Fogueteiro via Coina and Penalva to the CP system at Pinhal Novo, thereby providing an alternative to the ferry connection between Lisbon city centre and Barreiro on the south bank of the Tagus, the terminus for passenger trains to and from the south of Portugal.

Following an unsuccessful attempt to interest the private sector in a design, build, operate and maintain package for the cross-Tagus link, Lisbon rail authority GNFL awarded a contract for civil works in August 1995 to a consortium of DSD, American Bridge, Weiss & Freytag and Teixera Duarte. The group had submitted a bid of Esc35.89 billion. Subsequent contracts were to be let for tracklaying, signalling, electrification, rolling stock and operation of the link.

It was originally hoped that the cross-Tagus link would be in service by April 1998, in time for the opening of Expo '98 in Lisbon later that year. However, timing on the project slipped, and a more probable start date was October 1998. The Expo site is to be served by a new Eastern (Oriente) station, connected to the Lisbon–Oporto main line near Braço de Prata and the Lisbon orbital route. Spanish architect Santiago Calatrava has designed the new station, which was due for completion in December 1997.

International links
In May 1996 representatives of the Portuguese government met with European Commission officials to discuss the possibility of European Union funding for a new international passenger service. Using existing and planned infrastructure and a new connection between the Portuguese and Spanish networks over the River Guadiana, presumably at Vila Real de Santo António, the new service would run between the Spanish cities of La Coruña and Seville via Oporto, Lisbon and Faro.

Various other options have been examined for connecting Lisbon to Europe's developing high-speed network. An upgrade of the Beira Baixa (Entroncamento–Castelo Branco–Guarda) route was proposed in May 1996, whilst CP is known to have considered a direct Lisbon–Irún link. RENFE of Spain has expressed a preference for a route feeding into its emerging Madrid–Barcelona high-speed line.

Improvements to existing lines
Lisbon—Oporto upgrading
The electrified Lisbon—Oporto line (Linha do Norte) generates half CP's income, and its redevelopment became an urgent need with the 1991 completion of a motorway between the two cities. Following a study by the UK consultancy Transmark, in April 1991 the government authorised investment in infrastructure and new rolling stock to allow 220 km/h passenger operation between Lisbon and Oporto, with tilt-body trains covering the 340 km in two hours. A lift of maximum freight wagon axleload to 25 tonnes is also an objective.

On 26 July 1994 CP signed a Esc5.5 billion five-year project and construction management contract for the Linha do Norte upgrading programme with a consortium of ICF Kaiser International, W S Atkins and Fernando Braz Oliveira. A total of Esc175 billion is to be spent on infrastructure, which includes renewal of 600 track-km, realignment of 60 track-km for 220 km/h operation and provision of an additional 75 track-km. UIC 60 rail on monobloc sleepers is being installed and the project involves the construction of 160 new bridges and a 1 km viaduct.

Catenary on the Linha do Norte is being renewed and the route resignalled. Level crossings are being eliminated or given automatic protection in conjunction with installation of CTC and the Ericsson ATP system, which will permit a lifting of maximum passenger train speed. Layouts at 42 stations are being remodelled to reduce path conflicts of trunk and local trains, and to avoid speed restriction of non-stopping trains.

CP intends the Linha do Norte upgrading programme to be complete by 1999 and the route has been divided into nine sections for the letting of works contracts. During 1995, contracts were let for civil engineering, track, catenary and signalling and telecommunications work on the Braço de Prata–Alverca (17.8 km) section of the route; in early 1997 it became plain that this would not be finished in time for Expo 98, as had originally been intended. Tenders were called for similar work on the Albergaria—Alfarelos (49 km) and Pampilhosa—Quintans (34.7 km) sections.

Lisbon network redevelopment

In 1993, CP announced a Esc600 million, three-year upgrading programme to modernise the Lisbon—Azambuja service, including new rolling stock, station remodelling and refurbishment at Alverca, Azambuja (completed in 1995 in conjunction with the Linha do Norte programme) and Vila Franca de Xira, resignalling and the introduction of train radio.

CP has allocated Esc3.2 billion for raising capacity on the 27 km Lisbon—Sintra line, which carried 67 million passengers in 1991. The money will be spent on resignalling the route as far as Cacém with ESTWL90 equipment, eliminating level crossings, renovating stations and remodelling track layouts. It is planned to introduce centralised traffic control by 1998, permitting 25 trains an hour in each direction. Four tracks in place of the present two will eventually be in service between Lisbon and Cacém (17.3 km). By the start of 1996, 3.1 km of the route between Campolide and Benfica had been expanded to four tracks, with trains operating at 4 minute headways at peak hours and serving a new station at Queluz-Massamá.

In addition to minor works under way at the start of 1996 to improve interchanges with the Lisbon metro, a modernisation programme costed at Esc60 billion has been proposed for the Lisbon—Cascais route. Level crossing elimination, better bus interchanges and new car parks for rail commuters form the major objectives of the programme, which could be completed by 2002.

Oporto improvements

Recent investment programmes have made provision for a new train maintenance facility at Oporto and the conversion of the 1,000 mm gauge Lousado—Guimarães branch to 1,668 mm gauge. The 1,000 mm gauge Oporto—Póvoa de Varzim and Senhora da Hora—Trofa routes (49.4 km in total) are to form part of a new Esc100 billion light rail system planned for Oporto. A contract to build and initially operate the 68 km network was awarded in early 1997 to Siemens, which beat GEC Alsthom, a consortium led by Adtranz and a consortium of Spie Batignolles, Bombardier and Ansaldo to the contract.

Elsewhere on the CP Oporto network, doubling from two to four tracks between Oporto and Ermesinde is planned. Electrification from Ermesinde eastwards to Marco de Canaveses and double-tracking between Ermesinde and Caíde (completed as far as Valongo in 1995) were under way at the start of 1996. In 1995 the Oporto transport authority GNFP called tenders for rebuilding the Lousado—Nine section of the Oporto—Valença (Linha do Minho) route and double-tracking the 14 km Valongo—Cete section of the Oporto—Pocinho (Linha do Douro) route.

LRT for Coimbra—Serpins branch

Approval for the conversion of this 38 km branch to light rail operation was granted on 20 January 1994, some two years after an initial proposal was made by the city of Coimbra. The city and CP are jointly to manage the project, funded in part by development of railway and municipal lands along the route. Total cost is Esc1.1 billion, and EU funding was to be sought.

Beira Alta route

Modernisation of CP's prime international route to Spain, the Beira Alta, is a priority. This runs 201.6 km from Pampilhosa, south of Oporto on the Lisbon main line, to the Spanish border at Vilar Formoso; from here there is a direct Spanish route to the French border via Salamanca and Burgos. The 202 km of single track within Portugal is at present manually signalled, relies operationally on telephonic communication, and threads rugged country that demands a ruling gradient of 1.8 per cent, a minimum curve radius of 300 m and 12 tunnels. As a result, it has difficulty in operating its present traffic of some 30 trains daily.

The Beira Alta line is now to be electrified, resignalled and undergo substantial realignment to ease its most severe curves and permit 160 km/h operation. This will entail complete reconstruction of two segments, in addition to level crossing elimination. Completion may cut as much as two hours from Lisbon—Paris passenger train timings, and the Esc38 billion cost of the project has been supported in part by the European Union.

Siemens-built Class 5600 electric locomotive hauling an Oporto—Lisbon service (Mick Alderman) **1997**

Diesel locomotives

Class	Wheel arrangement	Power kW	Speed km/h	Weight tonnes	No in service	First built	Builders Mechanical	Engine	Transmission
9001/003	Bo-Bo	425	70	46	3	1959	Alsthom	SACM/MGO	E Alsthom
9004/006	Bo-Bo	440	70	46	3	1959	Alsthom	SACM	E Alsthom
9021/031	Bo-Bo	530	70	46.65	11	1976	Alsthom	SACM	E Alsthom
1001/1006	C	120	41.5	30.4	6	1948	Drewry	Gardner	M Sinclair
1021/1025	B	320	65	36	5	1968	Moyse	Deutz	E Moyse
1051/1068	B	90	38	28.3	13	1955	Moyse	Moyse	E Moyse
1101/1112	Bo-Bo	190	56	41.2	11	1946	GE	Caterpillar	E GE
1151/1186	C	190	58	42	36	1966	Sorefame	Rolls-Royce	H Rolls-Royce
1201/1225	Bo-Bo	480	80	64.7	25	1961	Sorefame	SACM	E B&L
1321/1337	Co-Co	750	120	87	17	1968	Alco	Alco	E GE
1401/1467	Bo-Bo	765	105	64.4	65	1967	Sorefame	EE	E EE
1501/1521	A1A-A1A	1,290	120	111	17	1948	Alco	Alco	E GE
1551/1570	Co-Co	1,290	120	89.7	20	1973	MLW	MLW/Alco	E GE Canada
1801/1810	Co-Co	1,530	140	110.3	10	1968	EE	EE	E EE
1961/1973	Co-Co	1,680	120	121	13	1979	MLW	MLW	E GE Canada
1901/13	Co-Co	2,240	100	120	13	1981	Sorefame	SACM	E Alsthom
1931/47	Co-Co	—	120	116	17	1981	Sorefame	SACM	E Alsthom

Electric locomotives

Class	Wheel arrangement	Power kW	Weight tonnes	No in service	Builders Mechanical	Electrical
2501-2515	Bo-Bo	2,116	72	15	50 c/s Group	50 c/s Group
2551-2570	Bo-Bo	2,116	70.5	20	Sorefame	50 c/s Group
2601-2629	B-B	2,940	78	21	Alsthom	50 c/s Group
5600	Bo-Bo	5,600	88	30	Sorefame	Siemens

Diesel railcars

Series	Power kW	Speed km/h	Weight tonnes	No in service	First built	Builders Mechanical	Engine	Transmission
9101/103 (NG)	240	70	22	3	1949	Nohab	Scania Vabis	H Lisholm-Smith
9301/310 (NG)	320	70	37	8	1954	Allan	AEC	E Smith
9601/622 (NG)	383	90	64.36	22	1976	Alsthom	SFAC	E Alsthom
0101/115 (BG)	252	100	33.3	12	1948	Nohab	Saab-Scania	H Voith
0301/325 (BG)	360	100	5.5	24	1954	Allan	SSCM	E Smith
0401/419 (BG)	560	110	94.1	19	1965	Sorefame	Rolls-Royce	H Rolls-Royce
0601/0640 (BG)	775	120	110	20	1979	Sorefame	SFAC	H Voith
9701-40 (NG)	720	60	92	10	—	Fiat*		M
9501/502	245	84	30	2	1995	Fiat/Volvo	Volvo	H Voith
9401/406	222	51	30	6	1993	Fiat	Volvo	H Voith

* (acquired from Yugoslav Railways)

Electric railcars

Class	Output kW	Speed km/h	Weight tonnes	No in service	First built	Builders Mechanical	Electrical
2001/2025	1,095	90	117	24	1956	Sorefame	Siemen/AEG/Oerlikon
2051/2074-2082/2090	1,095	90	123.6	33	1956	Sorefame	Siemens/AEG/Oerlikon
2101/2124	1,280	120	132.8	24	1970	Sorefame	Siemens/AEG/Oerlikon
2151/2168	1,280	120	132.8	18	1977	Sorefame	Siemens/AEG/Oerlikon
2201/2215	1,280	120	132.8	15	1984	Sorefame	EFACEC
2301/2342	3,100	120	—	42	1992	Sorefame	Siemens

During 1995, track renewal work was completed between Baraçal and Guarda, in addition to tracklaying on new alignments between Baraçal and Cerdeira and double-tracking on the Pampilhosa—Luso section. Civil works on new alignments between Carregal do Sal and Fornos de Algodres were completed and tracklaying began. Station remodelling was completed in 1995 at Oliveirinha, Canas, Cerdeira, Noémi and Vilar Formoso, and 14 new road over/underbridges were opened in conjunction with the closing of 89 of the route's 319 level crossings.

Preliminary electrification work was also under way in 1995 at Pampilhosa, Oliveirinha and Vila Franca das Naves. Substations for traction current were completed at Mortágua, Gouveia and Sobral.

Sines—Pego
CP is upgrading 330 km of railway linking a power station at Pego with the port of Sines via Abrantes, Entroncamento, Setil, Bombel (Vendas Novas) and Ermidas. The programme includes electrification at 25 kV 50 Hz AC from Entroncamento to Pego and from Setil to Sines. Imported coal is the principal commodity moved over the Sines—Pego route, which carries 20 per cent of CP's total freight traffic. In 1989 the national power generation company had invited bids to build an 8.7 km branch from Abrantes to Pego, to install rapid discharge gear at the power station and to supply 160 65-tonne coal hopper wagons. Movements of coal to Pego by rail began in 1992.

CP expected to handle almost one million tonnes of coal between Sines and Pego in 1995, but target capacity is 1.6 million tonnes a year. In May 1995 CP completed upgrading work between Entroncamento and Pego (37 km), including electrification, at a cost of Esc200 million. Spie Enertrans began work to electrify the Setil—Bombel section of the route (72 track-km) in 1995, and CP was preparing to call bids for electrifying the remaining Bombel—Sines section.

In addition to resignalling, passing loops are being lengthened at 29 locations along the route to accommodate the coal trains; remodelling was completed at Setil in 1995. Total cost of the Sines—Pego programme is in the region of Esc70 billion. CP is believed to have considered further electrification to Funcheira and Castro Verde, to serve mineral deposits, and to Faro (costed at Esc25 billion).

Traction and rolling stock
At the start of 1996, CP's 1,668 mm gauge rolling stock fleet comprised 184 diesel locomotives, 81 electric locomotives, 40 diesel shunters, 190 emus, 80 dmus, 443 trailer cars, 488 passenger coaches and 3,743 freight wagons. For its 1,000 mm gauge network, CP had at its disposal 10 diesel locomotives, 48 diesel railcars and 29 trailers, 15 passenger coaches and 11 freight wagons.

During 1995, CP took delivery of a further 63 triple-unit car transporters converted from conventional freight wagons. A total of 82 such transporters has been provided for Ford/Volkswagen car traffic. A fleet of 50 wagons was modified for the transport of timber, with a further 50 to be converted in 1996.

Intercity trains
CP's target end-to-end timing of two hours for its upgraded Lisbon—Oporto route is based on the use of automatic body-tilting vehicles. In early 1992, with the ETR 460 'Pendolino' and X2000 in mind, CP invited proposals from Fiat and ABB for supply of eight to 12 tilting trainsets. In March 1996 an order for 10 six-car trainsets, valued at some Esc25 billion, was placed with Fiat (bodyshells and tilting equipment) and Siemens (electrical equipment). It was expected that Adtranz Portugal (formerly Sorefame) would undertake final assembly of the fleet; the first five units were to be delivered by mid-1998, in time for Expo '98, with the remainder in service by the end of 1999.

These Scania-powered railcars dating from the 1940s were re-engined in the 1980s and are still in service south of Lisbon *1997*

Meanwhile, upgrading is being undertaken on the existing intercity fleet: 44 passenger coaches have been refurbished by CP's EMEF subsidiary at a cost of Esc5 billion. The upgrading features remounting on Y32 bogies, fitting of retention toilets, double-glazing, high-capacity air conditioning and power doors. CP has also installed telephones on the premium 'Alfa' trainsets of the Lisbon—Oporto service and introduced a business car on this route.

Cross-Tagus trains
Bids for the supply of 22 single-deck or 18 double-deck four-car electric multiple-units for operation on the 25 of April bridge (see 'New lines' section above) were received in February 1996 from five bidders. The contract went to GEC Alsthom, which will build the trains in the double-deck format; local companies Efacec and Adtranz Portugal will share in the work. The first trains are due to be delivered in 1998.

Signalling and telecommunications
CP is concentrating signalling of its main line network on five electronic control centres, at Oporto, Coimbra, Entroncamento, Lisbon and Setúbal. The five centres were due to be operational in 1996.

Two technologies have been adopted. One is the British SSI (Solid-State Interlocking), which has been supplied by Dimetronic SA of Spain and Westinghouse Brake & Signal. The other is ESTWL90, a German system similar to one adopted by that country's DB AG, which has been furnished by Alcatel's Portuguese subsidiaries, Alcatel SEL and Alcatel Portugal. The local company Efacec assisted in various aspects, including track circuiting, cabling, level crossing automation and installation.

In late 1991 an Esc11.1 billion contract to resignal 260 single-track route-km and 36 stations south of Entroncamento, plus the Entroncamento—Mouriscas line, with 17 solid-state interlockings was awarded to Dimetronic SA of Spain and Westinghouse Brake & Signal Company of the UK. Known as the SISSUL scheme, this SSI project forms part of the Sines—Pego programme and is focused on two of the planned integrated electronic control centres, at Entroncamento and Setúbal. During 1995, new signalling controlling some 80 track-km around Ermidas and Alcácer and including six automatic level crossings was brought into service. Work began on the resignalling of the following sections in 1995: Setil—Vendas Novas, Bombel—Poceirão, Poceirão—Águas de Moura, Pinhal Novo—Poceirão and Pinhal Novo—Água de Moura.

Other SSI schemes are: Campanha, based on Oporto, and covering the route over the new Douro bridge to Gaia on the Lisbon main line; Souselas, covering the Lisbon—Oporto main line to the neighbourhood of Coimbra; and

the 'Three As' scheme involving Alverca, Alhandra, Azambuja and Setil. The resignalling of Alverca, Alhandra and Azambuja was completed in 1995.

The first ESTWL90 contract was awarded in 1992, providing for CTC and five solid-state interlockings on the Beira Alta line. The structure to house the CTC installation at Pampilhosa was completed in 1995.

EB Corporation of Norway (now Adtranz) received a CP contract for the delivery of Ericsson-type ATP speed-control equipment for installation on the Lisbon—Oporto line. The contract covers equipment for 300 vehicles. The local partner in this project is Efacec.

Track
Standard rail
1,668 mm gauge: 30-55 kg/m in 8 and 18 m lengths
1,000 mm gauge: 20-36 kg/m in 8 and 12 m lengths
Welded rail
Thermit process is used. Rail used weighs 54, 50, 45, 40 kg/m in 18 and 24 m lengths. The length of continuous welded rail is usually 840 m but occasionally 950 m
Crossties (sleepers)
1,668 mm gauge: 260 × 130 × 2,600 mm, spacing 605 mm
1,000 mm gauge: 230 × 120 × 1,800 mm, spacing 820 to 850 mm
Rail fastening: Screw spikes or bolts. RN flexible fastenings used with welded rail
Filling: Broken stone, gravel or earth
Max curvature
1,668 mm gauge: 5.9° = min radius 300 m
1,000 mm gauge: 29° = min radius 60 m
Longest continuous gradient
1,668 mm gauge: 8.3 km of 1.4% gradient with curves varying from 590 to 1,501 m in radius
1,000 mm gauge: 7.2 km of 2.5% gradient with curves varying from 75 to 500 m in radius
Max gradient
1,668 mm gauge: 1.8% = 1 in 55½
1,000 mm gauge: 2.5% = 1 in 40
Max altitude
1,668 mm gauge: 812.7 m
1,000 mm gauge: 849.7 m
Max axleload
1,668 mm gauge: 19.5 tonnes
1,000 mm gauge: 11 tonnes
Max permitted speed
1,668 mm gauge: 140 km/h
1,000 mm gauge: 80 km/h

UPDATED

PUERTO RICO

Ponce & Guayama Railway

Corporación Azucarera de Puerto Rico
Aguirre, Puerto Rico 00608
Tel: +1 809 853 3810

Key personnel
Executive Director: A Martinez
General Superintendent: J Rodriguez
Roadmaster: R Rodriguez
Traffic Manager: J Lopez
Purchasing Manager: R Rivera
Accountant: T Cartagena

Gauge: 1,000 mm
Route length: 96 km

Traction and rolling stock
The railway operates 22 diesel locomotives and 1,280 freight wagons.

VERIFIED

ROMANIA

Ministry of Transport

Bd Dinicu Golescu 38, Bucharest 78123
Tel: +40 1 617 2060   Fax: +40 1 312 3205

Key personnel
Minister: A Novac
Director General, Land Transport: V Neacsu

UPDATED

Romanian National Railways (SNCFR)

Societatea Naţională a Căilor Ferate Române
Bd Dinicu Golescu 38, 77113 Bucharest 1
Tel: +40 1 223 3637/223 0660/638 6550
Fax: +40 1 312 3205/312 3200

Key personnel
President: Virgil Ioan Leancu
Vice-Presidents
  Social Affairs: Dan Saileanu
  Strategy, Management and Marketing: Vasile Olievschi
  Financial: Gheorghe Dragan
  Operations: Virgiliu Nita
Directors
  Freight Commercial: Lucian Dobrescu
  Passenger Commercial: Ion Soare
  Traffic: Radu Cazacu
  Infrastructure: Alexandru Nazarie
  Traction and Rolling Stock: Mihai Ion
  Purchases: Ion C Ion
  Human Resources: Florica Druga
  Law: Vasile Păcureţu
  Property: Traian Tănase
  Revenue Control: Florin Petcu
  Financial: Mrs Silvia Popeangă
  Quality: Valeriu Dorobantu
  Technical, Planning, Investment: Vasile Dincescu
Deputy Director, International Relations: Virgil Daschievici

Gauge: 1,435 mm; 1,524 mm; 760 mm
Route length: 10,889 km; 60 km; 427 km
Electrification: 3,866 km at 25 kV 50 Hz AC

Political background
In mid-1991 the railway, formerly a department of the Transport Ministry, became an autonomous state enterprise, Societaţea Naţională a Căilor Ferate Romane (SNCFR).

In 1992 SNCFR obtained World Bank support to engage foreign consultants for a wide-ranging study of the restructuring measures necessary to transform the railway into a viable enterprise in a free market; this was completed by German consultants DE-Consult in early 1994. The study made recommendations for changes in the legal status of SNCFR and restructuring for business sector management as well as an appraisal of requirements to raise the railway's technical and performance standards to those of western Europe.

The recommendations are now being put into effect. A new law redefining the railway's legal status and its relationship with government was passed in 1996. The railway is reorganising its structure along western European lines, with separate accounting for infrastructure and operations and a public service contract with the state.

SNCFR has sought overseas aid from the World Bank and European Bank for Reconstruction & Development for a package of improvements, particularly for a modern telecommunications network, management information systems, infrastructure refurbishment, and locomotive and rolling stock renewal and refurbishment. SNCFR estimates it will spend US$4.5 billion on investment projects in the period 1997-2015.

Organisation
SNCFR is divided organisationally into eight geographical regions plus a special administration covering the Port of Constanţa.

Staff numbers were cut from 148,650 at the end of 1995 to 137,190 at the end of 1996.

Passenger operations
SNCFR emerged from the liberalisation of eastern Europe with its infrastructure and rolling stock in better condition than in some neighbouring countries, though in need of modernisation in many areas. Passenger traffic has declined to a lesser extent than freight traffic, largely because fares are held artificially low and competing road transport services are still somewhat disorganised. The passenger-km figures for 1996 was 18,356 million (18,879 million in 1995). For pre-revolution comparison, the 1985 total was 31,082 million passenger-km.

The major traffic flows are concentrated on radial routes from Bucharest known as *magistrale*. Most of these routes are electrified, though in some cases there are lengthy single-track sections. However, a weakness of the system is the often poor cross-country links between the main lines, to a large extent the result of the difficult terrain.

This centralisation on the capital leads to congestion, particularly for passenger traffic using the city's only inter-city station, the Gara de Nord, a situation exacerbated by the loss of several platforms for construction of the northwest extension of the Bucharest metro.

During 1994 the first branded premium 'InterCity' service was inaugurated, one daily train pair from Timişoara to Bucharest and return, using new German-built first and second class corridor coaches, plus reliveried restaurant and baggage cars. The main improvements are a schedule of 6 hr 25 min with two stops, an average of 82 km/h, which compares with the previous 'Rapid' schedule of 8 hr 30 min (63 km/h). Locomotives now work throughout without change. Despite a supplement which almost doubles the basic fare, loadings are reported as very healthy. Subsequent additions to the InterCity system are Bucharest to Iaşi and, from 4 April 1995, Galaţi–Bucharest–Craiova. Further additions can be expected when additional new or refurbished coaches become available.

In 1997, the first EuroCity service reached Romania. The 'Traianus' runs between Budapest, Hungary, and Bucharest. A new direct service between Timişoara in western Romania and Budapest was introduced at the same time: the service is provided by train 355, the 'Bega'.

Freight operations
Freight traffic has seen a reduction to around one third of its 1989 level. Freight tonnes in 1996 (1995 in brackets) were 105.0 million tonnes (105.1 million); 26,878 million tonne-km (27,179 million). For a pre-revolution comparison, 1985 statistics were 283 million tonnes; 74,215 million tonne-km.

Coal remains the dominant commodity. Main reasons for the losses in the early 1990s are major reductions in industrial output of traditional railway freight commodities; increased tariffs; poor market alignment; and sharper competition from other modes. By 1995, the market seemed to have stabilised.

The use of the belt line around Bucharest for freight traffic results in excessive delays, making rail uncompetitive for time-sensitive international traffic

Diesel locomotive built by Electroputere, with engine built under licence from Sulzer   **1997**

moving by container to and from the capital via the port of Constanţa. Modernisation of the infrastructure in this area is thus urgently required to enable SNCFR to compete effectively.

International links
The major international links are with Hungary in the west/ northwest, using the border crossing points at Curtici (near Arad) and Episcopia Bihor (Oradea). The former is the main link onwards to Budapest and Hungary, while the latter gives access to northern Hungary, Slovakia and Poland. Transit traffic between western Europe and Bulgaria, Greece and Turkey using this route and the Giurgiu/Ruse Danube crossing has become more significant since the break-up of the former Yugoslavia, though the combination of an indirect routeing, poor traffic security and perceived border delays has meant that much traditional rail traffic has been lost to road and Danube river competition. In order to try to alleviate some of these problems, a train ferry service was inaugurated between Constanţa and Samsun in Turkey in February 1995.

Other important international links exist into former Soviet Union territory in the north (Ukraine) and west (Moldova and Ukraine), though efficient operation here is hampered by the laborious gauge-changing operations necessary. This has been mitigated in some places, such as Galaţi, in the east, by the continuation of broad-gauge tracks across the border into Romania to major traffic objectives. In the case of Galaţi the Sidex steel complex is equipped with its own broad-gauge marshalling yard. However, once again the availability of surplus road haulage capacity along these international axes, offering a competitive service without the need for regauging or transhipment, has led to serious reductions in the volume of rail traffic.

Intermodal operations
At the end of 1992, a new swapbody (lightweight container) service was inaugurated between Antwerp, Belgium, and Bucharest. Typical transit time from Antwerp to Bucharest is six days. A new company, Trans-Rail, has been set up to handle the Romanian end of the business; it works in conjunction with Belgian freight forwarder BVBA Gebroeders Verstreken, Intercontainer of Basel, Switzerland and NV Interferry of Antwerp.

Steel-clad swapbody units, 7.82 m long, 2.5 m wide and 3.1 m high are used. They are fitted with standard ISO-type top lift positions, as the Bucharest terminal has only conventional container spreaders and no swapbody

handling equipment. Low-platform Multifret wagons from the Intercontainer pool are used.

In 1993 a new piggyback service for international heavy goods vehicles was inaugurated between Bucharest Progresul on a cross-border service into Bulgaria, and a similar service was planned into Hungary.

New lines
In October 1996, SNCFR advertised for companies prepared to tender to build new lines on the following routes: Vâlcele-Râminicu Vâlcea; Albeni-Seciuri; and Hârlău-Flămânzi. Financing was to be arranged by the winning bidders, with repayment guaranteed by the government of Romania.

Improvements to existing lines
SNCFR has ambitious plans for upgrading its lines. Priority is being given to upgrading to 200 km/h standards the main routes from the capital to western Europe, via Simeria—Arad, Craiova—Timisoara—Arad and Sibiu—Cluj—Oradea.

Traction and rolling stock
At the end of 1996 SNCFR owned 953 steam locomotives (most for use as stationary boilers), 1,060 electric locomotives, 2,298 diesel locomotives, 133 diesel railcars and six emus. For hauled stock, the numbers were: 6,082 passenger cars (including 156 sleeping, 49 couchette and 50 buffet/dining cars) and 140,961 freight wagons. Many vehicles — perhaps as much as half the fleet — were unavailable for service due to lack of spare parts and maintenance.

Both diesel-hydraulic locomotives (335, 520 and 930 kW) and diesel-electric locomotives (1,120, 1,560, 2,250 and 3,000 kW versions with engines built under Sulzer, Alco and Maybach licences) are operated by the railway. Electric locomotives are of two basic types: the Class 40/41/42 5,100 kW Co-Co built by ASEA and by Electroputere under an ASEA licence (SNCFR owns 930 of these machines); and the Class 43 3,400 kW Bo-Bo built by Rade Končar of Zagreb.

In 1992 Electroputere of Craiova delivered a new diesel-electric locomotive prototype, numbered DE626BLI, a 1,940 kW unit with a maximum speed of 100 km/h, though no further orders have been forthcoming. In 1995 the same company completed the rebuilding of a withdrawn SNCFR 3,000 kW diesel-electric locomotive as a straight electric. If service trials are successful, it is likely that the remaining 31 units of this class could be similarly rebuilt.

Much of the motive power, while serviceable, is technologically obsolete: the railcars are essentially of a 1930s design, the diesel locomotives use 1950s technology and the electric locomotives are based on Swedish early 1960s designs. There is therefore a clear need for fleet modernisation, in particular for a fleet of modern diesel and electric multiple-units, which would help to improve the passenger environment as well as reduce maintenance requirements.

To appraise the potential for replacement of locomotive and carriage combinations on medium-distance services by new-generation diesel multiple-units, two DB AG Class VT628.6 sets were hired from Duewag of Germany in early 1995. They were used on a variety of services and returned excellent availability and fuel consumption figures, as well as providing an attractive travelling environment for passengers. It is understood that SNCFR may now be interested in obtaining a fleet of such vehicles.

Although the passenger rolling stock has seen considerable renewal in recent years, including the purchase of double-deck coaches from the former East Germany, overall quality is poor and general upgrading is required to meet customer aspirations in a competitive market.

A technology transfer agreement has been reached with De Dietrich of France for manufacture by Astra works at Arad of French Railways-type Corail passenger cars. In 1997, Astra of Arad was building 200 of these Z1 type 200 km/h coaches for SNCFR.

Germany's DB AG has offered to sell SNCFR some of its IC passenger cars as they become superfluous with the introduction of more ICE high-speed trainsets. The financing of this move is unclear, however.

Signalling and telecommunications
At the close of 1993, automatic block covered 4,337 km. Centralised Traffic Control (CTC) was operational over 366 route-km, which included one 82 km stretch of double track where the system was computer-based. A new national telecommunications network is an urgent investment priority.

Electrification
In the second half of the 1980s electrification made steady progress and, with more than 1,100 km newly wired, electrified route-km rose by 50 per cent.

Routes most recently electrified have included the formidable Transylvania east-west alpine line of 229 km between Braşov and Teius; and in western Transylvania, from Ilia through Cluj to Dej in the north, as part of a north-south electrified route between Ukraine and Bulgaria avoiding Bucharest. Work on the 45 km non-electrified section between Ilva Mica and Iacobeni on the route from Dej to Suceava was completed in 1995.

Electrification schemes in progress covered: 16 km of double track between Tecuci and Barboşi, in the far east of the country, to establish a more direct electrified link between the north-south Kiev—Suceava—Bucharest trunk (completed in late 1994) and that from Bucharest northeastward to Galaţi; 13 km electrification and doubling of the route from Gura Motrului to Târgu Jiu, and its 28 km Drăgoteşti branch, in the lignite area west of Craiova.

Track
Rail weight: 49.4, 53.8, 60.3 and 64.6 kg/m (respectively 6,552; 758; 1,383; 3,925 km)
Sleepers: 61 per cent concrete, 39 per cent wood
Spacing: 1,334-1,800/km in jointed track; 1,667-1,840/km in jointless track; 1,467-1,784/km in curves of more than 500 m radius; 1,600-1,800/km in curves of less than 500 m radius
Fastenings: Types K, E1, E2, E3
Min curve radius: 350 m (main lines)
Max gradient: 2.8 per cent
Max permissible axleload: 20.5 tonnes

UPDATED

RUSSIAN FEDERATION

Ministry of Railways

Novo-Basmannaya 2, Moscow 107174
Tel: +7 095 262 1628   Fax: +7 095 262 9095

Key personnel
Minister of Railways, Russian Federation: N E Aksenenko
First Deputy Minister: O A Moshenko
Deputy Ministers
    Finance: I S Besedin
    Operations: V S Zakharenko
    Traction and Rolling Stock: A N Kondratenko
    Safety and Environment: G B Yakimov
    Personnel, Social Services: A O Bogdanovich
    Customer Services: E S Podavashkin
Board members
    Freight and Commercial: V M Logunov
    Passenger: V N Shataev
    Finance: A V Martynchuk
    Traction: V V Titov
    Wagons: S S Barbavich
    Economics and Development: B M Lapidus
    Civil Engineering: V N Sazonov
    International Relations: S L Molgin

One of Russia's many industrial railways: a mixed train on the metre-gauge Monyetnaya Peat Railway
1996

UPDATED

Russian Railways

Rossiiskie Zheleznie Dorogi (RZhD)
Novo-Basmannaya 2, Moscow 107174
Tel: +7 095 262 1628   Fax: +7 095 262 2411

Key personnel
Regional Managers
    Moskovskaya (Moscow): I L Paristyi
    Krasnoprudnaya ul 20, 107040 Moscow
    Tel: +7 095 262 5165
Oktyabr'skaya (October): A A Zaitsev
    Ostrovskogo Pl 2, 191011 St Petersburg
    Tel: +7 812 168 6040
Severnaya (Northern): V M Predybailov
    Volzhskaya nab 59, 150028 Yaroslavl'
    Tel: +7 0852 294400
Gor'kovskaya (Gorkii): O Kh Sharadze
    Oktyabr'skoy Revolyutsii ul 61, 603011 Nizhnii
    Novgorod
    Tel: +7 831 484400   Fax: +7 831 484477
Severo-Kavkazskaya (North Caucasus):
    V A Bezrukavenko
    Teatral'naya Pl 4, 344719 Rostov-on-Don
    Tel: +7 8632 594400
Yugo-Vostochnaya (South East): V G Atlasov
    Revolyutsii Pr 18, 394621 Voronezh
    Tel: +7 0732 504460/504450   Fax: +7 0732 504893
Privolzhskaya (Volga): M P Likhachev
    Moskovskaya ul 8, 410013 Saratov
    Tel: +7 8452 904013
Kuibyshevskaya (Kuibyshev): A S Levchenko
    Komsomolskaya Pl 2-3, 443030 Samara
    Tel: +7 8462 394400

Sverdlovskaya (Sverdlovsk): B I Kolesnikov
    Cheluskintsev ul 11, 620013 Ekaterinburg
    Tel: +7 3432 539216
Yuzhno-Ural'skaya (Southern Urals): I P Vorobiev
    Revolyutsii Pl 3, 454000 Chelyabinsk
    Tel: +7 3512 338482
Zapadno-Sibirskaya (Western Siberia): A K Borodach
    Vokzalnaya Magistral ul 12, 630004 Novosibirsk
    Tel: +7 3832 228822
Krasnoyarskaya (Krasnoyarsk): Yu G Shipovalov
    Gorkogo ul 6, 660049 Krasnoyarsk
    Tel: +7 000 221 1764
Vostochno-Sibirskaya (Eastern Siberia): G P Komarov
    Karla Marska ul 7, 644638 Irkutsk
    Tel: +7 3952 294400
Zabaikal'skaya (Trans Baikal): N Vorob'ev
    Leningradskaya ul 34, 672092 Chita
    Tel: +7 30222 61357
Dal'nevostochnaya (Far East): A P Ivanov
    Muraveva-Amurskogo ul 20, 680000 Khabarovsk
    Tel: +7 421 272263
Sakhalinskaya (Sakhalin): A B Vasilev
    Kommunisticheskii Pr 78, 693000 Yuzhno-Sakhalinskii
    Tel: +7 424 4400
Kaliningradskaya (Kaliningrad): G S Dyubko
    Kievskaya ul 1, 263039
    Tel: +7 0112 3300

Gauge: 1,520 mm; Sakhalin: 1,067 mm
Route length: 90,000 km; Sakhalin: 1,116 km
Electrification : 19,000 km at 3 kV DC; 19,800 km at 25 kV
50 Hz AC

Political background
In the days of the Soviet command economy, SZhD (Soviet Railways) carried over two and a half times the total freight carried by all 16 Class 1 carriers in the US (SZhD's 1990 freight volume was 3,857 million tonnes, 3,717 billion tonne-km). In passenger traffic, SZhD carried about twice as many passenger-km as the railways of

France, Germany, Italy and the UK combined (in 1990 SZhD carried 4,273 million passenger journeys, 417 billion passenger-km).

The railways are still by far the most important mode of transport in Russia. RZhD (Russian Railways) accounts for almost half of all passenger-km travelled, and over three-quarters of all non-pipeline tonne-km carried in the country. But with the break-up of the Soviet Union in late 1991 and the transition to a market economy, the former enormous traffic volumes are no longer assured, and in the short term the railway is having to adapt to compete with other modes.

Consultants commissioned in 1992 by the European Bank for Reconstruction and Development recommended that the Russian, Belarus, Ukrainian and Kazakhstan governments should give railway managements commercial incentives to increase efficiency. They did not recommend outright privatisation of RZhD at that stage but thought competition should be encouraged by allowing track access to private firms and to major customers for their own trains. They suggested that foreign aid would most usefully be channelled into track maintenance and telecommunications systems.

Before the consultants reported, it had already been decided to introduce flexible rate fixing, and also premium freight centres, where clients could negotiate the whole transportation process, including pick-up and delivery, storage and documentation, with a single service point. Exploitation of modern information technology would progressively enable these centres to monitor freight transits for the benefit of clients. Privately owned wagons were encouraged with special rates.

In July 1995 the Federal Railway Law was ratified. This specified that while non-transport-related facilities might be privatised the operating railway was not liable to denationalisation. (However, in early 1996 the Railways Minister found it necessary to promise strong opposition to the suggestion that the railways might nevertheless be privatised in response to pressure from Western banks.) The Railway Law also forbade strikes of operating workers and allowed the railways to sell off shipments whose transportation had not been paid for. The general strengthening of the railways' hand meant that stronger measures were taken against recalcitrant debtors. For a few days in 1995 the railways refused to provide mail cars, and relented only when the Federal Postal Service agreed to pay its enormous debts.

Some ancillary enterprises like equipment supply works have been privatised. In the case of train and station catering services, privatisation brought a decline in an already unappetising performance and the railways in some cases have been allowed to take them back.

Despite lack of investment, the railways can handle existing traffic comfortably, but the anticipated economic recovery is expected to put them under severe pressure in the longer term. The ten-year plan for the railways, published in 1995, addresses this problem and also envisages a 20 per cent freight-rate reduction, financed by reduced costs.

After a change of minister in April 1997 (the second such change within a year), the government stated that the immediate task of the railways was to reduce freight tariffs and at the same time pay the specified taxes and contributions to the pension fund. Over time, cross-subsidisation from freight to passenger services was to be steadily ended and the railways were to enter the

Riga-built emu on the October Railway at St Petersburg
1997

wholesale electric power market. On the Moscow Railway, big cost reductions have been obtained by eliminating the night shift wherever possible.

Less money from government
In 1994 central government severely restricted its grants for major projects and agreed to maintain finance only for the final tunnel, the Severo—Muiskii, on the Baikul—Amur Magistral (BAM) (see 'Intermodal operations' section below), the Amur bridge reconstruction at Khabarovsk and 130 new passenger vehicles. Overall, by 1995 government investment was about 96 per cent less than it had been three years earlier. Most capital projects are now financed by RZhD itself, but local authorities sometimes assist, especially with station construction/rebuilding projects and occasionally with the purchase of new rolling stock for commuter services.

No major line closures have occurred yet, but they have become a possibility: up to 3,000 km of routes were provisionally listed for closure in 1995-96. Some 9,000 km are regarded as warranting closure, and to lessen local opposition it is hoped that some of these will become industrial railways. Meanwhile the staff was reduced by some 50,000 in 1994, with further cuts planned.

Organisation
The Russian system had 19 principal railways or regions, including the Kaliningrad and Sakhalin systems. These railways were further subdivided into over 100 divisions. However, a start has been made in reducing the number of divisions, with a view to their complete elimination as a management level. In the first half of 1996 25 divisions were to have been eliminated, but only three disappeared. Merging of the railways has been recommended, leading to the formation of five or six big organisations. The BAM

Railway has already been divided between the Far Eastern and East Siberian railways, and the Kemerovo Railway has been merged with the West Siberian. However, there has been opposition to such amalgamations, largely from local political administrators reluctant to lose their 'own' railway and the tax-base it represents. By early 1997 the aim had become a division of the network into federal, regional and local railways. Stock construction and maintenance is to be managed by a single central organisation subordinated to the ministry.

In early 1997 there were 1,521,000 operating workers, a fall of 6 per cent over the previous year.

Finance
The former SZhD ran at a profit. Interest on capital was not charged as an expense, but even so it is thought that the railway made sufficient profit to cover this.

Traditionally, profits from freight operations have been used to cover losses generated by passenger operations. During the early 1990s, with freight traffic declining faster than passenger traffic, this arrangement seemed threatened. But all RZhD regions (except Sakhalin) returned a profit in 1994 with an overall profitability, after subsidies, of 21.9 per cent of income. A figure of 23 per cent has been reported for 1995 as freight traffic rose for the first time in some years. But an unexpected traffic decline has led to a continuing loss since 1996. Moreover, the balancing of passenger with freight profits has aroused complaints from Siberia, where passenger traffic is low and freight traffic is high.

Freight tariffs and long-distance passenger fares are now inflation-indexed. Problems and losses occur, however, when the government orders a price-freeze, as happened for the duration of the fourth quarter of 1995. Local authorities are involved in the setting of fares for

commuter services, and St Petersburg municipal council now subsidises suburban services. Highway competition, as well as a desire to stimulate traffic, has led to flexible (negotiated) freight tariffs for some commodities, while political pressures have dictated reduced rates for freight moving over 3,000 km in Siberia and the east. Further differentiation of tariffs can be expected. Rates for low-value freight were reduced by from one third to one half in 1995, with slight increases for high-value traffic.

Passenger operations
In recent years RZhD's passenger traffic has not suffered from the changes in the economy to the same extent as its freight traffic. In fact, a slight drop in the number of passenger journeys has been offset by an increase in passenger-km. Over 1996-2005 suburban traffic is predicted by the ministry to grow by some 43 per cent and long-distance by over 50 per cent. Some long-distance services are operated with formations up to 24 vehicles in length.

Services operating between the republics of the former Soviet Union now undergo lengthy customs inspections at the new state frontiers. For this reason, services from the centre to the Caucasus and the Black Sea are now routed via Voronezh rather than through Ukraine.

Obtaining reservations has become less time-consuming for passengers due to the spread of RZhD's electronic reservation system. The St Petersburg Railway Agency now offers international reservations through the European START-AMADEUS system.

The rising number of accidents and crime rate on the system makes travel less secure. Railway police officers, used previously to protect merchandise in transit, have spread to late-night commuter services and long-distance trains passing through unstable regions.

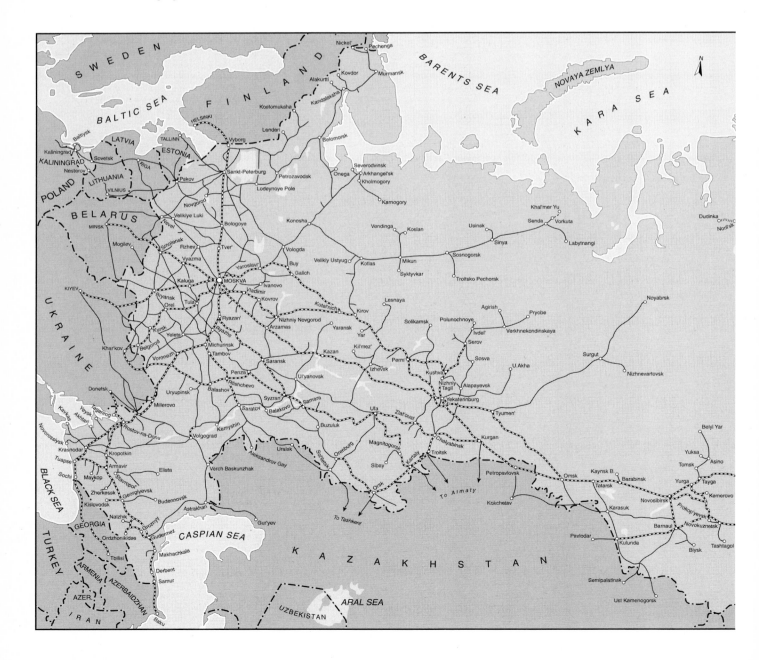

Overall the quality of customer service remains patchy, albeit improving. It is expected that a Federal Passenger Company (FPK) will be formed to handle passenger services and receive subsidies.

Traffic (million)	1994	1995	1996
Freight tonnes	1,053	1,030	908
Freight tonne-km	1,181,000	1,210,900	1,129,000
Passenger journeys	2,324	1,833	1,424
Passenger-km	228,000	193,800	n/a
		(Jan-Sept)	

Main commodities carried by rail (000 tonnes)

	1992	1993	1994
Coal	315,428	279,342	105,300
Coke	10,771	9,038	n/a
Oil and oil products	209,313	187,439	154,600
Manganese and iron ore	89,810	82,246	78,200
Ferrous metals	72,906	64,744	52,900
Chemical and mineral fertilisers	50,520	37,609	27,300
Cement	49,046	38,600	28,300
Timber	91,771	68,367	45,200
Grain	37,819	42,000	32,300
Construction materials	340,446	252,919	188,400

Freight operations

The economic changes in Russia, featuring the decline of heavy industry and the emergence of private enterprise road hauliers, have led to a decline in carryings on RZhD. All the main commodity groups saw a decrease in carryings in 1996 compared to 1992.

Hopes that the decline would flatten out in 1995 were disappointed, but rail's share of total common carrier freight shipments increased from 75 per cent in 1995 to 78 per cent in 1996.

The division of the SZhD freight wagon fleet amongst the republics of the former Soviet Union took place amicably, but the new states often suspect their neighbours of sending them wagons in doubtful order that require repair before being returned to the owning system. An automated wagon registration system at frontiers, with charges levied for the use of foreign wagons, was instituted in May 1996.

Industrial railways

Non-common-carrier lines belonging to particular industries, varying from short factory sidings to large local networks, are said to originate three-quarters of Russian railway freight. Total extent of these lines is probably around 30,000 km. In industrial areas they tend to be amalgamated into industrial railway transport enterprises which have steadily become privatised. One of the largest is the Moscow City Industrial Railway Company which serves 120 sites and owns 50 diesel shunters.

Intermodal operations

Intermodal traffic is to be developed. From 1996 a regular St Petersburg—Moscow service has been added to the existing Nakhodka—Moscow and Berlin—Moscow container services. Fixed-formation container trains have appeared on the Helsinki—Moscow route and piggy-back services are being phased in on the Helsinki and Trans-Siberian routes. Container flatcars for haulage in passenger trains are being introduced.

A Trans-Siberian container landbridge operation established in conjunction with the US shipping company SeaLand in 1991 is now recording significant success. Early teething problems of 'Trans-Siberia Express' service, as it is titled, have been overcome, with the outcome that the inaugural east-to-west rail transit time across Russia from the port of Vostochnyi, on the Sea of Japan, has been all but halved to 24 days. In early 1993 movement of SeaLand containers was averaging 900 a month and the load factor of westbound trains was almost 90 per cent. The original Trans-Siberian railway is now carrying up to 70 million tonnes of freight a year in total, whereas the relief route built by the USSR, the Baikal-Amur Magistral (BAM), is recording no more than 10 million tonnes.

A new multimodal freight terminal is being built at St Petersburg. Advice on the location, design, specifications, marketing and management of this terminal was provided by Sir Alexander Gibb and Partners of the UK, thanks to European Union funding.

New lines

Moscow—St Petersburg high-speed line

In September 1991 President Yeltsin decreed that a new high-speed route be created between Moscow and St Petersburg (formerly Leningrad).

A special company, RAO VSM, has been formed to study, build and operate the high-speed route. The French consultancy Sofrerail is taking a small financial interest in the Russian company, following the finding of its study that the project is economically and physically feasible. A technical co-operation agreement has also been concluded with DB AG (German Railways).

The present route between the two cities, 650 km long, logs annually about nine million long-haul passenger journeys, roughly three-quarters of which are end-to-end. The line also carries some 70 million tonnes of freight annually. There is heavy commuter traffic at each end of the route. Until 1987 about a quarter of the route could be run at 200 km/h by the prototype ER200 trainset, but today its schedule is half-an-hour longer because of the

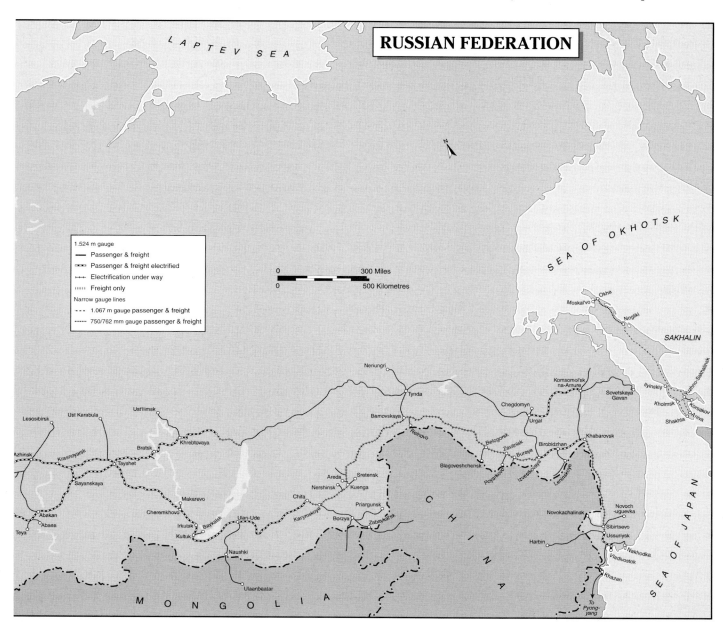

Škoda-built ChS7 double-unit electric locomotive at Chelyabinsk   **1997**

state of the track. Sofrerail attributed the latter in large part to systems of maintenance and renewal that were not apt either for the climatic conditions or the weight of traffic.

Sofrerail propounded four options. These ranged from a base of reorganised maintenance procedures, through expansion of the existing route's operating capacity and obtaining its availability for 200 km/h over 80 per cent of its length by adding third and fourth tracks in strategic locations, to construction of a new high-speed line to the west of the historic route. The last option was chosen, and in July 1993 construction was ceremonially launched of the St Petersburg—Novgorod section of the new 1,520 mm gauge line, which — finance permitting — will eventually extend to 654.3 km and will be 25 kV AC electrified for 300-350 km/h operation. The Russian government has a majority shareholding in the new company set up to build the line, and the other shareholders include the Moscow and St Petersburg city administrations and Sofrerail. Initial land clearance works have been hampered by wartime land mines and lack of funds — but in March 1996 RAO VSM announced an initial bond issue of 120 billion roubles.

By the end of 1996 70 per cent of the needed land had been acquired, and the remainder was secure. A site for the Moscow terminal has been selected near the existing Rizhskii station.

The project remains controversial. The former Railways Minister, Mr Fadeev, was reportedly hostile, as are environmentalists fearful of damage to the Valdai National Park. But the Prime Minister, Mr Chernomyrdin, and a deputy premier, Mr Bol'shakov, have both been in favour the latter being a former president of RAO VSM, but the sacking of Mr Bol'shakov in a cabinet reshuffle may prove a serious setback to the scheme. The total cost has been estimated at 40 trillion roubles (US$8-10 billion), with completion taking at least another seven years.

The main foreign investment so far is US$180 million from a British banking consortium for a new station in St Petersburg.

A new design of dual-voltage (3 kV DC and 25 kV AC) train has been proposed for the route. Tagged VSM-350, the train would have an axleload no greater than 18 tonnes.

After the St Petersburg route, a standard (1,435 mm) gauge Moscow—Smolensk—Krasnoye—Minsk—Warsaw high-speed line is proposed, to link in with the western European high-speed network. However, it is likely that improvement of the existing network will have a prior call on ministry funds.

Finnish connections
A new 126 km route between Kochkoma and Ledmozero in Karelia, near the Finnish border, was almost complete in 1995. Constructed by a private company, Gelleflint, the line has been designed to tap the mineral and forestry resources of the region. Gelleflint will interchange with RZhD at Kochkoma and with Finnish State Railways (VR) at the border.

Gelleflint proposes the development of a second line, a 180 km line from Karpogory to Vendiga, which in combination with the first new line and existing RZhD routes would establish the so-called No-We (North-West)

rail link from northeast Russia to ice-free Finnish ports on the Baltic. A start on construction was proposed for 1997.

In another development, agreement has been reached between VR and RZhD on a 68 km new line from Ruchei Karelski to the border with northern Finland at Alakurtti, with reinstatement of a 6.5 km line on an abandoned trackbed on the Finnish side of the border. This would allow mineral deposits in the Murmansk area to be tapped. Construction was due to begin in 1995.

New link with China
Several Japanese firms have entered joint ventures associated with development of the port of Zarubino, at the southeastern extremity of Russia, below Vladivostok. At present, rail access of China from this port involve a detour through North Korea. The Chinese are currently building a 1,435 mm gauge line from Tumen to Hunchun, near the Sino-Russian border. The plan now is to extend that across the frontier to Zarubino. On the Russian side it will be paralleled by a 1,520 mm gauge branch from the existing Russian line at Kraskino to the frontier station of Changlingzhi.

Dagestan
A new 80 km line avoiding Chechnya is being built in Dagestan. This will also reduce the length of the trunk route linking Russia with Azerbaijan.

Yamal peninsula line
Construction of a 400 km line from Vorkuta to gas and oilfields on the Yamal peninsula, which was put on hold in the early 1990s, has restarted; the line was 250 km long by late 1995. This will be the world's northernmost railway.

Amur-Yakutsk Railway
By May 1995 313 km out of the 830 km length of the Amur-Yakutsk line had been laid. Progress averages only 25 m of track per day.

Improvements to existing lines
The existing Moscow—St Petersburg main line is being reconstructed so that, by 2000, 200 km/h speeds will be possible. EBRD will aid in this, and also in the reconstruction of the Moscow—Voronezh and Moscow—Nizhnii Novgorod routes.

Track renewal and regauging to 1,435 mm gauge on the 47 km main line from Kaliningrad to Mamonova on the Polish frontier was completed in 1992-93 with German financial assistance. Elsewhere on the RZhD system, the condition of bridges requiring renewal or replacement has imposed a large number of speed restrictions.

An important new idea is to develop the Moscow ring railway as an outer circle line of the city metro system. Freight traffic on the ring railway is down by half, while the existing Circle line of the metro is heavily congested. Metro services would be introduced gradually section by section alongside, but separated from, continuing freight traffic. There would be some 36 new stations and interchange points with the existing metro system. If authorised, the first trains could run around the turn of the century.

A Russian-Finnish railway accord was signed on 16 April 1996. Projects include upgrading of the St Petersburg—Helsinki line for high-speed operation by 1999 with Pendolino tilting trains. International travel on this line grew by 32 per cent in 1994 and is forecast to reach one million passengers per year by 2000. Now the Finnish Railways are investing a European Union credit of US$335 million and have undertaken to find a further US$358 million by 1999. Some US$185-200 million is needed for the Russian section. Through high-speed trains to Turku are planned for 2005.

On the BAM line in Siberia, work on building the Severo—Muiskii tunnel has continued despite lack of cash. The BAM has excess capacity, and is in need of greatly increased economic activity in the area.

An improvement project has been proposed for railways on the island of Sakhalin in the Pacific, which were built to the 1,067 mm gauge. Freight from the mainland at present is shipped across the Gulf of Tartary on 1,520 mm gauge wagons on eight train ferries, and transhipped on the island into 1,067 mm gauge wagons for onward transit. To allow uninterrupted rail transit, there is a proposal to introduce a bogie changing facility at the port of Khomlsk on the island; clearances would also be enlarged in nine tunnels on the island's main line. For the long term, regauging of Sakhalin's railways at 1,520 mm and construction of a tunnel to the mainland are proposed.

A rather more exotic proposal is a two-tunnel rail link between Japan, Sakhalin and the Siberian mainland.

Traction and rolling stock
In 1993 the rolling stock fleet available for use comprised some 2,653 diesel and 5,043 electric locomotives, 37,940

Class VL60 locomotive at Orsk with a train from Moscow   **1997**

Electric locomotives

Class	Wheel arrangement	Output kW continuous/ one hour	Speed km/h	Weight tonnes	First built	Builders Mechanical	Electrical
3 kV DC							
VL8	2 × Bo+Bo	3,760/4,200	80/100	184	1953	N/T	N
VL10	2 × Bo-Bo	4,600/5,360	100	184	1976	N/T	T
VL10u	2 × Bo-Bo	4,600/5,360	100	200	1974	N/T	T
VL11	2 × Bo-Bo	4,600/5,360	100	184	1975	T	T
VL11m	2 × Bo-Bo	NA/6,680	100	184	1987	T	T
VL15	2 × Bo-Bo-Bo	8,400/9,000	100	300	1984	T	T
VL22m	2 × Co+Co	1,860/2,400	80	132	1941	N	N/D
VL23*	Co+Co	2,740/3,150	100	138	1956	N	N
ChS2	Co-Co	3,708/4,200	160	125	1958	Škoda	Škoda
ChS2t	Co-Co	4,080/4,620	160	126	1972	Škoda	Škoda
ChS200	2 × Bo-Bo	8,000/8,400	220	156	1975	Škoda	Škoda
ChS6	2 × Bo-Bo	8,000/8,400	190	164	1979	Škoda	Škoda
ChS7	2 × Bo-Bo	6,160/7,200	180	172	1983	Škoda	Škoda
25 kV AC							
VL60K*	Co-Co	4,050/4,650	100	138	1962	N	N
VL60pk	Co-Co	4,050/4,650	110	138	1965	N	N
VL65	Bo-Bo-Bo	4,680/5,000	120	NA	1992	N	N
VL80K	2 × Bo-Bo	5,920/6,320	110	184	1963	N	N
VL80T	2 × Bo-Bo	5,920/6,320	110	184	1967	N	N
VL80R	2 × Bo-Bo	5,920/6,320	110	192	1967	N	N
VL80S	2 × Bo-Bo	5,920/6,320	110	184/192	1979	N	N
VL85	2 × Bo-Bo-Bo	9,360/10,000	110	288	1983	N	N
VL86F	2 × Bo-Bo-Bo-Bo	NA/10,800	120	288	1985	N	N
ChS4	Co-Co	4,920/5,100	180	123	1965	Škoda	Škoda
ChS4t	Co-Co	4,920/5,100	180	126	1971	Škoda	Škoda
ChS8	2 × Bo-Bo	7,200/NA	180	175	1983	Škoda	Škoda
Dual Voltage 3 kV DC/25 kV AC							
VL82m	2 × Bo-Bo	5,760/6,040	110	200	1972	N	N

*Also operated in twin- and triple-unit versions
Abbreviations: D: Divamo; N: Novocherkassk; T: Tbilisi

Diesel locomotives

Class	Wheel arrangement	Power kW	Speed km/h	Weight tonnes	First built	Mechanical	Builders Engine	Transmission
TE3	2 × Co-Co	2,944	100	254	1953	V/K/Ko	2 × 2D 100	E ETM
TE7	2 × Co-Co	2,944	140	254	1956	V/K	2 × 2D 100	E ETM
2TE10M*	2 × Co-Co	4,416	100	276	1981	V/K	2 × 10 D100 or M1	E ETM
2TE10L	2 × Co-Co	4,416	100	260	1962	V/K	2 × 10 D100	E ETM
2TE10u	2 × Co-Co	4,412	100	276	1989	V/K	2 × 10 D100M1 or M2	E ETM
2TE10ut	2 × Co-Co	4,412	120	276	1989	V/K	2 × 10 D100M1 or M2	E ETM
2TE10V	2 × Co-Co	4,416	100	276	1974	V/K	2 × 10 D100	E ETM
4TE10S	4 × Co-Co	8,824	100	552	1983	V/K	4 × 10 D100	E ETM
TEM1	Co-Co	736	90	126	1958	B	2D50	E ETM
TEP10	Co-Co	2,208	140	129	1960	V/K	10 D500	E ETM
TEP60	Co-Co	2,208	160	129	1960	Ko	11D45	E ETM
TEP70	Co-Co	2,944	160	135	1973	Ko	2A5D49	E ETM
TEP80	Bo+Bo-Bo+Bo	4,412	160	180	1988	Ko	2-20DG	E ETM
M62†	Co-Co	1,470	100	116.5	1964	V/Ko	14D40	E ETM
2TE116	2× Co-Co	4,500	100	276	1971	V/Ko	2 × 1A5D49	E ETM
2TE136	2 × Bo-Bo+ Bo-Bo	8,832	120	400	1984	V/Ko	120DG(D49)	E ETM
2M62u	2 × Co-Co	2,942	100	252	1987	V/Ko	2 × 14D40	E ETM
TEM2	Co-Co	883	100	120	1960	V/B/P	PDIM or PDI	E ETM
TEM2um	Co-Co	994	100	126	1988	B/P	1PD-4A	E ETM
TEM7	Bo+Bo- Bo+Bo	1,472	100	180	1975	L/Ko	2-2D49	E ETM
ChME2	Bo-Bo	552	80	64	1958	ČKD	65310DR	E ČKD
ChME3††	Co-Co	993	95	123	1964	ČKD	K65310DR	E ČKD
ChME5	Bo+Bo Bo+Bo	1,470	95	168	1985	ČKD	K85310DR	E ČKD

* Also operated in triple-unit version (3TE10M)
† Also operated in twin- and triple-unit versions (2M62, 3M62)
†† A variant is classified ChME3T
Abbreviations: B: Bryansk; K: Kharkov; Ko: Kolomna; L: Lyundinovsk; P: Penza; V: Voroshilovgrad

Electric railcars or multiple-units

Class	Cars per unit	Motor cars per unit	Motored axles/car	Output/motor kW	Speed km/h	First built	Builders Mechanical	Electrical
3 kV DC								
ER1	10	5	4	200	130	1957	Riga/Kalinin	REZ, Dinamo
ER2	10-12	5-6	4	200	130	1962	Riga/Kalinin	REZ
ER22	8	4	4	220	130	1964	Riga	REZ
ER200	10	8	4	240	200	1974	Riga	REZ
ER2R	10-12	5-6	4	240	130	1979	Riga	REZ
ER2T	10-12	5-6	4	235	130	1987	Riga	REZ
ET2	10	6	4	NA	130	1993	Torzhok/Tikhvin	Tikhvin
ED2T	10	5	4	NA	NA	1992	Demikhovo/Tikhvin	Tikhvin
25 kV AC								
ER-9	10	5	4	180	130	1961	Riga/Kalinin	REZ
ER9P	10-12	5-6	4	200	130	1964	Riga	REZ
ER9M	10-12	5-6	4	200	130	1976	Riga	REZ
ER9E	10-12	5-6	4	200	130	1981	Riga	REZ
ER 9T	10-12	5-6	4	200	130	1988	Riga	REZ

Diesel railcars or multiple-units

Class	Cars per unit	Motor cars per unit	Motored axles/car	Power/motor kW	Speed km/h	First built	Mechanical	Builders Engine	Transmission
D1	4	2	2	540	120	1963	Avad/Ganz-Mavag	Ganz-Jendrassik 12VFE17/24	HM
DR1	6	2	2	736	120	1963	Riga	Zvezda M756B	H
DR1P	6	2	2	736	120	1969	Riga	Zvezda M756B	HM
DR1A	6	2	2	736	120	1973	Riga	Zvezda M756B	H
ACh2	1/2	1	2	736	120	1984	Studenka	Zvezda M756B	H

passenger cars and 548,000 wagons plus over 16,000 multiple-unit coaches.

RZhD's strained finances have continued to restrict deliveries of new rolling stock. Only 29 electric and 35 diesel locomotives were delivered in 1994, and the 1995 programme for new passenger coaches was cut from 980 to 320. Much of the available money is being channelled into factory reconstruction and emu production. In 1997, an order worth ECU48 million was placed with Adtranz for 21 electric locomotives, designated as class EP10. This Co-Co design has dual power supply and asynchronous motors, and nearly 80 per cent of components will be supplied by Russian factories.

Under an accord between the German and Russian governments reached in 1994, RZhD is taking delivery of 10 electric locomotives from Adtranz (worth DM40 million) and, at a concessionary price of DM500 million, 500 passenger coaches from former East German builder DWA; 191 new coaches were supplied in 1994.

Also approved by the Railways Ministry was the import of 26 electric locomotives from Škoda, 16 to be bought with hard currency and the remainder to be bartered for supply of electricity to the Czech Republic.

A shortage of passenger locomotives is forcing widespread use of freight traction for passenger services: an average of 800 to 1,200 electric and 605 diesel locomotives were in use in this way in 1995. Loco-hauled stock is being used to cover a shortfall of multiple-units; almost every diesel class appears on such work. A modernisation programme has been agreed for Hungarian-built class D1 dmus using a Zvezda engine and Kaluga electrical equipment.

Recently, numbers of new freight wagons delivered to the railway have fallen well below the number of withdrawals. RZhD acquired 10,400 wagons in 1993 and 7,600 in 1994.

Two Russian sleeping cars have been refurbished in Spain at RENFE's Malaga works as a pilot project for a possible 1,500 carriages.

New locomotive plans

Many of the traction suppliers to the former SZhD are located outside the Russian Federation. Procurement for the RZhD is being reorganised to minimise hard currency expenditure on imports and protect domestic employment.

Škoda in Czechoslovakia was SZhD's principal supplier of passenger electric locomotives in the days of the Comecon trading bloc. Now the Russian freight electric locomotive production facilities at Novocherkassk are being expanded to produce 100 passenger locomotives per year by 2000. A passenger version of Novocherkassk's new VL65 AC electric is on test, and Classes EP1 (AC) and EP2 (DC) are scheduled for series production from 1996 and 1997. Kolomna works, formerly concentrating on diesels, is to produce up to 100 Class EP100 (DC) and EP200 (AC) passenger electrics from 1998, incorporating the chassis of the TEP70 diesel locomotive. A new consortium, Novotecko, has been formed by Adtranz Italy and two Russian companies to design a new eight-axle 9 MW electric locomotive.

With the 'loss' of diesel loco-building capacity in Ukraine, steps are being taken to raise output from Russia's own plants. At Lyudinovo a new generation of standard diesel-electrics is to be developed in co-operation with GE Transportation Systems of the US, under a technology transfer agreement signed in July 1995; a prototype is to be built during 1996. A prototype 3,000 kW TEP400 mixed-traffic diesel locomotive is scheduled from Lyudinovo for 1998 and production of 80 per year from 2000. Kolomna plans to construct TEP80 and TEP71 passenger diesel locos from 1996 and 1997, to a maximum of 50 per year from 1999. Limited imports may continue in the form of 2TE116UP mixed-traffic locomotives from Lugansk.

Further co-operation is wanted with foreign firms concerning the latest semiconductor transformers, three-phase traction motors, microprocessor control and frame-hung traction motors. Foreign investment in more joint ventures is also being sought.

A Talgo tilting train was on test on the October Railway in early 1996, including high-speed trials on the Moscow–St Petersburg line.

New emu and dmu plans

Short-haul commuter travel is booming, despite draconian fare increases, because the government has provided suburban land for city inhabitants in a bid to encourage food production and cure urban shortages. Though RZhD owns just over 15,000 emu cars, nearly 30 per cent are close to life expiry, and their capacity cannot cope with a volume of commuter journeys that is rising beyond 2.4 billion a year.

The former source of emu car supply was the Riga works in Latvia, which Russia now finds expensive. In 1992, 100 emu vehicles were ordered from the Riga works, but the Russians are now developing their own domestic sources of supply.

Emu vehicles have been produced by the Torzhok missile wagon works, while the Tikhvin converted military plant has manufactured motor bogies. Current plans envisage an annual capacity of 750 carriages by 2001.

Novocherkassk produced its first 10-car emu in early 1996 (Class EN1). Production of 300 carriages per annum is planned from 1999.

The Demikhovo works, formerly a builder of narrow-gauge wagons for the mining industry, completed the first of 50 four-car emus in December 1992; Czech builder Škoda has a US$20 million stake in the new concern. Classes ED4 and ED6 are to enter series production in 1996 and 1999 respectively, with Novocherkassk electrical equipment. By 2000 the factory is intended to produce over 1,000 cars per year.

To replace the Hungarian, Latvian and Czech suppliers of dmus and railcars, the Lyudinovo locomotive plant has begun production of Class DL2 dmu motor cars, to be paired with trailer vehicles constructed by Tver. Full production of 150 carriages per annum is scheduled for 2003.

Double-deck coaches from France and Spain
In October 1992 a Russo-French technology transfer agreement covering double-deck passenger cars was concluded. ANF-Industrie of France is to assist Vagonmash to develop two works for manufacture and deliver 10 complete prototype double-deck coaches for intercity service, followed by 30 more in kit form for assembly in Russia. It will then supervise the manufacture by Russian plants of their first 50 coaches and co-operate in development of a commuter version, possibly at Torzhok. Vagonmash intends to manufacture up to 400 double-deck coaches annually.

In January 1995 RZhD signed a joint-venture contract with GEC Alsthom Transporte of Spain for the supply of double-deck coaches.

Orel locomotive depot   *1997*

Other new rolling stock includes the RZhD's first carriage with wheelchair access.

Signalling and telecommunications
Some 53,000 km of the RZhD network are equipped with the automatic block system, and 20,500 km with Centralised Traffic Control (CTC).

Although RZhD's signalling system is efficient, telecommunications are generally poor. The balance between fibre optic cable and satellite has still to be determined. The Krasnoyarsk Railway in association with the French Alcatel group has been trying a satellite communication system since 1991. Although Russia's great distances are cited as favouring satellites, a fibre optic cable from Moscow to Vladivostok is planned. This will also carry non-railway traffic, income from which will finance extensions. Meanwhile the Gorkii Railway is

reconstructing its signalling and communication system with a fibre optic digital system in association with the British GPT company; much of the equipment will be made locally.

Electrification
Lines around Moscow and in the Urals are electrified on the 3 kV DC system. Most lines electrified since 1956 have been equipped with the 25 kV 50 Hz AC system; routes recently electrified at this voltage include Khabarovsk—Kruglikovo and Mogocha—Chernyshevsk in the east and sections of RZhD's October (111 km), North Caucasia (115 km), South East (95 km), Volga (115 km) and Gorki (120 km) regions. Sections of the October (100 km) and Moscow (25 km) regions have recently been electrified at 3 kV DC. On the Trans-Siberian route the Zima—Slyudyanka section has been converted to 25 kV AC operation. New electrification on the Trans-Baikal Railway completes coverage from Moscow as far as Khabarovsk. Electrification is proceeding very slowly of the Trans-Siberian route's final gap of 603 km from Khabarovsk to Ussuriisk and it is being extended northwards from Konosha on the Archangel line.

Track
A severe backlog in track maintenance work has developed on RZhD in recent years. Ballast is in poor condition in many places. The EBRD report recommended that lighter, more mobile track maintenance equipment and advanced tampers should be used, and advocated a revision of maintenance methods. Western track machines have been purchased and a start made on producing Russian versions of them which initially will be devoted to the Moscow—St Petersburg, Moscow—Smolensk and Moscow—Samara main lines.

Rails: 75, 65, 50 kg/m
Continuous welded rail: 1993: 34,400 km
Sleepers: Ferro-concrete on 36,600 km
Sleeper spacing: 1,840/km on plain track, 2,000/km on curves of less than 1,200 m radius
Sleeper dimensions: 2,750 × 250 × 180 (wood); 2,700 × 250 × 193 (concrete)
Max axleload: 23.5 tonnes

DWA-built sleeper belonging to RZhD in international train at Aachen, Germany (Colin Boocock)   *1997*   *UPDATED*

SAUDI ARABIA

Saudi Railroad Organisation

PO Box 36, Dammam 31241
Tel: +966 3 871 2222   Fax: +966 3 827 1130

Key personnel
President: Nassir M Al-Ajami
Vice-Presidents: Fahad S Al-Balawi, Fahad M Al-Shehail
Directors-General
    Administration and Finance: Abdulla Ghanim Al-Oraini

Maintenance: Mohammed A Bubshait
Riyadh Branch: Abdulaziz S Al-Tammami
Projects: Hamad Abdulqadir
Operations: Mohammed Al-Maree
Directors
Personnel: Ibrahim H Al-Khashan
Finance: Omer Al-Khuzaim
Motive Power and Equipment: Ahmed Abdulla
Telecommunications: Fahad A Al Aqeel
Planning and Budget: Khamis M Al-Dossary

Controller of Finance: Saad A A Al-Abbad
Permanent Way: Hussain Murad Al-Balusi
Construction and Maintenance:
    Abdullah Saeed Balhaddad
Purchasing: Yousuf A Al-Farhan
Stores: Saeed Al-Qahtani
Representative for UIC Affairs: Mohammed A Bubshait

Gauge: 1,435 mm
Route length: 1,390 km (with branch lines & sidings)

Container train hauled by GM-built locomotives **1997**

Diesel locomotives

Class	Wheel arrangement	Power kW	Speed km/h	Weight tonnes	No in service	First built	Engine	Builders Transmission	
1100 (G18W)	Bo-Bo	746	110	62.2	16	1968	EMD	E EMD	
1100 (SW1001)	Bo-Bo	746	110	104.3	5	1981	EMD	E EMD	
1500 (F7 & F9)	Bo-Bo	1,119	110	118	6	1953	EMD	E EMD	
1200 (GP18)	Bo-Bo	1,119	110	111.4	1	1961	EMD	E EMD	
2000 (GP38-2)	Bo-Bo	1,492	110	113	1	1973	EMD	E EMD	
2000 (GT22CW)	Co-Co	1,678	110	108	3	1976	EMD	E EMD	
2000 (SDL38-2)	Co-Co	1,492	110	109.5	5	1978	EMD	E EMD	
3500 (SDL50)	Co-Co	2,611	160	120.4	6	1981	EMD	E EMD	
					10*	1985*			
3600 (CSE 26-21)	Co-Co	2,450	160	126	6	1981	Alco/Francorail	E Jeumont Schneider	

* With dynamic braking

Locomotive workshop **1997**

Improvements to existing lines

Principal infrastructure project of the 1980s was transformation of the Dammam—Riyadh main line. The 140 km of the existing route from Dammam to Hofuf were double-tracked and realigned for 150 km/h maximum speed, with continuously welded UIC 60 rail on concrete sleepers, the latter manufactured in a plant established locally at Hofuf. Beyond Hofuf a new and direct double-track route of 308 km was built for 150 km/h running.

New stations were built at Riyadh, Dammam and Hofuf. Traffic is controlled by route relay interlocking, tokenless block, with level-crossing automatic barriers worked by soft-lead batteries recharged by solar power.

The next major project is to be construction of a 100 km line from Dammam to the Jubail industrial complex. The project will be brought forward for approval in the 1995 to 2000 plan period.

Traction and rolling stock

In 1997 the railway was operating 59 diesel locomotives, 58 passenger cars (including nine restaurant cars) and 2,340 freight wagons. In October 1996, SRO signed a contract with General Motors of the US for the supply of seven locomotives, worth US$14.4 million.

A major maintenance workshop has been set up at Dammam with capacity for 78 main line locomotives and 33 shunting locomotives, with a maximum capacity of 20 locomotives at one time.

Type of coupler, passenger and freight: AAR Type E
Type of brake: Westinghouse air

Track

All main line track renewals are undertaken with continuously welded UIC 60 kg/m rail on prestressed concrete sleepers with elastic fastenings.

Rail types and weights: UIC 54, UIC 60
Crossties (sleepers): Prestressed concrete, 200 mm thickness, 2,600 mm long
Spacing: 1,667/km
Rail fastenings: Elastic, ballast cushion of 300 mm
Min curve radius: 565 m
Max gradient: 1%
Max permissible axleload: 29 tonnes

Traffic	1993-94	1994-95
Freight tonnes (million)	1.90	1.50
Freight tonne-km (million)	816	822
Passenger journeys	414,000	460,000
Passenger-km (million)	139	164

Finances (million Saudi Riyals)
Revenue

Passengers	13.695	14.639
Freight	63.705	62.292
Other income	14.005	11.469
Total	91.405	88.400

Expenditure

Staff/personnel	99.602	111.872
Materials and services	69.534	57.033
Depreciation	108.910	107.235
Other expenditure	6.118	6.100
Total	284.164	282.240

UPDATED

SENEGAL

Ministry of Equipment and Land Transport

Administrative Building, Dakar

Key personnel
Minister: Landing Sone

Société Nationale des Chemins de Fer du Sénégal (SNCS)

PO Box 175, Cité Ballabey, Thiès
Tel: +221 51 1013   Fax: +221 51 1393

Key personnel
Director-General: Mbaye Diouf
Director Delegate, Management Co-ordination:
 Ndiaga Ndiaye
Heads of Department
 Commercial and Freight: Fadel Kane
 Finance: Mor Kane
 Planning: Samba Fall
 Operations: Fadel Kane
 Traction and Rolling Stock: Cheikhou Diallo
 Infrastructure: Gamou Mbaye
 Computerisation: Fadel Kane
 Stores: Ibra Fall
 Personnel: Mame Babacar Sarr

Legal: Baye Ndaraw Fall
International Relations: Samba Fall

Gauge: 1,000 mm
Route length: 904 km

Organisation

As one of West Africa's most industrialised countries, Senegal has a railway system comprising two main lines running from Dakar to St Louis and Linguère in the north-east and the border with Mali in the east. The system was originally part of the Federal West African Railway Authority (AOF) before transfer to the Mali Federation in 1960. The disintegration of the Mali Federation caused

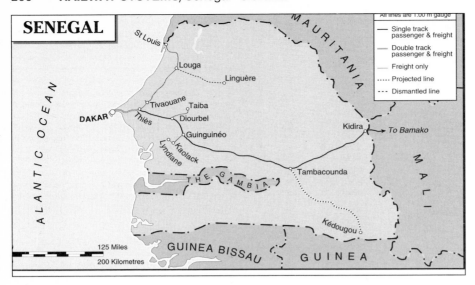

year, with payment linked to results. This target was comfortably exceeded, leading to an estimated 25 per cent rise in international tonnage in 1994-95.

Improvements to existing lines

Two projects are being assigned priority. First is the CFAFr19.6 billion renewal of track on the international main line between Tambacounda and Kidira. Target completion date is 1999.

The other project is installation of a third track between Hann and Thiaroye on the Dakar suburban route; this would be for the exclusive use of passenger trains, freeing up the other two tracks for freight. Earthworks had begun in 1997.

Traction and rolling stock

The stock of 29 diesel locomotives is mostly French built; French aid is financing GEC Alsthom maintenance of the railway's Alsthom AD16B locomotives. In 1996, a protocol was signed between the governments of Senegal and Canada that provides a grant of C$12.5 million to pay for five new locomotives from General Motors Canada; a further C$1 million from Senegalese sources will fund acquisition of a pool of spare parts.

In 1995, the number of passenger cars totalled 139. SNCS has acquired from France 24 stainless steel SNCF 'Mistral' cars of the 1950s and their four generator cars; these are now being used on the international trains to Mali.

The 'Little Blue Train' suburban service in Dakar was launched in 1987. There are seven five-car trains, with 10 dedicated Type AD16 locomotives as motive power. SNCS has refurbished 41 SNCF Type B10t 'Bruhat' passenger cars, and fitted them with ex-freight wagon metre-gauge bogies with their suspension refined.

In 1995, the freight wagon fleet totalled 662. SNCS and Mali have recently added 140 new wagons to the international pool.

Signalling and telecommunications

Automatic block colourlight signalling is operative on the 70 km of double track between Dakar and Thiès.

UPDATED

the division of the former Dakar—Niger system into two networks. The principal line extends 1,286 km from Dakar in Senegal to Koulikoro, the terminus of the railway in the landlocked neighbouring country of Mali.

SNCS was established in 1989 as successor to the former RCFS; it is an independent semi-public corporation and as such agrees a performance contract each year with the government.

In recent years, the growth of road transport has been a significant challenge for SNCS.

Passenger operations

There are four international expresses a week from Dakar to Bamako, the capital of Mali, which are overseen by a joint management board. Typically, these trains carry between 4,000 and 5,000 passengers a month.

A frequent push-pull service operates on the 29 km suburban route from Dakar to Thiaroye and Rufisque. Patronage on this route has boomed, with the service handling 6.3 million passengers in the year to July 1996.

Railcar services on domestic routes from Dakar to St Louis and Kaolack were lossmaking and were withdrawn in 1996.

Total passenger revenue grew from CFAFr1.12 billion in 1993 to CFAFr1.87 billion in 1995.

Freight operations

In terms of weight, the principal freight traffic is phosphates, transported by rail to the port of Dakar for export. In 1997, three trains a day were serving Taiba, a single daily train serving Lam-Lam, and a single daily train was serving Allou Kagne.

In 1997, SNCS was operating three trains of chemical products a day for the chemicals company Sefics between Taiba and Dakar, using wagons owned by Sefics.

In 1997, nine international freight trains a week were scheduled between Dakar and Bamako in Mali. Some 70 per cent of SNCS freight receipts and 50 per cent of gross tonne-km are generated by traffic with neighbouring Mali, though this constitutes only 14 per cent of total tonnage. Amongst other things, the railway has now captured 60 per cent of the container traffic between the coast and Bamako, in Mali. Freight traffic totalled 278 million tonne-km in the year to July 1996. Freight revenue in 1995 was CFAFr10 billion.

Following several years in which freight performance was marred by poor locomotive availability, in 1994 a four-year locomotive maintenance contract was agreed between SNCS and Canadian consultant Canarail, under which a target was set for 75 per cent availability in the first

---

SLOVAKIA

Ministry of Transport, Post and Telecommunications

Bratislava

Key personnel
Minister: Alexander Rezeš

VERIFIED

Slovakian Republic Railways (ŽSR)

Železnice Slovenskej Republiky
Klemensova 8, SK-81,361 Bratislava
Tel: +421 32 52 42/+421 204 70 07
Fax: +421 36 22 96

Key personnel
General Manager: Bartolomej Sinai
Deputy General Managers
    Finance: Pavol Dráč
    Strategy and Investment: Ján Kačica
    Property Management: Štefan Chocholák
    Operations: Ján Starinský
    Commercial and Rolling Stock: Miroslav Matúšek
    Personnel: Vladimír Klepanec
Divisional Managers
    Infrastructure: Ratislav Polcer
    Freight Traffic: Miroslav Horečný
    Passenger Traffic: Pavol Stetulič
    Rolling Stock: Miloslav Lužák

Management Board
Finance: Dušan Jakubec
Strategy: Jozef Gazda
Property Management: Valentín Forgáč
Legal Affairs: Tatiana Šloserová

Personnel: Eva Schwarczová
Purchasing: Ján Kováčik
Tariffs: Anton Kukučka
Operations: Štefan Hrivňák
Investment: Jozef Hudek

department, known as Infrastructure. Under its General Manager there are four chief engineers, responsible individually for: track, buildings and structures; electrical; signalling; and mechanical plant and vehicles. The department's annual budget of some R1.5 billion includes about R230 million for maintenance of the assets of the Rail Commuter Corporation.

The section responsible for design, procurement and maintenance of all rolling stock is known as Rolmat. It also covers engineering and research development.

Since 1991, the Spoornet workforce has dropped from nearly 120,000 to 63,000.

Passenger operations

Spoornet is principally a freight operator, but it still runs a few long-distance passenger trains. In 1994 main line passenger services totalled 122 trains weekly, based on 11 principal named trains.

The world-renowned 'Blue Train' between Pretoria and Cape Town still attracts tourist trade to the extent that its average load factor is 90 per cent. The case for ordering new rolling stock for the service is under study, but in the meantime the two 1972-built trains in use are being refurbished, with the first re-entering service in June 1997. The ultra-luxury train features rare Italian marble on the bathroom floors and hi-fi and video equipment in the more expensive compartments. There is an onboard laundry.

Freight operations

Separate business managements have been established for each major freight commodity group, such as coal, ores, timber, cement, steel and agricultural products.

A world first is claimed for Spoornet's in-house development of a hot box detector which, in measuring temperatures of boxes on passing trains, distinguishes whether boxes have white metal friction or roller bearings and works to the danger level appropriate for each type. Following success with a prototype near the Hex River Tunnel on the Johannesburg—Cape Town line, the detector is in mass production for installation on all Spoornet main lines.

Spoornet has a computerised Operating Information & Control System which provides instant information on the last reported movement of all wagonloads of goods for the benefit of both clients and of all levels of transport management. Approximately 100,000 vehicles and 5,500 locomotive movements on over 3,000 trains are reported daily from some 100 locations countrywide to one of the largest computer complexes in the Southern Hemisphere.

Richards Bay coal line

Coal and coke generate roughly two-thirds of Spoornet tonnage. A major component is the export flow from the Transvaal fields to Richards Bay on the Indian Ocean. Extremely heavy trains are run. Between the coalfields and Ermelo, the line is electrified at 3kV DC and trains comprise 100 CCL 5/7/8 wagons each carrying 84 tonnes, or 100 CCL 1/3 wagons each carrying 58 tonnes; both types are hauled by three Class 10E electric locomotives. At Ermelo these are combined into 200-wagon trains 2.4 km long for the 25 kV 50 Hz AC leg to Richards Bay. Payload is 18,400 or 14,200 tonnes depending on the types of train combined, and the total mass of the train can exceed 21,000 tonnes. Haulage is by four Class 11E locomotives.

The new type of coal wagon, designated CCL 8, has side plates of locally manufactured chrome steel, to counter the abrasive and chemical reaction on Corten steel of coal vibrating in transit. The CCL 8, which has an internal volume of 85.66 m³ and payload capacity of 84 tonnes for a tare weight of only 20.25 tonnes, is produced in permanently coupled pairs to suit the twin wagon tippler system at the Richards Bay coal terminal.

The tonnage of coal moved on the Richards Bay coal export line stood at 58.1 million tonnes in 1996, slightly down on the year before. Additional substations were installed on the 3 kV section in 1996, pushing capacity of the line to 65 million tonnes per year; in 1997, more substations were being installed on the 25 kV section, bringing annual capacity there up to 72 million tonnes.

Sishen-Saldanha ore line (Orex)

An 861km line from the iron ore fields at Sishen to the Atlantic Ocean port of Saldanha, known as Orex, is one of Spoornet's principal traffic arteries. The line suffered a decline in traffic during the mid-1980s ore glut, carrying less than 9 million tonnes in FY1986-87, but traffic has rebounded and a record 22 million tonnes were carried in FY1995-96. The line was run down during the period of

Spoornet diesel-electric locomotives

Class	Wheel arrangement	Power kW	Speed km/h	Weight tonnes	No in service	First built	Mechanical	Builders Engine	Transmission
33-000	Co-Co	1,605/ 1,490	100	91	59	1965	GE	GE 7 FDL-12	GE 761 A6
33-200	Co-Co	1,640/ 1,490	100	91	13	1966	EMD	EMD 16-645-E	EMD D 29CC-7
33-400	Co-Co	1,605/ 1,490	100	91	30	1968	GE	GE 7 FDL-12	5 GE 761 A6
34-000	Co-Co	2,050/ 1,940	100	111	119	1971	GE	GE 7 FDL-12	GE 5 GE 761 A13
34-200	Co-Co	2,145/ 1,940	100	111	47	1971	EMD	EMD 16-645-E3	EMD 29B
34-400	Co-Co	2,050/ 1,940	100	111	90	1973	GE	GE 7 FDL-12	GE 5 GE 761 A13
34-500	Co-Co	2,050/ 1,940	100	111	39	1977	GE	GE 7 FDL-12	GE 5 GE 761 A13
34-600	Co-Co	2,245/ 1,940	100	111	96	1974	GM SA	EMD 16-645-E3	EMD D 29B
34-800	Co-Co	2,140/ 1,940	100	111	55	1978	GM SA	EMD 16-645-E3	EMD 29B
34-900	Co-Co	2,050/ 1,940	100	111	30	1979	GE	GE 7 FDL-12	GE 5GE 761 A13
35-000	Co-Co	1,230/ 1,160	100	82	65	1972	GE	GE 7 FDL-8	GE 5GE 764-C
35-200	Co-Co	1,195/ 1,065	100	82	149	1974	EMD/ GM SA	EMD 8-645-E3	EMD D 29CCBT
35-400	Co-Co	1,230/ 1,160	100	82	100	1976	GE	GE 7 FDL-8	GE 5GE 764-C1
35-600	Co-Co	1,195/ 1,065	100	82	99	1976	GM SA	EMD 8-645-E3	EMD D29 CCBT
36-000	Bo-Bo	875/ 800	100	72	124	1975	GE	GE 7 FDL-8	GE 5GE 764-C1
36-200	Bo-Bo	875/ 800	90	72	101	1980	GM SA	EMD 8-645-E	D29B
37-000	Co-Co	2,340/ 2,170	100	125	92	1981	GM SA	EMD 16-645E-3B	EMD D31
38-000	Bo-Bo	1,500/ 780	100	74	50	1993	UCW	CAT 3508	Siemens ABB/6 FRA 5252
91-000	Bo-Bo	52/ 480	50	44	20	1973	GE	CAT D 379	GE 5GE 778

Spoornet electric locomotives

Class	Wheel arrangement	Output kW continuous/ one hour	Speed km/h	Weight tonnes	No in service	First built	Builders Mechanical	Electrical
3 kV DC								
5E1	Bo-Bo	1,940/ 1,456	100	86	400	1959	MV/UCW	4-MV 281/ 4-AEI 281 AZX/ 4-AEI 281 AX/ 4-AEI 281 X
6E	Bo-Bo	2,492/ 2,252	110	89	72	1970	UCW	4-AEI 293 AZ
6E1	Bo-Bo	2,492/ 2,252	110	89	916	1969	UCW	4-AEI 283 AZ
8E	Bo-Bo	800/ 704	75	81	100	1983	UCW	BBC/Siemens 4-1 KB 2820-0TA 02
10E	Co-Co	3,240/ 3,090	90	126	50	1985	UCW	Toshiba 6-SE-218
12E	Bo-Bo	2,492/ 2,252	150	84	5	1983	UCW	UCW/ AEI 283Z
10E1	Co-Co	3,240/ 3,090	90	126	79	1987	UCW	GEC 6X G425 A2
10E2	Co-Co	3,240/ 3,090	105	126	25	1989	UCW	Toshiba 6X SE-218A
25 kV AC								
EXP/AC	Bo-Bo	2,492/ 2,252	110	85	1	1975	UCW	50 c/s Group
7E	Co-Co	na/ 3,000	100	123	99	1978	UCW	50 c/s Group
7EI	Co-Co	na/ 3,000	100	123	50	1979	Dorman Long	Hitachi HS-1054-GR
7E2 (Series 1)	Co-Co	3,000	100	125	25	1982	UCW	Siemens 6-MG 680
7E2 (Series 2)	Co-Co	3,000	100	125	40	1983	UCW	Siemens 6-MG 680
7E3 (Series 1)	Co-Co	3,000	100	125	60	1983	Dorbyl	Hitachi EFF20 HS-1054-HR
7E3 (Series 2)	Co-Co	3,000	100	125	25	1984	Dorbyl	Hitachi EFF20 HS-1054-HR
11E	Co-Co	4,000	90	168	45	1985	GMSA	GM/ASEA 6X LJM 54D-1
50 kV AC								
9E	Co-Co	4,068/ 3,750	90	166	25	1979		GEC Engineers (Pty) GEC 6-GEC G415AZ
9E2*					6	1978	UCW	
Dual-voltage 3 kV DC/25 kV AC								
14E	Bo-Bo	4,000	130	92	3	1989	SLM	50 c/s Group
14E1	Bo-Bo	4,000	130	97	10	1996	SLM	

Abbreviations: MV: Metropolitan Vickers; UCW: Union Carriage & Wagon
* Ex-ISCOR 1978

low traffic, with track maintenance holidays and locomotives cannibalised for spares, but has since been built back up again.

All 31 of the fleet of Class 9E electric locomotives which work the line were expected to be back in traffic in 1997. The 9Es are capable of handling 18 million tonnes per year; a small stud of GE diesels handles traffic above this level and is assigned to trains which have to climb over steep gradients at times when electricity is expensive.

The rebuilding of infrastructure centres on treating cracked concrete sleepers and planing the rail surface.

Some 65,000 of the routes 1.4 million sleepers are being replaced in the period to 2002, and 650,000 are being treated with a silicon spray to prevent cracking. In early 1997 about 250 km of track needed planing and a machine was treating about 12 km a month.

In 1989 several world records were claimed when a 71,600 tonne train was run the length of the 861 km Sishen—Saldanha ore line. The train, 7.3 km long, was formed of 660 wagons and powered by five Class 9E electric locomotives at the head end, four more cut in after the 470th wagon, and at the rear, to avoid overtaxing the traction current supply, seven Class 37 diesel locomotives plus a fuel tank car and brake coach. Locomotive crews had radio intercommunication. Maximum speed was 80 km/h and average speed for the whole run 37.98 km/h. The feat culminated a research programme directed to increase the 14,500 to 21,800 tonne trainloads that are current practice on this line.

Intermodal operations

Spoornet's container division, CX, runs up to four daily 100 TEU trains each way between City Deep (Johannesburg) and Bayhead (Durban) terminals, as required. In addition, one 100 TEU train runs each way on weekdays between City Deep, Bloemfontein and Deal Party/Algoa Bay (Port Elizabeth), and East London Buffalo Harbour, and another links City Deep with Kimberley, De Aar and Cape Town's Belcon terminal. CX owns some 14,700 containers, and carried 444,386 TEU in 1995.

Spoornet is considering piggyback operation. Ten prototype well-floor wagons designated Abba have been built for trial use in Durban—Johannesburg container trains. Spoornet thinks of launching daily dedicated Abba trains between Durban and Johannesburg, and between Cape Town and Johannesburg. Private road haulage companies would carry out road collection and delivery.

A new type of full-length side-door container is being introduced for palletised goods.

GE-design Class 34-500 and 34-000 locomotives haul an Oudtshoorn—Port Elizabeth freight train past a Garratt steam locomotive (at left) on an excursion train (Mick Alderman)   ***1997***

Traffic (million)	1993-94	1994-95
Freight tonnes	164.0	171.6
Freight tonne-km	89,400	95,260
Passenger journeys	—	1.7
Passenger-km	—	—
Finances (R million)		
Revenue	1993-94	1994-95
Passengers		
(including commuter)	127.302	145.581
Freight	6,814.137	7,478.175
Miscellaneous revenue	1,589.997	1,576.822
Total income	8,531.436	9,200.578
Expenditure		
Labour	3,117.534	3,435.414
Materials and services	3,170.067	3,557.535
Depreciation	782.073	789.750
Total operating costs	7,069.674	7,782.699
Operating surplus/(shortfall)	1,461.762	1,417.879
Transnet management fee	81.497	61.399
Surplus/(shortfall)		
before financing costs	1,380.265	1,356.480
Financing costs	404.997	683.564
Surplus/(shortfall)	975.268	672.916
Pension fund costs	357.007	246.942
Retained surplus/		
accumulated loss)	618.261	425.974

Signalling and telecommunications

A sophisticated UHF train radio system operates on the Witbank—Richards Bay coal export line. Simpler VHF systems are being installed on branch lines where trains are controlled solely by radio. An electronic token system is being developed for branch line sections where train density taxes the capacity of pure radio control.

Intensive investigation of electronic interlocking cost-effectiveness has led Spoornet to develop a hybrid system in which non-safe functions, such as indications and through routeing, are performed electronically, and safe functions such as route locking and releasing are relay-based.

At the end of 1995, some 6,129 km was operated by CTC, 9,014 km by token block, 290 km by radio token, and 304 km by radio train order. At the same time, work was in progress on installing CTC between Touwsriver and De Aar (544 km), Port Elizabeth and De Aar (528 km), and Kimberley and Veertienstrome (77 km). The Johannesburg—Durban main line (726 km) is being equipped with hotbox detectors and train radio trunking, whilst the radio train token system is being installed between Rustenburg and Thabazimbi (137 km).

Traction and rolling stock

At the start of 1996 the railway was operating on 1,067 mm gauge 2,164 electric and 1,376 diesel locomotives, 3,660 passenger cars (including those operated by Metro), and 138,833 wagons. The resources on 610 mm gauge comprised 12 steam and 20 diesel locomotives, 24 passenger cars and 1,695 wagons.

Although Spoornet is now dedicated to Co-Cos for general main line use, in 1990 it took delivery for evaluation of three prototypes of a new Class 14E Bo-Bo design with dual-voltage 3 kV DC/25 kV AC capability.

With a 4,000 kW output and 160 km/h top speed, the 14E features self-steering bogies, fully suspended traction motors, three-phase asynchronous AC drive and control by an onboard complex of five microcomputers. The locomotives were built by SLM of Switzerland with electrical equipment from the 50 c/s Group. In 1996, Spoornet took delivery of the first 10 of a further 50 such locomotives, designated Class 14E1.

In 1990 an order for 50 electro-diesel locomotives was placed with Siemens. These Class 38 units, assembled by Union Carriage & Wagon Company, have a 1,500 kW rating as straight electrics and a Caterpillar Type 3508 eight-cylinder 780 kW engine to operate as diesel-electric. Initially, they released diesel locomotives operating on electrified routes to accelerate the end of steam power.

Type of braking: Vacuum and air
Type of coupler in standard use: Mainly E-type SASKOP (knuckle-type)

Track
Rail: 60 kg S-60 SAR, 60 kg UIC, 57 kg UIC A/B, 48 kg HCOB, 40 kg HCOB, 30 kG HCOB and 22 kg HCOB
Crossties (sleepers)
PY/FY concrete 2,200 × 250 mm
P2/F4 concrete 2,057 × 203 mm
Steel 40 and 30 kg
Wood 2,100 × 250 mm
Fastenings: Pandrol, Fist, E3131 chairs
Spacing: 700 mm: 1,440/km; and 650 mm: 1,538/km
Minimum curvature radius: 90 m
Max gradient: 1.67%
Max axleload: 29 tonnes

South African Rail Commuter Corporation Ltd (SARCC)

Private Bag X2, Sunninghill 2157
Tel: +27 11 804 2900   Fax: +27 11 804 3852

Key personnel
Chairman: J T M Edwards
Managing Director: Wynand P Burger
Chief Executive Officers
  Metro Rail: Zandile Jakavule
  Intersite Property Management: J Prentice
Senior Group General Managers
  Finance: Jakkie van Niekerk
  Communications: Mrs Connie Nkosi
  Management Services: Saag Jonker

Gauge: 1,065 mm
Length: operates over 1,276 km
Electrification: 3 kV DC

Metro Rail emus   ***1997***

Rail Commuter Corporation electric multiple-units

Class	Cars per unit	Motor cars per unit	Motored axles/car	Output/motor kW	Speed km/h	No of sets	First built	Builders Mechanical	Electrical
5M	11-14	3-4	16	220	100	350 (all series)	1957	UCW	GEC
6M	14	8	32	245	110	1 (prototype)	1983	Hitachi	Hitachi
7M	6	6	24	290	110	1 (prototype)	1984	MAN	Siemens/AEG/ BBC
8M	6	6	24	245	110	8	1987	Dorbyl	Hitachi

Metro Rail emu for Cape Town suburban service (Wolfram Veith) *1996*

Political background

In 1990 SARCC took over the infrastructure and rolling stock of the country's suburban services, with Spoornet running them under contract for the first few years but SARCC taking over from 1995 onwards.

In 1996, discussions were under way with a view to making city authorities responsible for commuter services in their areas. Concessioning on the Argentinian model was proposed. Also proposed was a move to make SARCC part of the Transnet holding company (see 'Political background' section in Spoornet entry above).

Organisation

SARCC's rail operations are branded 'Metro Rail'. This division of the company employed 10,357 people at the close of 1996.

Intersite is the division responsible for management and development of the company's property holdings. Its employee total at the close of 1996 was 80.

Overseeing the two divisions is SARCC's head office, employing about 40 people.

Finance

Surpluses have risen in recent years. In 1994-95, the surplus was R94 million on a subsidy of R1.25 billion; in 1995-96 the surplus was R155 million on a subsidy of R1.37 billion. Cost recovery from the farebox stood at 31 per cent in 1995-96.

Passenger operations

Metro Rail services operate around the larger coastal cities — Cape Town, Durban, Port Elizabeth and East London — and in the Johannesburg/Vereeniging/Pretoria metropolitan area.

In the newly stable political situation, patronage has started to grow again after declining substantially since the mid-1980s. This was largely due to strong competition from kombi-taxis and latterly the high level of violence

prevalent on some commuter routes. From a peak of 638 million passenger journeys in 1985-86, traffic reached a low point of 373 million journeys in 1992-93, but rebounded to 443.8 million in 1995-96 following successful efforts to counter politically motivated violence, which is now at an end.

New lines

A dozen new lines or extensions are proposed to extend rail service to developing suburban areas and seven, totalling 61 km, have been accorded priority for detailed studies. Varying in length from 3 to 18 km, the seven are costed out in total at R2.4 billion.

Improvements to existing lines

The new government's programme of National Reconstruction and Development has identified good-quality and inexpensive rail service as an essential part of the process of improving conditions in the township areas surrounding major cities. Accordingly, SARCC is embarking on a 10-year R600 million investment programme to improve and extend its services. The rolling stock fleet will be rehabilitated, and new stations are planned at several locations where substantial residential or educational developments are under way.

The entire 2,228 km of electrified track has been surveyed to ascertain its condition, and a start made on rehabilitation of 69 km of overhead on the Natal South Coast. Uniquely, heavily corroded steel is being replaced by glass fibre structures.

Traction and rolling stock

In 1997 the rolling stock fleet totalled 1,344 powered emu cars and 3,291 trailers. Apart from a few trains built in the 1980s, all stock is based on a design of 1957 vintage. Some R2.8 billion is to be spent on refurbishment of 4,000 cars in a 15-year programme. The aim is to raise comfort standards and reduce opportunities for vandalism.

Service improvements and the proposed extensions will require purchase of a further 300 cars, but the need to import technology and the devaluation of the rand has made such purchases problematic. In 1996, a R260 million loan from the Japanese government was being finalised for the purchase of new trains. Towards the end of the decade, 60 new coaches will be delivered under this arrangement, with the first new trains going to the Soweto line in Johannesburg.

Signalling and telecommunications

In 1997, automatic block was being installed on 70 km from Pretoria to Gauteng.

UPDATED

SPAIN

Ministry of Development

Plaza de la Castellana 67, Nuevos Ministerios, E-28071 Madrid
Tel: +34 1 597 7000   Fax: +34 1 597 8502

Key personnel
Minister: Rafael Arias Salgado y Montalvo
Secretary of State for Infrastructure and Transport:
   Joaquín Abril Martorell
Director General, Railways and Road Transport:
   Fernando José Cascales Moreno

VERIFIED

Catalan Railways (FGC)

Ferrocarrils de la Generalitat de Catalunya
Av Pau Casals 24, 8è, E-08021 Barcelona
Tel: +34 3 201 1144   Fax: +34 3 201 4683

Key personnel
Chairman: Enric Roig Solés
Director: Miquel Llevat Vallespinosa
Operating Director: Albert Tortajada Flores
Technical Director: Josep Lluís Arques Patón
Administration Director: Antoni Herce Herce
Personnel Director: Josep Lluís Portabales Iglesias

Gauge: 1,435 mm (Catalunya i Sarrià line); 1,000 mm (Catalans and Ribes—Núria (Abt rack) lines)

Class 254 diesel locomotive with empty potash wagons (John C Baker) *1997*

Route length: 45 km; 138 km (Catalans) and 12 km (Ribes—Núria)
Electrification: 1,435 mm gauge: 45 km at 1.5 kV DC
1,000 mm gauge: 63 and 12 km at 1.5 kV DC

Political background

In conjunction with efforts to create, by July 1996, a greater Barcelona transport authority with responsibility

for infrastructure and service planning and a new integrated fares structure, an agreement was signed in 1995 by central government and the Catalan government covering infrastructure investment on the FGC and Barcelona metro systems between 1995 and 1997. Some Pta9.9 billion was to be invested each year, with central government contributing (for the first time) Pta4.3 billion and the Catalan government Pta5.6 billion.

Organisation

FGC was created in 1979 and operates local railways in the Barcelona area. Its 1,435 mm gauge Catalunya i Sarrià line runs from the Plaça Catalunya terminus in Barcelona to Sant Cugat where it forks to serve Terrassa and Sabadell. A short branch (2 km) leaves the route at Gràcia within Barcelona itself to serve Avinguda Tibidabo.

FGC's 1,000 mm gauge Catalans line links Igualada and Manresa with Barcelona Plaça Espanya via Martorell. The 1,000 mm gauge Abt rack line between Ribes and Núria is isolated from the Catalans and Catalunya I Sarrià lines, connecting at Ribes with RENFE's 1,668 mm gauge Barcelona—La Tour de Carol route. FGC also operates one cable car system and four funicular railways.

Finance (Pta million)

Revenues	1994	1995
Passengers	3,992	4,166
Freight	488	527
Other income	327	452
Total	4,807	5,145

Expenditure	1994	1995
Staff/personnel	7,072	6,948
Materials and services	2,187	2,250
Depreciation	2,201	2,660
Financial charges	917	1,098
Total	12,377	12,956

Traffic (million)	1994	1995	1996
Freight tonnes	727,331	761,388	751,724
Freight tonne-km	47.99	50.19	47.58
Passenger journeys	42.5	42.6	44.9
Passenger-km	491.8	494.0	526.1

Freight operations

FGC is basically an intensive passenger service operator, but there are significant flows of common and potassium salts along the Catalans line. This traffic originates at mines served by the Súria and Sallent freight-only branches at the northwestern extremity of line and gains access to the port of Barcelona via another freight-only branch leaving the Catalans line at Sant Boi. Trains load up to 1,200 tonnes gross.

Improvements to existing lines

With the aim of increasing train frequencies, work began in 1994 on widening the tunnel to accommodate double track between Plaça Espanya and Ildefons Cerdà on the Catalans line. Under this programme, Plaça Espanya terminus is to be enlarged to give four tracks with platform faces and two stabling sidings, and a new station is to be built at Magòria. The programme was due for completion in September 1997.

Elsewhere on the Catalans line, work to double-track the Sant Vicenç dels Horts—Els Quatre Camins section was under way as part of FGC's long-term strategy to have two tracks in operation between Barcelona and Olesa de Montserrat.

Traction and rolling stock

At the start of 1996 FGC was operating three electric and 14 diesel locomotives, 63 emus, five dmus, eight other passenger cars and 182 freight wagons.

Diesel multiple-units

Class	Cars per unit	Motor cars per unit	Motored axles/car	Power/motor kW	Speed km/h	Units in service	First built	Builders Mechanical	Engine	Transmission
Catalans line										
3000	3	2	4	2×157	80	5	1955*	Macosa/MAN/ Ferrostaal	MAN	H DIWA

* Modernised 1985

Electric multiple-units

Class	Cars per unit	Motor cars per unit	Motored axles/car	Output/motor kW	Speed km/h	No in service	First built	Builders Mechanical	Electrical
Catalans line									
M5000/T6000	3	2	4	120	75	4	1960	SECN	Cenemesa
M5000/T6000	2	1	4	120	75	4	1960	SECN	Cenemesa
M211/T281/T291	3	1	4	276	90	7	1987	Macosa	Alsthom
M211/T291	2	1	4	276	90	3	1987	Macosa	Alsthom
M8000/T8100/ T8200	3	1	4	135	65	2	1949	SIG-MFO	Oerlixon
Catalunya i Sarrià line									
M111/T181	3	2	4	276	90	20	1983	MTM/ Alsthom	Alsthom
M112/TM122/ T182	4	3	4	180	90	5	1995	CAF/GATSA	ABB
Ribes—Núria abt rack line									
A	2	2	2	181	37	4	1985	GATSA/SLM	ABB

Diesel locomotives

Class	Wheel arrangement	Power kW	Speed km/h	Weight tonnes	No in service	First built	Builders Mechanical	Engine	Transmission
Catalans line									
700/1,000	Bo-Bo	570	70	44	7	1955	Alsthom	Alsthom	E Alsthom
700/1,000	Bo-Bo	590	70	48	3	1965	Alsthom	Alsthom	E Alsthom
254	Co-Co	1,200	90	79	3	1990	Meinfesa	GM 645 E3C	E GM/Cenemesa
Ribes—Núria line									
D9	B	300	37	23	1	1994	Stadler	Daimler-Benz 12 V 183 TA12	E ABB

Electric locomotives

Class	Wheel arrangement	Line voltage	Output kW	Speed km/h	Weight tonnes	No in service	First built	Builders Mechanical	Electrical
Ribes—Núria abt rack line									
E	C	1,500 DC	135	30	23	3	1929	SLM	BBC

The first five of 16 new Type 112 four-car emus ordered for the Catalunya i Sarrià line were delivered in 1995, to enable withdrawal of the elderly Type 400 units for renovation. The new trains were built by CAF and GEC Alsthom Transporte with ABB (now Adtranz) electrical equipment, and are formed of three motor cars and a trailer per set. Platforms at some underground stations will be lengthened to accommodate the four-car units.

In 1995 FGC ordered 20 Type 213 three-car emus from CAF, GEC Alsthom Transporte and ABB for the Catalans line. Derived from the Type 112 and similarly equipped with three-phase traction motors, the Type 213 was scheduled to enter service during 1998 following electrification of the Martorell—Igualada section. The central trailer vehicle of the Type 213 has a low-floor section to facilitate boarding from low platforms.

The Ribes—Núria Abt rack line is operated with three 265 kW units of 1929 vintage for haulage of a fleet of eight passenger cars, and four two-car trainsets with two 181 kW motors per car, delivered in 1985 and 1995. A diesel locomotive for the Ribes—Núria line was delivered by Stadler/SLM/ABB in 1995, as were two railcar trailers from GEC Alsthom Transporte for the Catalans line.

Signalling and telecommunications

The Catalunya i Sarrià line has ATP and CTC in operation along its entire length. Installation of ATO is planned for the Barcelona urban area (between Plaça Catalunya, Sarrià and Avinguda Tibidabo), to enable an appreciable increase in train service frequency, especially in the peak hours. The aim was to have 36 trains an hour departing Plaça Catalunya by 1997, a 20 per cent increase.

The Catalans line is equipped with the DIMFAP trainstop system between Barcelona and Manresa and between Martorell and Igualada (98 km).

Electrification

Electrification of the Martorell—Igualada branch (35 km) of the Catalans line was to be completed in 1997. Budgeted at Pta1.2 billion, this project was the major new scheme for the main FGC network covered by the funding agreement signed in 1995.

Track

Rail: 1,000 mm gauge: UNE 45 kg/m; UIC 54 kg/m. Abt rack line only: 20 kg/m
1,435 mm gauge: UIC 54 kg/m
Sleepers: Wood 2,400 × 240 × 140 mm*; and 2,000 × 230 × 140 mm
Concrete 2,400 × 300 × 200 mm*; and 1,900 × 260 × 209 mm
Fastenings: Direct or indirect elastic and direct rigid with ribbed plate on wooden sleepers
Min curvature radius: 150 m*; 100 m
Max gradient: 4.4%*; 2.5%
Max axleload: 20 tonne*; 15 tonne

* Catalunya i Sarrià line. Other dimensions refer to Catalans line

Class 112 emu for the Catalunya i Sarrià line

Class 450 double-deck suburban emu at Sitges (John C Baker)   ***1996***

and cereals. The upward trend appeared to be continuing in the first quarter of 1995 when a loss of Pta786 million was recorded, down 38.54 per cent on the same period in 1994. Turnover was up by Pta2 billion at Pta10.639 million.

A three-year investment plan costed at Pta7.2 billion was announced in 1996, aiming to restructure freight operations around seven different types of service and offer complete door-to-door logistics packages incorporating warehousing and onward distribution. Bulk traffic was to be conveyed by 'Indutren' services for different customers and products from the same sector, such as the petrochemicals industry; 'Maxitren' for single commodities, such as coal; 'Autotren' for car parts for different customers; and 'Jumbotren' for large volumes of general traffic. Non-bulk products were to be carried by general 'Almac' services, 'Logal' trains for consumer goods and 'Serliauto' trains for finished cars.

Elimination of wagonload business has been a major influence on the improved financial performance of the freight business sector. It has been estimated that wagonload traffic was carrying 20 per cent of freight traffic but responsible for 80 per cent of the sector's losses. By 1995 the network of freight depots served had been cut from 1,330 to 430 and the wagon fleet slashed from 36,000 to 1,500.

As part of its trainload strategy, the freight business unit complemented its established single-client regular 'Tren-Cliente' and seasonal 'Tren-Campaña' operations with a network of regular door-to-door services offering warehousing and distribution facilities. The first spokes in the TEM (Express Freight Train) network were daily Madrid–Barcelona and Madrid–Seville services introduced in 1994, carrying mainly consumer products such as drinks. The TEM network was to eventually comprise further radial services linking Madrid with Bilbao, La Coruña, Vigo and Valencia and Barcelona–Valencia–Seville and Barcelona–Vigo–La Coruña flows avoiding the capital.

All new RENFE freight wagons are designed for 100 km/h running with 22.5-tonne axleloads or 120 km/h with 20-tonne axleloads. The freight business is supported by SACIM, a system-wide, real-time data transmission system for traffic monitoring and control. It derives its data from a total of 257 terminals located throughout the rail system. Development of a real-time information system for freight customers known as 'Loginfo', to report the status of shipments, formed part of investment plans announced in 1996.

International traffic
International traffic has recently been growing at double the rate of domestic traffic and by 1995 represented some 25 per cent of non-intermodal freight business. A network of regular international freight services (TEMI), centred on Barcelona, is being established to complement the internal TEM services. A Barcelona–Cologne service was introduced in 1994, and by mid-1995 was operating three days each week with a journey time under 30 hours. In 1995 a thrice-weekly Setúbal–Lisbon–Oporto–Barcelona service was introduced; Italy, France, UK, Denmark, Belgium, Holland, Switzerland, Austria and Eastern Europe were under consideration as future additions to the TEMI network. A weekly service to Sweden began in 1996, using wagons owned by Nordwaggon and serving a new Combitrans terminal at Vicálvaro, near Madrid.

In April 1994, some 6,000 of RENFE's 16,000-strong specialised wagon fleet were suitable for operation beyond the French border via the wheelset-changing facilities at Irún/Hendaye and Port Bou/Cerbère. RENFE has owned a 20 per cent shareholding in Transfesa, the operator of these facilities, since 1995; SNCF has a shareholding of the same size. Wheelset-changing is preferred where less robust commodities such as new cars, car parts, citrus fruit and finished consumer goods are being carried. Cargoes such as wood, cereals and iron and steel products are usually transhipped, as are containers and swapbodies. Some 4,600 wagons belonging to other European railways are permitted to operate in Spain, and private wagon owners inside Spain (such as Transfesa) have 7,600 vehicles suitable for cross-border operation.

In 1995 the freight business units of RENFE and SNCF formed a working party to examine ways of easing traffic bottlenecks at the two border crossings. It was believed that the formation of a joint venture (a *Groupement Européen d'Intérêt Economique*) to manage operations at the two crossings, coupled with improved working patterns at the wheelset-changing facilities, had the potential to lift daily wagon throughput from 438 to 860.

Intermodal operations
Between 1993 and 1995 RENFE's intermodal business unit recorded a 30.7 per cent increase in traffic and a 26.6 per cent increase in tonne-km. An estimated 250,000 TEU were carried on domestic services in 1995 and at the start of 1996, over 60 container trains were in operation daily, serving some 34 terminals. In addition to port services and trains for single clients, some 55 timetabled TECO multiclient container trains were in operation daily, including services between Madrid and 14 centres, Barcelona and six centres, and Valencia and four centres.

Madrid Abroñigal forms the hub of the TECO network, but a larger replacement has been proposed in the shape of the Madrid Dry Port at Coslada, inside the triangle formed by the Madrid Chamartín–Hortaleza–Guadalajara, Guadalajara–Vicálvaro–Madrid Atocha and Vicálvaro–Hortaleza routes. Bids to operate the terminal,

costed at Pta2 billion, were invited in 1996 by a promoting consortium including the ports of Algeciras, Barcelona, Bilbao and Valencia. Growth has been marked at the port of Tarragona recently, and schemes to improve rail-served facilities at Algeciras, Bilbao and Valencia are being developed.

Azuqueca de Henares dry port
Since April 1996 RENFE's intermodal business has provided haulage for daily intermodal services operating between Barcelona and a new dry port at Azuqueca de Henares, located between Alcalá de Henares and Guadalajara on the Madrid–Zaragoza main line. These services were the first established in Spain under EU open access legislation and are operated and marketed by TCC Sea Train. Freight companies Transfesa and Cedes Logística Integral joined the Port of Barcelona and Barcelona Free Port to form TCC Sea Train, which itself is part of the TCC Puerto Seco consortium responsible for the development and management of the Azuqueca de Henares dry port.

The new dry port and its rail services have been developed at a cost of Pta900 million with the aim of reducing transit times between Barcelona and central Spain. Transfesa has provided wagons and Cedes swapbodies for the trains, scheduled to run daily in each direction between Azuqueca de Henares and the port and free port area of Barcelona. Served by a four-track rail terminal for containers, swapbodies and road semi-trailers, the Azuqueca de Henares dry port was to have storage capacity for 1,130 TEU. TCC Sea Train intermodal services to Oporto and destinations in southern France have also been reported as under consideration.

International services
In 1995 an estimated 200,000 TEU were carried on international services. By mid-1996, RENFE's intermodal business unit was handling 270 services each week between Spain and other European countries, a substantial increase from the six international services operated in 1992. Regular multiclient 'Euroteco' services link Spain with France, Germany, Italy and Portugal, with a Barcelona–Rotterdam service under consideration for introduction towards the end of 1996.

ICF intermodal services to and from Spain carried 120,000 TEU in 1995, with the bulk of this traffic (70,000 TEU) moving between Spain and Germany and mostly comprising chemicals and car components. The remainder of ICF Spanish traffic was carried to and from France, Italy, Switzerland, the UK, Scandinavia, Netherlands, Belgium and Portugal. In January 1996 ICF introduced additional services to Italy and Portugal, a Barcelona–Milan train operating four days a week in each direction and a weekly Bilbao–Lisbon/Leixões train.

Combiberia and Kombiverkehr retail space for containers and swapbodies on Tarragona/Granollers–Mannheim/Cologne and Zaragoza/Pamplona–Mannheim/Cologne services that mainly carry Opel car parts. RENFE and Transportes Olloquiegui began trials of Transtrailer bimodal equipment manufactured by Tafesa between Zaragoza and Cologne in 1995; Transtrailer units have also been used in trial service to carry Renault car parts between Douai, Flins and Sandouville in France and Palencia and Valladolid in Spain.

Class 269 electric locomotive with gauge-changing Talgo stock on a Geneva–Barcelona working at the border at Portbou (Marcel Vleugels)   ***1997***

It was hoped that bimodal equipment might help to relieve growing congestion at the crossing points of Irún/Hendaye and Port Bou/Cerbère on the French border. Intermodal traffic passing through Irún grew from 49.7 million tonne-km in 1994 to over 99 million tonne-km in 1995, and 126 million tonne-km were expected to be handled in 1996. At Port Bou, traffic grew from 71.7 million tonne-km in 1994 to 91.8 million tonne-km in 1995, and 114.8 million tonne-km were expected in 1996. RENFE was to invest Pta438 million to double transhipment capacity at Irún by the end of 1996, lifting throughput to 24 trains a day with the installation of a new gantry crane and an additional 1,668 mm gauge track and two extra 1,435 mm gauge tracks. To raise throughput at Port Bou to 23 trains a day, Pta150 million was to be spent on a new crane and other improvements.

Channel Tunnel
Freight operator Transfesa dispatched its first Channel Tunnel train, loaded with swapbodies containing Ford car parts, from Silla near Valencia via Port Bou to Dagenham east of London in October 1994. This dedicated service operates in each direction six days a week, using 300 wagons (which change wheelsets at the French border) purchased by Transfesa from Remafer and 300 13.6 m swapbodies with a capacity of 22 tonnes each. In 1995 direct services from UK terminals to Barcelona and Valencia were introduced by retailers ACI and CTL. In February 1996 Transfesa introduced a weekly intermodal service connecting Lisbon and Valencia with London, Glasgow and Birmingham via Madrid and Irún.

New lines
Madrid—Barcelona high-speed line
The original cost of the country's first high-speed line between Madrid and Seville, opened in 1992, had been calculated at Pta75 billion, although the final cost turned out to be Pta262.5 billion, excluding rolling stock. This drastic cost overrun has considerably influenced plans for the Madrid—Barcelona high-speed link which is to be constructed in stages. The new route is likely to reach the Barcelona area from the northwest via Martorell and serve a new station at La Sagrera within the city before continuing onwards to the French border and Narbonne. The Madrid terminus of the new line would be Atocha, the present and future hub of all 1,435 mm gauge routes serving the city.

Construction of the first two sections of the new high-speed line began in 1996 with civil works between Calatayud and Ricla (35 km) and Zaragoza and Lleida (137 km). Three contracts with total value of Pta29 billion were awarded for civil works on the Calatayud—Ricla section, expected to open to traffic in 2001 following electrification and installation of signalling budgeted at Pta8.4 billion and Pta5.6 billion respectively. The Zaragoza—Lleida section was expected to open in 2000 at a total cost of Pta135 billion; five of the seven civil engineering contracts for this section had been let by early 1996.

Class 311 diesel shunter with MTU engine

The first two sections of the Madrid—Barcelona high-speed line were initially conceived to relieve serious operating bottlenecks on the existing network and are to be built with sleepers allowing for conversion from 1,668 mm gauge to the 1,435 mm gauge of the Spanish high-speed system. Until the opening of the remainder of the Madrid—Barcelona high-speed route, the Calatayud—Ricla and Zaragoza—Lleida sections are to be used by 1,668 mm gauge trains travelling at up to 220 km/h.

The new Madrid—Barcelona route is to be engineered for a maximum speed of 350 km/h throughout, with a minimum curve radius of 6,000 m, 4.5 m between track centres and a maximum gradient of 2.5 per cent. Electrification and signalling will follow Madrid—Seville practice and RENFE is aiming for a Madrid—Barcelona journey time of 2 hours 30 minutes (less than half that of the fastest train to date) with an average speed of 242 km/h over the 605 km distance.

Although construction of the Zaragoza—Lleida and Calatayud—Ricla sections has been funded by central government, it is expected that between 50 and 70 per cent of the total cost of building the whole route (some Pta800 billion) will be provided by regional governments and the private sector, although a mechanism for involving the latter has yet to be determined. Mixed public/private build-and-operate mechanisms have been suggested, as have larger central government contributions financed by motorway tolls and increased road fuel taxes.

Barcelona—Narbonne high-speed line
The Madrid—Barcelona—Narbonne—Montpellier high-speed axis featured amongst the 11 infrastructure

projects selected to receive a total of ECU68.5 billion by 2010 at the 1994 Corfu summit of European ministers. In 1995 RENFE and SNCF formed a *Groupement Européen d'Intérêt Economique* known as SEM (*Sud Europa Mediterraneo/Sud Europe Méditerranée*) to carry forward the project for a high-speed line linking Barcelona with Narbonne. The joint venture will be responsible for development of the project and will oversee construction of the 280 km line, scheduled to open in 2004. Connecting with SNCF's TGV Méditerranée high-speed line at Montpellier, the new route will permit Barcelona—Paris journey times of around 4 hours 30 minutes, and will be used by freight trains between Barcelona and Perpignan operating at up to 160 km/h.

The total cost of the Spanish portion has been estimated at Pta170 billion and SEM's financial and economic studies for the project were to include the feasibility of placing the construction and operation of the route in the hands of a private-sector concessionaire. The concession was to be finalised by mid-1998, and it was anticipated that it would make provision for the concessionaire to receive financial support from the Spanish and French governments and the European Union.

In 1995 the Spanish and French governments signed an agreement covering the international Figueres—Perpignan section, including an 8 km tunnel under the Pyrenean chain at the Col du Perthus, as SEM arrived at an outline design for the route. By early 1996, SEM was updating earlier technical studies undertaken by Catalan Railways (FGC) from 1986 at the behest of the Catalan government, and it was hoped to revise earlier environmental impact studies by the end of 1996 with a view to defining a Barcelona—Narbonne alignment in 1997. FGC's studies had considered a route engineered for a maximum speed of 250 km/h. It was expected that trains would run at 300 km/h between Barcelona and Girona, at 250 km/h through Girona and at 350 km/h to the French border.

Other high-speed projects
In addition to the the Basque Y between Irún, Vitoria and Bilbao and the Zaragoza—Basque Y link, the revised PDI infrastructure plan makes provision for 1,435 mm gauge high-speed lines between Madrid and Valencia (with a branch to Albacete) and Madrid and Valladolid. The latter, along with the V-shaped Vitoria—Bilbao portion of the Basque Y, is intended to be built to 1,668 mm gauge for later conversion to 1,435 mm gauge. Existing infrastructure between Valladolid and Vitoria is to be upgraded.

With a view to starting construction of the Madrid—Valladolid and Vitoria—Bilbao routes in 1997, initial environmental appraisals were carried out in 1994. A 1996-98 infrastructure investment programme published by the Basque government in 1996 allocated Pta2.370 billion to the Basque Y project, but did not anticipate construction work starting before 2000. The Basque Y would take some 10 years to complete at an estimated cost of Pta400 billion; the project was allocated Pta150 million of central government funding in 1995 and Pta100 million in 1996.

Following studies conducted for central government and the region of Valencia, the latter has pronounced in

Class 447 suburban electric trainset

Refurbished (left) and unrefurbished Class 440 emus at Utrera (Bryan Philpott) **1996**

Electric locomotives

Class	Wheel arrangement	Output kW	Speed km/h	Weight tonnes	No in service	First built	Builders Mechanical	Electrical
3 kV DC								
250	C-C	4,600	160 100	124	40	1982	Krauss-Maffei/ CAF/MTM	BBC
251	B-B-B	4,650	160 100	138	30	1980	Mitsubishi/CAF	Westinghouse
269	B-B	3,100	140/80	88	105	1973	Mitsubishi/CAF	Cenemesa
269.200/ 500/600	B-B	3,100	180/200*	88	157	1973	CAF	Westinghouse
276.200	Co-Co	2,208	110	120	10	1956	Alsthom/Macosa/ CAF/MTM/ Euskalduna/ Babcock & Wilcox	Alsthom/Sice/ GEE/Oerlikon/ Westinghouse
3 kV DC/25 kV AC								
252	Bo-Bo	5,600	220	90	71	1991	Krauss-Maffei/ ABB/Henschel/ Meinfesa/CAF	Siemens ABB
1.5 kV DC/3 kV DC								
279	B-B	2,700	80/65	80	16	1967	Mitsubishi/CAF	Mitsubishi/ Cenemesa
289	B-B	3,100	70	84	38	1967	Mitsubishi/CAF	Mitsubishi/ Cenemesa

* Four Class 269.600 only

Diesel locomotives

Class	Wheel arrangement	Power kW	Speed km/h	Weight tonnes	No in service	First built	Builders Mechanical	Engine	Transmission
319-200	Co-Co	1,190	120	110	58	1984	Macosa	GM 567 C	E WESA
319-300	Co-Co	1,372	140	119	40	1991	Meinfesa	GM 645 E	E GM
319-400	Co-Co	1,372	120	116	10	1992	Meinfesa	GM 645 E	E GM
321	Co-Co	1,250	120	111	38	1967	Alco, CAF, Naval Euskalduna	Alco	E GE GEE
333	Co-Co	1,875	146	120	93	1974	Macosa	GM 645 E 3	E GM
352	B-B	1,470	140	76.3	7	1964	Krauss-Maffei Babcock & Wilcox	2 × Maybach-Mercedes MD 650/18	H Maybach-Mercedes
353	B-B	1,668	180	88	3	1969	Krauss-Maffei	2 × Maybach-Mercedes MD6652	H Maybach-Mercedes
354	B-B	2,340	180	80	8	1982	Krauss-Maffei	2 × Maybach-Mercedes MD 6652	H Maybach-Mercedes

Note: Classes 352, 353 and 354 are Talgo locomotives

Electric multiple-units

Class	Cars per unit	Motor cars per unit	Motored axles/car	Output/motor kW	Speed km/h	No in service	First built	Builders Mechanical	Electrical
1.5 kV DC									
442	2	1	4	524	60	6	1976	MTM	BBC
3 kV DC									
432	3	1	4	1,160	140	18	1971	CAF/Macosa	Mitsubishi/ Westinghouse
440	3	1	4	1,160	140	175	1974	CAF/Macosa	Mitsubishi/ CENEMESA
440R*	3	1	4	1,160	140	70	1981	CAF/Macosa	Mitsubishi/ CENEMESA
440R†	3	1	4	1,160	140	80	1981	GEC Alsthom/CAF	GEC Alsthom
444	3	1	4	1,160	140	14	1980	CAF/Macosa	Melco/GEC
446	3	2	4	1,200	100	170	1989	CAF/MTM/ Macosa	Mitsubishi/ ABB
447	3	2	4	1,200	120	81	1993	CAF/GEC Alsthom	Siemens/ABB
448	3	1	4	1,160	160	31	1987	CAF/Macosa	Melco/GEC
450	6	2	4	1,480	140	24	1994	GEC Alsthom/CAF	GEC Alsthom
451	3	1	4	1,480	140	12	1994	GEC Alsthom/CAF	GEC Alsthom
3 kV DC/25 kV AC									
AVE	10	2	4	1,100	300	17	1991	GEC Alsthom	GEC Alsthom

* Rebuilt for suburban services
† Rebuilt for regional services

favour of a route option for the Madrid–Valencia high-speed line with an estimated cost of Pta370 billion. This option would involve 403 km of new construction routed via Albacete and following existing routes between Albacete and Valencia. A Madrid–Valencia journey time of 1 hour 44 minutes is anticipated, which would attract some five million passengers a year and boost rail's market share in this corridor from 12 to 30 per cent. Other route options, including expensive alternatives via Cuenca, were between 350 km and 425 km in length and had estimates for cost ranging from Pta280 billion to Pta440 billion, with end-to-end journey times of between 1 hour 26 minutes and 2 hours 6 minutes.

The revised PDI infrastructure plan makes mention of the following branches from the Madrid–Seville high-speed route: Seville–Cádiz, Seville–Huelva and Córdoba–Málaga via Bobadilla.

Fixed link with Morocco
In 1996 the governments of Spain and Morocco announced plans to build a 38.7 km rail tunnel under the Strait of Gibraltar from near Tarifa in Spain to a point near Tangier in Morocco. Similar in design to the Channel Tunnel, the fixed link would comprise two single-track rail tunnels (7.5 m in diameter) either side of a smaller service tunnel (4.8 m in diameter). Shuttle trains carrying cars, road coaches and trucks would share the tunnel with through passenger and freight services.

The rail link between Spain and Morocco would be 1,435 mm gauge and would probably be connected to the proposed extension of Spanish high-speed network from Seville to Cádiz. It was hoped to open the tunnel (possibly with a single rail bore at first) by 2010, with forecasts suggesting that it might carry 10.7 million passengers and 7.6 million tonnes of freight a year by 2025. Although it was hoped to offer a concession to build and operate the tunnel for up to 30 years to the private sector, it was anticipated that public funding would be required to meet part of the estimated Pta500 billion cost of the project.

Improvements to existing lines
PDI projects
The revised PDI plan makes provision for upgrading the following existing lines for speeds of 200-220 km/h: Valladolid–Venta de Baños–Burgos–Vitoria, Venta de Baños–León–Monforte de Lemos, Madrid–Manzanares–Ciudad Real/Santa Cruz de Mudela, and Valencia–Alicante–Murcia. Complementary investment is earmarked for the modernisation of other routes, namely Monforte de Lemos–Orense–Vigo, Orense–Santiago–La Coruña, Fuentes de Oñoro–Valladolid, León–Pola de Lena, Palencia–Santander, Miranda–Castejón de Ebro, Madrid–Cáceres–Valencia de Alcántara, Cáceres–Mérida–Badajoz, Algeciras–Bobadilla, Santa Cruz de Mudela–Linares–Moreda–Almería, Linares–Córdoba, Moreda–Granada and Albacete–Murcia–Cartagena.

Mediterranean Corridor
As part of an ongoing programme scheduled for completion around 1999, the Murcia/Alicante–Valencia–Barcelona Mediterranean Corridor received Pta20.75 billion of investment in 1996. The programme aims to raise line speeds to 200-220 km/h over the 69 km of double track between Valencia and Castellón; curves are being eased, track and catenary renewed, and improved signalling installed.

Between Castellón and Tarragona the single track is being doubled and realignments undertaken that will shorten the distance from 206 km to 185 km. A new alignment is under construction between Alcanar and Camarles which includes bridging with a deck height of 29 m above the River Ebro at Amposta y L'Aldea. New routes through the towns of Benicàssim and Castellón are to be constructed at a cost of Pta23.5 billion, with funding provided by central government, the region of Valencia and local and municipal authorities.

Upgrading work between Font de la Figuera and Xátiva includes track doubling and installation of CR220 catenary for 220 km/h operation. A proposed cross-city tunnel under Valencia connecting the route to Barcelona with those to Madrid and Alicante has been costed at Pta51 billion. Forming part of the Valencia Intermodal strategy, the project includes a station beneath the city's existing RENFE terminus and would improve connections with metro and bus services.

Andalucian investment plan
The Andalucian regional government made public for

Talgo night train at Madrid Chamartín behind Co-Co diesel-electric locomotive (Colin Boocock)   **1997**

Diesel multiple-units

Class	Cars per unit	Motor cars per unit	Motored axles/car	Power/motor kW	Speed km/h	No in service	First built	Builders Mechanical	Engine	Transmission
597	2	1	1	381	120	6	1964	CAF/Fiat	Fiat	H Fiat/OM
592	3	2	2	213	120	69	1981	Macosa/Ateinsa	MAN	H Voith
593	3	2	2	206	120	61	1981	CAF/BWE	Fiat	M Fiat

consultation its own PDIA infrastructure plan early in 1994. Of a total budget of Pta4.9 billion, Pta319.2 million was earmarked to be spent on improvements to the rail network in the region up to 2007. Andalucia's strategy, which would involve greater spending than anticipated by central government for the area, has four principal objectives forming successive stages of the plan.

The first objective is the creation of a regional network from RENFE's existing Huelva—Bobadilla—Almería, Córdoba—Málaga, Cádiz—Jaén—Linares and Linares—Almería routes. This would involve upgrading the existing infrastructure and electrifying those sections of the putative network still operated with diesel traction, namely Utrera—La Roda, Bobadilla—Granada—Moreda and Linares—Moreda—Almería. In 1995 Andalucia awarded a contract worth Pta1.337 billion for upgrading work on the Tocón—Pinos Puente section of the Bobadilla—Granada—Moreda route.

The second objective is upgrading principal routes for services operating at 200-220 km/h to and from the high-speed line to Madrid at Seville and Córdoba. The routes concerned are Seville—Huelva, Seville—Cádiz, Córdoba—Málaga, Bobadilla—Granada, Córdoba—Linares and Espeluy—Jaén. The first three on this list feature on the national PDI plan as candidates for new broad-gauge high-speed feeders for the Madrid—Seville high-speed route.

Better links between Andalucia in the far south of Spain and the European rail network form the ambitious third stage of this far-reaching plan. In order to achieve this, new railway lines between Cádiz and Algeciras (the existing Bobadilla—Algeciras route is conspicuous by its absence from PDIA investment proposals) and Almería and Aguilas in Murcia are proposed. A further new line along the coast has been suggested to link Algeciras with Almería; the region's PDIA plan makes provision for a feasibility study.

Suburban services for the Seville, Málaga and Cádiz areas are the focus of the fourth stage, which foresees construction of new links and the reopening of the Huelva—Ayamonte line. In contrast, marginal routes such as Zafra—Huelva, Los Rosales—Zafra, Cordoba—Almorchon and Ronda—Bobadilla might be turned over to non-railway uses with potential for tourism such as long-distance footpaths under the PDIA proposals.

Suburban networks
As part of a 1990-98 investment strategy totalling Pta73.9 billion, the Ministry of Transport allocated Pta10.9 billion to suburban routes and railway access to cities in 1995. Madrid's suburban system was to receive the largest share (Pta5.75 billion), followed by Barcelona (Pta3.45 billion), Asturias (Pta900 million), Valencia and Seville (Pta400 million each). Part of a European Investment Bank long-term loan of ECU412.3 million

secured in 1994 was to be spent on infrastructure upgrading work in Madrid, Barcelona and Valencia.

In 1996 the government produced an investment plan for the Bay of Cádiz area, which proposed to spend Pta30.916 billion between 1996 and 2001 on infrastructure improvements for suburban services in Cádiz, San Fernando, Puerto Real, Puerto de Santa Maria and Jerez de la Frontera. A 1996-2001 suburban investment plan for the Madrid area costed at Pta133.2 billion was presented to regional and local authorities in 1995 for consultation; the plan included a new line from Madrid Chamartín to San Fernando de Henares via Barajas Airport, capacity improvements on routes into Madrid Atocha and better interchanges.

The 1996-2001 Madrid investment plan makes provision of Pta20 billion for a new 7.2 km line from Cantoblanco Universidad north of the city to stations at Valdelasfuentes and Avenida de España, serving the communities of Alcobendas and San Sebastián de los Reyes. Civil engineering contracts for the project were let in 1996, and it was hoped to complete the line by the end of 1998. Southwest of the capital, the Madrid regional goverment hoped to complete a new 29 km route from Vicálvaro to Rivas Vaciamadrid and Arganda del Rey in late 1998. Running for part of its length alongside an existing 1,000 mm gauge industrial railway, the new single-track 1,668 mm gauge electrified route was to be built with the help of private capital.

An upgraded 8 km link between Madrid's Príncipe Pío and Atocha stations (the 'Pasillo Verde'), including a new

burrowing junction at Atocha, opened to traffic in 1996. Major new interchanges with the metro at Nuevos Ministerios and Príncipe Pío have been provided.

Traction and rolling stock
At the end of 1995, RENFE's motive power comprised 501 electric locomotives, 302 line-haul diesel locomotives, 239 diesel shunting locomotives, 17 AVE trainsets, 1,821 emu cars and 402 dmu cars. The hauled passenger rolling stock fleet comprised 484 coaches, 298 couchettes and 151 sleeping cars, 23 restaurant/buffet cars, 584 Talgo coaches, 297 Talgo sleeping cars and 17 Talgo restaurant/buffet cars. In total 27,863 freight wagons were in service.

Intercity 2000 trainsets
RENFE's long-distance passenger business unit invited tenders in 1994 for the supply of 10 Intercity 2000 electric trainsets for around Pta10 billion, capable of seating up to 200 passengers at speeds up to 220 km/h. On 30 January 1996 10 three-car tilting trainsets based on the ETR 460 design for FS of Italy were ordered from a consortium of GEC Alsthom and Fiat for Pta9.058 billion. Seating 190 passengers each and to be deployed initially on the Madrid—Valencia route, the Intercity 2000 trainsets were scheduled for delivery between October 1997 and May 1998.

IR2D regional trainsets
In 1995 RENFE ordered 16 two-car IR2D diesel multiple-units from a consortium of CAF and ABB (now Adtranz). Intended for Regional Express services, the trainsets are derived from DSB's IC/3 model and feature hydraulic transmissions, aluminium bodyshells and movable driving consoles at each end to allow free passage between up to five units operating in multiple. Each two-car unit is powered by four water-cooled 300 kW diesel engines, has a maximum speed of 160 km/h and can accommodate 136 passengers.

Earmarked for regional corridors with high demand or strong potential for growth, the IR2D trainsets were due to enter service on the La Coruña—Vigo and Almería—Granada routes in early 1997. Under the terms of the supply contract, the building consortium has undertaken to guarantee for three years (or 500,000 km) minimum availability of 95 per cent and at least 100,000 km between failures. Maintenance costs have been set in the contract and RENFE is to compensated for IR2D fuel consumption in excess of one litre/km.

Suburban trainsets
RENFE's rolling stock acquisition policy of recent years has tended to concentrate on electric trainsets for its fast-expanding suburban services. Investment in suburban rolling stock (including refurbishment of existing trainsets) between 1989 and 1995 totalled Pta198.995 billion.

In total 170 Class 446 three-car electric multiple-units were constructed between 1989 and 1993 for the Madrid, Barcelona, Málaga and Bilbao areas. An improved version of the Class 446, the Class 447, has three-phase asynchronous motors, 15 per cent less weight and a 10 per cent lift of acceleration and deceleration rates. An initial batch of 70 trainsets was delivered between 1993 and 1994 for service in Barcelona (50) and Valencia (20).

Class 252 electric locomotive and Talgo Pendular 200 set at Córdoba on the Madrid—Seville high-speed line (Bryan Philpott)
    1996

An additional order for 46 trainsets was placed with the CAF/GEC Alsthom/Siemens/ABB (now Adtranz) consortium in 1994 for delivery between July 1995 and September 1996. This second batch was to be divided between the Barcelona and Valencia networks to create uniform single-deck emu fleets in these two cities and allow the transfer of Class 446 units from Barcelona to Madrid.

Double-deck emus have been purchased for the Madrid and Barcelona suburban systems. By March 1996 a fleet of 24 six-car Class 450 and 12 three-car Class 451 trainsets was in service, following an order placed in 1991. The latter comprised 15 Class 450 trainsets and 30 Class 450/451 power cars to be used in conjunction with 60 double-deck trailers delivered in 1990 for locomotive-powered push-pull operation.

The Talgo fleet

The latest model of Talgo coaching stock, the Talgo Pendular, has a passive body-tilting system designed to permit curve negotiation at a 20 per cent higher speed than the normal limit without discomfort to passengers. The range includes sleeping-car sets with wheelsets adjustable to gauge-change for international services. For details of these cars, see *JWR 1996-97*.

Of the 200 cars delivered between 1989 and 1990, 119 are variable-gauge cars for Madrid–Paris, Barcelona–Paris, Barcelona–Zurich and Barcelona–Milan international overnight services. In 1996 RENFE took delivery of a further 11 variable-gauge Talgo Pendular 200 cars costing Pta600 million, and ordered two nine-car sets of the same type. The cars were to be deployed on services between Madrid and destinations on the 1,668 mm gauge network reached via the 1,435 mm gauge Madrid–Seville high-speed line.

Talgo cars are owned by RENFE but maintained by the builder under contract. The present five-year contract, which also covers Class 352, 353 and 354 diesel-hydraulic locomotives built for Talgo haulage, specifies high-season coach availability of 97 per cent, dropping to 88 per cent in periods of low demand. In service, each trainset carries a Talgo engineer who can deal with any malfunction that may occur.

Signalling and telecommunications

At the end of 1994, RENFE had 1,908 km of its network equipped with automatic block signals and 3,282 km under the control of Centralised Traffic Control (CTC). Manual block equipment was in use on 6,609 km. Cab signalling (LZB system) was in use on 471 km of the network. Track-to-train radio is in operation on 3,850 route-km, with equipment installed in 1,065 traction units.

In 1996 a contract to equip the La Encina–Valencia and Valencia–Barcelona routes, 32 Class 252 electric locomotives and six 1,668 mm gauge AVE trainsets with Automatic Train Protection equipment over a period of four years was awarded to a consortium of ABB (now Adtranz) and Dimetronic. Fully compatible with the emerging European Train Control System, the ATP system for the Mediterranean Corridor incorporates ABB Ebicab 900 and Dimetronic TBS technology.

At the end 1995, automatic block signalling was being installed between Vara de Quart and Ribarroja (18 km) in the Valencia area. In Barcelona CTC was being installed between Moncada and Tarrasa (23 km), and in Madrid the Alcala–Guadalajara route (23 km) was being equipped with automatic block signalling. The LZB cab-signalling system was being installed on the Móstoles–Fuenlabrada route (42 km), which carries half of Madrid's total suburban traffic, to allow trains to run at 2 minute intervals.

Track
1,435 mm gauge routes
Rail: UIC 60 kg/m

Sleepers: Type DW monobloc concrete, spaced 1,667/km
Fastenings: Vossloh Type HM
Spacing between tracks: 4.3 m
Max gradient: 1.25%
Min curve radius: in general 0.5°, except stations and 30 km at 0.8°
Max axleload: 22.5 tonnes (up to 200 km/h); 17.2 tonnes (up to 270 km/h)

1,668 mm gauge network
Standard rail
Main lines: 54.5 kg/m for all relaying. 45 kg/m and UIC 54.1 kg/m in 12 and 18 m lengths
Sleepers
Wooden: Mainly creosoted oak, pine, and sometimes beech, 2,600 × 240 × 140 mm for ordinary track. For points, crossings 3, 3.5, 4 and 4.5 m of same width and thickness (centre crossing sleeper being 4,500 × 300 × 14 mm), and for expansion joints 2,600 × 350 × 140 mm. Special sleepers of up to 6.2 m used for diagonals on double-track
Reinforced concrete: Type RS or monobloc, thickness 250 mm
Spacing: 1,667/km
Rail fastenings: Screw spikes on wood sleepers and elastic clamps on reinforced concrete sleepers. Elastic fastenings for wood sleepers are also being tested.
Min curve radius: in general 250 m
Max gradient: 4.25% on Ripoll–Puigcerdá line
Longest continuous gradient: 8.27 km of 2%, with 5.85° curves (300 m radius) on 4.84 km
Max altitude: 1,494 m on Ripoll–Puigcerdá line
Max axleload: 22.5 tonnes

VERIFIED

Spanish Narrow-Gauge Railways (FEVE)

Ferrocarriles Españoles de Via Estrecha
General Rodrigo 6, Parque de las Naciones, E-28003 Madrid
Tel: +34 1 533 7000   Fax: +34 1 553 7904

Key personnel

President: José María Gurruchaga Zapiraín
Director-General: Miguel Angel Barrantes Romero
Secretary-General: Ignacio González Arrate
Directors
    Rolling Stock: Juan Carlos Albizuri Higuera
    Economy, Finance and Personnel: Miguel Pérez Pérez
    Communications: Aurora Moya Rodríguez
Commercial Operations Directors
    Asturias: Juan de la Cruz Pacheco
    Ferrol: Juan José Ruiz Varela
    Cantabria: C Cueto
    Bilbao-León: Juan José Valladares Moratiel
    Cartagena: E González

Gauge: 1,000 mm
Route length: 1,221 km
Electrification: 173 km at 1.5 kV DC

Political background

FEVE is a state-owned company established in 1965 to operate Spain's extensive network of narrow-gauge railways. Operation of several of these systems has since been transferred to local public operators, namely those established by the regional governments of Catalonia, Valencia, Majorca and the Basque country. The Cartagena–Los Nietos line may be the next to pass to local control.

Organisation

In 1994 the FEVE system comprised the Cartagena–Los Nietos line and the following railways in the north of Spain: Ferrol–Gijón; San Esteban de Pravia–Oviedo; Oviedo–Santander; Santander–Bilbao; León–Bilbao, and Gijón–Laviana; Oviedo–Collanzo.

Finance

In 1993, FEVE received Pta7 billion in subsidies and Pta3.5 billion in investment from the government. Income from passenger and freight traffic in 1993 amounted to Pta2.533 billion, 4 per cent up on 1992. Under central government investment plans, Pta6.4 billion was to be made available to FEVE in 1995 and Pta2.55 billion in 1996.

Passenger operations

Whilst long-distance services have been suffering from a drop in end-to-end patronage, traffic on shorter legs (40 to 50 km) has recently increased, particularly those popular with tourists. In the first eight months of 1995, when compared with the same period in 1994, passenger traffic grew by 2.7 per cent on the Gijón–Laviana route, by 2.8 per cent on the Gijón–Cudillero route and by 4.5 per cent on the Cartagena–Los Nietos route. Growth of 6.1 per cent was recorded on the Bilbao–Balmaseda route and of 13.2 per cent on the León–Guardo route following completion of major upgrading work.

FEVE also operates the 10-car 'Transcantábrico' land-cruise train on week-long trips from Santander to the west coast for connections to Santiago de Compostela and back. The trainset is available for private hire out of season, and has been used in conjunction with university seminars and other congresses in the area.

Freight operations

Freight traffic in the northern region of Asturias has in recent years declined as the region's smokestack industries have contracted. However, it is hoped that recent improvements to FEVE access to the ports of Gijón, Avilés and Santander could help to boost FEVE's block train workings of imported coal and fuel oil to nearby generating stations. In 1995 a new flow from Ferrol to a power station at Pontes de García Rodríguez (which would require construction of a 30 km branch) was under consideration.

New lines

EU regional development funds amounting to Pta5.215 billion were awarded to a Pta10 billion scheme approved in 1995 to develop 323,197 m² of land in Oviedo that includes FEVE's route to its terminus in that city. FEVE is participating with regional and city authorities and RENFE in the scheme, which also involves closure of FEVE stations at Fuso de la Reina, Caces, La Manjoga; construction of a new FEVE facility at RENFE's Oviedo station; new links to the Noreña and Laviana routes for through services; electrification between El Berrón and Oviedo; and metre-gauging and FEVE takeover of RENFE's Oviedo–Trabia route, scheduled for completion in 1997.

Improvements to existing lines

In 1993 the Ministry of Transport and the region of Castille and León signed an agreement to improve track conditions on the León–Matallana–Guardo section of FEVE's León–Bilbao route. Passenger services on the Matallana–Guardo–Bercedo portion of the León–Bilbao route had been suspended in 1992 due to the poor condition of the track. By the end of 1994, comprehensive track renovation and remodelling had been completed as

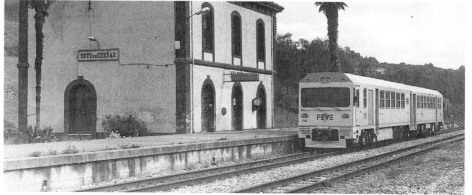

Type 2400 diesel multiple-unit at Soto de Dueñas (D Trevor Rowe)   *1996*

far as Guardo. Stations at León, San Feliz, Guardo and Puente Almuhey and workshops at Cistierna had been refurbished. Total cost of the work was some Pta886 million; the Pta159 million operating deficit of the León—Guardo section was to be assumed by the region.

Investment to improve infrastructure for Asturias region suburban services has included Pta272 million for the Gijón—Pola de Laviana route and Pta900 million allocated to upgrading the Oviedo—Pravia—San Esteban and Gijón—Pravia—Cudillero routes in 1996. On the Gijón—Pravia route, realignment has been undertaken at Perlora (0.5 km in length), Candás (2.8 km, including construction of a new station building) and Piedras Blancas (0.6 km). The work was carried out in conjunction with electrification and upgrading of the Pravia—Cudillero route and construction of a link at Pravia to permit through Gijón—Cudillero electric services.

On the Oviedo—Santander route, the station layout at El Berrón has been remodelled at a cost of Pta80 million. In 1996 the Cartagena—Los Nietos route was to receive investment of Pta150 million, and FEVE routes into Ferrol and León Pta150 million and Pta100 million respectively.

Traction and rolling stock
At the end of 1993 FEVE operated 74 diesel locomotives, 21 electric and 50 diesel trainsets, 13 diesel railcars, 21 hauled passenger cars and 1,069 freight wagons. A major new facility costing Pta1.4 billion was due to open at El Berrón in 1998, replacing existing rolling stock workshops in Oviedo and Candas.

Type of coupler in standard use: Alliance
Type of braking: Air and vacuum

Signalling and telecommunications
In conjunction with ongoing infrastructure investment in the Asturias region, automatic block signalling has been installed between Oviedo and El Berrón Noreña. Electronic interlocking has also been installed at Figaredo on FEVE's Oviedo—Collanzo route for Pta151 million. FEVE's 1996 investment plans made provision for Pta400 million to be spent on automatic block signalling and CTC for the Bilbao—Balmaseda route, and for some Pta200 million to be invested in signalling for the Asturias region.

Electrification
Electrification of the 74.4 km Langreo line from Gijón to Pola de Laviana was completed in 1994 at a total cost of Pta1.2 billion. Electrification of the Oviedo—Pola de Siero section of the Santander—Oviedo route has also been undertaken.

In conjunction with the Bilbao authorities FEVE has electrified its Bilbao—Balmaseda line (33 km) and installed double track on the 3.6 km between Zaramillo and Aranguren. The shared cost of the project amounted to Pta4.2 billion and electric services were introduced in late 1996. As part of Bilbao's restructuring plan, studies have been undertaken with a view to combining both RENFE and FEVE termini in Bilbao in a new purpose-built station, featuring interchange with both the urban metro and also urban bus routes.

Diesel locomotives

Class	Wheel arrangement	Power kW	Speed km/h	Weight tonnes	No in service	First built	Mechanical	Builders Engine	Transmission
1000	Bo-Bo	625	70	48	9	1954	Alsthom	SACM-MGO V12	E Alsthom
1050	Bo-Bo	680	70	48	14	1954	Alsthom	SACM-MGO V12	E Alsthom
1600	Bo-Bo	1,177	90	58	14	1982	MTM	SACM-MGO V16	E Alsthom
1650	Bo-Bo	1,177	90	60	10	1985	MTM	SACM-MGO V16	E Alsthom
1400	B-B	883	60	56	4	1964	Henschel	SACM-MGO V12	H Voith
1500	B-B	772	80	56	10	1965	GECO	Caterpillar	E GECO
1300	C	207	28	33.5	4	1964	SECN	Rolls-Royce	M Yorkshire
1300	C	161	28	33.5	9	1964	Westinghouse	Rolls-Royce	M Yorkshire

Diesel railcars or multiple-units

Class	Cars per unit	Motor cars per unit	Motored axles/car	Power/motor kW	Speed km/h	No in service	First built	Builders Mechanical	Engine	Transmission
2500	2	2	2	250	80	1*	1987	MTM	Pegaso	E ABB-MTM
2400	3	2	2	228	80	10	1983	MTM	MAN	E BBC
2400	2	2	2	228	80	15	1985	MTM	MAN	E BBC
2300	2	2	2	154.5	80	24		CAF/Macosa	Pegaso	H Voith
2300	1	1	2	154.5	80	7		Babcock		H
2200	1	1	4	220	75	6	1959	Esslingen	Bussing	H ZF

* Prototype

Electric railcars or multiple-units

Class	Cars per unit	Motor cars per unit	Motored axles/car	Output/motor kW	Speed km/h	No in service	First built	Builders Mechanical	Electrical
3500	2	1	4	4 × 121	80	2	1981	CAF	AEG/GEE
3500	3	1	4	4 × 121	80	6	1984	CAF	AEG/GEE
3500	3	1	4	4 × 121	80	13	1981	CAF	AEG/GEE
3800	2	1	4	4 × 119	80	16	1992	CAF	AEG/GEE

Type 3800 electric multiple-unit at Pola de Laviana (Mervyn Leah)   **1996**

Track
Rail: 35 kg/m, 45 kg/m and 54 kg/m
Sleepers: Concrete monobloc; and timber 2,000 × 240 × 130 mm
Sleeper spacing: 1,500/km plain track, 1,600/km in curves
Min curvature radius: Main line 100 m

Average curvature radius: 250 m
Max gradient: 3.6% between Cartegena and Los Nietos
Max permissible axleload: 15 tonne
Longest tunnel: 4 km, La Florida, between Gijón and Pola de Laviana

VERIFIED

Valencia Railways (FGV)

Ferrocarrils de la Generalitat Valenciana
Partida de Xirivelleta s/n, B de S Isidro, E-46014 Valencia
Tel: +34 6 357 8103   Fax: +34 6 357 8258

Key personnel
Managing Director: V Contreras
Managers
  Operations: F Garcia
  Finance: Jesus Cerverón Esteban
  Marketing: Jorge Beltrán Oliver
  Industrial Relations: Antonio Ruiz
  Rolling Stock: Manuel Sansano
  Workshops: Gonzalo Romero
  Communications: J Canales

Gauge: 1,000 mm
Route length: 123.6 km in Valencia; 92.6 km in Alicante
Electrification: 113.5 km at 1.5 kV DC

Political background
FGV was created in 1986 to take over from FEVE the local railways in the Valencia area, and also operates the non-electrified Alicante—Denia line.

FGV articulated LRV with ABB chopper-controlled motors and MICAS control, built by CAF

Improvements to existing lines
Valencia

FGV has completed the integration of the city's 1,000 mm gauge Llíria, Bétera and Villanueva de Castellón lines (Lines 1 and 2) as a regional metro via a 6.8 km city centre tunnel with eight underground stations.

Under an expansion programme for 1991-99 costed at Pta86 billion, an existing suburban line between Ademuz and El Grao was rebuilt as a 9.7 km double-track LRT route. Known as Line 4, the route opened in 1994 and carried some 10,500 passengers a day in its first week of operation.

Line 3 has been renovated between Rafaelbunyol and Palmaret (11 km) and the overground Palmaret—Pont de Fusta section abandoned in 1995 in favour of a new underground route to Alameda (3 km). From 1998 Line 3 will connect at Alameda with Line 5 to Avinguda, currently under construction. Line 5 will eventually link Nuevo Cauce in the west of the city with Cabanyal in the east.

Alicante

A total of Pta1 billion has been spent on upgrading work on the Alicante—Denia line, although no progress has been made on improving this isolated line's connection with the city centre at Alicante.

Electric railcars or multiple-units

Class	Cars per unit	Motor cars per unit	Motored axles/car	Output/motor kW	Speed km/h	No in service	Builders Mechanical	Electrical
UTA	2	2	1	220	80	40	CAF	ABB
3900	3	2				18	GEC Alsthom	GEC Alsthom

Diesel railcars or multiple-units

Class	Cars per unit	Motor cars per unit	Motored axles/car	Power/motor kW	Speed km/h	No in service	First built	Builders Mechanical	Engine	Transmission
MAN	2	1	2	210	80	8	1965	MAN	MAN	M Voith DIWA

Traction and rolling stock

At the start of 1994 FGV operated two 845 hp diesel-electric and two 465 hp diesel-mechanical locomotives, 61 electric and eight diesel trainsets.

Track
Rail: 45 and 54 kg/m
Sleepers: Stedef bibloc concrete 1,800 × 260 × 220 mm with Nabla fastenings; monobloc concrete 1,900 × 240 × 130 mm with HM-Vossloh fastenings; timber 1,900 × 240 × 130 mm

Sleeper spacing: 1,000-1,500/km in plain track; 1,250-1,500/km in curves
Max gradient: 2.4%
Max permissible axleload: 15 tonnes

VERIFIED

SRI LANKA

Ministry of Transport

PO Box 588, D R Wijewardana Mawatha, Colombo 10
Tel: +94 1 687311/687212
Fax: +94 1 694547

Key personnel
Minister: Mrs Srimani Athulathmudali
Advisor: P Rajagopal

UPDATED

Sri Lanka Railway (SLR)

PO Box No 355, Colombo 10
Tel: + 94 1 421281   Fax: +94 1 446490

Key personnel
General Manager: G P S Weerasoorriya
Additional General Manager (Administration):
 N M Weerasimghe
Additional General Manager (Operations): K A Pramasiri
Commercial Superintendent: P H Silva
Chief Engineer, Headquarters: T D S Peiris
Chief Engineer, Way and Works: W K B Wegerama
Chief Signal and Telecommunications Engineer:
 U C N Fernando
Chief Mechanical Engineer: S D M Mahindaratne
Chief Engineer, Motive Power: B A P Ariyaratne
Stores Superintendent: S P Samaranayake
Chief Accountant: H K Pathirage

Gauge: 1,676 mm; 762 mm
Route length: 1,459 km; 25 km

Organisation

SLR is based at Colombo, from where lines radiate north along the coast to Illarankulam, south to Matara and east to the Central Highlands. From the Central Highlands the main line runs to Talaimannar, where a ferry provides links with India's Southern Railway. Branch lines run to Trincomalee and Batticaloa, ports on the Bay of Bengal.

Political background

In 1993 the government introduced legislation to divorce the railway from the Transport Ministry and reconstitute it as the Sri Lanka Railway Authority under a new board of directors. The objective was to strengthen managerial control of the business. However, the railway has continued to suffer from political meddling, with fares too low to allow for investment and the service very rundown as a result; the civil war has exacerbated matters. In October 1996, commuters in Colombo clashed with police in protests over the state of the service after four passengers were killed riding on the footboard of an overcrowded train.

SLR's Hitachi M5 diesels are being re-engined with Paxman 12-cylinder Valenta engines   **1996**

The unrest led to political attention, with a Rs5 billion aid plan from the governments of the Netherlands, Germany and Japan announced. The money would be spent during 1997 on track rehabilitation (Rs1.7 billion), locomotive refurbishment (Rs800 million), workshop rehabilitation (Rs1.2 billion) and bridge replacement (Rs500 million).

The government also announced plans to seek private tenders on a build-operate-own or build-operate-transfer basis for electrification of the lines around Colombo, with Colombo—Polgahawela (73 km), Colombo—Kalatura South (42 km) and Ragama—Negombo/Katunayake Airport (30 km) identified for attention. The transport minister said the foreign investor undertaking this project would have to build its own power generation plant to ensure uninterrupted power supplies. It was estimated that 52 four-car trainsets would be needed for the service, which it was hoped to commission in 2000.

Passenger operations

Besides commuter services around Colombo, principally to Avissawella, intercity passenger services are now operated on four lines linking Colombo Fort with Matara, Kandy/Badulla, Trincomalee/Batticaloa and Kankesanturai in the southern, central, eastern and northern parts of the island respectively. An on-train radio communication system enables passengers to transmit urgent messages while on the move.

Freight operations

Freight traffic has suffered from lack of motive power, as the few locomotives which are available are often taken to power passenger trains.

Intermodal operations

Container traffic is expanding and is now managed by a dedicated company, Container Railway Freighters. In addition to the original container terminal at Colombo, there are now terminals in the tea plantations at Nuwara Eliya and Hatton. Another is likely to be established in the Katunayake free port and rail-served by an extension of the branch to Colombo airport. Further free trade zones to be established in the Colombo suburbs at Sapugaskande and at Koggala in the south offer fresh container traffic prospects. The aim is to develop unit container train services, but this will depend on SLR being able to come up with a dependable supply of locomotives.

New lines

In 1991 construction was formally inaugurated of a 120 km, 1,676 mm gauge, single extension of the South Coast line from Matara to the pilgrimage centre of Kataragama. A subsequent projection for a further 85 km to Badulla was a possibility. On the existing line to Badulla, construction of a 27 km branch from Nanu-Oya north to Ragala was approved by the government in 1993.

A further scheme surfaced in 1991, when bids were called by SLR to undertake a government-funded feasibility study of a 116 km projection of the West Coast line from Batticaloa to Pottuvil. Funding for this scheme, which is designed to open up a hitherto underdeveloped region, was sought from the Iranian government.

Diesel locomotives

Class	Wheel arrangement	Power kW	Speed km/h	Weight tonnes	No in service	First built	Mechanical	Builders Engine	Transmission
M2	A1A-A1A	1,063	80	79	9	1954	GM	GM 12-567C	E Generator D 12F
M2C	Bo-Bo	1,063	80	79	2	1961	GM	GM 12-567C	E Generator D 12F
M2D	A1A-A1A	977	80	79	2	1966	GM	GM 12-567E	E Traction motor D 29
M4	Co-Co	1,305	80	97.68	14	1975	MLW	Alco 12-25 103	E Generator GT 581PJ1
M5	Bo-Bo	1,175	80	66	16	1975	Hitachi	MTC-Ikegai 12V652TD11	E Alternator H1-503-Bb
M6	A1A-A1A	1,230	80	85.5	15	1980	Henschel	GM 12-645E	E Generator D 25L
M7	Bo-Bo	746	80	67	16	1981	Brush	GM 08-645E	E BA 1004A/BAE/507A
W1	B-B	857	80	60.55	33	1969	Henschel	Paxman 12YJXL	H MTU-Mekydro K 102-1016 PS
W2	B-B	1,173	80	65.3	9	1969	Lokomotivbau	Paxman 16YJXL	H MTU-Mekydro K 182 BU
Y	0-6-0	410		45	28	1969	Hunslet	Rolls-Royce DV 8T	H Rolls-Royce CF 13800
P1		98	32	20.12	2	1950	Hunslet	Ruston Hornsby 6 VPH	H Hunslet axle drive
N1	1-C-1	367	32	41.17	4	1953	Fried Krupp	Deutz 33	H Krupp LIB
N2	B-B	447	32		3	1973	Kawasaki	Detroit Diesel 16V71K	H Niigata DBG-138

Diesel railcars or multiple-units

Class	Cars per unit	Motor cars per unit	Motored axles/car	Power/motor kW	Speed km/h	No in service	First built	Mechanical	Builders Engine	Transmission
S3	4	1	4	656	80	14	1959	MAN	MAN L 12V18/21	H Maybach K 104 U
S4	4	1	4	656	80	3	1959	MAN	MAN L 12V18/21	H Maybach K 104 U
S5	4	2	4	577	80	3	1970	Hitachi	Paxman 8Y JXL	H MTU-Mekydro K 102 UB/55
S6	4	1	4	869	80	8	1975	Hitachi	Paxman 12Y JXL	H MTU-Mekydro K 102 UB
S7	4	1	4	760	80	9	1977	Hitachi	Cummins KTA-2300L	H Hitachi DW 2A
S8	5	1	4	1,055	100	20	1990	Hitachi/ Hyundai	MTU 12V 396 TC13	H

In 1995, 10 of these 1960s Henschel-built diesel-hydraulic locomotives were refurbished, with the original Maybach transmissions replaced by Voith turbo transmissions   **1996**

Improvements to existing lines

Conversion to broad gauge of the 63 km, 760 mm gauge Kelani Valley line to Avisawella, southeast of Colombo, is nearing completion. The project, designed to allow the line to cope with a growing commuter business, was executed in three phases. The first phase became operational for 1,676 mm gauge trains in 1991, and the second in 1993. The final 25 km section remains to be converted.

In mid-1997, a Rs500 million programme of bridge reconstruction on the southern coast line from Colombo to Matara was completed. The work, funded by Germany's Kreditanstalt für Wiederaufbau and undertaken by German contractors, involved replacement of two lattice girder bridges, one 200m long and the second 400m long.

Signalling and telecommunications

Work continues on extension of a centralised traffic control system based on Colombo. The equipment is L M Ericsson's JZA 711 electronic system. Double-line tracks operated by CTC are signalled with automatic block signals with a minimum headway of 3 minutes at an average speed of 48 km/h. In 1989 a grant of Rs16 million was secured from Sweden to finance colourlight resignalling in the Colombo area. An electronic passenger information system, diffusing through TV monitor screens, has been installed at Colombo Fort station.

A VHF/UHF telecommunications network supplied by ABB was completed in 1989. It extends from Colombo to Anurachapura and Nawala Pitiya, and from Kandy to Badulla. The railway has begun a phased computerisation programme as part of its effort to establish and maintain a high degree of operational efficiency and management control. Preliminary work has already commenced.

Traction and rolling stock

In 1995 SLR operated 144 diesel locomotives, 49 diesel railcars, 1,307 passenger cars and 2,497 freight wagons on 1,676 mm gauge. Lack of spare parts has led to cannibalisation of locomotives, meaning many fewer than those listed here are available for traffic.

Ten refurbished diesel-hydraulics were commissioned in 1996 under a programme originally instituted in 1985 but delayed for lack of funding. The locos were from the batch of 45 supplied by Henschel in 1965, and ABB Henschel won the order to rebuild them with Voith transmissions. The locos operate out of Kandy depot.

Type of coupler in standard use: Auto and screw, ARR standard

Type of braking: Vacuum

Track

Rail: Fb 39.9 and 36.26 kg/m

Crossties (sleepers): Wood and concrete, spaced 1,583/km

Fastenings: Dog and elastic spikes, Pandrol clips

Min curvature radius: 100.6 m

Max gradient: 2.7%

Max axleload: 16.5 tonnes

UPDATED

SUDAN

Ministry of Transport

PO Box 300, Khartoum

Key personnel
Minister: U Abdul Qadir

UPDATED

Sudan Railways (SRC)

PO Box 1812, Khartoum
Fax: +249 11 770 44

Key personnel
General Manager: Eng Hassan Khalifa Osman
Deputy General Manager, Technical:
Eng Ali Hummaida El Sheik

Regions: Eng Mohed El Bahi Ali
Finance: Eng Awad El Karim Ali Abdel Wahab
Regional Managers
Northern: Eng Awadella Hassan Bahagell
Eastern: Sayed A Halim Ahmaidia Tah
Central: Eng Adma Ibrahim Shurbalk
Southern: Eng A Rahamen El Daw Hamid
Western: Eng Hashim Mirgani
Department Managers
Traffic: Omer Mahmoud Mohed
Locos and Rolling Stock:
Eng Mahmoud Mohed Abdulla
Tracks and Construction:
Eng Abdel Rahim Mohed
Signalling and Telecommunication:
Eng Hassan Mohed Ahmed Nourabi
Public Relations: Bashir Mohed Tambal Sayed

Gauge: 1,067 mm
Route length: 4,595km

Political background

The single-track railway used to be the main transport mode in Sudan, but from the late 1970s onwards the mode has been in serious decline. Some rehabilitation was undertaken with foreign aid during the 1980s famine, but lack of spares and consequent poor availability of motive power severely hampered operations in the early 1990s; the situation eased when 10 new diesel locomotives arrived in January 1995.

The main line linking the capital Khartoum to Port Sudan carries over two-thirds of SRC's traffic.

Finance

Heavy losses in the 1980s were staunched when a new

extension of Centralised Traffic Control to the remaining 15 per cent of the route and provision of loops for 750 m freight trains, which will be able to travel the relaid main line at 120 km/h. Total cost of the project is put at SKr2 billion.

On the Gothenburg—Malmö line, construction of two parallel 8.5 km tunnels through the Hallandsås hills started in April 1993. The new tunnels will ease the maximum gradient on the line and eliminate a capacity bottleneck. It was originally expected that the project would be completed by 1996, but the difficult nature of the rock encountered has put it seriously behind schedule. Elsewhere on the West Coast Main Line, 20 km of new double track was opened during 1996. Further double-tracking work in 1997 will cost SKr2 billion.

Greater Stockholm
Quadrupling of the East Coast Line between Ulriksdal and Rosersberg north of Stockholm (in preparation for the Arlanda airport link) and double-tracking of the Älvsjö—Västerhaninge commuter line south of the capital were completed in 1996.

Systemwide projects
Banverket is spending SKr400 million across the network to reduce noise pollution from railway operations by installing soundproof triple glazing in homes near railway lines and constructing sound barriers. A total of SKr500 million is being spent on fitting some level crossings with automatic barriers and eliminating others.

Signalling and telecommunications
A new system to detect obstacles at level crossings has been ordered. The technology is based on magnetic sensors placed in the road. A pilot installation was being evaluated during 1997, and if this proved successful, the system would be introduced at all monitored level crossings.

The project to find replacements for 40-year-old relay-based interlockings at small stations and for traditional line blocking equipment reached the tender evaluation phase in mid-1997.

The radio block system for sparsely trafficked secondary lines, first taken into use in June 1995 on the Linköping—Västervik route, has now been extended to a second line. Projects will be initiated in 1997 regarding the control of point mechanisms and level crossings, and interfaces with other technology.

The programme to modernise Centralised Traffic Control (CTC) centres continues. Modern CTC technology employing workstations and full graphic interfaces is being installed at Boden, Gävle and Hallsberg.

A modified and improved type of serial ground-based equipment for Automatic Train Control (ATC) was evaluated in 1996 and will be introduced within Banverket's network, mainly at new ATC installations.

Telecommunications
The BV Telecom system comprises about 10,000 km of metal cable, 8,000 km of fibre optic cable, 80 digital telephone exchanges and 800 radio base stations. There are 26,000 subscriptions, of which 16,000 are used by Banverket or SJ and 10,000 are trackside telephones.

Ballast cleaning machine operated on Banverket tracks by contractor W F Hiebe (Göran Fält) **1997**

The fibre optic cable is a 12-fibre single-mode cable. Capacity is 2.5 Gb/s or 622 Mb/s long-distance and 34 Mb/s short-distance.

Capacity in the fibre optic cable is sold on commercial terms to external customers, of which SJ is one. Other major clients include Tele 2, Comviq, Telenordia and France Télécom, reflecting the deregulated telecommunications market in Sweden.

Electrification
The extension of Banverket's 130 kV 16 2/3 Hz power transmission line is continuing, with work on the Jörn—Boden section in northern Sweden in progress during 1997. In the Stockholm area, the Häggvik converter station will be connected during 1997.

In order to control the load flow and minimise transmission losses, an overall control system is under development. This system will use phase shift as the control parameter, rather than frequency as in the utility networks.

South of Stockholm along the South Main Line, a 130 kV 16 2/3 Hz transmission line between Norrköping and Nässjö via Mjölby is in the design stage. Once the overall control system is in operation, this line will be linked to the main 130 kV system through a connector from Mjölby to Hallsberg.

A further 130 kV link from Storvik through Bergslagen to Frövi and Hallsberg is under consideration. The Bergslagen area is very important for freight traffic, and the increase in power capacity that the 130 kV system would bring is essential to traffic growth.

As the 130 kV system is extended, another four rotary converter stations will be closed and one new static converter station built at Borlänge. The existing rotary converter station in Gothenburg will also be closed and a

static converter built in the same area. Contracts were to be signed during 1997.

Two lines linking the main line in northern Sweden with the coast were electrified during 1996-97: Bastuträsk—Skellefteå and Mellansel—Örnsköldsvik. Electrification of the Malmö—Ystad line in southern Sweden was completed in 1996.

Track
Standard rail: Type UIC-60 (60 kg/m) or BV 50 (50 kg/m)
On secondary lines: BV 43 (43 kg/m)
Crossties (sleepers)
Concrete
Type B10: 320 × 222 × 2,500 mm
Type S3: 320 × 250 × 2,500 mm
Wooden
Type 1: 240 × 165 × 2,600 mm
Rail fastenings
Wooden sleepers
On main lines: Hey-Back
On secondary lines: spikes, normally with baseplate
Concrete sleepers: Pandrol
Sleeper spacing
On main lines: 1,538/km on plain track; 1,538 or 1,667/km in curves of less than 500 m radius
On secondary lines: 1,333/km
Number of sleepers is increased to 2,000/km on the Kiruna—Riksgränsen ore line
Min curve radius: 300 m
Max gradient: 2.5%
Max permissible axleload: 22.5 tonnes (25 tonnes on the Kiruna—Riksgränsen ore line)

UPDATED

Swedish State Railways (SJ)

Statens Järnvägar
Centralstationen, S-105 50 Stockholm
Tel: +46 8 762 2000   Fax: +46 8 411 1216
Web site: http://www.sj.se

Key personnel
Chairman: Ms Berit Rollén
Director-General: Stig Larsson
Deputy Director-General: Tage Persson
Directors
  Passenger Services: Karl-Erik Strand
  Freight: Christer Beijbom
  Mechanical Engineering: Ragnar Hellstadius
  Estates: Per-Håkan Westin
  Finance: Bo Hamnell
  Personnel: Tage Persson
  Planning: Anders Lundberg
  Communications: Mrs Gunnel Sundbom

Gauge: 1,435 mm
Route length and electrification: (see Swedish National Rail Administration (BV))

Class X2-2 tiltbody electric train at Linköping on Three Lakes inter-regional service (Tom Ellett) **1997**

Finance (SKr million)

Revenue	1995	1996
Passengers	5,524	5,563
Freight	4,361	3,799
Other income	2,133	1,851
Total	12,018	11,213

Expenditure	1995	1996
Personnel	4,320	4,682
Materials/services	6,496	6,164
Depreciation	657	646
Financial items	44	174
Total	11,517	11,666

Organisation

The SJ Group consists of SJ, the railway and parent entity, together with subsidiary companies, most of which are members of the Swedcarrier Group. SJ itself has a headquarters general service organisation, below which it is divided into five divisions: Passenger Services (including parcels); Freight; Mechanical Engineering; Estates; and Data Processing.

Swedcarrier Group

AB Swedcarrier is a wholly owned subsidiary of SJ and functions as a liaison between the following companies: SJ Invest AB (internal financial services); SweFerry AB (ferry operations); AB Svelast (road haulage); CombiTrans Sweden AB (forwarding agency); TGOJ AB and Swemaint AB (rolling stock maintenance); AB Trafikrestauranger (catering); SwedeRail AB (consultancy); FAB Swe Re (captive insurance); Sve Rail Italia AB (associated marketing company).

Passenger operations

A distinction is made between trunk (main line) services, generally operated on hourly or two-hourly regular-interval timetables, and regional (secondary line) services, where timetables are specified by the regional transport administrations.

X2000 network expansion

SJ's premium intercity passenger services are branded X2000 and operated with Adtranz-built Class X2 tilt-body trainsets, designed for 200 km/h operation and first introduced between Stockholm and Gothenburg in 1990. By early 1996 there were 13 trains daily on this route, covering the 456 km in 3 hours.

X2000 services between Stockholm and Malmö started in 1995 and were increased to seven trains a day in January 1996, with a journey time of 4 hours 36 minutes. There were plans to reduce this to 4 hours 20 minutes on completion of infrastructure improvements in 1997, and for a non-stop service covering the journey in 4 hours. X2000 services also operate from Stockholm to Karlstad, Arvika, Falun, Mora, Sundsvall, Härnösand, Jönköping and Karlskrona, and between Gothenburg and Malmö.

The number of passengers using X2000 services increased by over 130 per cent in 1996, and the number of departures was double the 1995 figure.

Regional service improvements

Central government acts as purchaser for interregional passenger services on the trunk network which SJ cannot operate at a profit. All local services, including the suburban networks in Stockholm, Gothenburg and Malmö, are operated under contract to the 24 regional transport administrations.

The operation of services on secondary lines is subject to competitive tendering. In mid-1997, SJ held the contracts for all such routes apart from Ystad—Simrishamn in the far south of Sweden, where services are run by a local freight operator, Sydtåg AB (qv).

Regional transport administrations are also playing an increasingly important role in shaping secondary services on main lines. This has led to some blurring of the distinction between trunk and regional services, and a wide variety of solutions depending on local needs.

A shortened version of the X2, known as the X2-2, was introduced in 1994 on the Coast to Coast route from Gothenburg to Kalmar. Initially consisting of a power car and three trailers, some units had to be equipped with a fourth trailer in 1995 to cope with demand. X2-2 operation was extended to the Örebro—Mjölby—Katrineholm—Västerås—Uppsala corridor (known as the Three Lakes Link) in 1995.

New services on the Mälar and Svealand lines serving the populous area west of Stockholm (see Swedish National Rail Administration entry) are to be introduced progressively from mid-1997, employing seven further

Class Y2 dmu at Karlskrona in southern Sweden　　　*1997*

Electric railcars or multiple-units

Class	Cars per unit	Motor cars per unit	Motored axles/car	Output/motor kW	Speed km/h	No in service	First built	Builders Mechanical	Electrical
X1	2	1	4	280	120	94	1967	ASJ/Kalmar	ASEA
X2	7	1	4	815	210	21	1990	ABB	ABB
X2-1	5	1	4	815	210	4	1996	Adtranz	Adtranz
X2-2	4	1	4	815	210	14	1994	ABB	ABB
X9	2-4	2	2	170	115	42	1960	Carlsson	ASEA
X10	2	1	4	320	140	57	1982	Hägglunds	ASEA
X11*	2	1	4	320	140	44	1982	Hägglunds	ASEA
X12	2	1	4	320	160	18	1991	ABB	ABB
X14	2	1	4	320	160	18	1994	ABB	ABB

* Rebuilt from Class X10 in 1996

Electric locomotives

Class	Wheel arrangement	Output kW	Speed km/h	Weight tonnes	No in service	First built	Builders Mechanical	Electrical
Rc1	Bo-Bo	3,600	135	80	18	1967	Nohab/ASJ/Motala	ASEA
Rc2	Bo-Bo	3,600	135	77	86	1969	Nohab/ASJ/Motala	ASEA
Rc3	Bo-Bo	3,600	160	77	21	1970	Nohab/ASJ/Motala	ASEA
Rc4	Bo-Bo	3,600	135	78	128	1975	Nohab/Kalmar	ASEA
Rc6	Bo-Bo	3,600	160	78	100	1982	Hägglunds	ASEA
Rm	Bo-Bo	3,600	100	92	6	1977	Nohab	ASEA
Ue*	C	700	45	47.4	22	1987	Nohab/Motala/ASJ	ASEA
Uf†	C	720	60	50.4	12	1990	Nohab/Motala/ASJ	ASEA

Notes: Class Rc and Rm, thyristor control　　* Rebuilt from Class Ub　　† Rebuilt from Class Ud: radio-controlled

Diesel railcars or multiple-units

Class	Cars per unit	Motor cars per unit	Motored axles/car	Power/ motor kW	Speed km/h	No in service	First built	Builders Mechanical	Engine	Transmission
Y1	1	1	2	147	130	34	1979	Fiat/Kalmar	Fiat 8217.12.150	H Fiat SRM
Y1	1	1	2	210	130	40	1979	Fiat/Kalmar	Volvo THD 102 KB	H Allison
YF1	1	1	2	147	130	6	1981	Fiat	Fiat 8217.12.150	H Fiat SRM
Y2	3	2	2	294	180	12	1990	ABB-Scandia	KHD BF8LV 513CP	M ZFS HP 600
Y2*	3	2	2	310	180	5	1996	Adtranz	Cummins NTAA 855 R7	M ZFS HP 600

* Fitted with catalytic converters and particle filters

Diesel locomotives

Class	Wheel arrangement	Power kW	Speed km/h	Weight tonnes	No in service	First built	Builders Mechanical	Engine	Transmission
T44	Bo-Bo	1,235	90	76	120	1968 1983	Nohab Kalmar	GM 12-645E	E GM
V4	C	460	70	48	10	1972	Henschel	Deutz BF12M716	H Voith/Gmeinder
V5	C	460	70	48	40	1975	Henschel	Deutz BF12M716	H Voith/Gmeinder
Z66	B	218	70	32/34	25	1971	Kalmar	KHD F12 M 716	H Voith/Gmeinder
Z68	Bo	322	34	40	2	1984	Ageve Gävle	Scania Vabis DS1 14	HS Rexrath
Z70*	B	333	70	34	50	1990	ABB-Rac	Saab-Scania DSI 14	H Voith L3r 4U2

* Rebuilt from former Class Z65

Class X2 trainsets. Travelling times will be further reduced by the time these services are fully operational in 1999.

Improved regional services employing conventional two-car emus of Class X14 were introduced in 1994 between Nässjö and Skövde (linking the Stockholm—Malmö and Stockholm—Gothenburg main lines), and in 1995 between Norrköping and Tranås (on the Stockholm—Malmö main line).

Other regional services employ locomotive-hauled stock refurbished to InterRegio specification. New InterRegio services introduced in 1996 were Kalmar—

Växjö—Malmö and a commuter service between Gothenburg and Skövde.

Improved services on the Blekinge Coast line (Karlskrona—Hässleholm—Malmö/Helsingborg), introduced in 1992 and operated by Class Y2 dmus based on the Danish State Railways IC3 design, have led to a threefold increase in traffic. Following delivery of further Y2 units in 1996, three departures a day now continue to Copenhagen via the Helsingborg—Helsingør ferry. In an example of the growing coordination of intercity and regional services, Stockholm—Copenhagen connections are maintained through interchange at Hässleholm with Stockholm—Malmö X2000 services.

A new Linköping—Kalmar service introduced in mid-1996 employs Class Y2 dmus purchased by the Östergötland and Kalmar regional transport administrations. From mid-1997 some departures were extended to and from Stockholm, creating a new direct route between the capital and Kalmar.

Express parcels
SJ Passenger Services operates this business under the brand name SJ Express, in association with regional bus companies. There is a nationwide network of over 300 parcel points, including rail and bus stations, petrol stations and shops.

Freight operations
After a very successful year in 1995, SJ's freight business declined in 1996 because of a recession in the forestry and steel industries, increasing competition from road and sea transport and the deregulation of rail freight traffic. This led to a fall in market share, primarily in the international sector. SJ Freight has therefore initiated a series of measures aimed at restoring profits to an acceptable level.

Together with its intermodal subsidiaries, SJ Freight has developed a range of block train concepts aimed at specific sectors of the bulk freight market. Examples include TimberRail for wood, PipeRail for oil products and FreshRail for foodstuffs.

Wagonload traffic has been restructured and is now based on a network of 40 terminals close to the industries served. As far as possible, trains run between terminals without marshalling en route, which reduces transit time and cargo damage while improving punctuality.

In April 1996, traditional mail vans were superseded by a network of dedicated mail trains linking the three cities of Stockholm, Gothenburg and Malmö and operating at speeds of up to 160 km/h. These services are intended to be the first of a new generation of high-speed freight trains.

Together with Banverket and representatives of Swedish industry, SJ Freight is involved in a project entitled 'Freight Network 21' aimed at creating the right conditions, such as axleloads of 25 tonnes, for the future expansion of rail freight.

Freight sector organisation
The SJ Group's freight sector comprises SJ Freight together with Rail Combi AB, AB Svelast and CombiTrans Sweden AB. An associated company, Nordwaggon AB, is owned jointly by SJ and AB Electrolux. Two smaller companies, Ringborgs AB and Scanfreight AB, were acquired in 1996 to strengthen the group's position within the logistics sector.

Rail Combi AB is SJ's intermodal subsidiary, serving 14 terminals in Sweden. It handles sales of intermodal transport (trailers, swapbodies and containers) within the combined transport network, oversees SJ's international combined transport operations, and is responsible for rail connections with deep-sea container services.

AB Svelast is one of Sweden's largest road transport operators, working closely with SJ Freight and Rail Combi. About 40 per cent of its turnover is derived from distribution services to and from rail terminals. In 1995, SJ Freight and Svelast won a major contract to provide combined distribution facilities on behalf of paper manufacturer SCA.

CombiTrans Sweden AB is a forwarding agency specialising in international freight movements, including intermodal traffic. A joint venture with Norwegian State

Log train between Östersund and Sundsvall (Wolfram Veith)   *1997*

Railways (NSB), CombiTrans Combi AS, was established in 1996 with the aim of boosting rail's share of freight traffic between Norway and the continent via Sweden.

Nordwaggon AB's business is to rent out railway wagons for national and international freight traffic, and to maximise backloading northbound from mainland Europe. The number of wagons owned has grown from 50 to 2,000 over 10 years. A sophisticated electronic control system tracks wagons continuously, ensuring optimum utilisation. Nordwaggon has ordered 100 changeable-axle wagons (1,435 mm and 1,668 mm gauges) for new services to Spain.

Hansa Rail GmbH, owned jointly by SJ and Deutsche Bahn AG, markets transport between Sweden and Germany. A similar joint venture between SJ and Italian Railways (FS) is registered in Sweden as Sve Rail Italia AB.

Ferry operations
SweFerry AB runs shipping services for passengers and freight in the Öresund and the southern Baltic, in close co-operation with DSB Rederi A/S in Denmark and DFO (a DB AG subsidiary) in Germany. SweFerry operates seven vessels under the Scandlines brand on the routes Helsingborg—Helsingør, Helsingborg—Copenhagen, Limhamn—Dragør, Trelleborg—Sassnitz and Trelleborg—Rostock.

In December 1996, SweFerry introduced a new car-carrying catamaran on the Limhamn—Dragør route. New tonnage was due to enter service on the Helsingborg—Helsingør and Trelleborg—Rostock routes during 1997.

Traction and rolling stock
At the end of 1996, SJ operated 359 electric locomotives, 34 electric shunting tractors, 247 diesel locomotives and tractors, 275 emus, 17 dmus, 80 diesel railcars, 900 passenger coaches (including 38 buffet/dining cars, 93 sleepers and 95 couchette cars) and some 12,500 freight wagons.

To test the suitability of Rc-class locomotives for shunting duties, two examples of Class Rc4 were fitted with radio remote-control equipment in 1994-95. Three Class Rc1 locomotives were similarly equipped in 1996, and during 1997 the remaining 15 members of this class will be fitted with the same type of equipment.

A major order was placed in conjunction with DSB of Denmark in August 1997. The two companies are

purchasing 27 three-car bi-voltage emus from Adtranz for operation on the Öresund link when it opens in 2000; there is an option for a further 18 emus. Ten trains in the initial order are for SJ, the other 17 for DSB.

A further order for X2 trainsets placed with Adtranz in 1995 calls for seven complete sets, comprising a power car and four trailers, of which four sets were delivered during 1996. The order also included 26 additional trailers for existing sets. First deliveries of the last have allowed SJ to strengthen the sets operating X2000 services from Stockholm to Gothenburg, Malmö and Sundsvall, which now consist of a power car and six trailers.

This latest X2 order includes an option on a further six sets, possibly of a new variant with distributed traction equipment, and an option on a dual-voltage (15 kV 16 2/3 Hz AC and 25 kV 50 Hz AC) conversion of existing sets for services to Denmark via the Öresund fixed link.

A further five Class Y2 diesel multiple-units were delivered in 1996, funded by the Östergötland, Kalmar and Blekinge regional transport administrations (see 'Passenger operations'). Unlike previous deliveries, the new trains have Cummins engines and are fitted with catalytic converters and particle filters.

With X2 units taking over the main intercity services, SJ is refurbishing hauled coaching stock from the 1980s to a new InterRegio (IR90) specification, featuring a revised interior layout. The current rebuilding programme covers 70 coaches of types A7 and B7, which are reclassified AB9 and BFS9.

Type of braking in standard use: air
Type of coupler in standard use: screw

Traffic (million)	1995	1996
Freight tonnes	55.8	53.9*
Freight tonne-km	18,999	18,456*
Passenger journeys	99.3	99.0
Passenger-km	6,219	6,191

* Includes 12.3 million tonnes and 1,977 tonne-km carried by Malmtrafik AB between 1 July and 31 December

UPDATED

Sydtåg AB

PO Box 7018, S-291 07 Kristianstad
Tel: +46 44 106545   Fax: +46 44 106546

Key personnel
Managing Director: Jan Wallenkurtz

Route length: 80 km

Freight operations
Sydtåg AB began operations in 1991 and now transports

over 1,000 wagonloads of processed timber annually between Hanaskog and Kristianstad (18 km).

In October 1994 the company took over Malmö—Staffanstorp freight traffic (15 km) from SJ. It was hoped to increase this from 400 to 1,000 wagonloads per year. Principal flows are foodstuffs, and engineering, agricultural and cement products.

Further expansion came in January 1995 with the start of freight services between Ystad and Simrishamn (47 km). The company sees potential for 4,000 wagonloads a year, including sugar, foodstuffs, plastics and recycled materials. In addition, a contract was

secured to provide passenger services on this line for a four-year period from June 1995.

Sydtåg AB operates two diesel locomotives and five locotractors. For the passenger services two Class Y1 railcars are provided by the Kristianstad regional transport administration.

VERIFIED

Tågåkeriet i Bergslagen AB (Tågab)

Bangårdsgatan 2, S-681 30 Kristinehamn
Tel: +46 550 87500   Fax: +46 550 87503

Key personnel
Managing Director: Lars Yngström

Route length: 232 km

Freight operations
With over 15,000 wagonloads a year, Tågab is Sweden's largest independent shortline operator. In February 1994 the company took over feeder services on two lines in west central Sweden: Hällefors—Filipstad—Kristinehamn (105 km) and Bofors—Degerfors (18 km). Tågab supplies locomotives and drivers for certain SJ freight trains from Kristinehamn to Hallsberg and Karlstad. Haulage is also provided on occasion for Banverket works trains.

The company's main shareholders are its principal customers: Ovako Steel and crispbread manufacturer Wasabröd. Kristinehamn council holds a minority stake. Other traffic includes processed timber and liquefied petroleum gas.

Tågab operates three main line diesel locomotives (ex-Danish State Railways Class MY) and four diesel shunters. The company has its own workshop for heavy maintenance, which undertakes work for SJ and other operators.

VERIFIED

TGOJ AB

S-631 92 Eskilstuna
Tel: +46 16 172600   Fax: +46 16 172601

Key personnel
Managing Director: Curt Bylund
Traffic Manager: Sven-Olof Nehrer
Engineering Business Manager: Göran Ulin
Engineering Unit Managers
  Eskilstuna, Tillberga: L-G Olsson
  Malmö: L Eriksson
  Åmål: C Axelsson
  Örebro: R Johansson

Gauge: 1,435 mm
Route length: 689 km

Organisation
TGOJ is a subsidiary of the SJ Group and has operated rail services in central Sweden since 1877. The main activity now is engineering, with workshops at Eskilstuna, Örebro, Åmål, Tillberga (Västerås) and Malmö. The company employs 1,200 staff and has an annual turnover of SKr1 billion.

The engineering business undertakes overhauls, repairs, rebuilding and refurbishment on all types of rail vehicle and heavy road vehicles. Component maintenance is offered for diesel and electric motors, transformers, transmission and injection systems, hydraulics, and electronics. On-site service is available.

Passenger operations
TGOJ acts as SJ's subcontractor for the operation of certain local passenger services on behalf of the Västmanland regional transport administration.

Freight operations
Wagonload traffic is operated under a feeder traffic agreement with SJ Freight. TGOJ is responsible for services within its traditional area extending from Oxelösund via Eskilstuna to Grängesberg and Ludvika. Freight is transported to and from SJ's marshalling yard at Hallsberg. Total annual traffic is some 25,000 wagonloads.

In addition, bulk trains operate from the steelworks at Oxelösund to the plate works at Borlänge, returning with sheet metal products for export via the port of Oxelösund.

Traction and rolling stock
The fleet comprises 29 electric locomotives (Class Ma), five emus (Classes X21, X22 and X23), 27 diesel locomotives and 785 freight wagons.

TGOJ hires locomotives, multiple-units and wagons to SJ and Banverket.

VERIFIED

Woxna Express AB

PO Box 46, S-794 21 Orsa
Tel: +46 250 51270   Fax: +46 250 51270

Key personnel
Managing Director: Bo Persson

Gauge: 1,435 mm
Route length: 533 km
(127 km BV, 359 km IBAB, 47 km own tracks)

Freight operations
Woxna Express AB, which began operations in October 1993, runs freight services in the provinces of Hälsingland, Jämtland, Härjedalen and Dalarna. Traffic increased from 90,000 tonnes in 1995 to 185,000 tonnes in 1996, and the company now serves the Mora—Östersund, Bollnäs—Orsa, Arbrå—Kilafors—Lilltjära, Kilafors—Söderhamn and Söderhamn—Vallvik lines.

During 1997 the company was to start running on the Mora—Älvdalen and Mora—Vika lines, adding a further 57 route-km to its network.

Traffic is dominated by raw timber, wood pulp and export-bound processed timber, but charcoal and scrap metal are also carried.

Woxna Express AB has a staff of seven. One diesel locomotive is owned and two are hired from SJ.

UPDATED

SWITZERLAND

Ministry of Transport, Communications & Power

Bundeshaus Nord, CH-3003 Bern
Tel: +41 31 322 5711   Fax: +41 31 322 5811

Key personnel
Minister: Moritz Leuenberger

Political background
The federal government assumes financial responsibility for Swiss Federal Railways' (SBB) fixed installations, except where directly connected with SBB operations, workshops and traction current supply installations. The state's responsibility is purely financial. In its commercial sector, comprising InterCity passenger, wagonload, container and less-than-wagonload traffic, SBB has managerial freedom and should make an annually predetermined contribution to infrastructure costs. Deteriorating financial performance has prevented this, since the operating account is now in deficit.

The 57 so-called private railways (their private shareholders are in fact minimal) are supported by their Cantons. The federal government is statutorily obliged to top up their subsidy in two ways. It stabilises the railways' finances, including capital investment, at levels of contribution that reflect each railway's assessed value to the national or a regional transport system. Thus, support for the Bern—Lötschberg—Simplon (BLS), a trunk system of national importance, or the metre-gauge Rhaetian, socio-economically vital to the Grisons Canton, is much more generous than the backing for short local lines in more amiable terrain. Secondly, in the case of Alpine territory, railways like the Rhaetian or Bernese Oberland, federal subsidy finances local passenger and freight tariffs based on SBB prices; because of their abnormal upkeep costs such railways charge non-residents much higher rates.

In 1994 the federal council approved revision of the country's Railway Law (LCF) to put the SBB's Regional services on the same footing as those of the private railways. The Cantons will be required to share the costs of all Regional services, whoever provides them, sharing with the federal administration the annual determination of the total amount of subsidy to be provided, and the detail of services to be operated. This may be in conflict with the 'Bahn 2000' regular-interval service concept (see 'Political background' section in SBB entry).

Major change is now foreseen. New rail legislation proposed in 1996 would, if approved, adapt Swiss railways to the principles of open access for third-party operators, with track charge for infrastructure use, being introduced into surrounding European Union countries. This involves far-reaching changes to the concession principle of ownership and operations which has previously guided Swiss public and private rail competences. The new law was expected to come into effect in 1997.

VERIFIED

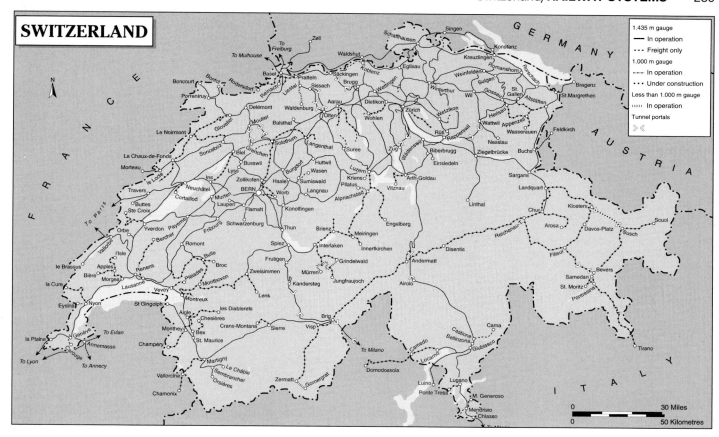

Appenzell Railway (AB)

Appenzeller Bahnen
Bahnhofplatz 10, CH-9101 Herisau
Tel: +41 71 351 1060   Fax: +41 71 352 3040

Key personnel
Director: Martin Vogt

Gauge: 1,000 mm
Route length: 60 km (5 km of rack rail)
Electrification: 60 km at 1.5 kV DC

Organisation
The system results from the 1988 merger of the Appenzell with the neighbouring St Gallen—Gais—Appenzell Railway. A 32 km line runs from Gossau, on the SBB St Gallen—Zurich main line, to Herisau, Appenzell and Wasserauen, in the Säntis mountain area, and attains a summit of 903 m above sea level at Gonten. A 20 km line extends from St Gallen to Teufen, Gais and Appenzell and is worked by seven rack-equipped electric trainsets. The third, 7 km line connects Gais and Altstätten Stadt and features a ruling gradient of 16 per cent.

In 1995 AB carried 3 million passengers for 32.3 million passenger-km, and 17,922 tonnes of freight.

Traction and rolling stock
In total the railway owned in 1993 one steam, two electric and one diesel locomotives; 14 electric trainsets; eight electric and one diesel railcars; and 36 other passenger cars (of which one incorporated a buffet).

VERIFIED

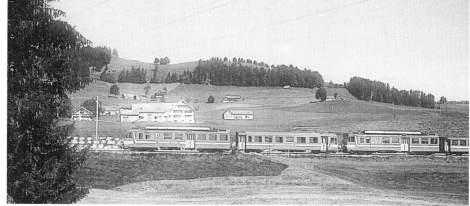

Appenzell Railway trainset
1996

Bernese Oberland Railways (BOB)

Berner Oberland-Bahnen, Wengernalp-Bahn (WAB) and Jungfraubahn (JB)
CH-3800 Interlaken
Tel: +41 33 828 7111   Fax: +41 33 828 7264

Key personnel
Director: Walter Steuri
Chief of Operations: Christian Balmer
Chief of Traction and Workshops:
  Dr Hans Schlunegger
Commercial Director: U Kessler

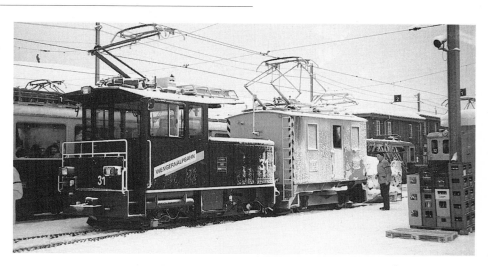

WAB locomotive by Stadler/SLM at Kleine Scheidegg
1996

Organisation

The BOB Group comprises the Berner Oberland-Bahnen (BOB), Wengernalp-Bahn (WAB) and Jungfraubahn (JB) systems, plus two rope-worked funiculars, the Harderbahn at Interlaken and the Allmendhubel at Mürren.

Berner Oberland-Bahnen

BOB operates 24 route-km of 1,000 mm gauge from Interlaken Öst to Lauterbrunnen and Grindelwald, electrified at 1.5 kV DC. Sections of route employ Riggenbach rack to cope with maximum gradients of 1 in 11.

Double track is to be installed over a 2.5 km section between Wilderswil and Zweilütschinen at a cost of SFr30 million, and curve radius eased from 120 m to 200 m over a further 5 km, enabling line speed to be raised from 40 to 70 km/h.

The BOB's latest rolling stock is three ABeh 4/4 II 43-tonne motor coaches and matching BDt control trailers. Each motor coach is powered by four ABB 314 kW series-wound DC motors. The braking system for direct-coupled DC motors is a combined regenerative and resistance brake with automatic changeover according to conditions in the supply system. The added control functions are performed by ABB's MICAS programmable system. Maximum speed is 70 km/h.

The railway also operates the 7.3 km 800 mm gauge Riggenbach rack Schynige Platte mountain railway (SPB) from Wilderswil, electrified at 1.5 kV DC, and the Bergbahn Lauterbrunnen-Mürren (BLM). The BLM comprises a cable funicular from Lauterbrunnen to Grütschalp and a metre-gauge line on the Lauterbrunnen valley's western wall from Grütschalp to Mürren.

Wengernalp-Bahn

Recording over 3.5 million passenger journeys annually, WAB operates an 800 mm gauge line running from Grindelwald and Lauterbrunnen to Kleine Scheidegg, 2,060 m above sea level and immediately below the Jungfrau mountain chain. It is electrified at 1.5 kV DC, and employs Riggenbach rack throughout. In 1996 an interlocking system with Alcatel-SEL axlecounter track release, specially designed for multitrain operation, was introduced between Lauterbrunnen and Wengen.

WAB has recently taken delivery of two locomotives to operate freight services to the village of Wengen, which is prohibited to road traffic. In 1998 Stadler will deliver four low-floor articulated driving trailers.

Jungfraubahn

JB records annually some 940,000 passenger journeys. It operates a 1,000 mm gauge line starting from Kleine Scheidegg, which tunnels through the Jungfrau range to attain the highest altitude of any European railway at Jungfraujoch, 3,454 m above sea level on the ridge between the Jungfrau and Mönch mountains. It employs the Strub rack system and is electrified at 1,100 V 50 Hz three-phase AC.

UPDATED

BOB Railways

Railway	BOB	SPB	WAB	JB	BLM
Route length	23.63 km	7.26 km	19.1 km	9.3 km	5.7 km
Max gradient	12%	25%	25%	25%	5%
Minimum curve radius	90 m	60 m	60 m	100 m	40 m
Steam locomotives	1	1	—	—	—
Electric locomotives	2	10	10	5	—
Electric railcars	10	—	28	14	4
Passenger cars	41	22	40	18	—
Baggage cars	10	—	—	—	—
Freight wagons	31	7	63	20	4

Diesel locomotives

Class	Wheel arrangement	Power kW	Speed km/h	Weight tonnes	No in service	First built	Builders Mechanical	Builders Engine	Transmission
BOB									
Tm 2/2	B (shunter)	110	30	15	1	1946	Stadler	Saurer	E BBC
HGm 2/2	B (shunter)	296	30	19.5	1	1986	Steck	Deutz	H Steck

Electric locomotives

Class	Wheel arrangement	Output kW	Speed km/h	Weight tonnes	No in service	First built	Builders Mechanical	Builders Electrical
BOB								
1.5 kV DC								
HGe 3/3	Co	295	45	36	2	1914	SLM	BBC
SPB								
1.5 kV DC								
Hc 2/2	B	220	12	16	10	1914	SLM	BBC/Alioth
WAB								
1.5 kV DC								
Hc 2/2	B	220	12	16	8	1909	SLM	BBC/Alioth
Hc 2/2	B	460	22	16	2	1995	Stadler/SLM	ABB
JB								
1.125 kV AC 3 phase								
Hc 2/2	B	283	18	15	5	1904	SLM	BBC

Electric railcars or multiple-units

Class	Cars per unit	Motor cars per unit	Motored axles/car	Output/motor kW	Speed km/h	Units in service	First built	Builders Mechanical	Builders Electrical
BOB									
1.5 kV DC									
ABeh 4/4	1	5	4	261	70	5	1965	SLM/SIG	BBC
ABeh 4/4	1	2	4	261	70	2	1979	SLM/SIG	BBC
ABeh 4/4 II	1	3	4	314	70	3	1987	SLM	ABB
WAB									
1.5 kV DC									
BDeh 4/4	11	11	4	110	25	11	1947	SLM	BBC
BDeh 4/4	7	7	4	110	25	7	1963	SLM	BBC
BDeh 4/8	6	4	4	110	25	6	1988	SLM	BBC/Sécheron
BDeh 4/8	4	4	4	201	28	4	1988	SLM	BBC
JB									
1.125 kV AC 3 phase									
BDeh 2/4	6	6	2	440	24	6	1955	SLM	BBC
BDeh 2/4	4	4	2	440	24	4	1966	SLM	BBC
BDeh 4/8	4	4	4	201	27	4	1992	SLM	ABB
BLM									
560 V DC									
BDe 2/4	1	3	2	49	25	1	1913	SIG	Alioth
Be 4/4	3	3	4	51	30	3	1963	SIG	BBC

BOB ABeh 4/4 II power car at Interlaken Ost
(Bryan A Stone)
1996

Bern—Lötschberg—Simplon Railway (BLS)

Genfergasse 11, CH-3001 Bern
Tel: +41 31 327 2727   Fax: +41 31 327 2010

Key personnel
Manager: Martin Josi

Commercial and Technical Manager:
  Dr Mathias Tromp
Finance: Hans Flury
Secretary: Heinrich Barben
Traffic Manager: Heinz Pulfer
Traction and Workshops Manager: Kurt Müri
Chief Engineer, Construction: Urs Graber

Route length: 115 km (BLS only); 130 km (other group railways)
Electrification: 245 km at 15 kV 16⅔ Hz AC

Organisation
The BLS main line from Frutigen through the Lötschberg Tunnel to Brig was opened in 1913. Certain regional

railways with special guarantees from the Canton of Bern were then incorporated in the Lötschberg system, though each retained separate financial and operating identity. The BLS group embraces the Spiez–Erlenbach–Zweisimmen Railway (SEZ), Gürbetal–Bern–Schwarzenburg Railway (GBS) and Bern–Neuchâtel Railway (BN). Much interoperation of rolling stock takes place. These arrangements were to be replaced in 1996 by a single overall BLS company. The group also owns 18 Lake Thun and Lake Brienz ships and the Interlaken bus company, Auto AG. The BLS company also owns BLS Alp Transit AG, a subsidiary set up to manage planning and possible building of the Lötschberg Base Tunnel.

The BLS system covers the main lines from Thun to Spiez and Interlaken, and from Spiez via the Lötschberg Tunnel to a junction with SBB at Brig. The Lötschberg route is one of Europe's vital international rail links. BLS also owns the Grenchenberg tunnel line between Lengnau and Moutier (MLB), which forms part of the shortest route between Geneva and Basel.

Passenger operations
Passenger traffic, including transit, fell by 4.3 per cent in 1994 to 8.8 million journeys, partly as Swiss tourism has declined. A further fall, to 8.39 million, was recorded in 1995.

Bern Canton supports integration and development of an RER (Regional Express) network (see SBB entry). For BLS this will principally entail part double-tracking of the Bern–Neuchâtel line, double-tracking throughout the Bern–Belp line, and provision of additional rolling stock. These requirements are only in part covered by investments planned with credits from federal and cantonal supports for the private railways covering the period up to 1997.

BLS provides the route for the Cisalpino (qv) tilting trains running between Basel and Milano from October 1996, bringing substantially reduced journey times.

Car shuttle
BLS runs a push-pull shuttle service for accompanied cars and coaches through the Lötschberg Tunnel between terminals at Kandersteg and Goppenstein. The trains are formed of 28 Talbot-built car-carriers, giving an hourly capacity of 550 vehicles.

Federal subsidy, halving tolls charged to users of this and the other transalpine tunnel auto-shuttles, was reduced in 1994; rates increased sharply. Though the number of cars carried in 1994 increased by 2.7 per cent to 1.275 million, there was a 5.3 per cent decline to 1.207 million in 1995.

Freight operations
Results for 1994 showed a 3 per cent growth in freight traffic, but an 8.5 per cent fall in revenue due to competitive pressure on tariffs. In 1995, BLS carried 6.736 million tonnes. BLS carries significant numbers of Intercontainer intermodal trains between Northern Europe and Italy, formerly routed through France, and in 1998 a piggyback corridor with enlarged profile will be available between Basel and Novara via the BLS route.

New lines
The federal council's transalpine tunnel decision of 1989 (see 'New lines' section in the SBB entry) provided for construction of both Gotthard and Lötschberg base tunnels.

The Lötschberg base tunnel would form part of a new 55 km route from Heustrich, between Spiez and Reichenbach, to a junction with the SBB's Rhône Valley main line, with ruling gradient 1 per cent. Like the Gotthard base tunnel, the Lötschberg will have clearance for piggybacked 4.2 m high lorries, as also the Simplon Tunnel, following the latter's track-lowering and equipment with a rigid traction current contact system (see 'Improvements to existing lines' section in SBB entry). The federal government would meet the cost, recovering roughly a quarter from road transport fuel taxation.

The twin-bore base tunnel would begin at Frutigen. Planned to fork at Km 27, the western arm would emerge, 33 km from Frutigen, on the SBB's Rhône Valley main line at Steg, giving a politically important automobile-carrying train service to the Canton Valais, replacing an Alpine motorway connection struck from the programme; it also completes a through route from the Lötschberg line to Lausanne and Geneva. The eastern arm is planned to lead into the Rhône Valley main line at Raron, west of Visp. Tunnel length to Raron Ost will be 35.9 km underground; this will feed traffic for Italy into the

Electric locomotives

Class	Wheel arrangement	Output kW	Speed km/h	Weight tonnes	No in service	First built	Builders Mechanical	Electrical
Re 465	Bo-Bo	6,400	230	84	8	1994	SLM	ABB
Re 4/4	Bo-Bo	4,980	140	80	35	1964	SLM	ABB
Ae 4/4	Bo-Bo	2,940	120	80	4	1944	SLM	ABB
Ae 6/8	1 Co-Co 1	4,400	100	140	1	1939	SLM	SAAS
Ae 8/8	Bo-Bo + Bo-Bo	6,470	120	160	3	1959	SLM	ABB
Ce 4/4	B-B	735	65	64	3	1920	SLM	ABB
Ee 3/3	C (shunter)	450	40	38	1	1943	SLM	SAAS
Eea 3/3	C (shunter)	600	75	50	1	1991	SLM	ABB

Electric railcars

Class	Cars per unit	Motor cars per unit	Motored axles/car	Output/motor kW	Speed km/h	No in service	First built	Builders Mechanical	Electrical
Be 4/4	1*	1	4	370	120	3	1953	SIG	SAAS
ABDe 4/8	2*	2	2	290	125	3	1954	SIG	ABB/SAAS
ABDe 4/8	2*	2	2	290	125	2	1957	SIG	ABB/SAAS
ABDe 4/8	2*	2	2	290	125	4	1964	SIG	ABB/SAAS
RBDe 4/4	1*	1	4	400	125	22	1982	SIG/SWS/SWP	ABB

* Most of these railcars are operated with additional trailers (some driving) as three- or four-car emus

Further upgrading will fit the BLS for 4 m high trucks   **1997**

Car driving on to the Lötschberg Tunnel shuttle train   **1996**

approach to the Simplon tunnel. Preliminary work began in 1994, but construction proper will not start unless a popular vote authorising financing is passed in 1997. Completion is foreseen in 2006.

BLS would operate an intensive road vehicle shuttle service through the base tunnel between terminals at Heustrich and Steg. In mind was a trainset with space for up to 100 private cars and six heavy goods vehicles but what has not been decided is whether accommodation for private cars would be double-deck; whether trainsets will have a locomotive at each end; and whether loops will be built at Heustrich and Steg to allow merry-go-round operation. Since this operation is recognised to be uneconomic (it results from political assurances that regional interests will be considered), its financing will also require clarification.

Improvements to existing lines
A 10-year programme to complete double-tracking of the 84 km Lötschberg main line was completed in 1992. The route can now accept 22.5 tonne axleloads and piggyback trailers of 4 m height. Maximum permissible speed remains 80 km/h between Frütigen and Brig, but 125 km/h through the Lötschberg Tunnel. Ruling gradient on both ramps is 2.7 per cent.

The route has reversible working, with crossovers at 4.5 km intervals. When stations are closed it is remotely controlled from three centres at Spiez, Kandersteg and Goppenstein. Track-to-train radio is operational between Thun and Goppenstein.

Frütigen station has been rebuilt and Spiez station is being both reconstructed and enlarged. Spiez is also to have a new signalling centre. In parallel to the SBB, the

BLS is installing ZUB 121 automatic train-control equipment.

The Bern—Thun section is one of the best aligned high-speed stretches in Switzerland. In a SFr86.7 million programme its 20.8 km from Gümlingen to Thun has been cleared for 160 km/h, with complete track renewal, easing of four curves, strengthening of 52 bridges, station improvements and resignalling for two-way working on each track.

While unaccompanied trailers up to 4 m high can be accepted on the Lötschberg route, tractor and trailer rigs of these dimensions are currently unable to use the line. Pending completion of the base tunnel, an interim SFr125 million has been drafted to enable Lötschberg RoLa ('rolling motorway') movement of trucks up to 4 m high at their roof corners. Completion of this project was expected in 1997.

The interim plan, proposing at first a gauntleted third track aligned near the bore's crown, was dropped in favour of lowering one of the tunnel's lines, rebuilding it with concrete slab track, and modifying the spacing of the two tracks, to secure the required clearance for bidirectional RoLa working on the one lowered line. This clearance cannot be obtained exclusively on one line through the approach tunnels, so RoLa trains will have to make more than one crossover between the two running lines, protected by special signalling, between Spiez and Brig.

Traffic (BLS only) (million)

	1994	1995
Freight tonnes	6.945	6.668
Passenger journeys	8.800	8,395

Traction and rolling stock

In 1995 BLS (including BN, SEZ and GBS) operated 51 electric locomotives, six electric shunting locomotives, 34 electric railcars, nine electrodiesel shunters, 27 diesel shunters, 34 control trailers, 172 other passenger coaches (including two restaurant cars), 31 baggage cars and some 200 freight wagons (including Lötschberg Tunnel car-carrying shuttle cars). There is also one steam locomotive.

In 1996, BLS ordered eight commuter trains from a consortium led by Vevey. Bombardier Talbot is supplying bodies and bogies and Holec the electrical equipment. The 47.4 m long trains will be akin to tramway vehicles.

Track (BLS only)
Rail
SBB IV (UIC 54E), 54 kg/m
Crossties (sleepers): Timber and concrete
Thickness: 150 mm timber, 235 mm concrete
Spacing: 1,666/km
Fastenings
Timber: Ke (bolted spring clips SKL 3)
Min curvature radius
Lötschberg line: 280 m
Other lines: 220 m
Max gradient
Lötschberg line: 2.7%
Other lines: 1.5%
Max axleload
Lötschberg line: 22.5 tonnes
Other lines: 20 tonnes

UPDATED

InterCity train on the Luogelkin viaduct on the south approaches to the Lötschberg Tunnel
1996

Bern—Solothurn Railway (RBS)

Regionalverkehr Bern—Solothurn
Bahnhofhochhaus, PO Box 119, CH-3048 Worblaufen
Tel: +41 31 925 5555   Fax: +41 31 925 5566

Key personnel
Manager: P Scheidegger

Gauge: 1,000 mm; mixed 1,435 and 1,000 mm
Route length: 56 km
Electrification: 52 km at 1.25 kV DC; 11 km at 600 V DC overhead

Organisation
RBS was formed by merger of the Solothurn—Zollikofen—Bern Railway (SZB) and Bern—Worb Railways (VBW). The RBS system is partly electrified at 600 V DC, the voltage of the Bern city tramway network with which both SZB and VBW were connected before the 1960s. At that time SZB's original surface route into Bern was superseded by a new segregated double-track route from Worblaufen which finally tunnelled 1.2 km to a new four-platform terminus beneath the reconstructed Bern main station. The VBW sytem was then mostly re-electrified at 1.25 kV DC and its route modified to funnel its trains into the new Bern subterranean terminus.

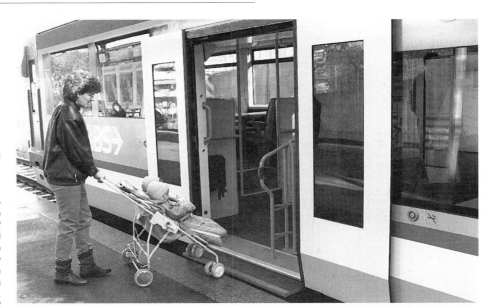

RBS low-floor LRV
1997

Passenger and freight operations
In 1996 RBS carried a total of 17.8 million passengers; 99,000 tonnes were carried.

Traction and rolling stock
In 1995 RBS operated six electric and two diesel locomotives; 15 electric power cars; 21 trailers; 21 two-car emus; 13 passenger cars; 12 freight wagons; and 63 transporters for 1,435 mm gauge wagons.

VERIFIED

Bière—Apples—Morges Railway (BAM)

Chemin de Fer Bière—Apples—Morges
Riond Bosson 3, CH-1110 Morges
Tel: +41 21 801 0805   Fax: +41 21 801 1184

BAM Type Ge 4/4 III locomotive at Vufflens-le-Château (John C Baker)
1995

In Switzerland, MThB also operates the 1,000 mm gauge, 18 km Frauenfeld—Wil Railway, electrified at 1.2 kV DC. It has been the first Swiss private railway company to compete with SBB and in Germany for operating concessions under new legislation, and was to operate local services on SBB's Lake Constance shore route. MThB employed 104 staff at the end of 1994.

Passenger operations
In May 1994 MThB introduced a cross-border fixed-interval service. With financial support from the German Baden—Württemburg provincial and local admin-istrations, the service runs from Weinfelden to Konstanz and over DB AG tracks to Singen and Engen. It is furnished with four new SBB-type 'Colibri' three-car electric multiple-units which were taken from a current SBB order for these units. In addition, the entire existing MThB rolling stock fleet has been adapted to meet DB AG

standards, including the fitting of INDUSI automatic train control equipment.

Traction and rolling stock
MThB operates two electric (one an Re 4/4 II) and three diesel locomotives, 10 electric power cars, 10 trailers and 14 other passenger cars. Five ex-DB 'Rheingold' vista-dome observation cars, and historic 'Orient Express' cars, are maintained for land-cruise train operations organised by the associated travel agency company Reisebüro Mittelthurgau.

The 1,000 mm gauge Frauenfeld—Wil Railway operates nine Be 4/4 motor cars, four driving trailers and 32 carriers for transport of 1,435 mm gauge wagons.

LOKOOP AG
In 1994, following tests of an ex-DR Class 142 electric locomotive, MThB agreed with South Eastern Railway

(SOB) to purchase 21 of these surplus locomotives. To do so, a joint company LOKOOP AG was formed by MThB and SOB, with finance from the Zurich and Thurgau Cantonal Banks. By mid-1995, two Class 142 locomotives had been sold to Fribourg Railways (GFM) and five were operational on SOB and eight on the MThB. The Emmental—Burgdorf—Thun (EBT) (now Mittelland Regional) group has also shown interest.

Electrical modifications to Swiss standards, including installation of electrical (resistance) braking, are performed on each locomotive by Stadler AG at Bussnang. MThB has shown interest in expanding its locomotive fleet in order to run through-trains between Germany and Switzerland and elsewhere, under the competitive freedoms given by EU Directive 440/91, and has already submitted tenders for various traffic flows.

VERIFIED

Montreux—Oberland Bernois Railway (MOB)

Chemin de Fer Montreux—Oberland Bernois
PO Box 1426, Rue du Lac 36, CH-1820 Montreux
Tel: +41 21 964 5511   Fax: +41 21 964 6448

Key personnel
Managing Director: F Jaussi
Assistant Director: M Sandoz
Marketing Manager: H Rickenbacher
Traffic Manager: J C Gétaz
Way and Works Manager: G Bridevaux
Traction and Workshops Manager: J M Forclaz

Gauge: 1,000 mm; 800 mm
Route length: 85.7 km; 10 km
Electrification: 95.7 km at 860 V DC

Organisation
The MOB Group comprises three electrified railways, funiculars (including the automatic 1.6 km Vevey—Chardonne—Mont Pèlerin Railway), ski lifts, coach operations, travel agencies and hotels and restaurants. The principal railway is the 75.3 km 1,000 mm gauge Montreux—Oberland Bernois (MOB); the Montreux—Territet—Glion—Naye (800 mm gauge, 10 km) and Vevey Electric (1,000 mm gauge, 10.4 km) railways have an essentially local role.

MOB's main line runs from Montreux via Gstaad to Zweisimmen. Its climb from Lake Geneva to Les Avants and the 2.4 km Col de Jaman Tunnel, at 7.3 per cent ruling grade, is the steepest adhesion line in Switzerland. The summit is 1,269 m above sea level. From Zweisimmen a branch runs to Lenk.

Passenger operations
Starting life as a local cross-country line, MOB began to court the tourist market in 1979 with introduction of the 'Panoramic Express'. The 'Super Panoramic Express' followed in 1985, and the 'Crystal Panoramic Express' in 1993. This was formed of an existing MOB power car between pairs of Breda-built panoramic cars obtained jointly with the Brig—Visp—Zermatt and Furka—Oberalp (FO) railways (for details see FO entry).

In 1995 MOB intoduced the Montreux—Lenk 'Golden Panoramic Express', operated with 'Super Panoramic Express' equipment rebuilt to 'Crystal' standards. This enabled MOB to operate six daily luxury panoramic services each way between Montreux and Lenk. 'Regional Panoramic Express' services, incorporating panoramic cars accessible without payment of supplement and compulsory reservation, run twice daily.

In 1995, MOB carried 2.5 million passengers and 49,374 tonnes of freight.

Improvements to existing lines
The Swiss federal council has approved MOB's proposal to extend the 'Panoramic Express' to Lucerne, requiring the laying of extra rails to accommodate 1,000 mm gauge trains on the 1,435 mm gauge tracks of Bern—Lötschberg—Simplon Railway (BLS) route from Zweisimmen through Spiez to Interlaken Ost. At Interlaken, MOB trains would take SBB's 1,000 mm gauge Brünig line to Lucerne. MOB envisages four trains each way daily, half provided by its own 'Panoramic' trains, half by the SBB, under the brand-name of 'Golden Pass'.

Class Ge 4/4 locomotive and 'Panoramic Express' cars at Chernex   *1996*

'Crystal Panoramic Express'

Electric locomotives

Class	Wheel arrangement	Output kW	Speed km/h	Weight tonnes	No in service	First built	Builders Mechanical	Electrical
De 6/6	Bo-Bo-Bo	1,230	55	63	2	1931	SIG	ABB
GDe 4/4	Bo-Bo	1,432	100	50	4	1983	SLM	ABB
Ge 4/4	Bo-Bo	2,400	120	62	4	1995	SLM	ABB

Diesel locomotives

Class	Wheel arrangement	Power kW	Speed km/h	Weight tonnes	No in service	First built	Mechanical	Builders Engine	Transmission
Gm 4/4	Bo-Bo	575	80	44	2	1976	Moyse	Poyaud	E Moyse-Leroy-Sommer
Tm 2/2	B-B	115	33	15	2	1953*	KHD	Deutz	H Voith-Turbo

* Rebuilt 1983-84

Although it supports the project, BLS is content to leave the provision of funding and rolling stock to MOB and SBB. The four Class Ge 4/4 electric locomotives delivered to MOB in 1995 are, unlike their predecessors, capable of modification to dual 900 V DC/15 kV 16⅔ Hz AC capability for through working from Montreux as far as Meiringen on the Brünig line. Beyond that point the Brünig line is rack-equipped. The 64-tonne 1,600 kW locomotives are designed for 120 km/h operation on the projected BLS mixed-gauge line.

Traction and rolling stock
MOB operates eight electric and two diesel locomotives, two diesel shunting tractors, 17 motored passenger units, 52 passenger cars and 112 freight wagons, plus numerous service vehicles.

UPDATED

Rhaetian Railway (RhB)

Rhätische Bahn
Bahnhofstrasse 25, CH-7002 Chur
Tel: +41 81 253 9121   Fax: +41 81 222 2501

Key personnel
Director: Silvio Fasciati
Chief Engineer: W Altermatt
Chief Mechanical Engineer: E Mannes
Chief of Finance and Services: H Bauschatz
Chief of Marketing and Operations: A Wieland

Gauge: 1,000 mm
Route length: 375 km
Electrification: 280 km at 11 kV 16⅔ Hz AC; 24.4 km at 2.4 kV DC; 60.7 km at 1 kV DC; 3 km at 1.5 kV DC

Organisation
The Rhaetian Railway is a vital means of communication in the mountainous southeast of Switzerland. Serving the Engadine, the valley of Poschiavo, the Davos area, Arosa and the Grisons Oberland, the railway connects the canton with the SBB network at Chur and Landquart, with the Furka—Oberalp Railway in Disentis/Muster, and with FS of Italy in Tirano. The territory is the most sparsely populated in Switzerland, with a population of some 170,000 averaging 23/km².

The core of the RhB network is electrified at 11 kV 16⅔ Hz, but the Bernina Railway from St Moritz to Tirano was electrified at its construction in 1908-10 at 1 kV DC and retains that system. The Bernina is the only Swiss transalpine line that avoids tunnelling, attaining a summit of 2,253 m above sea level at Alp Grüm; for 27 km, or 44 per cent of its total distance, it is graded at 7 per cent but is worked entirely by adhesion. The Chur—Arosa Railway of 26.4 route-km, which RhB absorbed in 1943, is electrified at 2.4 kV DC; on this line the ruling gradient is 6 per cent.

The RhB system as a whole has 118 tunnels and avalanche shelters aggregating 39 km in length and 498 bridges and viaducts totalling 12 km in length. Its longest tunnel is the 6 km Albula.

Traffic (million)	1993	1994
Freight tonnes	1.071	1.153
Freight tonne-km	53.7	58.6
Passenger journeys	8.991	8.864
Passenger-km	304.4	301.5

Finance (SFr million)		
Revenue	1993	1994
Passengers	98.9	102.7
Freight	35.5	36.1
Parcels and mail	10.3	9.7
Other	40.9	41.8
Total	185.6	190.2
Expenditure		
Staff/personnel	132.2	132.8
Materials/services	60.1	61.7
Depreciation	22.7	25.3
Total	215	219.5

Freight operations
Main constituents of RhB's considerable freight traffic are oil, cement, drinks, chemicals and timber. The wagon fleet includes sliding wall, insulated vans with electric heating and cooling to provide for winter haulage of fresh produce; power is provided by a busline from the train's locomotive.

RhB has a developing container traffic between Landquart and Thusis. It is developing a Bernina line terminal on the Italian frontier at Campocologno, believing that this route has all-weather advantages for traffic from northern Italy.

New lines
In 1981 RhB initiated plans for a 22.3 km cut-off from Klosters to Lavin, between Samedan and Scuol-Tarasp,

ABe 4/4 power car with ABB three-phase AC motors climbs through the Bernina pass to the RhB's summit, the highest on Europe's transalpine routes

RhB Class Ge 4/4 III locomotive at Samedan (Murdoch Currie)   **1996**

which would halve journey times between Landquart and the Lower Engadine. Journey times to Scuol-Tarasp from Zurich and Chur would be cut by 135 and 100 minutes to 2 hours 40 minutes and 1½ hours respectively.

The cut-off includes the 19.06 km single-track Vereina Tunnel under the Silvretta mountain range, currently under construction. The tunnel will have one passing loop, a ruling gradient of 1.5 per cent, and will be large enough to accommodate wagons conveying road vehicles up to 3.5 m in height. Maximum speed through the tunnel will be 100 km/h, allowing passage in 17 minutes.

From the Selfranga vehicle-loading terminal under construction at Klosters, a semicircular single-line tunnel on a gradient of 2.5 per cent will lead to the Vereina Tunnel portal via a short section of track in the open. The south terminal is at Saglians, between Susch and Lavin. Each terminal will have two loading tracks.

Total cost of the project, including SFr36 million for rolling stock, was estimated at SFr538 million in 1985; the federal government agreed to provide 85 per cent of the funding and gave its approval in 1986. Construction began in 1991, with completion scheduled for 1999 and commercial service due to start in 2000. The standard hourly service in each direction will be one conventional passenger train and one or two vehicle shuttles; the latter will increase to three in peak periods. There will be one or two daily freight services.

Improvements to existing lines
RhB has begun a major remodelling and upgrading of the Chur—Arosa branch. A plan to replace the 2.3 km traversal of Chur's streets by the Arosa branch from the station forecourt with a 3.3 km tunnel from the town's outskirts to a new underground facility has been dropped, but work is going ahead to convert the branch to RhB standard 11 kV 16⅔ Hz AC electrification. This work started in 1995 for completion in 1997.

Traction and rolling stock
In 1994 RhB operated 59 electric, 9 diesel and three electro-diesel locomotives; 42 electric railcars; 24 diesel and six electric shunting tractors; three steam locomotives (used for special trains); 329 passenger coaches (including eight restaurant cars); 53 baggage and mail cars; and 705 freight wagons.

Signalling and telecommunications
The RhB system, mostly single track, is colourlight signalled with automatic block under the oversight of seven control centres. The majority of passing loops can be switched for automatic operation by trains when their stations are unmanned. The entire system and all power units are equipped with the Integra 79 ATC system. Ground-to-train radio has been installed throughout the railway's network. The RhB has always relied upon Hardy vacuum brakes for its passenger and freight trains, enhanced by electric braking on all locomotives.

VERIFIED

Sihltal–Zurich–Uetliberg Railway (SZU)

Sihltal–Zurich–Uetliberg Bahn
Manessestrasse 152, CH-8045 Zurich
Tel: +41 1 202 8884   Fax: +41 1 202 9076

Key personnel
Chairman: Dr J Kaufmann
General Manager: Mrs Christiane V Weibel

Gauge: 1,435 mm
Route length: 29 km
Electrification: 19 km (Sihltal line) at 15 kV 16⅔ Hz; 10 km (Uetliberg line) at 1.2 kV DC

Organisation
SZU operates an intensive passenger service from Zurich over two routes, one to Sihlbrugg (the Sihltal line) and the other to Uetliberg.

Improvements to existing lines
Following the opening of SZU's tunnel extension from the outskirts of Zurich to the city's main SBB station in 1990, passenger traffic on the Sihltal line grew by 67 per cent. On the Uetliberg line, traffic grew by more than 150 per cent. As a result, the federal and canton governments financially supported a SFr137 million development plan, which included some double-tracking and new rolling stock.

SZU Be 4/4 railcars at Triemli (Murdoch Currie)   *1996*

Traction and rolling stock
SZU operates the Sihltal line with eight electric and four diesel locomotives, five electric railcars and 29 trailers, and 32 other passenger coaches. The Uetliberg line is operated with 14 electric railcars, four trailers and two other passenger coaches.

VERIFIED

South Eastern Railway (SOB)

Schweizerische Südostbahn
PO Box 563, CH-8820 Wädenswil
Tel: +41 1 780 3157   Fax: +41 1 780 3756

Key personnel
Director: Dr Ernst Boos

Gauge: 1,435 mm
Route length: 46.67 km
Electrification: 46.67 km at 15 kV 16⅔ Hz AC

Organisation
SOB, together with SBB and the Bodensee–Toggenburg Railway (BT), jointly operates an important cross-country intercity passenger service from Romanshorn and St Gallen to Lucerne, using the tracks of all three railways. The SOB segment of the route runs from Rapperswil to the SBB station at Pfäffikon, and from there to the SBB at Arth-Goldau. Branches serve Wädenswil and Einsiedeln.

Traffic (000s)	1994	1995
Freight tonnes	192	166
Freight tonne-km	1,846	1,573
Passenger journeys	3,690	3,840
Passenger-km	49,726	58,402

Finances (SFr 000)		
Revenue	*1994*	*1995*
Passengers	12,327	12,648
Freight	2,996	1,954
Other income	4,521	4,993
Total	19,844	19,595

Expenditure	*1994*	*1995*
Staff/personnel	20,455	19,600
Materials/services	10,265	10,773
Depreciation	4,582	4,685
Financial charges	64	35
Total	35,366	35,093

Traction and rolling stock
There are four Re 4/4 IV electric locomotives (ex-SBB); three electric and three diesel tractors; one diesel-electric locomotive; four RBDe 4/4, eight BDe 4/4 and three ABe 4/4 electric power cars; 11 driving trailers; and 36 passenger cars (including three buffet cars, one of which has been partially restored for charter and tour work).

In 1994 SOB purchased a surplus DR Class 142 electric locomotive for its exclusive use and subsequently agreed with Mittel–Thurgau Railway (MThB) to acquire a further 20 locomotives jointly. Two were sold to Fribourg Railways and four (equipped with rheostatic braking)

SOB 'Colibri' electric multiple-unit introduced in 1995   *1996*

Electric railcars

Class	Cars per unit	Motor cars per unit	Motored axles/car	Output/motor kW	Speed km/h	Weight tonnes	No in service	First built	Builders Mechanical	Electrical
ABe 4/4	1	1	4	706	80	46.5	14	1939	SIG/SLM/SWS	ABB/MFO/SAAS
BDe 4/4	1	1	4	2,060	110	72	8	1959	SIG	ABB
RBDe 4/4	2	1	4	1,714	140	70.5	4	1995	SWG/SIG	ABB

Electric locomotives

Class	Wheel arrangement	Output kW	Speed km/h	Weight tonnes	No in service	First built	Builders Mechanical	Electrical
Re 4/4 IV	Bo-Bo	4,960	160	80	4	1982	SLM	ABB

entered service with SOB through a leasing arrangement agreed with LOKOOP AG (see MThB entry).

The joint SOB/BT Lucerne–Romanshorn service is run by three sets of SBB-type Mk IV coaches, one SOB and two BT. Starting with the summer 1997 timetable, BT and SOB are running hourly direct trains between St Gallen and Arth Goldau(–Lucerne) using refurbished Mk I coaches as well as the Mk IVs. Four two-car emus of SBB's 'Colibri' type were delivered to SOB by Schindler Waggon in 1995.

Track
Rail: SBB-profile type I, 46 kg/m

Crossties (sleepers): Steel, concrete, wood, 150 × 260 mm
Spacing: 1,667/km
Fastenings: K and W on wood and steel sleepers. A on steel sleepers, B on concrete sleepers
Min curvature radius: 143 m
Max gradient: 5%
Max axleload: 22.5 tonnes

UPDATED

Swiss Federal Railways

Schweizerische Bundesbahnen (SBB)
Chemins de Fer Fédéraux Suisses (CFF)
Ferrovie Federali Svizzere (FFS)
Hochschulstrasse 6, CH-3030 Bern
Tel: +41 51 220 1111   Fax: +41 51 220 4265

Key personnel

Chairman: Jules Kyburz
President and General Manager, Finance and Staff:
    Dr Benedikt Weibel
General Secretary: Urs Schlegel
Deputy General Secretary: Jürg Scheidegger
Directors
    Traffic: Dr Hans Peter Fagagnini
    Infrastructure: Pierre-Alain Urech
Heads of Division
    Personnel: vacant
    Information Systems: Josef Egger
    Financial and Control: Michel Christe
    Audit: Ernst Bigler
    Medical: Dr Pierre-A Voumard
    International Relations: Jean-Pierre Membrez
    Rail 2000/Co-ordination of Train Service: Paul Moser
    Freight Traffic: Erwin Mauron
    Passenger Traffic: Paul Blumenthal
    Property Management: Vacant
    Traction and Train Services: André Urfer
    Rolling Stock: Theo Weiss
    Infrastructure Management: Hans-Jürg Spillmann
    Train Operation Management: Felix Loeffel
    Way and Works Direction: Dr Peter Winter
    Safety: Hans-Peter Hadorn
    Traction Current: Jörg Stöcklin
    Purchasing: Dr Max Lehmann
    AlpTransit: Peter Zuber
    Civil Engineering: Dr Peter Winter
    Telecommunications: Edward Stiefel

Gauge: 1,435 mm; 1,000 mm
Route length: 2,913 km; 74 km
Electrification: 1,435 mm gauge, 2,897 km at 15 kV 16⅔
Hz AC; 1,000 mm gauge, 74 km at 15 kV 16⅔ Hz AC

Political background

Heavy losses during the 1990s have prompted the Swiss government to put pressure on SBB to improve productivity and financial results. The railway has had some success in this, cutting the deficit from SFr496 million in 1995 to an estimated SFr153 million in 1997. This result, however, is after government subsidies: up from nil in 1970 to SFr2.4 billion in 1997.

The workforce has been cut from 39,000 in 1990 to 31,600 in 1997, but a further 12,000 jobs could go by spinning off non-core business.

Bahn 2000
In the 'Bahn 2000', or 'Bahn + Bus 2000' programme, the federal government is financing development of an expanded and closely integrated public passenger

Zurich S-Bahn train   *1996*

transport service nationwide by the next century. For railways, parliament in 1986 approved expenditure of SFr5.4 billion on SBB projects embodied in the plan. At the end of 1991 the federal government budgeted SFr1.3 billion to support the country's 57 private railways' 'Bahn 2000' investments.

SBB's expanded passenger train service plan for 'Bahn 2000' centred on hourly cycling throughout the timetable. Critical interchange points are the SBB stations at Basel, Bern, Biel, Lausanne, Lucerne, St Gallen, Sargans and Zurich. For symmetry, direct trains would run between each neighbouring pair of these centres on a timing that was slightly less than 1 hour, the residue of that hour being standing time for passenger interchange. Thus at each of these stations the full range of connections would be concentrated in a standard framework each hour of the day. On key routes, however, SBB's 'Bahn 2000' plan doubles InterCity or direct train service from hourly to half-hourly.

SBB's 'Bahn 2000' scheme called for about 130 km of new 200 km/h route, to secure competitive transit times, but also to cut running time between neighbouring hubs to the 1 hour required. (For details, see under 'New lines' section.)

SBB's major 'Bahn 2000' projects have not been able to proceed to plan. The initial cost estimate of SFr5.4 billion had, by 1993, swollen to SFr14-16 billion with increased construction industry costs, and through the addition of environmental safeguards enforced by objectors to several schemes. Objections to two segments of new 200 km/h infrastructure between Basel and Bern, and to a third between Zurich and Winterthur, resulted in delays and modification. In mid-1996 the Rothrist—Mattstetten section was started. The Adler Tunnel and cut-off near Basel are well in hand despite extreme difficulties with unstable terrain, but continuation to Olten from Liestal is still under review.

In 1993 the federal council required SBB to recast its 'Bahn 2000' plan to keep total cost within the 1987 budget, SFr8.1 billion, with subsequent cost inflation. This was exclusive of investment associated with the AlpTransit scheme for new transalpine base tunnels (see 'New lines' section). SBB's revised plan cost SFr 7.4 billion, allowing for 20 per cent overrun without infringement of the government's ceiling. This curtailed programme would achieve most objectives of 'Bahn 2000' by 2005. It would not accommodate the increased traffic expected from completion of the AlpTransit base tunnel plan. With tilt-body technology and double-deck coaches for InterCity services, some costly civil engineering to increase speeds and capacity has been saved.

Organisation

SBB is organised along business sector lines. The passenger sectors comprise: international traffic; domestic long-haul traffic; regional and conurbation traffic; and special traffic. The freight sectors are: domestic wagonload; transit, including intermodal; and special traffic. Each business 'buys' its services from production departments, being responsible for costs and for results.

Finance

For the past three years, the financial deficit has been on a downward trend: 1995's deficit of SFr496 million was reduced in 1996 to SFr293 million, and was set to be around SFr153 million in 1997. Total revenue in 1996 increased by 8.4 per cent to SFr6.767 billion, including federal support, which fell by 12.9 per cent to SFr2.394 billion. Support from the cantons rose from SFr15 million to SFr212 million in 1996.

Productivity measures being introduced include one-person crews for Regional trains and further substitution of buses for trains on poorly used Regional services. Stations are being closed or destaffed. The three-year 'lean infrastructure' programme begun in 1994 has rigorously embarked upon the removal of all track, points, crossings, and so on, surplus to normal requirements.

SBB's future remains the subject of debate, as its finances worsen and the demand for investment funds increases. The causes of its financial problems and the need for a revised contract with the state were set out by SBB in 1991. Its complaint, that it was not adequately compensated for its federally stipulated social services, notably the regional all-stations trains, was taken up in the 1994 revision of the Railway Law (discussed in the 'Ministry of Transport' section). International average real-money revenue per freight tonne continues to fall; in 1996 freight tonne-km fell by 9.5 per cent, and revenue fell by 9.7 per cent. Financial charges, depreciation and major maintenance costs have risen steadily. By 1997 SBB's annual capital outlay was set to scale SFr2.7 billion which, with interest on previous investment, would exceed annual passenger and freight revenue.

A federal law of 1987 requires rail and road to satisfy stringent noise emission standards by 2002. This will cost SBB approximately SFr2 billion.

Passenger operations

In 1996 passenger journeys, totalling 256 million, increased by 0.7 per cent, but passenger-km fell by 0.8 per cent to 11.6 billion.

Interior of bar car on CityNightLine train   *1996*

The cutbacks in 'Bahn 2000' civil engineering investment (see 'Political background' section above) mean that, outside the key Basel—Bern—Zurich triangle, within-the-hour scheduling of InterCity (IC) services between all adjoining pairs of hub stations will not be feasible. Half-hourly service frequency on some routes, such as Basel—Lucerne, may be limited to business peak hours. The 'Bahn 2000' objective, of connectional interlacing of Regional and long-haul trains to offer once-every-daytime-hour service between any pair of SBB stations, is affected by cuts in lightly used off-peak trains from many Regional services. SBB is transferring some Regional services from rail to bus. The abolition of conductors on Regional trains was complete by 1996.

Zurich RER

The Zurich RER (Regional Express) service, some 300 route-km, was inaugurated in 1990 (see *JWR 1996-97* for details). In 1989 Zurich Canton, which had put up SFr523 million for the RER project in 1981, approved a further contribution of SFr235 million. This was towards the SFr444 million cost of new infrastructure works, an outstanding feature of which is the boring of a 7 km tunnel between Wiedikon and Thalwil in the southeastern suburbs. This is part of a four-tracking of the existing double-track route shared by RER services and Gotthard and Chur route long-haul trains from the centre of Zurich to Thalwil; RER services will have exclusive use of the existing double-track skirting the Zurichsee. Other works include a flyover south of Effretikon.

Bern RER

In 1995 the first two routes of a four-line, 118-station RER network in Bern Canton became operational. The two routes were: Thun—Gumlingen—Bern—Fribourg; and Schwarzenburg—Bern—Konolfingen—Langnau. A third route, to become operational in 1998, is Biel—Lyss—Bern—Belp—Thun. The fourth route, planned for introduction in 1999, will link Angenthal—Burgdorf—Bern—Neuchatel/Murten.

Traffic (million)

	1995	1996
Freight tonnes	47.3	44.1
Freight tonne-km	8,156	7,382
Passenger journeys	254.0	255.8
Passenger-km	11,729	11,630

Finances (SFR million)

Expenditure	1995	1996
Personnel	3,481	3,259
Materials	1,278	1,233
Depreciation	847	883
Financial charges	676	691
Major maintenance	286	241
Other	172	753
Total	6,740	7,060

Revenue

Passengers	1,578	1,575
Freight	1,033	933
Compensation: regional passenger and piggyback freight	818	816
Support for infrastructure maintenance	1,450	1,497
Support for investment	311	318
Support for AlpTransit	8	—
Other	1,046	—
Total	6,244	—
Surplus (deficit)	(496)	—

Freight operations

In 1995 freight tonnage decreased by 0.4 per cent to 47.3 million. Recessionary conditions in Europe, despite growth of transit intermodal traffic, reduced overall freight revenue by 8 per cent. Since 1992, freight revenue has declined by a third, leaving it at SFr933 million in 1996.

Cargo Domicile, SBB's loss-making less-than-wagonload freight business, which had made heavy losses, was to be sold to a consortium of road hauliers previously used for deliveries.

An important experiment has been conducted with trains of 3,250 tonnes on the north-south route over the Gotthard pass; normal Gotthard loads are limited to 2,000 tonnes. The trials used a steel train from Germany to Italy, with two Class 460 locomotives on the front of the train and three in the middle. If capable of full-scale implementation, this method of working would considerably increase line capacity and productivity.

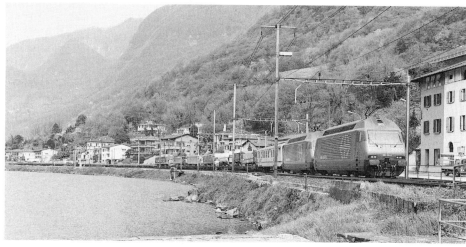

A pair of Class 460s hauling a Hupac 'RoLa' intermodal service near Capolago (John C Baker) **1996**

Intermodal operations

SBB is purely a wholesaler of train capacity to intermodal marketing concerns, notably the Swiss company Hupac (for contact details, see UIRR entry in 'Operators of International Rail Services in Europe' section), and the Swiss-based international company Intercontainer (qv), both of which own fleets of intermodal wagons. Hupac deploys a fleet of 345 RoLa ('Rolling Highway') low-floor well wagons for ro-ro movement of complete (tractor and trailer) highway trucks. Hupac also operates 25 couchette cars for RoLa trains' trucker crews and 1,750 pocket wagons for carriage of unaccompanied trailers and swapbodies.

Hupac's RoLa trains for accompanied highway trucks run between Basel and Lugano, between Freiburg-im-Breisgau (just inside Germany) and Lugano or Milan Greco Pirelli, and from Rielasingen to Milan Rogoredo. RoLa operation, however, cannot be marketed at a cost-covering price and is federally supported out of road-users' petrol/diesel tax. In 1993 this aid totalled SFr89 million.

SBB is a founder member of Intercontainer, the company jointly owned by European railway administrations which markets intermodal services throughout Europe. Intercontainer contributes almost half of SBB's transalpine intermodal traffic with long-distance container and swapbody trains.

New intermodal systems

The first bimodal operation has been launched by the Swiss food distribution company Migros, which annually sends 1.2 million tonnes of freight by rail. Ten Kombitrailers and 20 rail bogies operate from Migros' main Neuendorf centre to St Margrethen.

SBB and the private railways are partners in ACTS SA, a company formed to promote local container traffic. This achieves road-rail transfer without cranage; the Type Rs-x rail wagons, 800 of which are supplied by Tuchschmid AG of Frauenfeld, each have three 20 ft long platforms that can be swung outwards to back up to the rear of a road vehicle chassis equipped with a mechanism to slide a container from one vehicle to the other.

Gotthard route upgrade

The federal government allocated SFr1.46 billion for works, chiefly on the Gotthard route, and on approach routes Basel—Brugg—Arth-Goldau, to expand capacity for transit intermodal traffic pending completion of the new transalpine base tunnels (see 'New lines' section). The aim was to treble the Gotthard route's intermodal piggyback capacity from 160,000 to 470,000 units a year. This embraced unaccompanied semi-trailers, and RoLa movement of highway trucks. There would also be scope for annual throughput of some 330,000 containers and swapbodies.

The works were completed at the end of 1993. As a result, the maximum permissible format of Gotthard piggyback trains has risen from 17 to 36 flat wagons with a gross laden weight of 2,000 tonnes. Southbound, single-headed 16-wagon trains run to Dottikon, where they are coupled, so that the locomotive of the rear train becomes the radio-controlled mid-train power. A third locomotive is added to double-head the combined train. Northbound, combined trains are formed during the essential change-of-voltage repowering at the FS-SBB yard in Chiasso. The aim is to power these trains exclusively with the tranche of 75 Class 460 locomotives which SBB expressly ordered for the service. In 1994 the Gotthard route carried 44 piggyback intermodal trains daily.

The clearances of the Gotthard route allow unaccompanied trailers, 3.9 m high at their roof corners, on so-called 'pocket' wagons. If they have deflatable air

SBB's new locomotive sheds at Basel **1997**

The first of 58 'InterCity 2000' coaches ordered by SBB is rolled out of the Schindler factory at Pratteln in 1996
1996

suspension, 4 m high box trailers can be safely accommodated on the latest type of pocket wagon. But RoLa piggybacked trucks must not be higher than 3.8 m, whereas virtually unrestricted admissibility to RoLa trains of European trucks requires clearance for 4.2 m road vehicle height. That will be built into the new transalpine base tunnels.

New lines

'Bahn 2000' works

The longest stretches of new 200 km/h infrastructure proposed in the original 'Bahn 2000' plan were to be on the Basel—Bern route: one of 34 km between Muttenz, on Basel's outskirts, and Olten (which entailed tunnels of 4.7 and 12.8 km length, the Adler and Wisenberg respectively); and another of 54 km between the Olten area at Rothrist and Mattstetten, near Bern, with a branch to the Olten—Zofingen—Lucerne line. These give the 22 minute cut in Bern—Basel timings needed to secure under-the-hour running of direct trains, as between Bern and Lucerne or Zurich. But four-tracking between Basel and Bern would also handle the doubled direct passenger train frequency and anticipated extra international freight traffic via the Bern area following completion of the BLS Lötschberg route double-tracking.

The Rothrist—Mattstetten high-speed route survived the reappraisal of the 'Bahn 2000' project, and work started in 1996. It runs parallel to the N1 motorway and close to the existing railway as far as the region of Herzogenbuchsee, with a branch to an existing secondary line to Solothurn, to be upgraded to a fast route for trunk trains from Biel to Basel or Zurich. At Mattstetten the new line will make an end-on junction with the new Grauholz bypass.

The 9.5 km Grauholz bypass opened in 1995; it includes a 6.3 km tunnel. Its purpose is to keep Bern—Olten traffic clear of Zollikofen, where the old Olten—Bern and Biel—Bern lines saw some 300 trains a day. With full implementation of 'Bahn 2000' the total would rise to 500, including eight pairs of IC trains in each hour. The bypass starts 4 km out of Bern at Bern—Löchligut. The Grauholz bypass permits half-hourly Bern—Zurich IC service. Further east, the Rupperswil—Aarau segment, including Aarau station and a new tunnel under the town, will become a four-track high-speed section.

Of the planned Muttenz—Olten high-speed segment, only the Muttenz—Liestal stretch — which includes the Adler tunnel — is being built. This will segregate the Hauenstein and Bözberg routes out of Basel. Continuation through the new Wisenberg Tunnel would not produce transit time gains sufficient to warrant its high cost, and SBB considers that the required patterns of connections at Basel and Olten can be secured without it.

A third stretch of 200 km/h track, 9 km in length, was to be between Zurich Airport and Winterthur. This stretch required boring of the 8.4 km Brüttener Tunnel between Kloten and Winterthur. The entire scheme is now deferred.

Finally, 31 km of 200 km/h line were planned between Vauderens and Villars-sur-Glâne, on the main line from Lausanne to Bern. This, the only 200 km/h project with the sole aim of shortening transit time, was cut back to construction of a new tunnel at Vauderens that is essential

to provide adequate clearance for the new double-deck IC trainsets.

Among the SBB's other major 'Bahn 2000' schemes, the Rhône Valley route's last stretch of single track was due to be bypassed in 1996 by a new double-track tunnel between Salgesch and Leuk.

New base tunnels

The federal government's AlpTransit plan for new Gotthard and Lötschberg base tunnels, to enable the near-trebling of transalpine capacity for rail-based intermodal traffic, was approved by national referendum in 1992. The federal council adopted the AlpTransit plan, to resist European Union (EU) demands for a transalpine road corridor for 40-tonne trucks, in face of Switzerland's 28-tonne gross loaded weight truck limit, prohibition of night driving, a levy on heavy goods road transit, and noise and emissions controls. Railways claim 68 per cent of the Swiss transit freight market, although substantial diversion of road traffic via France or Austria occurs.

Using rights under the Swiss constitution, a private environmentalist initiative led to a national referendum on transit highway freight in 1994. Against federal government advice, in view of the likely strain on relations with the EU, the country voted to bar Swiss roads to all transit highway freight by 2004. Since neither transalpine base tunnel would be finished by then, rail congestion is inevitable.

Exploratory boring for the Gotthard base tunnel route began in 1995 (the Lötschberg project is considered in the Bern-Lötschberg-Simplon Railway entry). It will extend approximately 125 km from Arth-Goldau to the outskirts of Lugano, with the 57 km base tunnel as its centrepiece.

The base tunnel, starting at Erstfeld on the northern side, will be the world's longest rail bore; its summit, 571 m above sea level, will be some 600 m below that of the present Gotthard tunnel. The route is described in *JWR 1996-97*.

Clearances will be contoured for piggybacking of road lorries 4.2 m high. The base tunnel itself will be aligned and built so as to simplify its possible elaboration at some future date into the 'Y' form sought by eastern Switzerland. Other schemes exist, subject to financing, to improve access to the Gotthard base tunnel from eastern Switzerland, south Germany and Austria. Use of the Bodensee Toggenburg (qv) line from St Gallen southwestwards would bring Gotthard traffic from the east and northeast to Pfaffikon, up the SBB's Zurich line to Au and through a new Hirzel Tunnel, to a 'Y' near Zug with a new north-south double-track Zimmerberg Tunnel, to be bored from Thalwil to benefit traffic from Zurich (and the Stuttgart area of Germany) to Arth-Goldau.

Neither the Gotthard nor Lötschberg base tunnel can be finished before 2005. Internal differences in the Swiss Cabinet in 1994 led in 1995 to an independent reappraisal of the cost (about SFr15 billion) and returns, and it was shown that the SBB and BLS could not, as originally planned, pay back the cost from traffic income. Since this was a condition on which the 1992 popular approval was given, a further vote was due to be held in 1997 on a revised finance package, including increased use of fuel revenues. Although both lines should be finished in 2006, and the Transit Agreement with the EU requires both to be built, popular opinion and financial constraints may cause either tunnel to be delayed or cancelled.

Improvements to existing lines

The Rhône Valley main line to the Simplon Tunnel has been upgraded. Complete renewal of track with heavier rail and higher speed pointwork, realignments at Riddes and Ardon, renewal of overhead equipment, and resignalling accompanied by computer-based control, track-to-train radio and automatic speed control, equip the Martigny—Sion section for 200 km/h. There is provision for solid-state interlockings at Martigny and Sion. A new double-track tunnel replaces the last single-track section, the 5 km in difficult terrain between Salgesch and Leuk. Here, and from Leuk to Visp and (later) through the Simplon Tunnel, the speed limit is now 160 km/h.

To achieve clearance for piggybacked trucks of 4.2 m corner height, and to provide for higher passenger train speeds, the Simplon Tunnel's track is being renewed and its bed lowered. At the same time, a rigid traction current conductor replaces traditional catenary. The rigid conductor is closer to the tunnel crown giving 300 to 400 mm of extra clearance for intermodal piggyback trains. To avoid unacceptable interference with traffic, the works are executed in the least busy periods of the year, covering 3 to 5 km at a time, and the project is expected to take six to eight years in total.

Doubling of the Bad Ragaz—Landquart stretch of the Sargans—Chur line was completed in 1994. That of the

Tilting trains to be built for SBB will use technology developed using this test train formed with ex-British Rail Mk 3 sleepers by bogie manufacturer SIG
1996

Electric locomotives

Class	Wheel arrangement	Speed km/h	Weight tonnes	No in service	First built	Builders Mechanical	Electrical
610	Co-Co	125	120/124	120	1952	SLM	ABB/Oerlikon
410	Bo-Bo	125	57	42	1946	SLM	ABB/Oerlikon
411		125	57		1950	SLM	Sécheron
420	Bo-Bo	140	80	273	1964	SLM	ABB/Oerlikon/ Sécheron
430	Bo-Bo	125	80	20	1971	SLM	ABB/Oerlikon/ Sécheron
450	Bo-Bo	130	71	95	1989	SLM	ABB
Re 460	Bo-Bo	100	81	118	1993	SLM	ABB
620	Bo-Bo-Bo	140	120	88	1972	SLM	ABB/Sécheron
930	C	40/50	39/45	126	1928		ABB/Oerlikon/ Sécheron
Ee 6/6	C + C	45	90	2	1952	SLM	ABB/Sécheron
962	Co-Co	85	107	10	1980	SLM	ABB
Eem 6/6	Co-Co	65	104	1	1970	SLM	SAAS
15 kV/25 kV							
Ee 3/3 II	C	45	46	14	1957	SLM	ABB
1.5 kV/3 kV/15 kV/25 kV							
934	C	60	48	10	1962	SLM	Sécheron

New classifications have been reserved for forthcoming locomotives as follows:
  453 Possible three-voltage unit for Geneva and Basel S-Bahn projects
  462 Planned dual-voltage version of Re 4/4 VI

Electric railcars or multiple-units

Class	Cars per unit	Motor cars per unit	Motored axles/car	Output/motor kW	Speed km/h	No in service	First built	Builders Mechanical	Electrical
15 kV AC									
RAe 2/4	1	1	2	197	125	1	1935	SLM	ABB/MFO/ SAAS/SBB
511	3	3	4	204	125	18	1965	SWP/FFA	SAAS/ABB
512	4	2	4	281	125	4	1976	SWS/SWP/SIG	SAAS
560	2	1	4	412	140	65	1984	FFA/SIG/SWP/ SWA	ABB
524	1	1	4	497	125	80	1959	SIG/SWS	ABB/MFO
536	1	1	4	294	110	11	1952	SLM/SWP	ABB/MFO/ SAAS
546	1	1	4	201	75	1	1927	SIG/SWS	SAAS
1.5 kV DC									
Bem 550	2	—	—	600	100	5	1994	SWG-A/SWG-P/ SIG	ABB
1.5 kV/3 kV/15 kV/25 kV									
506	6	1	6	577.5	160	3	1961	SIG	MFO

Diesel locomotives

Class	Wheel arrangement	Power kW	Speed km/h	Weight tonnes	No in service	First built	Builders Mechanical	Engine	Transmission
843	B-B	1,093	140	80	4	1956	Krupp	Krauss-Maffei	H Maybach
842	Bo-Bo	611	75	66	1	1939	SLM	Sulzer	E ABB
840	Bo-Bo	620	75	72	26	1960	SLM	SLM	E Sécheron
	Bo-Bo	620	75	72	20	1968	SLM	SLM	E Sécheron
	Co-Co	956	75	106	4	1954	SLM	Sulzer	E ABB/ Sécheron
					10	1960			
930	C	326	65	49	5	1959	SLM	SLM	E ABB/ Sécheron
		326	65	49	35	1962	SLM	SLM	E ABB/ Sécheron
863	Co-Co	1,440	85	111	6	1976	Thyssen-Henschel	Chantiers de l'Atlantique	E ABB
Em 6/6	Co-Co	393	65	104	5	1971	SLM	SLM	E SAAS/ SSB/ABB
831	C	900	60	54	3	1992	RACO	Cummins	H
842	Bo-Bo	1,120	90	80	2	1992	Krupp	MTU	H

SBB HGe 4/4 locomotive on the metre-gauge Brünig line (Bryan A Stone)   ***1996***

Lucerne—Zurich line between Rotkreuz and Ebikon, and four-tracking between Olten, Aarau and Rapperswil, are to be finished in 1997; a third high-speed running line, with flyover, has been installed between Basel and Muttenz.

In preparation for expanded 'Bahn 2000' services, a new platform has been built at Basel SBB, and three of the station's other platforms extended. At Brig a new Platform 4 has been built for BLS trains and the track layout modified to suit. Morges, Winterthur and Aarau stations are being completely rebuilt.

Traction and rolling stock
In 1996 SBB operated 803 standard-gauge electric locomotives; 245 electric power cars; 121 diesel locomotives; 163 electric shunters; and 783 tractors. The rolling stock fleet of 4,392 passenger cars included 53 restaurant, 60 sleeping and 13 couchette cars. Freight wagons totalled 16,111, Swiss Post Office-owned postal cars 561 and baggage cars 333. Over 6,460 privately owned wagons were in use.

Class 460
The latest main line electric locomotive type is a 6.1 MW, 230 km/h 20-tonne axleload unit built by SLM with ABB (now Adtranz) electrical equipment known as Class 460. In 1992 the federal government agreed that the 75 Class 460 locomotives ordered in 1990 for Gotthard route piggyback traffic could be acquired on a leasing basis. They have been 87 per cent funded by Eurofima and for the rest by a leasing agreement with the Wilmington Trust Company (USA). Later a further 20 were ordered at a cost per unit of SFr6.9 million, bringing to 119 the total delivered by 1996.

Tilting train order
In 1996 SBB ordered 24 seven-car tilting trains from a consortium of Swiss industry in a contract worth some SFr500 million. The consortium is led by Adtranz and also involves Fiat-SIG and Schindler. The trains will be capable of travelling at 200km/h and are for use on curvaceous routes; SBB decided to opt for tilting trains to cut down the work required on building new lines for 'Bahn 2000'.

Delivery will be between mid-1998 and mid-2001. The first route on which the trains will work will be between Lausanne and St Gallen; Geneva to Basel will follow. Along with premier non-tilting services, the tilt trains will be marketed under the 'InterCity 2000' tag.

The tilting trains will have a multiple-unit format, with power distributed along the train. Two units will be able to work in multiple at peak times. The tilt system will be an electrically operated 'Neitec' system, which was tested by Fiat-SIG during 1995 in trials using former British Rail sleeping cars.

Coach fleet
In late 1993 SBB placed an initial order worth SFr157 million for 58 air conditioned 'InterCity 2000' coaches of various types, including nine driving trailers. The order went to a consortium of Schindler Waggon with Vevey Technologies and Alusuisse Lonza Railtec AG. As deliveries were drawing to a close in 1997, SBB placed a run-on order for 144 extra vehicles. The standard format of a push-pull double-deck IC formation is a Class 460 locomotive, six intermediate coaches and one driving control trailer. Total seating capacity is 755. Sets are capable of multiple-unit operation, so that a train can divide en route for service of two destinations. SBB estimates that its ultimate 'InterCity 2000' resources will include 130 Class Re460 locomotives and some 400 bilevel cars. First deliveries were made in mid-1996.

SBB's existing stock of over 400 Mk 4 coaches is to be modified to raise maximum speed from 160 km/h to 200 km/h. With push-pull 'InterCity 2000' services in mind, 60 driving trailers were ordered in 1994. Some 300 cars of earlier build, at present limited to 140 km/h, are being modified for 160 km/h operation.

ARGE Hotelzug, a consortium of Talbot, SGP and Schindler Waggon, has delivered a fleet (for details see German entry) of air conditioned double-deck vehicles of new design for operation in overnight 'Hotel Trains' of DACH Hotelzug AG, a joint venture of SBB and DB AG (ÖBB of Austria has dropped out of the venture). 'Hotel' train routes in Switzerland are: Zurich—Vienna (now run by ÖBB and not DACH), Zurich—Hamburg, and Zurich—Basel—Berlin.

Trainsets for local services
Delivery began in 1994 of 38 more of the 'Colibri' RBDe 4/4 motor car plus driving trailer units; this order was

fulfilled in 1996, and took the total stock of 'Colibri's to 126 two-car units. SBB is refurbishing to 'Colibri' standards other cars used in push-pull sets. The project involves 80 RBe4/4 motor cars, 56 BDt driving control and 445 intermediate trailers, all around 30 years old. SBB is progressively adopting one-person operation of trains on its Regional services. Where such services do not employ 'Colibri' emus, this requires the rebuilding of passenger cars with power-operated sliding-plug doors under the driver's control.

Signalling and telecommunications

Siemens ZUB1100 ATP (Automatic Train Protection) system has been selected and is to be applied to all main SBB routes, which involves equipment of 700 traction units and some 3,500 signal locations. The latter plan will cover about 80 per cent of all block sections. The first section to be ATP-operational was Bern—Thun. ATP had been installed at over 1,000 locations by the end of 1995,

and it was anticipated that most traction units would be ATP-equipped by 1996.

Partly in the cause of labour saving, but also to facilitate more bidirectional signalling to enlarge operating capacity, SBB has made adoption of solid-state interlockings a priority. Replacement of mechanical signalboxes had decelerated from between 15 and 20 a year to between 5 and 10 since the 1970s, because of other demands on a finite investment budget. The remaining 57 mechanical installations, 80 years old on average, rule 18 per cent of the railway's interlockings. SBB wishes to see them all replaced by 2000.

Almost as needy of renewal is the third of SBB's interlockings that are electromechanically controlled, and thus difficult to adapt for remote control from new route-setting panels. SBB is also one of Europe's leading railways in use of Automatic Vehicle Identification, using trackside radio-wave readers and transponder tags, designed by Alcatel-Amtech to UIC standard. The first

installations at Erstfeld, on the Gotthard route, and at Italian and French border stations in 1993, were followed by implementation throughout Switzerland, giving much improved rolling stock control and better customer information.

In common with the Lucerne—Stans—Engelberg Railway (qv), with which it shares tracks between Hergiswil and Lucerne, the Brünig route has been equipped with a ZSL90 system of ATP specially developed for narrow-gauge railways.

Electrification

Virtually the whole SBB system is electrified at 16 ⅔ Hz. The exception is the 12.7 km cross-border freight-only single line from Etzwilen to Singen in Germany. Partially closed in 1996, this line may close entirely in 1997 to avoid work on a bridge over the Rhine.

UPDATED

SYRIA

Ministry of Transport

PO Box 134, Damascus
Tel: +963 11 336801   Fax: +963 11 332 3317

Key personnel
Minister: Murfid Abdul Karim

UPDATED

Chemins de Fer Syriens (CFS)

PO Box 182, Aleppo
Tel: +963 21 213900/213901   Fax: +963 21 228480/ 225697

Key personnel
President and Director-General:
  Ing Mohammed Ghassen El-Kaddour
Directors
  Rolling Stock and Traction: Ing Abdel-Moneim El-Boum
  Planning and Statistics: Ms Fariza Melayess
  Movement and Traffic: Ismail Bader-Khan
  Fixed Installations: M Ismail
  Personnel, Legal: Abdel-Hannan Al-Haj Ali
  Financial Affairs: M S Nasser Agha
  Marketing: A M Battikh
  Signalling and Telecommunications:
    Ing Fahed Dassouki
  Technical: Amal Dabbaneh
  International Relations: Berge Partadjian
  Public Relations: Ihsan El-Khalidy

Gauge: 1,435 mm
Route length: 1,525 km

Organisation

All standard-gauge lines in Syria are operated by CFS, and comprise the lines from the Lebanese border via Homs and Aleppo to the Turkish border and, in the northeast, the connecting line between the Turkish and Iraqi borders. A line runs from the oilfields of Kamechli in the north to the port of Latakia (750 km). The Homs—Palmyra line was opened to phosphates traffic (destined for the port of Tartus) in 1980.

The extension of the railway from Homs southwards to Damascus (194 km) was opened in 1983 and the 80 km Tartus—Latakia line in 1992.

Passenger operations

In 1994, CFS recorded 2.5 million journeys for 567 million passenger-km; in 1995 this went down to 1.8 million journeys, 492 million passenger-km.

Freight operations

In 1994 traffic amounted to 4 million tonnes, for 1,190 million tonne-km; in 1995 carryings went up to 4.3 million tonnes, 1,285 million tonne-km.

Freight traffic is strong in bulk freight commodities such as phosphates and petroleum.

New lines

In 1981 a Soviet loan was secured to build a line from Deir Ezzor to Abou-Kemal on the Iraqi frontier (150 km). This will link up with Iraq's new Baghdad—Husaiba line, and should be finished during the 1990s. A study has also been undertaken of a new 203 km line from Palmyra to Deir Ezzor.

A 1,435 mm gauge line of 101 km is being built from the outskirts of Damascus to Deraa, near the Jordanian

frontier, to supersede the Syrian section of the 1,050 mm gauge Hedjaz Railway. The new line, which will have a branch from Sheikh Miskin to Suweida, will be engineered for 160 km/h operation. Completion is forecast during the 1990s. A new central station is to be built in Damascus.

Traction and rolling stock

In 1995 the railway was operating 183 diesel locomotives, 10 diesel railcars, 483 passenger cars (including 19 restaurant and 45 sleeping cars), 33 baggage vans and 4,319 freight wagons.

In June 1997, CFS signed a FFr350 million contract with GEC Alsthom to purchase 30 diesel locomotives, with funding from a letter of credit from the French government.

Wagon Pars of Iran was building 500 tank wagons for CFS in 1997.

UPDATED

Chemin de Fer du Hedjaz

PO Box 134, Damascus
Tel: +963 21 15 815

Key personnel
Director-General: Ing Akil Ismail
Directors
  Operations and Marketing: Fouad Irabi
  Traction Rolling Stock: N El Mammami
  Infrastructure, Signalling and Communications:
    M El Sakbani

Finance: Dib Habbouche
Planning: M Adib Dalbik

Gauge: 1,050 mm
Route length: 232 km

Organisation

In addition to its own route length, the CF du Hedjaz also operates the 67 km narrow-gauge Damascus—Zerghaya line on behalf of the Syrian government. Traffic has been at a very low level for several years. A standard-gauge line is being built to supersede this line (see CFS entry).

Traction and rolling stock

The railway owns 10 steam and seven diesel locomotives, six railcars, 51 passenger cars and 471 freight wagons.

VERIFIED

TAIWAN

Ministry of Transportation & Communications

2 Chang-Sha Street, Taipei
Tel: +886 2 349 2900   Fax: +886 2 381 2260

Key personnel
Minister: Chao-Shiuan Liu
Deputy Ministers: Jaw-Yang Tsay, Chi-Kuo Mao
Railways Department Director: Der-Chyr Huang

VERIFIED

Provisional Engineering Office of High Speed Rail

Key personnel
Director, Deputy Director: Fu Hsiang-wu
Director, Rolling Stock: K L Chen

VERIFIED

Taiwan Railway Administration (TRA)

3 Peiping West Road, Taipei
Tel: +886 2 381 5226   Fax: +886 2 383 1367

Key personnel
Managing Director: T P Chen
Deputy Managing Director: H J Sy
Chief Secretary: J Zu
Chief Engineer: J S Wu
Directors
   Operations: C L Shu
   Civil Engineering: M Z Huang
   Mechanical Engineering: H H Huiao
   Electrical Engineering: C T Lin
   Purchase and Stores: Y I Chen
   Planning: Y N Sheu
   Freight: S B Yau
   Accounting: C N Chai
   Personnel: C S Chi
   Data Processing: L T Lai
   Anti-Corruption Office: J L Lin
   Administration: C N Ma

Gauge: 1,067 mm
Route length: 1,108 km
Electrification: 519 km at 25 kV 60 Hz AC

Passenger operations
In the passenger sector TRA pursues principally the development of quality long-distance services with air conditioned rolling stock. These are the most remunerative because, although there is government control of fares, the ceiling imposed on long-distance fares is well above that set for local and commuter travel.

The cross-city tunnel in Taipei, opened in 1990, has eliminated traffic congestion caused by level crossings on Chunghua Road. It has also established a transport centre in the Taipei station area as a foundation for the emerging mass transit system. The project involved a new line starting from west of Sungchiang Road to the east of Wanhua station. It threads a new subterranean Taipei Main station. This multilevel through station, replacing the former terminal, hosts a cross-city emu service between Kee-Lung and Hsinchu.

Freight operations
In the freight sector, bulk commodities account for 60 per cent of the tonnage, with cement, limestone, grain and coal topping the list. Through its Railway Freight Service (RFS), TRA offers a total service, from door-to-door rail-and-truck transits between a dozen main centres to warehousing, responsibility for customs clearance and insurance. RFS has headquarters in Taipei, branch offices in eight other cities and service offices at 69 locations of the rail network.

Intermodal operations
TRA has two container terminals of its own at Kee Lung, one at Chi-Tu and the other at Wu-Tu. In addition, the railway serves the United Container Terminal's installation

at Pu-Hsui. TRA is also one of the financial backers of the China Container Terminal Corp and its Wu-Tu Inland Terminal in the Kee-Lung suburbs. The railway has further port container terminals at Tai-Chung and Su-Ao, and a Taipei area terminal at Cheng-kung.

The Kee-Lung and Kao-Hsiung port terminals and the Taipei inland terminal are interconnected by eight dedicated container trains each way daily. TRA has some 600 four-axle flat wagons capable of carrying 40 ft ISO containers.

Tonnage increased in each of the four years to 1993, reaching a record 19.8 million tonnes in that year, but fell back slightly to 19.6 million in 1994 and 19.2 million in 1995.

Traffic (million)	1994	1995	1996
Freight tonnes	19.6	19.2	16.5
Freight tonne-km	1,947	1,845	1,540
Passenger journeys	160.3	160.0	159.4
Passenger-km	9,505	9,489	8,969

Finance
TRA benefits from state funding for its major projects financed by the country's massive accumulation of foreign exchange reserves, which in 1991, standing at over US$82.4 billion, were the biggest of any country in the world. But TRA itself is in deficit, largely because of a burden of excessive staff and pensioners, and of government control of its charges.

New lines
In 1991 revised plans were approved for a US$16 billion, 350 km high-speed line from Taipei to Kaohsiung. To be built to 1,435 mm gauge, the route will begin at a rolling stock depot in eastern Taipei. It will traverse the capital alongside the existing 1,067 mm gauge route, adopting space in the cross-city tunnel originally reserved for two suburban service tracks. Emerging from the tunnel to serve an interchange with the TRA 1,067 mm gauge and the Taipei metro at Panchaio, the line will then be routed via Taoyuan, Hsinchu, Taichung, Chiai-i and Tainan. The distance between Taipei and Kaohsiung main stations will be 345 km; a further 17.7 route-km will serve depots.

Electrification will be at 25 kV 60 Hz AC. The aim is to engineer for 350 km/h maximum speed throughout, though initially commercial operation would not exceed 300 km/h. Minimum curve radius is specified as 6,250 m and ruling gradient as 2.5 per cent. As much as 28 km must be in tunnel in urban territory and a further 17 km in the mountains; a tunnel cross-section as capacious as 100 m² is proposed (by comparison, that of German high-speed NBS is 82 m²). As much as 75 per cent of the remaining route is expected to be on bridges or viaducts.

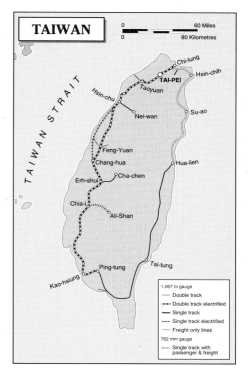

Prospective journey times are quoted as 85 minutes for Taipei–Kaohsiung non-stop services, predicating an average speed of 237 km/h; and 105 minutes for services making five intermediate stops. An inaugural fleet of 50 trainsets is likely, for which the choice of technology has yet to be made. Sofrerail of France is general design consultant.

A budget was approved in mid-1995 to cover the initial phases of land acquisition, planning and administration, and it was decided later that a minimum of 40 per cent of the projected cost would be sought from the private sector. Land acquisition started in late 1995 and in January 1997 two bids from private sector concerns were received. One consortium is led by China Development Corporation, Taiwan's largest merchant bank, and includes Bechtel as project manager and a large number of Japanese and Taiwanese firms.

A choice between the two consortia was due to be announced in November 1997. Contracts for civil works, electrical and mechanical, stations and operations would

Push-pull train for the West Coast Trunk Route. TRA is taking delivery of 32 of these trains from a Hyundai (South Korea)/GEC Alsthom (UK)/Union Carriage & Wagon (South Africa) consortium   **1996**

be awarded on a build-operate-transfer basis. The planned completion date is 2003.

The high-speed project forms part of a 30-year transport infrastructure plan. Projected investment includes the Kaohsiung metro, further development of the embryonic Taipei metro, and at a later stage metros for four other cities.

Improvements to existing lines

Following completion of double-tracking of the main line down the western side of the island of Taiwan, the government is funding double-tracking of the route on the eastern side, southward from Su-ao to Hua-lien; and also electrification of this line and its adjoining double-track line to the north, so as to have wiring throughout from Pa Tu, in the far north, to Hua-lien. South of Hua-lien, the North Link is to be upgraded with 50 kg/m rail to Tai-tung and the junction with the new South Coast Link. CTC is to be installed on this section. Target date for completion is 1998.

Continuation of the Taipei cross-city tunnel for 5.3 km from the main station eastward to Huashan and Sungshuan is proceeding. Over 2.7 km of the distance the rail alignment is integrated with a government expressway road project. The latter will be elevated above surface highways; and between the surface highway and the rail tunnel underground parking lots will be inserted. Plans have been laid for a western extension from Wanhua under the Tamshui river to an interchange at Panchaio with the metro and the prospective high-speed line.

Diesel locomotives

Class	Wheel arrangement	Power kW	Speed km/h	Weight tonnes	No in service	First built	Builders Mechanical	Builders Engine	Transmission
G12	A1A-A1A	1,060	100	78	50	1960	EMD	EMD	E EMD
G22U	Co-Co	1,230	100	78	39	1966	EMD	EMD	E EMD
G22CU	Co-Co	1,230	110	89	25	1970	EMD	EMD	E EMD
G22CU-2	Co-Co	1,230	110	90	8	1992	EMD	EMD	E EMD
GL8	A1A-A1A	705	100	65	12	1960	EMD	EMD	E EMD
GA8	Bo-Bo	665	75	54	11	1966	EMD	EMD	E EMD
GA18	Bo-Bo	820	75	54	4	1970	EMD	EMD	E EMD

Diesel railcars or multiple-units

Class	Cars per unit	Motor cars per unit	Motored axles/car	Power/motor hp	Speed km/h	Units in service	First built	Builders Mechanical	Builders Electrical
2100	1	1	1	220	95		1965	Cummins NHH-220	H Niigata DBS-100
2200									
2300									
2400									
2700	1	1	1	335	100		1966	Cummins NHHRTO-6-BI	H Niigata DBSI-100
2800	3	2	1	335	110		1983	Cummins NT855R4	H Niigata DBSF-100
2900	3	2	1	335	110		1986	Cummins NT85584	H Niigata DBSF-100
2800/2850	3				110	15	1982	Tokyu	
2900/2950	3				110	5	1986	Hitachi	
3000/3070	3				110	27	1990	Hitachi	

Electric locomotives

Class	Wheel arrangement	Output kW	Speed km/h	Weight tonnes	No in service	First built	Builders Mechanical	Builders Electrical
E100	Co-Co	2,100	110	72	18	1979	UCW	GEC
E200	Co-Co	3,130	110	96	39	1978	GE	GE
E300	Co-Co	3,130	100	96	39	1978	GE	GE
E400	Co-Co	3,130	130	92	18	1980	GE	GE
E1000	Bo-Bo	2,400	130	60	64	1996	UCW	GEC

Electric railcars

Class	Cars per unit	Motor cars per unit	Motored axles/car	Output/motor kW	Speed km/h	First built	Builders Mechanical	Builders Electrical
100	5	1	4	310	120	1979	BREL	GEC
200	3	2	4	116	120	1988	Socimi	Brush
300	3	3	4	125	120	1986	UCW	GEC
400	4	4	4	125	110	1991	UCW	GEC
500	4	3	4	250	110	1995 1996	Daewoo	Siemens

Traction and rolling stock

At the start of 1997 the fleet comprised 178 electric and 149 diesel locomotives, 141 diesel railcars and 81 trailer cars, 195 emu power cars and 75 trailers, 1,186 passenger coaches and 4,191 freight wagons.

In the mid-1990s, delivery was taken of 344 electric multiple-unit cars for Taipei suburban services being built by Daewoo Heavy Industries in South Korea. The cars have Siemens electrical equipment, comprising VVVF propulsion and control systems, and bogies by Adtranz.

In 1994, TRA placed an order with GEC Alsthom of the UK, Hyundai of Korea, and Union Carriage & Wagon of South Africa for 32 electric 130 km/h push-pull trainsets. The order comprises 64 power cars equipped with 2,200 kW asynchronous traction equipment and 336 trailer coaches. The first power cars were turned out in early 1996.

Signalling

Computer-aided CTC has been installed between Chunghua, Tainan and Pintong, and covers a total of 510 route-km. ABS is in service over 311 km.

Electrification

Under way is wiring of the East Trunk line from Pa Tu, near Chi-Lung in the north, as far as Hua-lien, a distance of 171 km. Altogether, wiring of 519 km was in progress at the end of 1996.

Type of coupler

Passenger cars: Tight lock automatic AAR-H
Freight cars: AAR E Type automatic
Type of braking: AAR Westinghouse air

Track

Rail: 37 and 50 kg/m; 100 lb/yd
Crossties (sleepers): In tangent track and curves over 600 m radius: 174 × 240 × 2,000 mm
In curves of 300 to 600 m radius: 201 × 240 × 2,000 mm
Spacing
In plain track: 1,760/km (wood), 1,640/km (concrete)
In curves: 1,800/km for radii less than 400 m
Rail fastenings: Pandrol clip
Min curvature radius: 5.82°
Max gradient: 2.5%
Max axleload: 18 tonnes

Finances (NT$ million)

Revenue	1994	1995	1996
Passenger	12,169	12,869	13,547
Freight	2,193	2,116	1,886
Parcels and mail	235	82	80
Other	3,927	5,433	4,471
Total	18,525	20,500	19,984

Expenditure			
Staff	15,339	16,774	17,378
Materials/services	5,026	5,154	5,687
Depreciation	2,647	3,185	2,791
Financial charges	4,632	3,018	3,290
Total	27,646	28,131	29,146

UPDATED

TAJIKISTAN

Ministry of Transport

Chepkin ul 35, 734012 Dushanbe

Key personnel
Minister: F Mukhiddinov

NEW ENTRY

Tajik Railways

Tajikskaya Zheleznaya Doroga (TZD)
Shapkina ul 35, 734012 Dushanbe

Key personnel
President: M Habibov
Deputy President: M Nuralyev
Chief Engineer: B Shodiyev

Traffic Manager: A Bulugin
Finance Director: M F Narzyev

Gauge: 1,520 mm
Route length: 423 km

Political background

The railway was founded as an independent organisation in October 1994.

In 1995 the railway carried 124 million passenger-km and 2,114 million tonne-km of freight. Traffic has declined precipitously since independence. The disturbed political situation has resulted in a mass exodus of Russians, and 90 per cent of railway specialist staff have been lost as a result. Further decline will occur if Uzbekistan completes its proposed Angren bypass of the Tajik Railways' northern section.

In 1996 an agreement was made with the Uzbekistan railway covering standardisation, cross-border workings of personnel, and access of Tajik students to Uzbek railway training institutions. Unfortunately this has not led to any noticeable improvement in cross-border operations.

Organisation

Formerly part of the USSR's Central Asian Railway, Tajik Railways consists of three lines, each isolated from the others by neighbouring states. In the south there are two branch lines from Termez in Uzbekistan, one to the Tajik capital Dushanbe and Yangi Bazar (93 km) and one to Kurgan Tyube and Vash (220 km). In the north, some 110 km of the east-west Andizhan—Samarkand line runs through Tajikistan. This portion is electrified eastwards as far as Khudjand (formerly Leninabad), but electrification work on the 59 km section towards Kanibadam has been suspended. A branch from Kanibadam stretches 53 km to Shurab.

Type 2TE10 double-unit locomotive at Dushanbe locomotive depot

1997

Passenger operations

In December 1995 Russian Railways refused to handle the Dushanbe—Moscow through service, citing poor quality rolling stock and mass ticketless travel. The through train was reintroduced on a thrice-weekly basis from October 1996, taking 87 hours for the journey.

Improvements to existing lines

Despite a shortage of track components, remedied partly by the lifting of redundant sidings, double-tracking of the northern line is taking place over busy sections, and the Kurgan Tyube branch is being extended to Kulyab.

Traction and rolling stock

Having initially only 29 locomotives, stationed at the country's only depot at Dushanbe, and finding itself with no track maintenance equipment upon independence, the railway has depended, to some extent, on equipment loaned by Uzbekistan's railway.

In 1997, the locomotive fleet comprised two double-unit locomotives of Type 2TE10, purchased in 1996; 24 double-unit locomotives of Type 2TE10V/L, of which 16 are serviceable; 10 shunting locomotives of Type TEM2 (all serviceable) and five shunting locomotives of Type ChM73 (of which only one is serviceable). The rolling stock fleet comprised 355 passenger coaches and 2,112 freight wagons.

UPDATED

TANZANIA

Ministry of Communications & Transport

PO Box 9423, Dar-es-Salaam
Tel: +255 51 37641 Fax: +255 51 36462

Key personnel

Minister: Philemon Sarungi
Deputy Minister: Gilvert Mululu
Principal Secretary: Dr George Mlingwa

UPDATED

Tanzanian Railways Corporation (TRC)

PO Box 468, Dar es Salaam
Tel: +255 51 46 054 Fax: +255 51 46 057

Key personnel

Chairman: J K Chande

Chief Commercial Manager: Ms Rukia D Shamte
Chief Mechanical Engineer: M Kabipe
Chief Civil Engineer: J Mabeyo (acting)
Chief of Manpower Development: N N Msoffe
Chief Supplies Manager: L R S Baseka
Chief of Finance: S A Riwa
Chief of Corporate Development and Management Services: J J Mungereza
Chief Signals and Communications Engineer: R Kisanga

Gauge: 1,000 mm
Length: 2,600 km

Political background

Following the formal break up of the East African Railways Corporation in 1977, Tanzania set up the independent Tanzanian Railways Corporation to operate the former EAR lines wholly within Tanzania.

By the end of the 1980s, TRC was rundown and in urgent need of investment capital. In a series of World Bank-inspired reforms, the railway's extensive lake-shipping operation was hived-off into a separate profit centre, staff numbers were reduced (down to 10,400 in 1995) and tariffs increased. Some rehabilitation of the system has been possible with funds made available from Canadian, European and Chinese sources.

Passenger operations

This business continues to perform badly, with the number of journeys halved from 2.5 million in 1992 to 1.3 million (694 million passenger-km) in 1995.

Diesel locomotives

Class	Wheel arrangement	Power kW	Speed km/h	Weight tonnes	First built	Mechanical	Builders Engine	Transmission
35	C	205	25	36.6	1973	Barclay	Paxman 8RPHL Mk 7	H Voith L320V
36	C	244	25	36.2	1979	Brush	Ruston-Paxman	E Brush
37	C	295	25	36.2	1985	Henschel	MTU Type 6Y 396	H Voith TC12
64	B-B	559	72	38.3	1979	Henschel	MTU Type EB	H Voith L520-UZ 12V 396 TCII
72	1Bo-Bo1	925	72	68.86	1972	GEC Traction	Ruston-Paxman 8CVST	E GEC
73	Co-Co	1,003	96	72	1975	Varanasi	YDMA4	E Varanasi
87	1Co-Co1	1,370	72	101.4	1966	Eng Elec	Ruston-Paxman 12CVST	E Eng Elec
88	1Co-Co1	1,490	72	110.9	1972	MLW	Alco 251C	E GE Canada

Freight operations

In 1995 freight traffic amounted to 1.3 million tonnes, for 1,354 million tonne-km. This was an increase of 20 per cent over levels of the late 1980s, achieved despite the threat posed by the new freedom of Tanzania's landlocked neighbours to resume use of South African ports.

A new prospect for increased traffic came with the 1993 agreement signed with the government of the neighbouring landlocked country of Burundi. TRC is providing dedicated trains for Burundi traffic between Dar es Salaam and its western terminus at Kigoma, where goods are transhipped to road vehicles for the cross-border journey to Burundi. New freight-handling depots at Dar and Kigoma provide rapid customs clearance facilities, and a special fleet of 80 wagons for the service has been donated by European Union sources (see below).

The Burundi service is seen as the prototype for similar operations serving other neighbouring countries, as TRC strives to regain the transit traffic lost at the start of the 1990s. A through service to and from Kenya via the Moshi—Taveta—Voi link was restored in 1996 after a 20-year interruption.

New lines

In 1991 Uganda and Tanzania reached agreement in principle for extension into Uganda of TRC's line from the port of Tanga to Arusha. The proposal is to project this line to Musoma on Lake Victoria and install a train ferry to connect Musoma with Uganda's capital, Kampala. A feasibility study, funded partly by Uganda, was carried out during 1994, but no further progress has been reported.

Traction and rolling stock

At the start of 1996 TRC owned 91 diesel locomotives, 97 passenger cars and 1,798 freight wagons.

In 1993 ABB Henschel delivered the last of nine diesel-electric DE2200 Co-Co locomotives at 1,565 kW power rating. 'Flexifloat' bogies give axle loadings under 14 tons to ease track wear.

ABB Transportation (now Adtranz) has carried out heavy overhaul on 11 Class 36 diesel shunters, and refurbished 79 passenger coaches at TRC's Dar es Salaam works. A batch of 27 coaches was supplied by India's ICF during 1996-97.

Signalling and telecommunications

Pursuant to an Italian government-financed study, WABCO Westinghouse was contracted to resignal the Dar es Salaam—Tabora section. The scheme is being executed in three phases: Dar es Salaam—Morogoro (201 km); Morogoro—Dodoma (456 km); and Dodoma—Tabora. The colourlight, interlocked signalling covers a distance of 850 km and involves entrance-exit electric interlocking at four major stations, panel interlockings in all other stations, and tokenless block working throughout.

Type of coupler in standard use: MCA-DA

Type of brake in standard use: Automatic air, Type EST4d

Track

Rail: 55, 60 and 80 lb/yd
Crossties (sleepers): Steel plain track, wood turn-outs
Fastenings: Fish bolts and nuts, fishplates, screw spikes, coach screws, Pandrol
Spacing:
  55 lb/yd: 1,430/km plain, 1,540/km curved track
  60 lb/yd: 1,405/km plain, 1,485/km curved track
  80 lb/yd: 1,402/km plain, 1,482/km curved track
Min curve radius: 8°
Max gradient: 2.2%
Max axleload: 14.7 tonne

UPDATED

Tanzania-Zambia Railway Authority (TAZARA)

PO Box 2834, Dar es Salaam
Tel: +255 51 860340/7 64191/9
Fax: +255 51 865187/865192

Key personnel

Chairman: S Musoma
Co-Chairman: Ronald Makuma
Directors
    Finance: Method A Kashonda
    Corporate Planning: Michael J Ngonyani
    Traffic: J Y Minsula
    Technical Services: L M Nsofwa
Regional Manager, Zambia: Morrison S Banda
Regional Manager, Tanzania: Hamis M Teggisa

Gauge: 1,067 mm
Route length: 1,860 km (891 km in Zambia, 969 km in Tanzania)

Political background

The Tanzania-Zambia Railway (TAZARA) was constructed following an agreement signed in 1967 between the governments of Tanzania and Zambia, and of the People's Republic of China. Under the agreement, China provided finance and technical services for construction of a railway from Dar es Salaam in Tanzania to Kapiri Mposhi in Zambia, together with equipment, two workshops and other auxiliary facilities. Operation began in 1975.

The loan repayment was to commence in 1983 and to be spread over 30 years, with each country responsible for 50 per cent. Due to their economic problems, however, both countries agreed in 1983 to reschedule the repayment terms; the start of repayment of the main loan was put back 10 years.

The Council of Ministers, consisting of three Ministers each from Zambia and Tanzania, is the body established by the two governments to exercise overall control on the railway. All the railway assets are vested in TAZARA, a corporate body whose principal organ is the Board of Directors consisting of five members each appointed by the two governments. For operational purposes, the railway is divided into two regions for Tanzania and Zambia, with headquarters at Dar es Salaam and Mpika.

TAZARA's gauge permits through traffic with contiguous railways in Central Africa, in particular Zambia Railways. Its performance, however, has been handicapped by serious problems of traction, rolling stock and track maintenance, of inadequate funds, and the international political strains of the continent. Whereas the railway's designed capacity was 5 million tonnes of freight a year, it has yet to register more than 1.5 million tonnes.

In the 1980s, TAZARA benefited from export/import traffic from Botswana, Malawi, Zaire, Zambia and Zimbabwe seeking to use Dar es Salaam instead of South African ports, but in the 1990s political change in South Africa enabled the landlocked states to resume use of ports in that country. By 1997, TAZARA was in deep trouble, with carryings down to 600,000 tonnes per year. An estimated US$7 million was owed by customers and there were few prospects of being able to collect the money.

In an effort to reverse the decline, the railway adopted a commercialisation policy with an aggressive approach to marketing. Armed police ride with freight trains to deter pilferers. Transit times have been cut, with the fastest freight trains taking four days (as opposed to ten in the past) to traverse the line. A gantry crane has been installed at Kapiri Mposhi.

Staff recruitment has been frozen, and it was planned that two-thirds of the 6,000 staff would be laid off once restructuring was complete.

Passenger operations

A long-established passenger service runs the length of the TAZARA line, from Dar es Salaam to Kapiri Mposhi, twice a week. In 1997, a twice-weekly express service, named 'Mukaba' eastbound and 'Kilimanjaro' westbound, was introduced.

There are also three-a-week services running on the Tanzanian and Zambian sections respectively.

Freight operations

Zambian exports, principally copper, have been the mainstay of TAZARA freight tonnage, but much of this is now routed through South Africa.

Improvements to existing lines

In a project funded by the Austrian Government, long-welding of rail is being installed between Dar es Salaam and Makambako (657 km); this project was ongoing in 1997. Completion throughout the route will remove a source of frequent delays due to misaligned or broken rail joints.

Traction and rolling stock

At the start of 1993 TAZARA operated 100 diesel locomotives (many of GE design), 97 passenger coaches (including nine restaurant cars) and 2,230 freight wagons.

In 1996, six CKD8B 2,200 kW diesel locomotives were ordered from Chinese manufacturers.

Type of coupler in standard use: Top action
Type of braking in standard use:
Passenger: Air
Freight cars: Air, vacuum

Track

Rail: 45 kg/m, 12.5 m length
Crossties (sleepers): Prestressed concrete 195 × 208 × 272 mm
Spacing: 1,520/km
Fastening: Electric (spring clip and bolt)
Min curvature: 200 m
Max gradient: 1 in 50
Max altitude: 1,789.43 m, Uyole near Mbeya
Max axleload: 20 tonne

Diesel locomotives

Class	Wheel arrangement	Power kW	Speed km/h	Weight tonnes	No in service	First built	Mechanical	Builders Engine	Transmission
1A (DFH1)	Bo-Bo	1,000	50	60	14	1971	Chintao	12V 189ZL*	SF 2010
1B (DFH-2)	Bo-Bo	2,000	100	80	57	1971	Chintao	12V 180ZL (28 locos)*/ MTU 12V 396TC12 (29 locos)	SE 2010 SE2010
DE (U30C)	Co-Co	3,200	100	120	29	1983	Krupp	GE 17 FDL 12HT	E GE
CKD8B	—	2,200	—	—	6	1997	Loric	—	—

* Class is being re-engined with MTU units

UPDATED

THAILAND

Ministry of Transport & Communications

5 Rajdammern Avenue, Bangkok 10100
Tel: +66 2 281 3422   Fax: +66 2 280 1714

Key personnel

Minister: Wan Muhammadnor Matha
Permanent Secretary: Mahidol Chantrangkurn

VERIFIED

State Railway of Thailand (SRT)

Rong Muang Road, Pathumwan, Bangkok 10330
Tel: +66 2 223 0341   Fax: +66 2 225 3801

Key personnel

Chairman: P Pakkasem
General Manager: S Shavavai
Deputy General Managers
    Operations: Saravudh Dhamasiri
    Development and Planning: Sriyoudh Sirivedhin
    Administration: Lt Sutep Yuktasevi
Assistant General Managers: Vichit Chansrakao, Taweesak Maneeepisith, Thasanai Chantarangkul
Traffic Manager: Jaroon Mahawat
Directors
    Finance and Accounting: Chan Waramuninthorn
    Signalling and Telecommunications:
        Thavorn Ratanavaraha
    Information Systems: Dr Chitsanti Dhanasobhon
Chief Mechanical Engineer: Paichit Tengtrairat
Chief Civil Engineer: Sanong Jotikasthira

Gauge: 1,000 mm
Route length: 3,865 km

Political background

Increasing the role of the private sector in joint developments with state enterprises is a longstanding goal. For the railway in particular, the objective has been to reduce government subsidy and attract private funding for modernisation and expansion. Some progress has been made. In 1990 the local subsidiary of Hopewell Holdings of Hong Kong signed a contract with the government and SRT to build and operate a 60 km elevated road and rail system in Bangkok (for full details see Jane's Urban Transport Systems 1997-98). A year later, the longstanding aim of exploiting the tourism potential of luxury trains was realised. Malaya Siam Royal Mail obtained a contract to run for the VSOE company the Thai portion of a luxury land-cruise train plying between Bangkok, Kuala Lumpur and Singapore.

Private sector participation is also being sought in the freight sector, where intermodal transport is seen as presenting a big opportunity for SRT. Accordingly, partners are being sought for establishment of a national road/rail container service to operate from the inland container depots now under development.

Further moves will focus on contracting-out of activities to reduce costs and improve efficiency; promotion of private participation in rolling stock procurement, operation and manufacturing; provision of privately owned freight-handling equipment; and joint ventures in land development. Leasing of locomotives and rolling stock is also to be adopted.

Finance

SRT recorded a loss of Bt577 million in 1994. Basic passenger and freight tariffs remain government-controlled and as a result SRT has difficulty in adjusting rates in step with increased costs. Another handicap is that the level of government subsidy has reduced, to about 15 per cent of SRT's total income, and does not cover the total costs of services which it must provide on social grounds.

Passenger operations

In 1994 SRT carried 87.3 million passengers, just 0.6 per cent down on the previous year. Passenger-km at 14,496 million showed a drop of 1.5 per cent, the decline being attributable mainly to a reduction in third-class travel.

With most freight traffic diverted away from the Bangkok area (see below), SRT plans a big expansion of suburban services. Centrepiece of the proposals is redevelopment of the Phaholyothin marshalling yard just north of the city centre, which would become a vast interchange between long-distance and suburban trains, the future services of the Hopewell and BMTA metro projects and buses. SRT will seek private sector partners to take the scheme forward.

Completion of double-tracking of the South and Eastern lines will facilitate introduction of regular-interval suburban services, allowing SRT to play a significant role in Bangkok's public transport for the first time. The Eastern line in particular is seen as providing an opportunity to demonstrate rail's capability as a tool of

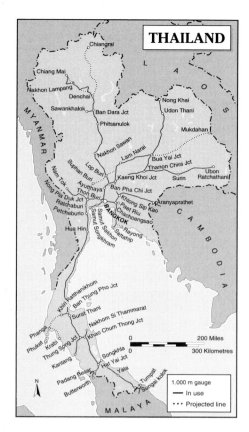

THAILAND

1.000 m gauge
— In use
··· Projected line

Diesel locomotives

Class	Wheel arrangement	Power kW	Speed km/h	Weight tonnes	No in service	First built	Mechanical	Builders Engine	Transmission
Davenport	Bo-Bo	375	82	48.12	24	1952	Davenport	Caterpillar LAD 397	E Westinghouse
Davenport	Co-Co	745	92	80	10	1955	Davenport	Caterpillar LAD 397	E Westinghouse
Hitachi	Co-Co	775	70	72	10	1961	Hitachi	MAN W 8V 22/ 30 m AUL	E Hitachi
HID	Co-Co	2,135	100	90	22	1993	Hitachi		E Hitachi
GE	Co-Co	985	103	75	50	1964	GE	Cummins VT 12-825 B1, VTA-1710-L GM 16V92 TA KT 38-L	E GE
Alsthom	Co-Co	1,790	95	82.5	52	1975	Alsthom	SEMT 16PA 4V.185 VG	E Alsthom
AHK	Co-Co	1,790	100	82.5	30	1980	Alsthom/ Krupp/ Henschel	SEMT 16PA4 185VG	E Alsthom
ALD	Co-Co	1,790	100	82.5	9	1983	Alsthom	SEMT 16PA4 185VG	E Alsthom
ADD	Co-Co	1,790	100	82.5	20	1985	Alsthom	SEMT 16PA4 185VG	E Alsthom
Krauss-Maffei	C	325	54	36	5	1955	Krauss-Maffei	MAN W 8V 17.5	H Voith 22A
Hunslet	C	180	19.5	30	4	1965	Hunslet	Gardner 8L 3B	H Voith
Henschel	B-B	895	90	52	26	1964	Henschel	MTU 12V4 93 TY 11 and MTU 12V3 96TC12	H Voith
Krupp	B-B	1,120	90	55	28	1969	Krupp	MTU 12V6 52 TB 11	H Voith
HAS	C	535	58	41.25	10	1986	Henschel	MTU 6V3 96 TC12	H Voith

Diesel railcars or multiple-units

Class*	Cars per unit	Motor cars per unit	Motored axles/car	Power/motor kW	Speed km/h	No in service	First built	Mechanical	Builders Engine	Transmission
BPD/BTD	2	1	1	235	85	4	1962	Niigata	Cummins NHHRS-6-B	H Nico
BPD/BTD	2	1	2	165 × 2	85		1967	Hitachi	Cummins NHH-220-B-1	H Nico
BPD/BTD	2	1	2	165 × 2	90	72	1971	Hitachi	Cummins NHH-220-B-1	H Nico
BPD/BIN	3	2	1	165	70	12	1971	Tokyu	Cummins NHH-220-B-1	H Nico
BPD	2	2	1	175	100	40	1983	Tokyu Hitachi Nippon	Cummins N855R2	H Nico
ASR	2	2	1	210	120	20	1991	BREL, UK	Cummins NTA 855 RL	H Voith
APD	2	2	1	175	100	63	1985	Nippon/ Kinki/ Kawasaki/ Hitachi/ Fuji/ Niigata	Cummins N855R2	H Nico
APN	Intermediate motor car		1	175	100	12	1985	Tokyu	Cummins N855R2	H Nico

* BPD = Bogie Power car for Diesel railcar with driving cab
BIN = Bogie trailer diesel railcar non-driving cab
APD = Air conditioned Power Diesel railcar with driving cab

BTD = Bogie Trailer for Diesel railcar with driving cab
ASR = Air conditioned Sprinter Railcar

urban development. Apart from Phaholyothin, several smaller freight yards around the city will become available for development once the new yard proposed at Mae Nam is commissioned.

Freight operations

On the freight side, in 1994 SRT transported 7.6 million tonnes for 3,072 million tonne-km, representing increases of 1.3 and 0.4 per cent respectively over the previous year. This was on account of improved carryings of commodities such as LPG, cement, sugar and timber.

New lines

Opening in late 1996 of the Khlong Sip Kao–Kaeng Khoi line, an 82 km link between existing Eastern and Northeastern lines, completed SRT's long-term plan to remove most freight traffic from the congested route through the centre of Bangkok. The new line provides direct access to the Sattahip port branch from the north.

In 1991 construction began of a 1.2 km 'Friendship' bridge over the Mekong river. Built with Australian finance, it was completed in 1994. It was conceived as a road crossing from Thailand to Laos (qv), but subsequently construction of a railway was undertaken. This forms part of a 20 km connection between SRT's Bangkok–Nong Khai line and Vientiane, the Laotian capital, which was due to be opened in 1997.

Engineering design for two other lines was in progress in 1996, both of them originally planned more than a decade ago. In the south, the branch that currently strikes westwards from Surat Thani would be extended some 160 km across difficult country to the burgeoning resort of Phuket. Even less hospitable terrain would be crossed by the proposed route of a 210 km link running northwards from Denchai on the Northern line to Chiangrai, some 350 km distant near the Myanmar border. As well as engineering considerations, consultants Acer Freeman Fox were to assess the likelihood of attracting private sector interest in the schemes.

Rebuilding of the so-called 'Death Railway' link with Myanmar was being discussed by the governments of the two countries in 1996.

Improvements to existing lines

The Bangkok Elevated Road and Train System, being built by a German/British consortium for Hopewell (Thailand) Ltd, will see SRT tracks mounted on an elevated structure along with a new metro and road, with property development underneath. The SRT upgrading and metro are due to be finished by the time of the Asian Games in December 1999; the new track will be laid by Balfour Beatty of the UK.

Double-tracking is under way on 234 km of route around Bangkok

Double-tracking on several routes is being carried out: for 43 km to Lop Buri on the line from Ban Pa Chi junction, some 90 km north of Bangkok (to be completed at the end of 1999); for 44 km on the Nong Khai line from Ban Pa Chi junction to Map Kabao (ready end 1999); for 46 km from Chachoengsao, junction of the Sattahip line, to Hua Mak (ready end 1999); and for 41 km from Bang Sue to Nakhon Pathom (ready end 1999). A third track is being installed over the 61 km between Klong Rangsit and Ban Pa Chi (ready mid-1999).

Plans see a further 317 km being doubled at a cost of Baht16.7 billion. This is largely accounted for by the 289 km line between Lop Buri and Chumsaeng, on which doubling work was to start in 1997. Track renewal and strengthening of infrastructure for 16 tonne axleloads will absorb a further Baht5.6 billion. Some 843 track-km will be relaid with 60 kg/m rail and more than 700 track-km resleepered in concrete, while several weak bridges will be replaced. Operation at 87 stations will be improved by installation of new layouts.

Traction and rolling stock

In 1994 SRT was operating seven steam, 190 diesel-electric and 54 diesel-hydraulic locomotives, 50 shunters, 222 diesel railcars, 1,164 passenger cars (including 107 sleeping, 18 restaurant, and 103 baggage cars) and 8,854 freight wagons.

In the investment programme period which ended in 1996, 99 wagons were being delivered by Ssangyong, South Korea, while 38 diesel-electrics were on order from GE, USA. Mid-1995 also saw delivery of 21 coaches bought second-hand from Queensland Rail, made redundant following electrification of Brisbane suburban lines.

An order was placed with Daewoo, South Korea, in 1995 for supply of 40 diesel railcars equipped with Voith turbo transmissions, of which 20 were delivered in 1995. The balance, plus a further 40 ordered later, were delivered in 1996. Daewoo also supplied 40 day and sleeper coaches to SRT in 1996.

Type of coupler in standard use:
Passenger cars: Type E, AAR-10A automatic, controlled-slack type
Freight wagons: Type E, AAR-10E automatic
Type of braking in standard use:
Locomotive-hauled stock: vacuum, air and dual-system; air will be standard in future

Signalling and telecommunications

A colourlight signalling project covering some 800 route-km and 109 stations was completed in 1994 along with two other small colourlight resignalling schemes. In total, 1,297 km of single-track route is now controlled by tokenless block.

Centralised Traffic Control (CTC) has been installed on the main line to Nong Khai between Bangkok and Ban Phaei. All the double and triple tracking schemes outlined above are being equipped with CTC and automatic block.

SRT is pursuing a level crossing elimination programme, with all crossings due to have gone by 2002.

Track
Rail

Type	Weight (kg/m)
BS 50 R	24.8
BS 60 R & 60 ASCE	29.77
BS 70 R	34.76
BS 70 A & 70 ASCE	34.84
BS 80 A	39.8
Others	37, 37.5, 42.5

In 1995-96, Daewoo of South Korea delivered 40 new railcars with Voith transmissions to SRT **1996**

Hitachi-built 90 tonne Co-Co locomotive powered by two Cummins KTTA50L engines **1997**

Min curvature radius: 180 m (turnouts 156 m)   **Max altitude:** 574.9 m
Max gradient: 2.6%   **Max axleload:** 15 tonnes

Sleepers

Type	Untreated hardwood	Creosote-treated softwood	2-block concrete (RS-type)	Monobloc pre-stressed concrete
Dimensions	150 × 200 × 1,900-2,000 mm	150 × 200 × 1,900 mm	1,710 mm long, block 209 × 274 × 600 mm	200 × 260 × 2,000 mm
Spacing	1,430-1,540/km	1,430-1,540/km	1,540/km	1,666/km
Fastenings	Dogspike, Dorken spike or Woodings clip	Dogspike, Dorken spike or Woodings clip	RN clip	Hambo elastic

UPDATED

TOGO

Ministry of Commerce and Transport

Lomé

Key personnel
Minister: Dedevi Michele Ekue

VERIFIED

Réseau des Chemins de Fer du Togo (RCFT)

PO Box 340, Lomé
Tel: +228 21 4301

Key personnel
President: David de Fanti
General Manager: Yawo Kalepe
Superintendents
    Administration and Finance: V K Dogbe-Tomi

Rolling Stock and Motive Power: K Alfa
Traffic: Polo Noelaki
Infrastructure: Y Akakpo

Gauge: 1,000 mm
Route length: 525 km

Organisation
Two main routes extend from the port of Lomé, the main line running 276 km to Blitta, and the so-called Ligne Frontalière 119 km to Kpalimé. The Coastal line, which

ran 47 km east to Aného, was closed in 1987. There are some branches, mainly serving the Lomé port area, plus a 58 km line linking Togblékové and Tabligbo, opened in 1979 for export clinker traffic and closed in 1984 when production ceased. Branches in the phosphates mining area north of Kpémé are operated by the Cie Togolaise des Mines du Bénin (CTMB).

Passenger and freight operations
Poor maintenance, due to lack of investment, led to a steady decline in traffic and as a result it was decided to let out railway operations in Togo to a private sector company under a management contract. This resulted in an upturn in traffic with 19 million tonne-km and 9 million passenger-km carried in 1994.

There is a twice-weekly passenger service between Lomé and Blitta. Freight trains run to Blitta, and the CTMB lines remain in service for phosphates traffic.

Traction and rolling stock
RCFT's stock consists of one Soulé and one De Dietrich railcar, and three GM and five Alsthom diesels; availability of the motive power is below 50 per cent. Out of service are a fleet of Henschel BB diesels and some ancient Renault railcars. There are 12 coaches, several of which are railcar trailers, plus some others locally built by Sotometo in 1990. Of some 240 wagons, 80 were designed for clinker traffic and many are dedicated to phosphates haulage.

Signalling and telecommunications
Telecommunication is mainly by telephone, though not all stations are equipped; this is supplemented by radio on the Blitta line.

Track
Rails: Weight unknown
Sleepers: Mostly steel, on older line sections also wooden, rails are fixed with plates and screws
Ballast: Crushed stone on all lines built after 1960 and on some parts of older lines
Medium speed: 35 km/h for railcars, lower for locomotive hauled trains

UPDATED

TUNISIA

Ministry of Transport

Tunis

Key personnel
Minister: M Zenaidi

NEW ENTRY

Tunisian National Railways (SNCFT)

Société Nationale des Chemins de Fer Tunisiens
PO Box 693, 67 Avenue Farhat Hached, Tunis
Tel: +216 1 249999   Fax: +216 1 344045/348540

Key personnel
President/Director-General: Ali Cheikh Khalfallah
Directors
  International Affairs: Mohamed Chabbi
  Administration and Finance: Raouf Toumi
  Rolling Stock: H Grira
  Operating: N Fitouri
  Audit and Control: Faouzia Ghardallou
  Fixed Installations: S Khanfir
  Legal: Khaled Jedidi
  Passengers: Fayçal Klibi
  Freight: Jalel Ben Dana
  Marketing: Mahmoud Amara
  Infrastructure: Mokhtar Fennira
  Track: Abdelhamid Jemmali
  Signalling and Telecommunication:
    Abdessalem Ben Dhiab
  Stores: Hachemi Chabchoub

Gauge: 1,435 mm; 1,000 mm; mixed 1,435/1,000 mm
Route length: 468 km; 1,684 km; 10 km
Electrification: 110 km of 1,000 mm gauge at 25 kV 50 Hz AC

Political background
In 1979 the government agreed to cover the cost of new

Railcar at Nabeul (Marcel Vleugels)   *1997*

infrastructure and to service the debts of loans for infrastructure payments.

Traffic (million)	1993	1994	1995
Freight tonnes	10.8	11.8	12.2
Freight tonne-km	2,012	2,224	2,302
Passenger journeys	28.1	28.3	27.7
Passenger-km	1,057	1,038	996

New lines
Several new lines are on the agenda. It is planned to rebuild the former Cap Bon line from Fondouk Djedid to

Henchir Lebna and extend it to Kelibia. Other schemes include two new north-south lines, one from Borj Mcherga to Kairouan and connections with the prospective Sousse—Kasserine route; and another further west from Gafour to Sidi Bouzid, whence there would be a fork southwest to Gafsa and southeast to Mazouna. Also projected is a new route around the coast from Monastir to Sfax via Mahdia.

Improvements to existing lines
Under a plan covering the 1992-2010 period, SNCFT aims to double-track throughout the key metre-gauge main line from Tunis southward to Sousse, Sfax and Gabès; in early 1997, SNCFT called tenders for provision of technical assistance for bridge strengthening and repair work on this route. Extension beyond Gabès to Medenine has begun, with ultimate projection to Tripoli in view.

Reopening is scheduled of: the line from Mateur to Tabarka, closed since 1984; the Mateur—Jedeida connection; the Mastouta—Merja link further south; and of line southwest from Sousse to revive a through route from the coast to Kasserine.

Traction and rolling stock
In 1996 SNCFT operated 173 diesel locomotives, 38 diesel railcars, six emus, 291 passenger cars and 5,097 freight wagons.

All railcars, locomotives and passenger cars are capable of bogie change and of operation on either gauge. Most of the passenger service has hitherto been provided by diesel railcars, but except for sets delivered by Alsthom in 1975 those used in secondary services are now elderly and inadequate to meet today's requirements.

Signalling and telecommunications
Automatic block installation, operative throughout the Tunis—Sousse—Sfax—Gabès single line, with relay interlockings at crossing stations, is being extended to the

Tunis suburban service (Marcel Vleugels)   *1997*

sections from Tunis to Djedeēda and Beja, Bir Kassa to Gafour, Sfax to Gabès and Gabès to Gafsa. The section from Sfax to Gafsa and Métlaoui has been experimentally equipped with track-to-train radio. All telephone lines are being progressively placed in ground-level ducts.

Electrification

It was announced in 1992 that electrification from Tunis to Bordj Cedria would be the centrepiece of a four-year development programme agreed with the Austria Rail Engineering Consortium, which was negotiating a credit from the Austrian government to cover the prospective Sch3,000 million cost of the plan. Other items included conversion of some 1,000 mm gauge lines to 1,435 mm, modernised communications, resignalling between Tunis and Bechar, and the necessary electric rolling stock.

In 1990 SNCFT invited bids for a feasibility study of electrifying its Tunis—Tebourba line as well as that to Bordj Cedria. Little progress has been reported on these projects.

Track

Standard rail

Standard-gauge: Flat bottom, 36-46 kg/m in lengths of 12-18 m

Metre-gauge: Flat bottom, 25-36 kg/m in lengths of 7, 8, 12 m

Welded joints: Thermit welding of rail joints

Diesel locomotives

Class	Wheel arrangement	Power kW	Speed km/h	Weight tonnes	No in service	First built	Builders
060GR12	Co-Co	1,047	100	92	5	1964	E GM
040 DF	Bo-Bo	698	90	59	9	1965	E GM
040 DG	Bo-Bo	698	80	48	6	1967	E Traction
060 DH	Co-Co	1,640	100	93	5	1973	E GM
060 DI	Co-Co	1,604	114	90	22	1973	E MLW
040 DK	Bo-Bo	895	116	64	20	1978	E MLW
040 DL	B-B	1,323	110	62	10	1981	H Ganz Mávag
060 DN	Co-Co	1,862	114	89	19	1983	H GE
060 DP	Co-Co	1,764	130	91	20	1984	H Bombardier
040 DO	B-B	1,764	130	64	20	1985	H Ganz Mávag
040 DD	Bo-Bo	294	70	39	8	1958	E Alsthom
040 GE	Bo-Bo	446	96	49	4	1962	E GE
040 GE	Bo-Bo	515	96	49	4	1965	E GE
060 DS	Bo-Bo	466	103	64	9	1977	E GE
040 DM	Bo-Bo	522	114	64	28	1983	E GE

Crossties (sleepers): Oak impregnated with creosote; metal; concrete RS type

Standard-gauge: 120 × 220 × 2,600 mm

Metre-gauge: 120 × 220 × 2,200 mm

Spacing: 1,500/km

Rail fastenings: Wood sleepers: spikes

Metal sleepers: clips and bolts

Concrete sleepers: special resilient fittings

Filling: Broken stone

Max curvature

Standard-gauge: 7° = min radius 250 m

Metre-gauge: 11.6° = min radius 150 m

Max gradient: 1 in 50

Max altitude: 952 m on Haidra to Kasserine line

Max speed, standard-gauge

Railcars: 100 km/h

Diesel trains: 70 km/h

Max axleload

Standard-gauge: 21 tonnes

Metre-gauge: 18 tonnes

UPDATED

TURKEY

Ministry of Communications

Ulâstirma Bakanliği, Ankara

Tel: +90 312 212 6730   Fax: +90 312 212 4900

Key personnel

Minister: A S Erek

Under-Secretary: O Tezmen

Director-General, Land Transport: M Mendilcioglu

UPDATED

Turkish State Railways (TCDD)

Türkiye Cumhuriyeti Devlet Demiryollari

Genel Müdürlügü Talatpasa Bulvan, Ankara

Tel: +90 312 309 0515   Fax: +90 312 312 3215

Key personnel

Chairman and Director-General: Tekin Çinar

Deputy Directors-General: Ms Nurhan Öç, Aydiner Sankaya, Ahmet Kabakçi, Cahit Söyler, Murat Bostan

Directors

Board of Inspection: Rasih Civelekoğlu

Secretariat of Security: Kemal Çiftçi

Permanent Way: Cevat Oktay

Traction: Haluk Akova

Commercial: Lütfi Özbek

Financial: Nevzat Türken

Operations: Süleyman Yavuz

Personnel: I Hakki Erol

Construction: Nurullah Tataragasiğil

Research and Planning: Feridun Akyüz

Training: Sebahi Balli

Marketing: Ünkur Gürses

Ankara Workshops: Fuat Açikgöz

Purchasing: Baki Mercan

Real Estate: Sabiha Öncü

Data Processing: Ms Ümran Özbozduman

Dining, Sleeping Cars and Tourism: Bedri Palamut

Marketing: Tankut Ergun

Signalling and Telecommunications: Mehmet Uras

Public Relations Manager: Turgay Doludeniz

International Relations Manager: Ms Fatma Kurdoglu

Affiliated Companies

Tülomsas (Eskişehir Locomotive and Motor Industry Establishment): Özkan Sain

Tüvasas (Adapazar Wagon Industry Establishment): Halil Özkan

Tüdemsaş (Sivas Railway Machine Industry Establishment): Hakki Çoşar

Gauge: 1,435 mm

Route length: 10,386 km

Electrification: 1,088 km at 25 kV 50 Hz AC

Finance

TCDD still has to balance its books with the aid of a considerable state subsidy. This covers track maintenance and the losses of uneconomic lines and services. It does not currently meet in full the shortfall between TCDD's revenue and expenditure.

Financially, TCDD has benefited from the rapid growth

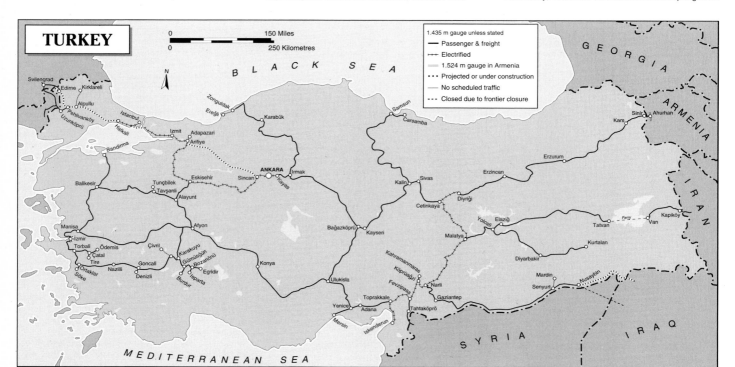

of traffic through the seven ports it manages: these now provide about a third of the corporation's revenues (about the same proportion as rail traffic, while government subsidy and non-operating revenues such as those from real estate make up the rest). Sale of the ports is likely to figure in the government's privatisation plans, which have already seen TCDD divest itself of a number of peripheral activities.

Mainspring of the railways' turnround has been an attack on the inefficiencies which previously prevented TCDD from grasping all commercial opportunities. The unacceptably high ratio of unserviceable locomotives, for instance, has been much reduced. TCDD has also invested substantial sums to modernise and rationalise the activity of its vehicle workshops. Manufacture of new high-capacity bogie freight wagons is being concentrated on the Tüdemsaş plant at Sivas. A drive has also been mounted to improve wagon productivity, in part by imposing demurrage charges on customers who are lethargic in unloading their cargoes. This has secured an improvement of about 10 per cent in turnround times.

TCDD's fundamental handicap persists, however, in that it cannot add competitive transit speeds to the considerable price advantage it offers over road transport, and to its availability when road movement is hobbled by winter conditions. Far too much of the rail system is still single-track and beset by sharp curves and severe gradients.

Passenger operations

Passenger business divides roughly half and half (in terms of passenger-km) between suburban and main line. Sirkeci has the most commuter traffic (944 million passenger-km in 1995), followed by Haydarpaşa (711 million), Ankara (380 million), Basmane (47 million) and Alsancak (15 million).

A feature in the long-haul sector is the development of good quality, first-class-only services. Recent additions to the long-haul rolling stock include business cars with telephone, telex and data modem equipment, new day cars and sleeping cars with individual shower/WC facilities for each compartment.

In 1991 a private company, Nesa of Istanbul, began operating its own premium-fare luxury car on Ankara–Istanbul trains; the company linked this rail operation with hire car facilities from each terminal. TCDD's service on the route was relaunched in 1994 following completion of electrification throughout. Now the 'Baskent Express' covers the 567 km from Ankara to Haydarpaşa (over the straits from Istanbul) in under five hours, with air conditioned cars providing a high standard of comfort.

For short-haul service TCDD has begun local manufacture of diesel railcars, while new Fiat dmus have been introduced on suburban lines round Izmir pending electrification. It also operates 20 two-car railbus sets bought second-hand from Germany.

Freight operations

The most important commodity is iron ore, at over four million tonnes, while coal (over two million tonnes) and construction materials (1.7 million tonnes) are also significant. International traffic is around one million tonnes annually.

In 1997, Turkish company Kale Group paid TCDD 2 billion lira for the right to operate freight trains between Bandirma and Sigirci for a year, cutting its transport costs by 40 per cent.

New lines

Ambitions for a high-speed passenger link between Ankara and Istanbul remain strong, despite financial and political problems. A 300km/h new line on the route has been proposed, but it is likely that this will prove too expensive for construction in the near future. As an interim step, TCDD had discussed with Fiat the purchase of 15 self-powered trainsets of Italian Railways' ETR450 type with the Fiat automatic tilt-body system. Acquisition would be facilitated by a credit from the Islamic Development Bank.

Government support has been forthcoming for the planned Bosphorus rail tunnel. A feasibility study for an 8 km double-track tunnel under the Bosphorus between Yenikapi, in Istanbul, and Haydarpaşa was made by Botek and the US consultancies, De Leuw, Cather and Sverdrup & Parcel. Responsibility for this project now lies with the Istanbul municipality, which has invited bids for a build-operate-transfer package. Besides main line traffic the tunnel would carry a suburban service connecting with the first line of the Istanbul metro, between Topkapi and

GM-designed diesel locomotive

1997

Diesel locomotives

Class	Wheel arrangement	Power kW	Speed km/h	Weight tonnes	No in service	First built	Mechanical	Builders Engine	Transmission
DH 33100	C	360	50	41.2	5	1953	MAK	Makma-304	H Voith
DE 33100	C	450	50	41.2	31	1953	MAK	KTA-1150	H Voith
DH 44100	D	800	80	58.9	5	1955	MAK	Makma-301A	H Voith
DH 6500	C	650	60	49.6	30	1960	Krupp	Maybach	H Voith
DH 3600	C	360	50	40.5	7	1968	MAK ELMS	MAK	H Voith
DH 3600	C	450	50	40.5	11	1968	MAK ELMS	Cummins	H Voith
DE 21500	Co-Co	2,150	114	111.6	29	1965	GE	GEFDL 12	E GE
DE 24000	Co-Co	2,400	120	112.8	307	1970	SMTE ELMS 16PA4-185	Pielstick	E Alsthom
DE 24000	Co-Co	2,000	120	112.8	21	1984	SMTE ELMS	Hedemora	E Alsthom
DE 18000	Bo-Bo	1,800	120	80	3	1970	SMTE ELMS	Pielstick 12PA4-185	E Alsthom
DE 18100	Bo-Bo	1,800	120	105	17	1978	SMTE ELMS	Pielstick 12PA4-185	E Alsthom
DE 22000	Co-Co	2,200	120	122.5	86	1985	GM	GM 645 E	E GM
DE 11000	Bo-Bo	1,065	80	68	85	1985	Krauss-Maffei	MTU 8V 396	E GEC
DE 11500	B-B	1,100	100	62	5	1960	MAK	Mercedes mB 820 B6	H Voith

Electric locomotives

Class	Wheel arrangement	Output kW	Speed km/h	Weight tonnes	No in service	First built	Builders Mechanical	Electrical
LE4000	Bo-Bo	1,620	90	77.5	3	1955	MTE	Alsthom/ Jeumont/SW
LE40000	B-B	2,945	130	77	13	1971	MTE	50 C/S Group
E43000	Bo-Bo-Bo	3,180	90	120	43	1987	Toshiba/ Tulomsaş	Toshiba
E4000	Bo-Bo	1,620	90	77.5	3	1995	Alsthom	Alsthom
E40000	B¹-B¹	2,945	90/130	77	13	1969	50 C/S Group	50 C/S Group
E43000	Bo-Bo-Bo	3,180	90	120	43	1987	Tülomsaş/Toshiba	Toshiba

Electric multiple-units

Class	Cars per unit	Motor cars per unit	Motored axles/car	Output/motor kW	Speed km/h	No in service	First built	Builders Mechanical	Electrical
E 8000	4	2	2	255	90	28	1995	Alsthom	Alsthom
E 14000	3	1	2	520	119	71	1979	Tüvasaş/50 C/S Group	50 C/S Group

Diesel multiple-units

Class	Cars per unit	Motor cars per unit	Motored axles/car	Power/motor LP	Speed km/h	No in service	First built	Mechanical	Builders Engine	Transmission
MT 5600	1	1	2	2 × 550	140	2	1992	Tüvasaş	Cummins KTA 19 R	H Voith T 320 RZ
MT 5700	1	1	2	2 × 280	120	15	1993	Fiat	Iveco	H Voith T211R
MT 3000	3	1	2	2 × 150	90	25	1960	Uerdingen	Bussing U10	EM
MT 5500	3	2	4	4 × 145	90	11	1961	Fiat	Fiat	H
DHM 3000	3	1	1	2 × 150	90	25	1989	Talbot	Bussing UIO	H ZF
Fiat 5500	3	2	2	4 × 145	90	11	1961	Fiat	203 0/762	H Fiat
DH 5600	1	1	1	410	120	6	1990	Tüvasaş/ Ganz-Hunslet	Cummins KTA-192	H Voith
DHM 5700	1	1	1	200	140	27	1993	Fiat	Iveco	

Levent on the European side of the Bosphorus. The government has allocated TL806 billion for fulfilment of this and other urban rail transport schemes.

Several routes have been proposed to reduce the distance between Ankara and the Armenian and Iranian borders, but high cost rules out early construction of any.

Better founded is a proposed line round the north shore of Lake Van, where elimination of the difficult train ferry crossing would allow TCDD to raise capacity closer to the substantial demand on this international axis. Design work was expected to be finished in early 1996, after which bids were expected to be sought for construction.

Traffic (million)	1993	1994	1995
Freight tonnes	15.8	14.6	15.1
Freight tonne-km	8,307	8,215	8,409
Passenger journeys	147	119	104
Passenger-km	7,209	6,335	5,797

Revenue	1993	1994	1995
(TL million)			
Passenger	611,283	1,173,507	2,004,841
Freight	1,660,506	2,389,374	4,482,380
Other income	2,222,308	5,158,494	8,162,558
Subsidies	1,884,755	2,700,544	4,309,516
Total	6,378,852	11,421,919	18,959,295

Expenditure	1993	1994	1995
(TL million)			
Railway personnel	5,556,142	8,518,512	13,196,536
Other expenditure	9,671,788	28,389,313	43,763,824
Total	15,227,930	36,907,825	56,960,360

Improvements to existing lines

A recent priority has been to realign, double-track, resignal and electrify the 577 km iron ore route from the Diyriği mines in east central Turkey southwards to the port of Iskerendun, also the site of a steelworks. A Saudi loan has financed this project and half its requirement of 80 4,000 to 4,500 kW locomotives. The high power is needed to attack the line's severe gradients. The objective is to double the line's present carrying capacity of 2 million tonnes a year.

Electrification has been complicated by the route's 92 tunnels with an aggregate length of 22 km. The contract was awarded to a Franco-Turkish consortium led by Société de Construction des Lignes Electriques and GTM Entrepose Electricité. The project has been two-thirds funded by France, the Saudi Fund for Development and the Islamic Development Bank. Even before the electrification is fully operational, a 285 km cut-off line has been proposed to shorten the distance to Iskenderun.

Under the 1993-97 Infrastructure plan a total of 1,762 route-km is being double-tracked, including: Incirlik—Toprakkale, 68 km, completed 1995; and Iskerendun—Toprakkale. During the currency of the plan TCDD also hoped to start double-tracking of the following sections: Narli—Malataya—Hekimhan, 252 km; Mersin—Yenice, 43 km; and Haydarpaşa—Gebze, 88 km.

At present TCDD's maximum speed is 120 km/h, and that is attainable only by the front-rank passenger train on parts of the Haydarpaşa—Ankara route. TCDD is aiming to ease curves on the route to a minimum 900 m radius, which along with further double-tracking and upgrading of permanent way would allow top speed to be raised to 160 km/h, but with a price tag of US$150 million.

Other objectives under TCDD's 1992-96 plan were renewal of 2,424 km of track and achievement of fully mechanised track maintenance. In the longer term, upgrading of the lines to the Black Sea ports of Zonguldak and Samsun is also proposed.

Traction and rolling stock

At the start of 1995 the fleet comprised 553 diesel, 59 electric and 58 steam locomotives, 99 emu cars and 68 diesel railcars. In addition, the railway operated 1,078 passenger coaches, among them 79 sleeping, 105 couchette, and 47 restaurant cars; and 19,132 freight wagons.

In early 1997, TCDD issued a tender for the supply of 60 electric locomotives, which were expected to cost US$240 million.

Type of coupling: Screw
Type of brake: Knorr and Westinghouse air

Signalling and telecommunications

Resignalling with CTC between Haydarpaşa and Ankara (520 km) was completed in 1993, and the Divriği-Iskenderun ore line is also finished. In 1995 work was in progress on resignalling between Istanbul and Kapikule on the Bulgarian border (CTC, 291 km), Kayas—Hanli (automatic block, 521 km), and Hanli—Cetinkaya (CTC, 224 km).

Electrification

TCDD's 1992-96 plan envisaged 2,460 track-km of electrification. By 1992, there was catenary throughout from Ankara to Haydarpaşa.

The 189 km from Cerkezöy to Kapikule, on the line to Bulgaria, was due to be completed in 1997.

The ore line wiring between Iskenderun and Divriği (577 km), was completed in mid-1995. The next line to be tackled will be the 701 km Kayaş—Çetinkaya artery, to link the ore line electrification with Ankara, on which TCDD hoped to start work in 1996 for completion in 2000.

Two suburban routes totalling 53 km are in Izmir are scheduled for electrification.

Track

Rails: 49.43 kg/m
Sleepers: Steel, wooden, concrete 2,400 × 220 × 200 mm
Spacing: 1,612/km
Fastenings: K
Min curvature radius: 190 m
Max gradient: 2.8%
Max axleload: 20 tonnes

UPDATED

Railcar at Izmir (M J Edwards)   **1997**

TURKMENISTAN

Ministry of Transport

Karla Marksa ul 24, 744014 Ashkabad
Tel: +7 3632 254 615

Key personnel
Minister: Sedar Djepbarov

UPDATED

Turkmenistan State Railway

Türkmenistanyn Döwlet Demir Yoly (TDDY)
Turkmenbashy ul 9, 744077 Ashkabad
Tel: +7 3632 255545   Fax: +7 3632 473858/510632

Gauge: 1,520 mm
Route length: 2,198 km all single track; no electrification

Organisation

The network comprises the western portion of the former Soviet Railways Central Asian Railway. Its main route is the 1,141 km Trans-Caspian line linking the port of Turkmenbashy (formerly Krasnovodsk), the capital Ashkabad and Chardzhou, near the border with

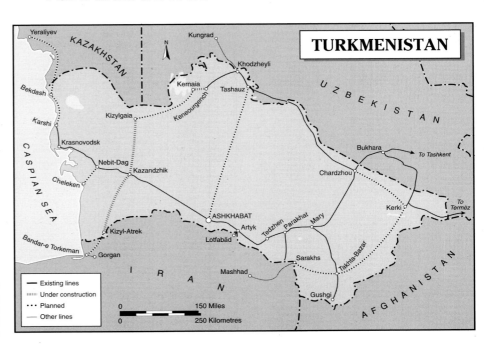

Uzbekistan. A branch from Mary to Kushka on the Afghan frontier is rarely used because of the unrest in Afghanistan.

Passenger operations
Passenger traffic in 1995 amounted to 1.9 billion passenger-km. A new fast service was introduced in 1993 from Turkmenbashy to the regional capital of Taschauz, covering the 1,600 km in 36 hours.

Freight operations
In 1995 the railway operated 8.6 billion tonne-km, mainly cotton and other crops, and oil.

New lines
Construction of the 122 km Tedzhen—Sarakhs—Mashhad line, linking Turkmenistan with Iran, has been completed; the line was opened in May 1996.

The branch to Kushka is to be the spring-off point for the proposed trans-Afghan railway, which was the subject of an accord signed between the Pakistan, Afghan and Turkmenistan governments in March 1994. The 800 km route, which has the strong support of the Pakistan government, would link Kushka with Chaman in Pakistan, via Herat, Farah and Kandahar in Afghanistan.

A link from Chardzhou in a southeasterly direction is under construction. This line will run along the south side of the Amu Darya river to Kerki where a new bridge is to be constructed with a link to the present isolated line at Kerkichi (on the Karshi Termez (both in Uzbekistan) route). This new river crossing will relieve pressure on the life-expired bridge at Chardzhou, for which a replacement is also being planned.

Traction and rolling stock
The current fleet of locomotives comprises some 233 double-unit locomotives of the 2TE10 derivatives, of which about 120 are available for service. Additionally, there are 98 shunters of types TEM2 and ChME3 of which about 60 are serviceable. Interest has been expressed in a potential re-engining exercise for the 2TE10M locomotives using (USA) General Electric technology.

UPDATED

Oil train at Ashgabat hauled by Type 2TE10 double-unit locomotive
1997

UGANDA

Ministry of Transport and Communications

PO Box 7087, Amber House, Kampala
Tel: +256 41 255028/235730

Key personnel
Minister: AK Kivejinja
Permanent Secretary: W O Wanyama

UPDATED

Uganda Railways Corporation (URC)

PO Box 7150, Nasser Road, Kampala
Tel: +256 41 254961/258051   Fax: +256 41 244405

Key personnel
Managing Director: E K Tumusiime
Chief Mechanical Engineer: S Kwesiga
Chief Civil Engineer: H Akora
Chief Rail Operations Manager: C Ntegakarija
Chief Administration Manager: G Kahangi
Chief Construction Unit Manager: C Musuuza
Financial Controller: S Sebunjo (Acting)
Assistant Chief Marketing Manager: E Hashaka
Assistant Chief Planning and Development Officer:
    F Mugenyi
Assistant Chief Signal and Telecommunications Officer:
    Ruth Kyohairwe
Public Relations Manager: E K Kabatangale

Gauge: 1,000 mm
Route length: 1,241 km

Political background
Uganda Railways Corporation (URC) was created after the 1977 dissolution of East African Railways (EAR). Since then it has suffered seriously from political dissension between its former partner countries in EAR, from the civil war in its own country and resultant damage, and from a decline in the performance of Ugandan industry and agriculture.

During 1995 and 1996 an easing of political tensions between the former EAR partner countries led to serious consideration of the practicality of reviving both the East African Community and much closer co-operation between URC and the neighbouring railways in Kenya and Tanzania, particularly in the areas of marketing, tariffs and accounting.

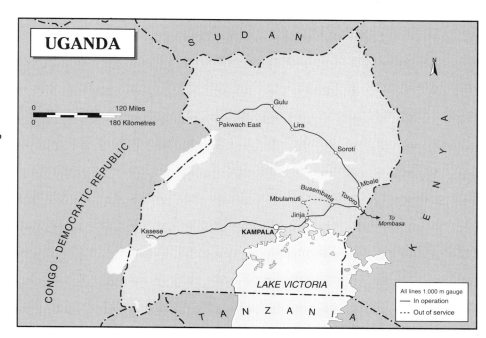

Class 73 locomotives
1997

Passenger operations

In 1990 traffic amounted to 1.5 million passenger journeys but fell off subsequently, with URC recording a mere 200,000 journeys (30 million passenger-km) in 1995. By 1997, all passenger services had been suspended, save for the weekly through international passenger train between Nairobi and Kampala (which was reintroduced in 1994 following reduction of political tension in the region). This uses URC locomotives and Kenya Railways coaches.

Freight operations

Freight traffic amounted to 459,000 tonnes in 1990; by 1995, carryings had doubled to 900,000 tonnes, 235 million tonne-km. Transport of emergency foreign aid for the neighbouring country of Rwanda was partly responsible for the increase in traffic.

Train ferry service

As a member of the African Central Corridor transport system, Uganda benefited from the provision of European funds for improvement of wagon ferry terminals and port facilities on Lake Victoria at Jinja, Port Bell, Mwanza, Musoma and Bukoba. Two URC train ferries ply between Port Bell in Uganda, Kisumu in Kenya and Mwanza in Tanzania, with occasional use of the Jinja terminal for traffic from the east of the country.

New lines

In 1991 agreement was concluded in principle with Tanzania for construction of a new link with Tanzania Railways. It was proposed to extend TRC's Tanga—Arusha line to Musoma on Lake Victoria, there to connect with the existing train ferry service for connection with Kampala.

In connection with the rehabilitation of the Lake Victoria train ferry service, the long-abandoned rail link between Kampala and Port Bell was reinstated in 1993.

Improvements to existing lines

URC started rehabilitation under a National Recovery Programme in 1980, commencing with signalling modernisation, financed by French aid, with station interlocking and tokenless block (which has since fallen into disuse); the construction of a workshop at Nalukolongo using German bilateral aid; new locomotive

International train for Nairobi, Kenya, at Kampala station; this is the only passenger service left on URC
1997

and rolling stock orders; and construction of new Lake Victoria wagon ferries.

A seven-year modernisation of the Tororo—Pakwach line was completed in mid-1993. However, operations are sometimes disrupted by continuing terrorist activity in the north of the country.

In 1987 the government received an Italian consultants' study of a US$150 million upgrading of the lightly built 333 km Kampala—Kasese main line. By 1989 a US$153 million aid scheme had been formulated, largely underwritten by the World Bank and Italy, to allow the work to go ahead. Completion would open up a valuable route from Mombasa to northeastern Zaïre. Unfortunately, the aid package was deferred and the route continues to deteriorate, with severe speed and axleweight restrictions.

Traction and rolling stock

At the start of 1996 URC was operating 57 diesel locomotives, 85 passenger coaches and 1,384 freight wagons. In 1991 the railway received 300 freight wagons from More Wear Industries of Zimbabwe, followed by a further 300 from the same source in 1992; 51 hoppers were delivered by Spain's CAF, also in 1992.

Surplus Henschel locomotives are hired out to neighbouring Kenya and Tanzania on a regular basis.

During 1995 negotiations were opened with ABB (now Adtranz) with a view to improving the utilisation of the Nalukolongo workshop by creation of a joint venture company which would take over management of the workshop and market its facilities on a regional basis.

UPDATED

UKRAINE

Ministry of Transport

Gorki ul 51, 252150 Kiev
Tel: +380 44 227 7351

Key personnel

Minister: O Klympush
Director, Railways: E Abdulajev
First Deputy Director, Railways: V Korenko

VERIFIED

Transcarpathian Railroads

294017 Uzhgorod, Universitetskaja Str 1
Tel: +380 3122 42662   Fax: +380 3122 37801

Key personnel

Managing Director: Ivan Ustich

Organisation

Transcarpathian Railroads is a private sector company set up to develop narrow-gauge railways in southwest Ukraine and neightbouring countries. Its first ambition was to take over the 80 km Beregova—Kusnitsa line run by the Ukrainian Ministry of Transport.

NEW ENTRY

Ukrainian National Rail Transport Administration

Derzhavna Administratsiya Zaliznichnogo Transportu Ukraïni (Ukrzaliznitsya, UZ)
Vulitsa Lisyenka 6, 252601 Kiev-34
Tel: +380 44 223 6305   Fax: +380 44 227 6593/0323

Key personnel

General Director: Vacant
Deputy General Directors
    Transport: Anatoly Slobodian
    Economics: Mykhailo Makarenko
    Development: Yuri Fediushyn
    Infrastructure: Anatoly Lashko
    Industry: Viktor Krutous
Departmental Chiefs
    Development: Arlikin Zubko
    Operations: Vasyl Koval
    Infrastructure: Volodymyr Buchko
    Freight: Leonid Petrenko
    Passenger: Yuri Yefimov
    Finance: Kostiantyn Opaterny
    Traction: Volodymyr Kuleshov
    Rolling Stock: Volodymyr Markhai
    Infrastructure: Volodymyr Buchko
    Foreign Affairs: Olexandr Yurtchenko
    Press and Public Relations Manager:
        Petro Moskalenko

Gauge: 1,520 mm
Route length: 22,564 km
Electrification: 3,924 km at 25 kV 50Hz AC, 4,624 km at 3 kV DC

Political background

UZ came into existence as a result of the break-up of the former USSR, in which the former Soviet Railways (SZD) maintained six regions in what is now the Ukraine: Donetsk, Lviv, Odessa, Dnipro, Southwest and Southern. Because these regions were controlled directly from Moscow, a new administration has had to be created in Kiev to manage UZ, reporting directly to the Railway Department of the Transport Ministry.

UZ is contiguous with the railways of Poland, Slovakia, Hungary, Romania, Moldova, the Russian Federation and Belarus; the last three are the only ones operating with the same gauge as UZ, though Poland, Slovakia and Romania each have cross-border 1,520 mm gauge lines, generally feeding large industrial complexes located near the respective borders.

In early 1997, the Ukrainian President declared himself dissatisfied with the railways which, he said, were producing worse results despite tariff increases, and were a source of crime and corruption. The General Director, Leonid Zhelezniak, was dismissed, although it was said that this was due to the wide opposition to the policy of eliminating railway divisions, a process that had been expected to be achieved by April 1997. The Dnipro Railway in particular was suffering from this reorganisation, and there was talk of its proximity to bankruptcy. Meanwhile the political problems of the Crimea found expression in demand for an independent Crimean Railway.

Finance

The high rate of inflation in Ukraine (in 1994 about 2,500 per cent) makes revenue data quite meaningless. However, passenger revenue for 1992 represented less than 5 per cent of UZ's total income, despite the high level of passenger activity.

Since separation from Russia, heavy increases in the costs of energy in the Ukraine — both diesel oil and electricity — have meant that these now form a much higher proportion of the railway's costs than formerly.

Some 575,000 persons work for UZ.

Passenger operations

In 1995, passenger traffic stood at 577 million journeys (1994 = 631 million); passenger-km stood at 63.759 billion (1994 = 70.881 billion).

The railways have no financial support from the state. In the five years 1992-96 only 17 passenger cars have been purchased. Although the Crimean government relieved

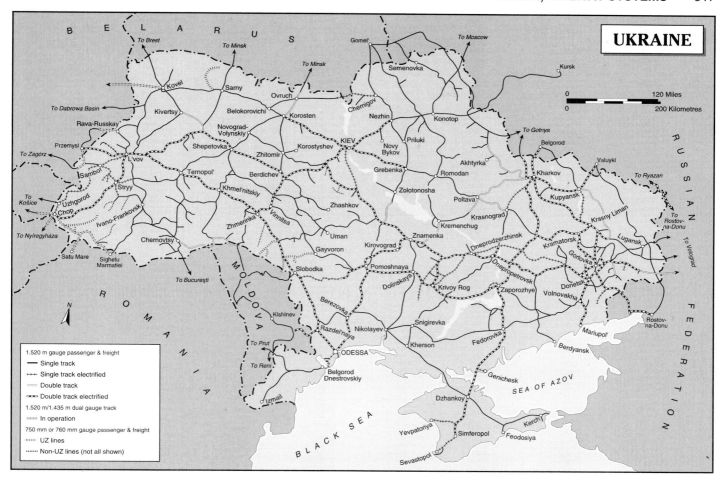

the railways of land tax, most local governments paid little heed to the government's exhortation to help the railways with passenger subsidies. In 1996, the railways therefore cut some services and put other pressures on local authorities, but with little result.

There is little road competition for passenger traffic; this reflects the high cost of fuel oil and the railway fares structure. In contrast to other former Communist countries, private interurban bus operation has not developed to any great extent, though there is already competition on the Moscow—Kiev—Kishinev (Moldova)—Bucharest—Turkey corridor from Turkish coach operators.

Freight operations

The major source of freight traffic is the heavily industrialised Donetsk region in the southeast.

Since the break-up of the USSR and SZD, freight traffic has declined by about 50 per cent. In 1995, the railway carried 360 million tonnes (1994 = 408 million); tonne-km stood at 195.762 billion (1994 = 200.423 billion). The Donetsk region generates over a third of freight traffic.

As with many neighbouring countries, the principal reasons for the decline in traffic are the reduction in industrial output following the loss of traditional markets, combined with an upsurge of competition, particularly from road hauliers for international traffic flows. Surprisingly, the navigable Dniepr river has not yet been a competitive factor.

Traction and rolling stock

In 1996 the rolling stock fleet comprised 1,943 electric locomotives, 3,158 emu cars, 2,067 diesel locomotives, 1,126 dmu cars, 9,900 passenger coaches and 220,061 freight wagons. (These figures are thought to include vehicles stored unserviceable as well as those in use.)

The main electric Classes are: VL8, VL10, VL11/11m, VL80 and VL82 families, ChS2, ChS4, ChS7 and ChS8, with emus mainly from the Riga-built ER2 and ER9 groups. The main diesel fleets are: TE3, TE7, TEP60, TEP70, 2TE10 family, M62 family, 2TE116 and 2TE121; dmus are of Classes D1 (Ganz Mávag), DR1, DR1A and DR1P (Riga).

During 1994 the financial situation had deteriorated to such an extent that freight traffic, wherever feasible, was being routed solely over electrified lines in order to reduce the consumption of diesel oil. More than 20 steam locomotives have been returned to service on shunting and trip work, mainly in the Lviv area.

It is proposed to build four new designs of twin-section Bo-Bo electric locomotives at Dnepropetrovsk: two freight Classes (DE1 — 3 kV DC; DE3 — 25 kV 50 Hz) and two passenger Classes (DE2 — 3 kV DC; DE4 — 25 kV 50 Hz) with projected hourly ratings of 6,280 kW and 7,960 kW for the DC and AC designs respectively; the first prototypes were expected to appear in 1996. Emus will be built at the Lugansk factory.

Fewer than 4,000 freight wagons were acquired in 1993, and 2,200 in 1994.

Signalling and telecommunications

The following types of signalling are in use on UZ (with km controlled in brackets): automatic block (13,605 km); interlocking control (3,355); semi-automatic block (7,466); automatic cab signalling (15,113); dispatcher control (8,495).

Electrification

Some 37 per cent of the Ukrainian system is electrified, slightly under half of the total length of wires being on the 25 kV AC system.

UZ has a rolling programme of electrification. The 47.5 km between Yagotin and Grebyonka were electrified by the end of 1994.

Lines in the programme are as follows:

1994-96: Podvolochinsk—Krasnoe (141 km)
1994-96: Zhemerinca—Padvolochinsk (163 km)
1994-98: Lubotin—Poltava Yuzhnaya (116 km)
1994-2000: Grebyonka—Poltava (203 km)
1997-2001: Poltava Yuzhnaya—Lozovaya (177 km)
2001-2002: Poltava Yuzhnaya—Burty (137 km)
2001-2004: Novomoskovsk—Krasnograd (99.4 km).

Track

To overcome a shortage of rail, in 1995 each of the six railways in UZ was required to close 200 km of poorly utilised track in order to provide materials for maintaining the main lines.

Class VL8 Bo-Bo+Bo-Bo electric locomotive with a freight train in the Donetsk area   **1997**

Rail: 65 kg/m (34,620 km); 50 kg/m (11,330 km)
Sleepers: Concrete, wood
Spacing: 1,840/km in plain track, 2,000/km in curves
Min curve radius: 200 m
Max gradient: 1.4%
Max axleload: 22.5 tonnes

UPDATED

Diesel multiple-unit at Charcysk Voksai
1997

UNITED KINGDOM

Department of the Environment, Transport and the Regions

Great Minster House, 76 Marsham Street, London SW1P 4DR
Tel: +44 171 271 5000   Fax: +44 171 271 5972
Website:
    http://www.coi.gov.uk/coi/depts/GTE/GTE.html

Key personnel
Deputy Prime Minister and Secretary of State for the Environment, Transport and the Regions:
    John Prescott
Minister for Transport: Gavin Strang
Minister for Transport in London: Glenda Jackson
Permanent Secretary: Andrew Turnbull
Director of Railways, Public Transport and Shipping:
    David Rowlands
Head of Railways Directorate: Roy Griffins

Organisation
The privatised railway in the UK is regulated by three autonomous bodies: the Office of Passenger Rail Franchising (qv), the Office of the Rail Regulator (qv) and the Railway Inspectorate of the Health & Safety Executive (qv). However, the Department of the Environment, Transport and the Regions retains direct responsibility for the administration of subsidies for environmentally beneficial transfer of freight from road to rail. Since April 1994, grants have been payable not only for rail loading and unloading facilities that remove freight from roads, as they had been since 1974, but also to offset track access charges.

UPDATED

Office of Passenger Rail Franchising

Goldings House, 2 Hay's Lane, London SE1 2HB
Tel: +44 171 940 4200   Fax: +44 171 940 4210

Key personnel
Director of Passenger Rail Franchising: John O'Brien
Deputy Director: Chris Stokes
Head of Public Affairs: Paul Moon
Chief Press Officer: Paul McKie

Political background
Under the Railways Act 1993 the Director of Passenger Rail Franchising is responsible for securing the provision of railway passenger services on the Railtrack system by entering into franchise agreements, with franchisees being selected through a competitive tendering process.

The Franchising Director is the route through which public subsidy into the privatised railway system is funnelled; where necessary (which at the outset of the privatised railway was over the whole system with the

Traffic (million)	1993-94	1994-95	1995-96	1996-97
Passenger journeys	713.2	702.2	718.7	—
Passenger-km	30,187	28,650	29,210	32,200

exception of Gatwick Express), the Franchising Director pays subsidies to franchisees to operate services.

The units for franchising are the 25 train operating companies (TOCs) which were formed out of the former British Rail. The first TOCs to be franchised were Great Western Trains, which is responsible for the main line services operating out of London Paddington, and South West Trains, operating long-distance and suburban services out of London Waterloo: these two companies were handed over to private sector operators in February 1996. Further franchises were let throughout 1996, and all 25 were in the private sector by April 1997.

OPRAF's role is now to monitor performance and adherence of TOCs to their franchise agreement, until the termination of the franchises and rebidding takes place — which for most companies is in 2002-03.

UPDATED

Office of the Rail Regulator

1 Waterhouse Square, 138-142 Holborn, London EC1N 2ST
Tel: +44 171 282 2000   Fax: +44 171 282 2040

Key personnel
Rail Regulator: John Swift QC
Group Directors
    Economic Regulation: Chris Bolt
    Railway Network: C J F Brown
    Passenger Services: J A Rhodes
Directors
    Resources: Peter Murphy
    Non-executive: Ann Foster, Stephen Glaister,
        Sir Wilfrid Newton
Chief Legal Adviser: M R Brocklehurst
Head of Private Office and Public Affairs: Keith Webb
Chief Information Officer: C I Cooke

Political background
The role of the Rail Regulator in the newly privatised railway is to protect the consumer, both passenger and freight, from abuses of monopoly power. This he does by licensing operators, approving agreements for track, station and light maintenance depot access and investigating closure proposals. Through the network of rail users' consultative committees, he also protects the interests of passengers.

In performing those functions he has a duty to promote: the use of the rail network; competition in the provision of rail services; and efficiency and economy by those providing services.

The Rail Regulator also has a role in facilitating through ticketing and other benefits associated with a national network.

Competition
Soon after the restructuring of the British Rail passenger business, competition began emerging between companies operating parallel services: the most marked example was between Gatwick airport and central London.

However, while introduction of on-rail competition was originally one of the main aims of the government's reforms of the industry, the difficulty in selling franchises if new franchisees faced the prospect of immediate direct competition led to a tempering of the policy. The Rail Regulator has limited competition until at least 2002: 'open access' passenger operators (that is, those without a franchise) will be barred before April 1999, and 'substantial restrictions' will exist for three years after that.

UPDATED

Railway Inspectorate of the Health & Safety Executive

Rose Court, 2 Southwark Bridge, London SE1 9HS
Tel: +44 171 717 6501   Fax: +44 171 717 6547

Key personnel
Chief Inspector of Railways: Stan Robertson
Deputy Chief Inspectors of Railways
    Technical Branch (RI 1): A Cooksey
    Strategy, Planning & Privatisation Branch (RI 2):
    R J Smallwood
    Field Operations Branch (RI 3): V Coleman

UPDATED

Association of Train Operating Companies

1 Eversholt Street, London NW1 1DN
Tel: +44 171 214 9143   Fax: +44 171 214 9127

Key personnel
Director-General: Major-General James Gordon
Director of Operations: Alec McTavish

Political background
The Association of Train Operating Companies (TOCs) was set up to administer schemes that required the joint participation of the 25 passenger TOCs formed out of the old British Rail. ATOC's most important role is to administer the division of monies derived from tickets for journeys which cross TOC boundaries, but it also performs a role as a trade association, acting for the TOCs where there is benefit to them in acting collectively.

VERIFIED

British Rail

British Railways Board
Euston House, 24 Eversholt Street, PO Box 100, London
NW1 1DZ
Tel: +44 171 928 5151   Fax: +44 171 922 6994

Key personnel
Chairman and Chief Executive: John K Welsby
Vice-Chairman: Christopher Campbell
Board Member, Finance and Planning: J J Jerram
Board Member, Personnel: Paul Watkinson
Solicitor: A F Sim
Secretary: P C Trewin

Railfreight Distribution
Enterprise House, 169 Westbourne Terrace, London
W2 6JY
Tel: +44 171 922 4285
Managing Director: James Mackay

Political background
Under the Conservative government's 1993 Railways Act,
the old British Rail has been split and sold off. By the
time of a general election in May 1997, BR had been
divested of all its operating railway functions save for
Railfreight Distribution: for this, a purchaser had been
selected (English, Welsh & Scottish Railway - qv), but the
deal awaited the approval of the European Commission.
BR was still responsible for non-operational railway land
(which was handed over to private sector agents for
administration) and the British Transport Police; an Act of
Parliament would be needed to wind up the company
completely.

While BR has been split into over 70 private sector
companies, there are three main constituents in the
privatised railway. Since April 1994, Railtrack (qv) has had
responsibility for infrastructure (tracks, earthworks and
signalling). Three rolling stock leasing companies (qv in
'Rolling stock leasing companies' section) now own what
used to be BR's passenger traction and rolling stock fleet.
Thirdly, private sector companies have taken over the
operating function: the bulk of BR's freight business was
sold to English, Welsh & Scottish Railway (qv) in early
1996, while franchises for running the passenger Train
Operating Companies (TOCs) have been sold by the
Office of Passenger Rail Franchising (qv).

Franchisees pay Railtrack for the use of the tracks and
the rolling stock leasing companies for the use of the
trains. The Franchise Director underwrites losses on
unprofitable services and sets the broad levels of service
required.

In addition to the franchise system, the government
made provision for future competition on passenger
services. So-called 'open access' operators would be
able to compete for passengers on a franchise company's
territory, although provision was made to restrict this
competition in the first years of private sector operation. A
new government appointee, the Rail Regulator (qv), has
the task of guarding against anti-competitive practices
and overseeing and regulating the industry in the best
interests of passengers.

For freight, open access operations have been allowed
from the outset of the restructuring of the railway industry.
Two firms — electricity generator National Power (qv) and
Direct Rail Services (qv), a subsidiary of nuclear waste
processor British Nuclear Fuels Ltd — took early
advantage of this opportunity. Charges for use of the
tracks by operators such as these are payable to
Railtrack.

In addition to these developments with BR's main
operations, peripheral organisations have been sold. The
government raised a little over £4 billion from the sale of
British Rail. This was offset by a near doubling of the
subsidy required to run the passenger railway, from
around £1 billion annually under the old BR to over
£2 billion in subsidy to the privatised TOCs in FY1996-97.
Under declining rates of subsidy signed up to by the
TOCs, overall subsidy is set to go below £1 billion again in
FY2002-03. The Conservative government which
undertook the privatisation stressed that the newly
privatised companies would have access to conventional
private sector financing, meaning that investment in the
railway industry would not be dependent on government
authorisation. When Labour gained office in May 1997, it
decided to leave the railway in private sector hands.

Intermodal operations
By April 1997, the only railway operations being
undertaken by British Rail were the container and

Class 92 hauling van train bound for the Continent on 750 V DC line in Kent (Brian Morrison)   **1996**

swapbody services operated through the Channel Tunnel
to mainland Europe by the company's loss-making
Railfreight Distribution (RfD) division. Agreement had
been reached on the sale of RfD to English, Welsh &
Scottish Railway (qv), but approval for this transaction
was required from the European Commission. At issue
was the dowry with which RfD was being transferred: in its
FY1995-96 accounts, BR wrote off its £300 million
investment in RfD and agreed to pay for RfD £200 million
of minimum usage charge payments to the Channel
Tunnel infrastructure owner, Eurotunnel, in the years up
until 2006.

RfD began running revenue-earning freight trains
through the Channel Tunnel in June 1994. Intermodal and
auto-carrying services are the two most important types of
rail freight to use the tunnel. In addition, some
conventional freight, such as steel, uses the new route.

Build-up of traffic on long-distance routes to Italy and
Spain has been encouraging, but on the shorter-distance
routes to the main continental markets of France,
Germany and the Low Countries, RfD has been squeezed
by very low road haulage rates made possible by a price
war between Eurotunnel and the ferries over lorry traffic
crossing the Channel. This meant that, two years after
services began, RfD was only carrying around three
million tonnes per annum; before opening of the tunnel, it
was anticipated that the market for cross-Channel rail
freight would amount to about six million tonnes per
annum.

By mid-1996, RfD was operating around 160 trains a
week through the Tunnel. The agreement between
Eurotunnel and the railways allows for up to 35 trains each
way per day to use the Tunnel.

RfD is limiting its role to that of a wholesaler, selling
complete train haulage through the Tunnel. It deals
directly with large companies with large capacity
requirements — for instance, a deal has been signed with
Spanish company Transfesa concerning movement of
complete trainloads of car parts for the Ford Motor
Company between Spain and the UK. For intermodal less-
than-trainload shippers, RfD has helped establish a
number of joint venture companies to retail container
slots through the Channel Tunnel.

RfD has a 10 per cent holding in Combined Transport
Ltd, a joint venture company and UIRR associate formed
by RfD, French and German intermodal companies and
road hauliers, to promote use of combined or intermodal
technology on Anglo-Continental freight services (for
address, see UIRR entry in 'International rail operators'
section). In 1992 a competing company, Allied
Continental Intermodal (ACI) was formed by
Intercontainer, SNCF and RfD, with a 50/25/25
shareholding split (for address, see Intercontainer entry in
'International rail operators' section).

ACI and CTL compete for intermodal traffic to a range
of destinations on the Continent. For Belgium—UK traffic,
a joint venture company known as Unilog has been
formed (for address, see 'International rail operators'
section). This began operations in June 1994 with a
pendulum service daily between Duisburg in Germany, a
terminal at Muizen in Belgium, and London and
Manchester in the UK.

The initial Channel Tunnel services operated from
intermodal terminals on Railtrack's West Coast route:

London (Willesden), Birmingham (Landor Street),
Manchester (Trafford Park), Glasgow (Mossend) and
Liverpool (Royal Seaforth).

In 1996, services began to two terminals on the East
Coast route: Wakefield and Doncaster. The latter, used
mainly for car trains from the continent, was set up in a
joint venture between the local authority and the private
sector; it was not part of the original network of terminals
planned by RfD. Other private sector initiatives resulted in
new Channel Tunnel intermodal terminals being opened
during 1997 at Hams Hall in the West Midlands and
Daventry in the East Midlands. Others have been
proposed for Avonmouth port near Bristol, Wentloog in
South Wales, near Heathrow airport in west London and
Temple Mills in east London.

On the complex ACI and CTL networks, for the first few
years of operation, trains are feeding into London from
the regional terminals and marshalling takes place at a
new yard at Wembley in northwest London; if traffic builds
up sufficiently, it is the intention that direct trains will run
from the British provinces to Europe.

Traction and rolling stock
Brush Traction built 46 Class 92 dual-voltage (750 V
DC/25 kV AC) Co-Co locomotives with Adtranz GTO
three-phase AC drives to handle trains through the
Channel Tunnel and on the British domestic network. The
126 tonne Class 92s have 5,000 kW rating in AC
operation, 4,000 kW in DC, and a maximum starting
tractive effort of 400 kN. Railfreight Distribution has
bought 30 of these machines, Eurostar (UK) seven, and
SNCF (French Railways) nine. Class 92 locomotives were
originally intended for sleeper services through the
Channel Tunnel as well as freight trains, but the uncertain
future of the European overnight services (see Eurostar
(UK) entry) means they may not be needed for this role.

A complex safety certification procedure by Railtrack to
ensure stray currents from the new locomotives would not
interfere with lineside signalling has limited the Class 92s
to the route from Wembley in north London to Fréthun, at
the French end of the Channel Tunnel. It had originally
been intended that they would work through to Scotland,
but the cost of altering signalling equipment on the West
Coast main line and other routes has proved prohibitive.

A fleet of wagons for Channel Tunnel operation has
been built. Arbel Fauvet Rail in Douai, France, has built
450 Multifret wagons. These run coupled in pairs; they are
designed for swapbody transport through the tunnel. The
Arbel-built wagons were ordered by RfD; Intercontainer of
Basel, Switzerland, and SNCF have ordered a further 540
Multifret wagons from Remafer of Reims, France (paid for
two-thirds by Intercontainer, one third by SNCF).
Intercontainer and the two railway administrations plan an
eventual fleet of 1,800 swapbody wagons for Channel
Tunnel work.

For transport of finished cars through the tunnel, which
is a major source of traffic, RfD has taken delivery of 300
fully enclosed car-carrying wagons, permanently coupled
in units of five wagons, from Arbel Fauvet Rail. The SNCF
subsidiary STVA and Gefco, a Peugeot Talbot subsidiary,
already own large fleets of car carriers which are
compatible with the British loading gauge.

UPDATED

Anglia Railways

Anglia Railways Train Services Ltd
15-25 Artillery Lane, London E1 7HA
Tel: +44 171 465 9000   Fax: +44 171 465 9015

Key personnel
Managing Director: Andy Cooper
Commercial Director: Tim Clarke
Production Director: John Smith

Political background
Under the arrangements put in place by the 1993 Railways Act, the franchise to run operations on Anglia Railways was let in December 1996 to GB Railways Group

plc, a company set up to run rail franchises by Michael Schabas, formerly transport adviser to property developers Olympia & York. Shares in GB Railways are traded on the London Alternative Investment Market.

The franchise was let for a term of seven years and three months. Anglia Railways will receive from the Franchising Director support, in 1996 prices, of £35.9 million in the first full financial year of the franchise, declining to £6.3 million in the last year of the franchise.

Revenue in FY95-96 was £38 million and in March 1996 the company employed 731 staff.

Passenger operations
Anglia Railways operates intercity passenger services over 600 route-km between London's Liverpool Street

terminus and Ipswich and Norwich. It also operates local trains on branches in East Anglia.

Under the franchise agreement, GB has committed to running a half-hourly weekday service on the London—Norwich route by September 2000.

Traffic (million)	1996-97
Passenger journeys	5.4
Passenger-km	526
Train-km	6.1

Traction and rolling stock
On the London—Norwich route Anglia uses 10 trains of Mk 2 stock, powered by Class 86/2 locomotives mostly leased from Eversholt. For local services eight Class 150/2 two-car dmus and seven Class 153 railcars are leased from Porterbrook.

GB has undertaken to lease a fleet of modern, air conditioned trains to replace the Class 86 + Mk 2 combinations on the London—Norwich route.

NEW ENTRY

Diesel railcars or multiple-units

Class	Cars per unit	Motor cars per unit	Motored axles/car	Power/motor kW	Speed km/h	Cars in service	First built	Mechanical	Builders Engine	Transmission
150/2	2	2	2	210	120	16	1986	BREL	Cummins NT855R5	HM Voith T211r
153	1	1	2	213	120	7	1987*	Leyland Bus	Cummins NT855R5	HM Voith T211r

* Rebuilt as single cars by Hunslet Barclay 1991

Cardiff Railway

Cardiff Railway Co Ltd
Brunel House, 2 Fitzalan Road, Cardiff CF2 1SA
Tel: +44 1222 499811   Fax: +44 1222 480463

Key personnel
Managing Director: Tom Clift
Commercial Director: Paul Brereton
Procurement and Contracts Manager: Rosalie Malcolm

Political background
Under the arrangements put in place by the 1993 Railways Act, the franchise to run operations on Cardiff

Railway was let in October 1997 to Prism Rail plc (qv), a company set up by a consortium of bus companies. Prism also runs the South Wales & West Railway, LTS Rail and West Anglia Great Northern franchises.

The franchise was let for a term of seven years and six months. Prism will receive from the Franchising Director support, in 1996 prices, of £19.9 million in the first full financial year of the franchise, declining to £13.3 million in the last year of the franchise.

Revenue in FY95-96 was £6.2 million and in January 1996 the company employed 1,315 staff.

Passenger operations
Cardiff Railway Co operates local services on a 138 km network centred on the Welsh capital, Cardiff. Trains run

up the valleys to the north of Cardiff and to Barry and Penarth in the south.

As part of the franchise agreement, Prism has committed itself to the introduction of six new through services per weekday and Saturday from Pontypridd: three each to Manchester and Portsmouth.

Traffic (million)	1996-97
Passenger journeys	5.9
Passenger-km	94.7
Train-km	3.1

New lines
Prism is investigating the feasibility of a rail link to Cardiff Airport.

Traction and rolling stock
Cardiff Railway is an all-diesel-operated franchise worked with second-generation dmus. The company leases Class 143 and Class 150 dmus from Porterbrook.

NEW ENTRY

Cardiff Railway diesel multiple-units

Class	Cars per unit	Motor cars per unit	Motored axles/car	Power/motor kW	Speed km/h	Cars in service	First built	Mechanical	Builders Engine	Transmission
143	2	2	1	152	120		1985	Alexander/ Barclay	Cummins LTA10R	H Voith T211r
150/2	2	2	2	210	120		1986	BREL	Cummins NT855R5	HM Voith T211r

Central Trains

Central Trains Ltd
Stanier House, 10 Holliday Street, Birmingham B1 1TH
Tel: +44 121 654 4215   Fax: +44 121 654 3554

Key personnel
Managing Director: Mark Causebrook
Commercial Director: Glen Kennedy
Production Director: David Fry

Political background
Under the arrangements put in place by the 1993 Railways Act, the franchise to run operations on Central Trains was let in March 1997 to National Express Group plc (qv), a bus and airport operator which has also won the Midland Main Line, Gatwick Express, ScotRail and North London Railways franchises.

The franchise was let for a term of seven years and one month. NEG will receive from the Franchising Director and the local authority Centro support, in 1997 prices, of £187.5 million in the first full financial year of the franchise, declining to £132.6 million in 2003-04.

Central Trains revenue in FY95-96 was £65.6 million and in September 1996 the company employed 2,617 staff.

Passenger operations
Central Trains operates services over a 2,400-km route network covering large part of central England, with many lines extending into Wales and East Anglia. It also

Central Trains electric multiple-units

Class	Cars per unit	Motor cars per unit	Motored axles/car	Power/motor kW	Speed km/h	Cars in service	First built	Builders Mechanical	Electrical
323	3	1	4	146	144		1993	Hunslet TPL	Holec

Central Trains diesel multiple-units

Class	Cars per unit	Motor cars per unit	Motored axles/car	Power/motor kW	Speed km/h	Cars in service	First built	Mechanical	Builders Engine	Transmission
150/0	3	3	2	210	120	6	1985	BREL	Cummins NT855R5	HM Voith T211r
150/1	2	2	2	210	120	62	1985	BREL	Cummins NT855R5	HM Voith T211r
150/2	2	2	2	210	120	10	1986	BREL	Cummins NT855R5	HM Voith T211r
153	1	1	2	213	120	20	1987*	Leyland Bus	Cummins NT855R5	HM Voith T211r
156	2	2	2	210	120	40	1987	Met-Cam	Cummins NT855R5	HM Voith T211r
158/0	2	2	2	275/300	145	72	1989	BREL	Cummins NTA855R	HM Voith T211r

* Rebuilt 1991

operates an extensive network of local services in the Birmingham/Wolverhampton conurbation for Centro, the local Passenger Transport Executive.

Traffic (million)	1996-97
Passenger journeys	30.5
Passenger-km	1,090
Train-km	27.0

Traction and rolling stock
For electric services around Birmingham, Central uses 22 three-car Class 323 emus (13 from Porterbrook, nine from Centro). For its premier diesel-worked long-distance routes, the business leases Class 158 dmus from Angel Trains. Other trains in use include Class 150, 153 and 156 dmus.

NEW ENTRY

Chiltern Railways

Chiltern Railways
Western House, 14 Rickfords Hill, Aylesbury, Buckinghamshire HP20 2RX
Tel: +44 1296 332100   Fax: +44 1296 332126

Key personnel

Directors
Managing: Adrian Shooter
Financial: Tony Allen
Personnel: Caroline James
Production: Owen Edgington
Sales and Marketing: Alex Turner

Political background

Under the arrangements put in place by the 1993 Railways Act, the Chiltern Railways franchise passed in June 1996 to M40 Trains, a joint venture of the Chiltern's management, the John Laing construction group and venture capitalists 3i. The new owners have undertaken to cut subsidy levels over a seven-year franchise from £16.5 million in the first year to £2.1 million in the final year, acquire new trains and maintain the level of services prevailing when it took over.

Chiltern Railways diesel multiple-units

Class	Cars per unit	Motor cars per unit	Motored axles/car	Power/motor kW	Speed km/h	Cars in service	First built	Mechanical	Builders Engine	Transmission
165/0	2/3	2/3	2	260	120	79	1990	BREL	Perkins 2006-TWH	Voith T211r

The Chiltern route has benefited from total modernisation in the past five years, with new trains, a new signalling system and station refurbishment. This has prompted strong revenue growth, from £15 million in FY93-94 to £26 million in FY95-96; the franchisee's plans assume this revenue growth will continue, and that turnover will be around £38 million by the end of the franchise.

Passenger operations

Chiltern runs services over 270 km on two routes out of London's Marylebone station: to Aylesbury via Amersham and to Birmingham Snow Hill via High Wycombe. The franchisee's ambitious revenue growth plans assume changing the character of the company's operation from one where commuter traffic to London predominates to one where medium-distance traffic, from such places as Leamington Spa to London, is of significance as well.

Traffic (million)	1996-97
Passenger journeys	8.1
Passenger-km	324
Train-km	5.63

Traction and rolling stock

Chiltern operates a fleet of modern 'Turbo' Class 165 diesel multiple-units owned by the Angel Trains leasing company; there are 22 two-car and 11 three-car units. Maintenance of the fleet has been subcontracted out to the trains' manufacturer, Adtranz.

With finance being provided by the leasing company Porterbrook, the company has ordered from Adtranz four new three-car 160 km/h units to improve services on its Birmingham route; these are intended to enter service in 1998.

UPDATED

Connex South Central

A subsidiary of the Compagnie Générale d'Enterprises Automobiles group of France
Connex South Central Ltd
Stephenson House, 2 Cherry Orchard Road, Croydon CR9 6JB
Tel: +44 181 667 2500   Fax: +44 181 667 2555

Key personnel

Directors
Managing: Geoff Harrison-Mee
Commercial: Gary Cooper
Production: David Sawyer

Political background

Under the arrangements put in place by the 1993 Railways Act, the Network SouthCentral franchise was transferred to London & South Coast Ltd (later renamed Connex), a subsidiary of the French CGEA group, in April 1996. The franchise will run for seven years.

Support payments from the Franchise Director to Network SouthCentral will decline from £85.3 million in the first year to £34.6 million in 2003.

South Central revenue in 1994-95 was £157 million.

Passenger operations

Connex South Central runs services on a 714 km network of 750 V DC electrified lines out of London's Victoria and London Bridge termini to Gatwick Airport, Brighton and other towns on the south coast of England.

Traffic (million)	1996-97
Passenger journeys	86
Passenger-km	2,091
Train-km	22.5

Traction and rolling stock

Connex South Central runs about 240 four-car electric multiple-units and some diesel multiple-units (for the non-electrified Uckfield line), on lease from the three ex-British Rail rolling stock leasing companies. Inner-suburban services are run by sliding-door units, while most of the longer-distance services are still run by slam-door stock built in the 1960s. There were no requirements in the franchise for the new owner of the company to make arrangements to renew any of the rolling stock, although there was a clause in the agreement which allowed for the franchise to be extended beyond seven years in the event of new trains being ordered.

Connex South Central electric multiple-units

Class	Cars per unit	Motor cars per unit	Motored axles/car	Power/motor kW	Speed km/h	Cars in service	First built	Builders Mechanical	Electrical
319/0*	4	1	4	247	160	80	1987	BREL	GEC
421/3	4	1	4	185	145		1964	BR	EE
421/4	4	1	4	185	145		1970	BREL	EE
422/2	4	1	4	185	145		1965	BR	EE
422/3	4	1	4	185	145		1970	BREL	EE
423	4	1	4	185	145	148	1967	BR	EE
455	4	1	4	185	120	184	1982	BREL	GEC
456	2	1	2	268	120	48	1990	BREL	Brush

* Dual-voltage 750 V DC/25 kV AC

Connex South Central diesel-electric multiple-units

Class	Cars per unit	Motor cars per unit	Motored axles/car	Power/motor kW	Speed km/h	Cars in service	First built	Mechanical	Builders Engine	Transmission
205/0/1	3	1	2	450*	120	30	1957	BR	EE 4SRKT	E EE507
207/0/1	2/3	1	2	450*	120	11	1962	BR	EE 4SRKT	E EE507

* Diesel engine rated at 450 kW

UPDATED

Connex South Eastern

A subsidiary of the Compagnie Générale d'Enterprises Automobiles group of France
Fourth Floor, Friars Bridge Court, 41-45 Blackfriars Road, London SE1 8NZ
Tel: +44 171 620 5505   Fax: +44 171 620 5522

Key personnel

Managing Director: Richard Fearn
Directors
Finance: Frank Johnson
Production: Tony Goff
Personnel: Hugh Dunglinson
Planning: Yves Lallement

Political background

Under the arrangements put in place by the 1993 Railways Act, the franchise to run operations on the former South Eastern Division of British Rail was let to Connex, a wholly owned subsidiary of the French CGEA group, in August 1996. Connex also runs the neighbouring Network South Central franchise (qv).

The franchise was let for a 15-year term; it is expected to become profitable in that time. Connex will receive from the Franchising Director support, in 1996 prices, of £124.5 million in the first year of the franchise, turning to a premium payment of £2.8 million in 2011.

Connex South Eastern revenue in FY93-94 was £205 million, and in FY95-96 it was £233 million. In December 1996, Connex South Eastern employed 3,763 staff.

Passenger operations

Connex South Eastern runs services on a 773 km network out of London's Charing Cross and Victoria stations to south London, Kent and East Sussex. South Eastern is the biggest of the 25 train operating companies in terms of passenger-km; it moves around 100,000 commuters into London every weekday morning.

Traffic (million)	1996-97
Passenger journeys	113.4
Passenger-km	2,768
Train-km	28.2

Class 421 stock at Orpington. The franchisee has undertaken to rid Connex South Eastern of slam-door stock by April 2006 (Brian Morrison) **1996**

Connex South Eastern electric multiple-units

Class	Cars per unit	Motor cars per unit	Motored axles/car	Power/motor kW	Speed km/h	Cars in service	First built	Builders Mechanical	Electrical
411/5	4	2	2	185	145	240	1956	BR	EE
421/4	4	1	4	185	145	84	1970	BREL	EE
423	4	1	4	185	145	296	1967	BR	EE
465/0	4	2	2		120	392	1992	ABB/Brush	GEC
465/2	4	2	2		120	200	1992	GEC	GEC
466	2	1	2		120	86	1993	GEC	GEC
365/5*	4	2	2			64	1994	ABB	GEC

* Dual-voltage 750 V DC/25 kV AC, operates only on DC lines

Traction and rolling stock

Virtually all South Eastern's territory is electrified on the 750 V DC third rail system.

The company's inner-suburban services are run with modern Class 465 Networker emu trains (674 vehicles) leased from the Eversholt and Angel Trains companies.

In mid-1997, the longer distance services were being operated with a fleet of Mk 1 slam-door stock dating from the 1950s and 1960s. This included 240 Class 411 emu vehicles, 296 Class 423 emu vehicles and 84 Class 421 emu vehicles.

Plans have been formulated for retiring these vehicles. South Eastern's share of the Class 365 Networker Express fleet owned by Eversholt was introduced into service on routes from London Victoria in July 1997. However, with only 16 trains (64 vehicles), this would make only a limited impact on the fleet of Mk 1 stock.

In June 1997, Connex announced plans for replacing the Class 411s: 30 Class 375 four-car 'Electrostar' trains were to be ordered from Adtranz, with the new trains to be introduced into service with the October 2000 timetable. At the same time, Connex took options on up to 800 'Electrostar' vehicles; if all are ordered, this will allow replacement of the complete slam-door fleet on Connex South Eastern and Connex South Central.

In its franchise agreement for South Eastern, Connex committed to provide new rolling stock for the replacement of Class 421 and 423 stock by April 2006, so that within 10 years of the granting of the franchise all slam-door stock would be gone. One possibility, if Connex decides against more 'Electrostars', is to adopt the 'Networker Classic' solution: this idea, proposed by Adtranz and leasing company Angel Train Contracts, involves reusing Class 423 underframes and merely replacing the superstructure. If this solution is adopted, subsidy terms with the Office of Passenger Rail Franchising will be renegotiable.

The Channel Tunnel Rail Link, due to open in 2003, will have a number of paths reserved on it for domestic services; new trains will be required for this. The Franchise Director will seek to reach agreement with Connex to run domestic services on the route; in the event that agreement is not reached, a bidding competition to find an operator will be arranged.

UPDATED

CrossCountry Trains

CrossCountry Trains Ltd
Meridian, 85 Smallbrook Queensway, Birmingham B5 4HA
Tel: +44 121 654 7028   Fax: +44 121 654 7482

Key personnel
Chairman: Stephen Murphy

Political background
Under the arrangements put in place by the 1993 Railways Act, the franchise to run operations on British Rail's InterCity CrossCountry division was let in January 1997 to the Virgin Rail Group Ltd (qv), a subsidiary of the Virgin airline company. Virgin also runs the West Coast Trains franchise (qv).

The franchise was let for a 15-year term. Virgin will receive from the Franchising Director support, in 1997 prices, of £112.9 million in the first full financial year of the franchise, reversing to a premium payment from Virgin to the Franchising Director of £10 million in 2011-12.

CrossCountry revenue in FY95-96 was £108 million and in March 1996 the company employed 842 staff.

Passenger operations
CrossCountry runs long-distance passenger services throughout Britain, although few of its services reach

CrossCountry diesel locomotives

Class	Wheel arrangement	Power kW	Speed km/h	Weight tonnes	No in service	First built	Mechanical	Builders Engine	Transmission
43	Bo-Bo	1,680	200	70		1976	BREL	Paxman Valenta 12 RP2000L	E Brush MB190
47/4	Co-Co	1,920	153	125		1963	BR/Brush	Sulzer 12LDA28C	E Brush TM64-68

CrossCountry electric locomotives

Class	Wheel arrangement	Output kW	Speed km/h	Weight tonnes	No in service	First built	Builders Mechanical	Electrical
86/2	Bo-Bo	3,010	160	86.2		1965	BR/EE	EE

London. Its route map has the form of a cross intersecting in Birmingham, with northern axes serving Scotland and the north of England and southern axes serving the west of England and the south coast.

Traffic (million)	1996-97
Passenger journeys	12
Passenger-km	1,928
Train-km	14.8

Traction and rolling stock
CrossCountry operates InterCity 125 diesel trains leased from Angel and Porterbrook and seven-coach conventional trains hauled by ageing Class 86 electric and Class 47 diesel locomotives.

From May 2000, Virgin will begin to replace the existing loco-hauled rolling stock with a fleet of 128 new dmu vehicles. The InterCity 125s will be replaced by 24 seven-car dmu trains by May 2004. In the meantime, the existing stock will be refurbished.

NEW ENTRY

Direct Rail Services

A subsidiary of British Nuclear Fuels plc
B536 Sellafield, Seascale, Cumbria CA20 1PG
Tel: +44 1946 776819   Fax: +44 1946 775604

Key personnel
Managing Director: Max Joule
Operations Manager: Neil McNicholas
Business and Administration Manager: Allison Crayton

Political background
Under the 1993 Railways Act, the government made provision for third party and own-account operators to begin rail freight operations on the Railtrack network.

Two traditional customers of the railways have taken advantage of the legislation by setting up their own rail freight operations: National Power (qv) and British Nuclear Fuels Ltd. BNFL established a new subsidiary for the purpose: Direct Rail Services.

Freight operations
DRS began freight operations in December 1995. Its initial operations centred on BNFL's own requirements, carrying flasks of imported spent nuclear fuel from the port at Barrow about 60 km along the Cumbrian coastline to the BNFL reprocessing plant at Sellafield, and also chemicals from further afield required by the plant. In July 1997, it began third party operations, with a trial piggyback milk tanker operation between Cumbria and London. The next traffic was expected to be spent nuclear fuel rods travelling between power stations around Britain and Sellafield.

Traction and rolling stock
Initially, DRS purchased 10 ex-BR Class 20 diesel locomotives that had been used on Channel Tunnel construction operations. By cannibalising some of the machines for spares, an operating fleet of five machines was established. These normally operate as two pairs (with built-in redundancy in the event of a locomotive

Ex-BR Class 20 refurbished for use by DRS   *1996*

failure) and a spare. Brush Traction of Loughborough was contracted to refurbish the machines.

In 1997, DRS significantly expanded its fleet so that it would have the capacity to expand operations. It purchased six Class 37 diesels from Eurostar (UK) that had been earmarked for hauling sleeper trains from Europe to the West of England and South Wales, but which were no longer needed due to a reassessment of the promise of this sleeper market. It also acquired 12 Class 20s which Racal BRT owned for telecom-munications infrastructure engineering, but which Racal BRT found it did not require as it decided to hire in traction from English, Welsh & Scottish Railway.

UPDATED

English, Welsh & Scottish Railway

English, Welsh & Scottish Railway Ltd
McBeath House, 310 Goswell Road, Islington, London
EC1V 7LL
Tel: +44 171 713 2300   Fax: +44 171 713 2420

Key personnel
Chairman: Ed Burkhardt
Managing Director: Ian Braybrook
Directors
    Marketing: Randy Henke
    Operations: Barry Graham
    Engineering: Jim Fisk
    Human Resources: Les McDowell
    Finance: William Sunnucks
General Managers
    Marketing (Infrastructure Services): Kim Jordan
    Marketing (Business Development): Julian Worth
Planning Director: Graham Smith
Manager, Financial Planning: Susan Norton

Political background
English, Welsh & Scottish Railway has purchased most of British Rail's freight operations. The company is owned by Wisconsin Central Transportation (qv) of the USA with financial partners Fay, Richwhite & Co, Berkshire Partners and Goldman Sachs. The consortium first acquired the mail carrier Rail Express Systems in December 1995, and then bought the three bulk carriers, Loadhaul, Main line and Transrail, in February 1996. These four companies have been amalgamated under the English, Welsh & Scottish Railway banner; EW&SR operates freight and mail trains over Railtrack metals. In 1997, EW&SR reached agreement with British Rail on the transfer of Railfreight Distribution, BR's continental freight carrier, to EW&SR; the transfer became embroiled at the European Commission in a dispute initiated by some continental railways concerning taxpayer support to RfD, because of the terms on which the operation was to be transferred (see BR entry).

Finance
Wisconsin Central Transportation Co owns a 34 per cent share in EW&SR. EW&SR contributed US$22.8 million to WCTC's 1996 profits of US$48.4 million.

Passenger operations
Although EW&SR is principally a freight carrier, it inherited from Rail Express Systems a nationwide operating licence for passenger trains which is used for the charter trains which the business hauls for tour operators.

Class 37 locomotive in English, Welsh & Scottish livery (Darren Ford)   *1996*

Freight operations
EW&SR's bulk freight principally comprises coal for electricity generation, iron ore and semi-finished steel movements, aggregates for the road-building and construction industries, and petroleum.

Coal for electricity generation, which 10 years ago contributed two-thirds of British Rail's freight revenues, is a market in decline for EW&SR. National Power (qv), Britain's biggest power-generating company, has taken advantage of powers in the 1993 Railways Act to set up its own rail haulage operation. NP's new locomotives and wagons are capable of moving 8 million tonnes of coal each year; in 1995, the company burnt 35 million tonnes altogether. In addition to this, coal is being supplanted by gas as a fuel source for electricity generation. Contracts put in place under the transitional arrangements for the privatisation of the coal industry, under which the electricity generators are required to burn 30 million tonnes of British coal each year, expire in March 1998, when yet more coal-fired generating capacity was expected to be retired.

The aggregates market depends on the road-building programme, which has been curtailed under government spending restrictions. Mendip Rail (qv) is EW&SR's most important customer in this sector.

The British steel industry has been buoyant in recent years, and in early 1996 EW&SR's Transrail unit signed a new 10-year contract with British Steel for the movement of iron ore in South Wales which will see the number of trains hauling ore on the 75 km Port Talbot—Llanwern route increase from 28 to 40 per week.

In the petroleum market, rail in the UK is now largely confined to niche products, such as liquid petroleum gas and bitumen, that cannot easily be moved by pipeline.

Despite the pessimistic traffic forecasts in most of EW&SR's bulk haul markets, the company intends to build up traffic again by attention to customer service and by recapturing market share from road hauliers in areas where rail has lost out to road in recent years, such as the transport of coal supplies to cement works. In order to acquire the flexibility needed to quote in these markets, in early 1997 EW&SR struck a deal with Railtrack in which the latter agreed to low marginal rates of track access charges in return for an assured fixed rate each year. In FY1996-97, Railtrack track access charges for freight stood at £159 million: the bulk of this sum was paid by EW&SR.

As well as rebuilding traffic in the traditional bulk-haul markets, EW&SR chairman Ed Burkhardt has expressed interest in building up a wagonload business which can appeal to the general merchandise market. BR had abandoned this market as unviable, but in 1994 the Transrail business — then being groomed for privatisation — established a new wagonload business, known as 'Enterprise', with nightly services between London/Southwest England and Scotland. This operation has been significantly expanded under EW&SR's auspices.

In addition to moving freight for industrial customers, EW&SR moves ballast, rails and other construction materials for engineering work on the track; as a result, the infrastructure company Railtrack is EW&SR's biggest customer. Future trends for this traffic are uncertain: Railtrack is tackling a backlog of renewal work with an expanded works programme, but innovation in the way works are carried out and different methods being used by contractors could lead to a reduction in demand for traditional materials trains.

Royal Mail traffic
When it purchased Rail Express Systems, EW&SR inherited a 10-year contract for the movement of mail by rail which took effect shortly before privatisation.

Many European countries are abandoning the use of railways for mail movement, but the Royal Mail division of the British Post Office made a strategic decision to stick with rail, subject to a rethink in the way the mode is used. The plan, known as 'Railnet', took effect in September 1996.

Railnet is capitalising on rail's strengths in the medium-distance market (150 to 500 km), leaving short-distance mail movement to road vehicles and longer distances to aircraft. The Post Office has made a £150 million investment to establish Railnet, which has been complemented by £30 million from the Rail Express Systems division of EW&SR.

The investment money has been spent in two areas, new depots and rolling stock. The Post Office has built a

Bimodal RoadRailer vehicles are being used on a trial basis between Aberdeen and Northampton *1996*

Freight and parcels locomotives inherited by EW&SR

Class	Number in service
08	179
09	20
20	5
	93
31/4	14
33	19
37/0-3	128
37/4	31
37/5-7	85
37/9	6
47	146
56	118
58	50
60	100
73/0	1
73/1	23
86/2	7
86/4	8
86/6	—
87/1	—
90	5
92	—
Total	**1,038**

Class 325 dual-voltage emus for the Post Office at ABB's Derby Works (Brian Morrison)   **1995**

27,000 m² depot at Willesden, in northwest London, adjacent to the West Coast main line; smaller depots are being built in Glasgow, Newcastle, Warrington, Doncaster, Bristol Parkway, Stafford and Tonbridge. Instead of departing from the main London termini, the Travelling Post Offices (in which mail is sorted on the move) now leave from Willesden, and the new depots allow movement of mail on and off trains to be removed from the main stations, where it interferes with passenger movements.

Adtranz in Derby has built 16 four-car electric multiple-units for the Post Office. Dedicated to hauling mail in new portable containers, these bivoltage units are able to operate on the 750 V DC network south of London or on the 25 kV AC network north of the capital; they are capable of coupling to diesel locomotives for operations on non-electrified lines. In addition to the new trains, existing vans and locomotives in the EW&SR fleet have been refurbished as part of the Railnet programme. A fleet of about 60 30-year-old Class 47 diesel locomotives has undergone a life extension programme aimed to prolong time in service by about 10 years. Vans for carrying mail have been fitted with new security doors and lighting, and 43 old driving vehicles from redundant suburban electric trains have been converted by Hunslet-Barclay in Kilmarnock into propelling control vehicles, to ease reversing moves into the new mail depots.

Intermodal operations

Most intermodal movements in the UK are handled by Freightliner and Railfreight Distribution, but EW&SR does

have some limited intermodal operations. In 1996, trials were undertaken with three bimodal RoadRailer vehicles, carrying paper from Aberdeen in Scotland to Northampton; in 1997, these vehicles were used for trials for a potentially even more significant customer, the food store Safeway (other major food stores had also expressed interest in this technology). In late 1995, the Main line unit of EW&SR moved some trial loads of containers from the east coast port of Harwich to Doncaster, under contract to Stena Line; this was converted to a regular flow in 1997.

EW&SR is also taking an interest in the plans of the Piggyback Consortium (a grouping of local authorities and rail industry interests) to establish a route with a generous loading gauge capable of taking road trailers from Scotland to the Channel Tunnel. Railtrack has undertaken studies to determine the cost of bridge-raising work on the West Coast main line for this project, and Thrall Car of the US has built a prototype spine wagon at Rosyth, Scotland, in conjunction with British partner Babcock. Service trials were due to take place with the new vehicle in 1997 and EW&SR is co-operating in plans to initiate a piggyback service from Scotland to London using the new vehicle.

Traction and rolling stock

EW&SR inherited a fleet of some 1,000 diesel locomotives and around 20,000 wagons when it acquired the three bulk-haulage businesses, adding to the 150 diesel and

electric locomotives, 130 Travelling Post Office vehicles and 400 vans in the Rail Express Systems fleet. Unlike the passenger franchises, EW&SR does not lease this rolling stock but owns it outright. In addition to the stock listed here, EW&SR operates Mendip Rail's fleet of eight Class 59 diesel locomotives used on stone and ore trains in the UK, plus many privately owned wagons.

Many of the locomotives EW&SR inherited from BR date back to the 1960s and are in need of replacement. Accordingly, in May 1996 EW&SR ordered 250 new 2,240 kW DC-drive diesel-electric locomotives from General Motors in the US; these machines will be geared for heavy freight haulage, with 120 km/h top speed. The first machine is due to be delivered in late 1997, with the balance following over the next 10 years.

In addition, a further 30 locomotives are needed for fast mail traffic, with a top speed of 200 km/h.

EW&SR is also following a policy of scrapping many of the older vehicles in the wagon fleet and acquiring new models in their stead. In July 1997, a deal was announced in which US builder Thrall Car would take over the former Adtranz carriage factory at York, UK, to supply wagons to EW&SR; 2,500 wagons are to be produced over five years.

UPDATED

Eurostar (UK) Ltd

EPS House, Waterloo Station, London SE1 8SE
Tel: +44 171 922 6180   Fax: +44 171 922 4424

Key personnel

Managing Director: Hamish Taylor
Directors
   Deputy Managing: Malcolm Southgate
   Customer Services: Gordon Bye
   Executive Commercial: Ian Brooks
   Marketing: Mark Furlong
   Information Technology: Paul Tomlin
   Business: Andrew Wilby
   International Sales: Christopher Leadbeater
   UK Sales: Adrian Watts
   Public Affairs: Debra Aspin
Operations Managers: David Murray, Phil Bassett
Personnel Manager: John Hodgson
Union Railways Chief Executive: John Neerhout

Political background

Eurostar (UK) Ltd is responsible, in conjunction with other European railways, for the operation of international high-speed passenger services between London, Paris and Brussels via the Channel Tunnel. It was previously known as European Passenger Services Ltd (EPSL).

In May 1994, EPSL was transferred out of British Rail ownership and became a company owned directly by the government. This was in preparation for the transfer of EPSL to the private sector consortium chosen to build the Channel Tunnel Rail Link, a new £3 billion, 108 km high-

speed line from London to the tunnel. Assets worth some £800 million would be transferred, comprising the British share of the fleet of Eurostar trains, Waterloo International station in central London and the North Pole Eurostar maintenance depot in west London.

In June 1994 four private sector consortia were invited to bid to build the line on a build-and-operate basis: the winning consortium was London & Continental Railway (LCR). LCR has been awarded the assets of Eurostar and there will also be a cash injection of about £1.4 billion from the government — although this will not be paid until the later stages of the project, to ensure the line is actually built. The government has also written off £1.3 billion of debt in Eurostar.

LCR took control of EPSL in May 1996. The consortium comprises: civil engineering consultants Arup (2 per cent), US construction company Bechtel (18 per cent), railway designers Halcrow (2 per cent), electricity supplier London Electricity (12 per cent), bus, coach and rail operator National Express (17 per cent), French rail consultancy Systra (14 per cent), airline operator Virgin (17 per cent), and investment bank S G Warburg (18 per cent).

An equity offering was planned for 1998 to raise funds to build the new line.

Finance

Failure to meet the traffic targets set when the Eurostar services were being planned meant that when LCR took over EPSL, the company was running at a loss. A rapid turnround in the financial fortunes of Eurostar was required if LCR was to be able to afford to build the new

high-speed line. LCR set itself the aim of doubling the number of passengers travelling on Eurostars within a year, from 3 to 6 million, and the company has an aspiration to carry 10 million people annually by the end of the century.

The company suffered a setback in late 1996, when a fire in the Channel Tunnel disrupted operations for six months while repairs were undertaken, but by mid-1997 Eurostar was close to achieving the six million passengers per year rate of travel it was seeking.

Passenger operations

Eurostar's principal routes are between London and Paris (up to 17 trains a day in 1997) and London and Brussels (eight trains a day in 1997). Services on these routes were first introduced in November 1994. Some services stop at the intermediate stations at Ashford, Calais Fréthun and Lille. The London–Paris train takes 3 hours, the London–Brussels trip 3 hours 15 minutes (2 hours 40 minutes when the new high-speed line is open in Belgium in late 1997 — for details see Belgian entry).

A direct daily train from Waterloo serves Marne-la-Vallée on the LGV Jonction (Paris bypass line), for the nearby Disney complex. Seasonal skiing trains to the French Alps were planned for late 1997, with three Eurostar trains adapted to take 1.5 kV DC supplies from the overhead in the French regions.

Services between the Continent and destinations north of London, using shorter trains than those on the 'Three Capitals' services, were due to start in late 1997. The first services were expected to run from Manchester, with Manchester–Paris direct, Manchester–Paris via

A Paris-bound Eurostar calls at Ashford International (Colin Boocock)   **1996**

Eurostar electric trainsets

Class	Cars per unit	Line voltage	Motor cars per unit	Motored axles/car	Output/motor kW	Speed km/h	No in service	First built	Builders Mechanical	Electrical
373/0	10	25 kV AC 750 V DC 3 kV DC	2	4/2	100	300	22 j	1994	GEC	GEC/Brush
373/1	8	25 kV AC 750 V DC 3 kV DC	2	4/2	100	300	7	1995	GEC	GEC/Brush

(j) BR allocation of half-trains for London—Paris/Brussels services. A further 32 half-trains are allocated to France and 8 to Belgium

Birmingham and Glasgow/Edinburgh/Newcastle—Paris on the eventual route map.

A service of sleeping car trains between Britain and the Continent was planned, but this service has been dogged by technical problems with the new coaches built for the service and worries about whether it would be financially viable. In 1997, plans for running sleeper trains from the British regions to Europe were scrapped, as it was thought such services would be unprofitable. The future of sleeper services from the British capital, with London Waterloo—Dortmund/Frankfurt (with division for the two German destinations at Aachen) and London Waterloo—Amsterdam routes originally planned, hung in the balance; routes penetrating deeper into Europe were under study for their likely viability. Mid-1999 was the earliest likely starting date if Eurostar (UK) and its continental partners do decide to initiate sleeper services.

New lines
In December 1996, Parliamentary approval was granted for the building of a new high-speed route between London and the Channel Tunnel. The new route, planned to open in 2003, should reduce the journey time between London and Paris via the tunnel by some 35 minutes to around 2 hours 30 minutes and that to Brussels to 2 hours 10 minutes.

Construction of the new route was scheduled to begin in 1998 and will be directed by Union Railways, a subsidiary of LCR. London & Continental Engineering, a joint venture of four of LCR's shareholders (Bechtel, Ove Arup, Sir William Halcrow and Systra) has been appointed under an arm's length contract to design the project and to manage its construction by third party contractors for Union Railways.

Of the new route's 108 km, 26 km will be in tunnel, the main structure being a 20 km tunnel on the approaches to St Pancras. The line includes junctions on to the 750 V DC existing route near Ashford so that international trains

from the high-speed line can serve Ashford International station on the historic route; non-stop trains will be able to bypass Ashford. Another link to the historic network near Gravesend will allow trains to access the Waterloo terminal on the south side of London. The government has selected Ebbsfleet, in north Kent, as a site for an intermediate station, and LCR also plans to develop a new international station at Stratford in east London. LCR plans a link from the high-speed line to the West Coast main line; the company hopes to build up traffic from British provincial cities on the West Coast main line to the Continent.

Under the terms of the government's agreement with LCR, the Franchise Director will have access to a number of paths on the high-speed line for express commuter services to St Pancras. Between Ashford and Ebbsfleet two paths have been set aside in the off-peak, four in the peak; from Ebbsfleet to St Pancras, four paths in the off-peak and eight in the peak have been reserved for the Franchising Director's use. Connex South Eastern (qv) will be offered first refusal on operation of these services.

Major new stations
An initial London terminal for international passenger trains has been created on the north side of Waterloo station. Platforms 16-21 have been remodelled to provide five 400 m international platforms under a striking curved glazed roof. The terminal is designed to handle up to 6,000 passengers per hour in peak periods, with segregation of arriving and departing passengers.

A second London station is to be built at St Pancras to act as the terminal for the Channel Tunnel Rail Link (see 'New lines' section above), with the aim being to finish the work in 2003. LCR intends to make full use of the magnificent St Pancras train shed, designed by the 19th century engineer William Barlow, and St Pancras Chambers, designed by Sir Gilbert Scott. Six platforms in the train shed will be given over to international services,

and three for Midland main line trains; a fourth platform for the latter will be built outside the train shed on the west side of the station. Two low-level platforms will be provided on the west side of the station for Thameslink services, to replace the present cramped station at King's Cross Thameslink.

The CTRL station at Stratford, east London, also due to open in 2003, will provide an intermediate stop for international and domestic services using the Channel Tunnel Rail Link. Two island platforms, largely underground, are planned. The new station will have a wide range of connectional opportunities with domestic main line, London Underground and Docklands Light Railway services.

At Ashford, Kent, a new international station opened in January 1996. Here, passengers starting or ending their journeys in the southeast of the country can change onto internal services. The project has involved extensive modification of the existing station, with new platforms and customs facilities to seal off the international part of the station from the domestic part.

Traction and rolling stock
For the London—Paris/Brussels 'Three Capitals' service via the Channel Tunnel, 31 300 km/h Eurostar trainsets have been built by GEC Alsthom; these are some of the most technologically sophisticated trains in use in the world today.

Each Three Capitals train consists of 18 trailers, articulated in two separable rakes and with a 68 tonne power car at each end of the train. The latter has to accommodate three voltages (25 kV on SNCF, 3 kV on SNCB and 750 V in the UK) but within a 17 tonne axleload maximum. Total continuous output under 25 kV wires is some 14,000 kW, which necessitates powering one outer bogie of each half of the trailer consist; on 3 kV DC it is 7,200 kW and on 750 V DC third rail, 4,300 kW. Asynchronous, inverter-controlled three-phase motors with microprocessor control and GTO thyristors are employed.

Each air conditioned trainset includes first and standard class accommodation, two bar-buffet cars, two family compartments and facilities for nursing mothers. Each set is arranged as two self-contained power cars and nine trailer halves, easily separable from each other in case of emergency in the Channel Tunnel. Much of the technology has been derived from the SNCF's TGV design.

For through services between Paris and the British provinces, a 14-trailer format is being used. Like the 18-car sets, these trainsets incorporate provision for onboard conduct of British and French immigration plus Customs processing of passengers.

Eurostar (UK) Ltd's share of the Eurostar trainset fleet is 11 18-trailer and all seven 14-trailer units. Of the remaining 18-trailer sets the SNCF's share is 16 and the SNCB's four. (Details in the table refer to the half trains into which the Eurostar units are separable.)

European overnight services
Eurostar (UK) Ltd and Continental railway administrations are co-operating in the purchase of rolling stock for an operation of overnight train services between UK and Continental centres. Orders were confirmed in July 1992 for 139 cars for these services, to be built by GEC Alsthom Metro-Cammell.

Following 'Hotel Train' principles, the cars' accommodation includes sleeping berths with *en suite* facilities, reclining-seat cars, and service cars with luggage, bar and catering facilities.

Production of the sleeper cars fell seriously behind schedule, during which time the market for Anglo-Continental sleeper trains was reassessed (see 'Passenger operations' section above). Finished vehicles emerging from the Metro-Cammell factory in 1997 were being placed into secure store.

UPDATED

Eurotunnel

Operating headquarters: PO Box 69, F-62231 Coquelles, France
Tel: +33 3 21 00 60 00   Fax: +33 3 21 00 60 01

London Office
130 Wood Street, London EC2V 6HU
Tel: +44 171 726 2270   Fax: +44 171 726 2280

Paris Office
140-144 Blvd Malesherbes, 75017 Paris
Tel: +33 1 43 18 62 00   Fax: +33 1 43 18 62 49

Key personnel
Co-Chairman: Patrick Ponsolle
Co-Chairman designate: Robert Malpas
Group Chief Executive: G-C Chazot
Director, Purchasing: Pierre-Yves Rogez

Director, Railway Relations: Jim Evans
Manager, Railway Business Unit: Bob Reid

Gauge: 1,435 mm
Route length: 60 km
Electrification: 60 km at 25 kV, 50 Hz

Political background
Anglo-French government agreement to construction of a

Cars driving onto a shuttle train at the Eurotunnel terminal at Cheriton, Kent **1995**

rail-only tunnel under the English Channel was announced on 20 January 1986. The scheme chosen by the British and French governments was that proposed by the consortium of the Channel Tunnel Group and their French partners, France Manche (CTG-FM), which is now known as Eurotunnel.

Agreement on payments to be made by British and French Railways for use of the Channel Tunnel was reached in May 1987 after protracted negotiation. Minimum usage charges will be paid each month, even if the traffic in any one month does not reach the forecast level. The railways agreed to pay these usage charges for the first 12 years of the Tunnel operation. In return, the railways won entitlement to use 50 per cent of the capacity of the Tunnel, as varied from time to time through the concession period. Protection clauses allowing for reduction in minimum usage payments if the Tunnel is not available for use were also written into the agreement.

The Tunnel was handed over by the builders, Trans Manche Link, to the operators, Eurotunnel, in December 1993. The Tunnel complex comprises a service tunnel 4.8 m in diameter, connected every 375 m by cross-passages on either side to two railway tunnels 7.6 m in diameter. These tunnels run for 50 km, with 38 km under the sea, connecting terminals at Cheriton near Folkestone, Kent, and Coquelles, near Calais in northern France.

Eurotunnel spent the first half of 1994 on final commissioning work, and the Tunnel was formally opened by Her Majesty Queen Elizabeth II and President François Mitterrand on 6 May 1994. However, as tests were still incomplete, revenue-earning services were unable to start straightaway. The first shuttle trains carrying lorries ran on 19 May, while the first conventional freight train (carrying new Rover cars bound for Italy) ran on 1 June. Through London—Paris/Brussels Eurostar passenger trains and car-carrying shuttles began in late 1994.

Finance
Construction of the Tunnel system cost some £10 billion. This was well in excess of preconstruction estimates, and the cost over-run put some strain on the funding of this wholly privately financed project. Over 60 per cent of the revenue was expected to be derived through tourist traffic in the summer months: Eurotunnel was hoping that its first summer of full operations, in 1995, would be sufficiently fruitful to see the company through to a steady income stream. However, fierce competition from ferries constrained revenues and in September 1995 Eurotunnel suspended interest payments on its £8 billion debts in order to force its creditor banks into a financial restructuring of the company's debtload.

A serious fire on a freight shuttle in the tunnel in November 1996 deepened the company's difficulties. While insurance would cover loss of revenues while freight shuttles were suspended for six months for repair of the tunnel and analysis of the safety of operations, it would not cover lower-than-average earnings in the period while traffic was built up again while confidence was being restored.

For 1996 as a whole, turnover was £483 million and operating expenditure £516 million, giving an operating loss of £33 million. Le Shuttle revenue was up 29 per cent on the year before as a result of increased traffic.

An £8.5 billion restructuring of the company's finances, which involved the banks swapping debt for equity and the two governments agreeing an extension of the company's concession beyond 2052 until at least 2086, was approved by the company's shareholders in July 1997. The concession extension depended on Eurotunnel meeting certain demands insisted on by the two governments, concerning promotion of rail freight through the tunnel and sharing of the corporation's profits with the governments.

Passenger operations
Passenger operations through the Channel Tunnel are of two types. Cars and road coaches are transported through the Tunnel on Eurotunnel's shuttle trains, while London—Paris/Brussels foot passengers are conveyed on Eurostar trains (for description of the latter, see Eurostar (UK) Ltd entry).

The 'Le Shuttle' car-carrying trains began operations in late 1994, initially for shareholders and other invitees and later as a 'turn-up-and-go' service. The 'Le Shuttle' trains operate between elaborate terminals just beyond the tunnel mouths, at Cheriton in England and Coquelles in France. The main running lines at each are in a loop, with a flyover to avoid conflict between incoming and outgoing trains, so that shuttle trains are in continuous Anglo-French circuit without reversal. Terminal-to-terminal journey time is about 35 minutes.

To use the shuttle service, car and coach drivers simply drive off the motorway into the Eurotunnel terminal, negotiate customs and immigration posts and then drive on to the train. Unlike the 'Le Shuttle Freight' services for lorries, the car and coach users of the service stay with their vehicles for the transit of the Tunnel, and no railway coaches with seating are provided for them.

Freight operations
Freight operations through the Channel Tunnel are of two types. Lorries are transported through the Tunnel on Eurotunnel's 'Le Shuttle Freight' trains, while intermodal and conventional rail freight is conveyed in trains operated by the national rail authorities (for description of the latter, see 'Intermodal operations' section in British Rail entry).

To use the shuttle service, lorry drivers simply drive off the motorway into the Eurotunnel terminal, negotiate customs and immigration posts and then drive on to the train. A minibus driving along the platform picks the drivers up and delivers them to a club car for transit of the Tunnel. A free meal is served en route, and another minibus on the other side of the Channel takes the drivers back to their vehicles. Journey time is around 35 minutes start to stop.

Traction and rolling stock
Locomotives
Eurotunnel has bought 38 5.6 MW Bo-Bo-Bo electric

locomotives with GTO converter three-phase AC drive for shuttle operations. They were built by Brush of Loughborough, with electrical equipment from ABB (now Adtranz) of Switzerland. There is a locomotive at each end of each shuttle train, with either machine capable of powering the shuttle should the other one fail.

In May 1996, an additional four locomotives to the same design were ordered from the same builders.

Eurotunnel has also purchased five Krupp/MaK diesel-electric locomotives for yard and maintenance work.

Tourist shuttles
The Euroshuttle Consortium Wagon Group, comprising chiefly the Canadian-owned multinational Bombardier, was contracted to build 108 covered single-deck transporters for coaches; 108 double-deck covered 'tourist' transporters for private autos; and 18 single-deck and 18 double-deck loading cars.

The 'tourist' shuttle cars are formed into nine single-deck and nine double-deck sets, each of 12 transporters. Each set is flanked by loader vehicles. The normal 'tourist' train shuttle format combines a bilevel and single-level set, each with its two loader cars, and has a locomotive at each end. It thus totals 30 vehicles and is 792 m long.

The 26 m long 'tourist' transporters were built to a height of 5.6 m and a width of 4.1 m, with floor level 1,050 mm above rail. The single-level cars can thus accommodate vehicles up to 4.2 m high. Each rake is a continuous roll-on/off roadway — on both floors in the bilevel rakes. There are 6 m wide side-loading/exit doors on each side of the bilevel rakes' 26 m long loading vehicles (DDL), with separate entrances/exits for each deck: internal ramps lead from the relevant entrance/exit doors to the upper deck. The unprecedented 4.1 m width of the cars achieves an internal width of 3.75 m on each deck, leaving room for auto passengers to dismount and use toilet facilities in the transporters during the journey. The bilevel cars (DDC) are semi-permanently coupled in threes, with the centre car housing stairs and WCs.

To avoid the structural problems of doorways big enough to pass road coaches, the single-deck rakes' 26 m long loading vehicles (SDL) have telescopic hoods of steel coil-carrying wagon character, so that 18 m of their floor length can be laid open during loading/unloading.

Freight shuttles
The shuttles for road freight vehicles were built by an Italian consortium. There are 228 single-deck transporters for heavy road freight vehicles, 33 loading wagons for same, and nine club cars in which the lorry drivers ride through the Tunnel. A standard 'Le Shuttle Freight' consist is: Bo-Bo-Bo locomotive, club car, loading/unloading wagon, 14 lorry transporter wagons, loading/unloading wagon, 14 lorry transporter wagons, loading/unloading wagon, Bo-Bo-Bo locomotive.

In March 1996, Eurotunnel ordered sufficient extra wagons to make up a further two freight shuttles (with an option on four more). The order was placed with Arbel Fauvet Rail of Douai, France: 72 shuttle wagons are due for delivery in March/April 1998, and there is an option on 144 additional wagons for delivery in 1999. Costamasnaga of Italy has been contracted to build three new club cars, with an option on another two.

Signalling and telecommunications
The initial operating plan provides for a three-minute headway in each direction. Half the 20 hourly paths in each direction can be occupied by Eurotunnel's shuttle trains. The Tunnel is equipped with the TVM430 signalling and Automatic Train Protection (ATP) system adopted for French Railways' TGV Nord. The maximum speed possible is 200 km/h, but in practice the Eurotunnel shuttle trains are limited to 140 km/h, international passenger trains to 160 km/h and freight trains to 120 km/h.

Track
Rail: UIC 60 kg/m
Sleepers: Twin block concrete encased in rubber boot and cast into floor slab with no tie bars
Spacing: 600 mm
Fastenings: Sonneville S75
Max gradient: 1.1%

UPDATED

Freightliner

Freightliners Ltd
CP323, 3rd Floor, The Podium, 1 Eversholt Street,
London NW1 2FL
Tel: +44 171 214 9491   Fax: +44 171 214 9279

Key personnel
Directors
Managing: David Rutherford
Finance: Douglas Downie
Terminals: John Williams
Rail: Alan Gailey
Commercial: Bill Shiplee

Political background
Freightliner was formerly the loss-making division of British Rail running deep-sea container services from the ports to inland destinations. As part of the BR privatisation process it was put up for sale, and in May 1996 it was sold to a management buyout group.

In its last year in BR ownership, FY95-96, Freightliner made an operating loss of £20.2 million on a turnover of £87.9 million. In order to make the business saleable, the government agreed to pay Freightliner subsidy of £75 million over the first five years of private sector operation, to offset track access charges from Railtrack.

Intermodal operations
Freightliner serves the five main container ports in the UK: Felixstowe, Southampton, Liverpool, Tilbury and Thamesport. About 70 trains a day link these ports to inland terminals.

Freightliner currently carries around 450,000 containers a year. The new owners' financial projections assume volume growth of about 50 per cent over the next five years: this is based on steadily growing container volumes being landed at the ports, and an assumption of modest traffic capture from road hauliers. The plan was exceeded in the first year in private ownership, with

Class 90 locomotive on a container train   *1996*

volumes rising in excess of 10 per cent. Freightliner is currently competitive when compared to road on distances in excess of 300 km; the new owners intend, by cost cutting, to squeeze that minimum down to around 200 km, to bring the vital seaboard-to-Birmingham market within rail's compass.

A new service, 'Freightlinerbulk', was launched in April 1997; it is aimed at capturing flows of liquid and dry bulk containers currently moving by road.

Traction and rolling stock
Freightliner owns 40 ageing locomotives: 30 Class 47 diesels, and 10 Class 86 electrics. In addition, it leases 60

locomotives from the Porterbrook leasing company: 30 Class 47s, 20 Class 86s and 10 relatively modern Class 90 electrics.

Porterbrook owns the modern wagon fleet operated by Freightliner: 696 container flats and 93 'Lowliner' intermodal wagons, of small-wheel design, capable of carrying 9 ft containers on Railtrack main lines.

The traction and rolling stock fleet is thought to contain sufficient spare capacity to accommodate the new owners' ambitious expansion plans without any need for further acquisitions.

UPDATED

Gatwick Express Ltd

A subsidiary of National Express Group
Gatwick Express Ltd
52 Grosvenor Gardens, London SW1W 0AU
Tel: +44 171 973 5005   Fax: +44 171 973 5048

Key personnel
Managing Director: M Mackintosh
Marketing Director: D Brickell
Financial Controller: J North

Political background
The Gatwick Express franchise was the only one let by the Franchising Director that did not require a subsidy from the outset. The franchisee will pay a premium (in 1996 prices) of £4.6 million in the first year, increasing to £22.6 million in 2010-11.

Gatwick Express revenue was £27 million in 1994-95.

Passenger operations
Gatwick Express operates a shuttle service over the 43 km route between Gatwick Airport (London's second

largest — Heathrow is the biggest) and the terminus at Victoria in central London. The service works on a quarter-hourly frequency throughout the day, and the trip takes 30 minutes.

Traffic (million)	1996-97
Passenger journeys	3.7
Passenger-km	155
Train-km	2.09

Traction and rolling stock
Gatwick Express leases 13 Class 73/2 electro-diesel

locomotives, 74 Mk 2 coaches and 10 driving trailers from the Porterbrook leasing company. The stock dates from the 1960s and 70s, and leases expire in April 1999.

In April 1997, Gatwick Express announced that it had reached agreement with the manufacturer GEC Alsthom and leasing company Porterbrook on the acquisition of eight new eight-car trains under a lease and maintain contract.

Gatwick Express electro-diesel locomotives

Class	Wheel arrangement	Output kW	Speed km/h	Weight tonnes	No in service	First built	Builders Mechanical	Electrical
660/750 V dc third rail								
73/2	Bo-Bo	1,190*	45	76.8	13	1965	BR/EE	EE

* 600 hp on diesel traction

UPDATED

Great Eastern Railway

Great Eastern Railway Ltd
Hamilton House, 3 Appold Street, London EC2A 2AA
Tel: +44 171 922 4774   Fax: +44 171 922 4870

Key personnel
Managing Director: Bob Breakwell
Commercial Director: Mike Turner
Operations Director: David Sargent

Political background
Under the arrangements put in place by the 1993 Railways Act, the franchise to run operations on Great Eastern Railway was let in January 1997 to FirstBus plc, a bus operator which also has a stake in Great Western Trains (qv).

The franchise was let for a seven year and three months term. FirstBus will receive from the Franchising Director support, in 1997 prices, of £29.0 million in the first full financial year of the franchise, reversing to a premium payment to the Franchise Director of £9.5 million in 2004.

Great Eastern Railway electric multiple-units

Class	Cars per unit	Motor cars per unit	Motored axles/car	Power/motor kW	Speed km/h	Cars in service	First built	Builders Mechanical	Electrical
312	4	1	4	201	145	96	1976	BREL	EE
315	4	2	2	82	120	172	1980	BREL	GEC
321/3	4	1	4	268	160	308	1988	BREL	Brush

Great Eastern Railway revenue in FY95-96 was £120 million and in March 1996 the company employed 1,423 staff.

Passenger operations
Great Eastern Railway runs suburban services on a 263 km route network out of London's Liverpool Street terminus, serving Colchester, Ipswich and Southend.

Traffic (million)	1996-97
Passenger journeys	48
Passenger-km	1,488
Train-km	10.0

Traction and rolling stock
Almost all of GER's territory is electrified on the 25 kV AC system. The company's rolling stock fleet comprises 24 Class 312 emus leased from Angel and 43 Class 315 and 77 Class 321 emus leased from Eversholt.

For its non-electrified Sudbury service Great Eastern hires an Anglia Railways Class 153 diesel coach.

NEW ENTRY

Great North Eastern Railway

A subsidiary of Sea Containers Ltd
Main Headquarters Building, Station Rise, York YO1 1HT
Tel: +44 1904 653022   Fax: +44 1904 653392

Key personnel
Chief Executive: Christopher Garnett
Marketing and Sales Director: Lorraine Flower
Production Director: Mike Tham
Personnel Director: Jonathan Metcalfe
Customer Operations Director: Mike McKechnie

Political background
Under the arrangements put in place by the 1993 Railways Act, Great Northern Railway, a subsidiary of the shipping and hotels group Sea Containers, was awarded the franchise for the InterCity East Coast route in March 1996; the trading name of the line was changed later that year to Great North Eastern Railway. The franchise runs for seven years, with subsidy declining from £67.3 million in the first year to zero in the seventh year. Revenue in FY94-95 was £206 million.

Passenger operations
GNER operates intercity services on a 1,480 km network out of King's Cross terminus in London to West Yorkshire, the North East of England and Scotland.

Traffic (million)	1996-97
Passenger journeys	11.9
Passenger-km	3,352
Train-km	15.9

Traction and rolling stock
GNER operates 31 InterCity 225 electric trains owned by Eversholt Leasing and nine diesel InterCity 125s owned

Class 91 locomotive with Mk 4 coaches (John C Baker)   *1997*

by Angel Trains. Mid-life refurbishing of the diesel trains began in August 1996. In August 1996, Sea Containers acquired the one-off Class 89 Co-Co electric built by Brush Traction; this is providing cover for Class 91 InterCity 225 locomotives, which are being sent to works for treatment to improve their reliability. In July 1997, Sea Containers bought nine Mk 3 sleeping cars which had

been in use on charter trains; these were to be stripped out and fitted with seats, to provide an extra vehicle in GNER's InterCity 125 trains.

In September 1997, GNER ordered two 11-car tilting trains from Fiat of Italy for the London—Edinburgh route, with an option for six further trains.

UPDATED

Great Western Trains

Great Western Trains Co Ltd
Milford House, 1 Milford Street, Swindon SN1 1HL
Tel: +44 1793 499400   Fax: +44 1793 499451

Key personnel
Managing Director: Richard George
Finance: Barry Ward
Fleet: Ian Cusworth
Marketing: John McCallion
Public Affairs Manager: Knowles Mitchell

Political background
Under the arrangements put in place by the 1993 Railways Act, Great Western Holdings took over the operation of intercity services out of London Paddington terminus in February 1996; GWH also holds the North Western Trains franchise (qv). GWH is a joint venture

between the former British Rail management on the line, the FirstBus company and the 3i investment company. The Great Western franchise will run for 10 years, subject to investment in refurbishing of rolling stock by the company; if this investment is not undertaken, it will revert to a seven-year term.

Subsidy for the first year will be £53.2 million, which will fall to £38.2 million in 2002-03. Total revenue in 1993-94 was £156 million.

Passenger operations
GWT operates intercity services on a 1,367 km route network out of London Paddington to South Wales and the West of England. It also operates a sleeper service out of London Waterloo to Devon and Cornwall.

GWT was planning to increase the frequency on the London—Bristol route to half-hourly in the summer 1998 timetable.

Traffic (million)	1996-97
Passenger journeys	15
Passenger-km	2,043
Train-km	13.4

Traction and rolling stock
GWT leases 41 InterCity 125 sets from Angel Trains Contracts. It also leases four Class 47 locomotives and some 20 sleeping and day coaches.

GWT's InterCity 125 coaches are currently being refurbished in a four-year mid-life programme at Railcare, Wolverton.

Acquisition of new diesel multiple-units (possibly with a tilt capability) or splitting the eight-coach InterCity 125s into four-coach half-sets were being reviewed as means of increasing capacity on Great Western.

UPDATED

Refurbished Great Western InterCity 125 diesel high-speed train   *1997*

Heathrow Express

4th Floor, Cardinal Point, Newall Road, Hounslow
TW6 2QS
Tel: +44 181 745 1615   Fax: +44 181 745 1631

Key personnel
Group Rail Strategy Director: Rod Hoare
Managing Director - Operating: Ben Harding
Finance Director: Mike Singh
Rail Strategy Manager: Paul Le Blond

Passenger operations
Heathrow Express was established with the aim of introducing a dedicated airport express service between London's principal airport, Heathrow, and the rail terminus at Paddington. The company is wholly owned by airport operator BAA.

The exit from Paddington has been electrified by Railtrack on the 25 kV AC overhead system for the new service. A new Airport Junction has been built 19 km out of Paddington. Here a new 6 km line, owned by Heathrow Express, has been built to the airport itself; virtually all the new line is in tunnel. The line is double track to a station under the Central Terminal Area, and then single track to a station under Terminal Four; if a fifth terminal is built at the airport, another line would be built to T5 from the CTA, with trains splitting for Terminals 4 and 5 from the CTA.

Siemens was awarded the contract to build 14 four-car emu trains for the new service, with CAF of Spain undertaking mechanical construction.

Problems with the tunnel under the airport have set back the expected opening date, which is now June 1998. The service will comprise four trains an hour in each direction travelling at a maximum of 160 km/h, with the Paddington—Heathrow journey taking 15 minutes.

Heathrow Express intended to begin an interim service to a temporary station at Airport Junction in late 1997, with a bus shuttle to the airport. This is being marketed as 'Fast Train'.

In late 1996, BAA announced that it intended to initiate a second service from central London to Heathrow, with the new service starting in 1999. This will be a stopping service operating from St Pancras terminal, giving good connections for passengers using main line services from the North and also providing a service for airport workers residing in west London. Frequency will be the same as the Paddington service (four trains an hour) but journey time will be much longer (35 minutes as opposed to 15). Railtrack has to electrify a short section of line in north London to allow the new service to start; target opening date is 1999.

It is expected that 12 extra emu vehicles will be ordered to operate the St Pancras service.

UPDATED

Heathrow Express emu
1997

Island Line

Island Line Ltd
St John's Road Station, Ryde, Isle of Wight PO33 2BA
Tel: +44 1983 408585   Fax: +44 1983 817879

Key personnel
Managing Director: Alan Cracknell
Commercial Manager: Jane Aslett
Operations Manager: Adrian Earle

Political background
Under the arrangements put in place by the 1993 Railways Act, the franchise to run operations on the 13.6 km railway on the Isle of Wight was let in October 1996 to Stagecoach Holdings plc (qv), a bus operator.

The franchise was let for a term of five years. Stagecoach will receive from the Franchising Director

Island Line electric multiple-units

Class	Cars per unit	Motor cars per unit	Motored axles/car	Power/motor kW	Speed km/h	Cars in service	First built	Builders Mechanical	Electrical
483*	2	2	2	130	75	29	1938	Met-Cam	GEC

* Built for London Transport, converted for Isle of Wight 1989-90

support, in 1996 prices, of £2.012 million in the first full financial year of the franchise, declining to £1.751 million in the last year.

Revenue in FY95-96 was £0.729 million and in March 1996 the company employed 44 staff.

Passenger operations
Island Line operates passenger services on a 13.6 km line between Ryde and Shanklin on the eastern coast of the Isle of Wight.

Traffic (million)	1996-97
Passenger journeys	0.69
Passenger-km	5.18
Train-km	0.28

Traction and rolling stock
Island Line is operated with former London Underground electric trains.

NEW ENTRY

London & Continental Railways Ltd

3-5 Rathbone Place, London W1A 1DA
Tel: +44 171 314 1000   Fax: +44 171 580 9082

Key personnel
Chairman: Sir Derek Hornby
Chief Executive: Adam Mills

Political background
London & Continental Railways is the consortium which in 1996 won the build-and-operate concession for the Channel Tunnel Rail Link, the high-speed line from the Channel Tunnel to London. It is the parent company of Eurostar (UK) Ltd (qv).

VERIFIED

LTS Rail

LTS Rail Ltd
Central House, Clifftown Road, Southend-on-Sea, Essex
SS1 1AB
Tel: +44 1702 357889   Fax: +44 1702 357823

Key personnel
Chairman: Bob Howells
Managing Director: Ken Bird

Production Director: David Franks
Business Development Manager: Andrew Ayers

Political background
Under the arrangements put in place by the 1993 Railways Act, the LTS Rail franchise was won by Prism Rail (qv) in May 1996. The franchise was let for 15 years on the understanding that Prism would acquire new rolling stock. The franchisee has also given undertakings to invest at least £14 million on station improvements, and to build a new interchange station at West Ham in east London.

LTS Rail will receive financial support from the Franchising Director, in 1996 prices, of £29.5 million in the first year, declining to £11.2 million in 2010-11. LTS Rail revenue was £53 million in 1993-94.

Passenger operations
LTS Rail operates commuter services on the lines out of London Fenchurch Street to Tilbury, Southend and Shoeburyness, with the route network extending to 129 km in all.

Traffic (million)	1996-97
Passenger journeys	21.3
Passenger-km	535
Train-km	5.48

LTS Rail electric multiple-units

Class	Cars per unit	Motor cars per unit	Motored axles/car	Power/motor kW	Speed km/h	Cars in service	First built	Builders Mechanical	Electrical
302	4	1	4	143	120	108	1958	BR	EE
310/0	4	1	4	201	120	144	1965	BR	EE
312	4	1	4	201	145	84	1976	BREL	EE

Traction and rolling stock

LTS Rail leases 84 ageing 25 kV electric multiple-units from the Eversholt (63) and Angel Trains (21) leasing companies. The 27 oldest units, Class 302, will be scrapped over the next year as they are replaced by sliding-door-equipped Class 317 units released from the Great Northern line by the introduction into service there of new Class 365 Networker Express trains.

To meet the requirements of the 15-year franchise term, LTS Rail intends to acquire stock to replace the other slam-door units by the turn of the century. In March 1997, Adtranz was selected to fulfil a £17 million order for 44 'Electrostar' four-car emus to be acquired by Porterbrook and leased to LTS Rail.

UPDATED

Mendip Rail Ltd

Marston House, Marston Bigot, Frome, Somerset BA11 5DU
Tel: +44 1373 453 533   Fax: +44 1373 452 303

Key personnel
Operations Director: Alan Taylor

Freight operations
Mendip Rail was formed by two aggregates companies, Foster Yeoman and ARC, to manage the rail movement of stone from the company's quarries in the west of England. Mendip Rail owns nine Class 59 diesel locomotives, plus a fleet of wagons. English, Welsh & Scottish Railway (qv) operates trains for Mendip Rail.

A downturn in road-building activity in the UK has prompted Mendip Rail to find other uses for surplus capacity in its fleet. In 1997, one of Mendip's Class 59s was dispatched to Germany, where it will work in a joint venture with DB AG (German Railways) on the haulage of stone delivered by ship from Scotland to northwest German ports and then transported by rail for the reconstruction of Berlin. Other Class 59s are being hired by EW&SR for haulage of iron ore trains in South Wales.

UPDATED

Mendip Rail Class 59 locomotive in Foster Yeoman livery (Michael J Collins)   **1996**

Merseyrail Electrics

Merseyrail Electrics Ltd
Rail House, Lord Nelson Street, Liverpool L1 1JF
Tel: +44 151 709 8292   Fax: +44 151 702 3074

Key Personnel
Managing Director: Richard Parkins
Directors
Commercial: Roger Cobbe
Production: John White

Political background
Under the arrangements put in place by the 1993 Railways Act, the franchise to run operations on the Merseyrail Electrics system was let in January 1997 to MTL Trust Holdings Ltd, a group with roots in bus operations in Liverpool. MTL also runs the Regional Railways North East franchise (qv).

The franchise was let for a term of seven years and two months. Unlike other franchises, the Merseyrail Electrics one is essentially a management contract, with Merseytravel (the local authority) retaining the revenue risk, setting the fares, marketing train services and controlling timetables. Merseytravel is responsible for 89 per cent of the costs of running the network.

MTL's task is to operate the trains more efficiently and to deliver improvements in areas such as reducing fare evasion and improving passenger comfort and security. MTL has committed £6.8 million to a programme of security enhancements. MTL will receive, from the Franchising Director and Merseytravel, support in 1997 prices of £80.7 million in the first year of the franchise, declining to £60.8 million in 2003-04.

Passenger revenue in FY95-96 was £18.7 million; in March 1996, the company employed 1,207 staff.

Passenger operations
Merseyrail Electrics runs services on two lines comprising 120 route-km serving the Liverpool suburban area. The Wirral line, extending under the river Mersey, links Liverpool with West Kirby, Ellesmere Port, New Brighton and Chester. The Northern line links Liverpool with Ormskirk, Kirkby, Southport and Hunts Cross.

Traffic (million)	1996-97
Passenger journeys	22
Passenger-km	250
Train-km	5.6

Traction and rolling stock
The Merseyrail Electrics system is electrified on the 750 V DC third rail system. The company runs 32 Class 507 and 31 Class 508 emus leased from Angel Train Contracts.

NEW ENTRY

Merseyrail electric multiple-units

Class	Cars per unit	Motor cars per unit	Motored axles/car	Power/motor kW	Speed km/h	Cars in service	First built	Builders Mechanical	Electrical
507	3	2	2	82	120	96	1978	BREL	GEC
508	3	2	2	82	120	93	1979	BREL	GEC/Brush

Midland Main Line

A subsidiary of National Express Group
Midland Main Line Ltd
Midland House, Nelson Street, Derby DE1 2SA
Tel: +44 1332 262045   Fax: +44 1332 262561

Key personnel
Directors
Managing: Nick Brown
Fleet: Russ Stimpson
Marketing: Andrew Harvey

Political background
Under the arrangements put in place by the 1993 Railways Act, the Midland Main Line franchise was let to the National Express Group (qv), a company with interests in the airport and bus industries, in April 1996; NEG also operates the Gatwick Express, ScotRail, Central Trains and North London Railways franchises. The Midland Main Line franchise was let for a 10-year term, although if the company fails to acquire new rolling stock by the turn of the century it will revert to a seven-year term.

A subsidy of £16.5 million will be paid by the Franchising Director in the first year with decreasing

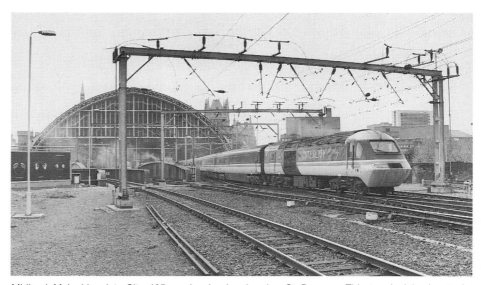

Midland Main Line InterCity 125 service leaving London St Pancras. This terminal is due to be redeveloped to house trains from the Continent off the Channel Tunnel Rail Link as well as domestic services (Brian Morrison)   **1996**

amounts thereafter until Year 5, when the franchise is forecast to turn profitable. In the second half of the franchise there will be payments to the Franchising Director by the franchisee, with the premium being around £10 million in Year 10.

Passenger operations

Midland Main Line operates intercity passenger services on a 480 km route network running out of London St Pancras station to Leicester, Derby, Nottingham and Sheffield.

Traffic (million)	1996-97
Passenger journeys	5.8
Passenger-km	758
Train-km	5.1

Traction and rolling stock

Midland Main Line leases 15 InterCity 125 sets from the Porterbrook leasing company.

In June 1997, the company ordered 13 two-car diesel multiple-units for May 1999 delivery from Adtranz, with finance from Porterbrook; the deal includes maintenance

of the new trains by the manufacturer. There is an option on trailer vehicles to make up some three-car sets if traffic warrants. The dmus will be used to provide frequent services to smaller intermediate stations on the route, allowing an increase in frequency to principal stations using InterCity 125 sets. A hub at Leicester, where the dmus will interchange with the IC125s, is planned.

UPDATED

MTL

MTL Trust Holdings Ltd
Edge Lane, Liverpool L7 9LL

Political background

MTL Trust Holdings Ltd was a bus operator which took advantage of the 1993 Railways Act to enter the rail

industry, winning the Regional Railways North East and Merseyrail Electrics franchises.

NEW ENTRY

National Express Group

National Express Group plc
Worthy Park House, Abbots Worthy, Winchester, SO21 1AN
Tel: +44 1962 888888   Fax: +44 1962 888898

Key personnel

Director, Train Division: Richard Brown

Political background

National Express Group was a coach, bus and airport operation which took advantage of the 1993 Railways Act, winning five out of the 25 passenger franchises on offer, making it the largest single operator. The franchises won were Gatwick Express, Midland Main Line, Central Trains, North London Railways and Scotrail; the group also has a minority holding in London and Continental Railways. The

size of the company's railway operation is now considerably larger than National Express's pre-existing road transport and airport business.

NEW ENTRY

National Power plc

Rail Business Department, Ferrybridge Rail Workshops, Knottingley, West Yorkshire WF11 8SB
Tel: +44 1977 632392   Fax: +44 1977 632390

Key personnel

Rail Business Manager: Chris Elston
Rail Operations Engineer: Ian Johnson
Rail Safety & Training Officer: Richard Pike
Train Control & Planning Officer: John Protheroe

Political background

Under the 1993 Railways Act, the government made provision for third party and own-account operators to begin rail freight operations in competition with the established operations of British Rail, which have themselves now been transferred to the private sector (see British Rail entry). The new entrants would buy train paths from Railtrack (qv).

In 1995, National Power took advantage of this legislation by setting up its own operations. As part of a wider agreement on coal transport, National Power and English, Welsh & Scottish Railway agreed in late 1997 that NP's rail assets would be incorporated within the EW&SR fleet in April 1998.

Freight operations

National Power took delivery of its first rolling stock in 1994: a Class 59 diesel locomotive built by General Motors in Canada, plus a rake of wagons. These are for hauling limestone for flue gas desulphurisation purposes to NP's Drax power station; the equipment is operated on NP's behalf by English, Welsh & Scottish Railway.

Bogie coal hopper and Class 59 locomotives owned by NP (Brian Morrison)   **1996**

For commencement of its own-account operations, NP ordered five more Class 59 locomotives from GM, plus five rakes of bogie wagons (with bodies from Finland and low track force bogies from Powell Duffryn Standard in the UK). The locomotives were delivered in August 1995, and NP started its own operations in November 1995.

The new equipment is used for NP's core traffic, movement of coal from pits and ports to power stations. The five rakes have an annual carrying capacity of about 8 million tonnes; NP's total coal burn is about 30 million tonnes per annum.

UPDATED

Northern Ireland Railways Co Ltd (NIR)

Central Station, East Bridge Street, Belfast BT1 3PB
Tel: +44 1232 899400   Fax: +44 1232 899401

Key personnel

Managing Director: Edward Hesketh
Directors
   Finance: Brian Delaney
   Human Resources: Alan Mercer
   Operations: Andy Watt
Chief Mechanical Engineer: Mal McGreevy
Marketing Executive: Cieran Rogan
Infrastructure and Property Executive: John Barnett

New locomotive for cross-border passenger services
1995

Gauge: 1,600 mm
Route length: 342 km

Organisation
Northern Ireland Railways is part of Translink, a state-owned corporation which manages public transport in the province.

Finance
Turnover in FY1996-97 was £21.5 million.

Passenger operations
NIR operates a cross-border intercity service jointly with Irish Rail between Belfast and Dublin. It also operates services within the province from Belfast on routes to Bangor, Larne and Londonderry.

Some 6.2 million passenger journeys were recorded in FY96-97 — thus maintaining the high levels achieved in 1995 when patronage jumped by 7 per cent, thanks to low levels of terrorist activity in the province.

Freight operations
A limited freight service operates in Northern Ireland, in the form of cross-border traffic worked to and from Adelaide yard in Belfast by Irish Rail.

New lines
A £29 million Belfast cross-harbour rail link incorporating the longest bridge in Ireland was opened in 1994. The new route comprises a 2 km single-track line, 1,424 m of it on viaduct, between Yorkgate and Belfast Central stations. A crossing loop has been provided at the site of a future station at Donegall Quay; the station itself was awaiting funding.

The project represents a significant advance for NIR, as it allows the railway to consolidate all its passenger activities on Belfast Central station; before construction of the bridge, Larne services terminated at Belfast Yorkgate, on the other side of the river Lagan.

Upgrading to passenger standards of the line from Bleach Green to Antrim has been authorised to capitalise on the new cross-harbour link. The £8 million scheme will cut Belfast—Londonderry journey times by some 20 minutes and will permit operation of through Dublin—Londonderry services without reversal when it is finished, in 1999 it is hoped.

Improvements to existing lines
Under a £100 million joint project with Irish Rail (qv), most of the Belfast—Dublin main line has been upgraded from 110 km/h to 145 km/h top speed. The project was due to be finished in 1998, with the Belfast approaches the last part to be done. The European Union has funded 75 per cent of the project.

The work has involved curve realignment and the raising of speed restrictions through Lisburn, Portadown, Poyntzpass and Dundalk. Some overbridges have been rebuilt, allowing 9 ft (2.75 m) high containers to be carried on the line.

In conjunction with the introduction of new rolling stock (see below), a 1 hour 35 minute journey time for passenger trains between Belfast and Dublin will be possible when the project is finished. Nine services will run in each direction per day, with each trainset running three round trips per day (rather than the two achieved with the old stock).

Major new stations
A new four-platform station in Belfast's Great Victoria Street was opened in September 1995. The station is at the end of a short reopened stub-end branch from the Lisburn—Belfast Central line, with spurs leading in both directions. Trains from Bangor, Ballymena and Larne reverse in the station and continue on to Lisburn or Portadown, with the same pattern applying in the reverse direction.

The new station gives good access to the city centre and Belfast's bus station. This £7 million project attracted 75 per cent European Union funding.

Traction and rolling stock
NIR has 10 diesel-electric locomotives, 30 dmus and 25 passenger cars.

In January 1994 NIR ordered two 2,390 kW JT42HCW Co-Co diesel-electric locomotives from General Motors of North America, as its contribution to a pool of four such locomotives to be jointly maintained with Irish Rail for cross-border services; it took delivery of the locomotives in July 1995. A pool of coaches was also ordered by the two organisations for this service (see Irish Rail entry for details), with squadron service beginning in September 1997.

NIR is studying options for the renewal of the Class 80 dmus dating from 1974.

Signalling and telecommunications
NIR uses two signalling systems. Centralised traffic control (CTC), with entry-exit colourlight route setting panels, controls 185 km. Block instruments control 155 km. In early 1996, CTC was being extended from the border to Portadown (30 km).

Track
Rail: 113 A FB (135 km); 95 lb BH (72 km); 50 kg FB (171 km)
Crossties (sleepers): Prestressed concrete and timber, spaced 1,150/km in plain and 1,300/km in curved track.

Fastenings: Pandrol PR401
Min curvature radius: 180 m
Max gradient: 1.25%
Max axleload: 18 tonnes

UPDATED

Diesel locomotives

Class	Wheel arrangement	Power kW	Speed km/h	Weight tonnes	No in service	First built	Mechanical	Builders Engine	Transmission
201	Co-Co	2,388	143	112	2	1995	GM	EMD 12-710 G3B	*E* GM
110	Co-Co	1,678	129	102	3	1980	GM	EMD 12-645E3B	*E* GM
100	Bo-Bo	1,007	129	69	3	1970	BREL/Hunslet	GEC Diesels/Paxman 8CSVT	*E* GEC
104	Bo-Bo	821	129	—	2	1956	Metro Vick	GM-EMD 645E	*E* AEI

Diesel railcars or multiple-units

Class	Cars per unit	Motor cars per unit	Motored axles/car	Output/motor kW	Speed km/h	Units in service	First built	Mechanical	Builders Engine	Transmission
80	3	1	2	175	112	21	1974	BREL		*E*
450	3	1	2	175	112	9	1985	BREL		*E*

New developments in Northern Ireland

To Londonderry

Larne

Bleach Green Junc.

Antrim

Whiteabbey

Yorkgate

Great Victoria St.

Central

Crumlin

BELFAST

Lough Neagh

Lisburn

Portadown

To Dublin

0 | 12 Miles
0 | 20 Kilometres

— Existing lines
--- Cross-harbour bridge opened in Nov.1994 Great Victoria St. opened in Sept. 1995
—— Freight line due to reopen to passengers in 1997

Telephones Telephones

Waiting area at reopened Great Victoria Street station in Belfast city centre **1996**

North London Railways

North London Railways Ltd
Melton House, 65-67 Clarendon Road, Watford WD1 1DP
Tel: +44 1923 207770   Fax: +44 1923 207069

Key personnel
Managing Director: Charles Belcher
Commercial Director: Bryan Leaker
Production Director: Steve White

Political background
Under the arrangements put in place by the 1993 Railways Act, the franchise to run operations on North London Railways was let in March 1997 to National Express Group plc, a bus and airport operator which has also won the Midland Main Line, Gatwick Express, ScotRail and Central Trains franchises.

The franchise was let for a term of seven years and six months. NEG will receive from the Franchising Director support, in 1997 prices, of £48.6 million in the first full financial year of the franchise, declining to £16.9 million in 2003-04.

NLR revenue in FY95-96 was £54 million and in March 1996 the company employed 1,148 staff.

Passenger operations
NLR operates suburban services out of London's Euston station and on the North London orbital line; the route network extends to 321 km. It planned to introduce a Watford—Gatwick service over the West London line in May 1998.

Traffic (million)	1996-97
Passenger journeys	28
Passenger-km	772
Train-km	8.6

Traction and rolling stock
NLR's principal route, from Euston to Northampton, is electrified at 25 kV AC overhead; for this line, the company leases 37 Class 321s emus from Eversholt.

Local routes around London are electrified with a mixture of 25 kV AC overhead and 750 V DC third rail, and for these the business leases 23 Class 313 dual-voltage emus from Eversholt.

On the Bletchley—Bedford and Gospel Oak—Barking diesel-worked branch lines, NLR uses first-generation dmus. Under the terms of the franchise agreement, NEG will replace these with new or refurbished stock by February 1999.

North London Railways electric multiple-units

Class	Cars per unit	Motor cars per unit	Motored axles/car	Power/motor kW	Speed km/h	Cars in service	First built	Builders Mechanical	Electrical
313*	3	2	2	82	120	69	1976	BREL	GEC
321/4	4	1	4	268	160	148	1990	BREL	Brush

* Dual-voltage 750 V DC/25 kV AC

NEW ENTRY

North Western Trains

North West Regional Railways Ltd
PO Box 44, Rail House, Store Street, Manchester M60 1DQ
Tel: +44 161 228 2141   Fax: +44 161 228 5003

Key personnel

Managing Director: Peter Strachan
Commercial Director: Chris Kimberley
Production Director: Alex Green

Political background

Under the arrangements put in place by the 1993 Railways Act, the franchise to run operations on North Western Trains was let in March 1997 to Great Western Holdings, the GW management/FirstBus/3i joint venture which operates Great Western Trains (qv).

The franchise was let for a seven years and one month term. GWH will receive from the Franchising Director and local authorities support, in 1997 prices, of £184.3 million in the first full financial year of the franchise, declining to £125.5 million in the final year.

North Western Trains revenue in FY95-96 was £47.8 million and in September 1996 the company employed 2,917 staff.

Passenger operations

North Western Trains operates local services on an 1,800 km route network in northwest England, including all the suburban services around Manchester, and in north Wales.

Traffic (million)	1996-97
Passenger journeys	25.1
Passenger-km	730
Train-km	23.7

Traction and rolling stock

NWT has a large stud of second-generation dmus. From Angel Trains, the business leases 55 two-car Class 142s and 29 two-car Class 150s. From Porterbrook, 12 single-car Class 153, 18 two-car Class 156 and eight two-car Class 158 dmus are leased, along with 17 three-car Class 323 emus. On the North Wales coast line, NWT uses Mk 1 coaches hauled by locomotives hired in from English, Welsh & Scottish Railway; there are also a number of first-generation emus and dmus still in use.

To replace the Mk 1 stock, GWH ordered 27 new dmu trains worth £64 million from GEC Alsthom. The order comprises nine 200 km/h three-car sets and 18 160 km/h sets (seven three-car and 11 two-car). It will also spend £1.5 million on the refurbishment of existing trains.

Class 153 dmu at Blaenau Ffestiniog (Peter J Howard)   **1997**

North Western Trains electric multiple-units

Class	Cars per unit	Motor cars per unit	Motored axles/car	Power/motor kW	Speed km/h	Cars in service	First built	Builders Mechanical	Electrical
304	3	1	4	155	120	12	1960	BR	BTH
305/1/2	3	1	4	153	120	48	1960	BR	GEC
309/2	4	1	4	210	160	32	1962	BR	GEC
323	3	1	4	146	144	51	1993	Hunslet TPL	Holec

North Western Trains diesel multiple-units

Class	Cars per unit	Motor cars per unit	Motored axles/car	Power/motor kW	Speed km/h	Cars in service	First built	Builders Mechanical	Engine	Transmission
101	2/3	1/2	2	112			1956	Met-Cam	Leyland	M
150/1	2	2	2	210	120	58	1985	BREL	Cummins NT855R5	HM Voith T211r
150/2	2	2	2	210	120		1986	BREL	Cummins NT855R5	HM Voith T211r
153	1	1	2	213	120	12	1987*	Leyland Bus	Cummins NT855R5	HM Voith T211r
156	2	2	2	210	120	36	1987	Met-Cam	Cummins NT855R5	HM Voith T211r
158/0	2	2	2	275/300	145	16	1989	BREL	Cummins NTA855R	HM Voith T211r

* Rebuilt 1991

NEW ENTRY

Prism Rail

Prism Rail plc
32 Ludgate Hill, London EC4M 7DR

Tel: +44 171 213 9650   Fax: +44 171 248 2512

Key personnel

Chairman: Godfrey Burley

Political background

Prism Rail was a company established by four bus companies — Blazefield Holdings, EYMS Group, Lynton Travel Group, and Q Drive Holdings — to take advantage of opportunities offered by the 1993 Railways Act. Prism won four franchises: Cardiff Railway, LTS Rail, South Wales & West and West Anglia Great Northern (all: qv). Shares in Prism are traded on the London Alternative Investment Market.

Finance

In the 14 months to April 1997, Prism Rail made £5.1 million before exceptional items. Passenger revenue totalled £104 million, subsidy payments £85.5 million and other income £9.7 million. Operating expenses of £194.1 million comprised Railtrack charges (£88.9 million), rolling stock leasing (£34.1 million), staff costs (£35.8 million) and other operating expenses (£35.3 million).

NEW ENTRY

Railtrack

40 Bernard Street, London WC1N 1BY
Tel: +44 171 344 7100   Fax: +44 171 344 7101
Web site: http://www.railtrack.co.uk

Key personnel

Chairman: Sir Robert B Horton
Chief Executive: Gerald Corbett

Directors
Engineering and Production: Brian Mellitt
Commercial: Richard Middleton
Safety and Standards: Rod Muttram
Line Safety: Aidan Nelson
Finance and Systems: Norman Broadhurst
Passenger Business: Brian Burdsall
Freight Business: Robin Gisby
European Affairs: David Moss

Civil Engineering: Nigel Ogilvie
Human Resources: David Armstrong
Major Projects: Gil Howarth
Project Delivery: Martin Reynolds
Procurement: John Abbott
Property: Bob Hill
Corporate Affairs: Philip Dewhurst
Solicitor and Secretary: Simon Osborne
Deputy Secretary: Jacqueline Holman

In 1996, Railtrack completed upgrading of the North London orbital line for regional Eurostar trains. The floor of the tunnel at Hampstead (pictured) had to be lowered to give the necessary clearances   **1997**

Financial Controller: Philip Berridge
Zonal Directors
  London North East: Nick Pollard
    Tel: +44 1904 524111
    Fax: +44 1904 523556
  Scotland: Paul Prescott
    Tel: +44 141 335 2424
    Fax: +44 141 335 3572
  North West: Chris Leah
    Tel: +44 161 228 8500
  Great Western: Nick Josephy
    Tel: +44 1793 499500
    Fax: +44 1793 515748
  Southern: Chris Jago
    Tel: +44 171 620 5012
  East Anglia: Michael Holden
    Tel: +44 171 922 4833
    Fax: +44 171 922 4822
  Midlands: vacant
    Tel: +44 121 654 2161
    Fax: +44 121 654 4871

Gauge: 1,435 mm
Route length: 16,536 km
Electrification: 2,970 km at 25 kV, 50 Hz AC overhead;
1,958 km at 750 V DC third rail

Political background
Railtrack was set up in the reforms engendered by the 1993 Railways Act (for description, see 'Political background' section in the British Rail entry). It is the rail infrastructure authority on the UK mainland, owning the track, stations and signals and controlling the timetabling of trains. Its income comes from the train paths it sells to train operating companies; charging policy is subject to scrutiny by the Rail Regulator.

Railtrack was floated on the London Stock Exchange in May 1996, in an exercise which raised some £1.9 billion for the UK government.

Finance
In FY96-97, Railtrack recorded turnover of £2.437 billion and operating profits of £339 million. Income comprised track access payments from passenger train operating companies (£2.119 billion), freight operators (£159 million), property rental (£120 million) and other sources (£39 million). Operating costs for 1996-97 were £2.098 billion.

Improvements to existing lines
Thameslink 2000
A £560 million plan to upgrade an existing north-south line under London to RER (Regional Express) standards was agreed by the government and Railtrack in the run-up to flotation of the company in early 1996. Railtrack agreed to undertake the project, known as Thameslink 2000, in exchange for being floated with lower debt levels than would otherwise have been the case.

The historic Thameslink route beneath the City of London, which has been used by through trains since 1988, suffers from serious capacity constraints. Thameslink 2000 involves major infrastructure work to eliminate some flat junctions south of the river Thames, and at St Pancras a new low-level station and new connections to adjacent main lines will be built as part of the rebuilding of the station for the Channel Tunnel Rail Link (see Eurostar (UK) entry). Power supplies in the central tunnelled section will be enhanced.

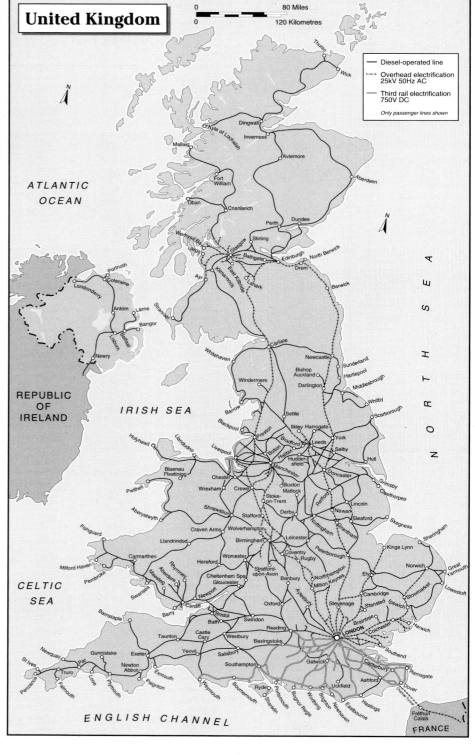

United Kingdom

0 ——— 80 Miles
0 ——— 120 Kilometres

Diesel-operated line
Overhead electrification 25kV 50Hz AC
Third rail electrification 750V DC

Only passenger lines shown

On completion of the project, probably in 2003, the present Thameslink service between Bedford and Brighton will be supplemented by services between King's Lynn and Peterborough north of the Thames, and Ashford, Dartford, Horsham and Guildford, south of London.

West Coast modernisation
The West Coast main line, which connects London with Birmingham, Manchester, Liverpool and Glasgow, has had only limited investment since its electrification in the mid-1960s. Plans by British Rail to modernise it in the early 1990s came to nothing and a decision on investment in the route had to await privatisation of the railways.

With the reorganisation of the railway industry, Railtrack has taken on responsibility for the infrastructure side of the West Coast project. In October 1996, the Franchise Director and Railtrack reached agreement on a £1.35 billion infrastructure upgrading programme on the route, while the franchise agreement for West Coast Trains signed by Virgin (qv) in early 1997 ensures that new trains will be built for the line.

The infrastructure upgrading programme includes signalling system upgrading, catenary renewal, upgrading of the traction current supply system and some minor work to improve alignments. While a 'Core Improvement Programme' which accounts for the largest share of the money will see replacement of worn-out assets, some £150 million of the £1.35 billion overall project is going to finance improvements in the route (rather than just like-for-like replacements). Known as 'PUG 1' (Passenger Upgrade One), the £150 million of improvements will be in place by 2002, when the new trains are scheduled to arrive, and will enable them to run at speeds up to 200 km/h (the present speed limit on the route is 175 km/h). Virgin's aspiration is that PUG 1 will be followed by PUG 2, enabling the new trains to run at speeds up to 225 km/h from 2006.

A central plank of the upgrade project is renewal of the signalling on the line. For this, Railtrack is proposing radio Transmission Based Signalling (TBS), with cab displays of the speed permitted and elimination of traditional wayside signals (except at busy junctions where signals would be retained for non-TBS equipped rolling stock). In early 1996, Railtrack awarded two parallel development contracts for the TBS to Transig (a consortium of Adtranz and Westinghouse Signals) and a consortium of GEC Alsthom and Siemens. It seemed likely that a variant of the

TBS being developed under the international European Train Control System initiative would eventually be chosen for the West Coast main line. However, in early 1997 the TBS programme was running into problems which might delay its implementation.

Signalling and telecommunications

Solid State Interlocking (SSI) has been a standard feature of recent resignalling projects. The interlocking is performed centrally by microcomputers which communicate through serial datalinks with lineside terminals directly controlling signalling equipment. To achieve the required levels of safety and availability, cross-checking duplicate or triplicate systems are used (hardware redundancy). Built-in diagnostic facilities enable faults to be detected and rectified speedily.

Major resignalling schemes lately completed or under way adopt the Integrated Electronic Control Centre (IECC) concept.

In an IECC, solid-state interlocking is used to prevent conflicting routes being set and, in place of a conventional panel, high-resolution colour VDUs are employed. Automatic route-setting is provided for the entire control area; manual route-setting is necessary only in exceptional cases. The signalling system provides data for comprehensive passenger and management information systems within an integrated communications network.

IECCs recently installed include one at Ashford, Kent, which controls international trains from close to the Channel Tunnel mouth to within a few kilometres of the terminus at Waterloo.

Signalling projects under way in 1997 included resignalling of the London—Southampton main line west of Wimbledon, and the London—Colchester line beyond Stratford. Work has begun on the first stage of an IECC for Manchester.

Taking a further technological step forward, Railtrack now envisages the use of transmission-based signalling (see 'West Coast modernisation' in 'Improvements to existing lines'). In a policy document issued in early 1997, Railtrack envisaged three levels of signalling in future: transmission-based signalling on the main intercity routes, conventional colourlight signals in suburban areas where conversion of large numbers of trains to TBS would be uneconomic, and axle counter or radio electronic token system for rural lines.

UPDATED

Regional Railways North East

Regional Railways North East Ltd
Station Rise, York YO1 1HT
Tel: +44 1904 653022   Fax: +44 1904 523075

Key personnel

Managing Director: Paul Davison
Commercial Director: Mike Hodson
Production Director: Stuart Baker

Political background

Under the arrangements put in place by the 1993 Railways Act, the franchise to run operations on Regional Railways North East was let in March 1997 to MTL Rail Ltd, a subsidiary of MTL Trust Holdings Ltd (qv), a group with roots in bus operations in Liverpool. MTL also runs the Merseyrail Electrics franchise (qv).

The franchise was let for a seven year and one month term. MTL will receive from the Franchising Director and local authorities support, in 1997 prices, of £224.5 million in the first full financial year of the franchise, declining to £145.6 million in 2003-04.

Regional Railways North East revenue in FY95-96 was £68 million and in September 1996 the company employed 2,960 staff.

Passenger operations

Regional Railways North East runs services on a 2,055 km network in northern England, including express services across the Pennines and local services around big cities such as Leeds and Newcastle.

Traffic (million)	1996-97
Passenger journeys	39
Passenger-km	1,265
Train-km	32.9

Regional Railways North East electric multiple-units

Class	Cars per unit	Motor cars per unit	Motored axles/car	Power/motor kW	Speed km/h	Cars in service	First built	Builders Mechanical	Electrical
308	3	1	4	154	120	66	1961	BR	GEC
321/9	4	1	4	268	160	12	1991	BREL	Brush

Regional Railways North East diesel multiple-units

Class	Cars per unit	Motor cars per unit	Motored axles/car	Power/motor kW	Speed km/h	Cars in service	First built	Mechanical	Builders Engine	Transmission
141	2	2	1	152	120		1984	BREL	Leyland TL11	H Voith T211r
142	2	2	1	170	120		1985	BREL	Cummins LTA10R	H Voith T211r
144	2/3	2/3	1	170	120		1986	Alexander	Cummins LTA10R	H Voith T211r
153	1	1	2	213	120		1987*	Leyland Bus	Cummins NT855R5	HM Voith T211r
155/1	2	2	2	213	120		1988	Leyland Bus	Cummins NT855R5	HM Voith T211r
156	2	2	2	210	120		1987	Met-Cam	Cummins NT855R5	HM Voith T211r
158/0	2/3	2/3	2	275/300	145		1989	BREL	Cummins NTA855R/ Perkins 2006-TWH	HM Voith T211r
158/9	2	2	2	275	145		1989	BREL	Cummins NT855R1	HM Voith T211r

* Rebuilt 1991

Traction and rolling stock

The majority of Regional Railways North East's services are run with second-generation diesel multiple-unit vehicles.

Class 158 dmus (31 two-car and 17 three-car) leased from Porterbrook operate the company's premier services, while Class 142, 144, 153, 155 and 156 dmus are used on local services. On electric services from Leeds to Doncaster, three Class 321/9 emus leased from

Porterbrook are employed, while on the Leeds—Skipton line first-generation emus of Class 308 leased from Angel Trains are used. Under the terms of the franchise agreement, MTL has committed to introducing 16 new three-car emus by December 2000 to replace the Class 308s.

NEW ENTRY

ScotRail

ScotRail Railways Ltd
Caledonian Chambers, 87 Union Street, Glasgow G1 3TA
Tel: +44 141 332 9811   Fax: +44 141 335 4592

Key Personnel

Managing Director: Alistair McPherson
Finance Director: Alex Lynch
Director of Corporate Affairs: John Boyle

ScotRail electric multiple-units

Class	Cars per unit	Motor cars per unit	Motored axles/car	Power/motor kW	Speed km/h	Cars in service	First built	Builders Mechanical	Electrical
303	3	1	4	155	120		1959	Pressed Steel	Metro-Vick
305/2	4/3	1	4	153	120		1960	BR	GEC
314	3	2	2	82	120		1976	BREL	GEC/Brush
318	3	1	4	268	145		1985	BREL	Brush
320	3	1	4	268	120		1990	BREL	Brush

ScotRail diesel multiple-units

Class	Cars per unit	Motor cars per unit	Motored axles/car	Power/motor kW	Speed km/h	Cars in service	First built	Mechanical	Builders Engine	Transmission
101	2	2	2	112		22	1958	Met-Cam	Leyland	M
117	3	2	2	112		21	1959	Pressed Steel	Leyland	M
150/2	2	2	2	210	120	28	1986	BREL	Cummins NT855R5	HM Voith T211r
156	2	2	2	210	120	96	1987	Met-Cam	Cummins NT855R5	HM Voith T211r
158/0	2	2	2	275/300	145	94	1989	BREL	Perkins 2006-TWH	HM Voith T211r

Political background

Under the arrangements put in place by the 1993 Railways Act, the franchise to run operations on ScotRail was let in March 1997 to National Express Group plc (qv), a bus and airport operator which has also won the Midland Main Line, Gatwick Express, North London Railways and Central Trains franchises.

The franchise was let for a seven-year term. NEG will receive from the Franchising Director and Strathclyde Passenger Transport Authority support, in 1997 prices, of

£280.1 million in the first full financial year of the franchise, declining to £202.5 million in 2003-04.

ScotRail revenue in FY95-96 was £104.9 million and in March 1996 the company employed 3,977 staff.

Passenger operations

ScotRail operates services on a 3,032 km network covering Scotland, including the Glasgow suburban network (which accounts for over a third of revenue). It also operates sleeper services between Scottish cities and London.

Traffic (million)	1996-97
Passenger journeys	53.4
Passenger-km	1,673
Train-km	32.1

Traction and rolling stock

ScotRail operates only multiple-unit trains, save for on its sleeper services, where Class 87s are hired in from Virgin West Coast to haul the Mk 3 sleeper vehicles.

NEG has committed to introducing, by March 2000, 38 new three-car emus for the Strathclyde network and nine new three-car dmus for the Edinburgh—Falkirk—Glasgow route.

NEW ENTRY

Sea Containers

Sea Containers Services Ltd
20 Upper Ground, London SE1 9PF
Tel: +44 171 805 5000   Fax: +44 171 805 5903

Key personnel
President: James Sherwood
Vice-President, Rail: Christopher W M Garnett

Political background
Sea Containers has its roots in the container leasing industry and has of late diversified into railways. It operates the luxury Venice-Simplon Orient Express tour train and in 1996 took over intercity operations on the London—Edinburgh route, which it is marketing as the Great North Eastern Railway (qv).

NEW ENTRY

South Wales & West Railway

South Wales & West Railway Ltd
Western House, 1 Holbrook Way, Swindon SN1 1BY
Tel: +44 1793 515391   Fax: +44 1793 515404

Key personnel
Managing Director: David Weir
Finance and Systems Director: Andrew Sinclair
Fleet Director: Mark Brand

Political background
Under the arrangements put in place by the 1993 Railways Act, the franchise to run operations on South Wales & West Railway was let in October 1997 to Prism Rail plc (qv), a company set up by a consortium of bus companies. Prism also runs the Cardiff Railway, LTS Rail and West Anglia Great Northern franchises.

The franchise was let for a term of seven years and six months. Prism will receive from the Franchising Director support, in 1996 prices, of £70.9 million in the first full financial year of the franchise, declining to £38.1 million in the last year of the franchise.

Revenue in FY95-96 was £44.5 million and in January 1996 the company employed 1,398 staff.

Passenger operations
South Wales & West runs interurban services from South

South Wales & West Railway diesel multiple-units

Class	Cars per unit	Motor cars per unit	Motored axles/car	Power/motor kW	Speed km/h	Cars in service	First built	Mechanical	Builders Engine	Transmission
143	2	2	1	152	120		1985	Alexander/ Barclay	Cummins LTA10R	*H* Voith T211r
150/2	2	2	2	210	120		1986	BREL	Cummins NT855R5	*HM* Voith T211r
153	1	1	2	213	120		1987*	Leyland	Cummins NT855R5	*HM* Voith T211r
158/0	2	2	2	275/300	145		1989	BREL	Cummins NTA855R	*HM* Voith T211r

* Rebuilt 1991

Wales to Manchester and Birmingham, Bristol, Portsmouth and the West of England. It also runs rural services over much of South Wales and the West of England. Total route-km operated over: 2,523.

Traffic (million)	1996-97
Passenger journeys	12.9
Passenger-km	728
Train-km	18.8

Traction and rolling stock
South Wales & West is an all-diesel-operated franchise worked with second-generation dmus. For its interurban routes, South Wales & West employs Class 158 dmus leased from Angel Train Contracts. For local services, it leases Class 153 single cars from Angel and Class 143 and 150/2 dmus from Porterbrook.

As part of the franchise agreement, Prism has committed to refurbishing the whole of the 78-vehicle Class 158 fleet. This includes renewing carpets, seats and interior trim, and improving air conditioning and toilets. The refurbishment programme is to be completed before April 1999.

NEW ENTRY

South West Trains

A subsidiary of Stagecoach Holdings
South West Trains Ltd
Friars Bridge Court, 41-45 Blackfriars Road, London SE1 8NZ
Tel: +44 171 928 5151   Fax: +44 171 620 5015

Key personnel
Managing Director: Brian Cox

Political background
Under the arrangements put in place by the 1993 Railways Act, a franchise to run South West Trains for seven years passed to the bus company Stagecoach (qv) in February 1996; Stagecoach also operates the Island Line franchise. Subsidy from the Franchise Director is set to fall from £54.7 million in the first year of operation to £40.3 million in the final year.

Revenue in 1994-95 was £230 million.

Passenger operations
South West Trains operates commuter trains in southwest London and long-distance services from London Waterloo to a triangular area of southern England stretching from Portsmouth in the east to Exeter in the west. Total route-km operated over: 940.

Traffic (million)	1996-97
Passenger journeys	110.7
Passenger-km	3,276
Train-km	31.5

South West Trains electric multiple-units

Class	Cars per unit	Motor cars per unit	Motored axles/car	Power/motor kW	Speed km/h	Cars in service	First built	Builders Mechanical	Electrical
412	4	2	4	185	145	28	1957	BR	EE
421/4	4	1	4	185	145	136	1970	BREL	EE
423	4	1	4	185	145	308	1967	BR	EE
442	5	1	4	300	160	120	1988	BREL	EE
455	4	1	4	185	120	274	1982	BREL	GEC

South West Trains diesel multiple-units

Class	Cars per unit	Motor cars per unit	Motored axles/car	Power/motor kW	Speed km/h	Cars in service	First built	Mechanical	Builders Engine	Transmission
159*	3	3	3	300	145	66	1993	ABB/ Babcock/ Thorn	Cummins NT855R1	*HM* Voith T211r

* Built as Class 158 and converted before entering service

Traction and rolling stock
Most of the area covered by South West Trains is electrified on the 750 V DC system. SWT operates some 230 four- and five-car electric multiple-units owned by all three of the ex-British Rail rolling stock leasing companies, plus 22 three-car Class 159 diesel units owned by Porterbrook which are used on the line from Waterloo to Salisbury and Exeter. In 1997, SWT placed an order with GEC Alsthom, with financing from sister company Porterbrook Leasing, for 30 new four-car emus to replace slam-door stock on the Waterloo—Reading line.

UPDATED

Stagecoach

Stagecoach Holdings PLC
20 Charlotte Street, Perth PH1 5LL
Tel: +44 1738 442111   Fax: +44 1738 643648

Key personnel
Chairman: Brian Souter

Rail operations office:
Stagecoach (South) Ltd
Lewes Enterprise Centre, 112 Malling Street, Lewes, East Sussex BN7 2RB
Tel: +44 1273 480248   Fax: +44 1273 474206

Key personnel
Director: Brian Cox

Political background
Stagecoach has its roots in the bus industry, having grown fast following bus deregulation in the UK in the 1980s. With that market approaching maturity, it turned its attentions to overseas bus acquisitions and to the opportunities offered by the 1993 Railways Act in the UK. It won the first franchise to be let, South West Trains (qv), and subsequently acquired the Island Line franchise. It also purchased Porterbrook (qv), one of the three rolling stock leasing companies formed with the British Rail rolling stock fleet. Porterbrook was initially sold to a management buyout team and then acquired by Stagecoach in late 1996.

The rail industry now accounts for over 40 per cent of Stagecoach's turnover.

NEW ENTRY

Thames Trains

Thames Trains
Venture House, 37-43 Blagrave Street, Reading RG1 1RY
Tel: +44 118 957 9453   Fax: +44 118 957 9648

Key personnel

Managing Director: Roger McDonald
Commercial Manager: Nick Illsley
Production Manager: David Franks

Political background

Under the arrangements put in place by the 1993 Railways Act, the franchise to run operations on Thames Trains was let in October 1997 to Victory Railway Holdings Ltd, a joint venture between bus operator The Go-Ahead Group plc and the management of Thames Trains. The Go-Ahead Group is also part of a joint venture running Thameslink (qv).

The franchise was let for a term of seven years and six months. Victory Railways will receive from the Franchising Director support, in 1996 prices, of £33.2 million in the first full financial year of the franchise, declining to zero in the last year of the franchise.

Thames Trains revenue in FY94-95 was £46.5 million and in February 1996 the company employed just over 1,000 staff.

Passenger operations

Thames Trains operates suburban services out of London's Paddington station along the Thames valley to Reading and Oxford. The company also runs services between Oxford and Worcester, Reading and Basingstoke and Reading and Gatwick Airport. Total route-km operated over: 584.

As part of the franchise agreement, Victory has committed to increasing the Oxford—Paddington weekday frequency to half-hourly in 1998.

Traffic (million)	1996-97
Passenger journeys	26.8
Passenger-km	756
Train-km	12.1

Traction and rolling stock

Thames Trains uses only modern 'Turbo' diesel units built by Adtranz. The fleet consists of Class 165 and 166 dmus leased from Angel Train Contracts.

Thames Trains diesel multiple-units

Class	Cars per unit	Motor cars per unit	Motored axles/car	Power/motor kW	Speed km/h	Cars in service	First built	Mechanical	Builders Engine	Transmission
165/0	2	2	2	260	120	10	1990	BREL	Perkins 2006-TWH	H Voith T211r
165/1	2/3	2/3	2	260	145	91	1992	ABB	Perkins 2006-TWH	H Voith T211r
166	3	3	2	260	145	63	1993	ABB	Perkins 2006-TWH	H Voith T211r

NEW ENTRY

Thameslink

Thameslink Rail Ltd
Friars Bridge Court, 41-45 Blackfriars Bridge Road, London SE1 8NZ
Tel: +44 171 620 5222   Fax: +44 171 620 5099

Key Personnel

Managing Director: Euan Cameron
Commercial Director: John Cimelli
Production Manager: Keith Pym

Political background

Under the arrangements put in place by the 1993 Railways Act, the franchise to run operations on Thameslink was let in March 1997 to GOVIA, a joint venture combining the British bus operator Go-Ahead Group plc and Via GTI, the French transport group.

The franchise was let for a seven year and one month term. GOVIA will receive from the Franchising Director support, in 1997 prices, of £2.5 million in the first full financial year of the franchise, reversing to a premium payment to the Franchise Director of £28.4 million in 2004.

Thameslink revenue in FY95-96 was £76 million and in March 1996 the company employed 522 staff.

Passenger operations

Thameslink runs cross-London suburban operations through a tunnel linking King's Cross to Blackfriars. Long-distance services run between Bedford and Brighton, and inner-suburban services between Luton and Wimbledon. Total route-km operated over: 225.

Traffic (million)	1996-97
Passenger journeys	27
Passenger-km	923.6
Train-km	10.0

Improvements to existing lines

Railtrack is committed to a £560 million upgrade of the Thameslink lines in a project known as Thameslink 2000. This will see upgrading of the power supply and signalling through the central London tunnels, improvements in track layouts to increase capacity in south London, and a new station adjacent to St Pancras to replace the cramped King's Cross Thameslink station. Target completion date is 2003, at which point Peterborough, King's Lynn and Letchworth to the north of London, along with Littlehampton, Eastbourne, Horsham, Dartford and Ashford to the south of London, will be brought into the service net.

The Franchising Director wishes to be in a position to refranchise the services currently operated by Thameslink at the time of the introduction of Thameslink 2000 services. Accordingly, under the terms of the franchise agreement, while the franchise can continue until 1 April 2004, the Franchising Director will have the right to terminate the franchise agreement at any time from five and a half years after the commencement date.

Traction and rolling stock

Thameslink operates over 25 kV AC overhead electrified lines to the north of London and 750V DC third rail in the south. The changeover point is at Farringdon in central London.

The company's rolling stock comprises solely Class 319 dual-voltage emus leased from Porterbrook; there are 66 four-car units in the fleet.

Thameslink Rail electric multiple-units

Class	Cars per unit	Motor cars per unit	Motored axles/car	Power/motor kW	Speed km/h	Cars in service	First built	Builders Mechanical	Electrical
319/0	4	1	4	247	160		1987	BREL	GEC
319/1	4	1	4	247	160		1990	BREL	GEC

NEW ENTRY

Virgin Rail

Virgin Rail Group Ltd
120 Campden Hill Road, London W8 7AR
Tel: +44 171 229 4738   Fax: +44 171 229 5834

Key personnel

President: Richard Branson
Chairman: Stephen Murphy
Director: Will Whitehorn

Virgin Rail Management
West Wing Offices, Euston Station, London NW1 2HS

Key personnel

Chief Executive: Brian Barrett
Finance Director: Alan Tomlin

Managing Director, Virgin Trains: Chris Tibbits
Director, Business Development and Industry Affairs: Ivor Warburton
Director, New Business Development: Dominic Ryan

Political background

Virgin Rail Group was established to oversee the rail franchises won by Virgin in the British Rail privatisation programme, CrossCountry Trains Ltd (qv) and West Coast Trains Ltd (qv). The two ex-InterCity businesses give Virgin an extensive route map covering much of the country. Ambitious revenue growth projections for the two businesses mean that, if they are met, Virgin's rail revenue will exceed its air revenue by 2003-04.

Organisation

Virgin Rail Group oversees the activities of Virgin Rail Management, which in turn supervises the operations run by Virgin Trains' Managing Director Chris Tibbits in Birmingham. CrossCountry and West Coast are run as one from the Birmingham office, although to meet the rules of the Office of Passenger Rail Franchising they are legally separate entities.

NEW ENTRY

West Anglia Great Northern

West Anglia Great Northern Railway
Hertford House, 1 Cranwood Street, London EC1V 9GT
Tel: +44 171 928 5151   Fax: +44 171 465 9015

Key personnel

Managing Director: David Burton

Financial Director: Nick Wood
Operations and Safety Director: Norman West

Political background

Under the arrangements put in place by the 1993 Railways Act, the franchise to run operations on West Anglia Great Northern was let in December 1996 to Prism Rail plc (qv), a company set up to run rail franchises by a consortium of bus companies. Prism also runs the Cardiff Railway, South Wales & West and LTS Rail franchises; shares in Prism Rail are traded on the London Alternative Investment Market.

The franchise was let for a term of seven years and three months. Prism will receive from the Franchising

WAGN Railway electric multiple-units

Class	Cars per unit	Motor cars per unit	Motored axles/car	Power/motor kW	Speed km/h	Cars in service	First built	Builders Mechanical	Electrical
313*	3	2	2	82	120	123	1976	BREL	GEC
315	4	2	2	82	120	72	1980	BREL	Brush/GEC
317	4	1	4	247	160	188	1981	BREL	GEC
322	4	1	4	268	160	20	1990	BREL	Brush
365	4	2	2	—	160	100	1994	ABB	GEC

* Dual voltage, 25 kV AC, 750 V DC

Director support, in 1996 prices, of £52.9 million in the first full financial year of the franchise, reversing to a premium payment from Prism of £24.8 million in 2004.

Revenue in FY95-96 was £119.8 million and in March 1996 the company employed 1,585 staff.

Passenger operations
West Anglia Great Northern operates suburban services on a 413 km route network out of London's King's Cross and Liverpool Street stations, with services reaching as far north as King's Lynn.

Traffic (million)	1996-97
Passenger journeys	50.5
Passenger-km	1,496
Train-km	16.5

Traction and rolling stock
WAGN is exclusively operated by electric multiple-unit trains operating on the 25 kV AC overhead system. The company leases 41 Class 313s, 18 Class 315s, 47 Class 317s, five Class 322s and 25 Class 365s. All are leased from Eversholt, except the Class 317s which are owned by Angel Trains.

Prism has committed to refurbishing all the units used on outer-suburban services to a standard comparable to the new Class 365s, and to install more comfortable seats on the Class 315s.

NEW ENTRY

West Coast Trains

West Coast Trains Ltd
Meridian, 85 Smallbrook Queensway, Birmingham
B5 4HA
Tel: +44 121 643 4444   Fax: +44 121 643 4557

Key personnel
Chairman: Brian Barrett

Political background
Under the arrangements put in place by the 1993 Railways Act, the franchise to run long-distance passenger services on the West Coast main line was let to Virgin Rail Group (qv), a subsidiary of the airline operator Virgin, in March 1997. Virgin also runs the CrossCountry franchise (qv).

The franchise was let for a 15-year term; it is expected to move into profit in 2002-03. Virgin will receive from the Franchising Director support, in 1997 prices, of £76.8 million in the first full year of the franchise, turning to a premium payment of £220.3 million in 2011-12.

Passenger revenue in FY95-96 was £219 million, and in April 1996 the company employed 3,880 staff.

Passenger operations
West Coast Trains runs services on a 1,087km network out of London's Euston terminus to the West Midlands, northwest of England and central Scotland.

Traffic (million)	1996-97
Passenger journeys	13.2
Passenger-km	2,917
Train-km	16.5

West Coast electric locomotives

Class	Wheel arrangement	Output kW	Speed km/h	Weight tonnes	No in service	First built	Builders Mechanical	Electrical
86/1	Bo-Bo	3,730	176	85.0	3	1965	BR/EE	EE
86/2	Bo-Bo	3,010	160	86.2		1965	BR/EE	EE
87/0	Bo-Bo	3,730	176	83.3		1973	BR/EE	AEI
90/0	Bo-Bo	3,730	176	82.5		1987	BREL	GEC Alsthom

West Coast Trains diesel locomotives

Class	Wheel arrangement	Power kW	Speed km/h	Weight tonnes	No in service	First built	Builders Mechanical	Engine	Transmission
B	Co-Co	1,190/1,120	133	123	1	1952	Clyde Eng	EMD16-567C	E EMD
S	Co-Co	1,450/1,340	133	123	4	1957	Clyde Eng	EMD 16-567C	E EMD
T	Bo-Bo	710/650	100	70	3	1962	Clyde Eng	EMD 8-567CR	E EMD

Improvements to existing lines
On 8 October 1996, the Office of Passenger Rail Franchising and Railtrack jointly announced the signing of a £150 million infrastructure investment plan, over and above the £1.35 billion being spent to renew the line's core infrastructure, to allow tilt trains to run at 200 km/h from 2002.

Traction and rolling stock
The West Coast main line is electrified at 25 kV AC and long-distance services are currently in the hands of Class 86 (leased from Eversholt), 87 and 90 locomotives (both leased from Porterbrook) powering push-pull trains of Mk 3 stock.

The centrepiece of Virgin's plan for the line is a commitment to replace virtually the entire rolling stock fleet with a new fleet of 40 high-speed trains for delivery from 2001 onwards, with services operated at 200 km/h starting in 2002 (the current maximum is 175 km/h). The new trains will be capable of running at 225 km/h.

The new trains will bring the current 2 hr 30 min journey time between London and Manchester down to 2 hours, while 20 minutes will be lopped off the Birmingham timings.

NEW ENTRY

Class 90 locomotive used on Virgin's West Coast Trains franchise

UNITED STATES OF AMERICA

Department of Transportation

400 7th Street SW, Washington DC 20590
Tel: +1 202 366 4000

Key personnel
Secretary: Rodney Slater
Deputy Secretary: Mortimer L Downey
Associate Deputy Secretary and Director, Office of Intermodalism: Michael P Huerta
General Counsel: Stephen H Kaplan
Assistant Secretaries
    Government Affairs: Steven O Palmer
    Public Affairs: Steven J Akey
    Policy: Frank E Kruesi
    Budget and Programmes: Louise F Stoll
Director, Executive Secretariat: Margarita Rogue

Surface Transportation Board

1925 K Street NW, Washington DC 20423-0001
Tel: +1 202 565 1674   Fax: +1 202 927 6107

Key personnel
Chairman: Linda J Morgan
Vice-Chairman: Gus A Owen
Member of Board: Vacant
General Counsel: Henri F Rush
Secretary: Vernon A Williams

Organisation
A proposal to reorganise the US Department of Transportation (USDOT) first made in January 1995 has not been acted upon. Under the proposal as formulated by the Secretary's office, 10 agencies would be consolidated into three, one of which would be an Intermodal Transportation Administration, including both the current Federal Transit Administration and Federal Railroad Administration, with the intent of streamlining operations and procedures for greater efficiency. A companion proposal called for some 30 capital grant programmes to be consolidated into one US$24 billion annual Unified Transportation Infrastructure Investment Program (UTIIP).

In place of the suggested reforms, the Secretary's office announced in January 1996 the Operation Timesaver initiative with an emphasis on an Intelligent Transportation Infrastructure (ITI) to be built in the next decade, especially in the 75 most populous urban centres. The rail industry does not appear to play a major part in this initiative, except as an element of Intelligent Transportation Systems (ITS) projects in the areas of traveller information systems and improved rail-highway crossing devices.

USDOT field offices are expected to show greater responsiveness to state and local agencies which are generally taking on more decision-making responsibilities. In 1997, the Administration introduced its NEXTEA (for National Economic Crossroads Transportation Efficiency Act) to succeed the ISTEA (Intermodal Surface Transportation Efficiency Act) which was in its last year of six. The Administration proposal was pegged at $175 billion for six years, compared to $157 billion for ISTEA. The levels are about the same if the effect of inflation over six years is taken into account. Several technical studies undertaken by USDOT during 1996, to ascertain the extent to which ISTEA funds have reached the intermodal industry, are being published.

Also receiving much attention recently is the ITS (Intelligent Transportation Systems) initiative, which consultants forecast will be a $400 billion market by 2015, although that figure is 87 per cent consumer-related product development and placement. Again, as a public policy issue, it is uncertain how much, if any, investment will be targeted towards either freight transportation, rail industry activity, or urban goods movement.

Surface Transportation Board
USDOT now includes the three-member Surface Transportation Board (STB), which replaced the Interstate Commerce Commission (ICC) and assumed its responsibilities in matters such as rail mergers. In July 1996 the STB unanimously approved the $3.9 billion acquisition of Southern Pacific by Union Pacific (UP). STB was to monitor the acquisition for five years, watching for any adverse competitive developments that would require additional conditions and to ascertain that the substantial trackage rights granted by UP to Burlington Northern Santa Fe were being utilised effectively.

In the matter of Conrail (qv), the STB essentially told CSX and Norfolk Southern to agree to a disposition of the assets or the STB would rule on such a disposition. By the second quarter of 1997, all three companies had entered a joint petition with the STB for an expedited proceeding.

A 1996 ruling by the STB makes mergers and acquisitions between short lines, where neither party has revenue in excess of $20 million, not subject to Board approval.

Under the terms of the ICC Termination Act the STB is authorised to exist until September 1998. It may then be disbanded or change status.

The 'SurfBoard's' annual budget is $12.3 million with about a quarter of that coming from fees.

UPDATED

Federal Railroad Administration

1120 Vermont Street NW, Washington DC 20005
Tel: +1 202 632 3133   Fax: +1 202 632 3705

Regional Administrators of Railroad Safety
Region 1: 55 Broadway, 10th Floor, Room 107, Cambridge, Massachusetts 02142
Tel: +1 617 494 2321
Region 2: Scott Plaza 2, Suite 550, Philadelphia, Pennsylvania 19113
Tel: +1 610 521 8200
Region 3: 1720 Peachtree Road NW, Suite 440 North Tower, Atlanta, Georgia 30309
Tel: +1 404 347 2751
Region 4: 111 N Canal Street, Suite 655, Chicago, Illinois 60606
Tel: +1 312 353 6203
Region 5: 8701 Bedford Euless Road, Suite 425, Hurst, Texas 76053
Tel: +1 817 334 3601
Region 6: 1807 Federal Building, 911 Walnut Street, Kansas City, Missouri 64106-2095
Tel: +1 816 426 2497
Region 7: 650 Capital Mall, Room 7007, Sacramento, California 95814
Tel: +1 916 551 1260
Region 8: Murdock Building, 703 Broadway Street, Suite 650, Vancouver, Washington 98660
Tel: +1 206 696 7536

Key personnel
Administrator: Jolene Molitoris
Deputy Administrator: Donald M Itzkoff
Chief of Staff: Robert Land
Chief Counsel: S Mark Lindsey
Directors
    Budget: Kathryn B Murphy
    Civil Rights: Miles S Washington
    Public Affairs: David Bolger
    International Policy: Ted Krohn
Associate Administrators
    Railroad Development: James T McQueen
    Policy: (vacant)
    Safety: Bruce M Fine
    Administration: Raymond J Rogers
    Research and Special Programs: Travis P Dungan

Organisation
The Federal Railroad Administration develops rules and regulations to implement national transportation law affecting railroads. FRA rules apply to some 40 major areas, including driver qualifications; maximum permissible hours of service for railroad personnel; conduct of railroad police; rolling stock safety standards; alcohol and drug testing; and level crossing and signalling system safety.

FRA also manages research and development projects and shares the responsibility for the Pueblo (Colorado) National Test Center with the Association of American Railroads.

UPDATED

Federal Transit Administration (FTA)

Department of Transportation, 400 7th Street SW, Washington DC 77820-590
Tel: +1 202 366 4040   Fax: +1 202 366 9854

Key personnel
Administrator: Gordon J Linton
Deputy Administrator: vacant
Director, Public Affairs: Bruce Frame
Director, Policy Development: Richard Steinman

Organisation
The Federal Transit Administration (FTA) was formerly the Urban Mass Transportation Administration and is the agency responsible for providing federal financial assistance to US cities to improve mass transit. Grants for capital projects, including the acquisition of rolling stock, involve 80 per cent federal and 20 per cent local funding; FTA also provides funds for public transport planning, research and operations.

FTA has eight field offices.

UPDATED

CLASS I FREIGHT RAILROADS

The following section lists Class I railroads. In June 1992 the Interstate Commerce Commission revised its definition of railroad classifications. The annual qualifying revenue threshold for Class I status was raised from a gross of US$92 million to US$250 million. One Class I carrier reclassified in consequence was Florida East Coast; it was replaced by Wisconsin Central (qv) which exceeds $250 million since the acquisition and integration of the Algoma Central and the ex-UP Duck Creek subdivision.

The second section lists the more important companies in the Class II (gross revenue US$20-249.9 million) and III categories. The Class II category includes 15 Regional railroads.

Following this is a section on passenger operators. This includes Amtrak, which is a Class I railroad.

Boston and Maine Corporation

A subsidiary of Guilford Transportation Industries Inc, Rail Division

Iron Horse Park, North Billerica, Massachusetts 01862
Tel: +1 508 663 1130   Fax: +1 508 663 1199

Key personnel

Chairman, President and Chief Executive Officer:
   David A Fink
Vice-Presidents
   Executive: F Colin Pease
   Marketing and Sales: Thomas F Steiniger
   Engineering: Stephen F Nevero
   Finance: Michael A Holmes
   Law: John R Nadolny
   Transportation: Sydney B Culliford
   Mechanical: James P Coffin
   Purchases and Stores: Stewart P Park Jr
Assistant Vice-Presidents
   Human Resources: Roland E Dinsmore
   Engineering and Chief Engineer, Design and
   Construction: Vinay V Mudholkar
General Attorney and Claims: J R L Gay

Gauge: 1,435 mm
Length: 2,532 km

Organisation

The principal lines of the Boston & Maine run north and west from Boston through the states of Maine, New Hampshire, Vermont, Massachusetts and in eastern New York state, where it makes connections at Albany and Schenectady with other lines.

In 1983 Guilford Transportation Industries (GTI) took over the B&M. GTI also owns the Maine Central. The railroads preserve their separate identities in some areas (for example equipment), but are being operated as an integral system with common management. As a result of past disputes with the labour force over working practices, management is exercised by another GTI subsidiary, the Springfield Terminal Railway Co.

Since the second quarter of 1995 all shipping documents have carried the Guilford name in order to simplify relations with customers. Guilford is privately held and revenue and performance data are not a matter of public record.

Freight operations

About 85 per cent of B&M's freight tonnage is received from connecting lines and two-thirds of it terminates on the system. Forest products from northern New England and Canada predominate.

Intermodal operations

B&M has built a major new intermodal facility called the Devens Inland Port and Distribution Center which opened in late 1993. This facility handles domestic and international containers, piggyback traffic and bulk transfer services; it serves as an extension of the port of Boston. Both the Devens Port and the Ayer automobile facility (see below) are targets of Norfolk Southern in a run-through arrangement which will see NS negotiating reciprocal rights with CP (St Lawrence & Hudson) in order to reach Albany, then a similar arrangement with B&M to serve Massachusetts, since CSX is acquiring Conrail's assets in New England.

Improvements to existing lines

The state of Massachusetts has announced a plan to spend $158 million to raise clearances across the state to accommodate double-stack trains. Phase I has consisted of clearing the section from Devens to Mechanicville, New York, to make connection to CP (St Lawrence and Hudson division).

In 1993, B&M upgraded the Ayer automobile unloading facility and installed 112 lb continuous welded rail on the Worcester main line.

Traction and rolling stock

The railroad operates with a fleet of 45 diesel locomotives of which the largest tranche is 32 GP40/GP40-2 models.

UPDATED

Burlington Northern Santa Fe (BNSF)

2650 Lov Menk Drive, Forth Worth, Texas 76131-2830
Tel: +1 817 333 2000   Fax: +1 817 333 7997

Former Santa Fe offices
1700 East Golf Road, Schaumburg, Illinois 60173-5860
Tel: +1 708 995 6000   Fax: +1 708 995 6219

Key personnel

Chairman:
President and Chief Executive Officer: Robert D Krebs
Senior Vice-Presidents
   Chief Financial Officer: Denis E Springer
   Chief Operating Officer: Donald G McInnes
   Law, and General Counsel: Jeffrey R Moreland
   Chief of Staff: Douglas J Babb
   Employee Relations: James D Dagnon
   Coal and Agricultural Commodities Business Unit:
   Gregory T Swienton
   Merchandise Business Unit: Matthew K Rose
   Intermodal and Automotive Business Unit:
   Charles L Schulz
Vice-Presidents
   General Counsel: Richard E Weicher
   General Tax Counsel: Daniel J Westerbeck
   Litigation: Gary L Crosby
   Government Relations: A R (Skip) Endres
   Finance, and Treasurer: Patrick J Ottensmeyer
   Controller: Thomas N Hund
   Investor Relations and Corporate Secretary:
   Marsha K Morgan
   Corporate Relations: Richard A Russack
   Marketing (UP/SP Lines): Peter J Richershauser
   Operations (UP/SP Lines): Ernest (Buck) Hord
   Intermodal Marketing: Steve Branscum

Gauge: 1,435 mm
Length: 69,600 km

For map, see p353

Organisation

BNSF was created in 1995 with the merger of two major railroads, namely the Burlington Northern and the Santa Fe. BNSF's territory lies principally to the west of the Mississippi river, serving 27 US states and two Canadian provinces; a major rival is the Union Pacific/Southern Pacific system.

BN itself was the product of a 1970 merger involving the Chicago, Burlington & Quincy; Great Northern; Northern Pacific; and Spokane, Portland & Seattle railways. In 1980 BN bought out the St Louis–San Francisco Railway (the Frisco).

The core of the Santa Fe Railway was a high-speed Chicago–Los Angeles route, with feeder lines in the western and mid-western states.

The administrative and executive functions of the merged railroads have been consolidated in Fort Worth, Texas, and a reduced managerial staff has been retained at the Schaumburg, Illinois, address of the former Santa Fe in recognition of the traffic levels in the Chicago area and while work is scheduled on closer integration of certain software such as train location and control (which SF had upgraded in its own territory shortly before the merger).

Union Pacific/Southern Pacific merger
In response to some significant opposition to the UP/SP merger the UP has sold the BNSF some 560 km of track and additionally arranged up to 6,100 km in trackage rights in order to provide competition in areas that would otherwise have had only single-carrier service. The three principal elements of the deal were (a) allowing BNSF into New Orleans directly, (b) connecting BNSF's extensive Pacific northwest trackage with California's Central Valley and Bay area, via Oregon (Klamath Falls) and northern California to offer a single line haul much shorter than the alternative through Idaho, Wyoming and over the Rockies again, and (c) giving BNSF access to the Denver–Stockton corridor which would otherwise have been a UP monopoly.

Typical of the new service options under trackage rights available is a Houston–Memphis service with interline connection via Illinois Central to Illinois. Systemwide, nearly 1,000 major manufacturing and distribution services can now call on BNSF for service. The Surface Transportation Board has stated that it will require periodic reports from BNSF in order to determine that the trackage rights concessions have achieved their purpose in satisfying shippers' concerns about competition. In the short-term, the arrangements have stretched the BNSF's resources of power and crews and was one factor contributing to a weak first quarter in 1997.

Finance

The BNSF concluded 1996 with greater than $8 million in total freight revenues. For 1995, BNSF reported $6.18 billion, which was the sum of a full year's revenues for BN and the revenues from Santa Fe after the September merger.

Carloadings for 1996 were running almost at the same level as 1995 and were forecast to end the year at 6.87 million; the expectation for revenue tonne-km was in the order of 650 billion. The operating ratio (expenses as a percentage of income) for 1996 was 78.6, compared with 79.5 for 1995.

The first quarter 1997 earnings were reported 20 per cent lower than in 1996, attributable to extreme climatological events (western floods; snow in the northern plains states) and to merger-related complications, such as the separate softwares controlling operations on the pre-merger networks. The 6,400 km of track that BNSF can serve within the merged UP system have made an impact on asset management as BNSF has assigned power, rolling stock and crews to the new territory, leading to temporary shortages elsewhere.

Finances (US$ millions)

	1996
Revenues	8,187
Operating income	1,748
Income after taxes and other items	889

Line sales

BNSF's line/track rationalisation programme has been relatively conservative compared to those of other Class I railroads. In 1996, 406.5 km of track, in western Kansas, Oklahoma and Colorado, were sold to the Cimarron Valley Railroad.

Dash 9-44CW locomotive built by GE for BNSF (F Gerald Rawling)

1997

Freight operations

Part of the rationale for the merger of BN and the Santa Fe was that the two companies were major players in different traffic areas: the BN's top commodities were coal, lumber and forest products out of the northwest, and agricultural commodities, while Santa Fe was pre-eminent in intermodal business and the distribution of automobiles. By merging two largely complementary territories, the BNSF offers single-line service from the Gulf of Mexico to Canada and from the southwest to the upper midwest. As a product of the trackage agreement with UP/SP, the BNSF will increase its presence in transborder traffic to and from Mexico.

Transport of coal is BNSF's largest source of rail freight tonnage, contributing 41 per cent of revenue ton-miles. Coal is in a virtual tie with intermodal as a revenue producer for the combined railroad bringing in $1.97 billion in 1996 compared to intermodal's $2.09 billion. The two combined bring in half of BNSF's total revenues.

Over 200 million tonnes of coal was originated by the combined properties in 1996. Low sulphur coal from the Powder River Basin of Montana and Wyoming accounts for most of BNSF's originations. This is hauled to close to 60 coal-burning electricity generating stations chiefly in the north central, south central, mountain and Pacific regions. Hauls to power plants in the east are rising (some coal is transferred onto navigable rivers at the limit of BNSF trackage).

Nearly all the coal tonnage originated by BNSF is carried in unit trains and 99 per cent of the business is run under contract. The trains typically consist of 108 wagons and, depending on the difficulty of the grades encountered, from three to six locomotives. On a typical working day BNSF has about 190 unit coal trains on the move; about three-quarters of them will be formed of customer-owned wagons. In the 25 years since the first unit trains were loaded in the Powder River Basin coalfield, BN has moved 2 billion tonnes in total and invested more than $3 billion in track systems and train operations infrastructure. In 1996, part of the capital programme included purchase of three complete new aluminium trainsets to complement the eight that were acquired in 1995.

BNSF serves a significant area of the major grain-producing regions located in the midwest and Great Plains and transports large quantities of whole grains to domestic feed lots, major milling centres, and to the Pacific northwest, Gulf and western Great Lakes ports for export. Agricultural commodities produce about 10 per cent of revenues.

BNSF serves the timber producing regions of the Pacific northwest and the southeast, hauling significant volumes of lumber, plywood and structural panels, wood chips, wood pulp, paper and paper products. For 1996 this group produced 6.8 per cent of revenues. Fluctuations in the level of forest products traffic result from general economic conditions as reflected in new housing starts and levels of industrial production, from competition with other modes, and export demand.

In other commodity groups, in the first half of 1996 chemicals accounted for 9.3 per cent of 1996 revenues; consumer products, 5.7 per cent; minerals, 3.9 per cent; metals, 4.9 per cent; vehicles and machinery, 4.8 per cent.

New international links

With the introduction of the North American Free Trade Agreement (NAFTA), BNSF spread its net to encompass service to both Canada and Mexico (via El Paso), as well as its US heartland.

Premerger partnerships had been struck with CP Rail, where BNSF operates intermodal trains between Texas and Toronto and Montreal, and with CN North America for movement of freight between western Canada and Chicago.

An agreement with the South Orient Railroad Co signed in 1992 gives BNSF alternative access to the Mexican rail network. Trains from Ojinaga in north Mexico travel via Presidio, Texas, to join the BNSF system at Dallas/Fort Worth. The UP-SP merger conditions also gave BNSF access to Eagle Pass, Texas, from San Antonio.

Intermodal operations

Increasing containerisation of internal US freight has benefited both the former BN (which has been moving for several years into domestic container business) and the former Santa Fe. Intermodal freight is now the number one revenue producer for BNSF, generating $2.09 billion in 1996. The 1995 tally for trailers and containers moved was 2.5 million.

Since 1991 both the Santa Fe and BN components of the railroad have been teamed up with road haulier J B Hunt to provide intermodal service between the midwest and Pacific northwest; this partnership continues. Other partnerships are in effect with UPS and its refrigerated MarTrac subsidiary, as well as several LTL (Less than TruckLoad) carriers.

In 1996, BNSF, Norfolk Southern and Conrail formed a domestic intermodal equipment project called NACS (North American Container System), which will encourage shippers to use containers in most major markets where there is double-stack service available and taking advantage of the restriction-free interchange of NACS containers.

BNSF now offers double-stack service for refrigerated containers in international traffic. Power for the refrigeration plant in up to nine containers conveyed on a five-platform double-stack wagon is supplied from a container, carried in the centre platform, which holds two diesel-generator sets (one for back-up) and a large fuel tank.

Recent additions to BNSF's stack-train resources include 106 stand-alone heavy-lift 'Husky-Stack' well wagons from Gunderson. The builder claims that the car, designed primarily for domestic market weighty container traffic, can accept 60 per cent more load than conventional articulated double-stack wells. It is therefore adaptable to such freight as lumber, plywood, paper and solid waste. The 48 ft well can take a 48 ft container below and stack a 53 ft container above.

Since the UP/SP merger, BNSF has introduced dedicated intermodal services on the following new lanes: New Orleans—Arizona and New Orleans—California; St Paul, Minnesota—California; and Texas—Pacific northwest/Vancouver. As recently as April 1994, BN had withdrawn from the Texas market.

Improvements to existing lines

BNSF's 1996 capital expenditures were a record $2.2 billion, and the 1997 forecast was $1.85 billion (these figures cover both infrastructure and rolling stock items). For 1996 the programme covered $1.45 billion in track signals, bridges, tunnels and other infrastructure items. Of the 69,600 km of BNSF track, a total of 19,200 (28.5 per cent) was resurfaced in that year. The company put in 1,440 km of rail; 3.2 million wood sleepers and 362,000 concrete sleepers. The company also overhauled 500 of its current locomotives.

Some $800 million was directed at capacity expansion projects, including negotiations with the Washington Central (qv) for track to reach the Pacific northwest.

Finding itself acutely short of capacity to the northwest ports and major markets, BNSF purchased and re-opened the Stampede Pass line to create a third route. The company has budgeted $125 million in the 1997-99 period for upgrades, including raising clearance in the 2.9 km Stampede Pass tunnel to accommodate double-stack container trains.

The Argentine Yard in Kansas City is receiving a complete $90 million rehabilitation over the course of two years; the intermodal facilities at Corwith (Chicago) and Hobart (Los Angeles) were both upgraded to handle over one million lifts annually, and the completed San Bernardino expansion project has raised the capacity there to 400,000 units per annum. Corwith is at 675,000 lifts presently, and during 1996 the road haulier J B Hunt built an exclusive terminal on 19 acres adjacent to Corwith and with a private internal road, speeding transfers of Hunt-owned containers and trailers onto intermodal trains of the former Santa Fe railroad. Also, several new markets that opened up as a product of the UP-SP track rights access agreement will require capital improvements.

Traction and rolling stock

At the end of 1996 the BNSF locomotive fleet had been rationalised to 3,023 units from 4,100 available pre-merger. But, during the 1996-97 winter there were power shortages.

BNSF became the first North American freight railroad to opt in volume for AC three-phase traction motors, ordering 350 SD70M-AC 4,000 hp (3,000 kW) locomotives from Electro Motive Division of General Motors in March 1993, subsequently adding 54 to the order. The locomotives have Siemens electrics, EMD's EM 2000 microprocessor control package and a new radial bogie. They are being promoted for their all-weather traction, improved fuel efficiency, lower emissions and lower maintenance requirements.

BNSF estimates that three of the new machines do the work of five SD40s. Most of the new locomotives have been used on coal service.

The $675 million order is being executed over four years; it was anticipated that by the end of 1996 all units would be on the property, as well as the order for 164 Dash 9-44CW units from GE that were ordered by Santa Fe and began arriving in mid-1996.

In May 1997 BNSF announced an order for an additional 405 locomotives to be delivered in the period 1997-2000. From EMD will come 26 SD75I units in 1997 and 105 SD70MAC units in 1997-98 with a further 104 (unspecified) in 1999 and 2000. From GE will come 170 Dash 9-44CW units in 1997-98. As part of the agreement with EMD a contract maintenance facility will be built at BNSF's intermodal property in City of Commerce, California. EMD already operates four such facilities in Chicago; Barstow, California; Alliance, Nebraska; and Glendive, Montana.

Parts supply

BNSF broke new ground with a three-year $25 million logistics contract struck with Consolidated Freightways in August 1996. CF's CF Motor Freight carrier will provide just-in-time delivery of railroad parts and supplies to the entire BNSF system. The project is intended to allow BNSF to return rolling stock to service faster and to release rail equipment used for transporting spares for use by shippers.

Power by the hour

BNSF continues with its 'Power by the Hour' contractual arrangements with locomotive manufacturers. The contracts involve 100 General Electric Dash 8 units through a leasing intermediary, LMX Inc, and 100 SD60 units from GM-EMD via another intermediary, Oakway Inc; actual fleets in 1995 had been reduced to 197 by attrition and accidents and these units also were beginning to show up more off-line during 1996.

The suppliers (LMX and Oakway) guarantee availability in the form of a number of kilowatt hours from the fleet. The manufacturer, supplier and the purchaser (BNSF) negotiate support functions — basically the manufacturers oversee BNSF workshop employees in the performance of a maintenance regimen.

Shops restructured

During 1996 the Galesburg, Illinois; Springfield, Missouri; and Denver, Colorado, locomotive shops were all closed. Galesburg and Denver were retained as fuelling points.

Trough Train

In 1991 BN took delivery, from Bethlehem Steel, of two prototype articulated five-unit open-top hoppers called Trough Train. The production series, all aluminium, built by Johnstown America and delivered during mid-1995, consists of 22 'troughs' per train, with each trough made up of 13 jointed segments totalling 85 m in length. Total train length is around 2 km.

Capacity represents a 40 per cent increase over the equivalent in standard cars. The first train entered service with a St Louis utility, Union Electric, and BNSF has ordered an additional set for 1996 delivery. The adjoining, close-connected bodies have overlapping floors and sides above articulating bogies, so that each 22-unit set forms one continuous trough.

Grainporter 2000

Grain processor Cargill Inc ordered 480 Grainporter 2000 cars from Johnstown America, built of aluminium, weighing only 24 tonnes and offering a payload of 105 tonnes. Burlington Northern had the first 10 production units in trial service after the design was tested at the Pueblo, Colorado, facility of the Association of American Railroads. The design has now been improved to a 116 tonne payload and grain company A E Staley has ordered 280 of these wagons.

AllRailer

BNSF is collaborating with Wabash National, the builder, to develop the AllRailer, a fully enclosed car transporter and the first such vehicle for Wabash. It will be changeable between a two-tier and a three-tier configuration and use the same slack-free couplers from RoadRailer. Performance tests have been conducted at Pueblo and in-service (revenue) trials were to start in 1997.

Northern Star boxcar

Trinity Industries and DuPont co-operated to build two boxcars out of hardcore composite materials for BNSF to

Combined locomotive roster

Class	kW	No in service	Source
MK12G	895	2	Lease/MK
EMD units			
GP7	1,120	94	SF
GP9; GP9B	1,120	88	BN; SF
GP10	1,340	16	BN
GP15-1	1,120	25	BN
MP-15	1,120	5	BN
GP18	1,340	1	BN
GP20	1,490	57	BN; SF
GP28M; 28P	1,340	50	BN
GP30	1,715	77	SF
GP35	1,865	148	SF
GP38, 38-2, 38E, 38-2B	1,490	315	BN; SF; EMD†
GP39; 39E; 39M; 39V; 39-2	1,715	284	BN; SF
GP40E; 40M; 40X; 40-2	2,240/2,600	63	BN; SF
GP50; 50L	2,685	47	BN; SF
GP53; 53L	2,240	60	BN
GP60; 60M; 60B	2,835	122	SF
SD9	1,270	77	BN
SD38-2; 38P	1,490	20	BN; GATX†
SD39	1,865	20	SF
SD40; 40C; 40E; 40G; 40-3 DF40-2	2,240	927	BN; SF; EMD†
SDF40-2	2,240	18	SF
SD42B; 42E; 42L; 42P	2,240	78	BN; EMD†
SD43L	2,240	5	BN
SD45; 45-2; SDF45; SDFP45	2,685	104	SF
SD60; 60E; 60M; 60MAC	2,835/2,985	200	BN; EMD†; OWY†
SD70M	2,985	372	BN
SD75M	3,200	76	SF
SW-10; 10B	745	54	BN
SW-1	450	1	BN
SW-12	895	49	BN
NW-12	895	1	BN
SW-15	1,120	71	BN
SWBLW	1,120	1	BN
Slugs	—	11	BN
EMD subtotal		**3,017**	
GE units			
B23-7	1,715	77	SF; MNCW*
B30-7; 7A	2,240	127	BN
B39-8	2,910	98	LMX*
B40-8; 8W	2,985	119	SF
U30C; C-30-7; SF30C	2,240	301	BN; SF
C-33-7	2,460	41	BN
C40-8W	3,085	152	SF
C44-9W	3,280	249	BN; SF; BNSF**
GE subtotal		**1,694**	
Grand total		**4,711**	

† EMD/GATX/OWY units are from lease fleets; OWY = Oakway, EMD's power by the hour division
* LMX = Locomotive Management, GE's power by the hour division
MNCW = units acquired by BN from Metro-North, still running with old numbers
** last 100 at C44-9W delivered to BNSF post-merger

test. The car is built in two pieces. The walls, ends and floor are all one moulding; the roof is the other piece. This reduces thermal leak potential to the only interface, between the sides and roof. The payload is 98 tonnes, compared to a more normal 72.5 tonnes for an insulated steel car. Both the thermal efficiency and the economics will be studied.

Signalling and telecommunications
BN opened its $120 million network operations centre (NOC), called the James J Hill Center and designed in co-operation with Union Switch & Signal, in Fort Worth, Texas, in April 1995. The centre provides tactical control of four functions, namely:
—Business Processes and Functions (that is trains, crews and power) through TSS (Transportation Support Systems);
—Information Technology (that is asset management, strategic and tactical planning systemwide);
—Human Resources;
—Facility Design.
BNSF is adopting the DigiCon dispatching system, and dispatchers from offices in St Paul, Minnesota; Alliance, Nebraska; Springfield, Missouri; and Seattle, Washington, are being moved to Fort Worth.

The 125 workstations at Fort Worth are individually climate and lighting controlled and include personal storage spaces. The building is built to withstand tornadoes; its walls are of half a metre thick, steel-reinforced concrete.

There is design capacity to include Santa Fe properties; SF opened its own similar facility within the last two years using a different systems architecture and different software, though the management objectives were the same. Combining and/or reconciling the two systems is a continuing systems engineering challenge.

BNSF and the UP are in the second year of co-operating with the Federal Railroad Administration to test Positive Train Separation (PTS) on 1,350 km of track in the Pacific northwest, comprising some track owned separately by each participant and some jointly operated, with the UP on the BNSF under trackage rights. Amtrak is a participant. GE Harris Railway Electronics is the systems integrator, involving both Forth Worth (BNSF) and Omaha (UP) dispatch centres. PTS displays safe train operating instructions in the cab, alerts train crew to potential conflicts and overrides, that is stops the train, if there is no crew response. The results will be shared nationally with the industry.

UPDATED

Conrail

Consolidated Rail Corporation
2001 Market Street — 19A, PO Box 41419, Philadelphia, Pennsylvania 19101-1419
Tel: +1 215 209 2000   Fax: +1 215 209 1338
Website: http://www.conrail.com

Key personnel
Chairman, President
and Chief Executive Officer: David M LeVan
Senior Vice-Presidents
    Finance: H William Brown
    Intermodal Service Group: Cynthia A Archer
    Core Service Group: John P Sammon
    Mergers: Bruce B Wilson
    Merger Consolidation: George P Turner
    Law and Government Affairs: Timothy O'Toole
    Finance: John A McKelvey
    Operations: Ronald J Conway
    Organisational Performance: Frank H Nichols
    Unit Train Service Group: Timothy P Dwyer
    Automotive Group: Lester M Passa
Vice-Presidents
    Operational Services: Richard S Pyson
    Controller: Donald W Mattson
    Treasurer: Thomas J McFadden
    Service Delivery: Gary M Spiegel
    Washington Counsel: William B Newman Jr
    Customer Support: Gerald T Gates
    Operating Assets: John M Samuels
    Continuous Quality Improvement: John T Bielan Jr
    Risk Management: Lucy L S Amerman
    Information Systems: Albert M Polinsky
    Service Design and Planning: Hugh J Kiley
    Labour Relations: Dennis A Arouca
    Corporate Communications: Craig R MacQueen
    Corporate Secretary: James D McGeehan

Gauge: 1,435 mm
Length: 19,630 km

Political background
Conrail was created as a private, profit-making corporation by an Act of Congress and began operations in April 1976. It comprised most of the rail properties of a group of bankrupt companies: the Central of New Jersey, Erie Lackawanna, Lehigh & Hudson River, Lehigh Valley, Penn Central and Reading lines. Conrail is now a freight railroad providing service in 14 states in the northeast and midwest, plus the District of Columbia and the province of Québec, Canada.

Following an unsuccessful attempt by the government to sell off Conrail to Norfolk Southern, the federal 85 per cent stake in Conrail was floated on the open market in 1987. The flotation was successful and realised $1.9 billion. Conrail would thus remain a system intact until broken up some time in 1997. It is a publicly traded company, listed on the New York Stock Exchange.

Break-up of Conrail
On 15 October 1996, CSX Corporation agreed to buy Conrail for $8.1 billion in a friendly deal that would have required the approval of the Surface Transportation Board (qv). Norfolk Southern countered with a $9.1 billion offer. The issue was fought out in the pages of the nation's business press as well as in the courts. Conrail stockholders opposed the 'friendly low bid' by CSX. Also in consideration was a legal issue of whether the virtual monopoly in the New York market, given to Conrail to improve its start-up position in 1976, could be transferred to CSX if there was a challenger (NS). The Surface Transportation Board effectively told the parties to agree between themselves on a settlement, tacitly recognising the break-up of Conrail. By the second quarter of 1997 the deal was in two parts:

(a) CSX would acquire Conrail for $10.5 billion (the price after having been bid up by NS)
(b) NS would immediately acquire about 58 per cent of Conrail for $5.9 billion, approximately.

The three parties then each withdrew their separate positions before the STB and jointly filed for an expedited proceeding. In June 1997, the STB said it would rule on the deal within a year.

Assuming the deal gets the green light from the STB, CSX will get a St Louis—Indianapolis—Cleveland—Buffalo—Syracuse—Albany—New York route (the once New York Central 'water level' route).

NS will get the ex-Pennsylvania line Chicago—Pittsburgh—East Coast (some of which, at the west end, it had been buying up already) and the 'southern tier' line across New York State.

Areas around Detroit, Philadelphia, in New Jersey and in the Monongahela coalfield are likely to be jointly owned, but NS will also get the old Reading route between Hagerstown and New York.

Competitive access asked
During the Conrail break-up negotiations, several companies have asked the STB, and also approached state governments, for access conditions, either on their own behalf or that of a partner.

CN has asked for access to New York via the 'southern tier' route and the New York, Susquehanna & Western Railway (qv). The St Lawrence & Hudson, which has a haulage agreement with NYS&W, has also asked for New York access. Both Canadian railroads have expressed concern that competitive access from the north has been largely ignored.

Opposing the UP-SP merger
Conrail had earlier been one of the parties most opposed to the merger between the Union and Southern Pacific

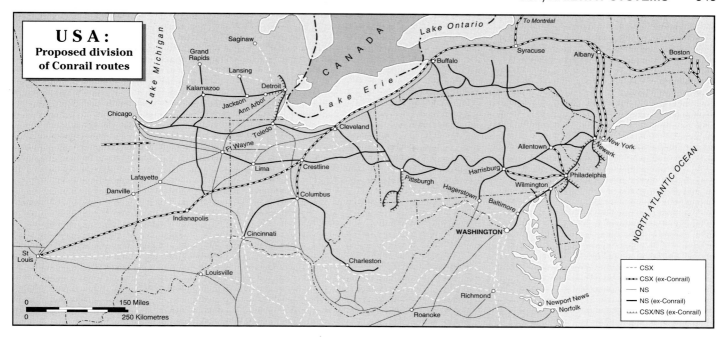

USA:
Proposed division
of Conrail routes

systems, or at least most demanding of conditions. In September 1995 Conrail offered $1.9 billion for SP lines in Illinois, Missouri, Arkansas, Louisiana and Texas as far as El Paso (known in the industry as 'SP:East'), but was rebuffed by UP, which later included the lines in the package that was offered to the BNSF for trackage and haulage agreements.

Organisation

In early 1994 Conrail established four major service groups for its freight business in a reorganisation. The four groups are: Automotive; Intermodal; Unit Trains; and Core Service Group, which respectively produce 16, 20,19 and 45 per cent of annualised revenues.

Finance

Results for 1996

For 1996, Conrail's revenue totalled $3.714 billion, little changed from 1995. Net income was $342 million, up $78 million, mainly reflecting Conrail's continuing cost-containment initiatives.

Line disposals

Prior to asset disposition being put on hold pending break-up of Conrail a significant component of Conrail's disposal programme was the 'Conrail Express' partnership project in which lines are spun off in 'clusters' around a hub, analagous to the way in which feeder services in the airline industry work. The extent of imitation even allowed for Conrail to paint the short line motive power in a 'Conrail Express' paint scheme. During 1996 Conrail disposed of a 125 km cluster in Connecticut (to RailTex); 157 km of track in Pennsylvania to the Reading and Northern; parts of the Pekin Secondary, the former Peoria and Eastern Railroad in Illinois, to Norfolk Southern; 61 km of the Williamsburg cluster and about 50 km of the Carnegie cluster, both in Pennsylvania.

In the first quarter of 1997 the project was suspended while CSXT and Norfolk Southern examined all of Conrail's remaining properties. A pending deal for Railroad Development Corporation to acquire 295 km of lines in Southern New Jersey was not executed, and six other 'clusters' have been retained.

Investment

In 1995, Conrail invested US$494 million; the final 1996 figure was expected to be closer to $450 million. In July 1993, Conrail had adopted a revised 1993-97 five-year plan in which a goal was set for investing 80 per cent of operating income in capital improvements. Much of Conrail's capital improvement programme was cancelled, or slowed, after October 1996.

Freight operations

Automotive Group

Conrail transports nearly 20 per cent of all finished vehicles manufactured in North America, as well as being the largest Class I haulier of parts. In total, Conrail serves 23 assembly plants and 59 component factories. Finished cars are moved in dedicated trains in damage-resistant multilevel wagons which are only switched at a handful of

specialised terminals. Special logistics centres cater to the industry's sourcing and delivery schedules and in late 1994 Conrail introduced a logistics management programme called PartStream, covering a total of more than 300 origin/destination combinations.

At Buffalo, New York, Conrail operates a 'Synchronous Support Center' to serve General Motors. Auto parts and supplies from western New York and Ontario are trucked to the Buffalo centre, then loaded on to railcars for transport to GM assembly plants in Missouri, Kansas and Texas. In Toledo, Ohio, Conrail operates a 'Sequence Center' to serve Chrysler. At the Toledo facility pick-up truck frames are received on specially equipped flatcars then sorted, sequenced and transloaded for truck delivery to the assembly plant in production line order.

Conrail purchased 466 bilevel racks in 1993 and added a further 300 valued at $10 million in the first half of 1994. By mid-1994, Conrail's autorack fleet numbered 5,500 fully enclosed units, 2,900 trilevel and 2,600 bilevel.

Commodity-specific programmes

Conrail has an aggressive programme to develop commodity-specific traffic. Following the successful introduction of backhaul rates for canned, bottled and packaged foodstuffs into the east-west traffic lane out of New York/New Jersey, Conrail made a similar rate offer to food and beverage shippers in New York, Massachusetts, Pennsylvania and Michigan who ship into the southeast states.

Another example is the SteelNET rail-truck distribution system based on 15 transhipment centres in key towns and cities. Conrail transports iron and steel products in gondola and coiled steel wagons from most major mills in the northeast and midwest to the SteelNET facilities (or to warehouses on connecting railroads, giving shippers access to markets across the country). At the SteelNET centres, the shipments are stored and/or transferred to

trucks for local delivery as needed. Each SteelNET centre is operated by an independent warehouse company. Eleven of the SteelNET facilities are climate-controlled to meet special storage requirements for high-quality sheet steel used in the manufacture of motor vehicles and appliances.

Conrail has also begun shipping steel production in double-stack intermodal trains, using specialised equipment known as STEELSAVER. In conjunction with CWS Inc, a Chicago-based trucking company specialising in steel shipping, Conrail is offering a new service using double-stack trains which is being marketed as SteeLINK.

A service, modelled on SteelNET and called 'Press Runner', started in February 1995; the new service expedites the movement of paper from mills in Maine to Chicago. The service operates in co-operation with Guilford Industries and has cut two days off transit times.

Conrail's Bulk Transfer Connection offers shippers door-to-door delivery of dry or liquid bulk commodities. The services include premium long-distance rail haulage and bulk transfer to tank or truck through a network of 15 Conrail Flexi-Flo terminals. In late 1996, Conrail sold its Flexi-Flo facilities to a joint venture of Savage Industries and Matlock Systems Inc; both companies are established in the bulk transfer industry and between them already have 54 similar properties.

Conrail is the first major railroad to adopt the self-discharge hopper train manufactured by Conveying & Mining Equipment Inc of Houston. The train, branded 'Conrail Conveyor', is used by a New Jersey company to deliver stone from a quarry to two asphalt plants, and also sand.

In 1992 a rail connection was completed to the New York—New Jersey Port Authority's Auto Marine terminal on Upper New York Bay, an important import-export auto gateway; major users include agents for BMW, Hyundai

One of Conrail's lease fleet, an SD40 locomotive, is second in the consist behind a CP SD40 at Schiller Park Yard in Chicago (F Gerald Rawling)
1996

and Mazda. In 1994 the Port Authority of New York & New Jersey began building a state-of-the-art on-dock rail terminal in two stages, the first to handle 100,000 containers (which has opened) and the second to add capacity for a further 150,000 boxes. The final cost will be $8.5 million.

Finances (US$ million)

Operating revenues	1994	1995	1996
Total	3,733	3,686	3,714

Operating expenditure

Way and structures	499	485	
Equipment	815	766	
Transportation	1,379	1,324	
General, administrative and other	350	655*	
Total	3,127**	3,230*	3,113†
Income (loss) from operations	606	456	601

** Including special charge of US$84 million
* Including asset disposition charge of US$285 million
† Including special charge of US$135 million for voluntary separations

Other income (expenditure)

Interest	(192)	(194)	(182)
Unusual items	(154)	–	–
Other, net	118	130	112
(Taxes)	(208)	(128)	(189)
Total	(282)	(192)	259
Net income (loss)	324	264	342

Intermodal operations

Two concerns, United Parcel Service (UPS) and the US Postal Service, account for a third of Conrail's intermodal business, and four of the railroad's 36 daily or near-daily intermodal trains (which Conrail brands 'TrailVan') are exclusive mail trains.

In May 1992, J B Hunt, a major truckload highway carrier, announced an intermodal transport agreement with Conrail for moving containers between Chicago and the northeast via rail intermodal service. This followed agreements with other railroads, signalling J B Hunt's major move into container transport. In 1993, Hunt announced plans to convert its traffic in this corridor to double-stack.

Other important customers are the shipping lines for which Conrail (in partnership with other railroads) operates transcontinental double-stack container trains from west coast ports to the conurbations in the US northeast.

Conrail's interline/runthrough arrangements with contiguous railroads include:

- the 'South Runner'; daily to and from four points on the IC and 10 points on Conrail, via St Louis
- the 'DownEast Express'; linking points on the Guilford network, as far north as Maine, to Conrail's intermodal system.

Compared to other railroads, Conrail's investment in its intermodal terminals has been modest. Some, such as those in Chicago, will call for some substantial improvements by whichever railroad (of CSX, NS) acquires them.

Conrail Direct
Conrail Direct is Conrail's multi-modal subsidiary. It creates trucking alliances to extend Conrail service outside the range of its rail system. In April 1997, Milwaukee was added. Previously, Conrail Direct was offered to Kansas City; Albany, New York; Minneapolis/St Paul; Waterville, Maine; Des Moines, Iowa.

RoadRailer joint venture
April 1993 saw the launch of Triple Crown Services Company, a truck-rail joint venture of Norfolk Southern and Conrail in which the two railroads are equal partners; NS had been operating RoadRailers through its Triple Crown subsidiary for some years beforehand, and the creation of the joint venture extends its reach into the important northeastern market. The two railroads formed the joint venture to create a domestic retail intermodal product, operated with bimodal RoadRailer vehicles and other intermodal equipment, to compete for truckload business. CN moves Triple Crown equipment as far as Toronto in Canada.

Triple Crown Services provides a single point of sales and accountability for door-to-door intermodal service on

hauls over 640 km. It aims to maximise return on investment through high equipment utilisation, broad geographic scope and increased market share. It uses state-of-the-art equipment including 48 and 53 ft domestic containers and RoadRailer units. Initial major traffic corridors are New York–Chicago, Chicago–Atlanta, and Atlanta–New York.

It is expected that the Triple Crown system will become 100 per cent owned by Norfolk Southern in the disposition of Conrail assets.

Improvements to existing lines

A typical year's track programme for Conrail included installation of nearly 320 km of rail, more than one million ties (sleepers), and surfacing of approximately 4,800 km of track.

A major facility project is under way to build a new yard at Pitcairn, near Pittsburgh in Pennsylvania, at a cost of $7 million.

Conrail committed $44 million to a joint programme with the state of Pennsylvania ($31 million) to provide double-stack clearance across Pennsylvania. Construction started in September 1993, and was completed in 1996.

The new double-stack route runs from Cleveland into western Pennsylvania and through Pittsburgh, Johnstown, Altoona, Harrisburg and Reading to Philadelphia. In conjunction with the programme, Conrail was working closely with the ports of Philadelphia, Pittsburgh and Erie to bring additional business to these centres. The railroad recently signed an agreement with AmeriPort, the new intermodal facility in Philadelphia, and has transported international cargo, traditionally offloaded on the west coast, from the port of Philadelphia to Pittsburgh.

A second phase of the programme, to be undertaken in conjunction with CP Rail (now the St Lawrence & Hudson), was intended to establish a north–south double-stack route between Philadelphia and New York state.

Traction and rolling stock

Since December 1995 Conrail has introduced to service its order for 106 SD80M-AC locomotives from EMD (General Motors) and put them in service with the unit train and intermodal sectors. In 1997 it bought EMD's two demonstrators also. These 5,000 hp (3,730 kW) units are equipped with HTCR radial trucks and the EM2000 microprocessor control system, plus the vibration-isolated WhisperCab, called the I-cab, which is separated from the locomotive body by a diaphragm. They are also fitted with the 710G3B power plant, the first 20-cylinder engine GM has installed since 1975. Their new 22,000 litre fuel tank makes it possible to run from Chicago to New Jersey without refuelling. Simulations of operations told Conrail that the ideal power combination for its median trainload is two units of 5,000 hp (3,730 kW) each.

Previously, in 1995, Conrail ordered 90 SD60Is, after a satisfactory trial of the I-cab on one of the order for SD60M units. As a means to getting the locomotives into service promptly, Conrail assembled 45 of the order at its Altoona locomotive shops using kits provided by the EMD works at La Grange, Illinois and London, Ontario.

A lease programme was introduced in 1995 when Conrail allocated 60 of its C40-8Ws and 65 of its C30-7 units to a subsidiary, Locomotive Management Services (LMS), in a joint venture with General Electric, the builder of those models. Conrail is responsible for servicing the locomotives. The two principal clients of LMS to date have been the Union Pacific and the Canadian Pacific; as their new locomotive orders arrive, more of the LMS units are returning to Conrail service. Separately, Conrail has made some of its large GP38 fleet available for sale or lease.

The Altoona shops continue to rehabilitate units in small lots under contract for customers, including: a repeat order for GP40s for New Jersey Transit passenger service; five GP38s refurbished for Amtrak; 26 of Amtrak's best F40s to be reconditioned, and a number of units to be refurbished for general purpose deployment by RailTex (qv).

Conrail received the first of 200 new Coilshield-2 cars, which were being added to the pre-existing fleet of 700 such wagons. Each car has a 42 ft trough able to load 222,000 lb of coils up to 84 inches in diameter.

Signalling and telecommunications

Conrail developed a satellite-based system termed Remote Perishables Monitoring (RPM) to safeguard high-value fresh fruit and vegetable cargoes in transit. RPM continuously monitors refrigerator unit operation, internal

and ambient temperatures, fuel level and thermostat setting. The mobile RPM unit, which includes a satellite transmitter, transmits routine 'OK' status messages to an operations control centre, but communicates immediately if it detects a malfunction requiring repair or servicing. Satellite messaging is provided by American Mobile Satellite Corp, which supplies the transmitter; the sensory mechanism and refrigeration monitor are provided by Lee Mechanical Inc.

EDI developments
In November 1995 Conrail and Canadian National became the first pair of major rail companies to link up via the Rate EDI (Electronic Data Interchange) Network to replace paper billing of interline movement with electronic linkage.

The list following is the Conrail locomotive roster at the beginning of 1996. Since that date CR has disposed of large numbers of SD40s, GP10s, U23Cs, SW1200s, SW1500s, either to scrap, to leasing companies, to rebuilders, or as part of the Conrail Express programme.

Diesel passenger units

Unit nos	Model	Make	Quantity
4020-4022	E8A	EMD	3
Total			3

Road freight diesel units

Unit nos	Model	Make	Quantity
2175-2185	GP30	EMD	2
2255-2361	GP35	EMD	21
3621-3688	GP35	EMD	8
3000-3274	GP40	EMD	44
3275-3403	GP40-2	EMD	127
4101-4208	SD80MAC	EMD	108
5500-5574	SD60M	EMD	75
5575-5614	SD60I	EMD/CR	45
5615-5659	SD60I	EMD	45
6241-6357	SD40	EMD	69
6358-6524	SD40-2	EMD	165
6654-6666	SD45-2	EMD	13
6700-6834	SD50	EMD	135
6840-6867	SD60	EMD	28
6960-6999	SD40-2	EMD	40
Total EMD units			819
1900-2023	B23-7	GE	117
2030-2040	B30-7R	GE	11
2800-2816	B23-7	GE	17
5000-5059	B36-7	GE	58
5060-5089	B40-8	GE	30
6600-6609	C30-7	GE	10
6550-6599	C30-7A	GE	50
6610-6619	C32-8	GE	10
6620-6644	C36-7	GE	25
6000-6021	C39-8	GE	22
6025-6049	C40-8	GE	25
6050-6229	C40-8W	GE	180
Total GE units			555
Total road freight units			1,374

Diesel road switcher units

Unit nos	Model	Make	Quantity
7513-7597	GP10	EMD	75
1600-1699	GP15-1	EMD	100
7635-7939	GP38	EMD	148
8040-8281	GP38-2	EMD	235
6925-6959	SD38	EMD	35
Total EMD units			593
6900-6918	U23C	GE	18
Total GE units			18
Total road switcher units			611

Diesel yard switcher units

Unit nos	Model	Make	Quantity
8632-8646	SW900	EMD	5
8701-8721	SW900	EMD	10
9400-9424	SW1001	EMD	25
8922-9140	SW9	EMD	16
9315-9381	SW1200	EMD	58
9500-9620	SW1500	EMD	116
Total EMD units			221

Motor trailer units

1000-1023	MT-4	ALT	24
1100-1118	MT-6	GE	19
1119-1128	MT-6	CD	10
Total motor trailer units (slugs)			53
Total diesel yard switcher units			379

UPDATED

CSX Transportation Inc (CSXT)

A business unit of CSX Corporation
500 Water Street, Jacksonville, Florida 32202
Tel: +1 904 359 3100   Fax: +1 904 359 1899
Website: http://www.csxt.com

Key personnel

President and Chief Executive Officer:
  Alvin R Carpenter
Executive Vice-President, Chief Operations Officer:
  Gerald L Nichols
Executive Vice-President, Finance: Michael J Ward
Executive Vice-President, Sales and Marketing:
  John Q Anderson
Senior Vice-Presidents
  Technology: John F Andrews
  Sales and Marketing: Duane H Cassidy
  General Counsel: P Michael Giftos
  Employee Relations: Donald D Davis
  Transportation and Mechanical: Carl N Taylor
Vice-Presidents
  Corporate Secretary: Patricia J Aftoora
  Employee Relations: R H Cockerham
  Merchandise Marketing: John E Giles
  Engineering: J N Reese
  Mechanical: W Michael Cantrell
  Field Operations: C W Gooden
  Financial Planning and Analysis: Frederick J Favorite
  Service Design: Renee D Rysdahl
  Corridor Development: A B Aftoora
  Operations Support: F E Pursley
  Human Resources: Sally B Basso
  Supply and Services: John W Basso
  Chemicals: C P Jenkins
  Coal Sales and Marketing: R L Sharp
  Automotive: D R Hawk
  State Relations: M J Ruehling
  Risk Management: J Edward Codd
  Corporate Communications and Public Affairs:
    T M Fiorentino
  Controller: C J O Wodehouse
Chief Engineers
  Maintenance of Way: R A Cross
  System Reliability: R Kenneth Beckham
  Train Control: R M Kadlick
Chief Mechanical Officers
  Locomotive Operations: David L Petway
  Cars: M L Wall
  Engineering and Quality Control: G C Martin
Vice-President and General Manager, Chesapeake &
  Ohio Business Unit: T G Forst
General Manager, Cumberland Coal Business Unit:
  D S Green
General Manager, Florida Business Unit: P D Sandler

Gauge: 1,435 mm
Route length: 29,608 km

Organisation

CSXT is a rail transportation and distribution company operating in 20 US states, the District of Columbia and Ontario, Canada.

It is one of five related transportation companies that make up CSX Corporation. The other component CSX companies are:

● Sea-Land Service Inc, a container shipper operating 83 ships and 161,428 containers of various kinds serving 100 ports in 70 countries and territories;

● CSX Intermodal Inc (CSXI — qv) which operates a network of intermodal terminals in North America and offers truck drayage, chassis management and leasing services;

● American Commercial Lines (ACL), the largest barge operator in the US with 120 towboats and 3,300 barges together with supporting marine facilities;

● Customised Transportation Inc (CTI), which is a contract logistics services company.

Non-transportation holdings of CSX are the Greenbrier resort in White Sulphur Springs, West Virginia, Grand Teton lodge in Moran, Wyoming, and Yukon Pacific Corporation in Anchorage, Alaska. CSX Real Property Inc disposes of CSX assets surplus to operating requirements.

The holding company, CSX Corporation, is publicly traded on the New York Stock Exchange.

Formation of CSXT

In 1980 Chessie System Inc merged with Seaboard Coast Line Industries to form the CSX Corporation. At first the

SD40 (left) and SD50 locomotives give rear-end assistance to a train of triple-deck autoracks on the climb from Cumberland, Maryland, to Sand Patch Summit on CSX's Baltimore-Pittsburgh main line (Bob Avery)
1996

rail constituents, Chessie System Railroads and Seaboard System Railroad (a revised title), maintained their separate identities, managements and operations, but in 1986 they were co-ordinated into a single system, CSX Transportation Inc (CSXT). A multimodal structure was developed to maximise deregulation's opportunities, stress the importance of the train as a link in a total distribution chain, and structure a competitively credible door-to-door transport system. Thus CSXT and its trucking operation, Chessie Motor Express, were welded into a new total transport system.

In early 1986 CSXT bid successfully for control of Sea-Land, the major container shipping line. This gave CSXT control of Sea-Land terminals throughout the world. To optimise the scope for synergies of its marine and land intermodal activity a new company, CSX Intermodal (CSXI), was formed to handle all CSXT and Sea-Land intermodal operations. It became operational at the start of 1988.

Bid for Conrail

In October 1996, CSX made an agreed bid for Conrail (qv), valuing the Philadelphia-based company at $8.1 billion. As expected, Norfolk Southern (qv) vigorously contested the merger and initiated a hostile bid valued at $9.1 billion. By January 1997 CSX had acquired about 20 per cent of Conrail stock and NS about 10 per cent. Conrail stockholders ceased to tender to CSX. The Surface Transportation Board expressed a desire to see the parties reach a 'negotiated and balanced' settlement. NS then sent CSX and Conrail a proposal to divide Conrail. CSX agreed to amend its merger proposal, rebid for Conrail at $115 share (a gross valuation of $10.5 billion) and resell about 58 per cent of Conrail to NS. Both CSX and NS were expected to resort to the capital markets for about $2 billion each to finance the acquisition. The approximate disposition of Conrail is shown in the attached map. CSX will get much of what was once the New York Central plus a shared interest in desirable trackage around Detroit; New York—New Jersey and in the Pennsylvania/West Virginia coalfields. By March 1997, the CSX, NS and Conrail legal teams had filed a joint consenting petition for an expedited disposition by the STB, a process which was expected to take three to six months.

Lines and territories

The Chessie System principally comprised the former Chesapeake & Ohio and Baltimore & Ohio Railroads and their subsidiaries, such as the B&OCT (Baltimore & Ohio Chicago Terminal). The ex-Chesapeake & Ohio Railway's principal lines extend from the coalfields of southern West Virginia and eastern Kentucky eastward to the port of Newport News; westward to Louisville, Cincinnati and Chicago; and northward through Colombus and Toledo to Detroit.

The former Baltimore & Ohio system operates in 11 states and the District of Columbia. Principal lines extend from Philadelphia, through the port of Baltimore and Washington to Cumberland, Pennsylvania, and thence by separate routes to Chicago and St Louis.

Seaboard System was formed in 1983 through the merger of Seaboard Coast Line Railroad and the Louisville & Nashville Railroad. Former Seaboard main lines extend from Chicago to the Gulf of Mexico along the Atlantic coastal plain, serving all major Atlantic ports from

Virginia to Florida; the system also serves several ports on the Gulf of Mexico, including Tampa, Mobile, Pascagoula and New Orleans.

In the south and southeast, ex-Seaboard lines serve the rich coal-producing fields of eastern Kentucky.

CSXT has not pursued line rationalisation as vigorously as Conrail or NS.

Business units

In early 1994 CSXT established the C&O Coal Business Unit. This unit manages all aspects of the railroad's business operations on the principal coal-hauling lines of the former Chesapeake & Ohio Railway. Strategic business units established previously are CSX Intermodal; Cumberland Coal Business Unit, covering coal operations on the lines of the former Baltimore & Ohio Railroad; and Florida Business Unit for phosphate and fertiliser in south-central Florida.

Service lanes

CSXT has established four service lanes (out of a projected seven); in each lane a large geographic area is supervised by a general manager responsible for all transportation functions. In many respects the lanes are a recreation of pre-CSXT rails, for example the Chicago lane is essentially the one-time Louisville & Nashville and Monon. Service lane management, the business units, and system support from sales and marketing are meshed in each territory to improve customer response, service reliability and asset deployment.

Finance, rail only (US$ million)

	1994	1995	1996
Operating revenue	4,625	4,819	4,909
Total operating expenditure	3,696	3,951	3,782
Operating income (loss)	929	868	1,127
Net income after other charges	610	727	855
Operating ratio	79.9	77.9	77.0

Finance

CSX reported consolidated transportation operating revenue of $10.5 billion in 1996, the second consecutive year over the $10 billion mark and a fifth year of increase. Gross expenses were $9.014 billion. Of those figures, rail contributed $4.909 billion to group revenue, up $90 million from the previous year. Rail operating expenses were $3.782 billion compared to $3.951 billion in 1994, a decline of $169 million. The operating ratio (operating expenses as a percentage of income) for 1995 declined to 77.0 per cent from 77.9 per cent a year earlier. Due to the substantial reduction in expenses, operating income was a record.

As a result of agreements negotiated in 1993 and similar ones reached previously, CSXT now operates through freight trains with only a conductor and driver on virtually its entire system. Efforts are now under way to extend these agreements to local and yard crews; the declared target is a systemwide crew size of 2.25 compared to the 2.4 in 1995 (and 2.7 in 1993).

Total CSXT rail workforce in 1995 was 28,559 employees. CSXT announced early in 1997 that it was going to set up several locomotive driver training courses in colleges and universities to train drivers as many existing drivers are expected to retire in the near future.

Including locomotive purchases, the annual capital investment programme for CSXT in 1996 was $764

AC4400 CW locomotive built for CSX by General Electric; the lightning logo on the cabside denotes AC traction motors   ***1995***

Rail commodities by wagon loads

| | Wagon loads in thousands | | | Revenue in $ millions | | |
	1995	1996	Change % 1995-1996	1995	1996	Change % 1995-1996
Automotive	357	367	+2.8	503	520	+3.4
Chemicals	406	408	+0.5	700	719	+2.7
Minerals	414	428	+3.4	375	379	+1.0
Food and consumer	179	167	−6.7	207	199	−3.9
Agricultural products	280	254	−9.3	336	323	−3.9
Metals	301	277	−7.9	291	290	U/C
Forest products	456	443	−2.8	464	472	+1.7
Phosphates and fertiliser	512	511	U/C	279	282	+1.1
Coal	1,678	1,711	+2.0	1,523	1,584	+4.0
Total	4,583	4,566	−0.4	4,681	4,765	+1.8
Other revenues				138	144	
Total rail revenue				4,819	4,909	+1.9

million, a level unchanged from the previous year. Similar annual programmes were expected to be in the range of $600-650 million in the years up until 1998.

Passenger operations
CSX is principally a freight railway, but it operates commuter services for Maryland's Rail Commission on lines to/from Washington Union station (see MARC entry). In 1996, CSX and MARC signed a five-year contract extension.

Freight operations
In 1996, total rail merchandise wagon loads (at 4.57 million) were virtually unchanged from a year earlier, but revenues in most commodity sectors showed improvement. Year to year comparisons for wagon loads and revenues are shown in the accompanying table.

Performance Improvement Teams
Operating in such areas as safety, productivity, asset utilisation, and cost containment, 'Performance Improvement Teams' have saved CSXT a total of $500+ million since their introduction in 1992; their 1996 contribution was valued at $106 million. CSXT has calculated that if car cycle time could be reduced by one day per load, systemwide average, that translates into 86,000 additional loads, if available, per year from existing assets.

Beginning in 1996, CSX targeted three areas: terminal improvements, industrial switching, and network operations. During 1996, improvements in locomotive repair, car repair and maintenance of way procedures were achieved under PIT.

Improvements to existing lines
A 20 ft (6 m) vertical clearance, suitable for double-stack operations, has been achieved on the Atlanta–New Orleans–Jacksonville triangle. CSXT will construct similar clearances in the Chicago–Nashville–Augusta (Georgia), traffic lane and the Nashville–Birmingham (Alabama), Macon (Georgia) corridor.

Traction and rolling stock
At the close of 1995 CSX Transportation listed 2,781 diesel locomotives; the higher horsepower units arriving on the railway will displace several of the older, smaller classes which will be made available to short lines and third parties.

In 1993 CSXT signed an agreement with General Electric Transportation Systems to purchase 297 new diesel-electric locomotives in the period 1994-98; 138 were commissioned in 1996 and over half are now in service. CSXT added 55 to the order in 1996 and also ordered 25 SD70MACs from General Motors. The accompanying fleet table does not reflect the number of older models which are either stored serviceable or being offered to rebuilders. Included in the GE package are 250 units with AC traction motors, of which 197 will be 4,400 hp (3,280 kW) and 53 will be 6,000 hp (4,475 kW). CSXT had a brief trial with the 6,000 hp demonstrator in early 1996 and became the first US railroad to introduce the unit in regular service. The power plant for the 6,000 hp units has been developed by GE in collaboration with Deutz MWM of Cologne, Germany. Two other of CSXT's CW44ACs are being used as a testbed for GE's self-steering bogie.

Compared to conventional 4,000 hp (3,000kW) DC units the 4,400 hp AC unit can deliver 29 per cent more starting traction, 30 per cent overall improvement in all-weather adhesion and 27 per cent improvement in dynamic braking capability. Each of the new locomotives is expected to replace two older models, resulting in lower maintenance costs, increased fuel efficiency and greater service reliability. Since the late 1980s mean time between failures for locomotives has risen from around 30 days to around 90 days and the new orders are expected to raise the figure again.

At the close of 1996, CSXT-owned freight wagons totalled 97,792 of which 15 per cent were boxcars, 25 per cent open-top hoppers, 18 per cent covered hoppers, 25 per cent gondolas and 16 per cent other types.

CSXT rebuilt 4,500 coal cars in 1995 at its Raceland, Kentucky, car shop as part of 6,000 (4,475 kW) additions

CSXT diesel locomotives, January 1996, including orders

Type	Number operated
B23-7	44
B30-7	81
B36-7	120
B40-8	20
BQ23-7	9
C30-7	94
C40-8	147
FP7A	1
FP7B	1
GP15T	25
GP30M	62
GP38	123
GP38-2	188
GP39	17
GP39-2	20
GP40	164
GP40-2	390
MP15	10
MP15AC	55
MP15T	42
RDMT	25
RDSLUG	130
SD20-2	5
SD35	6
SD35M	2
SD38-2	5
SD40	19
SD40-2	388
SD45-2	4
SD50	144
SD60	10
SW1200	1
SW1500	20
SWMT	33
U18B	46
U23B	38
U36B	16
CW40-8	268
CW44-9	44
CW44AC	253*
TOTAL	3,060

*being delivered; convertible to CW60AC when 6,000 hp (4,475 kW) power plant is available

and replacements/rehabilitations; in 1995 150 gondolas were refitted with racks for coil and slab steel.

Signalling and telecommunications
CSXT has been developing a pilot Advanced Train Control System (ATCS) on its Bone Valley line east of Tampa, Florida, which was also CSXT's testing ground for AEI (automatic equipment identification). Predominantly involved in phosphates haulage from mines to ports, this line is well suited to the trial because its traffic is hauled by a dedicated stud of locomotives.

Track
Rail type & weight: T-rail, 17.6 kg/m to 69.6 kg/m
Sleepers: Hardwood (101.5 million) 2,600 x 180 x 230 mm; concrete (250,000) 2,600 x 210 (railseat)/180 (centre) x 270 mm. Spaced 1,950/km (wood) and 1,640/km (concrete)
Fastenings: Cut spike, wood; Pandrol clips, wood in more than 6° curves and for concrete sleepers
Max curvature: 14°, main line; some branches up to 30°
Max gradients: approx 2.5%, main line; approx 2.9% branch lines
Max permissible axleload: 34.8 tonne

UPDATED

CSX Intermodal Inc (CSXI)

301 West Bay Street, Jacksonville, Florida 32202
Tel: +1 904 633 1000
Website: http://www.csxi.com

Key personnel
Chairman: Vacant
President and Chief Executive Officer: Ronald T Sorrow
Vice-Presidents
  Operations: Frank K Turner

Marketing and Pricing: Alan Peck
Finance: Asok Chaudhuri
Sales: Jim Williams
  Human Resources: William Schultz
Vice-President and General Counsel: Mark Hoffman

Organisation

CSXI, formed in 1988, is an integrated door-to-door intermodal carrier, operating both a nationwide container distribution service (with the backbone of the traffic being the inland haulage of containers landed by sister CSX company Sea-Land) and piggyback trains in the east of the country on the CSX system. CSXI's double-stack container trains use the CSX system to reach destinations in the east of the country but also serve other areas on other railroads.

CSXI operates independently of parent CSX Corporation but during 1995 was brought closer to the parent in several ways, including a relocation. Employment was reduced by 16 per cent in 1995, partly in response to flat demand for trailer business which was adversely affected by aggressive truck competition. CSXI has its own autonomous senior management group and, since 1993, has reported separate financial results.

Assets owned and leased at the end of December 1996 were 4,002 domestic containers, 5,124 rail trailers, 33 intermodal terminals, 28 motor carrier operations terminals and 18 servicing facilities. Compared to a year earlier there was effectively a one-for-one swap, with 500 containers acquired and disposal of 500 trailers. CSXI's 33 fully mechanised intermodal terminals, staffed by its own employees, serve every major port. CSXI daily manages and monitors 41 dedicated intermodal trains, including 13 transcontinental double-stack trains. Trucking operations are fully integrated, and CSXI's drayage operations, if considered alone, would constitute the largest such service in North America. A subsidiary, CSX Services, handles chassis leasing and equipment maintenance at 17 facilities, manages the container pick-up and delivery process and schedules availability.

In a restructuring and asset management move in June 1996, CSXI grouped its terminals into six geographic regions, each with a general manager.

European joint venture

CSXI is part of a joint venture partnership that also involves Deutsche Bahn AG (German Railways) and NS (Netherlands Railways). The new company, trading under the acronym NDX (see entry in 'Operators of international rail services in Europe' section), is headquartered in the Netherlands and, since early 1997 has been providing ocean and rail connecting intermodal service to the Netherlands and Germany, with Belgium, Italy, Switzerland, Austria, Poland, the Czech Republic and

Transferring containers between drayage truck and double-stack train **1996**

Hungary as future markets. CSXI chaired the first year of a revolving chairmanship, and John B Padalino, formerly Vice-President, Sales with CSXT, is Managing Director of NDX.

Finance

CSXI recorded operating revenue of $674 million in 1996. Expenses were $639 million, producing net operating income of $35 million, a 17 per cent increase over 1995.

Volume was 980,000 trailers and containers, much the same as in 1995.

The capital programme in 1996 was a conservative $24 million, less than half the figure for 1994 or 1995. CSXI will develop a new Atlanta terminal and expand in New Orleans.

Intermodal operations

Service extends to all continental US states, three adjoining Canadian provinces and Mexico. CSXI's sister

company Sea-Land connects to Alaska. The company's fastest growing service is its 48 ft domestic container network dubbed 'Frequent Flyer', which offers nationwide door-to-door service. Recently, especially buoyant flows have been the Pacific Northwest to Southeast (the Carolinas, Georgia, Florida) and California to New England, the Northeast and middle Atlantic states.

In the area of customer service CSXI has the USA's first advance ordering system for domestic containers, which was expanded to include trailers in 1993, and operates CSXI Customer Service, 24 hour, seven-day shipment tracing using EDI.

CSXI's 'Iron Highway' experiment, a train of flat wagons aimed at ease of loading and unloading in poorly-equipped yards in marginal markets, has been put on hold, purportedly while the parent company focuses on the allocation of Conrail assets.

UPDATED

Illinois Central Railroad

455 North Cityfront Plaza Drive, Chicago, Illinois 60611-5504
Tel: +1 312 755 7500 Fax: +1 312 755 7839

Former Chicago, Central & Pacific offices:
PO Box 1800, 402 East 4th Street, Waterloo, Iowa 50704
Tel: +1 319 236 9200 Fax: +1 319 236 9259

Key personnel

Chairman: Gilbert H Lamphere
President and Chief Executive Officer: E Hunter Harrison
Senior Vice-President, Marketing: Donald H Skelton
Senior Vice-President, Operations: John D McPherson
Vice-Presidents
  Maintenance: David C Kelly
  General Counsel: Ronald A Lane

Chief Finance Officer: Dale W Phillips
Human Resources: James M Harrell
Controller: John V Mulvaney

Gauge: 1,435 mm
Length: 4,320 km (excluding Chicago, Central & Pacific)

Organisation

Illinois Central Corporation is a holding company, listed on the New York Stock Exchange. Its principal subsidiary is the Illinois Central Railroad (IC), in the wake of the mergers now the sixth largest Class I railroad in the US at 4,320 km. It was incorporated in 1851 as the United States' first land grant railroad. The IC worked through a 20-year cycle of acquisitions, mergers and divestments from 1972 to 1992, to attain a core operation in six states in the heartland of America, running on a north-south axis from the Great Lakes to the Gulf of Mexico and providing

freight rail connection between some 2,000 communities, including Chicago, St Louis, Memphis, New Orleans and Mobile. IC interchanges little of its traffic with other railroads; it still originates 74 per cent of its traffic on its own territory (the highest figure in the industry) and 46 per cent never leaves the IC.

Its last major divestiture was the sale of the electrified commuter network in Chicago and south suburbs to Metra (qv). A merger with Kansas City Southern was discussed in 1994 but was not consummated. In 1996, it took a step toward turning back the clock when it agreed to acquire one of its earlier spin-offs, the Chicago, Central & Pacific. The company was formerly the Iowa Division of the Illinois Central Gulf Railroad, which sold it off for $75 million in 1985. Together with the small Cedar Valley Railroad it made up CC&P Holdings Inc, which the present Illinois Central bought back in June 1996 for $139 million plus taking over $18 million of capital leases.

The principal CC&P routes run 817 km from Chicago to Council Bluffs, Iowa; and 206 km from Tara to Sioux City, Iowa. The 602 km segment from Chicago to Tara is equipped with a mix of automatic block, CTC (centralised traffic control) and automatic train stop, permitting operation at 65 km/h overall and in some places up to 100 km/h. Former CCP rolling stock is being numbered into IC series.

Finances (US$ million)	1994	1995	1996
Revenues	595.3	645.3	657.5
Expenses	395.0	414.8	416.3
Operating income	200.3	230.5	241.2
Net income after taxes, special items and so on	113.9	118.4	136.6

Finance

In 1996 IC reported revenues of $657.5 million (up 1.9 per cent on 1995); operating income of $241.2 million (an increase of 4.6 per cent) and net income of $136.6 million (15.3 per cent up on 1995). On a *pro forma* basis, if CC&P

IC has acquired the Chicago, Central & Pacific Railroad; two GP locomotives owned by that road are seen in Cicero intermodal yard, Chicago (F Gerald Rawling) **1996**

had belonged to ICR all year, the performance for 1996 would have been: revenue, $697 million; expenses, $442 million; operating income, $255 million; net income, $143 million.

The company's 'Plan 2000' calls for gross revenues of $800 million (before CCP acquisition) by the end of 1999 and an operating ratio (operating expenses as a percentage of income) of 60. In 1996, the operating ratio was 63.6.

The (erstwhile) Interstate Commerce Commission reported the company as the only Class I railroad whose earnings exceeded the industry's cost of capital for six consecutive years. Internally, the company targets a 14 per cent return on capital by 2000. All levels of employees are involved in the company's performance bonus scheme.

In 1994, IC spent $57 million to convert high-cost leases into low-cost leases or to buyout leases, plus a further $17 million on track, yard improvements and traffic control. The 1997 capital programme is forecast at $172 million of which $93 million is targeted at track, structures and a freight car upgrade programme. Another $60 million is for the dry bulk and liquid bulk projects in Baton Rouge (see section on Freight operations).

Freight operations

IC's prime commodity is coal, which in 1996 accounted for 22 per cent of the year's 960,000 carloadings and for 13 per cent of total revenues. Coal business in the 1995-96 period was flat.

Grain, milled grain and food products together represented 17 per cent of carloads; export grain surged in the third quarter of 1995 but then declined sharply in 1996. A 1997 upswing is to be expected in this very cyclical business. The railroad has established itself as an integral part of the nation's grain distribution system by providing year-round service to the agricultural sector. IC maintains a strong advantage over other rail carriers as it provides a direct access to the Gulf of Mexico. Unit grain trains provide grain shippers with rates that are competitive with trucks and barges. IC is also well positioned to supply feed to the burgeoning poultry industry in southeast states. Grain, at 39 per cent, is the prime *raison d'être* for the CCP.

At the southern end of the railroad, chemical complexes produce a significant contribution to IC's traffic base in the form of 15 per cent of carloads and, significantly, 24 per cent of revenues. The 145 km stretch between Baton Rouge and New Orleans is particularly rich in such natural resources as lime, salt, sulphur, crude oil and natural gas.

One of the nation's heaviest paper mill concentrations is to be found in the IC-served states of Alabama, Tennessee and Louisiana. Since IC is the major railroad in Mississippi, a major timber-producing state, the wood, pulp, and paper products industries combine to generate 15 per cent of total carloadings and 17 per cent of revenues. Metals, bulk commodities and consumer products make up the balance of loads.

New business developments include a $52 million bulk transfer facility on 180 acres (73 ha) near Baton Rouge where the IC will directly access barge and ocean vessels. IC created a new subsidiary, IC RailMarine Terminal Company, to construct and operate the site. Private industry ventures which will be served by IC trains include: a Georgia Pacific distribution centre in University Park, Illinois; a Birmingham Steel melt shop in Memphis; a $200 million joint project of Birmingham Steel and GS Industries into DRI (Direct-Reduced Iron) at a plant adjacent to the IC's Baton Rouge development; and a chemical complex for Shintech, near Geismar, Louisiana.

Intermodal operations

Intermodal activity continued strong from 1995 into 1996 (10 per cent increase in units, 9 per cent increase in revenues), reflecting internal growth and the contribution of contracts with CSX, Southern Pacific (for its Texas market), Canadian National and Wisconsin Central. The former SP traffic may revert to UP. New or improved partnerships have recently been structured with Schneider National, CSX Intermodal and CWS Inc. J B Hunt was added to the list of partnerships in 1996.

Transit time for dedicated intermodal trains between Chicago and New Orleans is under 27 hours.

The transformation of IC's former classification yard at Harvey, Illinois, into an intermodal facility (called the Moyers Intermodal Terminal) continues. After a $6 million partial re-engineering, Wisconsin Central became a tenant and by the end of 1996 Canadian National moved its 95,000 loads a year passing through Chicago into a 67 acre (27 ha) site within the IC yard but with exclusive access/egress separate from the Moyers gate. Inclusive cost for four parallel simultaneous 2.7 km tracks and supporting infrastructure was $16.8 million. CN forecasts growth to 250,000 loads within three years as traffic via the St Clair tunnel (linking Ontario and Michigan) is booming. IC moves CN traffic directly to Memphis and the Gulf.

The Memphis intermodal facility (where CSX is a tenant) was improved during 1994 at a cost of $4.3 million. Following a new interchange arrangement with BNSF for traffic in the southeast states to/from northwest states traffic lane, IC has reopened its intermodal ramp in Mobile, Alabama. The bulk handling facility at Moyers Yard (for plastic pellets) was to be doubled in capacity in 1997 in response to industry demand. IC plans to market aggressively intermodal traffic on the CCP.

Collapsible container system

Illinois Central was the originating railroad for a trial of a collapsible container developed by SEEC Inc, of Mendota, Minnesota, with input from the US Department of Energy. Each Collapsible Intermodal Container (CIC) can move around 25 tonnes.

The trial involved movement of fly ash from a coal burning utility. Each CIC was hoisted in and out of an open top hopper car with conventional overhead crane equipment. The method solves the dust problem

associated with the transport of fly ash, plus offers the railroad backhaul traffic. The trial did not lead to an order by IC but several industries have expressed interest in developing a smaller CIC that would require cheaper, off-the-peg handling equipment.

Traction and rolling stock

In 1996 IC rostered 386 line-haul and 98 switching locomotives (not including CCP units) and attained 92 per cent daily availability. Owned or leased freight wagon stock totalled 16,600+, and IC continues to convert high-cost leases to lower-cost rollovers or to purchases. IC also owns 900 pieces of highway equipment (tractors and trailers). Early in 1995, IC ordered 20 SD70 locomotives rated at 4,000 hp (3,000 kW) and costing $26 million; after modifying some components, IC ordered another 20 machines in 1996; these were delivered in the fourth quarter of that year. The railroad had not bought new for 20 years previously. IC's 35 early model SD40s were upgraded to SD40-2 standards, by VMV Enterprises in 1995. Several of the older classes are being retired or sold; the SD20s are a favourite model for remanufacturers.

Signalling and telecommunications

By the close of 1996 it was the intent that all 4,320 km of the core railroad would be controlled by a DigiCon CTC (Centralised Traffic Control) system; $11 million was allocated to this item in 1995. IC has adopted Union Pacific Technologies' Transportation Control System for monitoring of traction and freight car status, car distribution, and generation of shipping documents and switching orders.

Diesel-electric locomotives: all GM-EMD

Class	No owned end 1996
SW-14	98
GP 10/11‡	105
GP-26	2
GP-38	1
GP-38A	11
GP-38D	16
GP-38-2	53
GP-40R	37
SD 40/40A	18
SD-40G	17
SD 40-2	63
SD 40-X	1
SD 70	40
SD 20	22
Total	464

‡ Rebuilt GP9

UPDATED

Kansas City Southern Railway Company

114 West 11th Street, Kansas City, Missouri 64105-1804
Tel: +1 816 983 1303   Fax: +1 816 983 1192

Key personnel

President and Chief Executive Officer:
Michael R Haverty
Senior Vice-President, Chief Operating Officer:
Albert W Rees
Senior Vice-Presidents
Marketing and Sales: William W Graham
Finance: Joseph D Monello
Senior Vice-President, General Counsel and Secretary:
Richard P Bruening
Vice-Presidents
Transportation: John Fenton
Sales: Robert D Wood
Marketing: David C Bastress
Business Unit Operations: Steve Hefley
Intermodal Business Unit: Vaughan Short
Engineering: David W Brookings
Vice-President and Chief Mechanical Officer: Eric R Post
Director, Purchasing: Sammie L McCain
Superintendent of Locomotives: Fred Haywood III
Superintendent, Car Department: John E Foster
Signal Engineer: Stanley R Taylor

Gauge: 1,435 mm
Route length: 4,690 km operated, 6,610 km of track
Employees at end of 1995: 2,905

Organisation

Kansas City Southern Industries (KCSI) is a diversified holding company. Transportation Services is one of three principal operations and the railway (KCSR) is the largest component of that group. In 1996, KCSI entered into a joint venture with GATX to create Southern Capital Corporation to continue the leasing operations of rolling stock and maintenance equipment, with KCSI as its major client. Transportation Services contributes more than 62 per cent of KCSI consolidated revenues.

In June 1993, KCSR acquired for $213 million the 78 per cent shareholding of MidSouth Corporation which it had not previously purchased, and the two railroads were officially merged from 1 January 1994. KCSI is a partial owner of the Kansas City Terminal Railway Co.

NAFTA railroad

KCSI has become a major player in the Mexican market. The roots of this expansion date back to 1995, when the company formed an alliance with Transportacion Maritima Mexicana (TMM) to explore joint venture prospects in connection with the North American Free Trade Agreement (NAFTA) cross-Gulf intermodal movements, and privatisation of the Mexican railways.

Through the partnership KCSI acquired a 49 per cent stake in the Texas-Mexican Railway (qv).

Of greater significance, though, was the allegiance KCS formed with TMM to bid successfully on the 50-year concession to run the Ferrocarril del Noreste, 3,850 km of track which is reported to carry 60 per cent of Mexico's rail freight. The core line is Mexico City—San Luis Potosi—Monterrey—Nuevo Laredo, with branches to Veracruz, Tampico, Aguascalientes, Metamoros. The operating company will be Transportacion Ferroviaria Mexicana, and one-quarter of the stock remains with the Mexican government for two years. The purchase price, US$1.4 billion was almost triple that bid by the UP and a partner and is almost five times revenues. Industry observers and market analysts were surprised, but for TMM it represents a step toward vertical integration across modes. For KCS it represents a link in the NAFTA railroad and a potential single carrier through route, Mexico City—Chicago, as well as access to an estimated 80 per cent of the Mexican population.

KCS will connect the new I&M Rail Link property (qv) at Kansas City which will extend its reach to the upper Midwest and Canada.

To put another piece in the jigsaw, KCSR has created a new subsidiary, KCS Transportation Co, which has moved to acquire the Gateway Western (qv). By linking up the GWWR, the KCS and the Tex-Mex, KCSR can create 'the NAFTA railroad' from Chicago to the Mexico border.

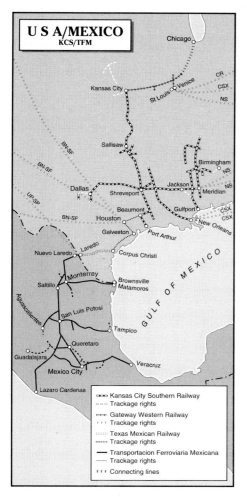

U S A/MEXICO KCS/TFM

Legend:
- ▭▭▭ Kansas City Southern Railway
- ▭ ▭ ▭ Trackage rights
- ▬▬▬ Gateway Western Railway
- ' ' ' Trackage rights
- ::::: Texas Mexican Railway
- ······ Trackage rights
- ▬▬ Transportacion Ferroviaria Mexicana
- ── Trackage rights
- ' ' ' Connecting lines

KCS diesel locomotives, May 1996

Model	Number	Builder/Rebuilder	Date of delivery (or of last rebuild)
GP7	1	EMD	1955-58
GP9	5	EMD	1953
GP10	76	EMD/ICG	(1968-74)
GP18	2	EMD	1960-63
SW1001	3	EMD	1974-81
SW900	1	EMD	1988
SW1500	44	EMD	1966-72
MP15	5	EMD	1975
GP38-2	34	EMD	1973-78
GP40-2LP	86	EMD	1979-81
SD40	7	EMD	1966-71
SD40-2	89	EMD	1972-80 (1995)
SD40X	4	EMD	1979
SD45-3	10	EMD/Helm	(1996)
SD50	9	EMD	1981
SD60	46	EMD	1989-91
Total*	435		

*Does not include 10 slugs or 4 F9s (in business train use)

At the same time KCSR will connect to CSXT at East St Louis.

Further expanding its interests in Latin America, KCSI formed a partnership with Mi-Jack products and a consortium of Panamanian business interests to win an exclusive concession to operate the 77 km Panama Railroad Company.

Divisions restructured
In December 1995 the railroad was formally restructured into two divisions. One is centred upon KCSR's spine line which runs south from Kansas City to Beaumont and Port Arthur, Texas, with trackage rights to Omaha, Topeka, Houston and Galveston. The second route division basically is east-west from Alabama to Texas and includes the line to New Orleans. The main freight yard, Deramus, is at Shreveport, Louisiana; KCSR also has its principal car and locomotive shop at Shreveport.

The 1996 capital programme included a $30 million reconstruction/expansion of the yard at Jackson, Mississippi.

Finance
KCSR produced revenues in 1996 of $492.5 million (2 per cent down on 1995); expenses were similarly reduced, at $415.3 million. Net income after taxes and interest expenses was $17.1 million. The operating ratio (operating expenses as a percentage of income) stood at 78.9, excluding non-recurring costs and expenses.

Freight operations
Carloadings in 1996 totalled 808,048, a decline of 2.8 per cent on the previous year. Coal loads led the commodity sectors at 179,612 (22.2 per cent of total), followed by intermodal (18.5 per cent); chemicals (12.2 per cent); pulp and paper (11.4 per cent) and lumber/wood (9.4 per cent).

Intermodal operations
Intermodal business, chiefly between New Orleans and Dallas, increased modestly for several years but took off in 1994. Growth continued in 1995 and again in 1996; totals for 1996 were 149,349 carloads, an increase of 11.5 per cent over 1995.

KCSR signed a new agreement with trucking company Schneider National in January 1994 to handle traffic through Kansas City. Later in the year KCSR created a service partnership with Norfolk Southern to operate each way daily in the Dallas–Atlanta market, offering a 'Hotshot 20' train to compete with trucks on parallel Interstate 20. KCSR handles the train west of Meridian, Mississippi, and installed seven new sidings to facilitate crossing trains travelling in the other direction on the single-track line. KCSR calls its section west from Meridian 'the Meridian Speedway'. United Parcel Service and J B Hunt are now also major intermodal partners.

KCSR owns and operates six intermodal facilities: Dallas, Texas; Kansas City, Missouri; Sallisaw, Oklahoma; Shreveport and New Orleans, Louisiana; Jackson, Mississippi.

Improvements to existing lines
Around 48 per cent of KCSR's track-km is continuously welded rail (cwr). For 1996, KCSR's capital programme peaked at $135.1 million (a rate of 25.3 per cent of revenues and double the industry standard), principally on trackwork and signalling, including 135 km of cwr. New sleepers installed totalled 342,000, less than half that of 1994, but ballast poured was more than 59 per cent up on 1994 at 350,000 tonnes.

As a result of the track programme, systemwide speeds on the care system have been raised to 85.90 km/hour and future investment can be at a more conservative rate. The forecast for 1997 was $60 million, with a continuing investment in locomotives.

Traction and rolling stock
Traction and rolling stock at the end of 1995 comprised 435 diesel locomotives (403 owned; 35 on capital lease) and 15,285 freight cars (more than half leased). The locomotive fleet is composed entirely of GM-EMD models and has an average age of 17 years in service and an average kW per unit of 1,896 (2,058 for road units only). The newest units are 10 MK-remanufactured 3,600 hp (2,685 kW) SD45-3s leased from Helm in 1995; 22 ex-CN GP40-2LW units also from Helm and also rebuilt by MK retaining the original Canadian comfort cabs; and 20 rebuilt SD40-2s via VMV. In addition to the Deramus shop at Shreveport, Louisiana, KCSR has a locomotive repair facility in Pittsburg, Kansas and a car repair shop in Dallas, Texas.

The MidSouth locomotive roster was made up entirely of units transferred from Illinois Central when MidSouth was spun off from IC a decade ago; fleet rationalisation has already led to the retirement of the CF7 Class. Many of the surviving lower power GP model locomotives have been drafted into service with The Texas-Mexican Railway to augment power on trackage rights newly acquired from UP between Corpus Christi and Beaumont, Texas.

Signalling and telecommunications
KCSR has centralised traffic control (CTC) over 1,505 track-km with a centralised computer-aided dispatching system. It has 96 track-km of Automatic Block System (ABS). The entire system is cable-controlled by microwave and/or fibre optic cables.

UPDATED

Norfolk Southern Corporation

Three Commercial Place, Norfolk, Virginia 23510-2191
Tel: +1 757 629 2600   Fax: +1 757 629 2345
Website: http://www.nscorp.com

Key personnel
Chairman, President and Chief Executive Officer:
   David R Goode
Executive Vice-Presidents
   Law: James C Bishop Jr
   Finance: Henry C Wolf
   Transportation Logistics: R Alan Brogan
   Operations: Stephen C Tobias
   Marketing: L I Prillaman
Senior Vice-President, International: William B Bales
Vice-Presidents
   Personnel: Paul N Austin
   Labour Relations: Robert S Spenski
   Quality Management: Rashe W Stephens Jr

Research and Tests: Donald W Mayberry
Engineering: Phillip R Ogden
Coal Marketing: John W Fox Jr
Intermodal: Thomas L Finkbiner
Strategic Planning: James W McClellan
Law: William C Wooldridge
Controller: John P Rathbone
Public Relations: Robert C Fort
Public Affairs: James L Granum
Treasurer: William J Romig
Operations Planning and Budget: Harold C Mauney Jr
Public Affairs: John F Corcoran
Information Technology: Charles W Moorman
Taxation: James A Hixon
Merchandise Marketing: Donald W Seale
Internal Audit: Kathryn B McQuade
Transportation and Mechanical: Jon L Manetta
Properties: David A Cox
Vice-President: Thomas J Golian

Corporate Secretary: Dezora M Martin
President and Chief Executive Officer, North American
   Van Lines: R Alan Brogan
Vice-President, Corporate Planning, NAVL:
   Dennis Koziol
President, Triple Crown Services: Dan Cushman
President, Pocahontas Land Corporation: Daniel D Smith

Gauge: 1,435 mm
Length: 23,000 km

Organisation
Norfolk Southern Corporation (NS) is a holding company with headquarters at Norfolk, Virginia, established in 1982. It owns the Norfolk Southern Railway Company, the product of a merger of the Norfolk & Western and Southern railways, which was largely motivated by the 1980 creation of CSX (qv). It also owns North American Van Lines Inc and a natural resources subsidiary called

Pocahontas Land Corporation. It is a publicly traded company, listed on the New York Stock Exchange.

Route structure
The Norfolk & Western and Southern Railway merger was an end-to-end consolidation. The N&W stretched from Norfolk, Virginia, west to Kansas City, Missouri, and north into the key markets of Chicago, Detroit and Cleveland. The Southern blanketed the southeast, from New Orleans, Louisiana; Mobile, Alabama; and Jacksonville, Florida, north to Cincinnati, Ohio; and Washington DC; from the St Louis 'gateway' and Memphis, Tennessee, eastwards to the Atlantic ports of Norfolk, Virginia; Charleston, South Carolina; Savannah and Brunswick, Georgia. The railroads connected at 17 common points, with major connections at East St Louis, Cincinnati and throughout Virginia and North Carolina.

The two railroads now function as an integral unit.

Conrail break-up
Once unsuccessful in a solo bid for Conrail in 1986, NS has worked with Conrail in the last decade in joint market developments. To counter a proposed CSX-Conrail merger, which would have effectively locked NS out of the US northeast market, NS launched an all-cash bid for Conrail (see Conrail entry for details). Conrail shareholders opposed the merger with CSX while there was an alternative. The Surface Transportation Board advised the three parties to work out a solution and, as a result, NS will acquire 58 per cent of Conrail for about $5.9 billion, the principal assets being the former Pennsylvania main line across Pennsylvania, plus access to New Jersey and half of shared tracks in New Jersey and the Detroit region, two desirable markets.

Finance
In 1996 transportation operating revenues were $4.77 billion (up 2 per cent from 1995) and the railway accounted for $4.10 billion of that. Net income after provision for taxes was a record $770 million. Operating ratio (operating expenses as a percentage of income) for 1995 was 71.6, a two-point improvement over the previous year.

Revenue in all major market groups except paper/forest products rose in 1996. Coal revenues for 1995 were 32 per cent of total and were up by 3 per cent to $1.316 billion, partly explained by a shift to coal from nuclear generation by a couple of utilities. Automotive revenue improved over 1995 by 8 per cent to $488.7 million; metals/construction revenue increased 1 per cent to $358 million; agricultural revenues were flat at $393 million; paper/forest products declined 5 per cent to $513 million; chemicals picked up 4 per cent in revenues.

Norfolk Southern's motor carrier subsidiary North American Van Lines had $669 million in revenues and $637 million in expenses in 1996.

In 1996, Norfolk Southern's subsidiary Pocahontas Land Corporation realised $70.3 million in revenues from lessees who paid royalties to extract coal, gas and timber from PLC's 900,000 acres in six states.

Capital spending for 1997 was forecast to amount to $792 million including approximately $240 million for track and structures and $239 million for rolling stock. For 1996 the capital budget was $708 million. Several long-term projects commenced in 1997: $39 million will be spent on computer systems; $33 million on despatching systems; $28 million on bridge and trestle works; $21 million to replace pole lines systemwide and bring in electronics for track circuitry and train location.

In the first quarter of 1997, NS took a $77 million pre-tax charge for costs related to the Conrail purchase. As a result, net income was $128 million, 24 per cent below the previous year. Without the charge, both rail and motor carrier gross revenues were 3 per cent up over 1996 to a new quarter's record of $1.25 billion.

Workforce developments
In 1995, NS had 27,000 employees. NS implemented an early retirement programme in the fourth quarter of that year for which 470 non-union employees were eligible and for which an after-tax charge of $20.4 million was taken.

A significant development came in May 1996 when NS and its 2,900 locomotive drivers reached a five year agreement that foresakes traditional wage rises in favour of year-end bonuses similar to management and subject to NS's rate of return on capital invested, which in 1995 was 20.2 per cent. The offer to the drivers was for a 5 per cent bonus in 1996 and 1997 and 10 per cent for three years thereafter. This agreement is designed to bring

management and union interests into closer convergence through performance measures and a consolidated approach to winning business, partly by capture from trucking.

Freight operations
Coal
Coal is NS's most important commodity. Reserves of some seven billion tonnes of low-sulphur coal are located in NS territory. The principal sources are mines in Virginia, West Virginia, Kentucky and Tennessee. Export coal is shipped through the NS piers at Lamberts Point in Norfolk, Virginia.

Computer-controlled loading introduced at a mine in Kopperston, West Virginia, permits optimisation of loaded weight and direct transmission of an EDI (electronic data interchange) invoice to the customer and to the piers at Lamberts Point to anticipate the train's arrival.

NS continues to participate in movement of low-sulphur coal out of Wyoming to southern states utilities. Export coal rose 5 per cent in volume in FY95-96. Metallurgical coal sells in several European and South American countries. The railway's wagon fleet contains more than 3,000 new gondolas, including 600 with aluminium bodies, and 20,500 that have been rebodied in recent years. Some 3,500 were rebodied in 1995 and the project continued in 1996. By mid-1996 the coal car fleet was working at a 15 per cent improved level of utilisation compared to 1994. 1996 volume, all coal types, totalled 128 million tonnes.

In January 1995 NS launched a new intermodal coal service, dubbed COLTainer, with 1.1 million tonnes/year movement to Alabama Power Company's Gorgas plant near Parrish. The site has no rail siding and so all coal has to be trucked in. NS supplies Gorgas from a Berry, Alabama, mine; coal is transported in high-capacity containers which ride on flatcars for 38 km. At a point 13 km from the power station, the COLTainers are loaded on to special truck chassis for movement to Gorgas. The service is designed to control inventory by delivering in

shipment sizes equal to demand, thereby eliminating a stockpile.

In June 1996, NS opened a second conveyor-fed loadout, in Benedict, Virginia. The coal moves over 5.6 km of conveyors from a mine, not on the Norfolk Southern, in Harlan County, Kentucky.

Agricultural products
Agricultural traffic declined 4 per cent and revenues were flat in 1996. The forecast for 1997 was for modest growth. Inbound feed grain to the poultry industry is expected to stay firm and Norfolk Southern acquired a 12 million bushel (storage capacity) elevator near Champaign, Illinois, as a consequence of buying a segment of the former Peoria & Eastern from Conrail. Also in Illinois, Norfolk Southern will expand its facilities in Decatur to secure an expanding complex owned by the grain company Archer-Daniel-Midlands.

Automotive
Automotive traffic rose 8 per cent, revenues rose 9 per cent, and auto parts, reported separately, rose 21 per cent. Norfolk Southern opened two JIT (just-in-time) rail centres in Hagerstown, Maryland, and Buffalo, New York, and a third, in Dayton, Ohio, was proceeding for a 1997 start-up. The Wentzville GM plant near St Louis returned to full production in 1996; GM's Doraville, Georgia, plant returned to production after retooling and the new BMW plant at Greer hit full production, so in 1996 all plants on NS were running for the first time since 1992. Mercedes-Benz is scheduled to begin production at Tuscaloosa, Alabama, in 1997, and Toyota is building a new truck plant at Princeton, Indiana as well as planning to expand at Georgetown, Kentucky. Norfolk Southern handles/originates some 20 per cent of all new vehicle production in the US and Canada.

In the first quarter of 1997, Norfolk Southern announced that a major component, at $100 million, of its 1997 capital programme would be a mixing centre network (with four locations) to serve the Ford Motor

Transportation Finances (US$ million)

Rail Revenues	1993	1994	1995	1996
Coal, coke and iron ore	1,213.3	1,290.2	1,267.8	1,304.7
Merchandise	2,020.9	2,199.2	2,269.7	2,308.9
Intermodal	390.2	428.7	474.3	487.4
Other	121.5	—	—	—
Total	3,745.9	3,918.1	4,011.8	4,101.0
Rail Expenditures				
Way and structures	649.7	n/a	n/a	n/a
Equipment	660.3	n/a	n/a	n/a
Operating	1,390.5	n/a	n/a	n/a
General and administrative	899.2	n/a	n/a	n/a
Total	3,599.7	2,874.8	2,950.0	2,936.1
Net revenue				
From operations (including motor carrier)	860.4	1,065.4	1,086.3	1,197.0
Other income (expense)				
Interest income and other, net	136.8	85.2	141.8	115.6
Interest expense	(98.6)	(101.6)	(113.4)	(115.7)
Total	38.2	(16.4)	28.4	(0.1)
Income before taxes	898.6	1,049.0	1,114.7	1,196.9
Provision for taxes	349.9	381.2	402.0	426.5
Net income	772.0	667.8	712.7	770.4

RoadRailer in NS Triple Crown service

Intermodal coal transport for electricity generating stations without rail connection: four of these COLTainers fit on one customised flat car   **1995**

Diesel locomotives*

Type	Wheel arrangement	Power kW	Speed km/h	Weight tonnes	No in service	First built	Builders Mechanical	Engine	Transmission
SW1	B-B	448	72	88.7	5	1950	EMD	EMD	E EMD
SW1500	B-B	1,119	114	112.7	60	1970	EMD	EMD	E EMD
TC10†	B-B	783	114	114.8	4	1983	EMD	Caterpillar	E Kato
MP15DC	B-B	1,119	105	116.6	87	1977	EMD	EMD	E EMD
SD9/9M	C-C	1,306	105	165.6	10	1957	EMD	EMD	E EMD
GP38	B-B	1,492	105	112.5	109	1969	EMD	EMD	E EMD
GP38AC	B-B	1,492	105	129.9	114	1971	EMD	EMD	E EMD
GP38-2	B-B	1,492	105	117.5	252	1972	EMD	EMD	E EMD
GP40	B-B	2,238	114	124.9	56	1966	EMD	EMD	E EMD
GP40X	B-B	2,611	114	121.5	3	1978	EMD	EMD	E EMD
SD40	C-C	2,238	114	175.5	73	1966	EMD	EMD	E EMD
SD40-2	C-C	2,238	113	175.5	276	1972	EMD	EMD	E EMD
GP49	B-B	2,089	105	121.3	6	1980	EMD	EMD	E EMD
GP50	B-B	2,611	114	121.5	90	1980	EMD	EMD	E EMD
SD45	C-C	2,686	113	184.5	9	1970	EMD	EMD	E EMD
SD50	C-C	2,611	113	175.5	26	1980	EMD	EMD	E EMD
GP59	B-B	2,238	113	121.5	35	1986	EMD	EMD	E EMD
GP60	B-B	2,835	113	129.4	50	1991	EMD	EMD	E EMD
SD60	C-C	2,835	113	175.5	151	1984	EMD	EMD	E EMD
SD70	C-C	2,984	113	175.5	56	1993	EMD	EMD	E EMD
U23B	B-B	1,716	105	119.7	65	1972	GE	GE	E GE
B23-7	B-B	1,716	105	122.0	53	1978	GE	GE	E GE
B30-7A	B-B	2,238	105	126.5	22	1982	GE	GE	E GE
C30-7	C-C	2,238	113	175.5	79	1978	GE	GE	E GE
D8-32B	B-B	2,387	113	121.5	45	1989	GE	GE	E GE
B36-7	B-B	2,686	105	125.1	6	1981	GE	GE	E GE
C36-7	C-C	2,686	113	175.5	43	1981	GE	GE	E GE
C39-8	C-C	2,909	113	175.5	136	1984	GE	GE	E GE
D8-40C	C-C	2,984	113	179.1	75	1990	GE	GE	E GE
D9-40C	C-C	2,984	113	179.1	240	1994	GE	GE	E GE

* Booster and slave units are not shown

† Retired GP9s rebuilt with Caterpillar engines and Kato transmission for local switching duty

Company and eventually distribute three million vehicles annually from 21 Ford assembly plants to its national dealer network. The four mixing centres will be at Chicago; Fostoria, Ohio; Shelbyville, Kentucky; and Kansas City, Missouri. The four mixing centres will supply 16 distribution centres around the US.

Also, in Detroit, Michigan, at the Detroit Regional Distribution Center (DRDC), NS increased carloadings of auto parts from 15 per day in 1992 to 35 per day in 1993, a figure which had doubled again by 1995. Instead of the more usual practice, where parts are received by rail and distributed by truck, the DRDC works in the reverse. Auto parts are brought to DRDC by truck from a radius of approximately 400 km and sorted according to the particular daily requirements of 10 GM assembly plants in the US and Mexico; the parts are shipped out in boxcars to arrive at the plants on a just-in-time schedule. GM saves on inventory floor space and costs; NS charges by the car and has 650 high-capacity boxcars in dedicated service after adding 200 in 1995. Similar centres at Hagerstown, Buffalo and Dayton (the last under construction in 1997) operate in the same way and on a similar scale, that is 4,800 carloads annually.

NS and Conrail have 20 AutoRailers (a bimodal car-carrying wagon produced by RoadRailer) in test with Triple Crown Services.

Expanding business base

In a programme in which it often acts in partnership with state and local governments, in 1996, Norfolk Southern located on its network 73 new industries and supported 37 expansions to generate an estimated 100,000 additional carloads. Two online mini steel mills are under construction.

The Sandusky Dock Corporation, a NS subsidiary, completed its $10 million investment over three years to upgrade its Lake Erie transloading facility where four million tonnes of coal are transloaded annually.

Significantly, nine of the last twelve new auto assembly plants in the US have located on the NS system (see also Automotive section above).

Intermodal operations

Intermodal set both volume and revenue records in 1996: traffic was up by 5 per cent and revenues up by 3 per cent. NS's strategic alliances with other railroads allow the company to reach New York (via Conrail), Dallas (via KCS) and Miami (via FEC).

Capacity expansion projects were completed in 1995 at intermodal terminals in Charlotte, North Carolina; Columbus, Ohio; Birmingham, Alabama; and Norfolk, Virginia. Columbus and Birmingham can handle double-stacks. In 1996, either capacity was increased or equipment upgraded at Chicago, Norfolk, Atlanta, Cincinnati and Louisville. Cincinnati can now handle double-stack trains. Double-stack is now available in the New York—Atlanta traffic lane via an interchange with Conrail at Hagerstown, Maryland, which will become an NS property with the break-up of Conrail.

The NS, CSX Intermodal and the New York, Susquehanna & Western Corp contract to operate a six-day-a-week domestic intermodal service in the Chicago—New York market may be compromised by the Conrail break-up as both NS and CSX will have route alternatives. The same will be true of an NS-Canadian Pacific arrangement serving parts of New York State and Pennsylvania.

NS, Conrail and Union Pacific have formed a joint venture called EMP to provide domestic containers for intermodal customers at a total of 28 terminals. EMP features a real-time management support system. In April 1996 NS made EMP available in three traffic lanes that it is developing with KCS, namely Dallas to Atlanta, Charlotte, North Carolina, and Jacksonville, Florida. In 1996, EMP was extended to Los Angeles by arrangement with Southern Pacific (later UP).

NS has joined UP in a partnership to expand the latter's 'Passport Service' offering to NS customers. Passport Service is a system for providing rail service to the Laredo gateway into Mexico; from Laredo, after expedited customs clearance, 16 major Mexican markets are reached by contracted motor carrier. NS has added the service to 21 cities as far apart as Buffalo and Miami.

In March 1997 NS and BNSF announced an initiative to offer improved interline intermodal service between Louisville, Kentucky and six cities between Denver and Vancouver. Added to the offering will be seven cities in Arizona and California.

In early 1995 NS announced a seven-year contract with Hanjin Lines of Korea. NS has since invested $17 million to upgrade and add capacity to its Chicago Landers yard to serve as a distribution point, and will move all Hanjin traffic east of the Mississippi river.

Chicago and Atlanta are the test installations for SIMS, the Strategic Intermodal Management System, applied to identification and movement of trailers/containers; by 1997 SIMS will be in place over much of NS's intermodal network.

Triple Crown Services Company

In April 1993, NS and Conrail entered into an equal partnership named Triple Crown Services Company (TCSC) to offer domestic intermodal services based on a Chicago—New York—Atlanta triangle, using RoadRailer bimodal equipment. Conrail bought into TCSC for a $50 million investment. NS contributed to the partnership the assets and operations of its Triple Crown subsidiary established in 1986.

Triple Crown has its own sales force (and generally eschews third-party sales) and provides most of its own drayage through North American Van Lines.

In 1994 TCSC purchased 1,770 new 53 ft long Mark V trailer units and retired all the remaining 48 ft Mark IV units. For future years TCSC is looking at adding refrigerated ReeferRailers.

TCSC began service into New Jersey in 1994, making the New York City market accessible; it continues to target the Dallas/Fort Worth, Houston and Miami markets. TCSC has an impressive lane balance (percentage of backloading with cargo) of 94 per cent.

In 1995 came a major development: the Federal Railroad Administration authorised NS to make up trains to a maximum of 125 trailers where the previous limit was 100.

Thoroughbred Bulk Transfer (TBT)

TBT services increased in 1996 by the addition of a facility at Petersburg, Virginia, and an increase in capacity at Dalton, Georgia. A new location at Charlotte, North Carolina, which was to open in 1997, would bring the total to 10 TBT terminals.

Traction and rolling stock

At the start of 1996 NS's diesel locomotive fleet was 2,054 in number, following completion of half an order (125 of 240) for Dash 9-40C/CW units by General Electric. Deliveries were arriving in 1996 and 1997 at a rated 4,000 hp (3,000 kW) but with electronics for 4,400 hp (3,280 kW), and for NS are a first purchase of the wide-body cab, having previously favoured the more utilitarian version. As these arrive, some of NS's smaller size classes and some earlier models such as the C30-7s are being sold off to rebuilders and lessors. NS has a small number of leased units.

Except for some double-stack container cars, the downsized freight wagon stock of some 108,000 vehicles is almost entirely NS-owned; 17,000 were declared surplus during 1995, with 10,200 of those subsequently sold to generate $100 million in income. The leaner fleet was expected to show a 25 per cent or better increase in utilisation in 1996.

New wagons received in 1996 included 150 73 ft centrebeam cars and 150 coil cars to handle aluminium coils, in addition to grain hoppers and high-capacity boxcars. In 1996-97 NS acquired 297 hi-cube cars, including 157 for dedicated auto parts traffic.

In 1994 NS made a corporate decision to terminate its special steam train operations; most of the equipment except the locomotives was sold at auction.

NS is increasing its main line fuelling practice, in which locomotives are not uncoupled from trains but are fuelled directly from service trucks. That, and a new locomotive management system, combined to increase by 4 per cent the amount of time a locomotive is pulling trains, the largest year-to-year improvement in utilisation in a decade.

Signalling and telecommunications

Consolidation of traffic centres and extension of computer-aided dispatching has continued. With the 1992 completion of the Fort Wayne, Indiana, installation, and of another in Greenville, South Carolina, early in 1993, around 6,100 route-km and 70 per cent of all NS train-km came under computer-aided control.

The Fort Wayne centre, with equipment by Union Switch & Signal, controls an entire division embracing 2,400 route-km between Chicago and Buffalo and between Detroit and Cincinnati. At Greenville, a Harmon system controls a 4,200 route-km division between Washington DC and Atlanta, Georgia, and between Asheville, North Carolina, and Charleston, South Carolina. Both centres feature rear-projection screen overview displays, along with ability to configure dispatcher consoles to match personnel and traffic requirements on a per-shift basis.

NS has been in the forefront of the application of Automatic Equipment Identification (AEI), which permits quick and accurate location of any wagon anywhere on the system. One third of its rail fleet has been equipped with transponders and NS tracks nearly 40,000 wagons, shipments and locomotives every 24 hours using AEI as input to its two principal inventory and customer service systems. One, Thoroughbred Yard Enterprise System (TYES), is a car positioning and tracking project. The other, Centralised Yard Operations (CYO), consolidates all transportation department clerical functions in Atlanta to improve customer support services. NS is now conducting a pilot project on several multilevel autoracks using its automatic equipment monitoring (AEM) system which records and transmits data about the ride dynamics of the car (wagon); these data about ride-impact forces

will be analysed for future use in improving ride quality and damage-free shipments.

By the end of 1992, NS had installed a Computerised Crew Management System on six of its nine operating divisions, reducing errors in calling the proper crews for trains, and by mid-1997 all nine divisions should be served from the Atlanta office.

Track

In addition to a normal year's $240 million spending on rails, sleeper ballast and bridges, in 1996 NS completed the total reconstruction of its historic 8 km-long Lake Pontchartrain bridge on the north approach to New Orleans, mostly with its own forces. The 13-year job

involved over 80,000 tonnes of poured concrete and 170 km of steel and/or concrete pilings.
Rail type and weight: Chiefly 132 lb/yd, 65.6 kg/m; 115 lb/yd, 57 kg/m; 100 lb/yd, 49.6 kg/m; and 85 lb/yd, 42.2 kg/m.
Crossties (sleepers): Wood
Spacing: 1,970/km
Fastenings: 6 in cut spikes
Max curvature: 22°
Max gradient: 4.4%
Max permissible axleload (lb): 71,500±, 36 in diameter wheels; 78,750±, 38 in dia wheels

UPDATED

Union Pacific Railroad Company

1416 Dodge Street, Omaha, Nebraska 68179
Tel: +1 402 271 5000   Fax: +1 402 271 5572
Website: http://www.uprr.com

Alton & Southern Railway Co subsidiary
1000 S 22nd Street, East St Louis, Illinois 62207
Tel: +1 618 482 3239

Former Chicago & North Western office
165 North Canal Street, Chicago, Illinois 60606
Tel: +1 312 559 7000   Fax: +1 312 559 6495

Former Southern Pacific office
Southern Pacific Building, One Market Plaza, San Francisco, California 94105
Tel: +1 415 541 1000   Fax: +1 415 541 1929

Key personnel

Chairman President and Chief Executive Officer (UP Corporation): Richard K Davidson
President and Chief Operating Officer (UP Railroad): Jerry R Davis
Executive Vice-Presidents
   Marketing and Sales: James A Shattuck
   Operations: Arthur L Shoener
   Finance and Information Technologies:
      John J Koraleski
Senior Vice-Presidents
   Labour Relations and Merger Implementation:
      Thomas L Watts
   Customer Service, Planning and Delivery:
      Dennis J Duffy
   General Manager (Energy): Arthur W Peters
Vice-Presidents
   Law: James V Dolan
   Human Resources: Barbara Schaefer
   Finance and Quality: James R Young
   Purchasing: Charles Eisele
   Energy: Henry L Arms
   Engineering Services: Stan McLaughlin
   Transportation: R Bradley King
   General Manager (Intermodal): Michael F Kelly
   General Manager (Industrial Products): John T Gray
   General Manager (Agricultural Products):
      Drew R Collier
   General Manager (Chemicals): J Edward Sims
   General Manager (Automotive): Joseph W Leppert III
   Labour Relations: John J Marchant
   Strategic Planning: John H Rebensdorf
   Risk Management: Robert D Naro
   National Customer Service Center:
      James J Damman Jr
   Information Technologies and Chief Information
      Officer: Joyce M Wrenn
   Western Region: Robert F Starzel
Chairman and Chief Executive Officer of Overnite:
   Leo H Suggs
President and Chief Executive Officer, UP Technologies:
   L Merill Bryan Jr
President and Chief Executive Officer, Skyway Freight
   Systems: Kip Hawley
Manager, Commuter Rail: Julie K Brown

Gauge: 1,435 mm
Route length: 57,600 km

Organisation

Corporate structure
Union Pacific Railroad Company (UPRR) is one of four business units of the holding company, Union Pacific

A pair of GP38 locomotives used by UP subsidiary Alton & Southern at Gateway Yard, East St Louis (F Gerald Rawling)   *1996*

Corporation. The other units are Overnite Transportation, a trucking company; Skyway Freight Systems, a logistics and transportation company bought in 1993; and UP Technologies, a developer and retailer of computer systems and software. Two subsidiaries were sold in recent years: USPCI in 1994 and UP Resources, a gas, coal and soda ash company, in 1996.

Union Pacific is a publicly traded company listed on the New York Stock Exchange.

Acquisitions and sales
Union Pacific's aggressive acquisitions policy has made it the second mega-system in the US West after the merged Burlington Northern/Santa Fe entity (qv). It operates 57,600 km in 23 states and employs 54,800 people.

During the 1980s the UP absorbed the Missouri Pacific, Western Pacific and Missouri–Kansas–Texas (MKT) systems. While increasing its hold on strategic main lines in the US West, UP has been divesting itself of secondary routes. Between 1987 and 1994 UP sold, leased out or abandoned over 5,000 km of lightly used branch lines; the pace has been slower since then.

Losing out to BN in the 1994 bidding battle for Santa Fe, UP went on to purchase the 70 per cent of Chicago & North Western Railroad (CNW) it did not already own (total valuation of CNW: $1.2 billion), thus safeguarding its access to Chicago. With effect from 1 May 1995 CNW — until that date the eighth-largest freight railroad in the US — and its coal-hauling subsidiary Western Railroad Properties Inc, became subject to control by UP. After completion of the CNW purchase the UP system totalled 36,480 km.

The decisive stroke on the route to becoming a mega-system came in August 1995 when UP Corporation agreed to buy Southern Pacific, a deal which would in time give UP annual revenues approaching $10 billion. To counter opposition to the deal, UP announced an arrangement with BNSF in which BNSF would receive approximately 6,400 km of trackage rights (at a rate below industry average to entice BNSF) and could buy outright an additional 400 km of tracks. Included in this arrangement was the so-called 'central corridor', between Denver, Colorado, and Oakland, California. By early 1997, UP had realised $100 million from line sales to BNSF.

The Surface Transportation Board voted 3-0 in favour of a merger between UP and SP at the beginning of July

1996; the merger took effect on 12 September 1996 after none of the parties opposed to it had elected to mount a court challenge. As part of the deal UP acquired a 100 per cent interest in the Alton & Southern, a switching railroad in East St Louis, Illinois, which beforehand it had jointly owned with SP.

Final approval for the merger from the STB left the West of the US with two giant railroads, the BNSF and UP-SP systems. The final valuation of the latter transaction was set at $4.1 billion (compared to the $3.8 billion BN spent on taking over the Santa Fe).

Operating Plan
Union Pacific's Operating Plan has a strong echo of the erstwhile SP structure in that it features discrete routes, namely:
* the I-5, or West Coast, Corridor: California to Seattle;
* the Sunset Route: Los Angeles–Houston–New Orleans;
* the Overland Route: Midwest to Northern California;
* the Golden State Route: Midwest to Southern California;
* the Kansas–Pacific Route: Kansas City to Denver;
* Memphis–Texas–California route;
* Midwest–Arkansas–Texas route.
Some of these routes are to be the subject of major investment, for example, more than 160 km of additional double track is to be installed in the Sunset corridor and CTC will control the Golden State corridor.

The Kansas–Pacific route will be used to return empty coal trains to the Powder River basin via Topeka and Denver.

Finance

UP operating revenue in 1995 was $7.486 billion (up from $6.492 billion in 1994); operating income was $1.341 billion, up from $1.173 billion. Consolidated transportation income, after adding in CNW post-merger, was $619 million (up 9 per cent). In 1996, the operating ratio (operating expenses as a percentage of income) rose slightly to 79.1 from 78.1 the previous year, principally reflecting the influence of the former SP. Carloadings were up 18 per cent over 1995, to 6,632,000. A measure of productivity, revenue per carload, improved by 2 per cent, a second year of such improvement.

For 1996, UP's capital investment programme was

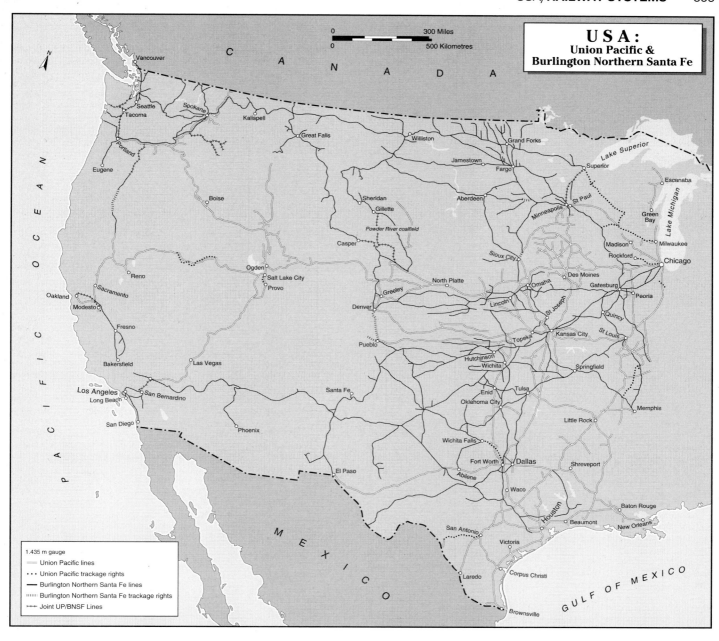

USA:
Union Pacific &
Burlington Northern Santa Fe

1.435 m gauge
══ Union Pacific lines
••• Union Pacific trackage rights
▬▬ Burlington Northern Santa Fe lines
||||| Burlington Northern Santa Fe trackage rights
⊢••⊣ Joint UP/BNSF Lines

$1.34 billion, consisting of trackwork, locomotives, rolling stock , terminal facilities and new technology.

UP adopted a capital budget of $2.2 billion for 1997. Of the total $1 billion was for track and structures; $615 million for 260 new locomotives and upgrades to some of the current fleet; $103 million for wagons. Application of the programme will be directed to addressing capacity constraints and power shortages on the ex-SP network.

Overnite Transportation
Union Pacific Corporation's Overnite Transportation business unit continued to struggle toward profitability in 1996. It lost $68 million on gross operation, revenues of $961 million, and is burdened with an operating ratio of 105.0. Purchased to complement UP's railway operations, Overnite is a 'top five' road carrier for small (less-than-truckload) shipments. Overnite operates in the eastern third of the US, east of the Mississippi river, using 166 service centres, 510 tractors and 1,800 trailers.

UP established a task force to address the future of Overnite after the 1997 results were in.

Passenger operations
In 1993 UP started commuter services, providing four daily trains each way on a 96 km line between Riverside and Los Angeles under contract to the Southern California Regional Rail Authority (qv); the contract permits up to 10 trains each way. Amtrak is the designated operator on the rest of the SCRRA Metrolink system.

As a consequence of the takeover of Chicago & Northwestern, UP is now contract operator to Metra for three Chicago area lines.

UP has set up a commuter rail development team to identify new opportunities by emphasising rail's 'green' credentials; approaches have been made to state and local authorities in San Jose, Stockton, Denver, Salt Lake City, St Louis, Seattle-Tacoma and Dallas-Fort Worth. There is a start-up planned for 1998 in the San Jose—Stockton corridor (see San Joaquin Railroad Commission entry). UP argues that commuter rail costs $7 million per mile to start up and is ready in 18 to 24 months, compared to $100 million per mile for highway construction and lead times in the 10 to 15 year range.

Freight operations
UP has a wide traffic mix, with coal from the Powder River basin, intermodal traffic from the Californian ports, and grain from the prairie states being important commodities. At the start of 1997 it was operating 2,100 trains daily.

By business unit and measured in carloadings the year-to-year changes were: *intermodal* — up 26 per cent; *energy* — up 26 per cent; *automotive* — up 20 per cent; *chemicals* up 14 per cent; *agricultural products* — up 13 per cent; *industrial products* — up 26 per cent. Essentially, the SP brought an average of 20 per cent in increased carloadings and the sector-specific percentages reflect that.

Significance of coal
Coal is the prime commodity on the Union Pacific. Output from the Powder River basin is now in excess of 100 million tonnes and train lengths have risen to 135 cars. This coalfield generates an average of 22 loaded trains a day. Output from mines in Utah and Colorado (served by former SP lines) reached new highs in 1996 in

response to better car and locomotive utilisation. The combination of higher payload and improved cycle times means the car replacement rate is conserved.

Deal with Wisconsin Central
Contributing to a surge in coal traffic on the former SP was a joint venture with Wisconsin Central (qv), which captured significant reciprocal movements of westbound ore and eastbound coal. Ore leaves Minntac (Minnesota Taconite) for Geneva Steel in Utah. The empties are made available to UP (ex-SP) to load with mountain low-sulphur coal for movement to midwestern utilities, depending on demand. The ore contract started out at 2.6 million short tons per year in mid-1994 and had already reached 3.8 million a year later. SP committed 70 locomotives and 14 trainsets each of 105 wagons to this business. WC put up 12 units and initially contributed 575 wagons until SP could receive new deliveries. UP now routes the trains around Chicago on the Elgin, Joliet and Eastern Railway (qv).

Soda ash expansion
UP continues to assist in the growth of the export soda ash business. It has improved transit time from Green River, Wyoming, to Portland, Oregon, to three days and has a share in a 30,000 short ton rail-to-ship storage facility which improves equipment turnaround. By the close of 1994 soda ash exports were running at 4 million short tons per annum, 90 per cent to the Asia-Pacific market and 10 per cent to Mexico, where UP also takes a part in a rail-only move. The heavy demand meant that rolling stock and power shortages were beginning to occur but UP has introduced distributed power to improve train times and equipment utilisation.

Customer service

The national Customer Service Center in St Louis interacts with UP's computerised Transportation Control System (TCS), which provides service representation with billing information and a profile of customer requirements, as well as online information on the status of shipments and the availability of wagons. Shippers now have the ability to interact directly with Union Pacific's TCS system. By using personal computers they can order wagons, trace shipments and enter billing information directly.

'Bottleneck' cases; open access

In 1996, power generating companies had several petitions before the STB to relieve 'bottleneck' cases, that is where only one railroad delivers to the utility but there could be multiple coal suppliers and multiple intermediate haulers. The utilities asked that the delivering railroad be required to establish a short-haul rate from any available proximate junction. UP and Conrail were the leading protagonists for the rail industry. The STB ruled in favour of the railroads, that is they are not required to move traffic to the nearest junction with another railroad, wherever a shipper requests. The issue was likely to be introduced into Congress by the shippers.

Intermodal operations

UP serves all major West Coast and all Gulf Coast ports. Most container traffic runs between West Coast ports and midwestern cities or New York, but regular double-stack trains also run between Houston and New Orleans. The fastest Chicago—Los Angeles double-stack train schedule is now 50 hours following the introduction of a new premium service.

In addition to these double-stack container trains, UP runs numerous dedicated container/piggyback trains daily between its major city and port hubs. Besides through services, competitive intercity connections are augmented by scheduled interchange between a number of trains at North Platte, Nebraska.

Intermodal returned to a growth pattern in 1996 as domestic demand rose.

Several major partnerships with trucking concerns continue (among the trucking partners are Schneider National, J B Hunt, Crete, and United Parcel Service), and UP has joined with Conrail and Norfolk Southern in the EMP partnership (for details see Conrail entry).

In the 1997 capital programme improvements were planned for the Seattle, Reno, Nevada, and Kansas City yards, plus completion of the Mesquito, Texas location.

Intermodal on the former SP

Intermodal was an important sector for SP, with the major ports of Los Angeles and Long Beach in southern California generating large quantities of container traffic which are handled in double-stack trains. Much of the 1996 increase in UP traffic (26 per cent more carloadings, 29 per cent higher revenues) is attributable to SP's contribution.

For the past decade these trains have been handled through the Intermodal Container Transfer Facility at Long Beach. SP signed a long-term lease until 2036 on the ICTF, which now covers 96 ha. An average of 75 trains a week serve the terminal, moving containers mostly for Pacific Rim shippers. The $100 million facility, a joint venture between UP and the ports of Los Angeles and Long Beach, is 6.5 km from the ports. It has 11 km of track and can load and unload five double-stack trains simultaneously.

In years to come the ICTF will be complemented by the $1.8 billion Alameda Corridor project. Designed jointly by the ports and the city authorities, the aim is to create a new high-capacity rail freight corridor linking the former Southern Pacific, Santa Fe and Union Pacific networks with container yards at the dockside. The ex-SP San Pedro branch forms the basis of the project, but it will be much improved and expanded. The corridor is designed to remove trucks hauling containers from the streets, and further to relieve traffic congestion by eliminating grade crossings on rail lines near the ports; to this end, part of the 32 km corridor will be sunk below street level, with streets crossing over the top of the trench. There will be rail access from the Corridor to the ICTF and Dolores yard. The project is being touted by the Administration as a paradigm in the area of innovative financing: USDOT has advanced a $400 million loan. Target project completion date is 2000.

Into Mexico

Since 1991 UP has operated run-through service into Mexico from the US, via Laredo, with American President

Double-stack container train operated for the K-Line ocean shipping company by UP   **1996**

Companies as the major customer. Expedited customs clearance and a dedicated intermodal terminal at Huehuetoca have strengthened the business.

SP also had important links with Mexico in its own right. Ex-SP double-stack container operations include a twice-weekly service from the Long Beach ICTF to Mexico City, interchanging with FNM (National Railways of Mexico) at El Paso/Ciudad Juarez.

Privatisation of Mexico's railways (see Mexico entry) has focused US attention on this market. Having lost out in a bid for the Ferrocarril del Noreste (Mexico's busiest line) to rival KCSI, UP gained a foothold with a 13 per cent stake in the GFM consortium which was successful in bidding for the 6,000 km Pacific-North route, which runs along Mexico's western coast.

Consolidated financial performance (in US$ millions)

	1994	1995	1996
Rail revenues	5,318	6,326	7,680
Tracking revenues	1,037	976	961
Other revenues	137	184	145
All	6,492	7,486	8,786
Operating expenses	5,248	6,145	7,253
Operating income	1,244	1,341	1,533
Income, net of taxes, interest, charges etc.	546	946	904

Improvements to existing lines

UP has a comprehensive track improvement programme which will be intensified in the short term as traffic is reorganised in the wake of the merger. The 1997 capital allocation to track and structures is $252 million. An additional $300 million per annum goes into maintenance.

A typical year for the railroad prior to consolidation with the SP was installation of one million new wooden sleepers, 200,000 concrete sleepers, 720 km of new and cascaded rail, plus extensive surfacing work. By the end of 1995 UP had 22,795 km of track with continuous welded rail installed and 14,272 km under CTC (centralised traffic control).

In the period 1995-96 capacity additions were made as follows:

- on the North Platte subdivision;
- east of Bailey Yard, North Platte, Nebraska;
- on the Yoder branch line in Nebraska, to handle empty coal trains returning to the Powder River mines; this will now be augmented by the Kansas City—Denver (ex-SP) route for the return of empties;
- at Marshall, Texas, 8 km of additional double track;
- added capacity in the Salt Lake City—Ogden corridor;
- restoration of former Rock Island trackage between Kansas City and Pleasant Hill.

Due to be a part of the 1997-1998 programme are:

- expansion of West Colton, California, yard;
- added track on Cajon Pass;
- track improvements at several Texas locations;
- track upgrades Denver—Topeka; including some triple-track;
- advance preparation for a second main line across much of Iowa;
- improvements to the Livonia, Louisiana, yard.

In Texas, a universal crossover between ex-UP and SP territories at San Antonio, plus several kilometres of sidings between San Antonio and Port Laredo, will improve staging of Mexico-bound trains.

UP closed 255 km of track in Nebraska for six days in June 1996, affecting 145 trains. In the six days the railroad replaced more than 28,000 sleepers; resurfaced 13 km and levelled the entire 255 km; replaced two bridges and made substantial improvements to crossings, switches and joints, creating added capacity for up to 100 extra trains a year in future.

In recent years daily coal train traffic has increased sixfold and been supplemented by several double-stack container trains on the main line between Omaha/Council Bluffs and Kansas City. As a result UP has been lengthening existing loops and installing new ones to an extent that virtually double-tracks the route. In all, the project has involved just over 1,200 km of track. To expedite the work and minimise the workforce needed, UP has been using an NTC (New Track Construction) machine designed by Tamper. In sequence, this lifts concrete sleepers from accompanying flat wagons and places them on the roadbed at a precise and predetermined spacing, places pads on the sleepers, and guides rail on to the sleepers ready for attachment of fastening clips.

Oregon double-tracking project

UP plans to spend more than $100 million in the years up to 2002 in double-tracking much of its main line through the Blue Mountains of eastern Oregon. Once completed, the more than 80 km of new double track will increase line capacity by at least 50 per cent. Most of the construction will be in 4 to 8 km segments. In many instances, it will link sidings to complete long stretches of double-track main line.

UP's main line over the Blue Mountains carries an average of 26 freight trains per day as well as two Amtrak passenger trains. During some periods, volumes reach up to 40 trains daily. While the number of trains has grown, so has the average length of trains. As a result, bottlenecks have developed on the line where long bulk commodity trains, forced to travel at low speeds due to track grade and curvature, occupy the main line track for long periods. This prevents high-speed, time-sensitive trains from passing. The track-doubling will overcome these difficulties.

Traction and rolling stock

With the addition of the SP roster, the UP now has 6,383 units, about one quarter of US locomotives. The average hp per unit at the beginning of 1995 was a notable 3,028 hp (2,260 kW) and continuing to rise with the addition of 4,000+ hp (3,000 kW) units.

UP operates the largest single tranche of units in North America in the form of the 1,075 SD40s, of various model variants. These continue to receive life-extending overhauls at about $400,000 each at a rate of 25 or so a year.

UP owns four 1955-vintage E9 diesel passenger locomotives used on business trains and excursions and a DDA40X. Considered the historic diesel fleet, all have been used at times in revenue service to cover power shortages. UP picked up seven F units from CNW and these are expected to be cannibalised to a working A-B-B-A set.

In addition, two steam locomotives (No 844, a 4-8-4 and Challenger 4-6-6-4 No 3985) appear on excursions and at exhibition events. The steam locomotives and the E9s operate with a fleet of 15 passenger cars comprising eight sleeping and seven dining cars: since the Norfolk Southern cancelled its steam programme in 1994 the UP is the only US road still supporting a regular steam programme.

Recent locomotive orders
UP took delivery of 195 new locomotives in 1996. In the three-year period 1995-97 UP has ordered or bought 565 high-power units with AC traction motors: 10 C60ACs from GE; 70 C44/60ACs from GE to arrive during 1997 at 4,400 hp (3,300 kW), but convertible to 6,000 hp (4,480 kW) in the future; 300 C44ACs and 185 SD90ACs from EMD.

The GM-EMD SD90MAC is being delivered at 4,300 hp (3,200 kW) and is also upgradable to 6,000 hp (4,480 kW). The performance of the 6,000 hp engines will be closely observed. Using data from nine 4,400 hp (3,300 kW) AC units (three UP and six loaned from CSX) in revenue service trials, plus testbed data from GE on the performance of the 6,000 hp engine, UP is predicting significant fuel savings, as much as 1,700 US gallons (6,430 litres) one way for a double-stack train in Chicago—California service, if two 6,000 hp AC units replace three 4,000 hp DC units.

LNG-fuelled locomotives
In mid-1994 UP took delivery of the first two MK1200G locomotives from Morrison Knudsen's Boise production line and assigned them to switching service at subsidiary company Los Angeles Terminal. The MK1200G runs solely on Liquefied Natural Gas (LNG) using a Caterpillar engine. Other innovations and features include an advanced LNG monofuel management system consisting of cryogenic tanks, process piping, vaporiser and controls; the MK-LOC microprocessor control system; and a high-visibility cab.

Distributed power
UP continues to set the pace for the development of 'distributed power', in which radio-controlled unmanned helper sets are put in mid-train or at the end of long consists, with the result that undesirable 'slack action' will be reduced by 50 per cent or better and track capacity can be increased. UP began introducing distributed power units in significant numbers in 1994 and by the end of 1996 a projected fleet of 300 units was due to be available.

Whereas UP used to split its unit coal, grain and soda ash trains to cross the Blue Mountains of Oregon in two sections, both crewed and requiring manned helper sets, the move can now be made with one crew and a total of six or seven distributed locomotives. Distributed power is also being applied to very long (180 to 190 wagons) soda ash trains between Green River, Wyoming, and North Platte, Nebraska and to many of the longer (135-car) coal trains.

Carrying the development a step further, UP has equipped three pairs of GE units with a 20,000 gallon (75,700 litre) fuel tender (one per pair) as a means to increase the range of its power without a refuelling stop, and stabilise the onboard fuel weight, and therefore the all-in locomotive weight, contributing to more consistency in applied tractive effort.

SP's fleet
SP contributed over 2,300 locomotives to the UP-SP pool, and 42,000 wagons. It immediately received 170 locomotives reassigned from UP to boost the fleet, raise the number of coal trains and halve the number of trains left standing for want of power. Some 600 container wagons were also borrowed to increase double-stack capacity on SP. By the close of 1996, UP has raised the availability of the ex-SP fleet from 87 per cent to 93 per cent.

Of the total ex-SP locomotive fleet, 891 are operated on a 'power by the mile' basis (rental is paid to leasing companies for work actually done). The last five classes of GEs, totalling 573 units, are in this category, as are 318 EMD units, that is all the GP60s, SD70s, and some of the GP40, SD40, SD45 series.

Freight wagons
UP's assets at the start of 1996 included 145,331 revenue-earning freight wagons, either owned or leased, 31 per cent of which were various kinds of hoppers. An additional 9,400 cars made up the track maintenance fleet. During 1996 UP added 2,263 new freight cars.

The wagon fleet had a 95.9 per cent availability in 1996, a third straight year of improvement.

Combined UP/SP locomotive roster at March 1997
(all types combined: line haul plus yard/hump/switch/transfer)

Model	hp	No in service
MK12G	1,200	2
EMD units		
GP7	1,500	47
GP9	1,500	12
GP15; 15-1; 15-1L	1,500	200
MP15; 15L; 15AC; 15ACL	1,500	193
GP30	2,300	6
GP35M	2,000; 2,500	19
GP38; 38-2; 38L; 38-2L; 38-3L	2,000; 2,300	469
GP39-2L	2,300	51
GP40; 40-2; 40-2L; 40M; 40X	3,000; 3,500	381
GP50	3,500	78
GP60	3,800	194
SD7	1,500	13
SD9	1,800	12
SD18	1,800	14
SD35R	2,000	11
SD38-2	2,000	22
SP39	2,300	2
SD40; 40-2; 40-2B; 40-2L; 40M; 40-2R; 40T	3,000	1,591
SD44-2	3,000	1
SD45; 45R; 45-2T	3,200; 3,400; 3,600	349
SD50; 50M	3,600	112
SD60; 60M	3,800	419
SD70; 70M	4,000; 4,300	50
SD9043AC	4,300	75
SW-10	1,200	57
SW-1000	1,000	3
SW-1200	1,200	7
SW-1500; 1500L	1,500	200
Slugs	n.r.	41
EMD subtotal		**4,629**
GE units		
B23-7	2,300	98
B30-7; 7A	3,000	157
B36B-7	3,600	16
B39-8	3,900	40
B40-8	4,000	51
C30-7; 7B	3,000	132
C36-7	3,750	60
C40-8; 8W	4,000	336
C41-8; 8W	4,135	199
C44-9; 9W	4,380; 4,400	274
AC44-9W	4,380	152
AC 44/60 (convertible); C60AC	4,380; 4,400, 6,000	356
GE subtotal		**1,871**
Total		**6,502**

List does not include the combined exhibition fleet of seven diesels and two steam locomotives; does not include tenders

An element of the 1997 capital programme will be directed at the wagon fleet. New purchases will include 553 bilevel autoracks; 315 aluminium coal cars at the new 315,000 lb (142 tonnes) gross weight; 155 small-cube hoppers for dense dry bulk commodities. A total of 1,750 existing cars (hoppers; boxcars; gondolas and reefers) will be rebuilt and/or overhauled.

Optimisation of locomotive use
UP continues to develop its successful management and productivity tool, the Locomotive Management System (LMS) developed jointly by Union Pacific Technologies and ALK Associates Inc. This computer-based system ensures that all trains are punctually furnished with traction, that the selected traction is most apt to a train's route and characteristics, and monitors each locomotive's status.

From its historical database of all trains run in the preceding five weeks, and comparison of that with the real-time traffic status obtained from TCS (see 'Signalling and telecommunications' below), LMS produces a traffic forecast for the ensuing seven days. Next, retrieving from TCS the locomotives' status report and, from another bank, the physical data of the UP rail system and train priorities, LMS simulates the following seven days' operations. This produces, for all prospective trains, optimal locomotive assignments in terms of type, power and individual unit location. Amongst other things, these allocations will have units due for maintenance within the next five days appropriately routed to a workshop area, and foreign locomotives directed to their owning railroad.

LMS modelling is run every six hours. The whole sequence takes between 20 and 30 minutes. Significantly, while fuel prices rose 13 per cent over the course of 1996, UP achieved a fourth straight year of incremental improvement in consumption, measured in gallons used per thousand gross ton-miles (1.37 versus 1.38 in 1995 and 1.41 in 1994).

Signalling and telecommunications
Harriman Dispatching Center
Union Switch & Signal has consolidated control of all UP trackage into the Harriman Dispatching Center in Omaha.

The most striking feature of the office is its panoramic, video-projected display of the UP system. While this wall display provides summary information, a visual display unit at each dispatcher's console offers a detailed view of operations at any of the 1,800 or so signal control points throughout the system.

The Harriman Center employs Computer-Aided Dispatching System (CADS). Using auto-routeing, dispatchers assign an identity and priority to each train. The computer then takes over and routes trains according to priority, while also automatically determining the meeting and passing of trains on single-track sections.

Positive Train Separation (PTS)
UP and Burlington Northern began a joint effort (including Amtrak) in PTS in April 1994, with field tests in Oregon. By late 1997 the tests were due to have been extended to multiple trains. Train dispatchers electronically provide train crews with operating instructions governing safe train movement. PTS can sound an alert and, if necessary, override train crew actions. The Harris Corporation is acting as systems integrator.

Transportation Control System
UP's marketing strategy rests on one of the most advanced technical bases in the industry. The heart of UP's service operations, the National Customer Service Center, would be impossible without the Transportation Control System (TCS) and the Automatic Call Directing (ACD) system. TCS schedules and monitors rail operations and performs the accounting function on every item shipped on the railroad. Wisconsin Central has adopted TCS as its primary management tool.

A new work order reporting system connects TCS computers directly with UP locomotives, enabling customers to have their data communicated to trains en route. This new system is being developed in conjunction with ATCS (Advanced Train Control System) and is expected to improve customer service and cut expenses by more than $20 million a year.

Union Pacific Technologies
A subsidiary of Union Pacific Corporation, Union Pacific

Technologies (UPT) specialises in developing computer systems for the transportation industry. It has had a major role in extending communications/data/management systems into former SP territory and in interfacing with BNSF over the 6,400 km of trackage and haulage access. For 1997-1998 the installation of TCS on the SP is a priority. Since 1993 it has installed a yard management programme at the 17 largest yards on the National Railways of Mexico (FNM) system and installed a computer upgrade at the FNM central office in Mexico City. With the onset of privatisation in Mexico, UPT foresees a large market for systems to connect the several new private properties that are evolving. UPT has taken on a Mexican partner to offer its products in Spanish language versions throughout Latin America. To explore the international market, UPT has joined with an IBM subsidiary, Integrated Systems Solutions Corporation.

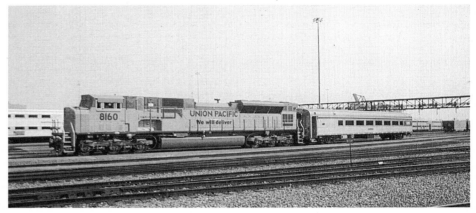

SD90MAC from GM-EMD; this model will be produced in a 6,000hp version (Jesse de la Pena)   **1996**

Track
Rail: 133 AREA, 60.3 kg/m
Crossties (sleepers): Wooden, 7 × 9 in × 9 ft
Spacing: 2,019/km
Fastenings: ⅝ × 6¼ in cut track spikes; Portec curve

blocs for curvative in excess of 6°
Max curvature: 20°; exceptionally 12°
Max gradient: Main line 2.33%, 4.0% branch lines

Max axleload: 65,750 lb (unrestricted operation), 78,750 lb (restricted)

UPDATED

Wisconsin Central Transportation Co

One O'Hare Center, 6250 North River Road, Rosemont, Illinois 60017-5062
Tel: +1 847 318 4600   Fax: +1 847 318 4615

Key personnel
President, Chairman and Chief Executive Officer:
    Edward A Burkhardt
Executive Vice-President and Chief Operating
    Officer: J Reilly McCarren
Executive Vice-President and Chief Financial
    Officer: Thomas F Power Jr
Vice-Presidents
    General Manager: J Edward Terbell
    Marketing: William R Schauer
    Finance: Walter C Kelly
    Planning: Earl J Currie
    Human Resources: Richard P White
    Chief Engineer: Glenn J Kerbs
    Mechanical: Robert F Nadrowski
    General Counsel: Janet Gilbert
Treasurer: Marty J Mickey

Route-km, track and trackage rights: 4,832 km

Organisation
Wisconsin Central Transportation Co (WCTC) is a holding company. Its main asset, one of seven wholly owned subsidiaries, is Wisconsin Central Ltd, the largest regional railroad in the US. Major gateways on the WCTC system are Chicago; Duluth/Superior; Green Bay; Milwaukee; Minneapolis-St Paul; and Sault Sainte Marie in the Canadian province of Ontario.

WCTC was formed in 1987 by taking over the Lake States Division of Soo Line. In 1993, WCTC acquired the Fox Valley Railroad Company and the Green Bay & Western Railroad Company through a wholly owned subsidiary, the Fox Valley & Western Inc, which is operated independently but shares a range of administrative functions.

Wisconsin Central has a policy of contracting out as little work as possible; this is car repair being carried out in the railroad's Fond du Lac workshops   **1996**

Shares in the company are traded on the NASDAQ exchange.

In 1996, the company had 2,086 employees. WCTC is still non-union, a condition confirmed in a September 1994 vote of operating personnel and a 1996 vote by engineering personnel. In 1996 WC offered to co-operate with the Federal Railroad Administration in conducting a one-person crew trial.

On 20 July 1993, WCTC took a minority interest in Tranz Rail (qv, formerly New Zealand Rail Ltd), which has since been floated on the stock exchange.

In January 1995, WCTC completed purchase of Canada's Algoma Central Railway (qv) via a wholly owned subsidiary known as WC Canada Holdings. Canada's National Transportation Agency cut 25 per cent out of its

subsidy for passenger trains on the Algoma Central, forcing WCTC to re-examine the service.

WCTC invested $45 million for a 32 per cent share in the partnership called English, Welsh & Scottish Railway (qv) which bought first the mail-hauling unit Rail Express Systems from British Rail in late 1995, and later bought BR's three trainload freight companies. The other stakeholders in EW&S are Berkshire Partners and Fay, Richards & Co Ltd.

The Surface Transportation Board has approved sale of 352 km by the Union Pacific to WC's affiliate, the Sault Sainte Marie Bridge Company, for $85 million. The properties, collectively called 'Duck Creek North', are in Michigan's upper peninsula and include the Escanaba ore dock.

In late 1997, Wisconsin Central was part of a consortium which acquired the Tasmanian freight operations of Australian National (qv).

Finance
The company's income, exclusive of the effects of extraordinary items, was $61.1 million for 1996 compared to $46.9 million for 1995, an increase of 30.2 per cent. Excluding some disputed charges, operating revenue for 1996 increased by $12.0 million or 4.6 per cent to $275.4 million. Volume, as measured by carloads handled (including as a carload each loaded trailer or container), for 1996 was 464,149 carloads compared with 436,286 carloads in 1995, an increase of 27,863 carloads or 6.4 per cent. Intermodal, paper, woodpulp, lumber, sand, stone and minerals, coal, steel, all improved.

The foreign holdings are important contributors to WCTC's finances. In the first quarter of 1997, WCTC had net income of $17.6 million, of which EW&S in the UK contributed $7.1 million and Tranz Rail in New Zealand $3.2 million.

A southbound train of hoppers on the WCTC system passes through Franklin Park, Illinois (John A Day)   **1996**

Key personnel
President: Dennis A Sudbeck
Master Mechanic: Gerald Fox

The D&IRR operates 222 route-km of former Milwaukee Road track between Dell Rapids, South Dakota, and Sioux City, Iowa, owned by the state of South Dakota. Its main activities are hauling aggregates, gravel and railroad ballast from its principal online shipper and owner of the working assets, the L G Everist Company. A former CNW line from Hawarden to Beresford is now a branch of the D&I and generates as many as 100 grain trains in a season. D&IRR operates 12 GM-EMD locomotives (10 GP9 and two GP20, which Everist maintains) and owns no other rolling stock. BNSF is the local service provider on two segments, Sioux Falls to Canton and Elk Point to Sioux City. Interchange is available via BNSF at Sioux Falls, South Dakota, and with BNSF, UP and IC (formerly CC&P) at Sioux City, Iowa.

VERIFIED

Dakota, Minnesota & Eastern Railroad Corporation

PO Box 178, 337 22nd Avenue South, Brookings, South Dakota 57006
Tel: +1 605 697 2400   Fax: +1 605 697 2499

Key personnel
President and Chief Executive Officer:
    Kevin V Shieffer
Vice-President, Marketing, Strategic Planning and Public
    Affairs: Lynn A Anderson
Chief Financial Officer: Kurt V Feaster
Vice-President, Transportation: Vernon L Colbert
Chief Mechanical Officer: David L Goodwin
Chief Engineer: Doug de Berg

Gauge: 1,435 mm
Route length: 1,878 km

Organisation
DM&E, formed in 1986, was the first railroad to be created by a major sale of Chicago & North Western trackage. It is the second longest US regional railroad, with Winona–Rapid City and Waseca–Mason City main lines as its core.
   In May 1995, DM&E acquired from the UP the 325 km 'Colony line' from Chadron, Nebraska, to Colony, Wyoming, which was also an ex-Chicago & North Western property. The DM&E meets this line at Rapid City, South Dakota.

Freight operations
Traffic in 1996 totalled 60,396 wagonloads (13.5 per cent up on the year before). Some 9,000 wagonloads were loaded onto barges at Winona, Minnesota.
   Grain is the main commodity, comprising approximately 42 per cent of wagonloads. Other important commodities are bentonite, kaolin, cement, scrap metal, scrap paper and bagged wood pellets. Future growth is expected in the form of inbound soyabeans for processing.

New lines
In June 1997, DM&E unveiled a plan for a $1.2 billion new project to extend into the Powder River Basin coalfield in Wyoming, a plan that excited opposition from Powder River incumbent operators Union Pacific and BNSF. The 1,050 km line from the Mississippi river in Minnesota to Rapid City, South Dakota, would be rebuilt, and a new 400-km link would be built into the coalfields. The project would take five years to complete.

Improvements to existing lines
Since the 1986 start-up, DM&E has expended $90 million on track and structures.
   DM&E's 1996 capital investment spending was $32.9 million, principally for track improvements, following completion of a financing package through the South Dakota state legislature to issue bonds for the purpose of upgrading 160 km of track between Wolsey and Pierre from 15 km/h to 65 km/h operation and effectively reduce east-west transit time by one day. The actual work involves installation of continuously welded rail, 55 bridge structure modifications, 35 turnouts and a number of passing loops.

Traction and rolling stock
DM&E operates 69 locomotives of GM-EMD origin, comprising SD10 (16), SD9 (14), GP40 (six), GP38 (four), GP38-3 (six) and GP9 (five) units and SD40-2 (12) and SD40-3 (six) units.
   In 1996 the capital programme was $32 million in new car orders from Trinity (500 vehicles) and Thrall (100), a combination of hoppers and gondolas.

UPDATED

Dakota, Missouri Valley & Western Railroad Inc

1131 22nd Street South, Bismarck, North Dakota 58504
Tel: +1 701 223 9282

Key personnel
President: Larry C Wood
Vice-President: Diane J Wood
General Manager: Roger C Wood
Transportation Manager: J P Ankenbauer

DMV&WR has 505.7 route-km and operates four GM-EMD GP35 locomotives.
   The company was created in 1990 to operate trackage leased from Soo Line (now Canadian Pacific) in North Dakota, principally from Oakes westward through Bismarck and north to Washburn. Freight wagons are supplied by CP Rail.

UPDATED

Dakota Southern Railway Company

PO Box 436, Chamberlain, South Dakota 57325
Tel: +1 605 734 6595   Fax: +1 605 734 6595

Key personnel
Chairman: Richard H Huff
President and General Manager: George A Huff IV

DSR operates over 299 route-km of track owned by the state of South Dakota; it has seven locomotives, including one Alco C420, one Alco S3, two GM-EMD SD7 and one SD9 and one GE 70-ton unit.
   The line, from Mitchell to Kadoka, generates 1,600 carloads a year, almost entirely grain and connects at Mitchell to BNSF. DSR has 110 covered hopper wagons on lease.

UPDATED

Danbury Terminal Railroad Co

In December 1992, Housatonic Railroad (qv) bought, from Conrail, 140.8 route-km in the vicinity of Danville, Connecticut, and obtained trackage rights on 89.6 km of Metro-North property to create an operating territory for its subsidiary, Danbury Terminal Railroad Company. In 1996, the company became fully integrated into the Housatonic and is no longer a separate entity.

UPDATED

Detroit, Toledo & Ironton Railroad

The DT&I was an independent railroad until 1982 when it was bought by Canadian National. In 1996, CN put it up for sale and the preferred bidder was RailTex (qv), at a reported $27 million, which would secure 233.5 km of track, 175 km of rights, and 110,000 annual carloads. It serves as a bridge line between Detroit and Cincinnati. Two major commodities are car parts northbound and finished autos southbound.

NEW ENTRY

Delaware Otsego Corporation

1 Railroad Avenue, Cooperstown, New York 13326
Tel: +1 607 547 2555   Fax: +1 607 547 9834

The Delaware Otsego Corporation is a publicly traded (on the NASDAQ exchange) non-rail holding company whose principal asset is the New York, Susquehanna and Western Railway (qv). The holding company also engages in real estate development to augment the railroad's traffic base.
   In May 1995, Delaware Otsego realised $5.2 million (pretax) from the sale of the Rahway Valley Railroad to the state of New Jersey. In January 1996, the company acquired a 40 per cent interest in the Toledo, Peoria & Western Railway (qv) for cash and stock valued at $2.25 million.

UPDATED

Duluth, Missabe and Iron Range Railway Company

500 Missabe Building, Duluth, Minnesota 55802
Tel: +1 218 723 2115   Fax: +1 218 723 2127

Key personnel
President: Robert S Rosati
Vice-Presidents
    Law: Robert N Gentile
    Finance: Joseph W Schulte
    Operations: F J Habic
    Marketing: R Vignovic
General Manager: P D Stephenson
Mechanical Superintendent: Charles E Voss
Chief Engineer: William H Harrison
Signals and Communications Engineer:
    Timothy R Luhm

DMIRR is a US Steel/Transtar (qv) property and has 736 km in track. It operates 69 locomotives, predominantly SD9s and SD38s, and 4,242 freight wagons. In 1995, the DMIRR acquired five reconditioned SD45T-3s from VMV and three more in 1996. Several SD9s were cascaded to other Transtar properties. The railway connects the Missabe Range iron ore deposits with the ports of Duluth and Two Harbors on Lake Superior, from where the ore is shipped to steel mills in the Great Lakes region. In 1994, DMIRR began to ship ore to Geneva Steel in Utah via Wisconsin Central and Southern Pacific.

UPDATED

Eastern Shore Railroad

PO Box 312, Cape Charles, Virginia 23310-0312
Tel: +1 804 331 1094   Fax: +1 301 311 2772

Key personnel
Vice-President and General Manager: Danny B Moore
Transportation Superintendent: Ira T Higbee

ESR has 113 route-km and operates two GM-EMD GP8 and four GM-EMD GP10 locomotives, and 27 freight wagons. It provides a ferry link to Norfolk News across the mouth of the Chesapeake Bay.

UPDATED

Elgin, Joliet and Eastern Railway Company

1141 Maple Road, Joliet, Illinois 60432
Tel: +1 815 740 6903   Fax: +1 815 740 6729

Key personnel
President (of Transtar): Robert S Rosati
Vice-Presidents
    Law: Robert N Gentile
    Operations: Frank J Habic III
    Finance: Joseph W Schulte
    Marketing: Rade Vignovic

General Superintendent: Mel S Turner
Director, Asset Management: James L Weis

EJ&E is a US Steel/Transtar (qv) property. Its route length is 320.2 km, and it has 54 locomotives and 4,850 freight wagons.

The EJ&E is the outermost of the three belt railroads encircling the Chicago area. Via 14 interchanges it connects with every Class I operator in the region. During 1996, several large railroads expressed interest in purchasing the EJ&E; UP has declared its intention to make a connection into the EJ&E in the vicinity of West Chicago and the EJ&E has granted overhead trackage rights. There is substantial civic opposition to this move in West Chicago. Metra (qv) has undertaken a feasibility study into the possibility of running circumferential commuter operations in the future on the EJ&E, to connect several routes radiating from Chicago.

UPDATED

Emons Transportation Group Inc

96 S George Street, York, Pennsylvania 17401-1436
Tel: +1 717 771 1700   Fax: +1 717 854 6275

Key personnel
Chairman and Chief Executive Officer:
   Robert Grossman
President and Chief Operating Officer: Alfred P Smith
Vice-Presidents: Steven H Hill, Scott F Ziegler, Matthew Jacobson

Organisation
Emons is a public company (traded on the NASDAQ exchange) which owns three short line railroads and operates rail/truck transloading and warehousing facilities. The latter include an intermodal terminal opened in September 1994 at Auburn, Maine, called Maine Intermodal Transportation Inc, served by the Emons-owned St Lawrence & Atlantic RR. The principal connection is with CN at Norton in Vermont for second morning service to Chicago; future plans include double-stack clearances on the route, which has attracted 16 new factories in the last two years. The State of New Hampshire intended to demolish the last clearance restriction in the town of Gorham and early 1997 data indicated continuing intermodal growth. The SLARR has access to a deep water port at Portland, Maine.

Emons also provides general logistics services to customers. The three short lines it owns are:
   Maryland & Pennsylvania RR Co, 41.5 km
   Yorkrail Inc, Pennsylvania, 25.5 km
   St. Lawrence and Atlantic RR Co, 264 km
For 1996 the company reported a 6.5 per cent increase in operating revenues to $14.9 million and net income of $0.47 million. Annual carloadings for 1996 were 34,550, an increase of 5 per cent over the previous year. With the inclusion of $1.6 million in government grants and loans, the group invested $4.6 million in its 1996 capital programme. The company maintains a fleet of 18 locomotives (four of which, GP18s, were added in 1996) and 600 boxcars.

UPDATED

Escanaba and Lake Superior Railroad

One Larkin Plaza, Wells, Michigan 49894
Tel: +1 906 786 0693   Fax: +1 906 786 8012

Key personnel
President: John C Larkin
Secretary and Treasurer: A K Larkin
Director, Marketing & Customer Services:
   Thomas J Klimek

ELSR operates 555 route-km with 21 locomotives, including several Baldwins. It owns 357 wagons and leases a further 550.

ELSR has connections through Green Bay to the Wisconsin Central system. There are several connections in other locations with the WC and its Sault Ste Marie subsidiary.

Principal traffic is paper waferboard and pulp outbound; chemicals and fertilisers inbound. Volume in 1996 was 14,000 carloads.

UPDATED

Farmrail System Inc

PO Box 1750, 136 E Frisco Street, Clinton, Oklahoma 73601-1750
Tel: +1 405 323 1234   Fax: +1 405 323 4568

Key personnel
Chairman, President and Chief Executive Officer:
   George C Betke Jr
Chief Operating Officer: Richard S Shaw

Farmrail System Inc comprises 566.4 km of line in western Oklahoma. It owns 286.4 km (ex-Burlington Northern) as Grainbelt Corp. It operates 284.8 km (ex-Rock Island and ex-Santa Fe) owned by the state of Oklahoma as Farmrail Corp. Employees: 32; locomotives: 15. Connections are made to Burlington Northern Santa Fe, Union Pacific and two short lines.

In mid-1995, the company assigned three GP9s to start up a subsidiary, Finger Lakes Railway, operating 176 km of lines centred on Geneva in upstate New York.

VERIFIED

Florida East Coast Railway Company

Florida East Coast Industries Inc
1650 Prudential Drive, Jacksonville, Florida 32207
Tel: +1 904 829 3421

Key personnel
Chairman and CEO: Winfred L Thornton
President: Carl F Zellers Jr
Vice-Presidents: William E Durham, L A Manz,
   Thomas R Ballas
Vice-President/Secretary: T Neal Smith
Comptroller: J Richard Yastrzemski

Organisation
FECRC is a Class II carrier. Its common stock is 54.5 per cent held by the St Joe Corp, Florida's largest private landowner. FECRC is one of two wholly owned subsidiaries of Florida East Coast Industries Inc, which also owns Gran Central Corporation, a property company which redevelops surplus rail property and other sites.

In May 1997, St Joe made a $428 million bid for the 46 per cent of FEC it did not already own. One scenario has St Joe absorbing the real estate activity and the railroad being merged or sold.

The railway's physical plant is 561.6 km of main track between Jacksonville and Miami; there is a 145.6 km branch line to Belle Glade on Lake Okeechobee. In addition, there are 251.2 km of yard and switching tracks and 294.4 km of second main and passing track. Main track is 132 lb rail on concrete sleepers; branch/yard track is 112/115 lb rail on timber sleepers. With a payroll of 1,035 in transportation in late 1996, the company has pared its workforce by 25 per cent since the start of 1993, but has recently been hiring again.

Finance
Revenues in 1996 were $172.9 million from transportation and $35.1 million from property. Net income before taxes in 1996 rose from $42.5 to $48.1 million, and net of taxes the company reported a $30.4 million in income. FEC's annual capital programme for railroad-related expenses is $12.9 million.

Freight operations
In addition to intermodal traffic, principal commodities are automobiles, crushed stone, cement, consumer products and foodstuffs. Traffic was basically flat or in slight decline in FY 1995-96, except for automotives which rose by 9.3 per cent. Gross tonne-km for 1996 were 6.5 billion.

Intermodal operations
Historically known for its interline intermodal business, especially through the ports of Jacksonville and Miami, FEC now originates or terminates 46 per cent of revenues online.

FEC opened a leased intermodal facility at Macon, Georgia, in March 1995, to extend its reach, but closed it in February 1996. The explanation for this was that growth was forecast to outgrow the facility but not by such a margin as to justify the expense of building, and owning, a larger site.

In another move to extend the company's intermodal reach, FEC took an 80 per cent equity position in International Transit Inc, a truckload hauler and drayage operator with 77 tractors, 1,360 trailers, and eight terminals in the Maryland-Georgia axis.

Traction and rolling stock
The all-GM-EMD locomotive fleet comprises 41 GP40 and GP40-2 units; 22 rebuilt GP9s; 11 GP38-2s; two SW9s; and two SW1200s. In 1994, FEC ordered its first six-axle units, four of which entered service on unit mineral trains and intermodal expresses.

At the close of 1996, the railway operated 2,635 freight wagons.

UPDATED

Gateway Western Railway

15 Executive Drive, Fairview Heights, Illinois 62208
Tel: +1 618 624 4700   Fax: +1 618 624 4731

Key personnel
President: Don Gill
Vice-Presidents
   Chief Financial Officer: Thomas King
   Marketing, Sales and Transportation: Jordan Buck
   Engineering and Mechanical: Paul Fetterman

Organisation
GWWR's route length is 656 km, of which 602 km is solely owned; the remainder is owned jointly or operated under rights. Annual carloadings: 60,000; employees: 225.

The railway was formed in 1990 to take over lines linking Kansas City, St Louis and Springfield, Illinois, and associated branches, formerly owned by the bankrupt Chicago, Missouri & Western. It has a long-term contract with BNSF (ex-Santa Fe) for haulage of that railroad's freight between Kansas City and East St Louis.

In 1995, it took over the Mill Street yard and six locomotives to service customers of the Kansas City Terminal railroad (which now only does traffic control and accounting). Also in 1995, the GWWR reached agreement with Conrail to haul the latter's intermodal traffic from St Louis to Kansas City where previously it went by highway.

GWWR operates a fleet of GM-EMD locomotives, comprising 10 GP38 and four GP40 line-haul units and 13 SW1500 switchers. Its 1996 capital programme for trackwork, signals and communications totalled $11 million. The forecast for 1997 was $5 million.

GWWR has trackage rights from Springfield to Chicago, which it is not presently using. The trackage rights have attracted the attention of the Kansas City Southern Railway (qv), enough for KCS to form a subsidiary for the purpose of acquiring GWWR.

UPDATED

Genesee & Wyoming Inc

71 Lewis Street, Greenwich, Connecticut 06830
Tel: +1 203 629 3722

Key personnel
Chief Executive Officer: Mortimer B Fuller III
Senior Vice-President and Chief Financial Officer:
   Mark W Hastings
Senior Vice-President: Alan R Harris
Senior Vice-Presidents
   Louisiana & Texas: Forrest L Becht
   Illinois: Spencer D White
   New York & Pennsylvania: Charles W Chabot
   Oregon: Robert I Melbo

Organisation
GWI is an operator of short lines and regional railroads. Its properties are:
• Genesee & Wyoming RR
• Allegheny & Eastern RR
• Buffalo & Pittsburg RR
• Rochester & Southern RR
• Pittsburg & Shaumut RR
• Louisiana & Delta RR
• Illinois & Midland RR
• Portland & Western RR
• Willamette & Pacific RR
In addition, in 1996 GWI bought Rail Link, an industrial switching company, from Varlen Inc.

Total trackage in the portfolio adds up to 2,425 km, about 55 per cent of it owned by the company.

In late 1997, GWI was part of a consortium which acquired the South Australian freight operations of Australian National (qv).

Finance

Operating revenues in 1996 were $77.8 million, 46 per cent up on year earlier, principally from acquisitions. Operating income was $14 million, up from $6.6 million. Carloads were almost double at 201,000, compared to 119,000 in 1995. Its 1996 capital programme was $16.6 million for rolling stock, track and buildings. The company is quoted on the NASDAQ stock exchange.

Traction and rolling stock

GWI owns or leases 113 locomotives and owns, leases or manages 1,133 wagons.

NEW ENTRY

Genesee & Wyoming Railroad Co

PO Box 101, 3546 Retsof Road, Retsof, New York 14539
Tel: +1 716 243 3770 Fax: +1 716 382 3186

Key personnel
Chief Executive Officer: Mortimer B Fuller III
President: Charles W Chabot Sr
Senior Vice-President: David J Collins

G&WR has 75 route-km of former Conrail trackage and 74 route-km of trackage rights in upstate New York.

This short line is the charter property of Genesee & Wyoming Inc (qv), a holding company headquartered in Connecticut and having a controlling interest in 12 shortlines and some 5,000 wagons.

UPDATED

Georgia Southwestern Railroad

908 Elm Avenue, Americus, Georgia 31709
Tel: +1 912 924 0812 Fax: +1 912 928 2619

GSWR is three consolidated RailTex properties totalling 552 km, generating 13,000 annual carloads. The former Georgia & Alabama and the former Georgia Great Southern are no longer reported separately. Connections to Class I railroads are CSXT (Bainbridge; Cordele) and NS (Albany; Americus; Arlington and Columbus).

NEW ENTRY

Great Western Railway Company of Colorado

Taylor Avenue Shops, PO Box 537, Loveland, Colorado 80539
Tel: +1 303 667 6883 Fax: +1 303 667 1444

Key personnel
President: David L Lafferty

GWR serves customers on 88 route-km of track. Interchanges are made with BNSF and UP; the latter brings corn in unit trains to GWR. The railway is an OmniTRAX company (qv) and undertakes major locomotive repair and rebuilding at Loveland for member companies as well as on contract. In 1996, GWR added two reconditioned SD9s to its locomotive fleet, in order to have sufficient power for the unit trains.

UPDATED

Green Mountain Railroad Corp

PO Box 498, Bellows Falls, Vermont 05101-0498
Tel: +1 802 463 9531 Fax: +1 802 463 4084

Key personnel
President and General Manager: Jerome M Hebda

Vice-President and Chief Engineering Officer:
  D M Lamoureux
Chief Mechanical Officer: S J Whitney
Operations Officer: K L Smith

GMRC has 83.9 route-km and operates five locomotives (one Alco RS1, four EMD GP9); 100 freight wagons; and eight passenger cars, including a dining car.

In 1996 the railroad recorded 4,000 carloads, 400,000 tonnes of freight, over 20 million freight tonne-km, 30,000 passenger journeys and 1.25 million passenger-km. The corporation is the operator of a mid-June to mid-October 'Green Mountain Flyer' tourist train.

GMRC is a partner in a marketing initiative that links up with the St Lawrence & Atlantic, the New England Central and the Providence & Worcester railroads.

UPDATED

Guilford Transportation Industries' Rail System

Guilford is the holding company for several rail assets, namely:
- The Boston & Maine (qv)
- The Maine Central (qv)
- The Portland (Maine) Terminal.

These properties are operated through a subsidiary, the Springfield Terminal Railway.

In May 1997, Guilford made a surprise (and unpriced) offer to the US Secretary of Transportation to buy or lease Amtrak's North East Corridor to provide both passenger and freight services.

The offer was not taken seriously by Amtrak; some analysts were suggesting it was made in response to a bid by Norfolk Southern to run Triple Crown intermodal services over the Amtrak line to Boston.

NEW ENTRY

Harbor Belt Line

See Pacific Harbor Line entry.
See also Anacostia & Pacific Co Inc entry.

Housatonic Railroad Co Inc

67 Main Street, PO Box 298, Centerbrook, Connecticut. 06409
Tel: +1 860 767 7476 Fax: +1 860 767 7419

Key personnel
President: John R Hanlon Jr.
Vice-Presidents
  Operations: Peter E Lynch
  Finance: Thomas E Curtin
  General Counsel: Edward J Rodriguez

The Housatonic RR, together with its subsidiary Danbury Terminal RR, operates freight service for 45 accounts on 259 km of tracks in the states of Connecticut, New York and Massachusetts; the lines are ex-New Haven, New York Central, Conrail, and Boston & Maine. HRRC also has freight rights to 141 km of Metro-North owned trackage. Connections are made to Conrail at Pittsfield, Massachusetts and Beacon, New York; and to the Boston and Maine at Derby, Connecticut. Paper products, limestone, chemicals, lumber are the principal commodities; total carloadings for the entire railroad are 4,500-5,000/year. It operates a lumber reload centre at Hawleyville, Connecticut.

UPDATED

Houston Belt & Terminal Railway Co

501 Crawford Street, Houston, Texas 77002
Tel: +1 713 222 1133

Key personnel
President and General Manager: Harlan W Ritter

Vice-President, Finance: Michael A Schensted
Chief Engineer: Satish C Malhotra
Superintendent, Signals and Communications:
  Richard M Sanders

Length: 435 km.

The railway purchased eight model MK1500D switchers featuring Caterpillar engines and MK-LOC microprocessors from MK Rail which displaced its previous fleet of 12. The contract for acquisition and long-term support is valued at $30 million. (See also the Port Terminal Railroad Association entry.)

UPDATED

Huron & Eastern Railway Co Inc

3720 East Washington Road, Saginaw, Michigan 48601
Tel: +1 517 754 2500 Fax: +1 517 754 8966

Key personnel
President: John H Marino
Vice-President and General Manager: Jack F Conser

H&ER is a Rail America subsidiary (qv) and one of its two charter properties. It operates over 315 km of route, and has four locomotives and 241 wagons. It also undertakes locomotive refurbishing and painting for other Rail America subsidiaries and for third parties.

UPDATED

IES Transportation Inc

2330 12th Street SW, Cedar Rapids, Iowa 52404
Tel: +1 319 398 4597 Fax: +1 319 398 4171

Key personnel
Vice-President and General Manager:
  Paul H Treangen
Chief Mechanical Officer: Angie Perez

The railway has 85 route-km; it operates 13 GM-EMD locomotives (five SW8; one SW900; one SW9; two SW1200; and four GP9 which were remodelled by National Railway Engineering in 1996) and 307 freight wagons.

IES is a holding company for the Cedar Rapids & Iowa City Railway, plus a barge terminal in Dubuque and a rail-to-track transfer facility in Cedar Rapids.

In 1996, a feasibility study was conducted (with Wilbur Smith, consultants, as prime contractor) to assess the potential for commuter rail on this system. The conclusion was that passenger services were unlikely to be justifiable.

NEW ENTRY

I&M Rail Link

1920 East Kimberley Road, Davenport, Iowa 52809
Tel: +1 319 344 7600 Fax: +1 319 344 7700

For map, see overleaf

Key personnel
President: Bill Brodsky
Executive Vice-President: J Fred Simpson
Vice-President, Operations: John Gruell
Chief Mechanical Officer: John Wiesch
Manager, Transportation: Dick Awe

In October 1996, Canadian Pacific announced that the successful bidder (from 15 applicants) for 1,829 km of track plus rights in five US states was the Washington Companies. In April 1997, I&M filed its tariff as the acquisition was cleared by the Surface Transportation Board. The I&M will have a customer base of 300+ and its prime connections will be made through Chicago, Kansas City and Minneapolis/St Paul.

NEW ENTRY

Illinois & Midland Railway Co

PO Box 139, Springfield, Illinois 62705
Tel: +1 217 788 8601   Fax: +1 217 788 8658

Key personnel
President and Chief Executive Officer: Mortimer Fuller

Gauge: 1,435 mm
Length: 194.7 km

The railroad was sold by its investor group owners in February 1996 to Genesee & Wyoming Industries (qv) which renamed it the Illinois & Midland. Its primary business is the haulage of coal to an electric utility. A power station online is converting from local coal to low-sulphur coal brought by SP from Utah.

Traction and rolling stock
G&W is changing the fleet mix of all EMD locomotives. Two SW1500s arrived to displace four SW1200s; all five SW1200s were sold to a Pioneer Railcorp (qv) subsidiary. The I&M fleet now numbers 14 (two SW1500; two SD18s; three SD9s; five SD20s; two RS1325s).

Track
Rail: 60 kg/m
Max curvature: 10°
Max gradient: 1.6%
Max axleload: 30 tonnes

NEW ENTRY

Indiana & Ohio System

PO Box 12576, 2856 Cypress Way, Cincinnati, Ohio 45212-0576
Tel: +1 513 531 4800   Fax: +1 513 531 4803

Indiana Southern Railroad
PO Box 158, Petersburg, Indiana 47567
Tel: +1 812 354 8080   Fax: +1 812 354 8085
General Manager: Dick Neumann

Key personnel
RailTex Regional Manager: Jim Bearden
General Manager: Bill Stevens
Operations Superintendent: Don Lee

The INOH has been a RailTex property since July 1996 when the assets of the former Indiana & Ohio Rail Corporation were acquired by the company for $9 million plus the assumption of $3.5 million in dept. This was RailTex's first acquisition of an established holding company and subsidiaries. The System is made up of 10 unconnected segments, each with one or more Class I connections into Conrail, CSXT and/or NS; it also connects with RailTex's new acquisition, the DT&I, in Cincinnati. The total track length is 357 km, including trackage rights. 1996 carloadings were 17,000.

One of the component properties, Indiana Southern Railroad, also operates the Pittsburgh Industrial Railroad as a satellite; the PIRR is 67 km of trackage west of Pittsburgh (including the Pittsburgh, Chartiers and Yonghiogheny) bought from Conrail in 1996 for $3 million.

The locomotive fleet at the time of purchase was 17 GM-EMD locomotives, namely four GP7, five GP9, one GP18, five GP30 and two GP35.

UPDATED

Indiana Harbor Belt Railroad Co

2721 161st Street, Hammond, Indiana 46323-1099
Tel: +1 219 989 4703   Fax: +1 219 989 4707

Key personnel
President: C W Dickieson
General Manager: C H Allen
Comptroller: J E DeWitt

Comprising 193.2 route-km, Indiana Harbor Belt (IHB) provides industrial switching and transfer services in northwest Indiana and northeast Illinois, especially to several steel plants in Indiana and to the GM-EMD La Grange locomotive plant in McCook, Illinois. It operates two yards at Gibson Transfer, Indiana, and Blue Island, Illinois. IHB is 51 per cent owned by Conrail and 49 per cent by CP (Soo). In 1996 traffic totalled 623,261 wagonloads, much the same as in the year before. Revenues at $78.4 million were up from $72.4 million in 1995. Expenses for 1996 were $69.93 million, up 5.6 per cent on the previous year.

IHB operates 89 GM-EMD locomotives, including 27 1,000 hp/746 kW NW2s, 11 1,200 hp/895 kW SW7s, five 1,200 hp/895 kW SW9s, 29 1,500 hp/1,119 kW SW15/ MP15s, two 2,000 hp/1,417 kW GP38-2s, two 2,000 hp/1,417 kW SD-20s; two SD39s and two SD40s. In recent years the railroad has acquired more main line locomotives and begun to reduce its fleet of switchers. The railroad also operates five power boosters, three diesel hump trailers and 1,518 freight wagons, of which 51 per cent are gondolas and 34 per cent coil cars.

Track is 115 lb rail on wood sleepers with spike fastenings spaced 2,031 per mile. Maximum curvature is 12½°, maximum gradient 1.5 per cent and maximum permissible axleload 39 short tons; 54 km of main line is CTC-controlled.

Employees in 1996: 774.

UPDATED

Indiana Hi-Rail Corporation

4301 SR1 North, Connersville, Indiana 47331
Tel: +1 317 825 0349   Fax: +1 317 825 0453

Key personnel
Trustee: R Franklin Unger
Vice-Presidents
   Operations: Pete Bell
   Marketing: Tim Yaeger
   Finance: James Owens

In early 1997, the company was in Chapter 11 receivership and its assets were being sold off. The Evansville area trackage had been sold and the Connersville—Evansville line was not operated. Trackage north from Connersville was on offer to a venture capital firm, Transmark. If this sale took place, the corporate centre might be downsized to an operations office and the trains run with leased stock.

UPDATED

Indiana Rail Road Co

PO Box 2464, Indianapolis, Indiana 46206-2464
Tel: +1 317 262 5140   Fax: +1 317 262 3347

Key personnel
President and Chief Executive Officer: Thomas G Hoback
Executive Vice-President and Chief Operating Officer:
   Thomas J Quigley
Manager, Equipment: R L Finley

Indiana Rail Road Co (IRRC) provides freight service over 249 route-km. In 1985 the company bought 188 route-km

serving coalfields in southern Indiana from Illinois Central and has since expanded. The railroad operates 19 locomotives, and recently acquired three additional GM-EMD SD18s (a total of seven are now in service) and nine GP16s. IRRC owns 40 freight wagons.

Rail is 44.6, 55.3, 56.8 and 62.74 kg/m; maximum gradient is one per cent and maximum permissible axleload 32.875 short tons. The 1997 capital investment programme was budgeted at $3.5 million, primarily for trackwork, a 40 per cent increase on 1996.

UPDATED

Iowa Interstate Railroad Ltd

800 Webster Street, Iowa City, Iowa 52240-4806
Tel: +1 319 339 9501   Fax: +1 319 339 9533

Key personnel
Chairman: Henry Posner III
President and Chief Executive Officer:
   Frederic W Yocum Jr
Executive Vice-President and Chief Financial Officer:
   Robert C Finley
Vice-Presidents
   Marketing: William A Haggerty
   Operations: William J Duggan
Superintendent, Operations: Gilbert P Peters
Chief Mechanical Officer: Frederick D Cheney Jr
Chief Engineer: Mark G Peterburg
General Manager, Intermodal: David Howland

The Iowa Interstate Railroad (IAIS) operates the former Rock Island main line from Council Bluffs, Iowa, to Bureau, Illinois, (724 route-km). Within Illinois, IAIS operates between Bureau and Blue Island over CSXT and Metra, connecting with all major railroads in the Chicago gateway. It also operates south from Bureau into Peoria, by exercising trackage rights over CSXT and the 59 km of the Lincoln & Southern. At Peoria it can offer an outlet for Iowa grain on the Illinois river and to Gulf ports.

The railroad's 1996 capital investment programme included a $5 million combined state, local and company investment in a new yard at Newton, Iowa, with intermodal capability. Newton is the location of the railroad's largest customer, Maytag Corporation.

In 1996 the IAIS turned over its entire intermodal operations to the C H Robinson Company. This contract is a new venture for both parties.

The IAIS locomotive fleet consists of 37 road diesels, chiefly GM-EMD GP38 (including four rebuilds from VMV added in 1994), GP7, GP8, GP9 and GP10. The railroad also operates five Alco diesels, including three ex-Providence & Worcester M420s rebuilt by Conrail in 1994 as M420Rs, and has leased two GP16s and four SD20s from National Railway Equipment to ease a continuing locomotive shortage. IAIS owns 469 freight wagons.

UPDATED

Iowa Interstate M420R locomotive at Blue Island, Illinois (F Gerald Rawling)   **1995**

Iowa Northern Railway Co

PO Box 640, 113 North Second Street, Greene, Iowa 50636
Tel: +1 515 823 5870   Fax: +1 515 823 4816

Key personnel
General Manager: Mark A Sabin

Iowa Northern (224 route-km) connects with Illinois Central (previously CC&P) and Iowa Interstate at Cedar Rapids, with Canadian Pacific (Soo) at Plymouth and with Union Pacific at Manly. Much of its annual 15,000 to 20,000 carloads of traffic is interchanged with the latter two railroads.

In December 1995 the company was bought by Iron Road Railways (qv) which is restructuring the business as a switching carrier. At the end of 1995, Iowa Northern operated seven GM-EMD GP9 locomotives and 40 freight wagons and employed 26 staff.

UPDATED

Iron Road Railways Inc

1300 Connecticut Avenue NW, Suite 903, Washington, DC 20036
Tel: +1 202 296 0535   Fax: +1 202 296 8434

Key personnel
President and Chief Executive Officer: Robert T Schmidt
Chairman: John F DePodesta
Vice-Presidents: Daniel R Sabin, B F Collins

Iron Road Railways was incorporated in 1993 to acquire, manage and invest in short line and regional railways. Two subsidiaries are Transportation Operations Inc (an operator of lines) and TOIX Equipment Corporation. Aggregated annual revenues are $55 million.

At the beginning of 1997 the six properties in the IRR stable were:
- Bangor & Aroostook Railway;
- Canadian American Railway;
- Windsor & Hantsport Railway;
- Iowa Northern Railway;
- Québec Southern Railway (Chemins de Fer du Québec Sud);
- Northern Vermont Railway.

The Québec Southern is the St Jean to Lennoxville section of the erstwhile Canadian Atlantic plus two branches; the Northern Vermont is all former CP trackage off the Canadian Atlantic extending south to Wells River, Vermont. The QSR also has trackage rights to reach the St Luc yard of the St Lawrence & Hudson (qv in Canada section).

The IRR combination of properties in upper New England and Québec is targeting traffic lost to truck haulage in the last decade and, in co-operation with several New England states, has begun to research the passenger market for east-west movement over the several contiguous properties.

UPDATED

Kankakee Beaverville & Southern Railroad Co

Po Box 136, Beaverville, Illinois 60912
Tel: +1 815 486 7260

Key personnel
President: F R Orr
Secretary and Treasurer: Kevin D Stroo

The railroad operates 249 route-km and has eight interchanges with other systems. The rolling stock fleet comprises one Alco C420 and four Alco RS11 locomotives and 265 freight wagons.

VERIFIED

Kansas South Western Railway

See Central Kansas Railway entry

Kiamichi Railroad Co LLC

PO Box 786, Hugo, Oklahoma 74743
Tel: +1 405 326 8306   Fax: +1 405 326 9353

Key personnel
Chief Mechanical Officer: Ralph E Allred

The company runs 30 locomotives, principally GM-EMD GP7, GP9 and GP38; and 418 various freight wagons on 370 route-km. It is a StatesRail property.

UPDATED

Kyle Railroad Co

PO Box 566, Third & Railroad Avenue, Philipsburg, Kansas 67661
Tel: +1 913 543 6527   Fax: +1 913 543 6539

Key personnel
General Manager: Dan A Lovelady
Superintendent of Operations: Charles C Frankenfeld

Kyle Railroad operates 1,114 route-km of line in Colorado, Nebraska and Kansas. It operates 36 locomotives and 792 freight wagons. The traffic base is predominantly grain and farm-related products. It employs 100 people.

UPDATED

Kyle Railways Inc

8687 East Via Ventura, Suite 310, Scottsdale, Arizona 85258
Tel: +1 602 443 3919   Fax: +1 602 443 4184

Key personnel
President: Rick Cecil
General Manager: Dan Lovelady

Kyle Railways Inc is a privately held corporation which wholly owns seven freight railroads totalling over 2,400 km. In the first quarter of 1997 StatesRail acquired all the shares of Kyle Railways Inc for an undisclosed sum and put the stock into a trust pending approval of the transaction by the Surface Transportation Board.

UPDATED

Lake Superior & Ishpeming Railroad Co

105 East Washington Street, Marquette, Michigan 49855-4385
Tel: +1 906 228 7979   Fax: +1 906 228 7983

Key personnel
President and General Manager: John F Marshall
Vice-President, Controller: Dewayne D Nygard
Superintendent, Transportation: William J Cooke
Chief Engineer: Theodor O Stokke

Lake Superior & Ishpeming (LS&I) is a self-contained private railroad which also shares tracks with Wisconsin Central. First built in 1896, LS&I is currently owned by the Cleveland-Cliffs Iron Co which has an interest in Empire and Tilden, the last two active iron ore mines in the Marquette range.

In 1996 the railroad handled 115,000 carloads, totalling 9.5 million tonnes. Of the 9.5 million, 8 million tonnes is outbound ore pellets and the balance is inbound materials, notably bentonite. Ore is moved in 11,000 tonne trains and loaded into lake shipping at LS&I dock, Marquette. The dock closes when Lake Superior freezes over, which usually occurs between January and April every year.

LS&I employed 175 people at the start of 1997. The railway amounts to 80 route-km, of which the 31 km main line is laid with 132 lb rail; the rest of the trackage consists of yards or spurs serving mines.

The rolling stock fleet at the start of 1994 consisted of 1,371 including 1,250 ore hoppers and 13 U30C and three U23C locomotives built by GE.

UPDATED

Laurinburg and Southern Railroad Co

PO Box 1929, Laurinburg, North Carolina 28353
Tel: +1 910 276 0786   Fax: +1 910 276 2853

Key personnel
President: Murphy Evans

The railway owns 45.1 route-km and also operates the 19 km Red Springs & Northern. Connection is directly to CSX or via the Aberdeen & Rockfish (qv) to NS. The 42-strong locomotive fleet is mostly leased to private industries and comprises 11 GM-EMD 1,000 hp/ 746 kW NW2, 13 GM-EMD 600 hp/447 kW SW1, one EMD SW9, three Alco 1,000 hp/746 kW S4, five Alco 1,000 hp/746 kW S2, seven GE 660 hp/492 kW and two GE 150 hp/111 kW units. The railway operates a fleet of 363 wagons.

UPDATED

Louisiana & Delta Railroad

402 W Washington Street, New Iberia, Louisiana 70560
Tel: +1 318 364 9625   Fax: +1 318 364 1716

Key personnel
President and Chief Executive Officer:
   Mortimer B Fuller III
Senior Vice-President: Forrest L Becht

The railroad is a GWI (qv) property and operates 14 branches totalling 180 route-km owned and an additional 180 km of trackage rights. It employs 45 staff. It owns 15 diesel locomotives of which 14 are CF7s.

It now connects to the BNSF which bought the line into New Orleans as a condition of the UP-SP merger.

UPDATED

Louisville & Indiana Railroad Company

2500 Old US Highway 31 East, Jeffersonville, Indiana 47130
Tel: +1 812 288 0940   Fax: +1 812 288 4977

Key personnel
President: John K Secor
General Superintendent: John H Sharp

Corporate office
53 West Jackson Blvd, Suite 350, Chicago, Illinois 60604
Tel: +1 312 341 1026   Fax: +1 312 362 1402

Key personnel
Chairman: Peter A Gilbertson

Louisville & Indiana (LIRC) is a wholly owned subsidiary of Anacostia & Pacific Co Inc (qv). Formed in 1994, the LIRC operates 171.2 km of main line track and 12.8 km of secondary track between Indianapolis and Louisville, Kentucky, formerly worked by Conrail. Annual carloadings amount to 23,000 and the railroad employed 35 people in 1996. The locomotive fleet consists of 10 GP7/9 units. Track is mostly 130 lb rail and is operable at FRA Class 3 (64 km/h). LIRC connects with four Class I railroads and five short lines.

UPDATED

Maine Central Railroad Company

Subsidiary of Guilford Transportation Industries Rail Division
20 Rigby Road, South Portland, Maine 04106
Tel: +1 207 828 6403   Fax: +1 207 828 6403

Key personnel
Chairman, President and Chief Executive: David A Fink
Vice-Presidents
   Transportation: Sydney P Culliford
   Marketing and Sales: Thomas F Steiniger
   Mechanical: James P Coffin
   Finance: Michael A Holmes

Gauge: 1,435 mm
Length: 1,187 km

Maine Central lies within the state of Maine, but another Guilford company, Springfield Terminal Railway, actually operates the system on account of the labour agreements advantageous to Guilford which are in force on the Springfield Terminal Railway.

Guilford will contribute $1.5 million to a $7 million new intermodal facility in Waterville, aimed at capturing truck traffic. Waterville will also be the originating/terminating point for the 'DownEast Express' operation started jointly with Conrail (qv).

Maine Central is also being positioned to combine with Boston & Maine (qv) and the New Brunswick Southern (qv in Canada section) to create an import-export business to and from New England via the port of Halifax, Nova Scotia.

At the start of 1994, 36 locomotives were in service: five GP7, two GP9R, eight GP38, one SD39, 10 U18B, four U23B and six Alco C424M.

UPDATED

Manufacturers Railway Co

2850 South Broadway, St Louis, Missouri 63118-1895
Tel: +1 314 577 1749   Fax: +1 314 577 3136

Key personnel
Chairman, President and Chief Executive Officer:
  Edward R Goedeke
Group Vice-President, Chief Financial Officer:
  Joel A Murnin
Senior Operations Director: Randy Weitzel
Director of Engineering: Kem E Conrad

The railway operates over 68.2 route-km and connects with all major carriers in the St Louis gateway, via Alton & Southern (qv) in particular. It is a wholly owned subsidiary of the brewing company Anheuser-Busch. In addition to switching the flagship brewery in St Louis and distributing certain beer brands nationally, for which the railway maintains a fleet of 146 boxcars, the subsidiary secures income from contract wagon and locomotive repair and modification. In late 1996 the company overhauled a trainset (two 'F' units plus six passenger cars) owned by the St Louis Car Company, which is now available for charter service. Manufacturers Railway operates 11 GM-EMD SW1500 and SW1001 locomotives.

There is also a subsidiary trucking operation that furnishes cartage (225 purpose-designed trailers) and warehousing services at five locations to serve the parent brewing company.

UPDATED

Maryland & Delaware Railroad Co

106 Railroad Avenue, Federalsburg, Maryland 21632
Tel: +1 410 754 5735   Fax: +1 410 754 9528

Key personnel
President: John C Paredes
General Manager: Eric Callaway

The company owns 191.5 route-km, four diesel locomotives.

VERIFIED

Maryland Midland Railway Inc

PO Box 1000, 41 North Main Street, Union Bridge, Maryland 21791-0568
Tel: +1 410 775 7718   Fax: +1 410 775 2520

Key personnel
Chairman and Chief Executive Officer: Maurice E Good
President: Paul D Denton
Chief Financial Officer: David Bordner
Vice-President, Planning: J A Chadwick Jr
General Manager: Wayne E Weszka

Maryland Midland operates 108 route-km and connects with CSXT at Highfield and Emory Grove. In 1995 the railroad employed 29 staff and handled 5,614 carloads of freight, 75 per cent of which were cement and coal. Gross

Manufacturers Railway locomotives at St Louis, Missouri (F Gerald Rawling)   **1996**

revenues of $3.669 million were recorded in 1995, of which $1.515 million was from provision of transportation and the balance from services, maintenance and equipment fees. Net income was $241,412.

The railroad operates six diesel locomotives (three GP9s and three GP38s) and 211 wagons, including 33 hoppers bought used in 1995.

VERIFIED

Maryland and Pennsylvania Railroad Co

See Emons Transportation Group Inc.

Mid-Michigan Railroad Inc/ Michigan Shore Railroad

432 East Grove Street, Greenville, Michigan 48838
Tel: +1 616 754 0001   Fax: +1 616 754 4444

Key personnel
General Manager: Jeff Forster
RailTex Regional Manager: Jim Beardon

Mid-Michigan and Michigan Shore are both RailTex (qv) properties, totalling 128 route-km and operated with three locomotives and 200 freight wagons. Together they handle around 11,400 annual carloads.

UPDATED

Minnesota Commercial Railway Company

508 Cleveland Avenue N, St Paul, Minnesota 55114
Tel: +1 612 646 2010   Fax: +1 612 646 8549

Key personnel
Chairman and President: John W Gohmann
Director of Operations: Wayne Hall Jr

The company owns 194.6 route-km; 18 diesel locomotives; 18 freight wagons. In recent years MCRC has been buying Alcos from the CN. The company provides industry switching and transfer in Minneapolis/St Paul. It has 59 employees.

UPDATED

Mississippi Export Railroad Co

PO Box 8743, Moss Point, Mississippi 39562-8743
Tel: +1 601 475 3322

Key personnel
President: D Gregory Luce Jr
Vice-President and General Manager:
  Michael W Bagswell

The company owns 167.3 route-km; four GM-EMD locomotives (two GP38-2, one GP9, one SW1500); 526 wagons.

VERIFIED

Maryland Midland GP38 and GP9 locomotives head a freight train through Westminster, Maryland (Bob Avery)

Missouri & Northern Arkansas Railroad

PO Box 776, Carthage, Missouri 64836
Tel: +1 417 358 8800   Fax: +1 417 358 6005

Key personnel
General Manager: Dave Smoot
RailTex Regional Manager: Jim Davis

The MNA is an 843 km RailTex (qv) subsidiary that started in 1992 on a former UP (ex-MoPac) line between Pleasant Hill, Missouri and Diaz Juction, Arkansas, with trackage rights from Pleasant Hill into Kansas City. In 1996 it generated 48,800 carloads. Other Class I connections are made to BNSF in four locations and to KCS at Joplin, Missouri.

NEW ENTRY

Mohawk Adirondack & Northern Railroad Corporation

8364 Lewiston Road, Batavia, New York 14020-1245
Tel: +1 716 343 5398   Fax: +1 716 343 4369

Key personnel
President: David J Monte Verde
Vice-President and General Manager: Jeffrey P Baxter
Marketing and Chief Financial Officer:
   Charles J Riedmuller

Totalling 244.8 route-km, Mohawk Adirondack & Northern (MA&N) is the largest of five railroads in the states of New York and Pennsylvania that together make up the Genesee Valley Transportation Company (GVTC). The others are Depew, Lancaster & Western; Lowville & Beaver River; and Falls Road Railroad in New York; and Delaware-Lackawanna in Pennsylvania.

During 1996 GVTC purchased 73.6 km of track from Conrail with a connection at Lockport, New York. GVTC also purchased an out-of-use yard in Niagra Falls, New York, which it will develop as a business park for customers.

MA&N operates several Alco models, RS11s, RS18s, displaced from the ex-Central Vermont.

UPDATED

Montana Rail Link Inc

PO Box 8779, Missoula, Montana 59807
Tel: +1 406 523 1500   Fax: +1 406 523 1493

Key personnel
President: William H Brodsky
Executive Vice-President: J Fred Simpson
Vice-President, Operations: Dan Walters
Chief Finance Officer: Thomas J Walsh
Operating Superintendent: John L Grewell
Chief Engineer: Richard L Keller
Chief Mechanical Officer: Melvin G Dinius

Montana Rail Link (MRL) is a subsidiary of Washington Companies, a diversified natural resources conglomerate. Anacostia & Pacific Co Inc (qv) also has an equity position in MRL. Formed in 1987 to run Burlington Northern's ex-Northern Pacific main line through Montana as a regional railroad, MRL provides a major corridor for rail traffic between central and southern US states and the Pacific northwest and Canada. Its western end is Spokane, its eastern end is Huntley near Billings; it traverses the Belt Mountains via Bozeman Pass, west of Livingston, at an altitude of 5,561 ft above sea level; it crosses the Continental Divide via Mullan Pass, west of Helena, at 5,546 ft above sea level. It also provides local service to more than 100 listed stations.

MRL is a Class II railroad and the fourth largest new regional formed in the US in the last 25 years. As of April 1996 it comprised 1,517 route-km; 462 km owned, 941 km leased and 106 km of trackage rights into Spokane. Employees numbered 1,126 in April 1996. Two-thirds of its route-km are cleared for 96 km/h operation, equipped with CTC and automatic block signalling.

Annual loads for 1996 were below 1995 levels in response to reduced bridge traffic (down 10 per cent). But originating/terminating traffic, which is only a quarter of all loads, was up 5 per cent. In January 1996 MRL began moving 115-wagon unit trains of low-sulphur coal from a road transfer siding at Lockwood to the Canadian port of Roberts Bank, British Columbia, for export to Japan, but shut down in June after falling behind on the contract. In 1996 capital expenditure amounted to $15 million, primarily for track components including 50 km of new curve track; 400 km of surfacing; 105,000 sleepers installed; 100,000 tonnes of ballast laid.

MRL rolling stock comprised 158 locomotives and 1,716 freight wagons (half of them boxcars) and cabooses in April 1996. The largest locomotive class is 65 SD45/SD45-2s after adding 18 ex-SP units in 1996. As many as a third of MRL's road locomotives are leased offline at any time; during 1996, MRL locomotives were leased to Burlington Northern Santa Fe and Canadian Pacific (20), and three spent five months on the Alaska Railroad to power work trains. MRL is contributing lease units to the start-up fleet of I&M Rail Link (qv).

Livingston Rebuild Center is also owned by the Washington Companies. In addition to some work for MRC, the LRC rebuilds and repaints for offline customers and, in 1996, began to offer a lease fleet for the first time.

In December 1996, MRL adopted the BNSF's TSS (Transportation Support System) to bring it in line with BNSF management practice.

UPDATED

Nashville & Eastern Railroad Corporation

514 Knoxville Avenue, Lebanon, Tennessee 37087
Tel: +1 615 444 1434   Fax: +1 615 444 4682

Key personnel
President: William J Drunsic
General Manager: Craig Wade

The N&ERR is the contracted operator for a four-county rail authority which owns the property. The company serves 210 route-km with eight ex-CSX U30Bs and one U36B locomotive; it connects with CSX at Nashville. Of the 10,000 annual carloads, 80 per cent are inbound and the primary commodities are lumber, plastics and beer.

For three summers, the state of Tennessee has funded an experimental commuter service into Nashville to relieve parallel Interstate 40. N&ERR provides passenger counts. The practice has not gone year round; outside of the summer season the parking facilities at the stations revert to bus park-and-ride lots.

UPDATED

Nebraska Central Railroad Company

400 Braasch, Suite B, Norfolk, Nebraska 68701
Tel: +1 402 371 9015   Fax: +1 402 371 4588

NCRC operates two former UP grain branches, the Stromsberg and Ord lines. The first branch connects to UP at Grand Island, the second at Central City. NCRC uses its own GP38s and borrows locomotives from UP when grain volumes reach unit train levels.

NEW ENTRY

Nebraska, Kansas & Colorado RailNet Inc

See North American RailNet Inc entry.

New England Central Railroad

2 Federal Street, St Albans, Vermont 05478
Tel: +1 802 527 3411   Fax: +1 802 527 3482

Key personnel
General Manager: Dale Carlstrom
RailTex Regional Manager: Jim Bearden

New England Central (NECR) is the name RailTex (qv) has assigned to the 549 km former Central Vermont property bought from Canadian National (CN). NECR began operations in February 1995 between East Alberg, where a frontier connection is made with CN, and New London, where NECR connects with Providence & Worcester. There is an intermodal ramp at Palmer, Massachusetts. NECR has been negotiating with CN to reach Montréal directly via 120 km of trackage rights.

Annual carloadings for 1996 were 30,000. The NECR locomotive fleet comprises 18 GP38s and GP40s rebuilt by Conrail and National Railway Engineering.

UPDATED

New England Southern Railroad

8 Water Street, Concord, New Hampshire 03301
Tel: +1 603 228 8580/+1 617 472 2425
Fax: +1 603 228 9571

Key personnel
President and General Manager: Peter M Dearness

The company owns and operates two properties, the NESR in New Hampshire and the Quincy Bay Railroad in Massachusetts. The NESR averages 2,200 carloads annually and the QBR moves 900. The NESR connects to the Boston and Maine (Guilford) at Manchester, New Hampshire; the QBRR connects to Conrail at Braintree, Massachusetts.

During 1996 and 1997 the company has a contract with the MBTA (qv in Passenger operators section) to perform two services:
(a) it brings in track materials for the contractor rebuilding the Old Colony lines (via the QBR);
(b) it will conduct running-in trials for the rolling stock that will be used in the Old Colony lines, namely 23 rebuilt locomotives from the former AMF Technotransport and 47 ex-Pullman cars being refurbished by Amerail (trials on the NESR).

UPDATED

New Orleans Public Belt Railroad

PO Box 51658, New Orleans, Louisiana 70151
Tel: +1 504 896 7410   Fax: +1 504 896 7452

Key personnel
President: Marc H Morial
General Manager: Ray Duplechain

The company owns 198 route-km; six GM-EMD locomotives (three SW1001 and three SW1500); and connects with UP, KCS and IC. It serves the Port of New Orleans and online industries.

UPDATED

New York & Atlantic Railway Company

21-16 Jackson Avenue, Long Island City, New York, 11101-5315
Tel: +1 718 433 3750   Fax: +1 718 433 3751

Key personnel
President: George L Stern
Superintendent: Stephen C Sanders

The company has contracted to operate freight services that were previously provided by the Long Island Railroad (qv); operations began in April 1997 and involve 27 employees. NYA is a subsidiary of the Anacostia & Pacific Company, Inc (qv). The 20-year operating concession has been assessed at $28 million per year — a $13 million fixed rental plus $15 million in user fees based on 1996 levels of activity.

NEW ENTRY

New York, Susquehanna and Western Railway Corporation

1 Railroad Avenue, Cooperstown, New York 13326
Tel: +1 607 547 2555   Fax: +1 607 547 9834

Key personnel
President and Chief Executive Officer: W G Rich
Executive Vice-President and Chief Operating Officer:
   C David Soule
Executive Vice-President, TP&W: Gordon R Fuller
Vice-President, NYS&W: Robert A Kurdock
Senior Vice-President and Chief Financial Officer:
   William B Blatter
Vice-Presidents
   Administration: William H Matteson
   Engineering: Richard J Hensel
   Operations: Joseph G Senchyshyn
   Controller: Robert E Pierce
   Treasurer: Frank Quattrocchi
   Marketing & Sales: Paul Garber
   General Counsel and Corporate Secretary:
      Nathan R Fenno
   Mechanical: David Boyd
   Revenue Accounting: Jane McArdle

New York, Susquehanna and Western (NYS&W) is wholly owned by the Delaware Otsego Corporation (qv) and operates over 800 route-km, of which 320 km is trackage rights. NYS&W covers territory from Syracuse and Utica, New York, through Pennsylvania to northern New Jersey. Between Binghamton and Buffalo, NYS&W has a haulage agreement with CP, using NYS&W supplied power and fuel. The Toledo, Peoria & Western is administered and despatched from Cooperstown.

From its junction with Conrail at Syracuse, NYS&W is now the regular route of Sea-Land double-stack container trains from the West Coast to the New York/New Jersey area. This was made possible by a renegotiated interchange agreement with Conrail and a $7 million investment in the line between Syracuse and Binghamton. The former route via Buffalo and the Norfolk Southern system is still used for CSXI domestic container trains from Chicago. Trains are handled at the CSXI-owned Little Ferry terminal in New Jersey. NYS&W has secured Hanjin's Pacific Rim—Northeast Coast container service, which is handled at a North Bergen terminal, and partners Union Pacific and Norfolk Southern in a weekly coast-to-coast stack train service from Long Beach, California.

Some years ago NYS&W opened a food-grade transfer facility for liquid sweeteners at Oakland, New Jersey, operated with New Jersey Tank Lines. The original yard reached capacity and in 1996 was doubled. In 1996 also, NYS&W relaid track to reopen a quarry. The Binghamton, New York, yard has been rebuilt. The railroad also has an automobile loading facility in North Bergen, operated by CT Services, and brings lumber to the New York/New Jersey Metropolitan market via a distribution centre operated by National Distribution in conjunction with Georgia Pacific. These facilities complement an already-strong sugar and plastics bulk transfer business.

Total revenue for 1996 declined to $32.3 million, 7 per cent below 1995. Net loss on the year was $1.165 million. With $15.8 million of revenue coming from CSXI and $6.3 million from Hanjin (both below 1995 levels), NYS&W is highly dependent on these two operators continuing their current movement patterns and both these multiyear contracts will be subject to some change in the context of the break-up of Conrail. The railroad's success is attributable in part to the constraints on Conrail imposed by ever-increasing New Jersey commuter traffic, although New Jersey Transit (qv) has expressed interest in introducing commuter services to the NYS&W system.

Rolling stock comprises 22 diesel locomotives (including three GM-EMD SD70M, four GM-EMD SD45, one GM-EMD F45, four GE B40-8, two Alco C430, one GM-EMD GP38, one GM-EMD GP40, three GM-EMD GP18, one GM-EMD GP9 and one GM-EMD NW2); 45 freight wagons; and 15 passenger coaches.

The 1997 capital programme anticipated spending of $15 million: $8 million for track and structures; $7 million for yards, terminals and related real estate; $1 million for motive power and equipment.

UPDATED

North American RailNet Inc

2300 Airport Freeway, Suite 230, Bedford, Texas 76022
Tel: +1 817 571 2356   Fax: +1 817 571 2335

Key personnel
Chairman & Chief Executive Officer:
   Robert F McKenney
President & Chief Operating Officer: Roger H Nelson
Executive Vice-President: William E Glavin

The company began operations in 1997. Its first property is the Nebraska, Kansas & Colorado RailNet Inc, 669 km in its namesake states and operated with five locomotives initially.

NEW ENTRY

Northern Plains Railroad

Devil's Lake, North Dakota
Tel: +1 701 662 6727

Key personnel
President: Gregg Hang
Vice-President, Operations: Robert Irwin

Established in November 1996, NPR was set up to operate 615 km of leased Canadian Pacific track, mostly in the state of North Dakota, commonly referred to in the industry as 'the Wheat Lines'. Connections to Canadian Pacific are available at Thief River Falls, Minnesota, or Kenmare, North Dakota. CP will provide the grain cars, set the rates and market the services. Cars handled in 1995 totalled 12,000, of which 90 per cent were outbound grain.

NEW ENTRY

Northwestern Pacific Railroad

4 West 2nd Street, Eureka, California 95501
Tel: +1 707 441 1625   Fax: +1 707 441 1324

Key personnel
Executive Director/Chief Executive Officer:
   Dan Hauser
Manager, Passenger Operations: Arthur Lloyd

NPRR uses 16 locomotives (4 SD9s, 12 GP7/9s) to operate between Eureka and Schellville. Trains meet at Willets and take four days to traverse the 560 km length. The NPRR started up in 1996 after the public agency, the North Coast Railroad Authority, purchased the Willets to Schellville section (it has previously acquired the Eureka to Willets section). The contract operator, California Northern, was displaced by NPRR but still provides a vital bridge 29 km from Schellville to Suisun City to connect to UP (ex-SP). Carloads for NPRR average 600/month. In an inauspicious start, the line was badly impacted by the west coast floods in 1997, incurring an estimated $5 million in damage.

Long-term, the public authority is reviewing property south into the area of San Rafael and Tiburon (in Marin County) as a commuter railway opportunity. Right-of-way is there and some out-of-service track. The commuter operator would be the Golden Gate Transit District.

NEW ENTRY

Ohio Central Railroad Inc

136 South 5th, Coshocton, Ohio 43812
Tel: +1 614 622 8118   Fax: +1 614 622 3941

Key personnel
President: William A Strawn
Chief Executive Officer: Jerry J Jacobson
Executive Vice-President: Michael J Connor

Director of Marketing: Marty Pohlod
Chief Engineering Officer: John Dulac
Chief Mechanical Officer: Tracy Young

The Ohio Central System is the collective name for the Ohio Central, Columbus & Ohio River, Ohio Southern, Youngstown & Austinstown Youngstown Belt, Warren & Trumbull and Ohio & Pennsylvania railroads, totalling 560 km. Together, the six railroads operate 35 diesel (five GP40s; one GP38; two GP35s; two GP30s; eight GP10s; two SW1500s; four SW1200s; one SW10; plus several Alcos and four slugs) and three steam locomotives for excursion trains (150,000 passengers/year), 13 passenger coaches and 38 freight wagons.

The company offers repair and rebuild service to other short lines in Ohio and Indiana and to independents such as grain elevator operators. It also has bought a number of ex-Conrail slugs and cannibalised them to make four serviceable units.

Track is 90 to 155 lb/yd rail on timber sleepers with plate and spike fastening. Maximum permissible axleloading is 35 short tons.

UPDATED

OmniTRAX Inc

252 Clayton Street, 4th Floor, Denver, Colorado 80206
Tel: +1 303 393 0033   Fax: +1 303 393 0041

Key personnel
Chairman and Chief Executive Officer: Robert E Smith
President: Dwight N Johnson
Vice-President, Research & Analysis: Dennis N Lindberg
Vice-President, Business Development: Stephen Gregory
Vice-President, Operations: Dennis McDougal
Vice-President, Real Estate: Clark Robertson
Managing Director: Mike Ogborn
Manager, Marketing and Sales: John P Reilly

OmniTRAX Equipment Inc

3310 Woodcrest Drive, Bettendorf, Iowa 52722-55378
Tel: +1 319 332 7959   Fax: +1 319 332 8505

Key personnel
President: John Gallagher
Vice-President: Jim H Griffiths

Quality Terminal Services Inc
2400 Westpost Parkway West, Haslet, Texas 76052
Tel: +1 817 224 7156   Fax: +1 817 224 7172

OmniTRAX Inc is the management company for properties owned or operated by the Broe Companies Inc. It is also involved in locomotive and wagon leasing through OmniTRAX Equipment Inc.

OmniTRAX also has property and other non-railroad subsidiaries. OmniTRAX Logistics provides distribution and inventory management services. OmniTRAX Switching Services Inc offers company or plant-specific switching. Quality Terminal Services Inc, a shared-ownership subsidiary, operates the 125 acre Alliance, Texas, intermodal terminal for BNSF, including switching and repair of trailers, containers, chassis. At the end of 1996 the operating companies in the OmniTRAX portfolio were:

   Central Kansas Railway Inc
   Chicago Rail Link
   Chicago West Pullman & Southern RR Co
   Georgia Woodlands RR Co
   Great Western Railway of Colorado Inc
   Great Western Railway of Iowa
   Great Western Railway of Oregon Inc
   Kansas Southwestern Railway Co
   Manufacturers Junction Railway Co (Chicago)
   Newburgh & South Shore RR Co
   Northern Ohio & Western
   Panhandle Northern RR Co

In November 1996 OmniTRAX was designated the successful bidder on 1,295 km of lines in northern Manitoba which are operated by Canadian National (qv).

UPDATED

locomotives still numbered in the NS roster, and 1,297 freight wagons. W&LE is a wholly owned subsidiary of the Wheeler Corporation.

During 1995 the railway restructured financially, and received a $2.4 million investment from the state of Ohio; in 1996 the Stark County Development Board used a $10 million state loan to build NEOMODAL, a North East Ohio intermodal facility at Masillon, which is targeted at a large market within a 180 km radius focusing on consumer perishables inbound and manufactured goods outbound. One feature of NEOMODAL is that all three MiJack cranes in the terminal are remote controlled, with units supplied by MaxTec International of Chicago. W&LE interchanges with Conrail, CSX and NS. In 1995, after an interval of 10 years, the railway reactivated the former Norfolk & Western ore dock at Huron, Ohio, for the purpose of moving taconite to a Wheeling-Pittsburgh Steel Company mill at Steubenville, Ohio.

In 1997, WLE received its first new car deliveries in several years, 23 covered coil cars.

UPDATED

Wichita, Tillman & Jackson Railway Co, Inc

4420 West Vickery Boulevard, Suite 110, Fort Worth, Texas 76107
Tel: +1 817 737 7288   Fax: +1 817 732 2610

Key personnel
Chairman and Chief Executive Officer of Rio Grande
  Pacific Corporation: Richard D Bertel
President, RGPC: Daniel P McShane

The WT&J operates over 163.5 route-km; it has six GM-EMD GP7 locomotives. The railroad consists of two short lines, one from the BNSF at Wichita Falls, Texas, to Altus, Oklahoma, and the other connecting Waurika, Oklahoma, on the Union Pacific with Walters, Oklahoma. Track in Texas is leased from the UP; in Oklahoma it is leased from the state. Annual carloadings are 7,700; wheat and sand are the main commodities. The workforce numbered 16 at the start of 1994.

WT&J is part of a holding company, Rio Grande Pacific Corporation, that also has the Nebraska Central (qv) and the Idaho, Northern and Pacific, each of which is locally managed.

UPDATED

Willamette & Pacific

See Genesee & Wyoming Inc entry

Winchester & Western Railroad Co

Virginia Division
PO Box 264, 126 East Piccadilly Street, Winchester, Virginia 22601
Tel: +1 540 662 2600   Fax: +1 540 667 3692

Key personnnel
President: W P Light
General Agent: P M Williams

New Jersey Division
PO Box 1024, Burlington Road, Bridgeton, New Jersey 08302
Tel: +1 609 451 6400   Fax: +1 609 451 7016

Key personnel
Trainmaster: M T Luczkiewicz
General Agent: F A Winkler

W&WR has 164 route-km of unsignalled trackage. The New Jersey Division operates with six GM-EMD GP9 locomotives. The Virginia Division operates with four GP9s and two Alco locomotives of model RS11. Winchester & Western has 346 freight wagons. Tonnage moved in 1995 was 1.3 million, up from 1.1 million in the year previous.

VERIFIED

Wisconsin & Southern Railroad Co

PO Box 9229, 5300 N 33rd Street, Milwaukee, Wisconsin 53209-10229
Tel: +1 414 438 8820   Fax: +1 414 438 8826

Key personnel
President and Chief Executive Officer:
  William E Gardner
Chief Mechanical Officer: James C Robertson

The company has 1,040 route-km, in three line clusters, including 418 km acquired with the purchase of the Wisconsin & Calumet Railroad from Chicago West

Pullman Transportation Corporation in August 1992. Wisconsin & Southern (WSOR) connects with Wisconsin Central, Union Pacific (formerly CNW) and Canadian Pacific at several locations. In addition, the railroad enjoys trackage rights over Metra between Fox Lake and Cragin and thence over Belt Railway of Chicago to reach BRC's Clearing Yard to connect with eastern and southern railroads.

WSOR has a fleet of 13 locomotives of several models, and 525 freight wagons. The company also operates the Northern Railcar workshop in Cudahy, Wisconsin, that specialises in rebuilding and maintaining privately owned passenger and freight vehicles and in custom-painting.

UPDATED

Wyoming Colorado Railroad Inc

452 Snowy Range Road, Laramie, Wyoming 82070
Tel: +1 307 721 2907

Key personnel
President: David L Durbano
Vice-President, Operations: Gregory L Kissel
General Manager: W Q Penno

WCRI operates over 186.6 route-km; it has five GM-EMD locomotives (two F7A, one F7B and two GP7).

VERIFIED

Yadkin Valley Railroad Co

401 Henley Street, Knoxville, Tennessee 37902
Tel: +1 615 525 9400   Fax: +1 615 546 3717

Key personnel
President: H Peter Claussen
Executive Vice-President: W Terry Hart
General Manager: Andy Anderson

This property was first sold by Norfolk Southern in 1989 as an element of NS's 'Thoroughbred' short line leasing initiative, then acquired in 1994 by Gulf & Ohio Railways. The YVRR totals 160 route-km based on Rural Hall, South Carolina. Annual carloadings are 11,000; corn, coal and soyabean meal are the three primary commodities. Interchange is with NS. The railway is operated with five GM-EMD GP9 and four GM-EMD GP10 rebuilds.

VERIFIED

PASSENGER OPERATORS

In certain conurbations regional authorities operate 'heavy rail' commuter services with their own equipment over track belonging to or acquired from railroad companies; elsewhere services are operated by railroads under contract. Details on these are included in this section.

Also included in this section is Amtrak, the federally owned Class I intercity passenger operator.

Proposals for high-speed passenger services in the USA and emerging commuter operations follow in separate sections.

Amtrak

National Railroad Passenger Corporation
Washington Union Station, 60 Massachusetts Avenue, New England, Washington DC 20002
Tel: +1 202 906 3000   Fax: +1 202 906 3865
Website: http://www.amtrak.com

Key personnel
President and Chairman of the Board: Thomas M Downs
Executive Vice-President and Chief Operating Officer:
  Dennis F Sullivan
Vice-President and Chief Financial Officer:
  Howard Nicholas
Vice-Presidents
  Passenger Marketing and Sales: Robert K Wehrmann
  Corporate Management: Anne W Hoey
  Re-engineering: Norris W Overton
  Human Resources and Labour Relations:
    Dennis R Wright
  High-Speed Rail: David J Carol
  Government and Public Affairs: Thomas J Gillespie Jr
General Counsel: Stephen C Rogers
Chief Executive Officers
  North East Corridor Business Unit:
    George D Warrington
  West Coast Business Unit: Gil Mallory
  Intercity Business Unit: Mark S Cane

Gauge: 1,435 mm
Route length owned: 1,256 km
Electrification: 554.6 km at 12 kV 25 Hz AC

Political background
Amtrak was created when the Rail Passenger Service Act was enacted in 1970. Services began in May 1971, establishing the first nationwide rail passenger service under one management in the USA.

Amtrak's rail passenger service is totally dependent upon the condition of track and related facilities that are owned, designed, maintained and operated by the private freight-hauling railroads. The only exceptions to this are where Amtrak owns its own track: in the Boston—New York—Washington North East Corridor (NEC), on short sections of track elsewhere, and in several major cities where the corporation has acquired passenger terminals.

Amtrak has been supported by federal capital and operating grants, the amount of which is annually budgeted by Congress as part of the overall transportation authorisation. The process generally consists of a joint House and Senate committee reconciling a House figure and a Senate figure with the requests submitted by Amtrak and by the Administration. Since November 1994 the Republican party has controlled both the House and the Senate in the US Congress, and contains a faction that argues for

eliminating Amtrak, purportedly as part of a balanced budget initiative.

This threat continues to drive much of Amtrak's policy and during 1995 Amtrak restructured significantly to make it more financially viable with the avowed aim of doing without any operating subsidy by 2002. An unwritten aspect of this intention is that Amtrak should be provided with adequate capital assistance (estimated at $600 million annually), but this does not appear to have universal support within Congress, where Amtrak continues to be a political football.

In the Administration's proposed six-year bill, NEXTEA (for National Economic Crossroads Efficiency Act), the proposal is for $2.5 billion for Amtrak over the six-year life of the bill. Capital funding is less than the $750 million per annum that could come from a federal petrol tax subvention (see below), but the Administration proposes to add intercity rail service (not necessarily Amtrak) to the list of eligible uses for flexible transportation programmes administered at the state level.

There is a House bill and a companion Senate bill before the Congress to allocate to Amtrak 0.5 cent of the 4.3 cents of federal petrol tax now going to (budget) deficit reduction. If passed, Amtrak could expect about $750 million/year based oncurrent contributions.

Privatisation of some services is under consideration. Certain Amtrak functions such as maintenance could be

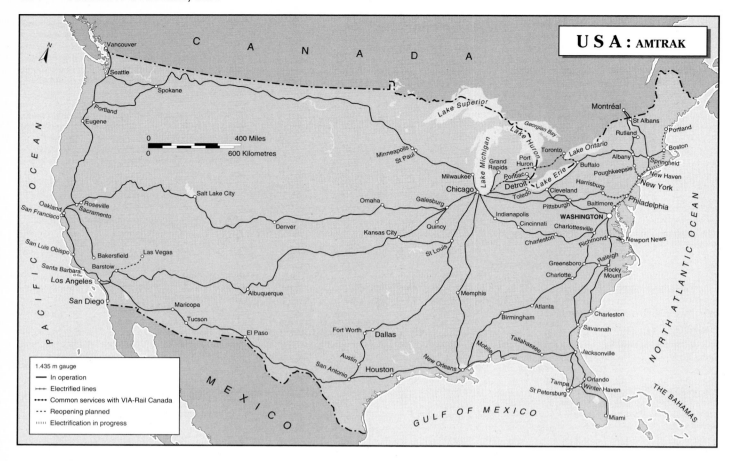

sold or contracted out, but this practice is currently confined by federal law to the area of food service, now seen as a potential source of profit for Amtrak. Some separable traffic generators, such as Auto-Train, which itself is profitable, are candidates for selling off.

Finance
Six-year strategic plan
In December 1994 Amtrak adopted a Strategic Business Plan. Dedicated capital, zero subsidies, and freedom to adopt standard business practices, were the foci.

In 1996, Amtrak reported a $300 million improvement to bottom line but still fell $82 million below target. Passenger revenue did not live up to expectations, although ticket yield (revenue per passenger mile) improved 13 per cent. Not all intended cost reductions were achieved.

A General Accounting Office report in July 1996 concluded that Amtrak was progressing toward the goals of the Strategic Plan but the core issues were still suitable capitalisation; increase in state contributions; productivity of equipment and labour; with the Intercity Business Unit being the most over budget in 1995.

Fiscal condition still precarious
In 1997, Guilford Transportation Industries offered (without giving any figures) to take over Amtrak routes in the North East Corridor, but this was widely thought to be a response to a proposal by NS to run container trains to Boston over Amtrak tracks, rather than a sensible proposal concerning Amtrak itself.

Following several years of underinvestment, Amtrak was forced in 1994 to resort to short-term private borrowing of $63 million to pay employees and suppliers. Thanks to an economy programme which saw cuts at 7.5 per cent in train-km, this expedient was not necessary during 1995, but in 1996 Amtrak drew $12 million against its line of credit.

Amtrak continues to work with Congress and the Administration to define the future for passenger rail in America. One proposal would have had Amtrak's future determined by a non-partisan grouping modelled upon the recent Base Closure and Realignment Commission. There have also been unsuccessful legislative initiatives to substantially relax Amtrak's inhibiting severance payment obligations. Another measure considered would recalculate the track-sharing formulae for commuter services, passing an estimated $50-60 million in additional costs to the commuter operators, primarily in the Northeast.

Amtrak budget (US$ million)

	FY94 Enacted	FY95 Enacted	FY96 Enacted	FY97 Enacted	Amtrak FY98 Request	Administration FY98 Request
Core operations	351.7	392.0	185.0	223.0	245.0	202.0
Core capital	195.0	230.0	230.0	223.0	751.0	200.0
Restructuring assistance	0.0	0.0	100.0	0.0	0.0	0.0
North East Corridor	225.0	200.00	115.0	255.0	*	200.0
Mandatory payments	137.0	150.0	120.0	142.0	142.0	142.0
Penn Station/Farley PO	0.0	21.5	0.0	0.0	0.0	23.0
High Speed Rail	0.0	0.0	24.0	25.0	0.0	20.0
Total	908.7	993.5	774.0	867.0	1,138.0	787.0

*NEC included in capital request

Representative Bud Schuster of Pennsylvania has commissioned a blue ribbon committee to examine Amtrak's future.

Financial achievements
In the financial year ending 1981 revenues covered only 48 per cent of total operating costs. Since then the operating ratio steadily improved to 80 per cent by 1993 but then it slipped to 77 per cent in 1994. Amtrak continues to aim for 100 per cent self-sufficiency and coverage of costs by revenues by 2002.

In FY96-97 passenger-related revenues, including fares, food and beverage income and 403(b) contributions (see '403(b)' services section below), rose 6 per cent over 1995 to $965 million, reversing two years of decline or flat revenue. While ridership fell by 2.2 per cent, it was less than expected in the light of service reductions, suggesting that the latter were astutely selected. The operating loss in FY96-97 was $764 million (compared with $808 million in 1995). Revenues rose 3.9 per cent to $1,554.8 million; expenses rose to $2,318.4 million, only 1 per cent over 1995.

Passenger operations
Amtrak's operations cover most of the mainland USA, but services vary in frequency. The most frequent services are on the North East Corridor (NEC) from Washington DC to New York City, where two or more trains operate each hour at speeds up to 200 km/h; services are also frequent between New York City and Boston and on certain routes in California. Additional trains introduced to key routes in 1996 left only two national routes with less-than-daily service.

As part of a 1996 restructuring exercise, Amtrak's

activities were reorganised into three strategic business units, namely North East Corridor, West Coast and Intercity. The company also created a 'sub' business unit in the North East Corridor. Trains other than Metroliners are marketed as *Northeast Direct*, with a modified colour scheme which may provide a source of ideas for similar sub-units with geographic identities.

Metroliner stock is being refurbished and a first 'Concept 2000' trainset was introduced during 1996. As a stand-alone product package, *Metroliner* operated in the black in 1996.

Track access
In the North East Corridor Amtrak owns its own tracks, but on other routes it has to buy track access from the freight railroads. The original track access contracts between freight railroads and Amtrak expired in April 1996 after a period of 25 years. By September 1996, negotiations had been concluded with several of the host companies and contract extensions agreed with Illinois Central (for 15 years) and Conrail (10). An impasse with Burlington Northern Santa Fe was referred to the Surface Transportation Board, then an agreement signed in October 1996 for a 15-year renewal. CSXT and Norfolk Southern have both commented publicly on the 'incompatibility' of freight and passenger services.

Under the track access agreements, Amtrak makes performance incentive payments to host railroads for dispatching its trains over their lines on time. An exponential formula has been adopted, so that at 90 per cent on-time performance, the host railroad has lost 50 per cent of its incentive opportunity; Amtrak's payouts are running in the order of one-third of potential maximum. In 1996 on-time performance across the Amtrak network

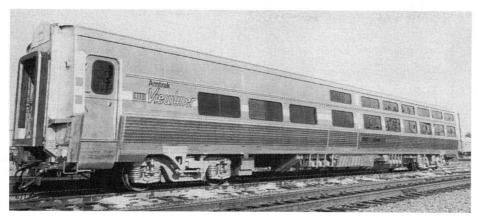

Prototype 'Viewliner' sleeping car

was 71 per cent; for short distance (less than 650 km) trips the figure was 76 per cent but long-distance services achieved only 49 per cent.

North East Corridor

Amtrak continues to enjoy a dominant presence in the North East Corridor, having raised its market share between Washington DC and New York City to 43 per cent; it now carries more passengers than either of the competing air shuttles and NEC is the only Amtrak business unit to produce a positive budget result. In the intermediate market its share is over 70 per cent. Improvements in onboard amenities and services (telephone, fax and conference facilities and complimentary meal service in extra-fare Club class) continue to encourage demand. Four trains daily now cover Washington—New York in 2 hours 30 minutes for the 362 km trip, inclusive of one intermediate stop.

'403(b)' services

Under the Rail Passenger Service Act of 1970, Amtrak can add new services to its existing network provided it has the equipment available and the additions will cover their operating costs requiring no additional federal support. Since this is rarely the case, Section 403(b) of the Act authorised Amtrak to initiate new routes with financial support from a non-Amtrak source. The latter could be a state, a group of states, a regional or local agency, or even an individual with the requisite financial backing.

Amtrak's conditions for considering new so-called 403(b) services are: that a state or states will shoulder 70 per cent of long-term losses, and that Amtrak's absorption of the remaining 30 per cent is subject to a maximum of $1 million annually; and that capital expenditure for station construction and other infrastructure improvements needed to initiate service are negotiated so that Amtrak's share does not exceed 30 per cent. Amtrak's ability to undertake a 403(b) service also depends on availability of spare rolling stock and Amtrak's ability to accept its share of any losses incurred in operation. The cost of using Amtrak's rolling stock must be shared by the applicant state(s), or the latter can provide their own. An applicant is free to shoulder all costs to get a service started if Amtrak is financially unable to take on any of the expenses involved, and in recent years the trend in new starts and service expansions has been towards 100 per cent state/local funding.

While several states made use of the legislation beforehand, Section 403(b) assumed greater importance when Amtrak introduced service cuts in 1995; a few states, such at Illinois, agreed to take a financial responsibility for specified intra-state services.

California has been a major player in the 403(b) arena, using the proceeds of a $1 billion bond issue in 1990 to purchase rolling stock for these services. In 1996, the California legislature passed a 'permissive' bill that allows local authorities to assume 403(b) responsiblity if they can offer current levels of service more cheaply or add service for the current expenditure. So far, eight counties in the Bay Area have formed a Joint Powers Authority with a view to BART (Bay Area Rapid Transit) acting as manager of rail services with Amtrak still the provider. In the Central Valley no initiative has started. In the San Diego—Los Angeles area several counties have proposed a cost-benefit feasibility study but have yet to assign funds.

A consortium of nine midwest states (Illinois, Indiana, Iowa, Michigan, Minnesota, Nebraska, Ohio, Wisconsin) have joined under the leadership of Wisconsin to fund a $688,500 study for what amounts to a 'Midwest business unit'. This short-term focus is on operational improvements, such as Chicago run-throughs, to save costs. The longer-term focus is on market development, new equipment and higher speeds, possibly with a regional visual identity. TAMS/COMSIS are the lead consultants. FRA put up $200,000 from the Next Generation Rail funding programme for the study; Amtrak is contributing $200,000.

Commuter contracts

Amtrak revenue from operating commuter services under contract to local agencies has continued to grow. In 1996, Amtrak recorded $234.4 million in revenue from commuter operations (10 per cent up on 1995) but only $84.4 million in facilities rental income (down from $92.4 million in 1995). A new contract for San Diego's 'Coaster' service worth $6 million was obtained in 1995 and increases in operating income were recorded over the previous year from MBTA (Boston), Metrolink (Los Angeles), San Francisco's Peninsula service, Maryland's MARC and Virginia Railway Express.

In 1995, commuter rail service was operated in the northeast states by or for the following agencies:

Maryland Department of Transportation (MARC): Washington—Baltimore—Perryville;

South Eastern Pennsylvania Transportation Authority (SEPTA): Philadelphia—Trenton, Marcus Hook, Downington;

Delaware Department of Transportation: service as far as Philadelphia—Wilmington;

New Jersey Department of Transportation: Trenton—New York Pennsylvania Station;

Metropolitan Transportation Authority: Pennsylvania station to the Borough of Queens;

Massachusetts Bay Transit Authority (MBTA): Attleboro—Boston.

Connecticut Department of Transportation: Shore Line East service between New Haven and Old Saybrook.

The Southern California Regional Rail Authority awarded Amtrak the contract to operate the ambitious commuter network it is developing in the Los Angeles area under the Metrolink identity. Five routes are now operational.

In 1996, both the Peninsula service and Metrolink contracts were renewed or extended.

Intermodal operations

Joint trials with the US Postal Service concluded with sufficient promise for Amtrak to order 13 RoadRailer bimodal van trailers, two intermediate rail bogies and 18 'Couplermate' adaptors from Wabash National. In late 1996 a pilot project was launched between Chicago and Philadalphia, plus Philadelphia and Jacksonville. From Jacksonville, trailers are hauled over the road to Orlando, Tampa and Miami postal stations.

Freight expansion possible

It was reported in the first quarter of 1997 that Amtrak would lease up to 600 freight cars to pursue express freight opportunities and capture such business from trucks. The plan is expected to create resistance on the part of the freight railroads, which are also interested in the same opportunity, but may turn out to have been a purely political ploy.

Improvements to existing lines

Excluding sections totalling 151 km that are owned by six regional commuter authorities, Amtrak has owned the 735 km Boston—New York—Washington North East Corridor route since 1976, including five of its stations: Baltimore, Wilmington, Philadelphia (30th Street), New York (Pennsylvania Station) and Providence. An improvement project (NECIP) on this route is continuing. The last stage to be inaugurated includes electrification to Boston (see 'Electrification' section), and the New York—Washington section is being upgraded to prepare for the introduction of high-speed trainsets. By mid-1994, 440 km of the North East Corridor was authorised for 200 km/h operation. During 1995 a further 100,000 concrete replacements were installed for timber sleepers.

Traction and rolling stock

Amtrak's main line fleet of locomotives and passenger coaches was further rationalised in 1996-97. By mid-1997 the average age of the locomotive fleet had been cut from 13.2 years to 7.4. Of the 215 life-expired F40s on the roster in 1995, only 60 remained. Several have been rebuilt as non-powered control cab units for push-pull services operating out of Chicago; the locomotive's power equipment is removed and the engine room converted to a baggage compartment. Amtrak has contracted with Conrail to recondition 26 of the most serviceable units.

Amtrak operates a fleet of 67 diesel locomotives to haul infrastructure maintenance trains and empty coaching stock. In 1995 five GP38s rebuilt by Conrail and 10 SW1000s rebuilt by National Railway Engineering were acquired, allowing Amtrak to retire a number of older units and return all leased units on the property.

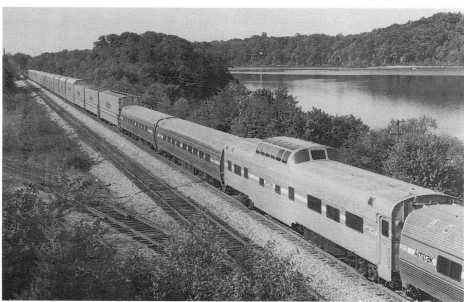

Washington DC—Florida Auto-Train; passengers ride in conventional rail vehicles, while their autos ride behind
1995

Amtrak and New York state (see 'High-speed rail projects' section) have co-operated to repower two existing Turboliner sets. The two partners have secured finance to convert all seven RTL sets at an inclusive cost of approximately $20 million (50 per cent local, 50 per cent federal money).

AMD-103

Amtrak received the first of its new 4,000 hp (2,985 kW) AMD-103 locomotives (known as the 'Genesis' fleet and also designated P40) from General Electric Transportation Systems in mid-1993, and the order for 44 units was completed in the first half of 1994.

A follow-on order for 98 additional 4,250 hp (3,170 kW) diesel-electric locomotives from General Electric was announced by Amtrak in May 1995. Designated model P42, these units will cost $255 million and replace up to 112 F40s.

The AMD-103 was tested to 185.5 km/h at the Pueblo test centre before entering revenue service at speeds up to 165 km/h. It has a monocoque carbody and bogies designed in co-operation with Krupp (now Siemens Schienenfahrzeugtechnik) of Germany. The AMD-103 also features an ergonomic cab, fuel capacity of 2,200 gallons (compared with an F40's 1,800 gallons). The P40 can be driven from its non-profiled end where there is a set of controls and a rear view window; this feature was not retained on the P42s.

A microprocessor control system monitors all subsystems, including fuel supply; the AMD-103 has been estimated to consume 15 per cent less fuel than older locomotives in the Amtrak passenger fleet. Mechanical parts are replaced via roof hatches as this is the first Amtrak locomotive type without side access to the engine compartment.

Half the units had arrived by the end of 1996; deliveries resumed in April 1997. In May 1997, the order was extended for an additional 30 units, 10 of which will be the dual-mode AMD-110 version. The first 1991-era series of GE units, the B-32 model, are being moved from California to Chicago for midwest short-haul routes, with a midlife overhaul in the Chicago shops. By the end of 1995, 10 3,200 hp (2,385 kW) dual-mode (diesel and third-rail electric) AMD-110 units had entered service, ordered to replace ageing FL9 locomotives.

F59PHI

At the start of the second quarter of 1997 Amtrak announced an order for 21 F59PHI units from GM, to be assigned to the West Coast Business Unit, for use on California 403(b) services and on Pacific northwest services.

High-performance trainsets

In April 1995 Amtrak announced the award of a contract to the Bombardier/GEC Alsthom consortium for 18 trainsets with active body-tilt, capable of 240 km/h operation, and 15 electric locomotives for use throughout the North East Corridor in conjunction with infrastructure improvements currently under way. Each 'American Flyer' trainset will consist of two power cars flanking six coaches, with a seating capacity of 345 per set; the trains will be equipped with the latest in electronic office suites and telecommunications to appeal to the business market. Total value of the contract for the rolling stock and up to three maintenance facilities is $754 million ($611 million for rolling stock only) and US/Canadian content will be 51 per cent or better. The operating contract contains significant performance specifications and penalties for failure to meet targets.

The combination of reduced journey times (New York–Boston down to 3 hours, New York–Washington to 2 hours 15 minutes) and an improved passenger environment (developed after services trials with X2000 and ICE trainsets) is expected to attract an annual increase of up to three million riders and up to $150 million in new revenues. Amtrak has contributed to a $15 million upgrade of the test track at the Association of American Railroads' Transportation Technology Center in Pueblo, Colorado, to test the American Flyer at up to 265 km/h and 12° of tilt.

Flexliner trials

In 1995 Amtrak hired two Adtranz IC/3 diesel Flexliner trainsets from Israeli Railways for two years. The trainsets were first demonstrated in Los Angeles–San Diego service. A visit to Canada followed, and at the beginning of April 1997 the sets were running as trains 301/302, the Kansas City–St Louis 'Mules'.

F40 diesel locomotives haul Amfleet single-deck cars on a '403(b)' service in California   **1995**

RoadRailer bimodal vehicle on trial with Amtrak   **1995**

Two AMD-103 units lead a P-32BH locomotive at Amtrak's 15th Street yard in Chicago (F Gerald Rawling)   **1996**

Passenger coaches

Total coaching stock at the start of 1997 was 1,730, averaging 20.7 years in service and achieving a 90 per cent availability rate.

Deliveries of 195 new Superliner II coaches from Bombardier began in early 1994 and by the end of 1996 were virtually completed. The Superliner II is basically an improved version of the original Pullman-Standard double-deck Superliner design, of which Amtrak owns 282.

Deliveries of Viewliner coaches, a new single-deck design, have been significantly behind schedule but Amerail (formerly Morrison Knudsen) had delivered 40 cars by the end of 1996. Despite the adoption of Superliner bogies, production Viewliners have cost $2 million each ($600,000 over estimate). An option for 172 additional coaches has expired and is unlikely to be exercised given the tight fiscal environment. A Viewliner sleeping car can accommodate 30 passengers in private compartments with self-contained washing and toilet facilities.

As a result of restructuring, Amtrak has been able to withdraw from service more of its Heritage (pre-1971) fleet and less than 200 such vehicles remained in service at the start of 1996. Several older passenger coaches are being stripped out and converted to baggage cars, taking advantage of their greater capacity than the current standard car.

The first series of Amfleet cars, the first new coaching stock ordered by the company, is now some 20 years old and several are being reconfigured for continuation in the North East Corridor business service. Amtrak had intended that the Viewliner coach, in several configurations, would become the standard single-deck car.

Signalling and telecommunications
New York CETC

A CETC office opened in New York in 1994, which controls interlockings from Morrisville, Pennsylvania, to New Brunswick, New Jersey. In conjunction with New Jersey Transit and Long Island Rail Road, Amtrak has commissioned a major simulation study to test operating scenarios, maximise track allocation and explore the opportunity for more through services to Penn station in New York City. The West Side Connection to the route to Albany, the Harold Avenue Connection to Long Island and two new connections to commuter lines at Kearney, New Jersey, are all controlled from the New York CETC facility; its completion has brought all of the NEC under CETC control.

Advanced signalling tests

Amtrak is participating in tests of three different advanced positive train control systems, to be carried out in conjunction with the Federal Railroad Administration. The new systems aim to allow higher operating speeds, provide increased track capacity and improve safety.

On Burlington Northern Santa Fe and Union Pacific routes in the northwest US, Amtrak is participating in trials of GE-Harris Positive Train Separation equipment in a mixed high-speed passenger/freight environment. In Illinois, the Advanced Train Control System developed in-house by the Association of American Railroads is being tested on the Chicago—St Louis route between Dwight and Springfield. In Michigan, the Incremental Train Control System developed by Amtrak and Harmon Industries is being tested on the 100 km between New Buffalo and Kalamazoo belonging to Amtrak.

Electrification
Extension to Boston

In total, 482.7 route-km of the North East Corridor is electrified at 12 kV 25 Hz AC. From New York to Boston, only the first 120.7 km as far as New Haven is at present electrified, and is mostly operable at 200 km/h.

With the financial backing of Congress, the US Department of Transportation, and the Coalition of Northeastern State Governors (CONEG) electrification is being extended from New Haven to Boston on the 25 kV 60 Hz AC system. The overall cost of the project has been estimated at $1.06 billion, with one-third of that for the electrical infrastructure and two-thirds for trackwork.

In May 1992 a contract worth approximately $300 million for the electrification component was awarded to a consortium of Morrison Knudsen, L K Comstock & Co Inc and Spie Group Inc. In light of Morrison Knudsen's then precarious financial condition, a new contract worth $321 million was signed in 1995 with a consortium of Balfour Beatty Group and Massachusetts Electrical Construction

Class	Wheel arrangement	Power kW	Speed km/h	Weight short tons	No in service	First built	Builders Mechanical	Builders Engine
Diesel locomotives								
F40PH	B-B	2,240	165	130/131	85	1976	GM	16-645 E3B
F59PHI	B-B	2,240	175	–	21	1997	EMD	12-710 G3B
FL9*	B-A1A	1,300	165	145	6	1957	GM	16-645 E
GP40H	B-B	2,240	165	132	8	1966	GM	16-645 E3B
P-32BH	B-B	2,390	165	129	18	1991	GE	FDL12
AMD-103	B-B	2,990	165	127	43	1993	GE	FDL16
AMD-103	B-B	3,135	165	127	98	1996	GE	FDL16
AMD-110DM*	B-B	2,390	175	127	10	1996	GE	FDL12
12 kV AC electric locomotives								
E60CP	C-C	3,580	145	183	2	1975	GE	
E60MA	C-C	3,580/ 3,800	145	183	11	1975	GE	
AEM-7	B-B	5,200	200	91	52	1980	GM/ASEA	

*Dual-mode: diesel & electric DC

Turboliners

Class	Cars per unit	Motor cars per unit	Motored axles/car	Power/motor kW	Speed km/h	Weight short tons	No in service	First built	Builders Mechanical	Builders Engine	Transmission
RTL	5	2	2	1 × 820 1 × 1,195	175	309	14	1976	ANF/Rohr Turmo XII	Turmo III	Voith

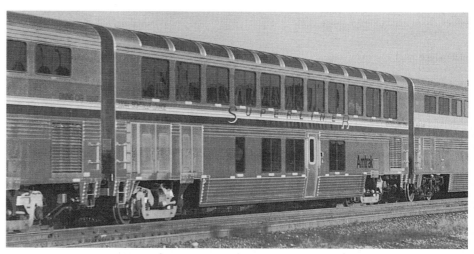

Domeliner lounge, a new model of Superliner double-deck car (F Gerald Rawling)   **1995**

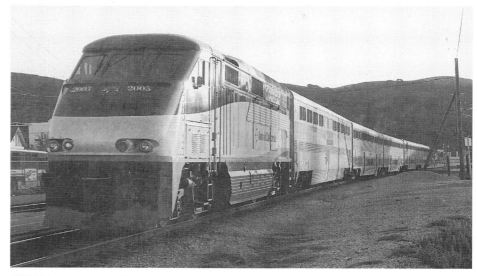

F59PHI locomotive and 'California Cars' working a Sacramento—San Jose 'Capitol' (Mick Alderman)   **1996**

Corporation; Siemens was the subcontractor responsible for substations. Work began in July 1996 and the project is now scheduled for completion by July 1999, when the best New York—Boston journey time should be cut by almost 1 hour to 3 hours or less.

Catenary renewal

In 1991, Amtrak and the Federal Railroad Administration decided to retain the 12 kV 25 Hz AC system on the southern end of the North East Corridor and spend an estimated $432 million to replace existing converters and renew/overhaul substations and catenary equipment. The alternative was to spend in excess of $540 million to convert the southern section to 25 kV 60 Hz AC.

Track
Rail: 70 kg RE
Crossties (sleepers)
Concrete: Thickness 241 mm, spacing 1,584/km
Wood: Thickness 178 mm, spacing 1,950/km
Fastenings: Concrete ties: Pandrol E2055
Wood ties: Cut spikes
Min curvature radius: 175 m (10.5°)
Max gradient: 1.9%
Max axleload: 32.88 tonne

UPDATED

Connecticut Department of Transportation

2800 Berlin Turnpike, PO Box 317546, Newington, Connecticut 06131-7546
Tel: +1 860 594 2900   Fax: +1 860 594 2913

Key personnel
Commissioner: J William Burns
Deputy Commissioner and Rail Bureau Chief:
    Harry P Harris
Rail Administrator: Lawrence J Forbes

Passenger operations
Amtrak is contracted to run an 81.4 km service between New London and New Haven, called 'Shoreline East',

serving six intermediate stations. Coaching stock consists of the 10 Pullman-Standard cars that were bought from Pittsburgh in 1990, plus 10 Bombardier Comet cars and 11 depowered Budd SPV2000 railcars that were remodelled by Amtrak's Wilmington workshops.

At the beginning of 1996 service was still basically weekday peak-only with two counter (stock positioning) movements; ridership increased during the year by 6.5 per cent to 1,185. Farebox recovery is in the range of 12 per cent. Six 3,000 hp (2,238 kW) diesel locomotives have been delivered from AMF Technotransport to improve service speeds in anticipation of overall corridor speed improvements as the result of electrification (see Amtrak entry).

The Connecticut DoT also oversees and subsidises jointly with the New York Metropolitan Transportation

Authority the New Haven line commuter service into New York operated by Metro-North (qv). Connecticut funds approximately 60 per cent of the New Haven line's operating shortfall and 63 per cent of capital costs.

ConnDot has been promoting bus shuttles to its stations to encourage 'reverse' commuting, which are now operating in Greenwich, Stamford, New Haven and Norwalk.

Overall, since 1989, the ConnDoT supported lines have seen a 121 per cent increase in intra-state commuting and an 89 per cent increase in trips 'imported' to Connecticut. ConnDoT has a $500 million capital projects 'wish list' for stations, parking, bridgework and so on — but there is no funding in place for these items at yet.

UPDATED

Dallas Area Rapid Transit

PO Box 660163, Dallas, Texas 75266
Tel: +1 214 749 3008

Key personnel
General Counsel: Roger Snoble
Vice-President, Commuter Rail & Railroad Management:
    Lonnie E Blades Jr
Commuter Rail Manager: Bonnie Duhr

Passenger operations
Dallas Area Rapid Transit (DART), in conjunction with Fort Worth Transportation Authority, introduced commuter services on a Union Pacific route to Fort Worth which is now owned by the two cities. The first stage, a 16 km three-stop service between Dallas and the South Irving Transit Center, opened on the last day of 1996; in time this service would be extended incrementally along the 54.5 km route to central Fort Worth, and to Dallas/Fort Worth International Airport, roughly halfway between the two cities, via a new 12.8 km branch from the existing infrastucture.

Traction and rolling stock
In 1995, DART sent its 13 ex-VIA RDC diesel railcars to GEC Alsthom/AMF Technotransport for rebuilding; in order to start services, DART worked with Herzog and Amtrak (for power), Amtrak and Connecticut DoT (for coaches), to create three short trainsets (one a reserve set) as a stop-gap until the RDCs arrived in the second quarter of 1997. The latest cost estimate on the RDCs is $2.5 million per rebuild. Each car seats 96.

UPDATED

Long Island Rail Road Co

93-02 Sutphin Boulevard, Jamaica Station, Jamaica, New York 11435
Tel: +1 718 558 7400   Fax: +1 718 558 8212

Key personnel
President: Thomas Prendergast
Executive Vice-President: Albert M Cosenza
Vice-Presidents
    Senior Vice-President, Operations: Thomas Waring
    Market Development and Public Affairs: Brian P Dolan
    Planning, Technology Development and Capital
    Program Management: John W Coulter Jr
Chief Engineer, Capital Program Management:
    Bruce DeVito
General Counsel and Secretary (acting): Roberta Bender
Chief Transportation Officer: James Dermody
Chief Engineer: Frederick E Smith
Chief Mechanical Officer: Hector Perez
Director, Procurement and Materials Management:
    John Hanrahan
Assistant Chief Engineers
    Signals, Communications and Power: Philip A Balkas
    Maintenance of Way: vacant

Gauge: 1,435 mm
Length: 1,120 km
Electrification: 237 km at 750 V DC third rail

Political background
Long Island Rail Road (LIRR) is a wholly owned subsidiary of the Metropolitan Transportation Authority (MTA), an agency of the State of New York, whose members constitute the railroad's board of directors.

Finance
LIRR's 1995-99 five-year plan, an element of the New York MTA's budget, calls for a $1.9 billion capital investment programme which is focusing on rolling stock renewal ($289.5 million), infrastructure maintenance ($243 million) and stations ($172 million).

Passenger operations
Passenger journeys in 1996 amounted to 74.4 million, up 1.2 per cent on 1996 and the fifth consecutive year of growth. Ridership fell by 3.5 per cent in the first quarter of 1996, possibly in reaction to a 9 per cent fare rise in Novemeber 1995, but recovered by year end.

The railroad serves the Long Island suburban counties of Nassau and Suffolk as well as certain communities in eastern Queens. It has nine branches which feed into three western terminals in New York City: Penn Station, Flatbush Avenue (Brooklyn) and Hunters Point Avenue

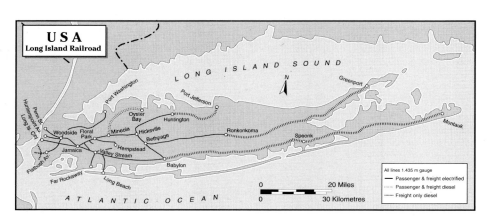

Electric railcars or multiple-units

Class	Cars per unit	Motor cars per unit	Motored axles/car	Output/motor kW	Speed km/h	No in service	First built	Builders Mechanical
M-1	2	2	4	640	129	758	1968	Budd
M-3	2	2	4	704	129	174	1984	Budd

(open only in peak hours and served only by diesel-powered trains). Penn Station handles 214,000 passengers daily; another 40,000 travel via Brooklyn and Hunters Point Avenue.

The focal point of the system is the eight-platform Jamaica station, where eight of the nine branches and the three approaches to the New York City terminals converge. During the rush hour, a train movement takes place on average every 30 seconds at Jamaica.

Freight operations
LIRR's freight division historically has produced a modest profit on a traffic volume of approximately 11,000 cars annually; it was offered for sale in early 1996. The purchaser, Anacostia & Pacific Company Inc (qv), formed the New York and Atlantic Railway subsidiary to operate the 430 km acquired, beginning in April 1997.

Improvements to existing lines
LIRR's $190 million Penn Station Improvement Project was under way in 1995, designed to improve access to, mobility through, and comfort and information in the Manhattan terminal. As a result of this project, LIRR's 214,000 daily patrons have experienced a 20 per cent increase in pedestrian space and a 40 per cent increase in access points throughout the station; five stairways, three escalators, five lifts to LIRR platforms and a new entrance on 34th Street have been provided. Other improvements

include upgraded signage and a master destination board, a new public address system, improved lighting, a customer waiting area with toilets and a climate-control system incorporating air conditioning for LIRR patrons on the concourse level.

Capacity at Penn station has been increased from 36 to 42 trains per hour. LIRR is studying access to Grand Central terminus via the 63rd Street tunnel for a further 24 trains per hour to New York City, and New York MTA has made initial funding of $50 million available to the project. Eastward extension of electrification is also under consideration.

The US Federal Highway Administration awarded LIRR, through New York DoT, a $3.9 million grant to test an Atlas (advanced train location and supervision) system, beginning with three trial locations in 1998. The partner is General Railway Signal. Full implementation by 2000 is envisaged. There are 308 grade crossings on LIRR's 1,120 km network.

Traction and rolling stock
Pending the arrival of new rolling stock in 1997, LIRR's passenger locomotive fleet comprised 28 GP38-2s of 2,000 hp (1,492 kW), 23 MP15ACs of 1,500 hp (1,119 kW) and three FL9ACs. A fleet of 13 de-engined GM F and Alco FA locomotives are used as cab control units in push-pull operation. For yard, transfer and maintenance work, LIRR operates eight SW1001

switchers of 1,000 hp (745 kW). LIRR leased seven switcher units to NY&A at the freight company's start-up.

The fleet of 1,125 passenger vehicles includes 760 Class M-1 multiple-unit cars, operated on inner suburban electrified lines in New York City, Nassau and Suffolk counties, and 174 Class M-3 cars acquired in 1984-86. Service to other points on the system is provided by diesel locomotive-hauled trains for which LIRR recently placed orders for new stock. Performance evaluation of dual-mode (diesel and third-rail electric) operation continues; LIRR runs one peak-hour train in each direction between the non-electrified Port Jefferson branch and Penn station using several of the 10 prototype Mitsui double-deck coaches between a pair of the FL9AC locomotives rebuilt by ABB Traction (now Adtranz).

New rolling stock ordered
In March 1995 LIRR awarded $250.2 million in contracts for the supply of locomotives and coaches. General Motors was to supply 23 DE30AC diesel-electric locomotives with AC transmission, in an order worth $70.7 million. Mitsui was to supply 114 double-deck coaches for push-pull operation, in an order valued at $179.5 million. The orders contained options for 23 locomotives (15 of which could be dual-mode) and 48 coaches and in 1996 a contract was placed for the supply of 10 dual-mode locomotives costing $39.5 million. Responding to local content requirements in contracts involving New York state funds, GM was to assemble the locomotives in the Schenectady area. Mitsui was to subcontract final assembly to Kawasaki Heavy Industries in Yonkers with Siemens of Germany collaborating on carbody design.

Market research has demonstrated a customer preference for 2+2 seating with wider seats to the 2+3 seating that was installed on the 10 prototypes in trial service for two years; consequently each cab car was to seat 139 rather than the 180 of the prototypes, with 145 seats in the standard coaches.

Track
Rail: 100 PS, 112, 115, 119 RE, 130
Sleepers: Wood 7 x 9 in by 8 ft 6 in, spaced 2,983/mile
Fastenings: Cut spike and Pandrol
Max curvative: 9° main line
Max gradient: 2.0%
Max permissible axleload: 33 short tons

UPDATED

Aerial view of Long Island's Caemmerer Yard on New York City's west side, used to store up to 320 cars between the morning and evening peaks

Maryland Mass Transit Administration: Maryland Rail Commuter Service (MARC)

5 Amtrak Way, PO Box 8718, BWI Airport, Maryland 21240-8718
Tel: +1 410 859 7406   Fax: +1 410 859 5713

Key personnel
Rail Administrator: Ronald L Freeland
Director of Passenger Services: Kathryn D Waters
Chief Mechanical Officer: John Kopke

Passenger operations
MARC provides Perryville—Baltimore—Washington DC services over 121.6 km of Amtrak's North East Corridor route (electrified at 12 kV 25 Hz AC) and Baltimore—Washington DC services over 61 km of CSXT. A Martinsburg—Washington DC service is provided over 116.8 km of CSXT track.

Amtrak operates the Washington—Baltimore—Perryville service with four electric locomotives and MARC's newer Japanese-built coaches. Two diesel-powered services are operated for MARC by CSXT. One is over former Baltimore & Ohio tracks between Washington's Union station and Baltimore Camden station. The other is from

GP40WH-2 locomotive rebuilt by Morrison Knudsen for MARC

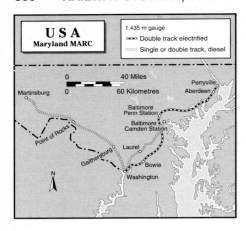

Washington to Brunswick, Maryland, and Martinsburg, West Virginia. CSX and MARC signed a five-year extension of the service contract covering 1997-2001.

MARC records about five million passenger journeys annually.

Improvements to existing lines

Federal funding has been appropriated in an amount of $13.5 million toward the total cost of extending the MARC network by 21.6 km to Frederick. The total cost of the project, including land acquisition, infrastructure improvements, stations and rolling stock has been estimated at $91.3 million

In 1996 MARC completed its first new station at Dorsey on the CSXT Washington DC—Baltimore route. Costing $5.2 million, the new station has parking space for 885 cars and its own links to the Maryland highway system. MARC has introduced limited-stop 'Speedliner' trains serving Dorsey.

Traction and rolling stock

MARC's locomotive fleet consists of four AEM7 electric locomotives; 19 GP40WH-2 (3,000 hp/2,238 kW) and six GP39-2 (2,300 hp/1,716 kW) diesel locomotives rebuilt by Morrison Knudsen. Two E9s are held in reserve.

In July 1997 MARC placed a $37.6 million order with a consortium of Bombardier and GEC Alsthom for six 200 km/h electric locomotives of the 'American Flyer' design being built for Amtrak.

The fleet of 106 coaches comprises 43 refurbished ex-New Jersey Transit vehicles and 63 coaches, including cab cars, built by Sumitomo.

In March 1995 MARC placed an order for 50 double-deck coaches, valued at $82 million, with Kawasaki Heavy Industries. Due to be delivered in 1997, the coaches were to be assembled at Kawasaki's Yonkers, New York, facility.

UPDATED

Massachusetts Bay Transportation Authority (MBTA)

10 Park Plaza, Room 5720, Boston, Massachusetts 02116
Tel: +1 617 222 3302   Fax: +1 617 222 4539

Key personnel

General Manager: Patrick J Moynihan
Director, Railroad Operations: John Brennan III
Chief Transportation Officer: Robert H Prince
Chief Finance and Administrative Officer:
   Ann O D Hartman
Chief Engineering and Maintenance Officer:
   William A MacDonald
Chief Mechanical Officer: David Diaz
Chief of Planning and Construction: Charles B Steward

Passenger operations

MBTA provides commuter service over 11 routes into Boston covering 435.9 route-km of ex-Penn Central and Boston & Maine trackage purchased in the 1970s. In 1988 the range of its services was extended along Amtrak's North East Corridor route to Providence, Rhode Island. All MBTA's services are operated by Amtrak (qv) under contract.

MBTA is also the operator of a co-ordinated network of four metro lines, five light rail lines, four trolleybus and 155 bus routes. An integrated fare system is in place allowing use of all modes, including heavy rail, with an inclusive, zone-based monthly ticket. The state of Massachusetts, directed by the governor's office, is looking into prospects for MBTA privatisation, beginning with functional areas such as revenue accounting, payroll and property management.

As of 1995, MBTA heavy rail operations were recording some 23 million passenger journeys and 675 million passenger-km a year, with revenues grossing between $40 and $45 million. The heavy rail services recover about 33 per cent of their costs from farebox revenues.

Improvements to existing lines

MBTA began operations over a 36.8 km extension of its network from Framingham to Worcester in late 1996. The project has been costed at $80 million, with the contract for infrastructure and signalling improvements awarded to Conrail.

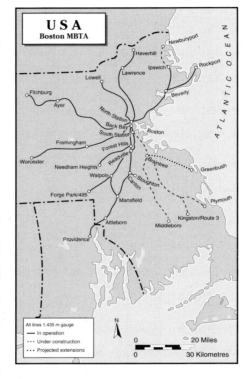

Old Colony Railroad services over three routes to Middleboro, Kingston and Scituate in southeastern Massachusetts were due to start in late 1997. This $560 million project, adding an additional 21 stations to the MBTA network, is forecast to increase arrivals at Boston's South station by the order of 15,000 passengers a day.

MBTA is receiving 23 rebuilt locomotives from the former AMF Technotransport (now owned by GEC Alsthom) and 47 remodelled ex-Pullman cars. Before entering service on Old Colony trains these were to be run in on the New England Southern (qv). The Old Colony services will use the extensively remodelled South Station which is now a major bus, taxi and metro interchange.

Several other network extensions, to both the north and south of Boston, are under study. A recent State Transportation Bond authorisation included $136 million for the development of rail projects.

Traction and rolling stock

MBTA operates 58 diesel locomotives (23 more are arriving) and 403 passenger cars. Rolling stock includes 25 F40PH-2C locomotives from GM-EMD, 18 F40PH and 12 F40PH2M locomotives remanufactured by Morrison Knudsen and one GP9 for shunting and maintenance duties. A contract worth $39.5 million was awarded to AMF Technotransport for 23 rebuilt locomotives to arrive in time for the completion of the Worcester and Old Colony projects.

The passenger coach roster includes 67 from MBB of Germany, 147 from Bombardier, 75 double-deck vehicles by Kawasaki and 58 coaches by Pullman-Standard. A further 17 Kawasaki vehicles have been ordered for 1997 delivery at a cost of $32 million and Amerail is performing mid-life overhaul on 51 Pullman-Standard vehicles for $30 million at the former MK Transit facility in Hornell, New York. A tranche of the MBB units will be reconfigured to serve as cab cars on the Old Colony lines.

MBTA has awarded a $166 million contract for the reconstruction of its Commuter Rail Maintenance Facility in Sommerville. Completion is scheduled for 1998.

Track

Rail: 65.5 kg/m
Crossties (sleepers): Wood 177.8 × 228.6 × 2,590.8 mm, spaced 2,017/km; and concrete 254 × 266.7 × 2,090.8 mm, spaced 1,641/km
Fastenings: Cut spikes with double shoulder tie plates or resilient fasteners with appropriate tie plates or adaptors
Max curvature: 13°
Max gradient: 3%
Max permissible axleload: 29.85 tonnes

UPDATED

Metra

Chicago Commuter Rail Service Board
(Northeast Illinois Regional Commuter Railroad Corporation)
547 W Jackson Blvd, Chicago, Illinois 60606
Tel: +1 312 322 6900

Key personnel

Chairman: Jeffrey R Ladd
Executive Director: Philip A Pagano
Deputy Executive Director: G Richard Tidwell
Chief Operations Officer: Vaughn L Stoner
Heads of Department
   General Administration: Dennis J Gallivan
   General Development: Gerald C Hoff
   Real Estate and Planning: Patrick McAtee
   Human Resources: Barbara Akins
   Treasury and Finance: Frank M Racibozynski

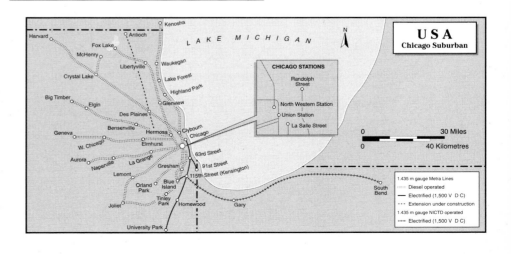

Metra diesel locomotives

Class	Builder's type	Wheel arrangement	Power kW	Speed km/h	Weight tonnes	No in service	First built	Mechanical	Builders Engine	Transmission
B32A	F40PH	B-B	2,390	142	118	28	1977	EMD	16-645E3B	E EMD
B32B/C	F40PH-2	B-B	2,390	142	118/120	86	1983	EMD	16-645E	E EMD
C32A	F40C	C-C	2,390	122	165	15	1973	EMD	16-645E	E EMD
B320	F40PHM-2	B-B	2,390	142	119	30	1991	EMD	16-645E3B	E EMD

Metra electric railcars

Class	Cars per unit	Motor cars per unit	Motored axles/car	Output/motor kW	Speed km/h	No in service	First built	Builders Mechanical	Electrical
S504A	1	1	4	120	130	8	1982	Sumitomo	GE
MA3A	1	1	4	120	121	130	1971	St Louis Car	GE
MA3B	1	1	4	120	121	35	1978	Bombardier	GE

Materials Management: Alfred Pierz
Transportation: Robert F Shive
Mechanical: Dennis D Ramm
Engineering: William K Tupper

Gauge: 1,435 mm
Route length: 335.6 km
Electrification: 98.95 km at 1.5 kV DC

Passenger operations

Metra is the commuter railroad operating arm of the Chicago Regional Transportation Authority (RTA). Its commuter rail system takes in the six counties of northeast Illinois. Including the operations conducted for Metra by Burlington Northern Santa Fe (BNSF — formerly Burlington Northern) and Union Pacific (UP — formerly Chicago & North Western) on their own infrastructure, the system embraces almost 800 route-km and 1,930 track-km, and covers most of the northeast Illinois region.

BNSF (one route) and UP (three routes) operate commuter services in the Chicago RTA area with Metra-owned equipment and under Metra direction through purchase-of-service contracts. Metra itself owns and runs the former Illinois Central (electric), Milwaukee Road and Rock Island services with its own train crews and equipment; since June 1993 it has operated the Norfolk Southern line to Orland Park, now called Southwest Service, under long-term lease. There are also two trains each way daily between Chicago and Joliet on the Illinois 'Central Heritage Corridor' route.

Total ridership in 1996 was 73,366,000, up 0.3 per cent

on 1995. On-time performance was reported at 97.3 per cent overall.

Improvements to existing lines

In August 1996 Metra introduced commuter service to the Wisconsin Central route from Franklin Park (on Metra's Chicago—Elgin line) to Antioch via nine intermediate stations. All-in start-up costs have totalled $119 million, including $13 million from non-Metra sources for land acquisition, stations and parking facilities. The 85 km line — now called the North Central service — has been equipped with electronic CTC and welded rail throughout, allowing operation at up to 95 km/h from the start.

Three daily return workings were to be provided initially on the Franklin Park—Antioch route, operating towards Chicago in the morning and outbound in the evening, with one midday cycle. Antioch serves the expanding commuter market from counties in southern Wisconsin contiguous to Illinois. The introduction of Metra service has required the installation or extension of five passing loops and annual ridership, presently 3,400, is forecast at 5,400 by the end of 1998. To accommodate 18 daily commuter services as proposed, the route would have to be double-tracked at an additional cost of $35 million, as Wisconsin Central freight traffic (including coal and ore in bulk) is now above 35 million annual tonnes (whereas it was little more than 1 million when Wisconsin Central was formed).

In response to rising demand, four trains were added on the Orland Park route. A new yard was opened at 179th

Street in Orland Park in 1996, when work began to install several sections of double track on the route.

Metra is a partner in evaluating the potential for commuter service on three routes: (a) the Aurora—Mundelein segment of the Elgin, Joliet & Eastern (qv) belt line; (b) an orbital route linking O'Hare and Midway airports using CSXT, Belt Railway of Chicago and Indiana Harbor Belt trackage; and (c) on the CSX line south to Beecher.

Capital programme

Metra's 1997 capital programme is set at $133 million. Included are $8 million for locomotive rehabilitation; $12 million for bilevel car rehabilitaiton; $24.5 million for bridges; $14.5 million for stations; most of the balance for track and signals.

The 1996 programme totalled $143 million but included the extraordinary expenses related to Wisconsin Central start-up.

Traction and rolling stock

At the end of 1996 Metra owned 129 diesel locomotives for revenue service, plus 175 electric railcars and 700 push-pull passenger coaches. A further nine locomotives are available for non-revenue services.

Highliner electric multiple-unit cars rebuilt by Amerail so as to be accessible to the disabled have been entering service on the Illinois Central route since the start of 1994; by mid-1997 the order was close to complete. By the end of 1996 the Rock Island and South West Service trains were accessible and the first cars were in service on the Milwaukee District lines.

For the introduction of its Franklin Park—Antioch service in August 1996, Metra performed a major rehabilitation of coaches in its own workshops.

Track
Rail: 115, 119, 131, 132, 136 lb/yd
Crossties (sleepers): Wood
Thickness: 7 × 9 in
Spacing: 1,988/km
Fastenings: Rail anchors
Max curvature: 7° 26′
Max gradient: 1.75%
Max axleload: 65,000 lb

UPDATED

Metro-North Railroad Co

347 Madison Avenue, 4th Floor, New York, New York 10017
Tel: +1 212 340 3000   Fax: +1 212 340 4037
Website: http://www.mta.nyc.ny.us

Key personnel
MTA Chairman: E Virgil Conway
MTA Executive Director: Marc V Shaw
President and General Manager, Metro-North:
    Donald N Nelson

Executive Vice-President: Genevieve T Firnhaber
Vice-Presidents
    Operations: George F Walker
    Planning and Development: Howard Permut
Assistant Vice-President, Operations: George F Walker
Chief Mechanical Officer: G Robert Bott
Director, Infrastructure Maintenance: Robert Lieblong

Gauge: 1,435 mm
Route length: 428 km
Staff: 5,393
Electrification: Hudson and Harlem lines (139 km), 600 V

DC third rail; New Haven line (116 km), 11 kV 60 Hz AC overhead

Organisation
Metro-North is one of five operating divisions of New York's Metropolitan Transportation Authority (MTA).

Finance
Revenue from passengers and other income totalled $300.4 million in 1996 (compared to $287.1 million in 1995) which was 58.7 per cent of expenses. On the New Haven line this figure reaches 66 per cent. Targets for Metro-North have been set at 62.3 per cent in 1997 and 64.6 per cent by 1998. There have been no fare increases on Metro-North in two years (but in Connecticut fares have gone up 9.5 per cent in the same interval). The MTA's internal cost control programme requires $3 billion in reduced expenses and $1.5 billion in increased revenue in the span of the 1995-99 five-year plan. Among other contributions, Metro-North has pared its employee total by 10 per cent.

Metro-North's capital investment programme is included in the overall MTA budget. Since 1983, Metro-North has expended $3 billion out of MTA's $22 billion. The 1995-97 Metro-North capital programme amounted to $12 billion.

Passenger operations
Metro-North's three main lines that run north out of New York City and east of the Hudson river are the Hudson, the Harlem and the New Haven lines. These three routes operate out of New York's Grand Central Terminal.

Service on the 158.4 km, 29-station New Haven line and its New Canaan, Danbury and Waterbury branches totalling 95.6 km, and 17 stations is provided by Metro-North pursuant to a contract between the Connecticut Department of Transportation (ConnDoT) and MTA/Metro-North. Stamford is the busiest station, boarding almost 5,000 passengers per weekday and receiving

M6 emu for New Haven line service

1995

2,100 arrivals. At New Haven connection is made with ConnDoT's Shoreline service which runs to New London. Capital improvements in Connecticut are funded by ConnDoT, which owns the infrastructure.

Metro-North also provides services west of the Hudson in the New York state counties of Orange and Rockland on the Port Jervis and Pascack Valley lines; trains on these lines run out of the Hoboken terminal on the New Jersey shore of the Hudson. These services are operated by New Jersey Transit (qv) under contract to Metro-North, which assigns part of its rolling stock fleet to NJT.

On the three main lines (Hudson, Harlem and New Haven), total passenger journeys in 1996 were 61.6 million. This was the highest figure recorded since 1945 and the sixth consecutive increase. Growth is occurring in weekend travel and reverse commuting, up 3.6 per cent and 6 per cent respectively, while the more traditional commuter market into New York City is essentially flat.

Improvements to existing lines
In 1996, Metro-North built its first new station since 1983, at Cortland, on the Hudson line, at a cost of $11 million, including parking. A further $9.6 million was spent on four major station upgrades on the Dover Plains line.

During 1996 Metro-North intended to install 45,000 concrete sleepers at a cost of $23 million, bringing the total made out of this material to 230,000 (13 per cent of the system's sleepers). For 1997, the target was a further 85,000 concrete sleeper installations, plus 35,000 replacement timber sleepers and 360 km of track resurfacing.

Two major items in Metro-North's 1995-97 capital investment programme were an estimated $175 million to rehabilitate Grand Central Terminal in New York City (for which $63 million was earmarked in 1995-96 with completion in stages into 1998) plus a revised estimate of $120 million for improvements to its elevated Park Avenue approach. Phase I of mechanical and electrical work was completed in 1995 on this 3.2 km viaduct, which carries 530 trains per day.

Design work has begun on an 8 km extension of the Harlem line beyond its current terminus at Dover Plains to Wassaic for opening in 1997 or 1998. A third track on the middle section of the Harlem line (between Mount Vernon and Crestwood) is planned as soon as environmental clearances are secured. This is currently estimated to cost $41 million.

Traction and rolling stock
At the end of 1995 resources comprised three electric and 48 diesel locomotives (10 of which are owned by ConnDoT), 683 emus and 88 conventional coaches (of which 30 are owned by ConnDoT). An additional eight locomotives are assigned to west of Hudson services and numbered in with NJ Transit rosters.

The majority of Metro-North's passenger cars serving the third rail electrified Hudson and Harlem lines are emus of Types M-1, M-2 and the most recent tranche of 54 M-6 three-car emus, which were delivered by Tokyu Car in 1987. As part of a major overhaul programme, 22 M-2 emus received attention in 1995, and a similar number was overhauled in 1996; the programme continues under outside contract while some M-1s, some M-3s and some Bombardier coaches were overhauled in-house.

Non-electrified lines are worked by locomotive-hauled trains, using a variety of diesel traction including FL9 electro-diesels equipped with third rail pick-up shoes for operating into Grand Central Terminal. Seven FL9s have been modernised: they have been rebuilt by ABB (now Adtranz) as FL9AC units with three-phase AC traction motors and a 3,200 hp (2,387 kW) EMD engine.

Five 3,200 hp (2,387 kW) P32AC-DM Genesis electro-diesel locomotives ordered from General Electric entered service in the third quarter of 1995 and a further seven are on order, costing $30 million, for 1998 delivery. In 1996, Bombardier completed an order for 34 passenger coaches valued at $41.5 million. Final assembly was undertaken at Plattsburgh, New York, and an option for a further 15 vehicles for 1997 delivery was exercised. Some of the new coaches are being allocated to services west of the Hudson, together with two new locomotives for which Metro-North was awaiting MTA purchase authority in 1997. Metro-North has contracted for design specifications for a coach body which can be built as either a conventional coach or an emu.

Future orders
In 1997, Metro-North was awaiting MTA approval to purchase a further 20 coaches from Bombardier and a third order for dual-mode locomotives. The new rolling stock would replace FL9 units and coaches dating from 1962. After extensive analysis, Metro-North concluded that a strategy of buying locomotives and coaches was more flexible and more cost-effective than replacing emus in kind. In recent years, Metro-North's emu fleet has been taxed by adverse weather conditions (including a 50-year record snowfall in the 1996-97 winter) and several power failures. However, Metro-North has continued to study the potential for adopting electric locomotives and double-deck coaches.

Maintenance
Heavy rolling stock repairs are undertaken at Croton-Harmon, while running repairs can also be carried out at Brewster and North White Plains. Some component repair is performed by outside contractors. There is a running repair facility at New Haven, Connecticut, for M-2, M-4 and M-6 emus. ConnDoT has funded the construction of an overhaul workshop in New Haven and a new maintenance and repair facility at Stamford.

For track, signalling, and electrification maintenance work, Metro-North operates a fleet of over 150 wagons and six GP35R locomotives rebuilt by Conrail's Altoona workshops.

Signalling and telecommunications
In 1991 Metro-North completed installation of CTC (centralised traffic control), cab signalling and ATC (automatic train control) throughout its main line system; this had been phased in over nine years for an outlay of $82.7 million. A new command centre, designed and built by GRS, has been completed on the sixth floor of Grand Central Terminal.

The only remaining segments without cab signalling are the single-track Danbury and Waterbury branches, and the Brewster North—Dover Plains section of the Harlem line. Metro-North dispatches for Amtrak and freight activity as far as New Haven.

Track
Rail: 119 RE and 132 RE predominantly, some 140 and 127

Crossties (sleepers): 7 × 9 in × 8 ft 6 in

Spacing: 1,968/km for wood ties; 1,640/km for concrete

Fastenings: Tie plates and cut spike for wood; Pandrol clips for concrete and some wood

Min curvature radius: 109 m

Max gradient: 3%

Max axleload: E72 loading for track design

UPDATED

Electric railcars or multiple-units

Class	Cars per unit	Line voltage	Motor cars per unit	Motored axles/car	Output/motor kW	Speed km/h	No in service	First built	Builders Mechanical	Builders Electrical
M-1	2	600 DC	2	4	110	160	178	1971	Budd	GE
M-2	2	600 DC and 12.5 kV AC	2	4	120	160	242	1973	GE	GE
M-3	2	600 DC	2	4	120	160	142	1982	Budd	GE
M-4	3	600 DC and 12.5 kV AC	2	4	120	160	54	1987	Tokyu Car	GE
M-6	3	700 DC and 13.2 kV AC	3	4	120	160	48	1993	Morrison Knudsen	GE
ACMU	1	600 DC	1	4	75	120	61	1962	Pullman-Standard	GE

Push-pull locomotive powered single coaches

Class	Speed km/h	Weight short tons	No in service	First built	Builder
Shoreliner Coach	160	45.5	136	1985	Bombardier

Diesel and electrodiesel locomotives (with third-rail pick-up shoes)

Class	Wheel arrangement	Power kW	Speed km/h	Weight short tonnes	No in service	First built	Mechanical	Builders Engine	Transmission
FL9	Bo-A1A	1,340	143	141	27	1957	EMD	GM 567 C	E EMD
FL9AC	Bo-A1A	2,310	160	137.5	7	1993	ABB	GM 710G3	E EMD
P32AC-DM	Bo-Bo	2,390	160	na	5	1995	GE	GE	E GE
F10A	Bo-Bo	1,300	130	125	4	1979 R	EMD	GM 567	E EMD
GP35R	Bo-Bo	1,490	110	131	6	1994 R	EMD	GM 567	E EMD
GP7u	Bo-Bo	1,120	105	124.5	1	1953	EMD	GM 567 C	E EMD
GP9	Bo-Bo	1,300	105	125.5	1	1955	EMD	GM 567 C	E EMD
GP40 FH2*	Bo-Bo	2,240	169	128.1	7	1988 92R	EMD/MK; EMD/CR	GM 16 645	E EMD

R year of rebuilding
* in New Jersey service

Electric locomotives

Class	Wheel arrangement	Line voltage	Output kW	Speed km/h	Weight tonnes	No in service	First built	Builders Mechanical	Builders Electrical
E10B	Bo-Bo	600 DC	745	50	126	3	1952	GE	GE

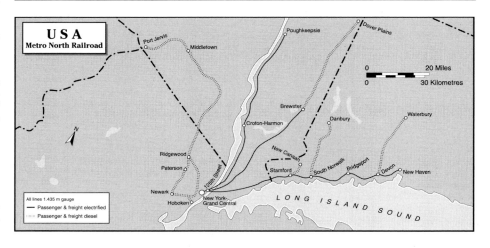

USA
Metro North Railroad

All lines 1.435 m gauge
— Passenger & freight electrified
⋯⋯ Passenger & freight diesel

New Jersey Transit Rail Operations Inc

One Penn Plaza East, Newark, New Jersey 07105 2246l
Tel: +1 201 491 7000   Fax: +1 201 491 8218

Key personnel
Executive Director: Shirley A DeLibero
Vice-President and General Manager of Rail Operations:
  Robert A Randall
Deputy General Manager, Hoboken Division
Operations: William R Knapp
Deputy General Manager, Infrastructure Engineering:
  Alison Conway-Smith
Deputy General Manager, Support Operations:
  Michael J Rienzi
Director, System Operations: James V Samuelson
Acting Assistant General Manager, Administration:
  Edward C McGittigan
Assistant General Manager, Contracts and Capital
  Programs: D C Agrawal
Chief Financial Officer: Charles Wedel

Gauge: 1,435 mm
Route length, owned: 513.4 km
Trackage rights: 231.5 km
Electrification, owned: 107.6 km at 25 kV 60 Hz AC;
26.4 km at 12 kV 25 Hz AC; 25.4 km at 12 kV 60 Hz AC
Trackage rights: 93.5 km at 12 kV 25 Hz AC

Passenger operations
New Jersey Transit (NJT) Rail carries 46.7 million passengers for 950 million passenger-miles annually over nine routes into Newark, Hoboken and New York City. Rail ridership in 1996 was 2.9 per cent up on 1994. There has not been a fare increase since 1990; overall, NJT fares (rail, bus and contracted services) cover 54 per cent of expenses. NJT Rail employs train crews, owns rolling stock and much of its network infrastructure (except Conrail and Amtrak routes), together with 145 stations. Weekday revenue trains operated total 591. NJ Transit (meaning commuter rail, bus and rail transit combined) lost $19.6 million in FY95-96, largely as a result of decreasing federal and state operating subsidies.

On the Jersey Coast line from New York Penn Station to Bay Head Junction, NJT operates its 'Jersey Arrow' electric multiple-units (as far as Long Branch) and trains hauled by GP40PH-2, GP40PH-2B, F40PH-2, and GP40FH-2 diesels. At weekends, diesel-powered trains

Arrow III cars being refurbished in ABB's plant at Elmira Heights, New York **1995**

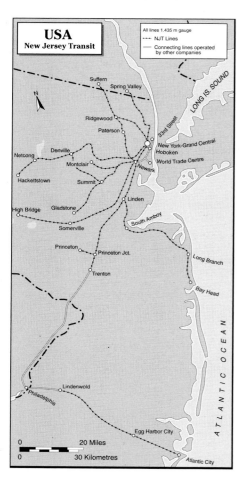

from Bay Head terminate at Long Branch where passengers transfer to emu services.

The North East Corridor service from Penn Station to Trenton and the branch to Princeton is provided by 'Arrow' emus. Services on the Raritan Valley line from Newark are powered by a range of new and rebuilt GM locomotive types (qv) and in 1994 was extended 13 km to a new terminus at Hackettstown.

The Morris and Essex lines, rewired to 25 kV AC in 1984, are operated principally with emus; some diesel-powered trains also run. As part of the major restructuring of services in association with the opening of the Kearny connection, push-pull trainsets powered by new ALP44 locomotives were introduced.

The Boonton, Port Jervis and Pascack Valley lines are served by diesel push-pull trains. Because the Port Jervis and Pascack Valley routes both extend into New York state, compatible equipment supplied by Metro-North (qv) is deployed alongside NJT stock.

Atlantic City services
Introduced in 1989, this service was extended into Philadelphia in 1993; it had previously terminated at Lindenwold for a metro connection to the city centre. In 1994 Amtrak pulled out of the Atlantic City market altogether and NJT rescheduled its service to provide all-day coverage. The service is run with a small fleet of five diesel locomotives and 18 coaches which are kept at Amtrak's yard north of 30th Street station. This service to Atlantic City continues to lose money out of proportion to other NJT rail services.

Improvements to existing lines
NJT's inclusive (all modes) 1995 capital investment programme was its largest to date at $623 million; the

1996 budget was $610 million. Each year's programme includes installation of continuously welded rail; renewal and rehabilitation of NJT's 622 bridges; and renewal of signalling and telecommunications infrastructure. Other recent areas of major expenditure include station renovation and improvements.

NJ Transit has continued to make significant progress in advancing major rail projects that will enable the state of New Jersey to meet forecast increases in demand through the 1990s and beyond 2000. Among these is the $69 million Kearny Connection project that in June 1996 was completed to link the Morris and Essex lines with the North East Corridor. This service is now marketed under the brand name MidTOWN DIRECT and already attracts 6,000 weekday riders. The connection enables through services to reach Penn Station in Manhattan, instead of terminating at Hoboken on the New Jersey shore of the Hudson, where a transfer to ferries or the PATH metro is necessary to reach Manhattan. In September 1996 the MidTOWN DIRECT service was extended to weekends also.

Design work has also continued on the Bay Street Connection, a link between the end of the Montclair branch (on the Morris and Essex line) to the Boonton line; this would allow Boonton services to gain access to the Kearny Connection and would permit closure of the southern end of the Boonton line into Hoboken.

The consortium of rail projects together is called the Urban Core Programme, which has been substantially supported by the US Congress and the FTA (qv).

Capacity at Penn Station
In conjunction with Amtrak, NJT has continued with design work to increase train frequency into New York City's Penn Station and raise total station capacity at peak

Electric locomotives

Class	Wheel arrangement	Output kW	Speed km/h	Weight tonnes	No in service	First built	Builders Mechanical	Electrical
ALP44	Bo-Bo	4,320	201	92.5	32	1990	ABB	ABB

Electric railcars or multiple-units

Class	Cars per unit	Motored axles/car	Output/motor kW	Speed km/h	No in service	First built	Builders Mechanical	Electrical
Arrow II	2	4	120	160	34*	1974	GE-AVCO	GE
Arrow III	2				91	1976	GE-AVCO	GE
Arrow III	1				29	1976	GE-AVCO	GE

*Arrow II withdrawals to start in 1997

Diesel locomotives

Class	Wheel arrangement	Power kW	Speed km/h	Weight tonnes	No in service	First built	Builders Mechanical	Engine	Transmission
GP40PH-2	Bo-Bo	2,238	169	133.8	13	1968	EMD	16-645 E3B	E EMD D77
F40PH-2	Bo-Bo	2,238	169	118.6	17	1996R	EMD/CR	16-645 E3B	E EMD D77
GP40FH-2	Bo-Bo	2,238	169	128.1	21	1987-1990*	EMD/MK	16-645 E3	E EMD D77
GP40FH-2	Bo-Bo	2,238	169	128.1	19	1994R	EMD/CR	16-645 E3	E EMD D77

* year of rebuild

periods from 20 to 30 trains. Work has included the design and construction of a new high-speed signalling system as well as improvements in and around Penn Station to accommodate increased passenger movements.

STV Consultants have been engaged in a large-scale simulation study of track occupancy between Newark and Jamaica on Long Island, involving the timetables of NJT, Long Island Rail Road and Amtrak. The study includes the routes to Spuyten Duyvil in the Empire Corridor and to New Rochelle in the North East Corridor. The instrument of analysis has been a family of software programs from Comreco and built around their RailPlan module.

Secaucus Transfer
Ground was broken in 1995 on this station (also part of the Urban Core Project) that will create a major New Jersey public transport interchange embracing all of NJT's north New Jersey lines. The multilevel facility, to be located in the Jersey Meadowlands (and estimated to cost $448 million by completion), will facilitate connections to Manhattan's Penn Station from all three lines in New Jersey that presently terminate in Hoboken. An

interchange is preferred to a direct rail connection as the north New Jersey lines are diesel-worked and only electric rolling stock is permitted in Penn Station. Services to Newark, the Jersey Coast, Trenton and Amtrak destinations will also be available via Secaucus.

New York, Susquehanna & Western
A proposed passenger service on the New York Susquehanna & Western railroad continues to be the subject of a consultant's planning and environmental impact study. The new service would call at Secaucus Transfer and diverge from the NJT Bergen line at Hawthorne to run into northern New Jersey or southern New York. Strategies for implementation have become increasingly complex as levels of freight traffic over the relatively basic infrastructure in question have increased significantly since the concept was first developed and have been further complicated by the jockeying for access to the New York-Northern New Jersey freight market as a by-product of the Conrail break-up.

Traction and rolling stock
At the end of 1995 NJT operated 28 electric and 78 diesel

locomotives, 300 emu cars and 389 other passenger coaches.

Recent items of major expenditure have included a futher 17 ALP44 electric locomotives (NJT had puchased 15 in 1990) to replace E60CP units. NJT has also ordered 96 Bombardier Comet IV model push-pull coaches to replace older Arrow II emus and these began arriving in 1997. NJT also spent $10.5 million to overhaul and upgrade some of its diesel locomotives.

Track
Rail: New rail standard 132 lb/yd (65.5 kg/m)
Crossties (sleepers): Hardwood
Thickness: Main lines 178 × 229 mm, yards 152 × 203 mm
Spacing: Running lines 1,989/km; yards 1,802/km
Fastenings: 152 mm cut spike, drive-on rail anchors
Min curvature radius: Running lines 194 m, yards 122 m
Max axleload: 20 tonnes at unrestricted speed; locomotives to 32.7 tonnes at restricted speed

UPDATED

Northern Indiana Commuter Transportation District

33 E US Highway 12, Chesterton, Indiana 46304
Tel: +1 219 926 5744   Fax: +1 219 929 4438

Key personnel
Chairman: vacant
General Manager: Gerald R Hanas
Chief Operating Officer: Kenneth R Peterson
Chief Counsel: Bjarne R Henderson
Chief Financial Officer: Dario M Brezene

Passenger operations
Following sale of the Chicago SouthShore & South Bend Railroad, Northern Indiana Commuter Transportation District (NICTD) took over full responsibility for its passenger services between Chicago and South Bend. From Chicago to Kensington operation is over Metra's electrified Illinois Central route. In 1993 a 1 km extension was opened to South Bend Airport.

NICTD owns 109.3 route-km, leases 20.2 route-km and has trackage rights over 22.9 km. Electrification at 1.5 kV DC overhead covers 141.4 km. Annual ridership is 3.3 million; the line continues to attract latent demand such that peak-hour trains average 110 per cent of seat capacity. Income from all sources including fares was $19.8 million in 1996, against expenses of $24.9 million. NICTD employs 280 people.

Improvements to existing lines
NICTD's capital investment programme for the near term involves continued improvements to infrastructure, especially stations, parking facilities and catenary. In 1996 the Dune Park station parking lot was enlarged and a new station building opened in Hammond, to complement the expanded parking there (1995). As of

NICTD train leaving Chicago (F Gerald Rawling)   *1995*

1996, 95 per cent of NICTD lines are laid with continuous welded rail.

In 1995, NICTD bought 7.7 km of CSXT right-of-way south from Hammond and secured an injunction to preserve the assets in place. Congressional funding has been promised for a major investment study concerning the introduction of NICTD passenger service to the route. One school of thought has advocated electrification and trainsets leaving/joining Chicago—South Bend services at Hammond, rather than the acquisiton of a small diesel-powered fleet.

Traction and rolling stock
NICTD operates a fleet of 48 Nippon Sharyo electric railcars and 10 trailers ordered through Sumitomo in two batches delivered in 1982-83 and 1992. Each power car has four GE 104 kW traction motors and maximum speed is 120 km/h. NICTD has built an extension to its Michigan City workshops for mid-life overhauls of the first batch.

UPDATED

North San Diego County Transit Development Board

311 South Tremont Street, Oceanside, California 92054
Tel: +1 619 967 2828   Fax: +1 619 967 0941

Key personnel
Executive Director: Richard L Fifer
General Manager: David C Wine
Manager, Rail Services: Betty Laurs

Passenger operations
In February 1995 North San Diego County Transit Development Board (NCTD) began operating its Coast Rail Express or 'Coaster' service over a 67.2 km San

Diego—Oceanside route. NCTD purchased 134 km of Santa Fe right-of-way between Oceanside and San Diego (including an Oceanside—Escondido branch which is being considered for a light rail) and continues to make capital improvements including six new and two remodelled stations, parking areas, passing loops and upgraded signalling.

Amtrak is the designated operator of Coast Rail Express under a five-year contract; the track is shared with its Los Angeles—San Diego services and Burlington Northern Santa Fe freight trains. Initial Coast Rail Express service comprised five trains to San Diego and one in the other direction at each weekday peak. In May 1995 a late evening train was added; in June a midday train was added. By February 1996 daily ridership had risen from

1,800 to 3,000. The target, after all the capital projects are on stream, is 4,200.

Traction and rolling stock
Bombardier supplied 16 double-deck push-pull coaches (eight cab cars and eight trailers) for the service, and Morrison Knudsen delivered five F40PHM-2C locomotives. An order was placed in 1996 for five more coaches from Bombardier. NCTD has begun design work for a rolling stock stabling facility at Stuart, 8 km north of Oceanside.

UPDATED

Peninsula Corridor Joint Powers Board

PO Box 3006, 1250 San Carlos Avenue, San Carlos, California 94070-1306
Tel: +1 415 508 6200   Fax: +1 415 508 6365

Key personnel
Executive Director: Gerald T Haugh
Director, Rail Services: Jerome Kirzner
Manager of Operations: Walt Stringer

Organisation
In 1992 the Peninsula Corridor Joint Powers Board, a three-county agency, purchased the 75.6 km Southern Pacific main line from San Francisco to San Jose for

$242.3 million. This is a long-standing commuter route previously operated under the sponsorship of the California Department of Transportation (CalTrans). There were options to purchase additional trackage on three branches (including the Tracy branch and its Dumbarton Bridge over San Francisco Bay) and an additional 40.9 km of line south to Gilroy. Amtrak was awarded the contract to operate the line; management is provided for the board by the San Mateo County Transit District. Amtrak's contract has been extended through to 2000 with a fixed price formula designed to contain cost overruns.

Passenger operations

The Peninsula commuter service, marketed as CalTrain, comprises a weekday service of 30 San Francisco–San Jose return trains. Four of these trains in each direction serve Gilroy beyond San Jose. Under a 10-year plan, service levels are to rise to over 100 trains a day. Weekday ridership averages 24,400, of which 600 presently comes from the San Jose–Gilroy section. Annual journeys exceeded 7.7 million in 1996, which was 8 per cent up on the previous year.

There are 34 stations, including an interchange facility at Tamien, 2 miles south of central San Jose, served by Santa Clara County's light rail system.

Bicycle accommodations

CalTrain market research has established that 9 per cent of passengers cycle to the station, and about 1,100 then use their bikes from station to work. CalTrain continues to install racks and lockers (now 700) at stations and is examining the on-train limit (presently 24).

Improvements to existing lines

The Joint Powers Board favours a long-term plan to relocate its San Francisco terminus to Beale and Market

CalTrain San Francisco—Gilroy service at Millbrae (Mick Alderman)   **1996**

Streets to connect with the city's light rail, metro, ferry, cable car and bus services. A conservative estimate for a project of this scope is in the order of $600 to $650 million.

The Muni light rail underground system is being extended to the current terminal at 4th & Townsend, providing improved service integration until such time as an extension of the commuter line can be engineered.

Traction and rolling stock

Services are operated with 20 3,200 hp (2,385 kW) F40PH locomotives from GM-EMD and 73 double-deck gallery coaches from Nippon Sharyo. The coaches include 21 push-pull cab control trailers. The F40PH units are configured for a maximum speed of 134 km/h.

The capital programme includes $31 million for up to 20 cars plus $7.5 million for three locomotives. The original 20 locomotives are approaching mid-life remanufacture. The Board is also studying the construction of a facility to perform heavy maintenance on all rolling stock. Late in 1996 a start was made on installing continuous welded rail on 10 km of double track.

UPDATED

Southeastern Pennsylvania Transportation Authority (SEPTA)

Sovereign Building, 714 Market Street, Philadelphia, Pennsylvania 19106
Tel: +1 215 580 4000   Fax: +1 215 580 5849

Regional Rail Division
1515 Market Street, 6th Floor, Philadelphia, Pennsylvania 19102
Tel: +1 215 580 5858

Key personnel
Chairman: Thomas M Hayward
Chief Operating Officer and General Manager:
John K Leary
Deputy General Manager: Howard H Roberts Jr
Assistant General Manager, Railroad: Michael T Burns

Gauge: 1,435 mm
Route length: 902 km
Electrification: 902 km at 12 kV 25 Hz AC

Passenger operations

SEPTA operates a multimodal network of public transport services throughout the five-county region of southeastern Pennsylvania. The commuter rail portion consists of 13 electrified lines radiating from Philadelphia.

The present Regional Rail system was formed in 1984 when the commuter lines formerly operated by the Pennsylvania and Reading railroads were linked by a four-track connection beneath central Philadelphia. SEPTA operates seven routes over tracks owned by SEPTA, Amtrak and Conrail. Connections are made with Amtrak and New Jersey Transit services.

In 1989, SEPTA extended service 15.5 route-km over Amtrak's North East Corridor to Wilmington, Delaware, under contract to the Delaware Transportation Authority. SEPTA continues to test the market for dedicated feeder bus routes from suburban stations to employment centres.

Livable Cities initative

In the largest single application of an FTA Livable Cities grant, the Beaux Arts station at Chester will be restored by mid-1999 at a cost of $7.5 million, to be a civic locus and public transport interchange for the current 4,300 riders.

Traction and rolling stock

The Regional Rail service is operated chiefly by a fleet of

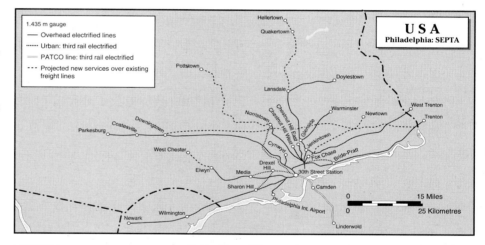

AEM7 electric locomotive with push-pull train   **1995**

Electric railcars or multiple-units

Class	Cars per unit	Motor cars per unit	Motored axles/car	Output/motor kW	Speed km/h	No in service	First built	Builders Mechanical	Electrical
Silverliner 2	1	1	4	110	135	36	1963	Budd	GE
Silverliner 2	1	1	4	110	135	17	1964	Budd	GE
Silverliner 3	1	1	4	110	135	20	1967	St Louis Car Co	GE
Silverliner 4	1	1	4	140	150	47	1974-75	GE	GE
Silverliner 4	2	2	4	140	150	184	1975-76	GE	GE

304 Silverliner electric multiple-unit cars. United Products Corporation was to refurbish the interiors of 231 Silverliner 4 cars under a contract valued at $14 million.

In 1987 SEPTA acquired seven AEM7 electric locomotives, featuring ABB (now Adtranz) electrical equipment and assembled by Bombardier to the GM/ ASEA design originally developed for Amtrak. A fleet of 35 passenger coaches was acquired from Bombardier at the same time, operated as seven five-car push-pull trainsets with the AEM7 locomotives.

Traffic (million)	1994	1995
Total passenger journeys	20.8	22.6

Finance (US$ million)	1994	1995
Revenue	61.55	70.20

Expenditure	1994	1995
Staff/personnel	96.07	—
Materials and services	49.92	—
Traction power	15.46	—
Other	3.58	—
Total	165.03	167.12

Type of coupler in standard use: N2A (emus) Tightlock Knuckle (push-pull cars)

Type of braking in standard use: 26C, PS68
Brake air and blended rheostatic (Silverliner 4 cars)

Track
Rail: 140 PS and RE, 132 RE, 131 RE, 130 REHF, 115 RE, 112 RE, 107 NH, 100 PS
Crossties (sleepers): Wood, thickness 175 × 200 mm
Spacing: 530 mm
Fastenings: Pandrol and spike
Min curvature radius: 125 m
Max gradient: 1 in 25

UPDATED

Southern California Regional Rail Authority

817 West Seventh Street, 7th Floor, Los Angeles, California 90017
Tel: +1 213 623 1194   Fax: +1 213 489 1469

Key personnel
Executive Director: Richard M Stanger
Deputy Executive Director: David Solow
Director, Operations: William Currier
Director, Equipment: William Lydon
Director, Engineering and Construction: David Boger
Director, Marketing and External Affairs:
   Adrienne Brooks-Taylor
Director, Finance and Passenger Services:
   Annette Colfax

Political background
In October 1992 the first three lines of a planned 650 km commuter rail system for the Los Angeles region came into operation. Start-up became practical after the Southern California Regional Rail Authority (SCRRA), which is co-ordinating the new services, purchased 544 km of right-of-way from Santa Fe in 1992; Santa Fe (now Burlington Northern Santa Fe) retained trackage rights for freight.

SCRRA serves five counties in the Los Angeles basin, which together have a population of 15.6 million. Because the area has been falling well short of targets set by the National Ambient Air Quality Standards, the elimination of car journeys is a major element of performance analysis for SCRRA's rail services. Ridership levels attained by late 1996 were claimed to represent 12,200 car journeys removed from the roads.

Passenger operations
Branded 'Metrolink', the first services introduced in 1992

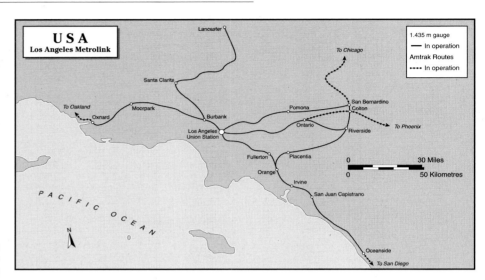

covered lines from Los Angeles Union Station to Moorpark (Ventura line), Montclair (San Bernardino line) and Santa Clarita (Santa Clarita line). Two lines were added in 1993: the Riverside line on the Union Pacific and the Orange County line to Oceanside; 17.4 km of route on the latter line has been double- or triple-tracked through Fullerton and Santa Ana.

A major project getting under way in 1997 is the rehabilitation of the 2.25 km single-track tunnel between Chatsworth and Simi Valley. Engineering will cost $1.2 million, implying a construction cost in the $12 to 15 million range.

In October 1995 Metrolink services were introduced between Riverside and Irvine via Anaheim and Santa Ana. At the start of 1996 the system comprised routes totalling

554 km and serving 42 stations. In the 12 months up to 30 June 1995, total passenger journeys were 4.4 million, a 33 per cent increase on the previous year. Fare income was $16.37 million, a 56 per cent rise, and covering 40 per cent of costs.

Promise of specials
In 1996, Metrolink ran several excursion specials from Riverside and inland communities to San Clemente. These sold out and were profitable. Metrolink is considering similar service to the Palm Springs resort area.

Traction and rolling stock
Metrolink services are operated by Amtrak under contract, using 23 low-emission GM-EMD F59PH locomotives, eight F59PHI units ordered by California Department of Transportation (CalTrans) and 94 double-deck coaches bought from Bombardier, with other similar vehicles on lease from GO Transit of Canada.

Track
Rail: 136, 119, 115
Crossties (sleepers): 83% wood; 17% concrete
Spacing: Wood: 2,006/ km; concrete: 1,630/km
Fastenings: (concrete) Pandrol clip, McKay Safelok
Min curvature radius: 10°
Max gradient: 3 %

UPDATED

Metrolink F59PHI locomotives with a Los Angeles—Moorpark service (F Gerald Rawling)
1996

Tri-County Commuter Rail Authority: Tri-Rail

305 South Andrew's Avenue, Suite 200, Fort Lauderdale, Florida 33301
Tel: +1 954 728 8512   Fax: +1 954 763 1345
Website: http://www.tri-rail.com

Operations Department
9400 NW 37th Avenue, Miami, Florida 33147
Tel: +1 305 693 8822   Fax: +1 305 693 0450

Key personnel
Executive Director: Gilbert M Robert
Deputy Executive Director: Jeffrey D Jackson
Chief Mechanical Officer: William D Volkmer
Chief Transportation Officer: Edward F X Connolly II

Passenger operations
The Tri-Rail commuter service, funded by the Florida Department of Transport, was introduced over 107 route-km of former CSXT tracks between Miami and West

Palm Beach in 1989. An extension north from West Palm Beach to Mangonia Park has made the service 118.4 km overall. There are now 18 stations on the line. The state of Florida financed the purchase of the Miami—West Palm Beach line for $264 million. Amtrak and CSXT continue to share the line; CSXT is responsible for maintenance. Tri-Rail's first choice for host railroad in the 1980s negotiations was Florida East Coast (FEC), which did not wish to pursue the concept at the time. Since 1994, consultations have been reopened with FEC.

Contract management of Tri-Rail operations is being provided until 1998 by Herzog Transit Services Inc for $10 million a year. A total of 179 trains run each week serving 18 stations, and in 1996 Tri-Rail recorded a total of 2.5 million passenger journeys, down 16 per cent from 1995. The downward trend has been blamed on service irregularities caused by track improvement projects. Revenues in 1995 were $5.05 million from fares, representing a 22.8 per cent recovery ratio. Politically, in 1997 Tri-Rail was probably less secure than at any time since its inception.

Following the loss in 1995 of $1 million in annual operating assistance from the state of Florida, Tri-Rail abandoned its flat fares in favour of a zonal structure. Transfers to local buses and the Miami metro system have remained free, but a fee is now charged to travellers transferring to Tri-Rail services.

Improvements to existing lines

A $30 million double-tracking project between Fort Lauderdale and Pompano Beach was completed in 1994. The five-year capital programme which extends through to 2000, involves double tracking the corridor and upgrading signalling, plus expanding park-and-ride. The 21 km of second main line so far installed is 135 lb rail with Pandrol clips.

Traction and rolling stock

At mid-1997 Tri-Rail's fleet consisted of 26 double-deck coaches (11 are cab cars), five F40PHL-2 locomotives, three F40PHC-2C rebuilt locomotives from Morrison Knudsen, and two ex-Amtrak reconditioned F40s.

UPDATED

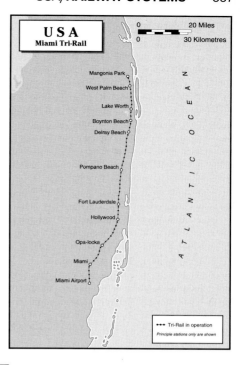

Virginia Railway Express (VRE)

6800 Versar Center, Suite 247, Springfield, Virginia 22151
Tel: +1 703 642 3808   Fax: +1 703 642 3820
email: gotrains@vre.org

Key personnel
Director of Operations: Stephen T Roberts
Managers
    Railroad Services: David Snyder
    Budget and Finance: Dale Zehner
    Marketing and Customer Services: Ann King

Organisation
Virginia Railway Express (VRE), a partnership of the Northern Virginia Transportation Commission and the Potomac and Rappahannock Transportation Commission, began commuter operations in June 1992 over two lines into Washington Union station, from Fredericksburg (87 km} and Manassas (53 km), serving 18 stations. Amtrak is the contract operator and services VRE rolling stock at its Ivy City facility north of Union station.

Passenger operations
From a daily ridership of 3,700 at start-up, patronage has climbed to 8,400. Total annual journeys for 1996 were 1.9 million. The farebox revenue, at $8.59 million, was 50 per cent of inclusive expenses.

Ticketing is a proof-of-purchase system with extensive use of ticket vending machines. VRE pursues a vigorous marketing programme, including free bus transfers; guaranteed ride home outside train times; and use of

Virginia Railway Express Washington DC—Manassas service at Burke, Virginia (Alex Mayes)

Amtrak trains in the same service corridors. VRE has combined with Washington Metropolitan Area Transit Authority to develop a joint fare structure.

Improvements to existing lines
VRE, Amtrak and Maryland Mass Transit Administration collaborated on a $4 million project to clear the route into Washington Union station for double-deck operations. MARC (qv) is also acquiring double-deck equipment and run-throughs between MARC and VRE will be practicable.

The 1996 capital programme was $15.3 million.

Traction and rolling stock
VRE motive power consists of 10 GP39-2C locomotives rebuilt by Morrison Knudsen and four GP40P-2C units rebuilt by AMF Technotransport. The passenger coach fleet comprises 38 vehicles built new by Mafersa and 29 ex-Massachusetts Bay Transportation Authority Budd RDC diesel railcars overhauled and depowered by Morrison Knudsen. VRE has been authorised to purchase 13 double-deck coaches at a cost of $23 million.

UPDATED

HIGH-SPEED RAIL PROJECTS

At the federal level, the Intermodal Surface Transportation Efficiency Act (ISTEA) required the US Department of Transportation to identify corridors where there is presently, or there can reasonably be expected to develop in the near future, 145 km/h or better operations. USDOT has identified six corridors as follows:
(1) Washington—Charlotte: 815 km
(2) Detroit—Chicago—St Louis/Milwaukee: 1,002 km
(3) Miami—Orlando—Tampa: 573 km
(4) San Diego—Los Angeles—Sacramento: 1,048 km
(5) Vancouver BC—Eugene OR: 742 km
(6) The Texas triangle (which was the subject of the Texas High-Speed Rail Authority) was added in 1996.
These corridors were added to two previously recognised corridors, namely the Washington—New York—Boston North East Corridor and the New York City—Albany Empire Corridor.

Dependent upon actual appropriations each of these corridors is eligible to receive up to $1 million per year for

the six years of ISTEA for level crossing hazard elimination. The FY97 appropriations bill for the Department of Transportation made the following provisions through the Federal Railroad Administration:
    $20.1 million for general railroad research and development;
    $195 million for the North East Corridor project; including $80 million towards the high-speed train sets;
    $24.7 million for Next Generation High Speed Rail studies, corridor planning, demonstration and implementation.
No provision was made for the National Magnetic Levitation Prototype Development programme.

Federal Railroad Administration — High Speed Rail division
(For address, see main FRA entry)
Tel: +1 202 366 6593   Fax: +1 202 366 0346

Key personnel
Director, High Speed Rail Staff: Mark Yachmetz

At the state level, several intercity corridors have been the subject of high-speed passenger rail attention. These are detailed in the following entries (except for the North East Corridor Improvement Programme, for details of which see Amtrak entry).

UPDATED

California

California Department of Transportation (CalTrans)

Division of Rail
PO Box 942874
Sacramento, California 94274-0001
Tel:+1 916 327 6219

Key personnel
Chief, Special Projects: Steve Zimrick
Division of Rail Transportation, Manager: Warren Weber

California Intercity High-Speed Rail Authority

PO Box 942874, MS-74
Sacramento, California 94274-0001
Tel: +1 916 324 1541

Key personnel
Executive Director: Dan Leavitt

The California High-Speed Rail Commission released its *Final Summary Report and 20-Year Action Plan* in December 1996, after which it was disbanded. The Authority replaces the Commission, with the task of raising both public support and funding, most probably with a bond issue referendum. In early 1997 the California Assembly and Executive were just beginning to appoint members.

In the Commission Report HSR was determined feasible, at a cost of $21 billion for an inclusive very-high-speed rail technology or $29 billion for maglev, with average speeds of 350 km/h and 495 km/h respectively, though very-high-speed rail would be slowed to 200 km/h or so in city limits. Annual ridership forecasts are 20 million for very-high-speed rail, 26 million of maglev. Both would have a positive farebox recovery ratio but both would require almost 100 per cent capital financing — which implies a statewide or regional tax of some kind to retire any bonds.

The core segment, San Francisco—Los Angeles via Bakersfield, would be covered in 2 hours 49 minutes by very-high-speed rail; 2 hours 3 minutes by maglev. The Commission opted for an inland, as opposed to coast route for the Los Angeles—San Diego section.

California Maglev Transportation Corporation

Key personnel
President: Joseph Vranich

This corporation has been formed in Nevada with the intention of developing a Transrapid maglev route between southern California and Las Vegas, Nevada. It has begun attempts to obtain venture capital, secure the use of highway rights of way and construct a test track from Las Vegas to the California state line. A franchise from the California Public Utilities Commission would be required for operations within that state.

UPDATED

Florida

Florida Department of Transportation: High Speed Transportation Program

605 Suwannee Street, Tallahassee, Florida 32399-0450
Tel: +1 904 487 4261   Fax: +1 904 922 4942

Key personnel
Secretary of Transportation: Ben G Watts
State Public Transportation Administrator: Marion Hart Jr
Managers
    Rail Office: J Fred Wise
    Rail Operations: Anne Brewer
    Rail Planning: Rob Hebert
HSTP Programme Manager: Charles H Smith
Rail Development Manager: Jack E Heiss
Project Manager: Nazih Haddad

Statewide Intercity Rail Passenger System
In February 1996 Florida's Department of Transportation (DOT) announced the award of a 40-year franchise to the Florida Overland Express (FOX) consortium to develop a public/private partnership to construct and operate a 523 km high-speed system connecting Miami, Orlando and Tampa. The consortium comprises Fluor Daniel, Odebrecht Constructors of Florida, GEC Alsthom and Bombardier, and proposed the adoption of French TGV technology. Florida pledged annual support of $70 million for 30 years and federal funding may also be used when available and where appropriate.

The consortium was to work with Florida DOT to develop its certification application which, if approved, will permit construction of the line. This certification process was expected to take between three and four years. The start of revenue operations between Miami and Orlando has been forecast for 2004, with a route to

Tampa opening in 2006. FOX has proposed to use existing corridors and rights-of-way for about 65 per cent of its dedicated 300 km/h high-speed system.

VERIFIED

Illinois Department of Transportation

Chicago—St Louis
Illinois Department of Transportation has studied this corridor and work to date has emphasised the Chicago—Joliet—Bloomington—Springfield—St Louis alignment. A consultant's report has suggested that investment in the order of $420 million is required to attain 200 km/h speeds and 3.5 hour journey times with tilting diesel or turbine equipment.

More recently, funds have been allocated to evaluate the Illinois Central (IC) alignment into Chicago, relatively free of level crossings and flat junctions and passing close to a proposed new regional airport site at Peotone. IC's recent track rationalisation programme may present opportunities for an exclusive passenger right-of-way over certain sections; the state is known to favour using diesel or gas turbine equipment on upgraded infrastructure. The city of Chicago Department of Transportation is reviewing terminus alternatives.

The Illinois Bureau of Railroads is investing $3 million to restore and resignal the Granite City section of the corridor between Alton and St Louis, where as much as 20 minutes could be cut from the present 45 minute journey time by easing track constraints on the east bank of the Mississippi river. The state is also applying a $1.75 million grant to install and test three vehicle-arresting barrier devices at level crossings in Chenoa, McLean and Hartford on the proposed high-speed route. Each device will be accompanied by a video impact detection system that will record each incident for the purpose of performance analysis; several crossing gate systems were also to be tested.

VERIFIED

Michigan Department of Transportation

425 W Ottawa, Lansing, Michigan 48909
Tel: +1 517 335 2921   Fax: +1 517 373 9255

Key personnel
Manager, Intermodal Section: James L Roach

Detroit—Chicago
Michigan continues to work with Amtrak and the Federal Railroad Administration (FRA) in the incremental development of higher speeds and more frequent service in the Detroit—Chicago Corridor including improvements to train control systems, track work, stations, and rolling stock. The state, FRA, and Amtrak are co-operating in development of a positive train control system of 110 km of track in Michigan owned by Amtrak; test speeds of 160 km/h were achieved in October 1996. Harmon Industries is supplying the equipment for this $21.6 million project with 55 per cent federal and 45 per cent state funding. In addition, a stop toward a safer service was achieved in 1996 with the closing of 12 private crossings (10 per cent of the total) in the corridor.

UPDATED

Missouri

Kansas City—St Louis
The state of Missouri has focused on a link between its two principal cities. Viability of such a service is considered to be at least partly influenced by service developments in the St Louis—Chicago market; no independent initiatives have as yet been put forward by Missouri, but a market test of the IC-3 dmu set was undertaken in 1996.

UPDATED

New York Department of Transportation

Policy & Program Bureau, Building 7A, Room 302, Albany, New York 12232
Tel: +1 518 457 5521   Fax: +1 518 457 3183

New York—Albany—Buffalo/Boston
New York has been active in high-speed rail developments for two decades and has invested more than $200 million in the same period to facilitate 160 km/h or better over long sections of the New York—Schenectady route. The state has estimated that an additional $800 million is needed for trackwork, signalling and train control, crossings, stations and fencing to bring the Schenectady—Buffalo section (450 km) up to a 160 km/h standard.

New York DOT re-engined and refurbished an Amtrak Turboliner set (Amtrak's contribution was $2 million) for 200 km/h operation in the New York—Albany Empire Corridor. Morrison Knudsen (now Amerail) installed a pair of TM-1600 Makila T1 turbines from Turbomeca and Amtrak rebuilt the non-powered cars at its Beech Grove, Indiana, workshops. The set has been tested in service at up to 200 km/h and in 1995 went on a demonstration tour of several midwest states. New York has secured some $20 million (including $10 million from federal sources) to start on the complete remanufacuring of the seven RTL Turbo trainsets. Service speeds will be limited to 175 km/h until various institutional constraints involving liability and suitable grade crossing controls can be resolved with the host railroad (Conrail, soon to be CSX) and the Federal Railroad Administration.

UPDATED

Texas

Texas Railroad Commission

PO Box 12967, Austin, Texas 78711-2967
Tel: +1 512 463 7288

A Texas High Speed Rail Authority was created by the Texas legislature's High Speed Rail Act to investigate the possibilities of high-speed rail in Texas, and to grant franchises for the construction, operation, maintenance and financing of high-speed rail routes in Texas if such routes were determined to be in the public convenience and necessity.

An attempt by the Authority to initiate construction of a TGV route in the early 1990s failed to come to fruition and under Texas law the Authority's independent existence ended in August 1995 when the enabling legislation was repealed. It is not altogether clear whether that creates a situation in which a consortium can feel free to launch a scheme without securing a franchise. Although no such consortium has positioned itself to be heir apparent to Texas TGV there is continuing dialogue between private interests and prospective host railroads. A more conventional certificate of public necessity and convenience would at least be likely to be required.

In future, high-speed rail initiatives will start in or through the Texas Railroad Commission or the Texas Department of Transportation. In 1997, HSR is, in effect, dormant. The 'Texas triangle' has been added to the list of USDOT designated lines, making any future project eligible for Federal funding participation.

UPDATED

Washington

Washington Department of Transportation

Transportation Building, PO Box 47383, Olympia, Washington 98504-7383
Tel: +1 360 705 7901   Fax: +1 360 705 6821

Key personnel
Rail Program Manager: Ken Uznanski

Strong interest continues in the 540 km Portland (Oregon)—Tacoma/Seattle (Washington)—Vancouver (British Columbia) 'Cascadia' corridor, using Burlington

Talgo Pendular 200 set at Seattle, Washington, forming the 'Mount Adams' to Portland (John Sully)

1996

Northern Santa Fe trackage for both high-speed services and commuter trains. The latter have been proposed as a congestion mitigation strategy competitive with the cost of new highway construction, but the failure of a March 1995 referendum to raise sales and petrol taxes for public transport investment has stalled such development until it is given another chance in another referendum.

Washington DOT secured contract engineering analyses to define track and other improvements necessary for 125 km/h services throughout and a 3 hours 55 minutes journey time. The eventual target is 200 km/h.

Phase I investment, committed by the state DOT, was directed at CTC installation, track superelevation, work on crossings, bridges and passing loops and some station modernisation for a total of $24 million (plus an additional $4 million from BNSF), out of a projected all-inclusive corridor cost of $315 million. In March 1994 Washington DOT leased a tilting 12-car Talgo Pendular 200 set from RENFE-Talgo of America for what became a popular six-month trial on Amtrak's Portland—Seattle (298 km) 'Mount Adams' service.

In May 1996 Washington DOT announced it had contracted to purchase two Talgo sets, one each for the 'Mount Adams' and the 'Mount Baker International', introduced in May 1995 between Seattle and Vancouver. The train operates at up to 125 km/h, at the threshold of high speed by Federal Railroad Administration standards. Amtrak has ordered a third train set to use on the 'Cascadia' and all three were expected to be in service by mid-1998, assuming the two states continue to fund their shares.

In March 1997, RENFE-Talgo awarded a $50 million contract to a new company, Pacifica, of Seattle, which was formed by the International Association of Machinist & Aerospace Workers for the purpose of building five trainsets. The last two will be built speculatively for sale to buyers outside the Pacific Northwest. A portion of Amtrak's order for F59PHI locomotives (see Amtrak entry) will power the new trains, now dubbed 'Cascade Services'.

UPDATED

EMERGING COMMUTER OPERATIONS

The following section contains details of commuter projects that appeared well advanced in mid-1997.

Denver Regional Transportation District

1600 Blake, Denver, Colorado 80202
Tel: +1 303 628 9000

Denver Regional Transportation District has been considering several new services, with the active participation of Union Pacific (UP) and Burlington Northern Santa Fe (BNSF). On UP, possible destinations from Denver include Golden, Boulder, Fort Collins and Cheyenne, Wyoming, and a service to Denver International Airport has also been proposed. UP ran a test train over 40 km of its tracks; some $140 million of capital acquisition and construction will be required to make a viable airport connection and commence service. Services would operate out of Denver Union station, as would those using BNSF routes.

VERIFIED

Georgia Department of Transportation

The Georgia State Transportation Board commissioned a study by LS Transit Systems Inc which concluded that there were 12 operable lines radiating from Atlanta. The most promising six could be in service by 2010 at a cost of $480 million for capital requirements and would then need $18 million a year in operating assistance. A multimodal transportation centre has been designed to anchor the system in Atlanta but no construction funding has yet been committed by either the public or the private sector.

VERIFIED

San Joaquin Railroad Commission

PO Box 1810, Stockton, California 95201
Tel: +1 209 468 3025   Fax: +1 209 468 8455

Key personnel
Interim Project Manager: Bob Stockwell

The San Joaquin Railroad Commission has been formed to develop service in the Stockton—San Jose corridor in California. Services would operate over Union Pacific (UP) tracks via station stops at Livermore, Pleasanton-Hacienda and Freemont. These major employment centres offer the prospect of filling seats twice, or even three times, in the 126 km corridor, which would relieve three of the most notorious highway bottlenecks in the greater San Francisco area.

Start-up service would comprise two trains each way, operated at peak times only and comprising one locomotive and three coaches. Forecasts have predicted up to 1,000 passengers each way daily within the first two years. Initial farebox recovery ratio has been targeted at between 43 and 48 per cent and, during a two-year developmental stage, UP would waive its track access charges.

The necessary series of signed agreements to start service, including a contract with a yet-to-be-named designated operator, was expected before the end of 1997 for early 1998 start up. The tentative marketing name is 'Altamont Express'. Additional services have been proposed to connect with San Francisco's BART metro system at Freemont and with Amtrak's San Jose—Oakland corridor.

In the second quarter of 1997 the Commission announced a $6 million order for three 3,200 hp (2,385 kW) F40PHM-2Cs from MotivePower Industries, to be built at Boise, Idaho. An option for six more is exercisable within a year. Eight Bombardier gallery cars are also on order.

UPDATED

OTHER US METROPOLITAN AREAS

The New York, Susquehanna & Western (qv) started a service called OnTrack in September 1994 in **Syracuse**, New York, using four RDC diesel railcars, of which two had been reconditioned by the operator. There is a midweek 'City Express' shuttle service connecting the Carousel Center shopping complex to a newly constructed Armory Square station and Syracuse University. On days when there is a major Syracuse University sporting event a shuttle runs from Armory Square to the Carrier Dome all-weather arena.

The Michigan Department of Transportation has signed a $400,000 study contract with DeLeuw Cather & Company to develop a plan and programme for the reintroduction of passenger services for **Detroit** and southeastern Michigan. The city of Detroit, General Motors, and the United Auto Workers have all endorsed the project.

The regional plan for **Cleveland**, Ohio, proposes service to Akron and Canton over Conrail trackage. The intended 1996 start-up was not attained but the proposal has received $7.7 million in development funding from the Federal government and has been endorsed by the Ohio Rail Development Commission.

The 20-year plan for metropolitan **St Louis** includes restoration of commuter service over 51 km to Pacific, Missouri, and intermediate suburbs, including Kirkwood which already has Amtrak service. A Union Pacific line south to DeSoto is under review. Consultancy Booz, Allen & Hamilton has been retained to carry out a feasibility study and preliminary design.

In Utah, Union Pacific has offered 37 km of track, between **Salt Lake City** and Draper, to the regional transit authority in anticipation of major reconstruction on a parallel highway in the near future. Service could eventually be provided from Ogden through Salt Lake City to Provo, a total distance of around 150 km.

Three counties in the **Tampa Bay** area of Florida are studying commuter rail options; the first service is likely to be between Tampa and Lakeland, half the distance to Orlando on CSXT. Federal funds of $2 million were made available in the FY97-98 appropriation bill.

The North Coast Transportation Authority has bought over 195 km of Northwestern Pacific (a subdivision of Southern Pacific's Western Division) trackage between **Willitts** and **Schellville**. The authority opted to be the freight operator while retaining ownership of the property as a potential commuter route for Marin County and San Francisco.

UPDATED

FEDERAL GRANTS

In the Federal Transit Act Section 3 New Start allocations for FY96-97 and FY97-98 (Section 5309.m.1.B; Miscellaneous Multi-Year Contracts) were several related to areas where there is no present service, as follows:

• $987,981 in FY96-97 for non-specified purposes in a Cincinnati-Northern Kentucky corridor to add to $1.191 million in prior years; these sums were reappropriated in FY97-98;

• For the Seattle—Renton—Tacoma corridor a sum of $3,952,375 remained unobligated from prior years;

• $493,990 in FY96-97 for Tampa—Lakeland, Florida, planning services; this was added to $496,250 still unobligated from FY95; further funds were available in FY97-98;

• $5,927,883 in FY96-97 for the Dallas/Fort Worth RAILTRAN project was added to $2,977,500 in prior years; the FY97-98 appropriation adds a further $15,143,599;

• $5,582 in FY96-97 for commuter rail in Vermont, between Burlington and Charlotte to add to $1,856,508 previously appropriated but not obligated; the FY97-98 appropriation adds a further $993,023;

• $1,234,976 in FY96-97 for the Memphis Regional Rail Plan; the FY97 appropriation adds a further $3,017,796;

• $4,198,917 in FY96-97 for the Cleveland—Akron—Canton commuter rail project; the FY97-98 appropriation adds a further $3,475,580;

Also in FY96-97 appropriation bill were sums for established commuter properties, as follows:

• $9,879,805 to Tri-Rail;

• $0 to MBTA for service expansion to New Bedford and Fall River; $744,375 remains unobligated from FY95-96;

• $9,879,805 to MARC; all sums from prior years are now obligated;

• $79,285,433 for the New Jersey Urban Core Project, to add to a total of $106,197,500 obligated in prior years;

• $14,226,919 to Metra for Wisconsin Central start-up, added to $10,421,250 obligated in prior years;

In the FY97-98 appropriation bill sums for established commuter rail properties were:

• $1,489,534 for LOSSAN, the Los Angeles—San Diego rail corridor; $8,397,834 remains unobligated from prior years;

• $8,937,206 for Tri-Rail (reappropriation);

• $496,511 for NICTD;

• $32,959,422 for MARC;

• $114,723,933 to NJ (Urban Core), a reappropriation;

• $496,511 to NJT for the West Trenton project;

• $2,979,069 to VRE.

Still in the obligations process are:

• $3,970,000 from FY95-96 to New Jersey Transit for the West Shore project and $21,559,000 to New Jersey for the Hawthorne—Warwick commuter rail project.

UPDATED

URUGUAY

Ministry of Transport & Public Works

Rincón 561, 8to piso, Montevideo
Tel: + 598 2 960509/957013   Fax: +598 2 962883

Key personnel
Minister: L Cáceres Behrens

UPDATED

State Railways Administration (AFE)

Administración de Ferrocarriles del Estado
PO Box 419, Calle La Paz 1095, Montevideo
Tel: +598 2 940805   Fax: +598 2 940847

Key personnel
President: V Vaillant
Vice-President: Dr F Caride B
Directors: O Lopez Balestra, J C Hernandez, E Silveira
Secretary-General: V Varela
General Manager: M Anastasia
Deputy General Manager: H Chapuis
Directors
  Legal Affairs: Dr R Jimenez
  Audit: E Garcia
  Special Projects: A Santos
Managers
  Finance and Accounting: G Leva
  Human Resources: J Ceriani
  Operations: H Riccardi
  Rolling Stock: J Lopez Baggi
  Infrastructure: G Tettamanti
  Communications: A Lujambio

Gauge: 1,435 mm
Route length: 2,073 km

Political background
In October 1991, legislation was passed which effectively reduced the role of AFE to that of track authority with responsibility for maintaining track and co-ordinating operations. It was to be financed via taxation and by charging fees to operators. The rump of AFE has been permitted to compete with private operators in providing services, although the future of the country's railways will depend on private companies owning and running their own motive power and rolling stock.

Of the current network, some 461 km are closed and a further 460 km only in partial operation. Track quality has been seriously prejudiced by the financial cuts of 1988 when substantial numbers of permanent way staff were shed. Total AFE staff numbers fell from 10,000 in 1987 to 2,100 at the start of 1994.

Finance
AFE's projected investment strategy for 1994-97 had US$30 million earmarked for track repairs and US$11.8 million to be spent on rolling stock. The remainder was reserved for the purchase of intermodal equipment. During 1996, out of a total investment budget of US$6.53 million, US$4.16 million was to be spent on major track improvements, US$1.55 million on freight wagon refurbishment and US$0.35 million on communications.

Traffic (million)	1993	1994
Freight tonnes	0.930	1.00
Freight tonne-km	NA	189

Passenger operations
In 1988, passenger services were withdrawn as an

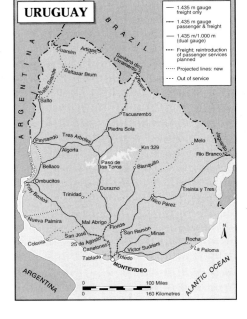

economy measure. In March 1990 a new political administration set out to restore passenger services by encouraging AFE to undertake joint ventures with the private sector. Between 1990 and 1992 several 'charter' trains were run and on 11 January 1993 regular passenger service was restored on the 118 km line linking Tacuarembó and Rivera in the north of the country.

Suburban service resumed between Montevideo and 25 de Agosto on 25 August 1993. By November of that year, the four trains running in each direction were carrying over 1,200 passengers a day on the 64 km route, with loadings reaching 1,500 a day by mid-1994. Uruguay's restored passenger services were managed by the private company Luxtol SA which was responsible for ticket sales, onboard service and the cleaning of trains and stations. AFE received a fixed amount per train-km which covers the hire of train crews and rolling stock.

Expansion and extension of the existing 25 de Agosto services to San José de Mayo and Florida was proposed. However, the return of the anti-rail political party in 1996 had a dramatic effect. The Ferrotransporte company managed by Luxtol had its August 1993 concession withdrawn. AFE itself took over the running of all trains in January 1997 and suspended indefinitely the deep rural Tacuarembó—Rivera train due to its lack of profitability. Although upgrading work on the 118 km route had resulted in a 2 hours 40 minutes end-to-end timing in 1993, by 1996 this had lengthened to 3 hours 45 minutes, despite faster railcars having replaced diesel locomotives and coaches. Intense political lobbying resulted in the Tacuarembó-Rivera train being reinstated on 3 March 1997. Furthermore, the timetabled four trains a day on the Montevideo—25 de Agosto commuter service were increased to five following the reinstatement of the Peñarol—Sayago feeder service.

Refurbished 1936-built Brill railcar on Montevideo suburban service (Peter Shearman)   **1997**

Freight operations

AFE expects its timber traffic to increase in the near future and is investing in track improvements accordingly. The railway's 10 new GE locomotives were purchased with this timber traffic in mind, and were expected to enable AFE to increase train lengths by 50 per cent and modify the pattern of its freight operations. New sidings to serve industrial customers, silos, containers and handling equipment for containers and pallets are also the subject of investment.

Intermodal operations

AFE's investment strategy for 1994-97 made provision for the purchase of two container cranes (US$0.56 million) and 150 bulk containers (US$0.9 million). By August 1994, 44 containers had been purchased for US$350,000.

New lines

Recent planning objectives have included development of the Littoral line and extension of the Central line northwards to a point known as Km 441 from its present terminus at Km 329. In conjunction with the latter project, US$3 million was spent on a new rail bridge across the Río Negro, but the scheme was later abandoned and the bridge converted for use by road traffic.

AFE has been reported as studying the possibility of constructing a new branch from the Montevideo—Fray Bentos line at Cardona to the recently expanded port of Nueva Palmira. The branch would be 70 km long.

Improvements to existing lines

AFE's Master Plan for Railway Reactivation unveiled in 1994 included the renewal of 1,500 km of track using sleepers imported from Bolivia; the railway later ordered 26 motorised track-inspection vehicles from Stelec—Geismar.

Electrification of the Montevideo—Progreso (26.4 km) section of AFE's route to 25 de Agosto was proposed as part of an LRT scheme under development in 1996. The upgraded infrastructure would be used by dual-mode LRVs similar to those adopted by the German cities of Karlsruhe and Saarbrücken.

Traction and rolling stock

At the start of 1993 the locomotive fleet comprised 24 Alco/GE and 18 Alsthom 825 hp (615 kW) diesel-electrics, seven diesel-hydraulics for shunting duties and four steam locomotives. In November of that year, AFE took delivery of 10 1,800 hp (1,340 kW) Type C18-7i diesel-electric locomotives built by GE Canada. The investment programme for 1994-97 made provision for the rebuilding of three shunting locomotives.

Passenger services are operated with refurbished equipment, namely six 200 hp (150 kW) Brill 60 railcars of 1936 vintage and 10 Fiat-Materfer coaches. The latter are hauled by Alsthom or newer GE locomotives. AFE has begun refurbishing four Ganz-Mavag diesel trainsets; the first was returned to service in September 1994. Its fleet of passenger equipment also comprises five ex-DB Uerdingen railbuses and 97 other passenger coaches (including 21 wooden-bodied vehicles and 10 Allan trailers used for charter trains), of which half have latterly been unserviceable.

At the start of 1993, AFE operated 2,413 freight wagons. The railway expected some future investment in new wagons to come from the private sector but made provision in its 1994-97 investment programme for the purchase of 200 all-purpose flat wagons, the conversion of 40 flat wagons to bulk hoppers and the fitting of roller-bearing wheelsets to 1,200 vehicles. The latter two projects were to be undertaken by AFE's own workshops.

Track

Rail: 20 kg/m (529 km); 30-40 kg/m (1,361 km); 40-50 kg/m (969 km); 50 kg/m or heavier (132 km)
Sleepers: Steel and timber
Min curve radius: Generally 500 m; less than 500 m over 97 km

UPDATED

UZBEKISTAN

Ministry of Transport

760001 Tashkent

Key personnel
Minister: T Rahimov

NEW ENTRY

Uzbekistan Railway

Uzbekistan Temir Yullari
T Shevchenko 7, 700060 Tashkent
Tel: +7 3712 324400

Key personnel
President: N Ermetov

Gauge: 1,520 mm
Route length: 3,656 km
Electrification: 480 km at 25 kV AC

Organisation

This network comprises the greater part of the former Soviet Railways Central Asian Railway, centred on the artery from Chardzhou in Turkmenistan to Bokhara, Samarkand, Dzhizak and Tashkent. It became an independent entity from January 1992. The northwest and far-eastern sections can only be accessed through the neighbouring states of Turkmenistan and Tadjikistan respectively which, given the political tensions in the

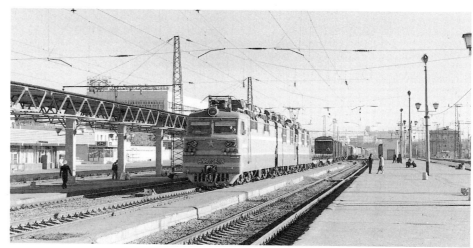

Class VL80 triple-unit locomotive with a freight train at Tashkent   **1997**

whole region, complicates the railway's operations considerably.

The railway is divided into five regional administrations: Tashkent, Ferganan, Bukhara, Aral and Karshi.

Passenger operations

The passenger business stood at 20.4 million journeys in 1993, for 5.9 billion passenger-km; by 1995, carryings had risen to 24 million journeys.

The extra costs associated with catering for this growth led to an increased financial loss for the railway, as a result of which fares were raised substantially in early 1995. Local authorities have contributed towards the cost of running new high-quality trains between major cities. Some trains have been leased to their staffs, and are said to be very presentable.

No new coaches had been purchased for the Central Asian Railway in the two years before the break-up of the USSR, and subsequently the lack of repair facilities has exacerbated the shortage of passenger stock. This situation should be remedied when repair facilites being built with Japanese credit come on stream at Tashkent.

Freight operations

Freight traffic has slumped following the break-up of the Soviet Union, with freight tonnage down from 90.8 million in 1991 to 57 million in 1993. An expected recovery in 1994 failed to materialise, with tonnage falling to 40 million. However, in 1995 volume increased to 46 million tonnes following improved international transits. The dominant traffics are cotton and construction materials.

New lines

In 1995, the 345 km Navoi—Nukus line was started, in the west of the country. This will enable rail access to the extreme northwest without the complications of transit through eastern Turkmenistan. There is also a project to link the Karshi—Kitab and Termez—Denau lines in the south, again bypassing Turkmenistan.

Class 2VL60 electric locomotive   **1997**

Work on this 220 km Guzar—Kumkurgan line began in 1996.

In the east, a bypass is proposed from Angren to the Kokand—Namangan line, hitherto accessed from Khavast through Tadjikistan. However, the very difficult terrain makes any early start on this project unlikely.

Improvements to existing lines
The modernisation, including electrification, of the main trunk route between Bokhara, Samarkand and Tashkent is continuing. This line's activity is expected to increase to some 25 freight and six passenger trains per day, including international traffic from Turkmenistan and Iran.

Traction and rolling stock
The current traction is as follows:
diesel (main line) locomotives 2TE10/3TE10 variants: 1,082 units (480 ½ double and triple locomotives); diesel (shunting) locomotives TEM2/chME3: 313 locomotives (all single units); electric (main line) locomotives 3VL80/VL80, 2VL60/VL60: 173 units (84 double and triple locomotives); electric multiple-units ER2, ER9: 90 units (45 sets). The ER2 units (24 two-car units) are stored out of use.

Electrification
Apart from the 354 km between Tashkent and Samarkand, only a few short industrial lines have been electrified. Some routes in the Fergana basin were electrified in 1993, including Khavast—Bekabad. Wiring is proceeding slowly on a further section of the main Central Asian route, the 275 km from Samarkand to Bukhara.

Passenger coaches total 1,450 (many are no longer serviceable).

Freight wagons total 32,500 (many are no longer serviceable).

UPDATED

VENEZUELA

Ministry of Transport & Communications

Caracas

Key personnel
Minister: C Zaa

Venezuelan State Railways (Ferrocar)

Instituto Autónomo Ferrocarriles del Estado
PO Box 146, Avenida Lecuna, Parque Central, Torre Este, Piso 45, Caracas 1010
Tel: +58 2 509 3500/1   Fax: +58 2 574 7021

Key personnel
President: L Hilzinger L
Vice-President: O Ramirez Osio
Vice-President, Legal Affairs: C Salazar
Vice-President, Marketing: Antonio Zapata
Vice-President, Internal Accounting: L Morales
Managers
    Construction: Olegario Braga
    Operations: C Alberto Buenaño
    Administration and Finance: I Antunez
    Planning and Budgets: G Vanorio
    Personnel: Mercedes Polo Mimo
    Property: R Gosselain

Gauge: 1,435 mm
Route length: 336 km

Political background
Recent legislation pertaining to Venezuela's ambitious railway construction programme has made provision for private funding to be used alongside public money.

Organisation
The Ferrocar system consists of the 176 km Puerto Cabello—Barquisimeto route with branches from Yaritagua to Acarigua and Morón to Tucacas.

Freight traffic, amounting to 315,000 tonnes (46.8 million tonne km) in 1994, consists of grain, fertiliser, sand and sugar cane waste (bagasse), often moving via private sidings serving industry.

Ferrocar has in the past operated passenger services on the 173 km Puerto Cabello-Barquisimeto line, but at last report no passenger services were operating.

At the end of 1994, Ferrocar employed 200 people.

Finance
Ferrocar's provisional investment budget for 1996 amounted to Br14.963 billion, including Br1.341 billion for major track improvements, Br567 million for workshops and repair facilities and Br13.055 billion for new lines, of which Br12.493 billion was to pay for civil works on the Cua—Puerto Cabello project.

New lines
National Railways Plan
Venezuela's revised National Railways Plan aims to create a 3,447 km system of lines of local, regional and national importance by 2020. The programme involves the eventual creation of four interconnecting systems that are known as the Central Western, Central Region, Eastern Plains and Western railways.

Central Western Railway
Ferrocar's existing routes form the core of this system.

Extension of the branch leaving the main line at Morón beyond its present terminus at Tucacas to Riecito and a total length of 109 km was hoped to be completed in 1996, when the project was allocated Br66 million. Construction, costed a total of Br2.3 billion, has been funded by Ferrocar and the national oil company PDVSA as the line will carry phosphates from deposits at Riecito to a petrochemical works at Morón. This traffic is eventually expected to amount to some 1.2 million tonnes a year, and Ferrocar sees potential for tourist services in the Tucacas and Chichiriviche areas.

A proposed 285 km extension would take the Riecito branch to Coro, Puerto Cardón and Amuay for oil industry traffic. This has been costed at Br15.5 billion for infrastructure and Br8.5 million for rolling stock. A total of Br10 million was allocated to studies for a 185 km Yaracal—Coro route in 1996.

In 1991, work began on a 45 km extension from Acarigua to Turén, for which financing had been approved. The majority of the civil engineering work had been completed by early 1994, but further funding was required before tracklaying and terminal construction could begin. Costed at Br0.7 billion, the Acarigua—Turén extension is expected to carry some 500,000 to 800,000 tonnes of freight (mostly agricultural produce) a year with potential for traffic to grow by 20 per cent a year.

From Turén, a 115 km extension is planned to El Baúl. From El Baúl, a further eastward extension would connect the Cental Western system with the proposed Eastern Plains network at El Sombrero. Engineering design work for Turén—El Sombrero route was under way at the start of 1994, as were funding negotiations with Spanish financiers.

Central Region Railway
The major Ferrocar enterprise now under way is the long-planned new east—west Central Region system, also known as the Central Trunk. This will extend from Caracas to Puerto Cabello via Cúa, Maracay and Valencia, and will link the capital and the central region of the country with the Central Western trunk at Puerto Cabello. It has been designated a project of national importance. At Puerto Cabello the Central Trunk would also connect with the Central Western, enabling the latter to rail coal and minerals to the Caracas conurbation.

After a call for tenders in 1989, an Italian-Japanese-Venezuelan consortium, Contuy Medio, led by Cogefar-Impresit SpA of Milan, won in 1991 the competition to build the first 43 km from Caracas to Cúa serving the expanding new town of Tuy Medio. A contract valued at US$800 million was eventually signed with the Venezuelan government on 29 May 1996, whereby the consortium agreed to meet 50 per cent of the construction cost. Ferrocar's 1996 investment budget made provision for a Br12.493 billion advance payment for civil works on the Caracas—Cúa route, expected to open in 2001 and carry some 180,000 passengers per day.

This first stage traverses difficult terrain, with a difference of 623 m in level between its extremities, and will involve a ruling gradient of 2.3 per cent and 10.6 km of tunnelling, including one bore of 6.8 km. The line will be electrified at 25 kV 60 Hz AC, and laid with a single track later to be doubled.

Maximum speeds of 100 to 120 km/h will be exploited by four-car emus consisting of two motor cars enclosing two trailers, each with a capacity for 448 passengers. CTC will be located in Caracas and there will be two intermediate stations. The Caracas terminus will be at Mercado for interchange with Line 3 of the city's metro system, currently under construction.

The second stage of the Central Region system is the 176 km Cúa—Puerto Cabello section. Private finance was expected to fund the project, costed at Br52.7 billion for civil works and Br12.6 billion for rolling stock; Ferrocar allocated Br213 million to further studies in 1996. The Cúa—Puerto Cabello route is to be engineered for 180 km/h passenger operation, but is also expected to carry heavy freight traffic once Venezuela's national network emerges. Ferrocar expects to eventually handle 96,000 passengers and 139,000 tonnes of freight between Caracas and Puerto Cabello every day.

Eastern Plains Railway
A proposed Eastern Plains system will be formed of south—north and east—west axes together totalling 938 km. The 394 km south—north route would start at Puerto Ordaz on the River Orinoco, connecting with the existing 141 km route to Ciudad Piar operated by Ferrominera for the transport of iron ore. From Puerto Ordaz, the new line heads north through Maturín for a deep sea port at Puerto Guiria on the Gulf of Cariaco, in the state of Sucre. Costed at Br32.5 billion for civil works and Br4.3 billion for rolling stock, the south—north axis is expected by Ferrocar to carry 12 to 21 million tonnes of iron ore a year.

In 1995, Br45 million was spent on surveying work for the Puerto Ordaz—Maturín—Guacarapo component (342 km) of the project, allocated Br75 million for further studies in 1996. In 1995, Ferrocar concluded agreements with the states of Anzoategui, Bolívar and Monagas to proceed with south—north axis of the Eastern Plains system (with branches to Barcelona and Guanta on the Caribbean) to be built either as a mixed private/state venture or by offering concessions. Expressions of interest were sought in 1996 by mining company CVG (qv) to construct a route from Ciudad Guayana (east of Puerto Ordaz) to Puerto Guiria or another Caribbean port.

The 544 km east-west line would run from Maturín via Zaraza and El Sombrero to a junction with the Central Trunk at Cagua. Traffic would consist mainly of agricultural produce moving westwards from the eastern plains, estimated to be in the region of 8 million tonnes a year. The Maturín—Cagua route has been costed at Br45.3 billion for civil works and Br6.5 billion for rolling stock.

Western Railway
This system's principal traffic would be coal and phosphates from deposits in the southwest of Venezuela, moving to tidewater for export. International links have also been considered and, in May 1996, Ferrovias of Colombia announced proposals for a new 126 km route from Cúcuta across the border to La Concha and La Ceiba on Lake Maracaibo in Venezuela. The proposed Western Railway's initial 116 km section from La Fría to La Concha would carry some 3 million tonnes a year, and has been costed at Br10.6 billion for civil works and Br0.9 billion for rolling stock. Construction of this route has been deemed a priority and was to be publicly funded to the tune of 50 to 80 per cent. In 1995, Br31.3 million was to spent on initial studies for the Urena—La Fría—La Concha—La Ceiba route, including geotechnical and hydrological work, and further La Fría—La Ceiba (243 km) studies were to receive Br198 million in 1996.

The Western Railway would also include three other routes. The first is El Vigía—La Ceiba—Barquisimeto (417 km), connecting the La Fría—La Concha—La Ceiba route with the Central Western system and costing Br33.2 billion for civil works and Br6.9 billion for rolling stock. This line would carry 7.9 milion tonnes a year according to Ferrocar's forecasts.

A second line, 472 km long, would head north from La Fría to a new port on the Gulf of Venezuela, known as Puerto Nuevo via Maracaibo, and the coal mining area of Guasare. Civil works are costed at Br41.9 billion. The third route runs for 446 km from Santo Domingo via Barinas to the southern branch of the Central Western at Turén. This route would carry 10 million tonnes of traffic a year, principally coal and phosphates. Civil works have been costed at Br38 billion.

Improvements to existing lines

In anticipation of heavier traffic expected to be generated by the extension of its branches (roughly twice the present amount) and the construction of other connecting trunk routes, upgrading work was undertaken on the track of the Puerto Cabello—Barquisimeto main line of the Central Western Railway in the early 1990s.

Traction and rolling stock

At the start of 1995, Ferrocar operated 17 diesel locomotives, namely six GM-EMD 1,300 kW GP9s, four GM-EMD 1,100 kW GP15-1s and two 110 kW shunting locomotives. Other rolling stock comprised 16 passenger coaches, 12 diesel railcars and 262 freight wagons.

Type of coupler in standard use: US Type E
Type of braking in standard use: Air

Track

Rail employed is ASCE 49 kg/m and UIC 60 kg/m on Dywidag concrete sleepers (2,500 × 227 × 300 mm) spaced 1,670/km and 1,336/km in curves. Minimum curve radius is 800 m, maximum gradient 1.4 per cent, maximum permitted axleload 31.75 tonnes, and maximum speed is 70 km/h.

VERIFIED

Ferrominera

CVG Ferrominera Orinoco CA
PO Box 399, Puerto Orduz, Bolívar State
Tel: +58 86 303111   Fax: +58 86 303656

Key personnel

General Superintendent, Piar Division: E Carabello
Superintendents
　Pao Division: H Brazon
　General Shops: M Aro G

Track and Structures: D Massiah R
General Supervisor: J Diaz

Gauge: 1,435 mm
Route length: 196 km

Freight operations

Ferrominera, a state-owned company, operates two railways in eastern Venezuela principally for the transport of iron ore to the River Orinoco. The line linking Ciudad Piar in the Cerro Bolívar range with Puerto Ordaz on the river is 141 km long, and that connecting El Pao with Palua on the Orinoco 55 km long. Annual carryings amount to some 30 million tonnes of freight.

Traction and rolling stock

Ferrominera operated a fleet of 36 diesel locomotives and 1,587 freight wagons in 1990. In 1996, Freios Knorr of Brazil was contracted to supply the company with 100 braking systems to be fitted to new wagons ordered from Transimpex of Bulgaria.

UPDATED

Los Pijiguaos Railway

CVG Bauxilum
Carretera Nacional Caicara–Puerto Ayacucho, Los Pijiguaos, Bolívar State
Tel: +58 2 572 1620   Fax: +58 2 993 7685

Key personnel

President: Pedro Mantellini
Executive Vice-President: José L Garcia G
General Manager: Gustavo Quintero
Mineral Handling Manager: Oscar Portes
Traffic and Railway Maintenance Superintendent:
　Juan Carlos Fermin

Gauge: 1,435 mm
Route length: 52 km

Freight operations

CVG Bauxilum operates a 52 km railway linking bauxite deposits at Los Pijiguaos with the Orinoco river port of Gumilla. Opened in 1989, the line carried 5 million tonnes in 1995.

Improvements to existing lines

A new mineral handling system has been installed which will allow the railway to carry 5.3 million tonnes of bauxite a year. The system incorporates an automatic loading station and an automatic car dumper, both with a capacity of 3,600 tonnes an hour, and allows six trains carrying 2,500 tonnes each at 60 km/h to be operated in a period of 8 hours.

Traction and rolling stock

At the end of 1995, the railway operated five diesel-electric locomotives, including GM-EMD SD38-2 and SW900 types, and 119 freight wagons, mostly 90 tonne gondolas.

Type of coupler in standard use: F150
Type of braking in standard use: 26L, 24RL, 6BL

Track

Rail: AREA 132 RE, 54.75 kg/m
Sleepers: Dywidag concrete, 2,500 × 227 × 300 mm
Spacing: 1,667/km
Fastenings: RN 300
Min curve radius: 36°
Max gradient: 1%
Max permissible axleload: 30 tonnes

VERIFIED

VIETNAM

Ministry of Communications and Transport

80 Tran Hung Dao, Hanoi
Tel: +84 4 25 2079

Key personnel

Minister: Buy Danh Luu
Railways Director: Nguyen Hieu Liem

NEW ENTRY

Vietnam Railways (DSVN)

Duong Sat Viet Nam
118 Duong le Duan, Hanoi
Tel: +84 4 254998   Fax: +84 4 254998

Key personnel

Director-General: Doan Van Xe
Deputy Directors-General
　Vu Duc Lan, Nguyen Trong Bach, Nguyen Minh Khue
Directors
　Da Nang Division: Phung Dinh Ngoan
　Ho Chi Minh Division: Dao Dinh Bihn
　Investment: Nguyen Ngoc Khoi
　International Relations: Nguyen Huu Bang
Deputy Director, International Relations:
　Nguyen Trung Hoe

Gauge: 1,435 mm; 1,000 mm; mixed gauge
Route length: 172 km; 2,205 km; 228 km

Political background

After a long period of stagnation, DSVN underwent reorganisation in 1994-95, following the government's agreement to separate infrastructure and operating costs from the beginning of 1995. The railway, freed from responsibility for upkeep and renewal of its infrastructure, nevertheless continues to manage day-to-day execution of these tasks and retains control over rolling stock maintenance and procurement. It is required to cover its operating costs as well as remitting 10 per cent of revenues to the government as a track access charge. In return, the government shoulders all costs associated with track, signalling, telecommunications and structures.

DSVN is not entirely free from government control, however, as it cannot set domestic fares at an economic level. In its first year of operation without subsidy, DSVN turned in a loss of D134 billion, but in 1995 it achieved the balance of revenue and expenditure that was intended to be the norm under the restructuring programme, largely by means of big increases in freight rates.

Despite the restructuring, funding remains problematical. Clearing the huge backlog of infrastructure and rolling stock maintenance could absorb as much as 400 billion dong annually, a sum which can only be delivered by new funding sources such as joint ventures with the private sector. DSVN controls all the country's railway manufacturing and service companies, many of which would benefit from foreign participation.

Organisation

The most important route is the main line linking Hanoi with Ho Chi Minh City (Saigon) (1,726 km); other routes radiate from Hanoi to the port of Haiphong (96 km) and Quan Trieu (mixed-gauge, 54 km), while two lines run to the border with China — northwest to Lao Cai and northeast to Dong Dang (mixed-gauge). A 1,435 mm gauge line runs from Quan Trieu to Kep and Halong.

Hanoi has a western orbital route, built in the 1980s, which diverges from the main line to the north at Dong Anh, crosses the Red River on the Thang Long bridge, and joins the southern main line to Ho Chi Minh City (Saigon) at Van Dien.

Passenger operations

By 1994, passenger traffic had fallen below 8 million journeys annually, with some 80 per cent of the passenger-km logged by the Hanoi—Ho Chi Minh City (Saigon) route. Traffic on this artery is expected to grow to more than 14 million journeys a year, a renaissance which started in 1994 with the commissioning of a new premium service, The Reunification Express, which cut the transit time by half to 36 hours. As a result, journeys rose 11 per cent to 8.8 million in 1995.

Further growth is expected on the two routes to the Chinese border. At Dong Dang, a metre-gauge DSVN train connects twice-weekly with a 1,435 mm Chinese Railways service to Pinxiang. On the 530 km all metre-gauge route from Hanoi via Lao Cai to Kunming in China, an inaugural direct service ran in April 1997. Four services a week were planned.

Radical improvement must await delivery of new rolling stock. Introduction of high-quality air conditioned coaches is seen as vital to help DSVN retain its share of the middle-distance traffic which has not yet yielded to bus competition. DSVN's Gia Lam works at Hanoi can now turn out coaches to a higher standard than the basic accommodation deemed satisfactory for local trains. These are based on the most recent cars supplied from India, but air conditioning equipment requires costly foreign exchange and it will be some time before sufficient cars are available to make a real impact.

Freight operations

Recent years have seen considerable growth in freight traffic. Tonne-km in 1994 were 1.37 billion; this figure rose to 1.75 billion in 1995. Severe weather in 1996 was expected to adversely affect final statistics for that year.

There is considerable potential for increased traffic with China, both over the 1,435 mm gauge route via Dong Dang and the metre-gauge line that provides a through connection from the port of Haiphong to Kunming. On the Dong Dang route (on which trans-shipment is required at the gauge change at the border) international services resumed in 1996, after having been broken off during a border dispute in 1979; there are now four freight services daily, aggregating 6,400 tonnes.

Intermodal operations

A joint venture between VSDN and New Zealand interests known as Rail Express has opened up the route between the port of Haiphong and Hanoi with a US$5million investment package. Just over US$3 million was contributed to this by the venture's New Zealand partner, Minzr Containers Ltd, a company established by engineering conglomerate Mc Connell International which is drawing in rail expertise from TranzRail.

VSDN has improved the track between the two cities and an on-dock rail terminal has been built in Haiphong. Rail Express obtained its operating licence in August 1996 and expected to start running three container trains a day (total capacity 60 TEU) between Haiphong and the capital during 1997. More powerful locomotives and new wagons are needed if the venture is to expand.

Once it is better established, Rail Express intends to expand by beginning services on the Ho Chi Minh City–Hanoi route. The port of Ho Chi Minh City has a throughput of 300,000 TEU, but currently none of these boxes goes by rail.

New lines

DSVN has long sought a link with Thailand, but this would require a line across intervening Laos (qv) which is only now building its first railway line. A line from Ho Chi Minh to Phnom Penh in Cambodia (Kampuchea) also figures in ASEAN proposals for improved links between member countries.

In 1995, ITF Intertraffic, a subsidiary of Germany's Daimler-Benz, studied proposals for a 15 km cross-city elevated railway to be built through the congested centre of Hanoi. Funding for feasibility and preliminary

engineering studies were being sought in 1996, and the current five-year plan includes a proposal to buy diesel railcars for suburban services. More recently, a 120 km line from Ho Chi Minh to the seaside resort of Vung Tau has been canvassed.

New links to ports are being studied. A 110 km double track line from the port of Vung Tau to Ho Chi Minh City could be built using the build-operate-transfer form of contract, if experience currently being gained on the first project in Vietnam to be built in this way, a power station near Hanoi, is favourable. Good access to a new deep sea port being built at Cai Lan, which will open in 2000, would be assured by construction of a 42 km cut-off between Yen Vien near Hanoi and Pha Lai.

Other proposed links are from Ho Chi Minh City to the tourist region of Dalat, and a railway from Lok Ninh to Da Nang.

Improvements to existing lines

The mammoth rehabilitation task continues to be hampered by funding shortages. Trackwork is largely ancient and in poor condition, with worn-out 30 kg/m rail. A particularly critical problem is the state of the system's numerous bridges and viaducts — 1,658 of them, with a total length of some 39 km. Over many metal bridges a speed limit of 5 km/h is imposed because of corrosion or other weaknesses.

Rehabilitation of the Hanoi–Ho Chi Minh main line, aimed at increasing passenger train speeds to 120 km/h, remains the priority in the investment plan for the years through to the end of the century. Relaying of 400 km of track with 40 kg/m rail, replacement of nine bridges and strengthening of 70 other structures is costed at Dong 2.5 billion.

The two routes to China, via Lao Cai and Dong Dang, are also earmarked for early attention.

Swiss assistance was sought for rehabilitation of the 89 km rack-and-adhesion line between the coastal town of Thap Cham and the central highlands city of Da Lat. Steam-worked before its closure in 1976, the restored line will be worked by new diesel locomotives.

Japanese loans agreed in 1995 have been used in part to fund rehabilitation work, in particular reconstruction of the many damaged or substandard bridges. Queensland Rail has also supplied technical assistance with

rehabilitation, while India's Rites has been working with DSVN since the 1970s.

Signalling and telecommunications

Semaphore signals and token-block working on the Hanoi–Ho Chi Minh–Dong Dang and Haiphong–Lao Cai lines is to be replaced by colourlights and semi-automatic block. Vulnerable lineside telecommunications cabling would be replaced by a digital telephone and information system that would eventually cover the entire network.

Traction and rolling stock

In early 1996, the railway owned 64 steam and 384 diesel locomotives, but of the latter only 300 were serviceable and only 180 or so in daily operation. Steam traction remains in use on account of the plentiful local supply of coal. Only half the stock of about 1,000 passenger cars and 4,700 freight wagons was serviceable.

Recent deliveries include 15 1,000 kW, 251 D-engined diesel-electric Co-Co locomotives, similar to Indian Railways' Type YDM4, from India's Projects & Equipment Corp (PEC); and from Belgian industry came 16 1,300 kW, 84-tonne diesel-electric Co-Cos with Cockerill engines. ČKD Praha has delivered 10 750 kW, 56-tonne Type DEV-736 diesel-electric locomotives for metre-gauge. Other diesel traction includes GE and Russian-built Type TY 300 kW units, and 13 locos bought secondhand from Queensland Rail in 1994.

The railway's urgent requirement is for locomotives of higher power, and hopes are pinned on the possibility of a technology transfer agreement with an overseas manufacturer that would equip Gia Lam works for diesel loco construction. A similar deal would probably be the only way of meeting the need for some 500 new coaches by 1999.

PEC supplied nine new coaches and 63 bogies for rehabilitation of existing coaches under a contract awarded in 1992, while India's ICF supplied 16 coaches (including five sleepers) in 1995. Another Indian manufacturer, Jessop & Co, supplied nine first class coaches in 1996, along with 72 bogies for locally built stock.

UPDATED

YUGOSLAVIA (SERBIA AND MONTENEGRO)

Ministry of Transport & Communications

Boulevard Avnoj 104, Belgrade

Key personnel
Minister: Z Vuković
Head of Rail Transport Division: B Djikanović

UPDATED

Yugoslav Railways (JŽ)

Jugoslovenske Železnice
Community of Yugoslav Railways
Railways of the Republic of Serbia
Railways of the Republic of Montenegro
Nemanjina 6, Belgrade 11000, Yugoslavia
Tel: +381 11 688722   Fax: +381 11 641352

Key personnel
Director-General: Dr Svetolik Kostadinović
Deputy Directors-General
  Traffic, Technical and Commercial: Radomir Jovanović
  Systems, Economics and Financial: Milan Grujić
Directors
  Traffic: Aleksander Jevtović
  Technical: Stanislav Stanković
  Commercial: Savo Vasilević
  Finance: Nadežda Milićević
  Planning and Accounting: Dragan Paripović
  Legal Affairs and Personnel: Mila Djordjević
  Revenue Control: Aleksa Miličić
  International Affairs: Vilibald Jurak
  Communications: Zeljko Valentic

The striking crossing of the Mala Rijeka valley on the Belgrade—Bar line   1996

Gauge: 1,435 mm
Route length: 3,987 km
Electrification: 1,377 km at 25 kV 50 Hz AC

Political background

Following the break-up of the former Yugoslavia, JŽ now comprises the railways of Serbia and Montenegro.

The war in parts of the former Yugoslavia seriously disturbed traffic flows and caused a significant reduction in industrial production. This was aggravated by UN

imposition of sanctions on Serbia, with fuel shortages a particular problem for the railways. Movement of international freight was at a standstill, while passenger traffic, ostensibly unaffected by sanctions, was greatly reduced.

Lifting of sanctions at the end of 1995 heralded a gradual resumption of normal operations, with international freight connections re-established in January 1996. The main route for international trains is now the (Hungary)–Subotica–Belgrade–Niš–Dimitrovgrad–

(Bulgaria) north-south transversal line. As regards western Europe, JŽ's summer 1997 timetable had direct passenger trains to Budapest and Vienna only; foreign visitors were being warned to beware of the dangers of rail travel in Yugoslavia, where the desperate economic situation has given rise to widescale theft of money and personal belongings from travellers.

Passenger operations

In 1993 JŽ carried a total of 32 million passengers, an increase of 8.7 per cent on 1992. The following year saw a decline to 26.2 million journeys, but growth resumed in 1995, when 28.4 million journeys were recorded for 2,654 million passenger-km. A key event of 1995 was opening of the underground Vukov Spomenik station in Belgrade.

Freight operations

A total of 7.8 million tonnes was carried in 1993, down 58.3 per cent on 1992, and the 1994 figure was lower still at 5.3 million tonnes. Ending of sanctions at the end of 1995 came too late to have much effect on the year's results — 5.8 million tonnes carried for 2,652 million tonne-km.

New lines

Completion of the 68 km Valjevo—Loznica line, which has been under construction for some time, remains an aim of JŽ.

Improvements to existing lines

JŽ plans modernisation of the Belgrade—Subotica and Belgrade—Bar lines, and rehabilitation between Podgorica and Nikšić. Negotiations have been carried out with several potential partners interested in collaborating in modernisation of the railways, including possible construction of high-speed lines.

The massive reformation of the Belgrade network, begun in 1976, continues to make erratic progress. The project aims to supersede the dead-end central station and its inconvenient approach from Zagreb with a new 12-track facility served by a through route tunnelled beneath the city.

The key elements of the scheme are a north-south line from Pont de Pančevo, near the Danube, to a junction with the existing southeastern exit from Belgrade's terminus beyond Topcider; and, at National Library on this new line, a triangular junction with another new route threading the city via a route through Central Station, then bridging the Sava River to rejoin the present exit from Belgrade terminus to Zagreb at Novi Beograd. Thus, the finished scheme will create through running from both northeast and southeast to the Zagreb direction. The project involves in all 13 km of tunnelling, as well as an elevated approach to the new Sava River bridge.

In 1996 services began to use the new underground station at Vukov Spomenik, 40 m beneath Belgrade's city centre.

Traction and rolling stock

At the start of 1996, JŽ owned 189 electric and 274 diesel locomotives, 45 emu and 100 dmu sets, 625 hauled passenger cars (including 77 sleeping, 75 couchette, 20

Diesel locomotives

Class	Wheel arrangement	Power kW	Speed km/h	Weight tonnes	No in service	First built	Mechanical	Builders Engine	Transmission
641-100	Bo-Bo	441	80	62	80	1960	Mávag	Ganz	E Ganz
641-300	Bo-Bo	685	80	64	30	1985	Ganz-Mávag	PYLSIIK	E Ganz-Mávag
642	Bo-Bo	606	80	64	28	1960	DD	MGO	E B&L
643	Bo-Bo	680	80	67.2	14	1967	B&L/DD	MGO	E B&L
645	A1A-A1A	1,820	120	100.2	4	1981	GMF/DD	GM	E GM
661	Co-Co	1,933	112	108/114	92	1961	GM	GM	E GM
662	Co-Co	1,212	120	99	2	1965	DD	MGO/DD	E R Končar/Sever
664	Co-Co	1,617	124	99/103	9	1972	GM	GM	E GM
734*	B-B	478	60	48/54	15	1960	MAK	Maybach GT06	H Voith
744	BB	882	66	82.5	5	1977	LIZ-SSSR	LIZ	H LIZ-SSSR
666	Co-Co	1,845	122	100	4	1978	GM-USA	GM	E GM
742	B-B	1,213	110	67.2	1	1971	MIN	ČSR	H Voith
761	C-C	1,617	120	97.8	2	1966	Kraus Maff-D	D	H Voith

* Ex-German Federal Class 260/261
B&L: Brissonneau & Lotz   DD: Duro Dakovic   RK: Rade Končar Zagreb

Electric locomotives

Class	Wheel arrangement	Power kW	Speed km/h	Weight tonnes	No in service	First built	Builders Mechanical	Electrical
441	Bo-Bo	3,400/4,080	140	78	94	1970	ASEA/R Končar	ASEA/R Končar
4610	Co-Co	5,100/5,400	120	126	95	1972	Electroputere	Electroputere

Diesel railcars or multiple-units

Class	Cars per unit	Motor cars per unit	Motored axles/car	Power/motor kW	Speed km/h	Cars in service	First built	Builders Mechanical	Engine	Transmission
712	2	1	4	2×213	120	15	1980	Duro Dakovic	MAN	H Voith
811	4	2	2	367	118	11	1974	Ganz-Mávag	Ganz-Mávag	M Ganz-Mávag
812	1	1	1	110	90	80	1958	Goša	MAN	M MAN

Electric railcars or multiple-units

Class	Cars per unit	Motor cars per unit	Motored axles/car	Output/motor kW	Speed km/h	Cars in service	First built	Builders Mechanical	Electrical
412	4	2	4	170	120	45	1980	RVR	RVR

restaurant and buffet cars) and 17,169 freight wagons.

JŽ has requested a credit of SwFr100 million from Eurofima to finance purchase of new vehicles and spare parts to rehabilitate existing stock. An initial tranche of SwFr10 million was agreed in February 1996. With the ending of sanctions, delivery resumed of 23 suburban emus ordered from RVR Riga in 1991. SAB-Wabco is supplying braking equipment to raise the maximum speed of 23 coaches to 200 km/h, under a contract which also includes technology transfer to Yugoslav industry.

Signalling and telecommunications

About 50 per cent of railway stations are equipped with station relay signalling; automatic block system, or interlocking are installed on about 40 per cent of lines, and Automatic Train Control (ATC) on 34 per cent of lines. CTC was commissioned on the Belgrade—Bijelo Polje line (311 km) and between Belgrade and Bar (481 km) during 1996, whilst automatic block is being installed over the Subotica—Belgrade—Niš—Preševo main line, totalling 840 route-km.

Lineside telecommunication cables and dispatching telephone systems with selective dialling and identification are installed on 37 per cent of lines.

Electrification

The only project currently proposed is for energisation of the Lapovo—Kraljevo—Požega route, which would provide alternative access to the Bar line for electric trains.

Track

Rail: UIC 45A is installed over 376 km; UIC 49 over 2,254 km; and UIC 60 over 206 km
Crossties (sleepers): Wooden, 2,600 × 260 × 160 mm; concrete, 2,400 × 300 × 192 mm
Spacing: 1,666/km
Fastenings: K, SKL-2 and Pandrol
Min curvature radius: 250 m
Max gradient: 2.5%
Max axleload: 22.5 tonnes

VERIFIED

ZAMBIA

Ministry of Communications & Transport

PO Box 50065, Block 33, Fairley Road, Ridgeway, Lusaka
Tel: +260 1 251444
Fax: +260 1 253260/262441

Key personnel

Minister: W J Harrington
Deputy Minister: Gilbert Mululu
Permanent Secretary with responsibility for railways:
   R C Mukuma

UPDATED

Zambia Railways Ltd (ZR)

PO Box 80935, Corner of Buntungwa Street and Ghana Avenue, Kabwe
Tel: +260 5 222201/9   Fax: +260 5 224411

Key personnel

Chairman: P S Chamunda
Chief Executive: Clement C F Mambwe
Directors
   Technical Services: Igwa U Sichula
   Traffic and Marketing: Chris C Musonda
   Finance: Goodson M Moonga
   Personnel: Ms Angela Malawo
General Managers
   Workshops: Bedford Lungu
   Central: H C K Nyimbili
   South: Baxton Siwila
   North: Kingston Mkandawire
Chief Civil Engineer: Yubya Mwanawina
Chief Mechanical and Electrical Engineer: Webster Mutambo
Chief Signal and Telecommunications Engineer:
   P C Lumumbe
Managers
   Traffic: David Mwaliteta
   Finance: A L Fernando

Marketing: Frank Kangwa
Purchasing and Stores: Francis Zulu
Passenger Services: Luke Mwanza
Freight Services: Hilary Mphuka

Gauge: 1,067 mm
Route length: 1,273 km

Political background

Formerly part of Rhodesia Railways (RR), Zambia Railways was segregated as an autonomous system in 1976. It comprises the old RR system north of the Victoria Falls Bridge, to which was added in 1970 the 164 km Zambesi Sawmills Railway from Livingstone to Mulobezi. RR remained a legal entity until 1996, when its assets were eventually divided between ZR and National Railways of Zimbabwe.

Since its independence, ZR has been handicapped by the political crises in the region and the problems of some neighbouring railways, which have clouded definition of the land-locked country's rail routes to the sea ports with

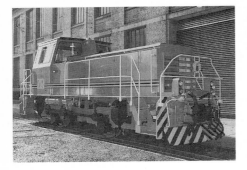

ZR has recently acquired some new shunting loco-motives from CMI Belgium   **1996**

uncertainty. Rail outlets are of critical importance to Zambia's copper industry, which generates 90 per cent of its exports. The TAZARA system's operating difficulties (see Tanzania entry) have restricted the potential of its route to Dar-es-Salaam, originally envisaged as Zambia's primary export rail route, and the Benguela Railway to Lobito in Angola has been affected by the unrest to the west. Assignment of copper traffic to the TAZARA or Victoria Falls routes is decided by the government.

ZR is a subsidiary of ZIMCO, a holding company for all state-owned enterprises, which also embodies the country's two road haulage companies. Since 1984, ZR has been a limited company, with freedom to set its own tariffs.

ZR's position as one of the poorest performers in the country's transport sector is changing under a restructuring plan which is currently being implemented. The railway is to concentrate on its core freight business, with substantial effort directed to productivity improvements. Staffing levels are being reduced, with the employee total down from 8,500 in 1993 to 5,400 in 1995. More foreign exchange will be earmarked to pay for automated track maintenance equipment, track renewals, mobile radios and motive power overhaul. Contract maintenance of rolling stock is under consideration, as is hiving-off the railway workshops to the private sector.

Hoped-for improvements were slow in coming through, however, not least on account of continuing low levels of investment in infrastructure rehabilitation. A spate of accidents in 1995 and 1996, attributed largely to poor track conditions, compounded the longer-term effects of theft and damage to signalling equipment. The problems were compounded following an aid freeze by western donor nations after the November 1996 election was boycotted by opposition parties, and the fragile economic liberalisation process which was due to see privatisation of the country's copper mines and other state-owned assets was in danger of stalling.

Passenger operations

In 1997, ZR was running a daily service over the 851 km between Livingstone and Kitwe (augmented by a thrice-weekly service on the Livingstone—Lusaka section of the route), two daily return trips between Livingstone and Victoria Falls (13 km) and a twice-weekly service between Livingstone and Mulobezi (163 km). For service details on the TAZARA line see Tanzania entry.

Passengers benefited from introduction of refurbished coaching stock in 1991, but this has done little to attract extra patronage. Traffic figures for 1995 were 1.3 million passenger journeys, 267 million passenger km — little more than half what they had been a decade before. Rolling stock shortages have conspired to reduce capacity even where demand has been strong and, in 1994, ZR arranged lease of 50 cars from Spoornet in South Africa to augment the Livingstone—Kitwe service.

A new express passenger service run by South Africa's Spoornet had been planned to link Lusaka and Johannesburg starting in 1992, but the project was abandoned because of the poor state of ZR's track.

Freight operations

Copper is the principal commodity carried, but this has been vulnerable to road competition. In addition to the constraints on performance due to fallible equipment, traffic growth has been restricted by several factors: slow turn-round of wagons at customers' sidings and on neighbouring railways; inflation and the depreciation of the Kwacha; and unsettled politics and strife in neighbouring countries. Traffic figures for 1995 were 1.9 million tonnes, 462 million tonne km — less than half what they had been a decade previously.

New lines

In 1989, the government released funds to complete a 24 km line from Chipata to the Malawi border at Mchinji, designed to provide another outlet for Zambian traffic. Having lain dormant for several years, tracklaying was in progress in 1994.

Improvements to existing lines

The main line between Livingstone and Kalomo consists of 80 lb/yd rail on wooden sleepers laid in 1945 or earlier and badly in need of replacement. The stretch from Kalomo to Mookamunga has been relaid with 90 lb/yd rail on concrete sleepers as part of the Third Railway Project of the World Bank. A further relay of 66 km using reclaimed 80 lb/yd rail was undertaken from Kaloma southward to Makoli in 1990-91. This work had US$5.2 million of assistance from the African Development Bank. On completion of these projects there still remains some 100 km of substandard track in the section. Elsewhere, lengthy sections require resleepering.

Canadian consultants Canarail were commissioned in 1994 to study ways of increasing capacity between Livingstone and Mulobezi.

Traction and rolling stock

In 1993, ZR was operating 60 main line diesel locomotives, comprising 56 General Electric U20C 1,330 kW (US-built and delivered in batches from 1967-76), four of the same type built by Krupp in 1980, plus 14 General Electric U15C 1,016 kW shunters. There were 77 passenger cars (six sleepers, 19 standard class, 36 economy class, three buffet/dining and six snack cars) and 6,713 freight wagons.

ZR also hires from Spoornet of South Africa and operates between 15 and 30 of its locomotives, and 50 coaches which were leased in 1994.

In 1990, employing internally generated funds of US$30 million, ZR ordered 15 Type GT36CU-MP locomotives from GM Canada. Delivery commenced in 1993.

Other recent deliveries were 100 bogie covered wagons from BN and 25 container flats from BREC, Belgium, while Braithwaite of India was supplying 20 sulphuric acid tank wagons in 1996-97.

Type of coupler in standard use: Alliance automatic, bottom-operated, Contour 10A

Type of brake in standard use: Vacuum

Signalling and telecommunications

The 851 km in total from Livingstone to Ndola and the Copperbelt branch section between Ndola and Kitwe are controlled by CTC (centralised traffic control) with multiple-aspect colour light signals. Sections outside CTC territory are worked on the token block system or, in the Copperbelt, on the train staff system. The CTC system was installed during 1961-64 and utilised open-wire carrier circuits along the line or rail. Operating from a centre at Kabwe, the CTC has now been renewed with all-electronic apparatus by Siemens AG at a cost of US$15.8 million. A total of 61 relay interlockings are remote controlled from Kabwe, whilst a further six stations have locally controlled relay interlockings.

The overhead line carrier system has been replaced by radio transmission because of theft and vandalism of wires, generators and batteries, with resultant interruption of the new CTC. The African Development Bank funded the US$9.14 million conversion which was finished in 1990.

Other recent projects include installation of a Mitsui digital multiplex microwave radio system between Ndola and Livingstone and upgrading of a computer mainframe. A start was made with purchase of hand-held radios for communication between yard staff and signalboxes. Installation of mains electricity was completed at a further 15 stations, replacing diesel generators.

Track

Rail: 45.13 kg/m

Crossties (sleepers): Wood, 127 mm thickness; concrete, 200 mm thickness; spaced 1,340/km in plain track, 1,400/km in curves, for concrete, 1,400/km in both cases for wood

Fastenings: Coach screw, clip and spring washer (triple coil) for wood, Pandrol for concrete sleepers

Min curve radius: 8.7°

Max gradient: 1.75%

Max axleload: 15.25 tonnes

UPDATED

Njanji Railways

PO Box, Lusaka

Key personnel
Managing Director: C Mayatwa

Gauge: 1,067 mm
Route length: 16 km

Organisation

This operation, started-up by the state copper mining company and now run independently, established a cross-city commuter service in Lusaka in 1990, largely over existing tracks. The two diesel railbuses originally employed proved inadequate for the demand, and now the service is provided by two locomotives and eight coaches hired from ZR.

The success of the limited service offered has stimulated plans for extension over ZR's main line to serve Ngwerere in the north and Chilanga to the south.

VERIFIED

ZIMBABWE

Ministry of Transport and Energy

PO Box Cy 595, Kaguvi Building, Causeway, Harare
Tel: +263 4 700693   Fax: +263 4 708225

Key personnel
Minister: Simon K Moyo

VERIFIED

National Railways of Zimbabwe (NRZ)

PO Box 596, Bulawayo
Tel: +263 9 363716   Fax: +263 9 363502

Key personnel
Chairman: A J Laurie
General Manager: Alvord Mabena

Assistant General Managers
  Finance: Alfred Nyalila
  Personnel and Administration: Samson Zumbika
  Technical Services: E S Marowa
  Operations: C M Chivonivoni
Chief Internal Auditor: D Sithole
Chief Accountant: L D Mkandla
Chief Traffic Manager: Welcome Phineas Lugube
Chief Planning Manager: Mazikhethela Banana

Chief Mechanical Engineer: Martin Kuzviwanza
Chief Manpower Manager: Eliot Mashingaidze
Chief Civil Engineer: J Nyawura
Chief Electrical Engineer: A C Dube
Chief Signal Engineer: D J Scott
Manager, Computer Services: Raphael S Wabatagore
Public Relations Manager: H Mondhlani
Manager, Marketing Development:
 Chenjerai Nziramasanga
Manager, Eastern Area: V Sithole
Manager, Southern Area: G W T Tyamzashe

Gauge: 1,067 mm
Route length: 2,759 mm
Electrification: 313 km at 25 kV 50 Hz AC

Political background

NRZ was created in 1967 out of Rhodesia Railways (RR), the northern portion of which became Zambia Railways. The old RR remained a legal entity until 1996, when division of its assets between the two countries was finally agreed.

An important condition attached to the Railway II Project agreed in 1991 was that the country's Railways Act be amended to give NRZ more commercial and financial freedom of decision making. NRZ would be required to act on normal business principles, with government involvement limited to appointment of the railway's management board.

The revised Act made provision for government assumption of financial responsibility for upkeep of rail infrastructure, for use of which NRZ would pay tolls. In 1995, the government decided that NRZ would be split into separate operating and infrastructure divisions, with the aim of improving the railway's ability to compete with road transport. However, due to scarcity of funds the government has been unable to take on World Bank inspired obligations to fund the infrastructure and pay for uneconomic passenger services kept running for social reasons. As no money could be expected from the government, NRZ was expecting a deficit of Z$240 million in 1996; with already high debt levels at banks, the corporation was in in a serious financial position.

Passenger operations

There is a daily train between the two largest cities, the capital Harare and Bulawayo, and tourist services between Bulawayo and Victoria Falls. A daily service operates between Harare and Mutare on the Beira Corridor route, and there are also services between Somabhula and Chiredzi in the southeast of the country.

Fare increases have contributed to the reduced passenger carryings evident since the record figure achieved in 1989, when 3.1 million journeys were made. In 1995 the total was 1.8 million.

A 1986 proposal for a Harare suburban electric system has been revived in part, and the project is being handled by the Ministry of Local Government, with NRZ's participation limited to technical advice. Sofretu was contracted to undertake a feasibility study of a 28 km link between the city and its satellite town of Chitungwiza.

Freight operations

The downward trend in freight movement apparent over

five years was reversed in 1995, when tonnage rose by 14 per cent to 12.3 million for 4,754 million tonne-km. This was some 10 per cent over budget, with increases in maize, chrome ore, cement, coke and sugar cane more than offsetting decreases in iron ore and tobacco.

Traffic continued to be affected by drought, with erratic rains in 1994-95 causing failure of the maize and wheat harvests but stimulating strong yields of sugar cane and tobacco. In addition, the railway was called upon to shift some 500,000 tonnes of grain to areas where disaster-relief supplies were urgently required. The arrival of rains for the 1996-97 growing season gave expectations of increased carryings of home-grown grain, while low water levels in the Kariba dam as a result of the shortfall of rain in previous years meant NRZ was asked to shift extra coal to coal-fired power stations to make up for lower output of hydroelectricity.

NRZ operates a merry-go-round operation supplying ore from Ngezi (on the Somabhula—Rutenga section) and coal from the Wankie Colliery Co at Hwange to the state-owned ZISCO iron and steel manufacturing complex at Redcliff. The trains employ purpose-built rotary tippler wagons by ZECO of Zimbabwe, the coal wagons having aluminium body sides; ore wagon payload capacity is 58.5 tonnes, that of a coal wagon 60.5 tonnes. Both iron ore and coal are loaded with trains on the move beneath overhead bunkers. Hauled by GM Class DE 10A 1,678 kW locomotives, the trains are formed of 60 wagons grossing over 4,500 tonnes, each powered by four DE 10A units. From loading to destination tippler takes 8 hours, while from Hwange source to Redcliff takes a coal train 16

hours. Coal for other destinations generally moves in unit trains of about 34 wagons.

In 1997, South African interests were proposing to develop an iron ore processing plant in the Manica province of Mozambique, using cheap local sources of natural gas to produce hot briquetted iron for the Asian market. The project would use Zimbabwean ore, meaning extra traffic for NRZ on the Beira Corridor if it comes to fruition.

Intermodal operations

Almost 90 per cent of the country's tobacco crop is exported in containers, along with tea, coffee, graphite, hides and skins, nickel and tin. Containerised imports for the Harare area's extensive industrial development include machinery, lubricants, bricks, iron and steel. NRZ's two container terminals are Dabcon, at Dabuka near Gweru, and Locon, at Lochinvar near Harare.

In 1996, users of the Beira Corridor through Mozambique agreed to pay a fee of US$5 per TEU or tonne of break-bulk cargo on the route in order to keep the line open. The poor state of permanent way on the Mozambiquan section had led to a severe derailment problem.

New lines

NRZ intended to make a start in late 1997 on upgrading the line from Heany Junction, just outside Bulawayo, to West Nicholson, and building a new line from West Nicholson to Beitbridge. This line would shorten by some 300 km the route from the second city of Bulawayo to the South African border. A joint venture was established in 1996 with a private company, New Limpopo Bridge, with a view to building the new link on a build-own-operate-transfer basis.

Improvements to existing lines

In 1997, the Zimbabwean section of the Beira Corridor was being upgraded at Umfeseri, with elimination of sharp curves and steep gradients in this area.

Traction and rolling stock

In 1995, NRZ owned 30 electric, 15 steam and 150 diesel locomotives; 325 passenger cars (including 17 buffet/dining, and 117 sleeping cars) and 11,898 freight wagons.

NRZ is continuing a major rationalisation and updating of its diesel locomotive fleet. For historic reasons, the fleet is a mix of 11 classes, embodying nine types of engine, and featuring both electric and hydraulic transmissions. A programme inaugurated in 1992 saw scrapping of 110 locomotives, mainly of Classes DH2, DE7 and DE8/8A. The principal Classes retained are DE10A (GM-EMD GT22LC-2), DE9A (refurbished GE U10B and U11B), and DE6 (refurbished GE U20C). NRZ hoped that improved diesel locomotive availability would allow it to retire, in 1997, all steam locomotives still employed on shunting work, with a few of these machines being retained for tourist specials.

NRZ hoped to retire, during 1997, the remaining steam locomotives still at work on shunting duties. This Garratt was photographed at Bulawayo (D Delaney)
1996

Class EL1 25 kV electric locomotive hauling a mixed freight (Marcel Vleugels)   **1996**

Electric locomotives

Class	Wheel arrangement	Output kW	Speed km/h	Weight tonnes	No in service	First built	Builders Mechanical	Electrical
EL1	Co-Co	2,400	100	114	30	1983	ZECO/SGP	50 c/s Group

Diesel locomotives

Class	Wheel arrangement	Power kW	Speed km/h	Weight tonnes	No in service	First built	Mechanical	Builders Engine	Transmission
DE 6	Co-Co	1,559	116	90.84	9	1966	GE-USA	GE 7-FDL-12	E GE-USA
DE 9A	Bo-Bo	732	103	61.3	64	1975	GE (U11B)	D 3512	E GE
								D11 JWAG Caterpillar (re-engined 1992-94)	
DE 10A	Co-Co	1,678	107	94.35	61	1982	GM USA/Canada	12-645E3 B (GM)	E GM
DE 11A	Co-Co	2,508	102	113.998	13	1992		16-645E3B	E
DE 2	1 Co-Co 1	1,095	88	114.8	3	1955	EE	EE 16 CSVT Mk II	E EE

For the future, NRZ is studying the possibility of using engines able to burn lower-grade fuels, microprocessor control systems, three-phase AC drives and electro-diesel designs. The last-mentioned is of interest because at present tonnages are not great enough to justify the capital costs of major electrification extensions, so that the ability of a locomotive to work unchanged from non-electrified into electrified territory would be valuable.

A new fleet of coaches was introduced during 1996, including sleepers and day coaches with reclining seats.

Type of coupler in standard use: Automatic centre buffer coupler, Alliance No 1 and 2 heads
  Passenger cars: 5 × 5 in, 5½ × 5 in shanks
  Freight wagons: 8 × 6 in, 7 × 5 in shanks
Type of braking in standard use: Vacuum on passenger and freight stock except for liner train wagons, which are on direct release airbrakes

Signalling and telecommunications

A new CTC (centralised traffic control) supervisory and remote-control system was commissioned on the Victoria Falls—Bulawayo section in 1993. However, its usefulness was reduced by continuing dependence on a vulnerable copper-wire pole route for communications. Consideration has been given to provision of a reliable microwave radio communications system to all stations and sidings. CTC now extends to almost 1,600 route-km.

Second-generation CTC equipment is being installed between Harare and Mutare (the Zimbabwean section of the Beira Corridor export route to the Indian Ocean) to replace the signalling system dating from 1960. Following a funding agreement with the African Development Bank, a Z$83 million contract for this was let to Siemens in January 1997, with completion scheduled for December 1998. As part of the work, the line will be equipped with a vandal-proof digital microwave radio system.

Reliability problems have also plagued the railway trunk dialling system in the coalfields and other areas. Use of Post Office facilities as a back-up continues to cost a substantial sum every year. Hot box detectors on the North Line have been removed due to poor telecommunications. As a result, accidents caused by broken axles are rife, causing losses running into millions of dollars.

Following the success of a temporary freight traffic control centre set up to cope with the additional grain traffic handled in 1992-93 under the drought relief programme, NRZ has established a permanent control centre to monitor freight operations country-wide.

Electrification

The 313 km route between Harare and Gweru is electrified on the 25 kV 50 Hz AC system. Rewiring was carried out in 1995 of 22 km of catenary over the original electrification test section between Gado and Samwari, where contact-wire breakages had been giving trouble for years.

NRZ has more Class EL1 electric locomotives than current traffic levels demand, so locomotive availability is maintained by cannibalising mothballed machines.

Track

Rail: UICE standard 54 kg/m (307 km of main line only); remainder of main line BS45 kg/m; branch lines BS45, 40 and 30 kg/m. A new standard rail, BS90A, has been adopted for all future use
Crossties (sleepers)

Type:	Thickness (under seat)
Concrete,	226 mm
Hardwood,	115 mm
Steel	10 mm; 13 mm

Spacing: 1,429/km
Min curvature radius: Main line 550 m, branch lines 300 m
Max gradient: 1 in 50
Max axleload: 20 tonnes

Traffic	1994	1995
Freight tonnes (000)	10,791	12,269
Freight tonne-km (million)	4,327	4,754
Passenger journeys (000)	2,138	1,837
Passenger-km (million)	651,421	545,977

Finance: (Z$ million)

Revenue		
Passenger	36.563	41.871
Freight	746.179	875.448
Parcels and mail	13.417	20.849
Other	42.672	55.743
Total	838.831	993.911

Expenditure		
Staff	494.850	548.557
Materials and services	341.295	459.106
Depreciation	17.386	21.613
Total	853.531	1,029.276

Operating surplus *(loss)*	(19.706)	35.365

UPDATED

MANUFACTURERS

Locomotives and powered passenger vehicles
Diesel engines, transmission systems and fuelling systems
Electric traction equipment
Non-powered passenger vehicles
Passenger coach equipment
Freight vehicles and equipment
Brakes and drawgear
Bogies and suspensions, wheels and axles
Bearings
Simulation and training systems
Signalling and telecommunications systems
Passenger information systems
Automatic fare systems and station equipment
Fixed electrification equipment
Permanent way equipment and services
Freight yard and terminal equipment
Workshop, repair and maintenance equipment
Turnkey systems contractors

LOCOMOTIVES AND POWERED PASSENGER VEHICLES

Alphabetical Listing

Adtranz
AGS
Alna Koki
Alusuisse Airex Composites
Alusuisse Road & Rail
Amerail
AMF
ANF-Industrie
Ansaldo Trasporti
Astarsa
Astra
Babcock & Wilcox Española
Badoni
Beijing
BEML
BHEL
BMZ
BN
Bombardier-Concarril
Bombardier Eurorail
Bombardier Inc
Bombardier Prorail
Breda
Brookville
Brush Traction
Bumar-Fablok
BWS
CAF
CFD
Changchun Railway Car Works
Changzhou Diesel and Mining
    Locomotive Plant
China National Railway Locomotive and
    Rolling Stock Industry Corporation (LORIC)
ČKD
CLW
Clyde
CMI
Daewoo
Dalian Locomotive & Rolling
    Stock Works
Datong Locomotive Works
De Dietrich Ferroviaire
Diema
Diesel Supply Co
DLW
Dorbyl
Duro Daković
DWA
Electroputere

Emaq
Energomachexport
Faur
Ferrostaal
Fiat
FIREMA Trasporti
Fuji Car Manufacturing
Fuji Heavy Industries
Ganz Ansaldo
Ganz-Hunslet
GE
GEC Alsthom
Gemco
General Motors Corporation
Gevisa
Goninan
Hanjin
Hitachi
Holec Ridderkerk UK
Hoogovens
Hunslet-Barclay
Hyundai
ICF
INKA
Jenbacher
Jessop
Kaelble-Gmeinder
Kalugaputjmach
Kawasaki
Keef
Kinki Sharyo
Kolmex
Kolomna
Konstal
Krauss-Maffei
LHB
Luganskteplovozstroj
Lyudinovo Locomotive Works
Mafersa
Materfer
Matra
Mecanoexportimport
Metrowagonmash
Michurinsk Locomotive Works
Mitsubishi Electric
Moës
MotivePower Industries
MSV
Muromteplovoz
National Railway Equipment Company
NEVZ
Newag

Niigata
Nippon Sharyo
Pafawag
PEC
Peoria Locomotive Works
Plymouth
Precision National
Qishuyan
Qualter Hall
Railcare
Rautarüükki
Reggiane
Relco
Republic Locomotive
RFS (E)
Ruhrthaler
RVR
Saalasti
SAN
Santa Matilde
Schindler
Schöma
SEMAF
SFL
Siemens SGP
Siemens Schienenfahrzeugtechnik
Siemens Transportation Systems
Siemens Transportation Systems Inc
Škoda
SLM
Stadler
Steele
Sully
Talbot
Techni-Industrie
Tokyu
Toshiba
Transrapid International
Transwerk
Tülomsas
Unilok
Union Carriage
Ventra
Vevey
Villares
Wagon Pars
Walkers
YEC
Zeco
Zephir

Classified Listing

BODYSHELLS AND COMPONENTS
Alusuisse Road & Rail Ltd
De Dietrich Ferroviaire
Ferrostaal
FIREMA Trasporti
Hoogovens
Mafersa
Techni-Industrie

DIESEL LOCOMOTIVES
Adtranz
Amerail
Astarsa
Babcock & Wilcox Española
Badoni
Beijing
BHEL
BMZ
Brookville
Brush Traction
Bumar-Fablok
CAF
CFD
Changzhou Diesel and Mining
    Locomotive Plant
China National Railway Locomotive and
    Rolling Stock Industry Corporation (LORIC)
ČKD
CLW
Clyde
CMI
Daewoo
Dalian Locomotive & Rolling
    Stock Works
Datong Locomotive Works
De Dietrich Ferroviaire
Diesel Supply Co
DLW
Dorbyl
Electroputere
Emaq
Faur
Ferrostaal
Fiat
Fuji
Ganz-Hunslet
GE
GEC Alsthom
General Motors Corporation
Gevisa
Goninan
Hitachi
Hyundai
Jenbacher
Kalugaputjmach
Kawasaki
Kolmex
Kolomna
Krauss-Maffei
Luganskteplovozstroj
Lyudinovo Locomotive Works
Materfer
Mecanoexportimport
Michurinsk Locomotive Works
Mitsubishi Electric
MotivePower Industries
Muromteplovoz
Newag
Niigata
Nippon Sharyo
PEC
Peoria Locomotive Works
Plymouth
Qishuyan
Reggiane
Republic Locomotive
Siemens SGP
Siemens Transportation Systems
Siemens Schienenfahrzeugtechnik
Stadler
Toshiba
Tülomsas
Union Carriage
Villares
Wagon Pars
Zeco

DIESEL MULTIPLE-UNITS AND RAILCARS
Adtranz
ANF-Industrie
BEML
Bombardier-Concarril
BWS
CAF
CFD
Daewoo
De Dietrich Ferroviaire
Duro Daković
DWA
Faur
Ferrostaal
Fiat
FIREMA Trasporti
Fuji
Ganz-Hunslet
GEC Alsthom
Goninan
Hanjin
Hitachi
Holec Ridderkerk UK
Hunslet-Barclay
Hyundai
ICF
INKA
Jenbacher
Kawasaki
Kinki Sharyo
LHB
Materfer
Mecanoexportimport
MSV
Niigata
Nippon Sharyo
Reggiane
RVR
Siemens SGP
Siemens
Stadler
Tokyu
Toshiba
Union Carriage

ELECTRIC LOCOMOTIVES
Adtranz
Ansaldo Trasporti
BN
Breda
Brush Traction
CAF
China National Railway Locomotive and
    Rolling Stock Industry Corporation (LORIC)
ČKD
CLW
Clyde
Daewoo
Datong Locomotive Works
Dorbyl
Duro Daković
Electroputere
Emaq
Fiat
FIREMA Trasporti
Ganz Ansaldo
Ganz-Hunslet
GE
GEC Alsthom
Gevisa
Hitachi
Hyundai
Jenbacher
Kawasaki
Kolmex
Krauss-Maffei
Mecanoexportimport
Mitsubishi Electric
NEVZ
PEC
Peoria Locomotive Works
Rautarüükki
Reggiane
Siemens SGP
Siemens Schienenfahrzeugtechnik
Siemens Transportation Systems
Škoda
SLM

Toshiba
Tülomsas
Union Carriage
Villares
Walkers
Zeco

ELECTRIC MULTIPLE-UNITS AND RAILCARS
Adtranz
Alna Koki
Amerail
ANF-Industrie
Ansaldo Trasporti
Astra
Babcock & Wilcox
BEML
BN
Bombardier-Concarril
Bombardier Prorail
Breda
BWS
CAF
China National Railway Corporation
Daewoo
De Dietrich Ferroviaire
Dorbyl
Electroputere
Ferrostaal
Fiat
Fuji Car Manufacturing
Fuji Heavy Industries
FIREMA Trasporti
Ganz Ansaldo
Ganz-Hunslet
GEC Alsthom
Goninan
Hanjin
Hitachi
Holec Ridderkerk UK
Hyundai
ICF
INKA
Jenbacher
Jessop
Kawasaki
Kinki Sharyo
Kolmex
LHB
Mafersa
Materfer
Mecanoexportimport
MSV
Niigata
Nippon Sharyo
PEC
Rautarüükki
Reggiane
RVR
Santa Matilde
Schindler
SEMAF
Siemens SGP
Siemens
Škoda
SLM
Stadler
Talbot
Tokyu
Toshiba
Union Carriage
Vevey
Villares
Walkers

HIGH-SPEED TRAINSETS
Adtranz
Ansaldo Trasporti
Breda
De Dietrich Ferroviaire
Fiat
FIREMA Trasporti
GEC Alsthom
GEC Alsthom Transporte SA
Hitachi
Kawasaki
Kinki Sharyo
Mitsubishi

...IN A WORLD HUNGRY FOR TRANSPORT SOLUTIONS

Where large numbers of people require fast and effective transportation every day, Goninan provides Quality solutions that are designed to meet customers' needs in price, style, comfort and timely introduction-to-service. Goninan products include double-deck electric passenger cars, self-propelled diesel passenger cars, and locomotive hauled cars that are proven, reliable, efficient and easy to maintain.

A. Goninan & Co. Limited is Australia's largest designer and manufacturer of rolling stock and provider of maintenance services to government and private railways. *Goninan Quality is **the** solution.*

GONINAN
QUALITY

A. Goninan & Co. Limited
(ACN 000 003 136)
Telephone 61 2 49235000 ◆ Facsimile 61 2 49235001

Nippon Sharyo
Siemens

**INDUSTRIAL, MINING AND SHUNTING
LOCOMOTIVES**
Brookville
CFD
Changzhou Diesel and Mining
   Locomotive Plant
CMI
Dalian Locomotive & Rolling
   Stock Works
Diema
Dorbyl
Faur
Ferrostaal
Ganz-Hunslet
Gemco
Hunslet-Barclay
Kaelble-Gmeinder
Keef
Konstal
Moës
Newag
PEC
Peoria Locomotive Works
Plymouth
Qualter Hall
Republic Locomotive
RFS (E)
Saalasti
SAN
Schöma
SFL
Steele
Ventra
Villares
YEC

LIGHT RAIL VEHICLES AND TRAMS
Adtranz
Alna Koki
ANF-Industrie
Ansaldo Trasporti
BN
Bombardier-Concarril
Bombardier Prorail
Breda
BWS
CAF
De Dietrich Ferroviaire
Duro Daković
Ferrostaal
Fiat
FIREMA Trasporti
Fuji Car Manufacturing
Fuji Heavy Industries

Ganz Ansaldo
Ganz-Hunslet
GEC Alsthom
Hyundai
Jessop
Kinki Sharyo
Konstal
Mafersa
Materfer
Nippon Sharyo
Rautarüükki
Schindler
SEMAF
Siemens SGP
Siemens
Stadler
Vevey

LOCOMOTIVE COMPONENTS
AGS
Alusuisse Airex Composites
Diesel Supply Co
Electroputere
Hoogovens
Lyudinovo Locomotive Works
Qualter Hall
Ruhrthaler
Sully
Techni-Industrie

LOCOMOTIVE REMANUFACTURE
Amerail
AMF
Brush Traction
Hunslet-Barclay
Jenbacher
National Railway Equipment Company
Newag
Precision National
Relco
Republic Locomotive
SFL
Transwerk
YEC

METRO CARS, MONORAILS AND PEOPLE MOVERS
Adtranz
Amerail
ANF-Industrie
Ansaldo Trasporti
Astra
Babcock & Wilcox Española
BN
Bombardier-Concarril
Bombardier Prorail
Breda
CAF

Changchun Railway Car Works
China National Railway Corporation
Daewoo
Fiat
FIREMA Trasporti
Fuji Car Manufacturing
Ganz Ansaldo
Ganz-Hunslet
GEC Alsthom
Hitachi
Holec Ridderkerk UK
Hyundai
ICF
Kawasaki
Kinki Sharyo
Konstal
Mafersa
Materfer
Matra Transport
Metrowagonmash
Mitsubishi
Nippon Sharyo
Rautarüükki
SEMAF
Siemens
Toshiba
Transrapid International
Union Carriage
Vevey
Walkers

**PASSENGER VEHICLE REFURBISHMENT AND
REPAIR**
Adtranz
Bombardier Prorail
Electroputere
Faur
Hunslet-Barclay
Newag
Railcare
Škoda

ROAD/RAIL LOCOMOTIVES
CFD
Saalasti
Unilok
YEC
Zephir

TILTING TRAINSETS
Adtranz
Fiat
Fuji Heavy Industries
Nippon Sharyo
Rautarüükki
Siemens

Company Listing by Country

ARGENTINA
Astarsa
Materfer

AUSTRALIA
Adtranz
Clyde
GEC Alsthom Australia
Gemco
Goninan
Walkers

AUSTRIA
Adtranz
Jenbacher
Siemens SGP

BELGIUM
BN
CMI
Bombardier Eurorail
Moës

BRAZIL
Emaq
Gevisa
Villares

CANADA
AMF
General Motors Corporation

CHINA, PEOPLE'S REPUBLIC
Beijing
Changzhou Diesel and Mining
    Locomotive Plant
China National Railway Locomotive and
    Rolling Stock Industry Corporation (LORIC)
Dalian Locomotive & Rolling
    Stock Works
Datong Locomotive Works
Qishuyan

CROATIA
Duro Daković

CZECH REPUBLIC
ČKD
Škoda

DENMARK
Adtranz

FINLAND
Adtranz
Rautarüükki
Saalasti

FRANCE
ANF-Industrie
CFD
GEC Alsthom
SFL
Sully
Techni-Industrie

GERMANY
Adtranz
Diema
Ferrostaal

Hoogovens
Kaelble-Gmeinder
Krauss-Maffei
Newag
Ruhrthaler
Schöma
Siemens Schienenfahrzeugtechnik
Siemens Transportation Systems

HUNGARY
Ganz Ansaldo
Ganz-Hunslet

INDIA
BHEL
CLW
DLW
PEC
SAN
Ventra

IRAN
Wagon Pars

IRELAND
Unilok

ITALY
Adtranz
Ansaldo Trasporti
Badoni
Breda
Fiat
FIREMA Trasporti
Reggiane
Zephir

JAPAN
Alna Koki
Hitachi
Kawasaki
Mitsubishi Electric
Niigata
Nippon Sharyo
Toshiba

KOREA, SOUTH
Daewoo
Hyundai

MEXICO
Bombardier-Concarril

NORWAY
Adtranz

POLAND
Bumar-Fablok
Kolmex

PORTUGAL
Adtranz

ROMANIA
Electroputere
Faur
Mecanoexportimport

RUSSIAN FEDERATION
BMZ
Kalugaputjmach
Kolomna

Lyudinovo Locomotive Works
Michurinsk Locomotive Works
Muromteplovoz
NEVZ

SOUTH AFRICA
Dorbyl
Transwerk
Union Carriage

SPAIN
Babcock & Wilcox Española
CAF

SWEDEN
Adtranz

SWITZERLAND
Adtranz
Alusuisse Airex Composites
SLM
Stadler

TURKEY
Tülomsas

UK
Adtranz
Brush Traction
GEC Alsthom
Hunslet-Barclay
Keef
Qualter Hall
RFS (E)
Steele
YEC

UKRAINE
Luganskteplovozstroj

USA
Adtranz
AGS
Amerail
Brookville
Diesel Supply Co
GE
General Motors Corporation
MotivePower Industries
National Railway Equipment Company
Plymouth
Precision National
Relco
Republic Locomotive

ZIMBABWE
Zeco

Adtranz

ABB Daimler-Benz Transportation GmbH
Group Holding Headquarters and Group Corporate
Centre
PO Box 130127, D-13601 Berlin
Telephone: +49 303 8320   Fax: +49 303 832 2000

Berlin office: Saatwinkler Damm 43, D-13627 Berlin

Key personnel
Group Executive Committee
President and Chief Executive Officer (CEO):
  Kaare Vagner
Executive Vice-President (EVP), Deputy CEO:
  Rolf Eckrodt
PAT and EVP, Business Segment A: Christer Bådholm
PAT and EVP, Business Segment B: Heinz F. Cronimund
PAT and EVP, Business Segment C: Rolf Eckrodt
PAT and EVP, Business Segment D: Chris Sheppard
EVP, Manufacturing & Technology: Joachim Gaissert
Chief Financial Officer and EVP: Ruben Ornstein
(PAT — Project Allocation Team Member) (Each EVP has
  specific regional, country or services responsibility,
  marked A, B, C, D or MT, CFO below)

Business segments and product ranges
A — Asia Pacific, Australia, Baltic, Canada, Denmark,
  Finland, Israel, Norway, Sweden, Turkey, USA
A — Rolling Stock: emus, dmus, metros, tilting trains, AGT
  systems (qv New Technology section)
B — Austria, Belgium, CIS, France, Greece, India, Italy,
  Netherlands, North Africa, Pakistan, Portugal, Spain,
  Sri Lanka, Switzerland
B — Rolling Stock: electric locomotives and traction
  equipment
C — China, Germany, Middle East
C — Rolling Stock: high-speed trains, diesel locomotives,
  LRVs
D — Sub-Sahara Africa, Ireland, Eastern Europe, Latin
  America, UK
D — Customer support: maintenance, repairs, aftersales
MT — Manufacturing, supply management, R&D
  processes, engineering, systematics, system lead
CFO — Control, accounting, legal, tax, treasury, project
  financing

ABB Daimler-Benz Transportation GmbH
Group Headquarters and Group Corporate Centre
Other Group corporate centres
Group staff officers (all senior vice-presidents (SVP))
SVP, Business Development & Acquisitions: Eberhard
  Beyer
Group: PAT and SVP, Group Marketing: Dieter Klumpp
SVP, Human Resources: Ian Butler
SVP, Representation, Public Affairs: Klaus Milz
SVP, Corporate Communications: Peter Polzer

Corporate Centres
Belgium
Adtranz (Europe) Ltd, Group Corporate Centre

Flexliner front modules attached to AM96 emu   *1997*

Rue Froissart 123-133, B-1040 Bruxelles
Telephone: +32 2 233 1161   Fax: +32 2 233 1162
Executive: Klaus Milz
Switzerland
ABB Daimler-Benz (Switzerland) Ltd
Affolternstrasse 44, CH-8050 Zurich
Telephone: +41 1 317 7398   Fax: + 411 317 7954
Executive: Heinz Cronimund.

**Groups with worldwide responsibility for designated
product range**
Germany
Total Rail Systems Group (TRS)
ABB Daimler-Benz Transportation GmbH
PO Box 130127, D-13601 Berlin
Telephone: +49 303 832 1701   Fax +49 303 832 2004
Executive (acting): Christer Bådholm
Signal Group (SIG) (qv Signalling & Communications)
ABB Daimler-Benz Transportation GmbH
PO Box 130127, D-13601 Berlin
Telephone: +49 303 832 1721   Fax +49 303 832 2003
Executive: Lars Afzelius

Fixed Installations (Electrification) Group (FIX)
Headquarters (qv Electrification section)
ABB Daimler-Benz Transportation (Deutschland) GmbH
Mainzer Landstrasse 349-351, D-60326 Frankfurt am
Main
Telephone: +49 69 750 7551   Fax: +49 69 750 7584
Executive: Anders Larsson

*Regional Transportation Companies, Regional and
Branch Offices*
RTC — Regional Transportation Company; BO — Branch

Office; Regional Office, with its RM (Regional Manager), is
the contact for countries where Adtranz has no own
office. Regional offices are usually attached to an RTC or
BO.

Albania: see Yugoslavia

Algeria: contact North-Africa Region Office RM in
Switzerland

Argentina (BO and Regional Office)
ABB Daimler-Benz Transportation (Argentina)
Av. del Libertator 2424, Piso 11a, RA 1425 Buenos Aires
Telephone: +541 808 8799   Fax: +541 808 8701 (808
8700 + extension 8488 for countries with tone-phone
system, USA and Brazil)
Executive: Eugenio-Jorge Vago (also RM for Argentina
and Chile)
RM, Latin America: Lutz Elsner

Australia (RTC and Regional Office)
ABB Daimler-Benz Transportation (Australia) Pty Ltd
PO Box 1387, Milton, Queensland 4034
Telephone: +61 73 858 2400   Fax: +61 73 367 2422
Executive: Lars Brodin (also RM for Australia, New
Zealand, Oceania, Indonesia)
Other plants in Dandenong, (Vic), Maryborough (Qld),
ABB Engineering Construction Pty, Ltd, Sydney (NSW)

Austria (RTC)
ABB Daimler-Benz Transportation Austria GmbH
PO Box 57, A-2351 Wr. Neudorf
Telephone: +43 22 364 040   Fax: +43 22 364 1858
Executive: Manfred Fischer

Bangladesh: Contact Southwest Asia Region Office in
Switzerland

Belgium
For Belgium, CIS (excluding Ukraine), Cyprus, France,
Greece, Luxembourg, Mongolia, Netherlands
Group HQ, Berlin (qv)
Telephone +49 303 832 1501   Fax +49 303 832 2004
Regional Manager: Wolfgang Wegener

Bhutan: Contact Southwest Asia Region Office,
Switzerland

Bosnia/Herzegovina: See Yugoslavia

Brazil (RTC)
ABB Daimler-Benz Transportation (Brasil) Ltda
Av. dos Autonomistas 1496, 06020-902, 06020-902
Osaco-SP
Telephone: +55 11 704 8405   Fax: +55 11 702 9318
Executive: Albert Blum
RM, Latin America: Lutz Elsner (qv Latin America)

Bulgaria (BO)
ABB Daimler-Benz Transportation (Bulgaria)
S Triadica Street, 1040 Sofia
Executive: Ivan Botev
Telephone: +359 2 981 4550   Fax: +359 2 981 4556
RM: John Kapala (qv Poland)

RS1 Regio-Shuttle light diesel power car   *1997*

MC double-power car with panoramic windows   1997

Cambodia: see Thailand

Canada: (BO)
ABB Daimler-Benz Transportation (Canada)
10300 Henri Bourassa, St Laurent, Quebec H4S 1Y4
Telephone +1 514 956 0691   Fax: +1 514 956 0424
RM: Ray Betler (qv USA)

Chile: See RM, Argentina

China: (RTC)
ABB Daimler-Benz Transportation (China) Ltd
Beijing Liaison office, (also Regional Office)
Unit 2501, Landmark Building, 8 North Dongsanhuan Bei
Rd, Chaoyang District, Beijing 100004
Telephone: +86 106 506 6214   Fax: +86 106 506 6218/9
Executive: Wilhelm Buckwar (also RM for Hong Kong,
China, Macao)

Changchun Adtranz Railway Company
5 Qingyin Road, Changchun, Jilin Province

ABB Daimler-Benz Transportation (China) Ltd
Shanghai Liaison Office
Room 1701, Hua Ting Guest House, 2525 Zhong Shan Xi
Lu, Shanghai 200030
Telephone: +86 216 439 5005   Fax: +86 216 439 5011
Executive: Andrew Lezala
RM: Wilhelm Buckwar (qv Beijing)

ABB Daimler-Benz Transportation (China) Ltd, Hong
Kong
Room 1301/2, Houston Centre, 63 Mody Rd, Tsimshatsui
East, Kowloon, Hong Kong
Telephone: +85 22 368 0155   Fax: +85 22 369 1874
Executive: Cyril Moore
RM: Wilhelm Buckwar (qv Beijing)
Other plant in Shenyang (qv Signalling section)

Croatia: see Yugoslavia

Cyprus: see Belgium

Czech Republic: (BO)
ABB Daimler-Benz Transportation (Czech)
Sokolovska 73, 18600 Praha 8
Telephone: +42 22 180 8112/111   Fax: +42 22 180 8114
Executive: Josef Schorm
RM: John Kapala (qv Poland)

Denmark: (RTC and Regional Office)
ABB Daimler-Benz Transportation (Denmark) a/s
Toldbodgade 39, DK-8900 Randers
Telephone: +458 642 5300   Fax: +458 641 5700
RM: Henrik Mortensen (for Israel)
Other plant in Hvidovre (qv Signalling section)

Egypt: (BO and Regional Office)
ABB Daimler-Benz Transportation (Egypt)
Commercial Centre-Office No. 33, Nile Hilton Hotel, Tahrir
Square, Cairo
Telephone: +202 579 0197/8   Fax: +202 579 0196
Executive and RM, Middle East: Rudi Stoecker

Ecuador: see Latin America

Finland: (RTC)
ABB Daimler-Benz Transportation (Finland) Oy
Atmitie 5c, FIN-00370 Helsinki
Executive: Markku Tanttu
Telephone: +358 1022 2060/10 2211   Fax: +358 1022
2066
(The general Helsinki area code is now 9 but all Adtranz or
ABB offices/companies in Finland are reached over their
common individual code 10)

France: see Belgium

Germany: (RTC)
ABB Daimler-Benz Transportation (Deutschland) GmbH
Am Rathenau-Park, D-6761 Hennigsdorf
German Adtranz company HQ
Telephone: +49 330 2890   Fax: +49 330 289 4050
Executive: Wolfgang Toelsner

ABB Daimler-Benz Transportation (Deutschland) GmbH
PO Box 100351, D-6128 Mannheim
Business Area Systems and Components, Executive:
   Uwe Stohwasser
Telephone: +49 621 3810   Fax: +49 621 381 8788

ABB Daimler-Benz Transportation (Deutschland) GmbH
Frankenstrasse 140, D-90461 Nürnberg
Business Area Mass Transit Executive: Wener Rauer
Telephone: +49 911 94560   Fax: +49 911 9456/1319
Other Plants in Berlin, Kassel and Siegen

ABB Daimler-Benz Transportation (Deutschland) GmbH
Mainzer Landstr. 349-351, D-60326 Frankfurt am Main

Telephone: +49 69 750 70   Fax: +49 69 750 7316
Fixed Installations Executive: Aders Larsson

Ghana: see South Africa

Greece: see Belgium

Hungary: (RTC)
ABB Daimler-Benz Transportation (Hungary) Kft
PO Box 52, H-1554 Budapest
Telephone: +361 270 5499   Fax: +361 270 5490
Executive: Matyas Racz
Holding company of MAV Dunakeszi Wagon
Manufacturing and Repair Ltd
Allomaf Setany 19, H-2120 Dunakeszi
Telephone +36 27 341 9517   Fax: +36 27 341 997
Executive: Lajos Varga
RM: John Kapala (see Poland)

India: (RTC)
ABB Daimler-Benz Transportation (India) Ltd
Guru Nanak Foundation Bldg, 15-16 Quatab Institutional
Area, New Delhi 110 067
Telephone: +91 11 686 8019   Fax: +91 11 686 6553
Other plant in Baruda
Executive: Viren P. Srivastava

Indonesia: (BO)
ABB Daimler-Benz Transportation (Indonesia)
Jl. Cikini Raya No. 69, Jakarta 10330
Telephone: +62 21 314 9115   Fax: +62 21 315 3963
Executive: Joachim Schulze-Warnecke
RM: Lars Brodin (see Australia)

Ireland: (BO)
ABB Daimler-Benz Transportation (Ireland)
Belgard Rd, Tallaght, Dublin 42
Telephone: +353 1 405 7368   Fax: +353 405 7370
Executive: Colin Blackwood
RM: Stig Svard (see United Kingdom, Derby)

Israel: see Denmark

Italy: (RTC)
ABB Daimler-Benz Transportation (Italy) SpA
Centro Direzionale Milano, Oltre 2, Palazzo Cedri, V le
Europa, I-20090 Segrate MI
Telephone: +39 22 684 01   Fax: +39 22 684 0555
Executive: Norberto Achille
Other plant in Vado Ligure, Roma

Japan: (BO and Regional Office)
ABB Daimler-Benz Transportation (Japan)
Roppongi First Bldg, 1-9-9 Rop, Minato ku, Tokyo 106
Telephone +81 35 562 0821   Fax: +81 35 562 0881
Executive: Gert Andersson (also RM for North-east Asia-
Pacific — Korea, Japan, Taiwan)

Korea: (RTC)
ABB Daimler-Benz Transportation (Korea) Ltd
143-42 Samsung-dong Kangnam-ku, Wonbang Bldg,
10th floor, 135-090 Seoul
Telephone: +82 2 569 1991   Fax: +82 508 2 4484
Executive: Gert Andersson

Laos: see Thailand

Latin America: Regional Office
ABB Daimler-Benz Transportation (Latin America)
762 South Military Trail, Deerfield Beach, FL 33445, USA
Telephone: +1 954 420 0302   Fax: +1 954 420 0798
RM, Latin America (Argentina, Brazil, Chile, Mexico, other
Latin American countries): Lutz Elsner

Libya: see Switzerland (North Africa Regional Office)

Luxembourg: see Belgium

Macedonia: see Yugoslavia

Malaysia: (RTC)
ABB Daimler-Benz Transportation Malaysia SDN BHD
Suite 27-02, Menara Lion, 165 Jalan Ampang, 50450
Kuala Lumpur
Telephone: +603 262 7366   Fax: +603 262 7335
Executive: Rauno Boga (also RM for South-East Asia-
Pacific (Cambodia, Laos, Malaysia, Myanmar, Singapore,
Thailand, Vietnam)

Malta: (RTC) — see Switzerland (North Africa Region
Office)

Networker Express Class 365 emu   1997

Mauritania: see Switzerland (North Africa Region Office)

Mexico: BO
ABB Daimler-Benz Transportation (Mexico)
Rubín Dario 281, Piso 8, 11580 Mexico
Telephone: +525 282 2053 Fax: +525 280 2054
Executive: Guillermo Carrion
RM for Latin America: Lutz Elsner, Florida (qv Latin America)

Middle East: see Egypt

Mongolia: see Russia

Morocco: see Switzerland (North Africa)

Myanmar: see Malaysia

Netherlands: see Belgium

Nepal: see Switzerland (Southwest Asia Region Office)

New Zealand: see Australia

Nigeria: see South Africa

Norway: (RTC)
ABB Daimler-Benz Transportation (Norway) AS
Stasjonsveien 1, N-2011 Stroemmen
Telephone: +476 380 9600 Fax: +476 380 9601
Executive: Ornulf Myrvoll

Pakistan: see Switzerland (Southwest Asia RO)

Philippines: (RTC)
ABB Daimler-Benz Transportation (Philippines) Inc
14th floor, JMT Bldg, San Miguel Ave, 1655 Pasig Metro Manila
Telephone: +632 634 2167 Fax: +632 634 2168
Executive: Lino P Pangan
Regional Manager: Gert Andersson (see Japan)

Poland: (RTC and RO)
ABB Daimler-Benz Transportation (Poland) Ltd
ul. Bitwy Warszawskiej 1920 r. nr. 18, PL-02-366 Warszawa
Telephone: +48 22 658 1020 Fax: +48 22 608 0766
Executive: John Kapala (also Regional Manager for Central Europe (Albania, Bulgaria, Romania, Hungary, Poland, - Bosnia/Herzegovina, Croatia, Macedonia, Slovenia, Czech Republic and Slovakia
Other site: Lodz, Warszawa, Zory (qv Signalling)
Pafawag
Fabryka Wagonów Pafawag SP ZOO
ul Fabryczna 12, PL-53-609 Wroclaw, Poland
Tel: +48 71 552258/562111 Fax: +48 71 562635/561289
(Adtranz holds 75 per cent of Pafawag the other 25 per cent is held by the Polish state)
General Director: Dipl Ing E Blaszczyk

Portugal: (RTC)
ABB Daimler-Benz Transportation (Portugal) SA
Rua Vice-Almirante Azevedo Cout, PO Box 60005, P-2701 Amadora Codex

Izmir LRVs   *1997*

Telephone: +351 1 496 9100 Fax: +351 1 499 1052
Executive: Manuel Norton
Other plant: Sines
Sorefame Division: address as above

Romania: (BO)
ABB Daimler-Benz Transportation (Romania)
16 I Cimpineau, 5th floor, R-70100 Bucuresti
Telephone: +401 312 0840 Fax: +401 312 0837
Executive: Franz Weber
Regional Manager: John Kapala (qv Poland)

Russia: (BO and RO)
ABB Daimler-Benz Transportation (Russia)
Pokrovskij Boulevard, Korpus 3, 1st floor, 10100 Moscow
Telephone: +70 95 207 2959 Fax: +70 95 230 2313
Executive and Regional Manager for CIS and Mongolia: Franz Weber

Singapore: (RTC)
ABB Daimler-Benz Transportation (Singapore) Pty Ltd
2 Ayer Rajah Crescent, 4th floor, Singapore 139 935
Telephone: +65 773 8797 Fax: +65 775 1328
Executive: Stanley Low
Regional Manager: Rauno Boga (qv Malaysia)

Slovakia: (BO)
ABB Daimler-Benz Transportation (Slovakia)
Nam SNP 15B, 81 106 Bratislava
Telephone: +421 732 3050 Fax: +421 732 6567
Executive: Rudolf Kvetan
Regional Manager: John Kapala (qv Poland)

Slovenia: see Yugoslavia

Spain: (RTC)
ABB Daimler-Benz Transportation (España) SA
Complejo Triada—Torre A, planta 4 a, Avenida de Burgos 17, E-28036 Madrid
Telephone: +341 383 6200 Fax: +341 383 6199

Executive: Jose Capparros
Other plants : Trapagaran 48510, Vizcaya; 28100 Alcobendas, Madrid (qv Signalling and Electrification sections)

South Africa: (RTC and RO)
ABB Daimler-Benz Transportation South Africa (Pty) Ltd
PO Box 857, Johannesburg 2000
Telephone: +27 11 806 9111 Fax: +27 11 887 0565
Executive and Regional Manager for Sub-Sahara Africa: Gert Kruger

Sri Lanka: see Switzerland (Southwest Asia RO)

Sweden: (RTC and RO)
ABB Daimler-Benz Transportation (Sweden) AB
Ostra Ringvdgen 2, S-72183 Vdster
Telephone: +462 132 2000 Fax: +462 114 8271
Executive and Regional Manager for Nordic Countries and Turkey: Staffan Hakanson
Regional Manager for Baltic States (Estonia, Latvia, Lithuania): Matts Holgersson
Other plants in: Helsingborg, Kalmar, Surahammar, Hdssleholm, Stockholm (qv Signalling section)

Switzerland: (RTC and RO)
ABB Daimler-Benz Transportation (Switzerland) Ltd
PO Box 8384, CH-8050 Zurich
Executive: Beat Mller
Regional Manager, North Africa Region (Algeria, Libya, Malta, Mauritania, Morocco, Tunisia) and Southwest Asia Region (Bangladesh, Bhutan, Pakistan, Nepal, Sri Lanka): Werner Bohli
Telephone: +411 318 3333 Fax: +411 312 6159
Other plants in: Geneva, Turgi

Taiwan: (RTC)
ABB Daimler-Benz Transportation (Taiwan) Ltd
6th F 1, 8 Min-Chuan 2nd Rd, Kaohsiung
Telephone: +88 67 335 5931 Fax: +88 67 335 5934
Executive: Charles Chen
Regional Manager: Gert Andersson (see Japan)
Other plant: Taipei

Tanzania: see South Africa

Thailand: (RTC and RO)
ABB Daimler-Benz Transportation (Thailand) Ltd
Manorom Bldg, 12th floor, 10501 Bangkok
Telephone: +66 2 249 7272 Fax: +66 2 671 7597
Executive and Regional Manager for Laos and Cambodia: Somkiet Prathanee

Tunisia: see North Africa Region Office, Switzerland

Turkey: (BO)
ABB Daimler-Benz Transportation (Turkey)
Özden Konak Ishani, Kat 9, Kasap Sokak No. 2, TR-80280 Esentepe- Istanbul
Telephone: +90 212 275 2811 Fax: +90 212 275 2821
Executive: Ali Savci
Regional Manager: Staffan Hakanson (see Sweden)

Uganda: (BO)
ABB Daimler-Benz Transportation (Uganda)
PO. Box 21821, Kampala
Telephone: +25 64 120 0419 Fax: +25 64 120 0419
Executive: Tom Barrow
Regional Manager: Gerrit Kruger

Class ALP44 locomotive for New Jersey Transit   *1996*

Class WAG 9 locomotive for Indian Railways   *1996*

Ukraine
Daimler-Benz AG, General Agent for Ukraine, wul. I.
Klimenko 5/2, 252680 Kiev 37
Telephone: +380 44 271 7842   Fax: +380 44 271 8555

United Kingdom: (RTC)
ABB Daimler-Benz Transportation (UK & Ireland) Ltd
Litchurch Lane, Derby DE24 8AD
Telephone: +44 133 234 4666   Fax: +44 133 226 6472
Executive and Regional Manager for UK and Ireland:
   Stig Svard
ABB Daimler-Benz Transportation (Rolling Stock) Ltd
Litchurch Lane, Derby DE 24 8AD
Executive: Stig Svard
Telephone: +44 1332 344666   Fax: +44 1332 292001

ABB Daimler-Benz Transportation (Customer support)
Ltd
Litchurch Lane, Derby DE 24 8AD
Telephone: +44 133 234 4666   Fax: +44 133 225 1884
Executive: Stig Svard
Other plants: Crewe, Chart Leacon, Doncaster, Ilford,
London, Manchester, Swindon

ABB Daimler-Benz Transportation (Total Rail Systems)
Ltd
St Dustan's Osmaston Rd, Derby DE 24 8B2
Executive: Keith Rands
Telephone: +44 133 226 6001   Fax: +44 133 225 1796
Other plants: Reading, Plymouth, Birmingham (qv also
Signalling section)

USA: (RTC and RO)
ABB Daimler-Benz Transportation (North America) Inc
1501 Lebanon Church Rd, Pittsburgh, PA 15236-1491
Telephone: +1 412 655 7000   Fax: +1 412 655 5860
Executive and Regional Manager for US and Canada:
   Ray Betler
Other plants: Pittsburgh, California, Elmira Heights, New
York, West Miffin, Pennsylvania

Yugoslavia
ABB Marketing (Eastern Europe) Ltd, General Agent for
Yugoslavia, also Albania, Bosnia-Herzegovina, Croatia,
Macedonia and Slovenia.
Schaffhauserstrasse 418, CH-8050 Zurich, Switzerland
Telephone: +411 318 2970   Fax: +411 302 0452
Regional Manager: John Kapala (see Poland)

Vietnam: (BO)
ABB Daimler-Benz Transportation (Vietnam)
138 A Giang Vo Street, Bo Dinh District, Hanoi
Telephone: +844 83 3625/6   Fax: +844 833 3883
Executive: Ernst Bening
Regional Manager: Rauno Boga (see Malaysia)

Corporate Developments:
ABB (Asea Brown Boveri AG, Switzerland) and Daimler-
Benz AG, Germany, merged their rail businesses in 1995
to form a new company. The 50:50 joint venture is called
the Adtranz (ABB Daimler-Benz Transportation Systems)

group and it has manufacturing subsidiaries (regional
transport companies — RTCs) in 25 countries, branch
offices (BOs) in 17 countries and several regional offices,
in most countries attached to an RTC or a BO. Two further
corporate centres are in Bruxelles and Zürich.

Adtranz acquired IVV (Ingenieur Gesellschaft für
Verkehrs-Planung und Verkehrs-Sicherung GmbH),
Braunschweig, in 1996. It was renamed ABB Daimler-
Benz Transportation (Signal) GmbH.

At the end of 1996, Adtranz and Changchun Car
Company, China (qv) signed a joint venture to produce
rolling stock for urban transport applications. CCC is
owned by the Chinese Railway Ministry and manufactures
1,200 passenger vehicles a year. From the beginning of
1997, a new company, the Changchun Adtranz Railway
Company, was formed with 51 per cent of shares owned
by Adtranz and 41 per cent owned by CCC. Planned
production is 160 vehicles a year.

Portuguese manufacturer, Sorefame, was renamed
Adtranz Portugal in 1996.

ABB Daimler-Benz Transportation (Hungary) KFT has
been established in Budapest as a Regional
Transportation Company and in 1996 acquired the
Dunakeszi Vaggon Manufacturing and Repair workshop
of MAV Hungary.

At the beginning of 1997 Adtranz acquired a 75 per
cent share of Pafawag, Poland, which manufactures
locomotives and it was renamed Adtranz Pafawag.

Jernbaneverket (the former infrastructure division of
NSB) and ABB Daimler-Benz Transportation (Norway)

Adtranz entered into a framework agreement, in
December 1996, for the supply of signalling products and
systems. Adtranz is supplying signal and interlocking
products and systems to Jernbaneverket. The agreement
runs until December 1999 and can be extended to
December 2001.

A branch office, ABB Daimler-Benz Transportation
(Uganda), has been established with Uganda Railways in
Kampala, following implementation of a joint venture with
the Uganda Railway Corporation (URC) for the
maintenance and upgrading of locomotives, railway
freight and passenger cars at the URC workshops at
Nalukolongo.

ABB Daimler-Benz Transportation (Switzerland) was
due to acquire the rolling stock business of Schindler
Waggon in January 1998. Schindler Waggon is a
subsidiary of the Schindler Group which manufactures
and maintains escalators and lifts. The component
manufacturing, construction/engineering and winding
technology divisions in Altenrhein continue with Schindler
Waggon and will eventually become independent
companies.

Products: Development, design, engineering, sales,
production, installation, maintenance and after sales
service of rolling stock, systems, components and
equipment for urban transport.

Electric and diesel traction vehicles for urban,
suburban and regional transport; and high speed,
including tilting trains; light rail vehicles; automated
guided vehicles; special vehicles.

Maintenance, refurbishment and after sales service for
rolling stock.

ECO2000 and LOCO2000 electric locomotives are
operating in Europe as DB Class 101 and Class 145, in
Italy with FS Class 412 and 464, and will in Greece with the
DE 2000, in Poland with PKB Class 112/113E as well as in
Russia with the EP10. LOCO 2000 traction units are
operating in Switzerland with SBB Class 460 and with BLS
Class 465, in Finland with VR Class Sr2, in Norway with
NSB Class EL18 and in Hong Kong with KCRC.
LOCO2000 derivatives are operating Euroshuttle trains
with Class 9000, in Britain and France freight trains with
Class 92, in Italy high-speed trains with FS ETR 500, and
India passenger trains with Class WAP5 and freight trains
with WAP9.

Contracts and deliveries
Australia
In a joint venture with Adtranz Australia, Walkers is
building five two-car emus for Westrail Perth. They will be
similar in design to previous emus and delivery is
expected during 1998. Each car carries 156 passengers.

Queensland Railways has taken delivery of 12 three-car
emus for suburban services around Brisbane and four
4-car interurban emus for the Queensland Gold Coast
service to Helensvale. A third series of six 3-car interurban
emus is in advanced production with deliveries expected
to be completed during 1997.

DB Class 101 electric locomotive (Adtranz Germany)   *1997*

Bangladesh

Bangladesh Railway (BR) has been taking delivery of 12 diesel-electric DE 1650 Co-Co metre-gauge locomotives since October 1996. They have a maximum speed of 100 km/h and will serve as motive power for passenger and freight trains between the cities of Dhaka and Chittagong. The locomotives have full width hoods which prevent unauthorised personnel riding along on any vehicle side.

Belgium

Belgian National Railways' (SNCB) contract for 240 Flexliner Front modules for AM 96 emus is under delivery, to be completed by 2000.

PR China

An X2000 by Adtranz Sweden has been ordered for the Guangzhou to Hong Kong line.

An Adtranz-led consortium has received the Shanghai Metro Corporation (SMC) order for a total rail system which involves development and building line 2 of the Shanghai Metro, running from East to West. The first part is expected to start commercial service by the end of 2001. The contract includes installation of the catenary system, telecommunications, remote control systems and 35 trains, each usually configured with six cars, but can be extended to eight cars.

The Guangzhou Metro Corporation (GMC) contract with the Adtranz/Siemens consortium to build a metro system for the city of Guangzhou is in advanced production. Adtranz has supplied 20 six-car trains (120 metro cars).

Kowloon-Canton Railway Corporation (KCRC) has taken delivery of two electric locomotives from the Adtranz/ITOCHU consortium. Similar to the Sr2 for Finnish State Railways, the locomotives were built by Adtranz Switzerland and SLM for delivery in 1997. Hong Kong—Lantau Railway (to the new Chek Lap Kok Airport) received the first of 23 emus in early 1997 from Adtranz/CAF. Deliveries were expected to be completed by the end of the year.

Denmark

Danish State Railways (DSB) has taken delivery of 44 three-phase driven, IR4 Flexliner emus for which Adtranz Denmark has provided the mechanical equipment and Adtranz Sweden the electrical equipment.

Six different Danish private railways have ordered 13 L2D dmus with deliveries starting in 1997. Derived from the DSB IC3 DMU, the L2D is a member of the Flexliner family with two cars, adapted for local and regional services, with a top speed of 140 km/h. The trailer car of the L2D, with floor height 600 mm above rail top, offers same-level boarding for passengers with prams, bicycles, heavy luggage or wheelchairs. Passenger capacity amounts to 129 seated and 60 standing. Up to five train sets can be coupled in multiple traction. Like all versions of the Flexliner family the L2D train sets are equipped with automatic couplers at both ends.

Egypt

Egyptian Railways (ER) is taking delivery of an additional 10 Type DE 2250 Co-Co diesel-electric locomotives from Adtranz Germany.

ENR is now operating 45 Co-Co ABU Tartour diesel-

Adtranz Blue Tiger freight locomotive   *1997*

electric locomotives supplied by the Adtranz Kassel plant in Germany. These are of a new modular design which permits one or two driver cabs, different track gauges, axle loads, clearance profiles and diesel engines within the range of 1,845 to 3,000 kW. ENR selected a design with one driver cab. The maximum speed is 80 km/h and total weight is 132 tonnes. The supply contract included a spare parts package, tools and comprehensive services, including training of personnel. Deliveries were completed in 1996. Since 1957 the Kassel plant has supplied over 400 diesel-electric locomotives to Egypt, including 68 DE 2550 units.

Finland

VR is taking delivery of its 20 electric Sr2 Bo-Bo locomotives from Adtranz/SLM Switzerland. The first two units Nos 2301 and 3202 were delivered to VR in 1996, with completion at the end of 1997. The Re Sr2 units run under 25 kV and have a maximum speed of 230 km/h.

France/Switzerland

SNCF/SBB

Eight SBB Colibri shuttle train sets consisting of power car and driving trailer, with immediate passenger cars added according to passenger volume, are being modified for two-system operation. They will serve as international regional express stock under two different single-phase AC catenaries, on the SBB with 15 kV along the Rhine line from Laufenburg and from Frick on the line Zurich to Basle, crossing into France and on the SNCF with 25 kV, continue to Muhlhouse. The first modified Colibri set was due to start in service in June 1997.

MC (Martigny-Le Châtelard) Railway continues across the French border connecting with an SNCF line of 56 km from Vallorcine—Chamonix—Mont Blanc to St Gervais—Les Bains/Le Fayet. SNCF is now operating three new Z800 double power cars with mixed adhesion/rack rail operation.

Two new Swiss MC double power cars of the same design as the SNCF vehicles also serve on this line. The five new units have panoramic windows. Built by Vevey Technologies and Adtranz Switzerland, they operate on third rail in France and overhead catenary in Switzerland.

Germany

German Railways (DB AG) has ordered 80 Class 145 electric freight locomotives and 145 Class 101 electric high-speed passenger locomotives from Adtranz Germany.

In production for DB AG are 80 Class 145 Bo-Bo freight locomotives with a maximum speed of 140 km/h. An option exists for another 400 units. They are designed for a catenary supply of 14 kV, and are at rated at 4,200 kW.

DB has started to take delivery of Class 101 Bo-Bo 14 kV high-speed electric locomotives for IC trains. These are from the ECO 2000 locomotive range with single-axle traction control, air conditioned driver cabs and engine room with centre aisle.

Since the end of 1996 DB has been receiving part of the order for 45 three-phase driven ET474 three-car trains for S-Bahn Hamburg from Adtranz/LHB. Deliveries were expected to be completed by the end of 1997. A contract for an additional 58 ET 474 trains is in production. Deliveries should start in 1999.

DB has placed an order with a consortium consisting of DWA and Adtranz, for 100 complete three-phase driven BR 481 emu eight-car trains for S-Bahn Berlin services. Each train will take 750 V DC, third rail, and have a maximum speed of 100 km/h. A second order for 400 complete BR 481 trains has been made. A preseries order for 10 complete trains has been delivered and passed type and acceptance tests. For the varied capacity demands, complete trains BR 481 can be split into half-trains (four cars) and quarter trains (two cars). Series production started 1997. Deliveries will extend to 2005.

Berlin Transport Company (BVG) has a contract with Adtranz for 25 HK four-car small-profile underground trains with three-phase drives, for delivery starting in December 1998. Out of a contract for 115 three-phase driven, standard profile H-type six-car underground 'Train 2000' units, two pilot trains were received during 1996. The first series-produced trains will be delivered in 1998.

Hamburg HHA (Elevated Railway) has a contract with Adtranz/LHB for a third series of 20 three-phase driven four-car DT4 trains. Power supply is 750 V DC third rail and train control is by MICAS which includes diagnostics with propulsion by eight water-cooled traction motors each rated 125 kW. Water heated by these contributes to passenger room heating.

The RS1 Regio-Shuttle introduced by Adtranz Germany is a new design of lightweight dmu with a 70 per cent low-floor, 760 mm above rail top. It has two double-doors and capacity is 76 seating and 94 standing. The trains will offer upholstered seats, space for wheel chairs, baby carriages and bicycles. It has a maximum speed of 120 km/h and can operate either as a single unit or, for larger passenger capacity, can be combined with a control car of the same overall design but without diesel engines. Alternatively, the RSI can act as a traction vehicle for freight wagons. Six regional railway companies have already ordered a total of 51 RS1 cars.

Adtranz Germany launched a tilting DMU design in 1996 for travel on curving tracks at higher speeds. It meets DB requirements for faster services on regional and branch lines. The first DB contract for 50 tilting Class 611 dmus was being fulfilled in 1997. A second DB contract for 50 tilting Class 612 dmus was expected to be completed in 1999.

The first three GTWm2/6 dmus with MTU diesel engine and DC traction motors (three-phase drive in future vehicles), which have the designation Class 596 Bm2/6, are now serving the DB non-electrified line Radolfszell—

Adtranz ML90 emu on Lisbon metro   *1997*

Stochack. The Swiss private railway Mittel—Thurgau Bahn (MThB) operates this line on behalf of the German Railways. The GTWm 2/6 units have been built by Adtranz Germany with contributions from DWA Bautzen, Germany and the Swiss companies Stadler Fahrzeuge, Busnang, Alusuisse Road and Rail, Zurich and Swiss Locomotive and Machine Works Ltd (SLM), Winterthur. This dmu is specifically intended for non-electrified suburban, regional branch and secondary lines.

Greece

Hellenic Railways Organisation (OSE) has ordered 25 DE 2000 diesel-electric locomotives from Adtranz Germany. Deliveries were due to start in 1997, with the locomotives capable of conversion to electric power upon the electrification of OSE's Athens—Thessaloniki main line. Hellenic Railway Organisation (OSE) started receiving its order for 25 diesel-electric DE 2000 Bo-Bo locomotives during 1997. The OSE network is being electrified between Thessaloniki and Athens and OSE specified that these locomotives should be capable of conversion to electric units by replacing as little equipment as possible. Adtranz will meet this condition by retaining the locomotive body, driver cabs, bogies, traction power converters and a major part of the electronic system. The three-phase squirrel-cage traction motors installed in the DE 2000 are already rated for the power of the future electric locomotive. This allows exchange of complete bogies between diesel-electric and electric locomotives. Adtranz plants in Germany, Austria and Switzerland are involved in the manufacture, assembly and commissioning of these locomotives. The maximum speed is 200 km/h.

India

IR is taking delivery of 33 electric locomotives derived from SBB's Class 460 design from Adtranz Switzerland, with mechanical parts by Adtranz Australia. Deliveries of 11 Class WAP 5 Bo-Bo passenger locomotives assembled by Adtranz Switzerland began in 1995 for completion in 1997. Deliveries of 22 Class WAG Co-Co freight locomotives were begun in 1996, with six assembled by Adtranz Switzerland and 16 delivered in semi-knocked-down configuration for completion by Chittaranjan Locomotive Works, India.

Israel

The Ports and Railway Authority contract for seven C3D dmus is in production and includes equipment from suppliers in Israel. These are intended for commuter services around Haifa and Tel Aviv but will also operate on regional lines. The C3D dmu is part of the Flexliner family which includes IC3D dmus and the IR4E emus of Danish State Railways as well as the L2D dmus of private Danish railways.

Italy

Italian Railways (FS) has ordered 50 Class E464 locomotives for regional passenger services from Adtranz Italy with electrical equipment from Adtranz Switzerland. Designed for push-pull operation, the E464 features a driving cab at one end and a luggage compartment at the other. Deliveries were due to start in 1998. Adtranz Italy, as a member of the Trevi consortium, took delivery of

electrical equipment for 60 power cars for 30 ETR500 high-speed trainsets ordered by Italian Railways (FS). Five of the trainsets are equipped to operate from three catenary systems (1.5 kV and 3 kV DC, 25 kV 50 Hz AC) for services to and from France.

Deliveries for 20 Class E412 Bo-Bo electric locomotives to FS from Adtranz Italy are now complete. Designed for Alpine transit services between Italy and Ausatria, the locomotives feature a power rating of 6 MW and take overhead current at 3 kV DC and 1.5 kV 16⅔ Hz AC. The maximum speed is 200 km/h.

Genova—Casella Railway has ordered two type E46 A electric power cars and two trailers from Adtranz Italy.

FS (Italian State Railways) and FNM (North Milan Railway) have contracts in production for a total of 82 double-deck emus with an Italian consortium comprising Adtranz, Ansaldo, Breda and Firema. The TAF (*Treni Alta Frequentazione*) consortium has ordered two power cars and two trailers for each train. Adtranz provides traction motors and motor bogies, other electrical equipment and assembly. Power cars will be three-phase driven and be supplied from 3 kV catenary. The trains will have 475 seats and a maximum speed of 140 km/h.

Satti (Ferrovie Torino-Ceres and Ferrovia Canavesana) has taken delivery of seven 3 kV emus, with a maximum speed of 130 km/h. Five operate in the Turin—Ceres line and two operate on the Canavesana Railway. Adtranz supplied the electrical equipment.

A Trento-Malè Railway contract for another Type E86 emu (as an addition to four units of an earlier order) is in production.

Sardinian Railways (FdS) is receiving from Adtranz and Breda eight diesel-electric ADe91 power cars and five trailer cars. These dmus operate on the 950 mm gauge regional lines near Cagliari, Sassari and Macomer.

Norway

Norwegian State Railways (NSB) is taking delivery of 22 Class EL 18 Bo-Bo electric locomotives from Adtranz Norway. The EL 18 is based on SBB's Class 460 design.

Adtranz Norway and Adtranz Sweden are supplying NSB with 18 non-tilting three-car emus for the Gardermoen airport line (one train in this order is to be fitted with tilt equipment for trial purposes). A further order has been received from NSB for 16 tilting four-car emus with an option for five more. Both have the same exterior and are technically of the same design, derived from the Swedish X2000 tilting train, but the four-car trains have a different interior for longer journeys. Production of the four-car trains will begin in 1998.

An additional four IC70 trains has been delivered. Each train consists of a power car, two non-driving trailers and a driving trailer. Power cars have three-phase drive, GTO power converters and the MICAS control system with diagnostics.

Pakistan

Adtranz and GE Transportation Systems are supplying Pakistan Railways with 30 Blue Tiger diesel electric locomotives, for delivery in 1998.

Poland

Polish State Railways ordered 50 electric locomotives from local manufacturer Pafawag, in which Adtranz holds

a 75 per cent stake. Eight of these locomotives are Class 112E, two-system units with 15 kV, 16.7 Hz AC or 3 kV DC supply, for international services between Warsaw and Berlin. The other 42 locomotives of Class 113E with 3 kV DC supply will operate on domestic express passenger and freight services. Their production is an international co-operation project between Adtranz companies in Poland, Italy, Germany and Switzerland. To a large extent, they will be similar to the Italian FS Class 112, now under delivery, and the propulsion is a derivative of the Locomotive 2000 concept.

Portugal

Adtranz Portugal (formerly Sorefame) is supplying Portuguese Railways with 10 four-car emus, in addition to an original contract for 42 four-car sets. It is also supplying seven two-car demus. Carris Lisbon received four LRVs. In 1993 Lisbon Metro received the first two three-phase driven, three-car prototype ML 90 emus, supplied from 750 V DC third rail. A further order for 17 ML90 emus was placed, followed by another in 1995 for 38 emus.

Russia

Russian Railways is taking delivery of 21 EP10 dual-voltage electric locomotives from Adtranz Switzerland. The EP10 is a Co-Co dual-system locomotive (25 kV AC and 3 kV DC) with a power of 7.2 mW and 160 km/h maximum speed.

South Korea

SMG (Seoul Metropolitan Government) has received 366 metrocars for the Seoul Metro, of which 183 are power cars, from Hyundai Precision Industries. Adtranz Sweden produced the propulsion systems with three-phase drive. In 1996 SMG received an additional 242 vehicles as part of an order placed in 1994.

Spain

CAF and Adtranz are supplying FGC (Ferrocarrils de la Generalitat de Catalunya) Barcelona with 16 suburban, 1,500 V DC supplied four-car S/213 LRVs with three power cars and one intermediate trailer. Adtranz is supplying complete electrical equipment, including inverters with water-cooled GTO modules and three-phase traction motors for an additional 20 four-car trainsets. Deliveries started in early 1997 and the trains were due to be in commercial service by January 1998.

RENFE has increased its suburban three-phase driven UT447 fleet with a second series of 46 trains. RENFE's UT447 stock now comprises 117 trainsets. RENFE is also taking delivery of 19 Flexliner IR2D dmus. Each unit has two aluminium-bodied cars and the maximum speed is 160 km/h. These units operate on the Vigo—Santiago—La Coruna line in the North of Spain.

CTB Bilbao opened Metro de Bilbao over a year ago with 24 emus equipped with GTO water-cooled drive inverters, three-phase asynchronous traction motors and MICAS S2 control system and diagnosis equipment.

Adtranz electrical equipment was specified by Metro Madrid for 50 two-car sets and it has ordered Adtranz electrical traction equipment for a further 63 vehicles built by CAF. The first two sets were due to be delivered in mid-1997 and the last six in 1998.

Sweden

Swedish Railways (SJ) has ordered seven X2000 high-speed tilting trainsets from Adtranz Sweden.

Adtranz and Bombardier Eurorail subsidiaries BWS and BN are supplying SL Stockholm with 12 LRVs. Delivery is expected to start in 1999. There is an option for 58 more.

Blekinge Lanstrafik AB and associated Kristianstad Lanstrafik in southern Sweden received a Y2 Flexliner three-car set in early 1997. There are now 15 Y2 Flexliner sets operating in Sweden.

SL Stockholm is taking delivery of 75 bi-articulated metrocars. They are formed into three-car trainsets, are designed for automatic operation and have advanced passenger information systems. Delivery started in early 1997.

Adtranz Sweden secured an order in 1997 from DSB Denmark for 27 three-car emus to operate on the Denmark—Sweden service via the Öresund bridge. There is an option for a further 18 emus. DSB will operate 17 emus and SJ Sweden 10. Delivery is between 2000 and 2001. The emu design specifies a maximum speed of 180 km/h, wide doors and low floor for fast urban operation.

Switzerland

Swiss Federal Railways (SBB) is taking delivery of 24 emu

Class DE1650 locomotive for Bangladesh Railways   *1997*

tilting trains from a consortium headed by Adtranz. Delivery of the preseries train was due in June 1998. From May 1999 one train per month will be delivered with completion in 2001.

The contract for 10 Class 465 Re 4/4 locomotives is in advanced production. BLS will operate and maintain the locomotives which will haul piggyback and container freight trains on the Lötschberg—Simplon line.

SBB took delivery of an additional 20 Regional Express trains (Zurich S-Bahn) during 1997. Each train comprises an SBB Class 450 Re 4/4 three-phase driven 3,500 kW locomotive with a single driver cab, with a maximum speed of 130 km/h, two intermediate passenger cars (one first class) and a second class driving trailer. The consortium producing the trains includes Adtranz Switzerland, Swiss Locomotive Works (SLM), Schindler Waggon Ltd (SWP) and Swiss Industry Company (SIG). Adtranz/SLM are producing the 20 locomotives.

An order for 11 GTW Be 2/6, low-floor, metre-gauge, articulated, electric LRVs is under delivery for Swiss private railways, with completion in 1998. Operating as single cars or multiple-units, the GTW Be 2/6 is designed for smaller regional and suburban railways.

MThB (Mittel-Thurgau Bahn) has ordered 10 GTWe 2/6 emus for 15 kV supply from Stadler/Adtranz. Rorschah-Heiden Railway (RHB) has ordered a BDeh 3/6 low-floor rack/adhesion rail car with electrical equipment from Adtranz, bogies from SLM and body from Stadler.

CMN (Chemin de Fer Des Montagnes Neuchateloises), a metre gauge regional railway in the Jura mountain area, has taken delivery of an additional power car BD 4/4 for supply from 1,500 V DC.

UK

The Eurotunnel contract for four further ESL 9000 Bo-Bo-Bo shuttle locomotives is in advanced production with Adtranz/Brush Electrical Machines (BEM). Delivery is for the first quarter of 1998. The ESL 9000 is of the 2000 family modular design with GTO power converters and MICAS S2 controls.

The 46 dual-system Class 92 electric locomotives for operation in France and UK have now been delivered. BEM is leader of the British-Swiss consortium which produced the Class 92 units; other members are Adtranz, Derby and Adtranz, Switzerland. The Class 92 locomotives operate on single phase AC 25 kV in France and the Channel Tunnel and on 750 V DC supply rail on the Railtrack system. The Class 92 is part of the 2000 range of locomotives. The Class 92 units could also haul passenger trains and their design provides for later addition of supply for electric systems of passenger coaches.

A Prism Rail subsidiary, LTS Rail, has ordered 44 25 kV four-car emus to be built at the Adtranz, Derby, works. Delivery is expected to start in 1999.

Connex Rail Ltd has ordered 30 Class 375 four-car

Class DE2250 locomotive for ENR Egypt **1997**

Electrostar emus for delivery by 2000. An option exists for a further 800 cars. They will operate on Connex South Eastern routes initially and will have air conditioning, corridor connections and CCTV. Adtranz will maintain the trains in association with Connex, the first 30 being maintained at the Adtranz Chart Leacon depot.

Repair and refurbishing has been carried out on 33 small-profile metro cars used on the Glasgow underground railway. Refurbishing and repair work has also been carried out on 452 London Underground Metropolitan line 'A' stock large-profile cars. All have been delivered.

Chiltern Railways has ordered four three-car Class 166 dmus and the contract includes the maintenance of the fleet.

National Express Group (NEG) subsidiary Midland Main Line has ordered a fleet of 13 Turbostar two-car dmus. The contract includes a seven-year maintenance agreement to be carried out in conjunction with the NEG maintenance facility MainCo at Derby. The trains will be air conditioned, with standard and first class accommodation. They will seat over 120 passengers, have luggage racks and overhead racks, public phone, on-board catering facilities and two toilets, one fully accessible by disabled travellers. Passenger information systems will keep passengers informed of journey status. If demand requires, the two-car configuration can be upgraded to three-car. Deliveries start early 1999.

USA

New Jersey Transit (NJT) has received a further 10 Class ALP 44 electric locomotives (type AEM 7) for single-phase AC operation at two different frequencies and voltages from Adtranz USA and Sweden. The ALP 44 is based on the type AEM 7, currently operating with Amtrak and other railway companies.

Amtrak and Adtranz are co-operating in the operation of a national two-year tour to show the capabilities of the Flexliner dmu for short to medium distances. Reports

show substantial increases in ridership with these trains in Kansas, Michigan, Wisconsin and North Carolina.

The Flexliner dmu is in operation with state and private railways in Denmark, Israel and Sweden. DSB also operates an emu version of the Flexliner.

SEPTA (South Eastern Pennsylvania Transportation Authority) is taking delivery of 222 stainless-steel metro cars with three-phase drive. The first preproduction cars were due to be delivered in the first half of 1997. Deliveries of series-produced cars started in mid-1997 and will be completed at the end of 1998.

BART (Bay Area Transit), San Francisco, has a contract with Adtranz to refurbish 200 out of 439 cars, for deliveries between 1997-99.

Developments

Adtranz and GE Transportation Systems (qv) have developed the Blue Tiger range of diesel-electric locomotives for the world market. The first, DE-AC33C, has modular construction allowing adaptation to customer requirements. Options include full-width driver cab, twin cabs, air conditioning, toilet, full width hoods and adaptability to various loading and track gauges. The Co-Co standard gauge prototype weighs 108 tonnes with an axle load of 18 tonnes and the diesel engine is rated at almost 2,400 kW. GE Transportation Systems provided the complete three-phase propulsion system with diesel engine, generator, traction motors including the controls, the cooling system and the electronic components for diagnostic and display systems. Blue Tiger is mounted on Henschel Flexi-float bogies.

Adtranz Portugal is leading a project called Safetrain Project – train crashworthiness for Europe/Railway Vehicle Design and Occupant Protection. The main objective of the project is to establish European standards for the construction of coaches to ensure the safety of passengers and crew in case of collision.

Blue Tiger diesel-electric locomotive family

Gauge (standard/narrow): 1,435/1,067 mm
Wheel arrangement: Co-Co
Weight: 108/132 tonnes
Axle load (min/max): 18/22 tonnes
Gross horsepower: 3,300 hp (2,430 kW)
Starting tractive effort (standard/narrow): 517/371 kN
Diesel engine type: GE 7FDL 12
Traction motor type (standard/narrow):
　GEB 15 A4/GEB 19 A1
Speed (standard/narrow): 120/160 km/h
Length over buffer beams: 22,000 mm
Max width: 2,800 mm
Max height (low profile/high profile): 3,710/4,080 mm
Wheel diameter (standard/avilable:
　1,067/1,016 mm (42/40 in)

UPDATED

AGS

PO Box 70, Trumbauersville, Pennsylvania 18970-0070, USA
Tel: +1 215 536 0333　Fax: +1 215 536 2025

Key personnel
President: Jean-Jacques Gaudiot
Marketing Manager: Jean-François Dentraygues

Products
Windscreens and other glass for rolling stock. Traction

fitted with AGS glass includes General Electric Dash-8 locomotives and new stock on the Frankfurt line in Philadelphia.

VERIFIED

Alna Koki

Alna Koki Company Ltd
4-5 Higashi Naniwa-cho 1-chome,
Amagasaki 660, Japan
Tel: +81 6 401 7283　Fax: +81 6 401 6168

Key personnel
President: Masatoyo Uji
Managing Director, Sales and Production:
　Yoshinobu Sugimoto
Director, Engineering: Shigeo Ueki

Products
Aluminium, mild steel and steel electric railcars and passenger coaches; light rail vehicles.

Recent contracts include the supply of 21 electric railcars for Hankyu Corporation; 60 electric railcars for Tobu Railway; 24 electric railcars for Osaka Municipal Transportation Bureau; 25 electric railcars and 32 light rail vehicles for Japanese private railways.

UPDATED

Series 3000 emu for Tobu Railway　　　　　　　　　　　**1997**

Alusuisse Airex Composites

Alusuisse Airex Composites
PO Box 6, Stickereistrasse, CH-9320 Arbon, Switzerland
Tel: +41 71 447 1010   Fax: +41 71 447 1020
email: airexcomposite@access.ch

Key personnel
General Manager: G Reif
Marketing Manager: T de Kalbermatten

Subsidiary
Alusuisse Airex Composites
CH-5643 Sins, Switzerland
Tel: +41 41 789 6600   Fax: +41 41 789 6660

Products
Design tooling and manufacture of large composite components for rail vehicles using sandwich technology.

Recent contracts include the supply of cabs for German BR424 family and ICT, Swiss RE460 locomotives, composite roofs for Talgo sets and floor panels for Italian ETR460 and 470 trainsets.

UPDATED

Alusuisse Airex composite locomotive cabs
1995

Alusuisse Road & Rail Ltd

Buckhauserstrasse 11, CH-8048 Zurich, Switzerland
Tel: +41 1 497 4422   Fax: +41 1 497 4585

Key personnel
Managing Director: Jürg Zehnder
Sales Manager: Giorgio De-Stefani

Corporate structure
Alusuisse Road & Rail Ltd is a subsidiary of Alusuisse-Lonza Holding Ltd, which operates plants in 15 countries. Alusuisse Road & Rail Ltd has entered into co-operation agreements with over 30 rolling stock manufacturers.

Products
Design and stress calculation of aluminium bodyshells; composite elements and interiors; manufacture of prototypes; static strain gauge and fatigue testing of bodyshells for passenger rolling stock and components; supply of aluminium semis (large extrusions up to 800 mm width); structural subassemblies (such as complete cab fronts for locomotives and railcars) and interior components of composite materials and others.

Recent contracts include low-floor suburban trainsets for Danish, German, Italian, Spanish and Swiss railways (main contractors Adtranz, Duewag, Fiat Ferroviaria, CAF and Stadler); suburban trainsets for FGC Barcelona and German railways (main contractors CAF and Duewag); double-deck coaches for Czech, Finnish, Italian and Swiss railways (main contractors MSV Studénka, Rautaruukki, Breda/Firema and Schindler); tilting trains for Czech, German, Italian, Portuguese, Spanish and Swiss railways (main contractors ČKD, Adtranz, Fiat Ferroviaria, GEC Alsthom, Patentes Talgo and Schindler); high-speed trains for French, German and Italian railways (main contractors GEC Alsthom, Adtranz/Duewag/DWA

Pendolino with FS, built by Fiat Ferroviaria using Alusuisse engineering and materials for bodyshell construction.
1997

and Breda); Transrapid (main contractor Thyssen Henschel).

UPDATED

Amerail

American Passenger Rail Car Co
900 East 103rd Street, Chicago, Illinois 60628, USA
Tel: +1 773 264 9730   Fax: +1 773 264 5218

Works address
Horton Street, Hornell, NY 14843
Telephone: +1 607 324 4570   Fax: +1 607 324 2361

Key personnel
President: Larry E Salci

Vice-President, Business Development: David R Bell

Corporate developments
Amerail was formed in October 1995 from Morrison Knudsen's MK Transit Group.

Products
Manufacture of trainsets for metro, heavy-rail commuter systems and inter-city systems; electrical rotating equipment; car door systems; microprocessor-based control systems; component parts.

Contracts include double-deck electric multiple-unit cars for Metra Chicago, metro cars for BART San Francisco, double-deck coaches for Caltrans California and inter-city sleepers for Amtrak.

UPDATED

AMF

AMF
1830 Le Ber Street, Montréal, Québec H3K 2A4, Canada
Tel: +1 514 925 3826/3618   Fax: +1 514 925 3828/3826

Key personnel
Senior Vice-President, Marketing and Sales:
Georg W Paffrath

Corporate developments
AMF is the company operating the Point St Charles workshops formerly owned by CN North America (qv).
In early 1996, CN and GEC Alsthom Canada agreed terms for the sale of AMF, with GEC Alsthom taking on 500 of AMF's 850-strong workforce (see GEC Alsthom).

Products
Locomotive and rolling stock refurbishment/ remanufacture. Recent contracts include the remanufacture of six locomotives for Roberval Saguenay (Alcan Group of companies) and 25 locomotives for MBTA Boston.
Contracts were received in 1996 for refurbishment of 13 diesel railcars for DART Dallas and for the overhaul of 40 aluminium double-deck commuter cars for GO Transit, Ontario, Canada.

UPDATED

ANF-Industrie

ANF-Industrie
PO Box 1, F-59154 Crespin, France
Tel: +33 3 27 23 53 00   Fax: +33 3 27 35 16 24

Key personnel
Chairman: Bernard Sorel
Managing Director: Bernard Dolphin
Directors
    Engineering: Philippe Van Berten
    TGV Product Line: Michel Roger
    Operations and Logistics: Jean-Claude Khouberman
    Double-Deck emu and dmu Product Line:
    Claude Maire
    Bogie Product Line: Jacques Rossi
    Urban Product Line: Francis Ancelet

Corporate structure
ANF-Industrie is the French subsidiary of the Bombardier Eurorail Group. The ANF manufacturing facility is located at Crespin, near Valenciennes, in northern France.

Products
Electric multiple-units, diesel railcars, metro trainsets, light rail vehicles and guided light transit vehicles.
ANF-Industrie manufactures the TER 2N (an emu for regional railways). The TER 2N project has been developed to meet the requirements expressed by eight French regions. SNCF has placed an order for 60 trainsets with options for a further 16. The first units were due to be delivered by the Autumn of 1997.
The first guided light transit vehicles (named TVR) for the city of Caen are being built by ANF.
The GLT is a bimode vehicle operating on rubber tyres but guided by a single rail; it is designed to offer the capacity and image advantages of a light rail vehicle with the flexibility of a bus. Propulsion is by electric motor, supplied by either overhead line or diesel generator.

The vehicle is 24.5 m long and 2.5 m wide with a height of 3.4 m. It seats 33 with 165 standing and weighs 24.5 tonnes (36 tonnes loaded). It is powered by two 200 kW electric motors. Guidance from a central and flush-fitted rail is to all four axles, with the first and fourth axles powered. Maximum speed is 70 km/h and the minimum curve radius is 12 m. Life expectancy of the vehicle is 20 years.
ANF-Industrie is fitting out the 30 TGV2N Duplex trainsets ordered by SNCF, comprising first-class trailers R2 and R3, and second-class trailer R7. Features of the TGV2N include seats equipped with retractable armrests and with head and footrests, velvet upholstery for seats, carpets in first and second class, telephone in trailer R2 and a nursery in R7.

UPDATED

Ansaldo Trasporti

Ansaldo Trasporti SpA
425 Via Argine, I-80147 Naples, Italy
Tel: +39 81 565 0111   Fax: +39 81 565 0698

Works
260 Via Nuova delle Brecce, I-80147 Naples, Italy

Other Offices
336 Viale Sarca, I-20126 Milan, Italy
Tel: +39 2 64451   Fax: +39 2 6445 4630

35 Via Dei Pescatori, I-16129 Genoa, Italy
Tel: +39 10 6551   Fax: +39 10 655 2610

50 Via Volvera, I-10045 Piossasco (Torino), Italy
Tel: +39 11 903 9111   Fax: +39 11 906 6500

Key personnel
Chairman: Bruno Musso
Vice-Chairman and Managing Director:
    Luciano Cravarolo
Co-General Manager: Decio Lordi
Vice-General Managers
    Central Research and Quality: Carlo Rizzi
    Business Development: Gabriele Testa
Directors
    Systems: Claudio Artusi
    Turnkey Vehicles and Power Supply: Giorgio Morrica
    Signalling and Automation: Walter Alessandrini
    Strategy and Marketing: Silvano Brandi

Subsidiaries
AT Signal System AB, Sweden
AT Signalling, Ireland
Transystem SpA, Italy
Segnalamento Ferroviario SpA, Italy
Union Switch & Signal Inc, USA

Corporate developments
The transfer was completed in 1997 of Breda Costruzione Ferroviarie and Bredamenarinibus to the Finmeccanica

Class E402 dual-voltage locomotive for Italian Railways   *1996*

Group, forming a conglomerate made up of Ansaldo and Breda (qv).

Products
Electric propulsion equipment, either rheostatic or electronic, for locomotives with AC and DC motors; electronic converters and controls; auxiliary apparatus; planning, designing and management methodologies for public transport: sale, assembly, start up and servicing.
Recent contracts include traction equipment for 73 E652 chopper-controlled locomotives for Italian Railways (FS); 60 ETR 500 high-speed trainsets for FS (supplied by the Trevi Consortium, of which Ansaldo Trasporti is a member); and 120 E402 electric locomotives with inverter drives and asynchronous traction motors for FS, with 80 equipped for operation at 3 kV DC and 25 kV 50 Hz AC.
Ansaldo Trasporti has been selected to build the Bursa light metro in Turkey as part of a consortium with Siemens.
A contract has been won to build the Copenhagen metro and covers, on a turnkey basis, the design, construction, supply and installation of an automatic urban metro system with 15 km of track and 15 stations. It also covers the supply of 19 driverless vehicles with ATC.

UPDATED

Astarsa

Astilleros Argentinos Rio de la Plata SA
Tucumán 1438, 1050 Buenos Aires, Argentina
Tel: +54 1 407014   Fax: +54 1 372 8647

Works
Calle Solis Rio Lujan, 1648 Tigre, Prov Buenos Aires
Tel: +54 749 107178

Key personnel
Executive Vice-President: E G Nottage
General Manager, Rail: G Molinari

Associated company
General Motors Corporation

Licences
MTE and GEC Alsthom (France and UK)

Products
Diesel-electric locomotives.

VERIFIED

Astra

Societatea Comercială Astra Vagoane Arad SA
Calea Aurel Vlaicu 41-43, R-2900 Arad, Romania
Tel: +40 57 231255/235379   Fax: +40 57 230998/230998

Key personnel
General Manager: George Albu

Technical Manager: Romulus Nosner
Marketing Director: Mihai Danciu

Products
Metro trainsets.
 Based on a 1,435 mm track gauge, the trainsets can comprise one, two or three two-car sets having a maximum total capacity of 3 × 554 passengers. All axles are motorised, being fed either by a third rail or from a

pantograph (750 V DC supply voltage). Supplied to the Bucharest Metro.

UPDATED

Babcock & Wilcox Española

Babcock & Wilcox Española SA
PO Box 294, Alameda Recalde 27, E-48009 Bilbao, Spain
Tel: +34 4 424 1761   Fax: +34 4 423 7092

Key personnel
President: R Gonzalez-Orus
Railway Division Manager: L Zubia

Products
Main line diesel-electric and diesel-hydraulic units, shunting locomotives.

Exports have featured diesel-electric locomotives for Colombia, Guatemala and numerous African railways.

VERIFIED

Badoni

Antonio Badoni SpA
Corso Matteotti 7, I-22053 Lecco, Italy
Tel: +39 341 364306   Fax: +39 341 367300

Key personnel
Chairman: Gualberto Lesi

Managing Director and General Manager:
 Giuseppe R Kramer Badoni
Sales Manager: S Dal Soglio

Products
Diesel-hydraulic shunting locomotives; radio-controlled shunters; hydrostatic transmission; freight wagons. The company's products include the Type GR214 100 kW

and GR245 370 kW diesel-hydraulic shunters of Italian Railways (FS).

VERIFIED

Beijing

Beijing 'February 7th' Locomotive Works
Changxindian, Fengtai District, Beijing 100072, People's Republic of China
Tel: +86 1 269/408   Fax: +86 1 325 7654

Key personnel
Factory Director: Xu Xiaozeng
Deputy Director: Li Guoan

Corporate structure
Member of China National Locomotive Rolling Stock Industry Corporation.

Products
Diesel locomotives; diesel engines; hydraulic transmissions; fuel injectors; fuel injection pumps; cardan shafts; and bogies.
 The BJ series of diesel-hydraulic locomotive is produced in 1,990 kW B-B and 3,980 kW B-B versions. The B-B has been in series production since 1975. Both models employ the Type 12V240ZJ-1,100 rpm 12-cylinder engine which is also manufactured in the works. The B-B weighs 92 tonnes, has a starting tractive effort of 23.1 tonnes, a continuous tractive effort of 16.27 tonnes at 24.3 km/h and a maximum speed of 120 km/h.
 The works also manufactures the Model DF7 Co-Co diesel-electric locomotive, for heavy shunting. It is fitted with a four-stroke 12-cylinder Vee engine of Type

12V240ZJ-1, exhaust turbocharged with intercooling, which has a rating of 1,470 kW at 1,000 rpm. The transmission is AC/DC alternator, employing silicon rectifiers.
 The Model DF7B Co-Co diesel-electric locomotive produced for freight traffic has a rating of 1,840 kW at 1,000 rpm and is equipped with rheostatic braking.
 To meet the needs of industrial and mining industries the works produces the Model GK1E diesel locomotive with a hydrostatic transmission system. The locomotive is powered by a six-cylinder Vee diesel engine, which has a 240 mm bore and a stroke of 260 mm, producing a maximum rating of 1,000 kW at 1,100 rpm.

VERIFIED

BEML

Bharat Earth Movers Ltd
BEML Soudha, 23/1 4th Main, SR Nagar, Bangalore 560 027, India
Tel: +91 80 222 4141   Fax: +91 80 222 6883

Works address
Bangalore Complex, New Thippasandra, Bangalore 560 075, India
Telephone: +91 80 528 2414   Fax: +91 80 528 5545

Key personnel
Chairman and Managing Director: Dr K Aprameyan
Chief General Manager: A Maruthachalam
General Manager (Research and Development):
 T Prabhakar Rae
See entry in *Non-powered passenger vehicles* section

Products
Electric multiple-units, diesel railbuses.
 Recent contracts for Indian Railways include the supply of a lightweight, two-axled, 1,676 mm gauge diesel railbus and electric multiple-units with DC traction equipment.

UPDATED

BEML diesel railbus for Indian Railways   1995

BHEL

Bharat Heavy Electricals Ltd
Bhopal 462 022, India
Tel: +91 755 586100   Fax: +91 755 540425

Head Office
BHEL House, Siri Fort, New Delhi 110049

Key personnel
Executive Director: H A Ghanekar
General Manager: R C Aggarwal
General Manager, Switchgear and Control Gear:
 D P Joshi
General Manager, Transportation: S P Bindra

Group Companies
Bharat Heavy Electricals Ltd
Jhansi 284 129

Tel: +91 517 440240/440615/440944   Fax: +91 517 443108/444360
General Manager: T S Nanda
Product Manager, Locomotives: Y Pathak

Products
Electric locomotives, diesel-electric shunting locomotives, traction transformers and control equipment.

Bharat Heavy Electricals Ltd
Transportation Business Department, Lodhi Road, New Delhi 110003, India
Tel: +91 11 461 6544 (Marketing)   Fax: +91 11 462 9423
General Manager: P C Dani
Deputy General Manager: S C Chopra

Products

Electric locomotives for 25 kV AC, 1.5 kV DC and dual-voltage operation. Diesel-electric locomotives for shunting and main line duties from 261 kW (350 hp) to 1,940 kW (2,600 hp).

Recent AC electric production includes 75 Class WAG-5 locomotives, 20 Class WCAM2 locomotives, 53 Class WCAM3 locomotives, all for Indian Railways, with delivery between 1996 and 1998. A 5,000 hp prototype with thyristor control has been undergoing trials at the Centre for Electric Transportation, Bhopal.

UPDATED

BMZ

JSC Bryansk Engineering Works
ulica Ulyanova 26, 241 015 Bryansk, Russian Federation
Tel: +7 832 55 8673/0030   Fax: +7 95 203 3395

Key personnel
Senior Marketing Manager: Natali Skrobova
Marketing Manager: Dmitri Melnichuk

Products
Diesel shunting locomotives, generator vans.

BMZ locomotives have been supplied to operators in Syria, Nigeria, Guinea, Poland, Bulgaria, Mongolia, North Korea and Cuba. Current production includes the TEM16 and TEM18 Co-Co diesel-electric locomotives for shunting and light main line duties. Both types are rated at

757 kW and are available for operation on 1,676 mm, 1,520 mm and 1,435 mm gauge.

VERIFIED

BN

BN Division of Bombardier Eurorail
Avenue Louise 65, B-1050 Brussels, Belgium
Tel: +32 2 535 5511   Fax: +32 2 539 0428

Main works
Vaartdijkstraat 5, B-8200 Bruges, Belgium
Tel: +32 50 401111   Fax: +32 50 401840

Rue du Long Trî 67, B-7170 Manage, Belgium
Tel: +32 64 519211   Fax: +32 64 557780

Key personnel
General Manager: B Dolphin
Manager, Engineering: M Thomas
Engineering Director: A Lanckriet
Operations Director: J Van den Bussche

Products
Electric and diesel-electric locomotives; light rail vehicles, metro cars and emus for suburban and main line duties.

In 1996, the Belgian (SNCB) and Luxembourg (CFL) railway administrations ordered, respectively, 60 and 20 dual-voltage (3 kV DC, 25 kV AC) electric locomotives. BN is responsible for the mechanical construction of 70 locomotives in collaboration with GEC Alsthom Acec Transport.

The last AM96 three-car emu for SNCB (Belgian Railways) was delivered in January 1996. The full order of 120 emus will be delivered in the next four years.

A second order for 25 four-car suburban emus for the Indonesian Railways (Perumka) is in the course of preparation.

Recent orders include 15 LRVs for Saarbrücken, produced in association with BWS (qv). The last dual-mode vehicle (able to operate on both light rail and main line systems) was delivered in September 1997.

Delivery of 80 low-floor LRVs for KVB Cologne was completed in February 1997. The third batch of 40 additional vehicles has been ordered for delivery in April 1998. 36 two-car mini-metro units will be supplied to RET Rotterdam from August 1998.

BN and GEC Alsthom ACEC are constructing 25 metro cars for STIB Brussels. Delivery is for 1999.

Adtranz and Bombardier Eurorail subsidiaries BWS and BN are supplying SL Stockholm with 12 LRVs. Delivery is expected to start in 1999. There is an option for 58 more.

UPDATED

AM96 emu for SNCB (Alain Janmart)
1996

Bombardier-Concarril

Bombardier-Concarril SA de CV
Paseo de la Reforma, 329 Mezzanine, Col. Cuauhtémoc, DF 06500, Mexico
Tel: +525 729 9903   Fax: +525 525 0438

Key personnel
President: Javier Rión del Olmo
Operations Vice-President: Serge Blamchet

Works
Sahagun, Hidalgo

Products
LRVs, metro cars, advanced rapid transit vehicles, freight cars.

Contracts
Include refurbishment of 256 MP68 rubber-tyred metro cars for Mexico City; 78 rubber-tyred metro cars for Line A, STC Mexico City; refurbishment of 234 rubber-tyred metro cars for STC Mexico City; 48 LRVs for Sistema de Tren Electrico Urbano, Guadalajara, Mexico; 23 LRVs for Metrorrey, Monterrey, Mexico; 16 LRVs for Electric Transport System, Taxqueña-Xochimilco, Mexico City.

NEW ENTRY   *TE90 LRV for Servicio de Transportes Eléctricos*   *1997*

Bombardier Eurorail

Avenue Louise 65, B-1050 Brussels, Belgium
Tel: +32 2 535 5511   Fax: +32 2 539 0428

Key personnel
President: Jean-Yves Leblanc
Managing Director: P Goulet
Vice-Presidents
   Finance: Y Vandeweyer
   Human Resources: P Scarborough
   Marketing: B van Dijk
   Legal Affairs: H Deslauriers

Indonesian office
Bombardier Eurorail
PO Box 28, Kuningan Plaza-South Tower, Suite 508, Jl,
H R Rasuna Said Kav.C11-14, Jakarta 12940

Corporate developments
In 1995, Waggonfabrik Talbot of Aachen, Germany,
joined the Bombardier Eurorail group following its
acquisition by Bombardier Inc.

Corporate structure
Bombardier Eurorail is the European subsidiary of
Bombardier Transportation of Canada. Details of the five

companies constituting Bombardier Eurorail will be found
in the following entries: ANF-Industrie, France; BN
Division, Belgium; Bombardier Prorail Ltd, UK;
Bombardier Wien Schienenfahrzeuge (BWS) AG, Austria;
Waggonfabrik Talbot, Germany.

UPDATED

Bombardier Inc

Bombardier Inc
Transportation Group
1101 Parent Street, Saint-Bruno, Québec J3V 6E6,
Canada
Tel: +1 514 441 2020   Fax: +1 514 441 1515

Key personnel
President: Jean-Yves Leblanc

The Transportation Group is responsible for all of
Bombardier's operations in the field of rail transportation
equipment and these are carried out by the Mass Transit
Division, Transportation Systems Division, Bombardier-
Concarril (qv) and Bombardier Eurorail (qv).

Mass Transit Division
address above

Key personnel
President: Michel Baril
Vice-President, Advance Engineering and Marketing and
   Sales, Canada: François Auger

Production facilities
La Pocatière, Québec G0R 1Z0; Kingston and Thunder
Bay, Ontario

The Mass Transit Division's American operations are
carried out through the following units:
Auburn Technology Inc
100 Orchard Street, Auburn, NY 13021, USA
Tel: +1 315 253 3241   Fax: +1 315 253 9175

Bombardier Transit Corporation
Suite 3260, 450 Lexington Avenue, New York NY 10017,
USA
Tel: +1 212 682 5860   Fax: +1 212 682 5767
President: Peter Stangl

Bombardier Transit Corporation — Other USA offices
3684 Marshall Lane, Bensalem, PA 19020, USA
Suite 713, 2011 Crystal Drive, Arlington, VA 22202
Suite 290, 1610 Arden Way, Sacramento, CA 95815
Suite 600, 5850 T G Lee Boulevard, FL 32822

Production facilities in USA: Barre, Vermont; Plattsburgh,
New York

Transportation Systems Division
PO Box 220, Station A, Kingston, Ontario K7M 6R2,
Canada
Tel: +1 613 384 3100   Fax: 613 384 5240

Key personnel
President: Jacques Laparé

Other offices
Suite 600, 5850 T G Lee Boulevard, FL 32822, USA
PO Box 113, 4th Floor, UBN Tower, Jalan P Ramlee, Kuala
   Lumpur, Malaysia
3/F, 367 Fu Hsing North Road, Taipei, Taiwan

ART Mark II car for Kuala Lumpur   *1997*

Products
Through its Transportation Group, Bombardier offers
urban, suburban and intercity vehicles including emus,
dmus, LRVs, metro cars, double-deck cars, monorail cars
and automated rapid transit vehicles.

Through a commercial and industrial co-operation
agreement with GEC Alsthom, Bombardier is responsible
for the marketing and manufacturing of the French TGV
high-speed train in North America.

New Developments
Bombardier's modern dmu is designed to meet the
stringent requirements of North America's railways. It is
suitable for new service start-ups which have low

passenger volume, for providing feeder service to remote
areas on a regional rail system and for allowing high-
frequency service during off-peak demand without the
use of a locomotive.

The technological improvements include a monitoring
system to control and provide diagnostic information
about the engines, as well as other major car systems,
stainless steel carbodies, and Bombardier's fabricated
lightweight B-65P outboard bearing trucks designed to
provide a smooth and stable ride at high speed.

The basic Bombardier dmu configuration is a coupled
pair with each car powered by two engines and two
transmissions having sufficient power to include an
intermediate trailer car if required. The modular carbody

Bombardier dmu for USA   *1997*

Emu for Deux-Montagnes commuter line in Montreal   *1997*

Products

Electric, diesel-electric and diesel-hydraulic locomotives; multiple-units and hauled coaches.

Recent contracts include 15 Class 252 high-speed electric locomotives for Spanish National Railways (RENFE). Four Class 269.600 locomotives have been rebuilt for RENFE with new bogies and transmissions and redesigned front ends for 200 km/h operation.

VERIFIED

CFD

CFD Industrie
9-11 rue Benoît Malon, F-92156 Suresnes, France
Tel: +33 1 45 06 44 00   Fax: +33 1 47 28 48 84

Key personnel

President: F de Coincy
Sales Manager: M Hallet

Principal subsidiaries

CFD Industrie, CFD Locorem, Belgium Desbrugeres, Batiruhr and CFD Bagnères, France

Products

Diesel locomotives from 150 to 2,000 kW, road-rail vehicles.

Track construction and maintenance company Scheuchzer SA, Switzerland, has ordered a 1,790 kW (2,400 hp) 80 tonne diesel locomotive. HCB Cement Group is taking delivery of an 80 tonne 559 kW (750 hp) shunting locomotive and an order has been received from Ethiopian Railways for four refurbished Class AD12 diesel-electric metre-gauge locomotives, similar to those which CFD supplied in 1995 to the Friguia aluminium plant in Guinea.

UPDATED

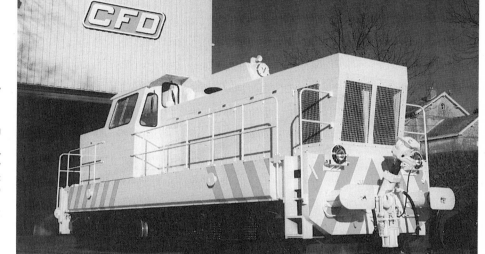

CFD diesel locomotive for Holderbank cement works, Switzerland   *1997*

Changchun Railway Car Works

5 Qingyin Road, Changchun 130062, Jilin, People's Republic of China
Tel: +86 431 790 1114   Fax: +86 431 293 8740

Key personnel

Managing Director: Ma Shu-Kun
Deputy Director: Teng Mao-gen

Corporate developments:

At the end of 1996, Adtranz and Changchun Car Company, China (qv) signed a joint venture to produce rolling stock for urban transport applications. CCC is owned by the Chinese Railway Ministry and manufactures 1,200 passenger vehicles a year. From the beginning of 1997, a new company, the Changchun Adtranz Railway Company, was formed with 51 per cent of shares owned by Adtranz and 49 per cent owned by CCC. Planned production is 160 vehicles a year.

Products

Development, design, production, sales, installation, refurbishment, maintenance and after-sales service for metro cars; electric multiple-units for main line applications, sleeping cars, dining cars, mail vans and passenger coaches.

Metro cars include DK20 and the DK9 with chopper voltage control. All cars are motored (4 × 86 kW) and designed to operate in multiples of two, four or six.

Changchun DK20 metro trainset   *1997*

Contracts include the supply of 217 cars to Iran and 174 cars to Beijing.

UPDATED

Changzhou Diesel & Mining Locomotive Plant

74 Xinshi Road, Changzhou, 213002 Jiangsu, People's Republic of China
Tel: +86 519 600656   Fax: +86 519 600443

Key personnel

Managing Director: Xie Yintang
Chief Engineer: Xu Di'an
Marketing Director: Wang Chenxian
Production Director: Wang Jianxun
Export Sales Director: Wu Leping

Products

Diesel locomotives from 60 to 750 kW. Electric locomotives for mining applications from 3 to 55 tonnes.

VERIFIED

China National Railway Locomotive and Rolling Stock Industry Corporation (LORIC)

10 Fuxing Road, 100844 Beijing, People's Republic of China
Tel: +86 10 6351 1620   Fax: +86 10 6351 1614/1600

Key personnel
Chairman: Du Jing-Xin
Vice Chairman and Managing Director: Wang Tai-Wen
Deputy Managing Director and Chief Engineer: Yang Anli
Deputy Manager of Import and Export Head Office: Cao Guo-Bing
Project Manager: Yang Xiong-Jing

Works addresses (the company comprises 35 production facilities and four research divisions)

Changchun Railway Car Works (qv)

Dalian Locomotive & Rolling Stock Works (qv)

Datong Locomotive Works (qv)

Beijing February 7th Locomotive Works
Changxindian, Beijing 100072, P R China
Tel: +86 10 63 886043   Fax: +86 10 63 257654

Sifang Locomotive and Rolling Stock Works
16 Hangzhou Road, Quingdao 266031, Shandong, P R China
Tel: +86 532 371 8168   Fax: +86 532 371 6656

Qishuyan Locomotive and Rolling Stock Works
Qishuyan, Changzhou 213011, Jiangsu, P R China
Tel: + 86 519 877 1711   Fax: +86 519 877 0358

Ziyang Diesel Locomotive Works
Ziyang 641301, Sichuan, P R China
Tel: +86 8419 624261   Fax: +86 8419 627176

Zhuzhou Electric Locomotive Works
Zuzhou 412001, Hunan, P R China
Tel: +86 733 843 1331   Fax: +86 733 843 2399

Taiyuan Locomotive & Rolling Stock Works
84 Jiefang North Road, Taiyuan 030009, Shanxi, P R China
Tel: +86 351 304 5411   Fax: +86 351 304 9563

Jinan Locomotive & Rolling Stock Works
73 Huaichun Street, Huaiyin District, Jinan 250022, Shandong, P R China
Tel: +86 531 795 5930   Fax: +86 531 795 7548

Yongji Electric Machine Factory
24 Tiaoshan West Street, Yongjii 044502, Shanxi, P R China
Tel: +86 359 802 3825   Fax: +86 359 802 2090

Products
Development, design, engineering, production, sales, installation, refurbishment, maintenance and after-sales service for electric, diesel-electric and diesel-hydraulic locomotives with various power ratings from 280 kW to 6,400 kW for passenger, freight and shunting services; passenger coaches; metro cars; freight wagons; rail-mounted cranes; diesel generator sets and components.

From 1986 to 1995, the Corporation has built 5,276 diesel locomotives, 1,656 electric locomotives, 18,362 passenger coaches and 232,926 freight wagons.

The annual output is over 650 diesel locomotives, 300 electric locomotives, 2,500 passenger coaches and 30,000 freight wagons. Most are 1,435 mm gauge.

CKD7 diesel-electric locomotive for Myanmar railways   **1997**

LORIC electric locomotives

Type	Wheel arrangement	Line voltage	Output (kW) continuous	Speed (km/h)	Weight tonnes	Length (mm)	First built	Builders
SS3B	Co-Co	25 kV/50 Hz	4,350	100	138	21,416	1992	Zhuzhou, Dafong, Taiyuan
SS4B	2(Bo-Bo)	25 kV/50 Hz	6,400	100	184	2 × 16,416	1995	Zhuzhou
SS5	Bo-Bo	25 kV/50 Hz	3,200	140	86	16,716	1990	Zhuzhou
SS6B	Co-Co	25 kV/50 Hz	4,800	100	138	21,416	1992	Zhuzhou
SS7	Bo-Co-Bo	25 kV/50 Hz	4,800	100	138	22,016	1992	Datong
SS8	Bo-Bo	25 kV/50 Hz	3,600	177	88	17,516	1994	Zhuzhou
AC4000	Bo-Bo	25 kV/50 Hz	4,000	120	96	19,160	1996	Zhuzhou

LORIC diesel locomotive

Type	Wheel arrangement	Transmission	Power (kW)	Speed (km/h)	Weight tonnes	First built	Builders
DF 4B	Co-Co	AC/DC	2,430	100/120	138	1984	Dalian/Ziyang
DF4C	Co-Co	AC/DC	2,650	100	138	1985	Dalian
DF4D	Co-Co	AC/DC	2,940	160	138	1996	Dalian
DF4E	2(Co-Co)	AC/DC	2 × 2,430	100	2 × 138	1994	Sifang
DF5	Co-Co	AC/DC	1,210	80	135	1981	Sifang, Dalian
DF6	Co-Co	AC/DC	2,940	118	138	1989	Dalian
DF7B	Co-Co	AC/DC	1,840	100	135	1990	Feb 7th
DF7C	Co-Co	AC/DC	1,470	100	135	1991	Feb 7th
DF7D	2(Co-Co)	AC/DC	2 × 1,840	100	2 × 138	1995	Feb 7th
DF8	Co-Co	AC/DC	3,310	100	138	1984	Qishuyan
DF9	Co-Co	AC/DC	3,160	140	138	1990	Qishuyan
DF10F	2(Co-Co)	AC/DC	2 × 2,200	160	2 × 123	1996	Dalian
DF11	Co-Co	AC/DC	3,680	170	138	1992	Qishuyan
BJ	B-B	hydraulic	1,990	120	92	1973	Feb 7th
DFH5	B-B	hydraulic	790	40/80	86/72	1976	Ziyang
GK0	B-B	hydraulic	590	30	80	1990	Sifang
GK0B	C	hydraulic	280	20	14-23	1992	Sifang
GK1	B-B	hydraulic	790	35/70	92	1989	Ziyang
GK1C	B-B	hydraulic	990	35/75	92	1991	Ziyang
GK1D	2(B-B)	hydraulic	2 × 990	50	2 × 90	1990	Sifang
GK1E	B-B	hydraulic	950	40/80	92	1991	Feb 7th
GK1G-B	B-B	hydraulic	1,000	35/70	100	1995	Jinan & DERI
GK2	C-C	hydraulic	1,375	65/100	120	1994	Ziyang
GKD1	Bo-Bo	AC/DC	990	80	84	1990	Dalian
CK5	B-B	hydraulic	515	76	60	1992	Ziyang
CK5A	B-B	hydraulic	571	36	60	1993	Ziyang
CK5B	B-B	hydraulic	310	10	60	1994	Ziyang
CKD5	Bo-Bo	AC/DC	280	45	28-40	1995	Dalian
CKD6	Bo-Bo-Bo	AC/DC	880	90	66	1995	Sifang
CKD7	Bo-Bo-Bo	AC/DC	1,250	90	76	1993	Dalian

LORIC electric railcars and multiple-units

Class	Cars per unit	Line voltage	Motor cars per unit	Wheel arrangement	Output (kW) per motor	Speed (km/h)	Weight (tonnes) per car	Total seating capacity	Length per car (mm)	No in service	First built
DK6	4	750V DC	4	Bo-Bo	76	80	35	188	19,000	4	1979
DK9	4	750V DC	4	Bo-Bo	93	80	35	188	19,000	4	1982
DK16	6	750V DC	6	Bo-Bo	76	80	35	188	19,000	116	1985
DK20	6	750V DC	6	Bo-Bo	80	80	35	Mc228/M247	19,000	42	1994
DKZ1	3	750V DC	2	Bo-Bo	130	80	35	160	19,000	3	1985
KDZ1	4	250V AC	2	Bo-Bo	150	140	54	103	25,500	4	1987

The DF range of diesel-electric locomotives, with four-stroke turbocharged diesel engines, and with AC/DC transmission, are the main types of locomotive for both passenger and freight traffic. The locomotives run on three-axle bogies with roller bearings. The electric motors are axle hung and the locomotives are designed for hauling trains of some 5,000 tonnes.

The GK range of diesel locomotives is intended for shunting and industrial applications. Most have hydraulic transmission and have B-B configuration to suit tight curves.

The SS range of electric locomotives features microprocessor control, anti-slip braking and AC/DC transmission.

The CK range of diesel locomotives is designed for markets other than China and features a lower axle load. These locomotives are in operation on the metre-gauge railways of Thailand and Myanmar.

LORIC is developing high-speed passenger trains with an operating speed of 160 km/h for the DF4D, DF10F, DF11 and SS8 locos. An SS8 locomotive reached 212 km/h in 1997.

Orders include nine diesel-electric locos for Myanmar and two diesel-electric locos for North Korea.

Recent orders include 12 3,200 kW 140 km/h electric locomotives, and two 2,650 diesel-electric locomotives for Iran, ten diesel-electric locomotives for Myanmar, six diesel-electric locos for Tanzania and 20 diesel-electric locomotives for Nigeria.

UPDATED

DF11 diesel-electric locomotive by LORIC   *1997*

SS8 electric locomotive by LORIC
1997

ČKD

ČKD Dopravní Systémi AS
Ringhofferova 115/1, 15500 Praha 5, Czech Republic

Commercial department
Českomoravská 205, 19005 Prague 9
Tel: +42 2 6603 8200   Fax: +42 2 6603 8801

Key personnel
Managing Director: Joseph Bouda
Commercial Director: Vítéslav Mamica
Technical Director: Jiři Nemecek

Products
Diesel-electric shunting and main line locomotives, battery shunting locomotives, tramcars, LRVs, refurbishment, consultancy.

The range includes two-, four- and six-axle types with outputs from 200 kW to 1,760 kW and track gauges from 760 mm to 1,766 mm. The locomotives are suitable for both passenger and freight operation.

Production of tilting trains has started, in association with Fiat, Siemens and MSV. Production has also started of new metro cars, in association with Adtranz and Siemens SGP,

Recent contracts include the supply of six Class T 239.1 diesel-electric shunting locomotives (327 kW), remanufacturing of 65 Class 735 diesel-electric locomotives as Class 714 for Czech Railways and 10 Class 708 diesel-electric locomotives (300 kW) for shunting and branch line applications.

UPDATED

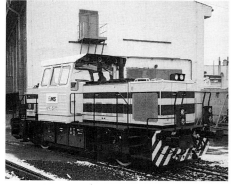

Class T239.1 diesel electric locomotive for Switzerland   *1997*

Class D12E diesel electric locomotive for Vietnam   *1997*

CLW

Chittaranjan Locomotive Works
Chittaranjan, 713331, Burdwan District, West Bengal,
India
Tel: +91 341 525642   Fax: +91 341 525641

Key personnel
General Manager: A P Murugeson
Chief Mechanical Engineer: S Sah
Chief Electrical Engineer: A K Jain
Chief Controller, Stores: Lt Col S Mandhani
Financial Adviser/Chief Accounts Officer: L C Majumder
Chief Personnel Officer: U P L Das

Products
Electric locomotives; traction motors, castings.
   CLW is developing a three-phase 1,492 kW (6,000 hp)
locomotive through a technology transfer agreement from
Adtranz.

UPDATED

Clyde

Clyde Engineering
PO Box 73, Factory Street, Granville, NSW 2142, Australia
Tel: +61 2 9637 8288   Fax: +61 2 9897 2174
A member of the Evans Deakin Industries Group

Branches (Workshops)
Sydney Road, Bathurst, New South Wales 2795
Somerton Road, Campbellfield, Victoria 3061
Wittenoom Road, Forrestfield, WA 6057

Key personnel
General Manager: B R Willmann
Group Sales Manager: Kevin C Thomson

Products
Diesel-electric and diesel-hydraulic locomotives; electric
locomotives; traction motors and associated rolling stock
equipment.
   Contracts for Westrail include nine narrow-gauge dual-
cab 2,260 kW diesel-electric locomotives, 15 standard-
gauge single-cab 3,000 kW diesel-electric locomotives, all
with steerable bogies and integrated cab electronics.

Class 82 locomotive for New South Wales State Railway Authority   1996

Diesel locomotive production since 1992

Class	Wheel arrangement	Transmission	Rated power (kW)	Max speed (km/h)	Total weight (t)	No in service	Year first built	Builders Mechanical parts	Engine and type	Transmission
Australian National Railways										
AN	Co-Co	electric	3,030	152	128	11	1992	Clyde/EMD	EMD 16-710G3	Clyde/EMD
82 class	Co-Co	electric	2,259	121	132	58	1994	Clyde/EMD	EMD 12-710G3A	Clyde/EMD

Electric locomotive production

Class	Wheel arrangement	Line voltage	Rated output (kW) continuous	Max speed (km/h)	Weight (t)	No in service	Year first built	Builders
Queensland Railways								
3300	Bo-Bo-Bo	25 kV	2,970	80	112	22	1994	Clyde

UPDATED

CMI

Cockerill Mechanical Industries SA
Avenue Greiner 1, B-4100 Seraing, Belgium
Tel: +32 41 30 24 46   Fax: +32 41 30 25 02

Key personnel
President: G Cartilier
Sales Director: J F Levaux

Products
Shunting locomotives of 185 to 1,500 kW, on two, three or
four axles, for all gauges and types of track. Amongst its

latest products is a shunting/branch line locomotive
featuring hydrostatic transmission.
   The company has developed a high-security radio
remote-control adaptable to all types of shunting
locomotive.

VERIFIED

Daewoo

Daewoo Heavy Industries Ltd
PO Box 7955, Daewoo Centre Building 23rd Fl, 541, 5-GA,
Namdaemun-Ro, Jung-Gu, Seoul, South Korea
Tel: +82 2 726 3181   Fax: +82 2 726 3186/726 3307

Works
462-18 Sam Dong, Euiwang City, Kyonggi Province,
South Korea

Key personnel
Chairman: Won Seok Yune
President: Ho Suk Choo
Executive Managing Director, Rolling Stock Division:
   Soon Hyuck Park
Director, Rolling Stock Overseas Marketing: Soo Hwan
   Kim

Products
Magnetically levitated vehicles, emus, dmus, diesel and
electric locomotives, passenger coaches, freight wagons,
bogies, electrical equipment.

DMV-92 maglev test car   1996

Emu cars for Seoul MRT   **1996**

Contracts
Daewoo has supplied more than 2,700 emu cars to domestic clients such as Korean National Railroad (KNR), Seoul Metropolitan Subway Corporation (SMSC) and Seoul Metropolitan Rapid Transit Corporation (SMRT). Also 344 emu cars have been supplied to Taiwan Railway Administration (TRA). The cars feature VVVF propulsion and control system, a train control and monitoring system, stainless steel carbodies and bolsterless bogies.

The State Railway of Thailand took delivery of 60 dmu cars in 1996. Other recent contracts include 200 emu cars for Inchcon Subway Agency, Korea and 86 dmu cars and 143 emu cars for KNR Korea.

New developments
Since 1989, for the purposes of research and development on future transport systems, Daewoo has carried out an intensive study of magnetically levitated vehicles. This work resulted in the manufacture of a magnetically levitated vehicle in 1992, DMV-92, for trials.

DMV-92
Levitation: electromagnetic suspension
Propulsion: single-sided linear induction motor
Line-voltage: 600 V DC
Capacity: 40 seats
Max speed: 110 km/h
Gross weight: 18 t

Daewoo diesel intercity multiple-units

Class (Manufacturer's own designation)	Cars per unit	Motor cars per unit	Motored axles per motor car	Transmission	Rated power per motor (kW)	Max speed (km/h)	Weight (t) per car (M-motor T-trailer)		Total seating capacity	No of car service 1996	Year first built	Builders Engine & type	Builders Transmission
DMU (SRT 20 cars)	3	3	1	hydraulic	—	120	—		232 (3 cars)	20	1995	Cummins NTA855R1	Voith T211rzz
DMU (SRT 60 cars)	2/3	2	1	hydraulic	—	100 (3 cars) 120 (2 cars)	—		208 (3 cars)	60	1996	Cummins NTA555RI	Voith Voith
DMU (KNR & POSCO)	3	3	2 (M) 1 (MCI)	hydraulic	—	120	M MCI	50 50	82 66	22	1996	Cummins NTA855-R1 NT-855-R5	Voith

Recent Daewoo electric railcars or multiple-units

Class	Cars per unit	Line voltage	Motor cars per unit	Motored axles per motor car	Rated output per motor (kW)	Max speed (km/h)	Weight (t) per car (M-motor T-trailer)		Total seating capacity (M-motor T-trailer)	Length per car (mm)	No of cars in service	Rate of acceleration (km/h/s)	Year first built	Builders Electrical equipment
Subway Commuter (SMSC)	4/6/8/10	25 kV AC/ 1,500 V DC	2/3/4/5	4	200	110	Tc M T1 T2	33.1 41.2 26.5 32.0	48 54 54 54	20	82	3.0	1993	Daewoo and GEC Alsthom
Subway Commuter (SMSC)	4/6/8/10	1,500 V DC	2/3/4/5	4	200	100	Tc M T1 T2	32.8 38.5 26.5 31.7	48 54 54 54	20	170	3.0	1994	Daewoo and GEC Alsthom
Subway Commuter (KNR)	6/8/10	25 kV AC/ 1,500 V DC	3/4/5	4	200	110	Tc M1 M2 T1 T2	33.0 40.0 42.0 27.5 32.0	48 54 54 54 54	20	88	3.0	1994	Daewoo and Toshiba (Japan)
Subway Commuter (TRA)	4	25 kV AC	2	4	250	110	EMC EP ET EM	42.3 39.7 37.8 43.0	60 60 60 60	20	344	2.9	1995	Daewoo and Siemens
Subway Commuter (SMRT)	6/8	1,500 V DC	3/4	4	180	100	Tc M1 M2 T1 T2 T1'	32.5 36.7 36.8 29.0 29.0 29.9	48 54 54 54 54 54	20	226	3.0	1995	Daewoo and GEC Alsthom

UPDATED

Dalian Locomotive and Rolling Stock Works

51 Zhong Chang Street, 116022 Dalian, People's Republic of China
Tel: +86 411 419 9386/460 2043
Fax: +86 411 460 3064/6447
Email: DLW@pub.dl.lnpta.net.cn

Key personnel
Vice-President, Marketing and Sales: Zong Baoquan
International Marketing and Sales: Jiang Hui

Corporate Developments:
Dalian Locomotive and Rolling Stock Works is part of LORIC (China National Railway Locomotive and Rolling Stock Industry Corporation (qv)

Products
Diesel locomotives of various power ratings for passenger, freight and shunting applications.

The DF10F, rated at 2 × 1,985 kW, is a double-unit diesel locomotive with each unit powered by a 12V240ZJ diesel engine. Each unit can be operated independently. Total weight of the locomotive is 92 tonnes.

The DF4C locomotive with a 2,650 kW power rating is a development of the DF4B. It includes new components such as the TQFR-3000B main alternator, ZQDR-410C motors, 16V240ZJC diesel engine and ABB VTC254-13 turbochargers. Total weight is 138 tonnes.

The Dong Feng DF4D locomotive with a 2,940 kW rated output is for use on main line services (max speed 133 km/h) and can haul 20 coaches. It is powered by the 16V240ZJD diesel engine.

The DF6 locomotive with a 2,940 kW power rating is a new generation of locomotive powered by a 16V240ZJD diesel engine developed in association with the British

Dong Feng 10C double-unit (2 × 2,210 kW) diesel-electric passenger locomotive   **1996**

series for main line passenger operation with a running speed of 140 to 160 km/h. It has three-phase AC drive and the traction motors have roller bearings. Maximum speed is 160 km/h and the axle weight is 20 tonnes.

The DF5 locomotive has a 1,210 kW power rating and an 8240ZJ diesel engine with three-phase AC drive. The locomotive is suitable both for shunting and industrial duties. Total weight is 135 tonnes.

The DF5B locomotive has a power rating of 1,840 kW and is based on the DF5 loco. It has a 12V240ZJF diesel engine with three-phase AC drive. The loco has a narrow hood, making it suitable for mining operations.

The CKD7 locomotive has a power rating of 1,250 kW and is powered by a CAT3516 diesel engine. It has been designed especially for Myanmar Railways, which specifies two cabs and Bo-Bo-Bo arrangement. It has a dual-vacuum/air brake and rheostatic brake system.

The CKD8A locomotive, designed for Nigerian Railways, is powered by the advanced 12V240ZJG diesel engine, with a maximum power of 1,800 kW and a maximum speed of 100 km/h.

The CKD8B locomotive with a 2,200 kW power rating which is powered by the 12V240ZJD diesel engine has been designed for Tanzania Zambia railways.

Contracts agreed in 1996 include six CKD8B locomotives for Tanzania Zambia Railways; 10 CKD7 locomotives for Myanmar Railways; 50 CKD8A locomotives for Nigerian Railways; 60 DF4D locomotives for Sino-Railways Construction Development Centre.

company Ricardo Consulting Engineers. Advanced technology from GE of the USA has also been incorporated in this locomotive, including the GTA 32A1 alternator, GE 752 AFC1 DC traction motors, dynamic brake with three-stage expansion, constant hp excitation and anti-slip/slide devices, and fault diagnostic system. Total weight is 138 tonnes.

The DF10F Co-Co locomotive is a version of the DF10

UPDATED

Datong Locomotive Works

1 Daqing Road, Datong 03708, Shanxi, People's Republic of China
Tel: +86 352 509 0124   Fax: +86 352 509 0984

Key personnel
Director: Zheng Xian Dao
Chief Engineer: Zhu Shun Nian
Chief Chartered Accountant: Gu Feng Ming

Corporate developments
Datong Locomotive Works is part of LORIC (China National Railway Locomotive and Rolling Stock Industry Corporation) (qv).

Products
SS3 passenger and freight electric locomotives; DF4 diesel-electric freight locomotive; DT20 diesel-electric shunting locomotive; DF4, DF8 combined piston of steel crown and aluminium skirt; ND5 combined piston of steel

crown and aluminium skirt for 7FDL diesel engines; forged aluminium piston and piston pins for diesel engines; bogies and parts for locomotives and rolling stock.

UPDATED

De Dietrich Ferroviaire

PO Box 35, F-67891 Niederbronn Cedex, France
Tel: +33 3 88 80 25 00   Fax: +33 3 88 80 25 12
Email: ddf@dx-net.fr

Key personnel
President: Michel Perricaudet
Vice-President: Denis Delcros
General Manager: Jean-Marie Bucher
Sales Manager: Daniel Sprauer

Corporate developments
The rolling stock activities of De Dietrich & Cie were transferred to a new company named De Dietrich Ferroviaire in 1995. De Dietrich Ferroviaire is owned by Ferromeca (51.25 per cent), De Dietrich Group (31.25 per cent) and GEC Alsthom (17.5 per cent).

Products
LRVs, dmus, emus, passenger coaches, remote-controlled shunters, haulage systems.

Recent contracts include the supply of 80 air conditioned lightweight regional dmus to SNCF and DB from a consortium of De Dietrich and LHB, Germany. Delivery is due to start in 1998. The 140 km/h railcars are powered by two 250 kW diesel engines. Each car has a low-floor area 550 mm above rail level, covering 60 per cent of the floor area. There are 85 seats per car. Up to three units can be coupled together.

50 mDDM double-deck electric power cars are being supplied to Netherlands Railways. It has three bogies and is designed to pull three or four double-deck coaches, The mDDM car carries 16 first class and 32 standard class passengers. Its 900 mm-wide doors open into vestibules at each end. Sound proofing insulates passengers from the engine compartment underneath and two roof-based heating/ventilation units are located in the vestibules.

Bodyshell components and passive crumple zones have been supplied for TER dmus for SNCF.

UPDATED

De Dietrich regional dmu   **1997**

mDDM six-axle double-deck motor car   **1997**

Diema

Diepholzer Maschinenfabrik Fritz Schöttler GmbH
PO Box 1170, Diemastrasse 11, D-49345 Diepholz,
Germany
Tel: +49 5441 304143   Fax: +49 5441 3046

Key personnel
Managing Director: Peter Benzien

Products
Standard- and narrow-gauge diesel shunting locomotives,
narrow-gauge diesel, electric battery or trolley wire-

powered mine locomotives, narrow-gauge industrial
locomotives, hydraulic tippers and motorised work
trolleys.

VERIFIED

Diesel Supply Co

Diesel Supply Co Inc
1601 Industrial Street, Hudson, Wisconsin 54016, USA
Tel: +1 715 386 3901   Fax: +1 715 386 7420

Key personnel
President: Paul J Kramer

Products
Supply of diesel-electric locomotives and locomotive
components, including bearings, power assemblies, light
bulbs and brake equipment.

Recent contracts include the supply of locomotives to
Raillink Inc, Mobile Locomotive, and Right Co-Op,
Kansas; and the supply of locomotive components to
shortline and industrial operators.

VERIFIED

DLW

Diesel Locomotive Works
Varanasi 221 004, (UP), India
Tel: +91 542 370551   Fax: +91 542 370603

Key personnel
General Manager: R K Jain
Chief Mechanical Engineer: M Sirajuddin
Controller of Stores: N K Mehndiratta

Chief Design Engineer: H C Gupta
Chief Project Manager: V K Pabby
Chief Marketing Manager: P Chandra

Products
Diesel engines of 1,000 to 2,300 kW; metre- and
1,676 mm-gauge diesel-electric locomotives; components for diesel locomotives. The plant was set up in
collaboration with Alco, USA and has supplied 3,650
locomotives, mainly to Indian Railways.

With conversion of most metre-gauge sections to broad
gauge (1,676 mm), production of metre-gauge MG
locomotives has been discontinued, except for orders
outside India.

Export orders include 15 metre-gauge 1,000 kW six-
axle locomotives to Vietnam National Railways and six to
Tanzanian Railways. Four 1,676 mm 1,939 kW (2,600 hp)
six-axle WDM2 locomotives have been supplied to Sri
Lankan Railways. Bangladesh Railways took delivery of
10 metre-gauge twin-cab locomotives in 1996.

New developments
WDP1: 1,676 mm gauge Bo-Bo loco for passenger work.
It has an Alco 251-C 12 cylinder diesel engine, upgraded
to 1,715 kW.
WDG2: 1,676 m gauge Co-Co loco for freight work with 16
cylinder Alco 251-C engine, uprated to 2,312 kW. Starting
tractive effort is 37.9 tonnes, compared to 30.4 tonnes
with the WDM2 loco.
WDM2: Freight/passenger Co-Co loco with 16 cylinder
Alco 251-C engine, uprated to 2,312 kW.
For high-speed operation (160 km/h) on broad-gauge,
DLW has designed a full-width twin-cab WDP2 Co-Co
locomotive. Three were due to be constructed in 1997.
In 1995, IR signed a contract with General Motors
(EMD), USA, for the supply of 3,095 kW AC drive
GT46MAC locomotives, as well as 12- 16- and 20-cylinder
diesel engines, produced at DLW. DLW is assembling
eight of these partially CKD locos with full production
starting in 1999.
DLW is manufacturing spares for diesel locomotives
including 6- 12- and 16-cylinder diesel power pack,
cylinder blocks and engine components.
DLW has been recommended for ISO 9002
certification.

DLW WDG2 1,676 mm-gauge diesel electric locomotive   **1997**

UPDATED

Dorbyl

Dorbyl Transport Products (Pty) Ltd
PO Box 229, Boksburg East 1460, Transvaal, South Africa
Tel: +27 11 914 1400   Fax: +27 11 914 1884

Key personnel
Managing Director: R C Duff
Technical Manager: D G Leggitt

Products
Mining battery locomotives, mining diesel locomotives,
underground pantograph locomotives, inspection
trolleys; 22-person gang trolleys and industrial shunting
locomotives from 10 to 65 tonnes.
Dorbyl started supplying locomotives from its
Boksburg works in 1960, building to General Electric
drawings and specifications. Over 850 locomotives have

been supplied. These include diesel-hydraulics and the
Spoornet Class 7E1 electric locomotives, of which a
contract for 110 has been delivered.

VERIFIED

Duro Daković

Railway Vehicles Factory Ltd
PO Box 94, 55102 Slavonski Brod, Croatia
Tel: +385 35 241926/232189   Fax: +385 35 232454

Key personnel
General Manager: A Milović
Marketing Manager: Antun Kaurić

Products
Diesel locomotives — diesel-hydraulic 220 to 730 kW;
diesel-electric 730 to 3,000 kW.

VERIFIED

DWA

Deutsche Waggonbau Aktiengesellschaft
Kablower Weg 89, D-12526 Berlin, Germany
Tel: +49 30 67930   Fax: +49 30 674 4560
Email: info@dwa.de
Web: http://www.dwa.de

Key personnel
See entry in *Non-powered passenger vehicles* section

Products
Diesel railcars and railbuses.
DWA has developed a double-deck low-floor railbus
featuring bus components and a diesel-electric railcar for

use on regional services. Produced in partnership with
Adtranz and other companies, the double-articulated
railcar is of modular design and features aluminium
bodyshells. Floor height for boarding is 570 mm and there
are seats for 136 passengers. Rated at 540 kW, the
railcar's drive unit is located in a short centre section and
drives a central frameless bogie.

DWA has developed a low-floor diesel railcar, LVT/S, for local lines between 50 km and 100 km. It is of modular design with a corrosion-resistant body of lightweight steel construction. It is designed for buffer loads of 1,500 kN over the side buffers.

The railcar is constructed using bus and tram technology and can be run in multiple units. Floor height is 600 mm and there are 64 seats with room for 41 standing.

UPDATED

DWA Type LVT/S diesel railcar
1997

Electroputere

SC Electroputere SA
Calea Bucureşti 144, R-1100 Craiova, Romania
Tel: +40 451 147753   Fax: +40 451 199897

Key personnel
Managing Director: Ion Lupulescu

Products
Diesel-electric Co-Co locomotives from 1,570 to 3,000 kW; electric Co-Co locomotives of 5,100 kW; electric shunting locomotives of 1,250 kW.

Electroputere co-operates with a large number of other factories in Romania supplying auxiliary machines and apparatus, the braking system control and supply equipment, metering equipment lamps and so on. Diesel

engines are manufactured by UCM Reşiţa and bogies by CAROMET Caransebeş.

Recent contracts include the supply of Type LE 2,900 kW electric locomotives to Romanian Railways; and 45 sets of locomotive components for Adtranz, including bogie frames, underframes, bodyshells and cabs (with driver's desks).

VERIFIED

Emaq

Emaq Industrial SA
PO Box 93609, Estrada Rio-Teresópolis, BR-116, Km 121, Magé, RJ Brazil
Tel: +55 21 633 2020   Fax: +55 21 633 2194

Key personnel
President: Admiral Jair M Pimentel
General Director: Eng Octavio T Yamazaki
Technical and Industrial Director: Eng Délio G Spitz
Commercial Manager: Eng Alexandre M Fuchs
Industrial Planning Manager: Eng Paulo R Sampaio
Manager: Eng Paulo R Padula

Products
Locomotives, diesel-electric and electric; rolling stock.

Recent contracts include the building of emus for CBTU.

VERIFIED

Energomachexport

Energomachexport
25A Protopopovsky per, 129010 Moscow, Russia
Tel: +7 095 288 8456   Fax: +7 095 288 7990
Email: in@eme.tsr.ru

(See also entry in *Bogies and suspensions, wheels and axles* section)

Key personnel
General Director: M Nosanov
Director, Transmash Department: G Stepnov
Advertising Manager: Natalia Kuznetsova

Products
Metro cars

NEW ENTRY

Faur

Faur SA
B-dul Basarabia 256, Bucharest 3, R-73249, Romania
Tel: +40 1 627 6275/624 2022   Fax: +40 1 312 8070/312 8071

Key personnel
General Manager: Trofin Ion
Production Manager: Vasile Nicodim
Product Development Manager: Voicu Ciprain
Sales and Marketing Manager: Brindus Zaharia

Corporate developments
In October 1994, Faur agreed to set up a joint venture with Anglo-French company GEC Alsthom to manufacture and refurbish locomotives and rolling stock. The joint company, GEC Alsthom Faur Transport, is 51 per cent owned by GEC Alsthom, with Faur holding the other 49 per cent.

Products
Diesel-hydraulic locomotives of 110 to 1,940 kW and diesel-electric locomotives of 745 to 1,120 kW for shunting, secondary and main line duties, produced

under licence from Sulzer, Alco, MTU, MAN, Voith, Clark, Adtranz, Gelenkwellen, Oerlikon, Knorr-Bremse and others.

Diesel railcars and tramcars

Recent contracts include a rolling programme to supply 10 LDH 195 kW locomotives a year over five years to sugar factories in Egypt, and overhaul of diesel locomotives for SNCFR, Romania.

V3A-93 tramcars with GEC Alsthom traction motors have been supplied to SNCFR Romania.

UPDATED

Ferrostaal

Ferrostaal AG
PO Box 101265, Hohenzollernstrasse 24, D-45116 Essen, Germany
Tel: +49 201 81801   Fax: +49 201 818 2822

Key personnel
Head of Transport Department: Christian Fritzen

Products
Main line, shunting and mining locomotives with diesel-hydraulic, diesel-electric and electric traction. Electric or

diesel-electric railcars, railbuses, light rail vehicles and other multiple-units for urban public transport; motor and trailer bogies; rolling stock components including wheels, axles, wheelsets, bearings, suspension parts, couplers and electrical equipment.

UPDATED

Fiat

Fiat Ferroviaria SpA
Piazza Galateri 4, I-12038 Savigliano (CN), Italy
Tel: +39 172 718111   Fax: +39 172 718306

Key personnel
Chairman: Marco Pittaluga
Managing Director and General Manager:
   Giancarlo Cozza

Vice-General Directors: Andrea Parnigoni, Piero Losa
Commercial Department Manager: Antonio Amoruso

Principal subsidiary
Elettromeccanica Parizzi

Products
Electric and diesel-electric locomotives.
Electric and diesel railcars; active tilt-body trains; multiple-

units; metro cars; LRVs; tramcars; bogies and components.

A recent product is the Type D145 centre-cab diesel-electric locomotive for shunting and light mixed traffic work, 38 of which have been delivered to Italian Railways (FS). Developed in conjunction with Elettromeccanica Parizzi, the D145 is also known as the Inloc because of its inverter and three-phase variable voltage frequency AC motor transmission. The Inloc pursues recent Fiat practice in adapting heavy road vehicle diesel engines to rail traction.

In 1990 the first E652 electric full chopper locomotives were delivered, representing an important evolution of the well-known E632. The power has been increased from 4,500 to 5,000 kW; the speed in one version only gives 160 km/h with unchanged tractive effort. Rated output is 5,000 kW (continuous) with a line voltage of 3 kV DC, and weight of 103 tonnes.

Fiat has recently supplied low-floor tramcars for Turin, and metro cars for Milan's Line 3.

Fiat's ETR 450 'Pendolino' trainsets, equipped with active body-tilt, have now run over 15 million km in Italian Railways' (FS) service.

The performance of the ETR 450 led FS to order 45 ETR 460 trainsets (of which 20 will be equipped for operation into France), the third generation of the 'Pendolino' trains. In addition to a contract with German Railways (DB AG) for bogies and a tilting system for 20 VT 610 diesel-electric railcars (produced in co-operation with local manufacturers), a contract was signed in 1992 with Finnish State Railways (VR) for two tilt-body 25 kV 50 Hz 'Pendolino' trainsets, with an option on a further 23 trains. Nine dual-voltage (3 kV DC/15 kV 16⅔ Hz AC) ETR 470 'Pendolino' trainsets have been delivered for international services between Italy and Switzerland.

In 1994 DB AG ordered 43 tilting 'Neitec' emus from Siemens/DWA/Fiat for inter-regional services. Fiat is also

ETR 460 electric trainset with active body-tilt

actively working with its partners in the Trevi consortium, Adtranz, Ansaldo and Breda, on the ETR 500 high-speed train for FS. An order for 30 trainsets of 13 vehicles (two power cars and 11 trailers) was placed with Trevi in 1992,

and an additional 30 trainsets were ordered in 1994; the latter will have dual-voltage traction equipment.

Sasib Railway has formed a consortium with Fiat called Italrail for LRT turnkey projects.

Fiat diesel railcars and multiple-units

Class (Railway's own designation)	Cars per unit	Motor cars per unit	Motored axles per motor car	Transmission	Rated power (kW) per motor	Max speed (km/h)	Weight (t) per car	Total seating capacity	Length per car (mm)	No in service 1994	Year first built	Builders Mechanical parts	Builders Engine and type	Builders Transmission
Aln668 (FS)	1	1	2	mechanical	230	91	40	68	23,540	3	1990	Fiat	Fiat	Fiat
Aln668 (FS)	1	1	2	mechanical	230	91	40	68	23,540	4	1992	Fiat	Fiat	Fiat
Aln668 (FS)	1	1	2	mechanical	230	118	40	68	23,540	3	1993	Fiat	Fiat	Fiat
Aln668 (FS)	1	1	2	mechanical	230	95	39.5	69	23,540	8	1993	Fiat	Fiat	Fiat
Aln680 (FS)	1	1	2	hydraulic	250	90	42.5	80	23,840	16	1994	Fiat	Fiat	Voith
Aln777 (FS)	1	1	2	mechanical	250	150	40	77	23,540	20	1992	Fiat	Fiat	Fiat
Aln777 (FS)	1	1	2	mechanical	250	150	40	77	23,540	16	1993	Fiat	Fiat	Fiat
TCDD	1	1	2	hydraulic	250	120	44.8	68	23,840	30	1992	Fiat	Fiat	Voith
VT610 (DB AG)	2	2	2/1	electrical	485	160	47.5	136	26,300	20	1991	Fiat/MAN MBB/Duewag	MTU	ABB/AEG Siemens

Fiat electric railcars and multiple-units

Class	Cars per unit	Line voltage	Motor cars per unit	Motor car wheel arrangement	Rated output (kW) per motor	Max speed (km/h)	Weight (t) per car (M-motor T-trailer)		Total seating capacity	Length per car (mm)		No in service 1994	Year first built	Builders Mechanical parts	Builders Electrical equipment
Low-floor streetcar	1	600 V DC	1	B + 2 + B	150	60		28.0	173		22,280	54	1987	Fiat	Ansaldo
ETR450	9	3 kV DC	8	1A + A1	350	250		44.0	460	M M*	27,350 25,600	15	1987	Fiat	Fiat/Marelli Ansaldo
ETR500 Prototype†	2	3,000 V DC	1	Bo-Bo	1,000	275	M T	72.0 40.0		M T	20,000 26,000	M1 T 1	1987	Fiat/Breda	Ansaldo/TIBB
Rome Metro (Lido)	6	1,500 V DC	4	B + B	220	100	M M* T	32.0 31.0 19.0	133		17,640	6	1987	Fiat	Ansaldo/Marelli
Milan Metro Line 3 Inverter	3	1,500 V DC	2	B + B	270	90	M T	32.0 40.0		M T	17,540 17,540	M26 T 13	1987	Fiat	Ansaldo/Parizzi/TIBB Marelli/Hitachi/Socimi
ETR500(*)		3,000 V DC		Bo-Bo	1,000	300	M T	72.0 40.0	714	M T	20,000 26,000		1989	Fiat/Breda	Ansaldo/ABB
Milan Metro Line 2		1,500 V DC		Bo-Bo	270	90	M T	32.0 40.0	16 8	M T	17,550 26,000		1991 1991	Fiat	Ansaldo/ABB/Marelli
ETR 460	9	3 kV DC	6	1A + A1	500	250		52.7	458	M M*	27,650 25,900		1992	Fiat	Parizzi
S200	6	25 kV 50 Hz	4	1A + A1	500	220		54.0	366	M M*	27,650 25,900		1992	Fiat	Parizzi
ETR 470	9	15 kV 16⅔ Hz 3 kV DC	4	1A + A1	500	200		54.4	500	M	27,650		1993	Fiat	Parizzi/Siemens

UPDATED

FIREMA

FIREMA Trasporti SpA
Viale Edison 110, I-20099 Sesto S Giovanni (Milano), Italy
Tel: +39 2 249 4396   Fax: +39 2 262 25380

Key personnel
Chairman: Dr G Bono
Managing Director: Dr D Marchiorello
General Manager: Dr R Cai
Export Manager: Dr M Fantini
Commercial Manager: Dr G Merola
Marketing Manager: Dr M Fantini

Business Units
Officine Stanga Cittadella
OMS Works
Corso Stati Uniti 3, I-35100 Padua, Italy
Tel: +39 49 899 6211   Fax: +39 49 899 6212

Cittadella Works
Via Rometta all'Olmo 5, I-35013 Cittadella (Padova), Italy
Tel: +39 49 597 1966   Fax: +39 49 940 0238

Fiore Officine Casertane
I-81020 S Nicola la Strada (Caserta), Italy
Tel: +39 823 258111   Fax: +39 823 466812/467691

Ercole Marelli Trazione
Viale Edison 110, I-20099, Sesto S Giovanni (Milano), Italy
Tel: +39 2 24941   Fax: +39 2 248 3908

Metalmeccanica Lucana
I-85050 Tito Scalo (Potenza), Italy
Tel: +39 971 485088/485089   Fax: +39 971 485072

Retam Service
Viale Edison 124, I-20099 Sesto S Giovanni (Milano), Italy
Tel: +39 2 249 4300   Fax: +39 2 249 4310

Products

Electric locomotives, high-speed trainsets, electric multiple-units, railcars, metro rolling stock and light rail vehicles.

Contracts include mechanical parts for 20 single-voltage (3 kV DC) and 23 dual-voltage (3 kV DC and 25 kV 50 Hz AC) E402 electric locomotives for Italian Railways (FS); electrical equipment for 26 E652 electric locomotives for FS; and mechanical parts for 12 E652 locomotives for FS.

Other contracts include the supply of 20 power car bodyshells, 56 first-class and 38 second-class light-alloy trailers, 40 trailer bogies, 12 sets of AC traction motors and 60 auxiliary static converters for 30 ETR 500 high-speed trainsets for Italian Railways (FS); 20 power cars, 77 trailers, 30 motor bogies, 154 trailer bogies and electronic equipment for 30 dual-voltage (3 kV DC and 25 kV 50 Hz AC) ETR 500 trainsets for FS; six Type E82 two-car 3 kV DC emus for SEPSA, Naples (Cumana and Circumflegrea Railways); five Type E84A 3 kV DC emus for COTRAL (Rome–Viterbo); 72 power cars and 32 trailers for 72 four-car double-deck emus for FS and North Milan Railway (FNME); and four two-car emus for Circumetnea Railway.

UPDATED

Top deck of double-deck emu in service with FS and FNME   *1997*

Class E402 dual-voltage locomotive for FS
1997

Fuji Car Manufacturing Co

Fuji Car Manufacturing Co Ltd
3 Shoho Building, 2-2-3 Nishishinsaibashi, Chuo-ku, Osaka 542, Japan
Tel: +81 6 213 2711   Fax: +81 6 213 4071

Key personnel
Export Sales: M Miyama

Products
People mover systems (FAST).

VERIFIED

Fuji Heavy Industries

Fuji Heavy Industries Ltd
Transport Equipment Division
Subaru Building 7-2, Nishishinjuku 1-chome,
Shinjyuku-ku, Tokyo 160, Japan
Tel: +81 3 3347 2436   Fax: +81 3 3347 2117

Main works
Utsunomiya Manufacturing Division
1-11, Yonan 1-chome, Utsunomiya, Tochigi 320, Japan

Key personnel
General Manager, Overseas Department: Y Hanaoka

Products
Diesel trainsets, tilting dmus and railcars.

VERIFIED

Ganz Ansaldo

Ganz Ansaldo Electric Ltd
Lövöház utca 39, H-1024 Budapest, Hungary
Tel: +36 1 175 3322   Fax: +36 1 156 2989

Key personnel
President: Gábor Kara
Managing Director: Paolo Smirne
Commercial Director: Maurizio Sauli

Production Director: Bruno Salucci
Purchasing Director: Anton Luigi Traverso

Products
Electric main line and shunting locomotives.

All of the electric locomotives for the Hungarian State Railways (MÁV) are produced by Ganz. These include 56 thyristor-controlled locomotives Type V63 with 3,600 kW output which operate with mixed traffic. Also the Type V46 which is a thyristor-controlled, four-axle shunting

locomotive with 800 kW output. MÁV has 45 of these in service and a further 15 were delivered recently.

Corporate developments
In 1991, Ganz Electric Works was merged with Ansaldo SpA to form Ganz Ansaldo Electric Ltd, a member of the Finmeccanica Group.

VERIFIED

Ganz-Hunslet

Ganz-Hunslet Részvénytársaság
PO Box 29, 1430 Budapest, Hungary
Tel: +36 1 210 1177/313 0887/1173 (Sales Office)
Fax: +36 1 210 1175/210 1180

Works
Vajda Péter utca 12, Budapest VIII

Key personnel
Chairman: Dr Gyula Várszegi
Managing Director: Stephen F Kostyal
Commercial Director: John A Kardos
Technical Director: Richard Lemmerer

Principal subsidiary
Ganz-Hunslet Special Rail Products (Ganz-Hunslet SRP)

Corporate developments
Ganz-Hunslet is a limited company and was formed from Ganz, established in 1844, and later Ganz-Mávag companies.

Products
Electric and diesel multiple-units, trams and LRVs, metro cars, diesel-electric and diesel-hydraulic locomotives, AC

electric locomotives for main line, shunting and industrial applications.

Deliveries during 1996/7 include three four-car intercity emus and two four-car emus for MÁV Hungarian State Railways. They have AC traction equipment in addition to microprocessor-control, data transmission and diagnostic equipment supplied by Adtranz (qv). KTMB Malaysia has taken delivery of 18 Series 8100 three-car commuter emus with stainless-steel carbodies and AC traction equipment supplied by Holec Ridderkerk, Netherlands. Final assembly and fitting out work took place at the Jenbacher plant in Jenbach, Austria.

UPDATED

Type DVM-14 diesel-electric locomotive

1995

Ganz-Hunslet intercity emu for MÁV Hungary
1997

GE

GE Transportation Systems
2901 East Lake Road, Erie, Pennsylvania 16531, USA
Tel: +1 814 875 5385   Fax: +1 814 875 5911
Web: www.ge.com/transportation

Key personnel
President and Chief Executive Officer:
   David L Calhoun
General Managers
Americas Locomotive Marketing: Stephen F Angel
Europe, Africa, Middle East Locomotive Marketing:
   Alex B Messerle
Asia Locomotive Marketing: Robert J Parisi
Global Service and Parts: David B Tucker
Manufacturing: Ted F Torbeck
Engineering: Daniel Sheflin

Affiliates
A Goninan Ltd, Australia (licensee)
Dorbyl Transport Products, South Africa (licensee)
GEVISA SA, Brasil (joint venture)
GE Harris Railway Electronics, USA (joint venture)
GE Locomotif, Indonesia (joint venture)

GE AC 6000 locomotive for Union Pacific Railroad
1997

MWM, Germany (joint project)
Adtranz, Germany (joint project)

Products
Diesel-electric locomotives (new, remanufactured and modernised); electric locomotives; locomotive control systems; financing and training programmes.

Locomotives
GE AC4400 CW (4,400 hp — 3,285 kW) and GE AC6000 CW (6,000 hp — 4,475 kW) diesel locomotives feature AC traction motors regulated by computer-controlled inverters with advanced high-performance traction control (single inverter per axle).

Dash 9 and Dash 8 diesel locomotive propulsion systems utilise DC traction motors in full-time parallel configuration supplied by rectified three-phase traction alternators (computer-regulated adhesion process).

Both models are microprocessor-controlled locomotives utilising integrated function computers and displays that replace add-on boxes and operator interfaces.

Dash 7 diesel models include the Constant Horsepower Excitation Control (CHEC) and the speed-based adhesion control (Sentry) systems with automatic wheel diameter calibration.

Electric locomotives are designed with DC traction motors in full-time parallel configuration supplied by phased thyristor control and fast, analogue-regulated adhesion control.

Genesis series passenger locomotives are available either as a straight diesel model or a dual-mode derivative, able to operate from a third rail electric supply or by using diesel power in non-electrified zones.

Technologies
The GE AC traction motor includes a low slip capability and is designed for 1 million mile overhaul intervals. AC locomotives feature direct air-cooled, easily replaceable phase module inverter systems (single inverter per axle).

Electronic fuel injection promotes fuel savings, reduces emissions, and lowers maintenance.

Split cooling reduces NOx emissions, improves fuel efficiency, and reduces engine temperatures.

GE Harris Railway Electronics LLC designs and integrates advanced electronic train and railway system products such as LOCOTROL® distributed power, electronic air brakes, computer-aided dispatching and Precision Train Control®.

HiAd (high adhesion) trucks (bogies) feature a low weight transfer design with 10-year overhaul intervals.

GE's steerable bogie, introduced in 1996, is a three-axle, three-motor, high-adhesion class truck designed to carry half the weight of the locomotive. The steerable bogies allow locomotives to negotiate previously prohibited curved track.

Integrated function controls use microcontrol computers to optimise locomotive operations. This feature includes display screens which simplify the operator-machine interface.

GE AC 6000 locomotive for CSX

1997

Dynamic braking grid isolation results in higher reliability and easier maintenance.

GE high-impact fuel tanks are puncture resistant and vented to prevent spillage.

Engines and Components

GE offers three diesel engine designs: GE 7HDL 16-cylinder, 6,000 hp; GE 7FDL 8-, 12-, 16-cylinder, 16-cylinder 4,400 hp; GE Alco 251 8-, 12-, 16-cylinder.

All AC, Dash 9, Dash 8, Dash 7 models feature a main generator consisting of a three-phase traction alternator feeding a full wave bridge traction rectifier. The GMG 196/198 generator is used on 6,000 traction hp (AC) and 4,400 traction hp (AC, Dash 9, and Dash 8) models.

Most AC, Dash 9, Dash 8, and Dash 7 models include a single stator traction alternator output with sufficient capacity to accommodate all volt-amp requirements through the entire speed range.

All AC, Dash 9, Dash 8, and Dash 7 models feature traction motors connected in a full-time parallel configuration in the propulsion mode to provide consistent propulsion behaviour; to enhance speed-tractive effort characteristics; and to eliminate motor transition contactor maintenance. The DC traction motor family consists of GE 752, GE 793, GE 794, GE 761, and GE 764 models. With the AC traction motor technology, 35 per cent adhesion is realised.

GE Transportation Systems has developed a locomotive architecture that promotes the development of railway-specific technology advancements.

GE Transportation Systems and Adtranz (qv) have developed, and produced the Blue Tiger range of diesel-electric locomotives for the world market. The first, Type DE-AC33C, has modular construction allowing adaptation to customer requirements. Options include full-width driver cab, twin cabs, air conditioning, toilet, full width hoods and adaptability to various loading and track gauges. The Co-Co standard gauge prototype weighs 108 tonnes with an axle load of 18 tonnes and the diesel engine is rated at almost 2,400 kW. GE Transportation Systems provided the complete three-phase propulsion system with GE 7FDL diesel engine, generator, traction motors including the controls, the cooling system and the electronic components for diagnostic and display systems. The propulsion equipment has one air-cooled traction power inverter per axle for individual axle control, integrated function computer and displays, dynamic

Blue Tiger Series AC/AC locomotive developed by GE Transportation Systems and Adtranz   **1997**

braking, computer controlled air brake system, microprocessor controls and AC motor driven auxiliary equipment.

Renewal Parts

GE Transportation Systems' global parts operation provides a comprehensive offering that currently serves more than 20,000 locomotives in over 75 countries through a network of over 50 regional distributors and agents worldwide.

Certified OEM quality new and remanufactured components provide dependable service for replacements, while a wide variety of performance-enhancing upgrades that increase adhesion of tractive/braking effort or reduce maintenance costs, fuel consumption or emissions, are available for older U-Series and ALCO locomotives as well as newer Dash 7, 8 and 9 models.

LMS

Locomotive Management Services (LMS) manages a variety of locomotive lease fleets including recently built Dash 8-40CW locomotives. The mission of LMS is to provide highly reliable and productive locomotives for lease to its customers on terms that are tailored to support the rail lines. Lease periods are flexible, ranging from short-term operating leases to long-term commitments. Full-time (for a specified time period) leases over a multi-year commitment can be ordered or offered. Longer term commitments ensure continued availability of quality lease locomotives during critical traffic periods at a predictable and manageable daily rate.

Service

GE Global locomotive maintenance service maintains over 2,000 locomotives in comprehensive service programmes. GE Transportation Systems provides customised maintenance solutions ranging from field technical support to full, turnkey maintenance facility operations. These programmes feature high performance through reliability-centred maintenance programmes, continuous training, supply chain integration and dedicated engineering support.

Training

GE Transportation Systems' training programmes are designed to focus on operator and maintenance personnel. Through this training, maximising railway fleet performance is accomplished by applying operating characteristics, protocols and maintenance tasks. Courses can be scheduled individually or as part of a complete training package at customer's sites or at the GE Learning Centre in Erie, Pennsylvania. Delivery methods range from videos, multimedia training modules, video conferencing, IFC AAR simulator and DID panel simulator, as well as custom-designed programmes.

UPDATED

GE AC 4400 locomotives for Canadian Pacific Railway Company
1997

GEC Alsthom

GEC Alsthom Transport Division
48 rue Albert Dhalenne, F-93482 Saint-Ouen Cedex, Paris, France
Tel: +33 1 41 66 90 00   Fax: +33 1 41 78 96 66
Web: http://www.gecalsthom.com

Key personnel

Managing Director: André Navarri
  Deputy Managing Director: Michel Moreau
  International Director: André Thiniègres
  Finance and Administration: Philippe Fondanaiche
  Industrial and Technical Department: Patrick Bikard
  Business Development: Pierre Lenfant

Corporate developments

GEC Alsthom was formed in 1989 by the merger of the Power Systems Division of GEC (UK) and Alsthom (France). It is jointly owned by General Electric Company, England, and Alcatel Alsthom, France.

Since then the company has made a number of

GEC Alsthom PBKA Thalys trainset   **1997**

acquisitions and involved itself in joint ventures including:
• Linke-Hofmann-Busch (LHB), Germany, together with its Scharfenberg subsidiary;
• Faur, Romania;
• AMF, Canada;
• Geo-Railmex, Mexico;
• Konstal, Poland;
• GTRM, UK.

With a turnover of ECU1.97 billion, the Transport Division of GEC Alsthom employs more than 17,000

people in seven European countries as well as North and South America and has sold its products to more than 50 countries over the past 10 years. Vehicles built to GEC Alsthom designs have been manufactured in 20 countries through technology transfer agreements.

Following a major reorganisation, the company comprises five operating groups—Passenger, Signalling, Locomotives, Equipment and Systems.

The company has entered into a number of joint ventures, including with the following companies:
• Bombardier (supply of high-speed stock to USA);
• Fiat (promotion of tilting train technology in UK);
• Siemens (high-speed projects in Asia);
• Mitsubishi and Telecite (electrical equipment).

GEC Alsthom Transport has now extended its capabilities and facilities to include whole-life maintenance.

Specialist business units have been created in the UK, Canada, Brazil and Spain, covering maintenance of the complete range from TGV-style trains to heavy-haul diesel locomotives.

In the UK GEC Alsthom has invested in a major

Jubilee Line train built by GEC Alsthom (Jubilee Line Extension Project) **1997**

infrastructure maintenance company, GTRM, released as part of the privatisation of British Rail. The work of this unit covers track and signalling maintenance. Also in the UK it has taken over the train maintenance depots of London Underground Northern Line and Gatwick Express.

GEC Alsthom has signed an agreement to take possession of railway manufacturing assets at Hornell, New York, which were previously owned by the American Passenger Rail Car Co, LCC (Amerail).

Works locations

Australia

GEC Alsthom Australia Ltd, Transportation Division
373 Horsley Road, Milperra NSW 2214, Australia
Tel: +61 7 772 7444   Fax: +61 7 774 4838
General Manager: Michael O'Rourke
(Locomotives and multiple-units)

Belgium

GEC Alsthom ACEC Transport
Rue Gambier Dupret 50-52, PO Box 4211, B-6001 Charleroi, Belgium
Tel: +32 71 445411   Fax: +32 71 445778
Managing Director: C Jauquet
(Traction equipment)

Brazil

GEC Alsthom Locomotives
Avenida Interlargos, 4211 São Paulo, Aeria Cap 04661.300
Tel: +55 1 524 1044
Managing Director: C A Almeida
(Locomotives)

GEC Alsthom Mafersa
PO Box 01404, 902 Sao Paulo
Tel: +55 11 284 6699   Fax: +55 11 289 5700
Managing Director: C A Almeida
(Rolling stock)

Canada

GEC Alsthom AMF Transport Inc
1830 Le Ber Street, Montréal, Québec H3K 2A4
Tel: +1 514 925 3618   Fax: +1 514 925 3826
Managing Director: M Montferrante
(Heavy maintenance and refurbishment of locomotives and coaches)

France

GEC Alsthom Transport
3 Avenue des trois Chênes, 90018 Belfort Cedex
Tel: +33 3 84 55 10 00   Fax: +33 3 84 55 17 37
Managing Director: J C Brimont
(Locomotives, shunters, TGVs and power cars for TGVs)

GEC Alsthom Transport
Avenue du Commandant Lysiak, 17001 Aytré, La Rochelle
Tel: +33 05 46 51 30 00   Fax: +33 05 46 30 62 68

Managing Director: Thierry Smaggh
(TGV trainsets, passenger coaches, mass transit vehicles and LRVs)

GEC Alsthom Transport
Rue Jacquart, 54494 Petit Forêt
Tel: +33 3 27 14 18 00   Fax: +33 3 27 14 18 01
Managing Director: M Krebs
(Double-deck cars, metro cars)

Germany

Linke-Hofmann-Busch GmbH, PO Box 411160, D-38233 Salzgitter
Tel: +49 5341 214041   Fax: +49 5341 213943
Contact: H J Jabbs
(Passenger coaches, mass transit vehicles and LRVs)

Mexico

GEC Alsthom Geo Railmex SA de CV
Leibnitz 20-10, Col Ansures, Del Miguel Hidalgo 11590
Tel: +52 2 254 1419   Fax: +52 2 545 5194
Managing Director: F Garcia Manso
Other works at Mexico City, Monterrey and Xapala
(Maintenance of locomotives and freight wagons)

Poland

GEC Alsthom Transport Poland (ex-Konstal)
Ul Katouvielka 104/Hala, PL 41500 Chorzow
Tel: +48 32 411427   Fax: +48 32 411427
Managing Director: H P Engel
(LRVs and passenger coaches)

Spain

GEC Alsthom Transporte SA
Paseo de las Castellana 257, 28046, Madrid
Tel: +34 1 334 5670   Fax: +34 1 334 5888

Managing Director: Miguel Iraburu
(Maintenance of passenger rolling stock)

Tel: +34 1 334 5800   Fax: +34 1 334 5801
Managing Director: J Gasol
(Manufacture and maintenance of diesel and electric locomotives and maintenance of AVE high-speed trains)

GEC Alsthom Transporte SA
Poligono Industrial del Mediterraneo, C/Mitxera, s/n, 46550 Albuixech, Valencia
Tel: +34 6 141 5000   Fax: +34 6 140 0816
Managing Director: J J Sanchis
(Locomotives)

United Kingdom

GEC Alsthom Metro-Cammell Ltd
PO Box 248, Birmingham B8 2YJ
Tel: +44 121 328 5455   Fax: +44 121 695 3695
Managing Director: Peter Murray
(Passenger cars and mass transit vehicles)

GEC Alsthom Railway Maintenance Services Ltd
PO Box 3799, Common Lane, Washwood Heath, Birmingham B8 2UG
Tel: +44 121 695 3600   Fax: +44 121 695 3650
Managing Director: Stephen Ollier
(Rail vehicle maintenance)

Products

Diesel-electric and electric locomotives, high-speed trainsets (TGV), trains for interurban, suburban, transit and metro operations, LRVs, passenger coaches, bogies and electrical propulsion equipment.

Metro trainsets, light rail vehicles, automated light vehicles, diesel and electric multiple-units and railcars, high-speed trainsets, electric and electronic traction equipment. Railway engineering: turnkey transport systems.

GEC Alsthom produces the TGV family of high-speed trainsets, first built for the Paris—Lyon high-speed line opened in 1981. Since then, GEC Alsthom has produced TGV-Atlantique trainsets for SNCF, AVE trainsets for RENFE, TGV-Réseau trainsets for use in France and Belgium, Eurostar trainsets for use through the Channel Tunnel and double-deck TGV-Duplex trainsets for SNCF's Paris—Lyon and Paris—Lille routes.

When the present contracts are completed, 525 TGV trainsets will be running in eight countries.

Contracts

Moroccan National Railways (ONCF) is taking delivery of seven Bo-Bo electric freight locos, with an option for two more. The power rating is 4,400 kW and power is taken at 3,000 kV DC and the operating speed is 120 km/h. Delivery is due to start in 1998.

A consortium led by GEC Alsthom Transporte with Adtranz and CAF is supplying CPTM Brazil with 30 four-car trainsets, with delivery expected in 1998.

GEC Alsthom's subsidiary, Linke-Hofmann-Busch, as leader of a consortium with Siemens AG, has won an order to supply DSB Denmark with 112 trainsets for delivery from 1998 onwards.

A fleet of six seven-car rubber-tyred trainsets for Santiago Metro Lines 1 and 2 is being supplied during 1997-98.

'Asytrit' locomotive for SNCF **1996**

An order for 28 Citadis trams has been received for Line 1 of Montpellier's future tram system. Each tram carries 271 and the fleet is scheduled for delivery in December 1998 for full service operation in 2000. The ultra-low-floor Citadis has a floor height of 350 mm and bogies with single-wheel hub motors. The floor is raised over the more traditional bogies and the body construction is aluminium alloy panels on steel frames. The bogie design has been bought in from LHB (qv) and specifies GEC's ONIX asynchronous traction motor.

Other contracts include 665 Type MP89 metro cars for RATP, Paris; 28 six-axle double-articulated LRVs for Rouen; 100 two-car TER dmus for SNCF; 30 double-deck TGV-Duplex high-speed trainsets for SNCF; 59 metro trainsets for London Underground Ltd's Jubilee Line Extension; double-deck emus for the Tagus crossing, Portugal and 106 metro trainsets for London Underground Ltd's Northern Line.

A fleet of seven four-car emus is being constructed for the Arlanda Airport line, Sweden.

In Hong Kong a major refurbishment programme has been completed covering extensive re-styling as well as half-life maintenance for the whole fleet of emus for the Kowloon—Canton Railway.

Diesel-hydraulic railcars have been supplied to Finland, passenger coaches have been delivered to India and suburban emus to Hamburg.

The company has supplied high-speed (TGV) trainsets for service in France and Spain and Eurostar high-speed trains for use through the Channel Tunnel. Other high-speed trains on order include those for the Thalys project in northwest Europe, the new high-speed line in South Korea and the FoX system in Florida, USA; some degree of local manufacture is planned for these export orders and when present contracts are completed the total will be 525 trainsets in four countries.

French National Railways (SNCF) is taking delivery of 30 BB36000 'Asytrit' locomotives from GEC Alsthom. The 6,000 kW locomotives feature asynchronous traction motors and are equipped to operate at 1.5 kV 50 Hz AC and 1.5 kV and 3 kV DC at up to 220 km/h.

GEC Alsthom, in association with Bombardier, has won an order to supply MTA Maryland with six high-speed locomotives to be operated by Maryland Rail Commuter Service (MARC). The locomotives are similar in design to the 15 BB36000 Asytrit locomotives currently being built for Amtrak.

TGV trainsets are being built for the Seoul—Pusan high-speed line in South Korea (where local assembly is taking place through a technology transfer agreement). The first trainset was completed early in 1997 and consists of 18 passenger cars plus two power cars. It is being tested on SNCF until 1998. A second train of a total of 46 trainsets was delivered direct to KNR mid-1997. TGV trainsets have also been built for the Thalys (Paris—Brussels—Cologne—Amsterdam) high-speed network.

TGV-Duplex trainsets

Trainset consist: M+8T+M
Motor axle layout (UIC): 2 Bo-Bo power cars
Electrical supply: 25 kV 50 Hz AC, 1.5 kV DC
Number of powered axles: 8
Total tare weight of trainset in running order: 424 t
Motor or carrying axle load: 17 t
Overall length M+8T+M: 200 m
Traction motors
   type: three-phase asynchronous
   number per trainset: 8
   location: underfloor
   type of transmission: gear reduction, spline shaft transmission and final drive gearbox

TGV Duplex, a double-deck design for the Paris—Lyon line   **1997**

The first TGV for the high-speed line in South Korea   **1997**

Max speed: 300 km/h
Passenger capacity
   first class: 197
   second class: 348

New developments

An emu for British train operating companies has been unveiled. Named Juniper, the bodyshell is to the same design as the existing Networker but slightly narrower, allowing universal route availability. It can take power from third rail or overhead and has a top speed of 160 km/h. The four-car set consists of two driving motors and two trailer composites and seats 246 in 2+2 configuration. It will be built at GEC Alsthom's Metro-Cammell works, Birmingham.

An order for eight Juniper sets (eight-car formation) has been received for the London Victoria—Gatwick Airport service.

The bodies, which will have ribbon-flush glazing will have three classes of accommodation, Executive, First and Standard. GEC Alsthom's Railway Maintenance Services will be responsible for maintenance of the fleet during the 15-year franchise period.

A further order has been received from Porterbrook Leasing, owned by Stagecoach, UK, for 30 Juniper emus. Delivery starts in 1998 and the fleet is expected to be in service by 2000 and will be used on London Waterloo to Reading services, replacing slam-door stock.

The fleet will be air-conditioned and have a maximum speed of 160 km/h. Each four-car emu will seat 266 in standard class with a further 24 in first class. Wider doors will allow two to alight/board at the same time. Bicycle racks will accommodate at least two bikes per set.

An order for 27 GEC Alsthom dmus for North Western Trains was received in July and includes an option for a further 50 vehicles. Some of these trains will be able to run at up to 125 mph. The trains will be built at GEC Alsthom's Washwood Heath plant and are expected to enter service in 2000.

GEC Alsthom, in association with Bombardier, has won an order to supply MTA Maryland with six high-speed locomotives to be operated by Maryland Rail Commuter Service (MARC). The locomotives are similar in design to the 15 BB36000 Asytrit locomotives currently being built for Amtrak.

378 metro cars for la Compania Anonima de Metro de Caracas (CAMC), Venezuela, are being refurbished. The contract includes training of personnel and maintenance of new equipment for a year. The work includes refurbishment of the traction control system, incorporation of IGBT technology to replace the static converter battery charger and installation of electrically controlled circuit breakers to replace pneumatically controlled circuit breakers. The first car will be supplied in 1998.

Istanbul Ulasim Ve Ticaret AS has ordered 32 metro cars for the Istanbul metro, similar to those being supplied for Caracas metro, Venezuela. They are being built at the Valenciennes factory and delivery is expected to start in 1998. A technology transfer agreement with local industry exists for the supply of a further 62 cars for Phase 2 of the metro.

UPDATED

Double-deck M12N emu for the Eole route in Paris   **1997**

INKA

PT (Persero) Industri Kereta Api (PT INKA)
Jalan Yos Sudarso No 71, Madiun 63122, Indonesia
Tel: +62 351 4623/4624/3554   Fax: +62 351 2892

Key personnel
President: Ir Istantoro
Marketing Director: Ir Haryono Subyantoro

Corporate developments
Formed for local freight wagon assembly chiefly from
Japanese manufactured kits. In 1989 PT INKA became
part of the state-owned Strategic Industries.

Products
Assembly and renovation of diesel and electrical multiple-
units. These are being undertaken in collaboration with
the BN division of Bombardier Eurorail, Belgium.

VERIFIED

Jenbacher

Jenbacher Energiesysteme AG
Achenseestrasse 1-3, A-6200 Jenbach, Austria
Tel: +43 5244 6000   Fax: +43 5244 63255
Web: http//www.jenbacher.com

Key personnel
Board Members: Siegmar Gerhartz, Gerd-Werner
Klawonn, Alfred Benk

Corporate developments
The company primarily makes engines, for use in
locomotives and railcars, though the main market for its
engines is in power generation. Jenbacher is owned by
the Auricon Group of Austria.

Products
Development, design, production and sales of diesel-
hydraulic, diesel-electric and electric locomotives from 50
to 3,000 kW for varying railway types and track gauges;
remanufacture.

Development, design, production and sales of diesel-
hydraulic, diesel-electric and electric railcars, railbuses
and multiple-units; refurbishment.

Contracts include: 60 four-axle diesel-hydraulic Class
2068 locomotives for Austrian Federal Railways for
shunting and other light duties. Features include low-
noise emission (70 dB), optimised exhaust gas
suppression and prevention of fluid emission. The class is
designed for a maximum speed of 120 km/h.

Other contracts include more than 100 Class 5047
diesel-hydraulic railcars and Class 5147 emus for Austrian
Federal Railways and for Styrian Railways. The cars are
designed for one-man operation on non-electrified
regional routes. Particular attention was paid to noise
absorption/soundproofing and vibration insulation. The
railcars have a maximum speed of 120 km/h and are
equipped with a sealed lavatory.

Jenbacher has completed deliveries of 18 three-car
emus for Malaysian Railway Administration (KTM). The
units feature stainless steel bodyshells, air conditioning
and seating for 224 passengers. Maximum speed is
120 km/h.

New developments
An articulated high-speed train for regional use based on
low-floor passenger saloons without wheels linked to two-

Jenbacher 5147 dmu   *1997*

Jenbacher articulated Integral set   *1997*

axle drive modules, which also have seats. Double-deck
or single-deck options, or a mix, are available and the
concept is named Integral. Train lengths can be specified
from three-section upwards.

UPDATED

Jessop

Jessop & Company Ltd, Calcutta
63 Netaji Subhas Road, Calcutta 700001, India
Tel: +91 33 243 2041/33 243 3420
Fax: +91 33 243 1610

Works
Dum Dum Works, 21 & 22 Jessore Road, Calcutta
700 028, India
Tel: +91 33 551 9922/5992   Fax: +91 33 551 2868

Key personnel
Managing Director: A K Sur
Director (Engineering and Commercial):
    P C Bhattacharya
Director (Production): P K Mukherjee
Secretary: R D G Raghavan
Senior Manager (Exports): Amit Ghosh

Products
Rolling stock including electric multiple-unit coaches,
LRVs, passenger coaches and freight wagons.

Contracts include 175 electric multiple-unit coaches for
Indian Railways. A total of 51 such coaches was delivered
to Indian Railways in 1993-94.

UPDATED

Kaelble-Gmeinder

Kaelble-Gmeinder GmbH
PO Box 1355, D-74803 Mosbach, Baden, Germany
Tel: +49 6261 80614   Fax: +49 6261 80660

Key personnel
Managing Director: Heinz Chr Mutz
Head of Rail Traction Division: Rudolf Mickel

Products
Diesel locomotives with electric, hydrodynamic or
hydrostatic power transmission systems and engine

output up to 1,100 kW, suitable for narrow-, standard- or
broad-gauge locomotives with dual-power systems,
(diesel-electric/electric, battery/electric) for operations in
tunnels; flameproof diesel locomotives for chemical
industries and flameproof battery locomotives for
underground mining operations; propulsion bogie
systems for application to any kind of special railway
vehicles, such as snow-ploughs, rail grinding and track
maintenance vehicles.

Examples are the Type D60C diesel hydraulic
locomotive and the dual-mode service locomotive. The
Type D60C is powered by an MWM water-cooled diesel
engine producing 463 kW which provides a maximum

speed of between 30 and 50 km/h in forward and reverse.
Total weight with ballast is 66 tonnes. The locomotive is
equipped with cardan shaft drive and hydraulic power
transmission. The dual-mode service locomotive which
has been supplied to Berliner Verkehrsbetriebe (BVB) is
fitted with a three-phase drive system and has a Bo-Bo
axle arrangement. It is powered by a 1,100 kW diesel
engine giving a maximum speed of 80 km/h. Radio-
controlled push-pull running, operated from the control
car, is available.

VERIFIED

Kalugaputjmach

Kaluga Locomotive Works
PO Box 4, 248 612 Kaluga, Russian Federation

Products
Locomotives.

VERIFIED

Kawasaki

Kawasaki Heavy Industries Ltd
World Trade Center Building, 4-1 Hamamatsu-cho 2-chome, Minato-ku, Tokyo 105, Japan
Tel: +81 3 3435 2588   Fax: +81 3 3435 2157/3436 3037

Works
1-18 Wadayama-dori 2-chome, Hyogo-ku, Kobe 652, Japan
Tel: +81 78 682 3133   Fax: +81 78 682 3134/671 5784

Key personnel
President: Hiroshi Ohba
Executive Vice-Presidents: Yoshiro Manabe,
    Junji Hayashi, Yukihiro Hirata, Tetsuro Takahashi
Senior General Manager, Rolling Stock Group:
    Sotaro Yamada

Subsidiary
Kawasaki Rail Car Inc, 1 Larkin Plaza, Yonkers, New York 10701, USA
Tel: +1 914 376 4700   Fax: +1 914 376 4779

Products
Electric, diesel-electric, diesel-hydraulic locomotives; high-speed trainsets, electric and diesel railcars, metro trainsets, automated guideway transit systems.

Kawasaki's R110A new-generation prototype metro train for New York   1996

Recent contracts include the supply of a DC inverter locomotive with an output of 3,390 kW to the Japan Freight Railway.

Other contracts include the supply of a Series 500 Shinkansen high-speed trainset to JR West; E2 and E3 Shinkansen high-speed trainsets for JR East; and an Automated Guideway Transit (AGT) system for Tokyo.

UPDATED

Keef

Alan Keef Limited
Lea Line, Ross-on-Wye HR9 7LQ, UK
Tel: +44 1989 750757   Fax: +44 1989 750780

Key personnel
Managing Director: Alan Keef

Products
Design, construction and refurbishment of light railway equipment including diesel-hydraulic, diesel-mechanical, mining and surface locomotives, steam locomotives, rolling stock and trackwork. Sole suppliers of Simplex locomotives and related spares.

Current contracts include two K100 diesel locomotives for TPC Ltd, Tanzania for sugar cane haulage.

UPDATED

Keef K80 diesel locomotive for Chhatak Cement, Bangladesh
1995

Kinki Sharyo

Head Office and Tokuan Factory
The Kinki Sharyo Co Ltd
3-9-60 Inada-Shinmachi, Higashi-Osaka City, Osaka 577, Japan
Tel: +81 6 746 5240   Fax: +81 6 745 5135
Email: KRSTAN@Kinsha.dp.u-netsurf.or jp

Key personnel
President: Junro Ono

Executive Vice-President: Shunji Matsumoto
Senior Managing Director, Rolling Stock: Teijiro Itoh
Managing Director: Hirokazu Iyota
Director, Manufacture: Hiroyuki Seki
Director, Domestic Sales: Yosuke Saida
General Manager, Rolling Stock: Shigehiro Ueda

Subsidiary company
Kinki Sharyo (USA) Inc
20 Walnut Street, Wellesley Hills, MA 02181, USA
Tel: +1 617 237 2075   Fax: +1 617 237 2079

Products
Electric and diesel railcars in steel, aluminium and stainless steel, including high-speed trainsets, electric multiple-units, metro cars and light rail vehicles.

Recent contracts include a Series 653 Limited Express emu for JR East (seven cars); Series 300 Shinkansen trainsets for JR Tokai (16 cars); Series 813 suburban emus (66 cars) for JR Kyushu; six cars for Teito rapid transit, Ginza Line; eight cars for Tokyo Metropolitan Government, Asakusa Line; 40 commuter cars for Kinki Nippon; Series 70 (linear motor) metro trainsets (eight

Kinki Sharyo double-deck express Vista car for Kinki Nippon Railway   1997

Kinki Sharyo Series 70 emu with linear induction motor propulsion   1997

cars) for Osaka Municipal Transportation Bureau; 84 cars for Kyoto Municipal Transport Tozai Line; 20 LRVs for Massachusetts Bay Transportation Authority, USA; 43 low-floor LRVs for New Jersey Transit, USA; 48 metro cars for Cairo Metro Line 2, National Authority for Tunnels, Egypt; 12 double-deck passenger coaches for KCRC Hong Kong.

Deliveries to JR West include Series 500 Shinkansen high-speed trainsets (10 cars), Series 207 suburban emus (27 cars), Series 681 Limited Express (9 cars) and Series 223 Suburban (20 cars).

UPDATED

Kolmex

Kolmex SA
Grzybowska 80/82, PL-00-844 Warsaw, Poland
Tel: +48 22 661 5000   Fax: +48 22 620 9381

Key personnel
Chairman: Andrzej Nâlecz
Commercial Director: Krystyna Stepaniuk

Products
Electric and diesel locomotives for main line, shunting and mining applications; Electric multiple-units, manufactured by Pafawag of Wroclaw; diesel railcars; trams.

The locomotives are manufactured by H Cegielski of Poznan (diesel), Pafawag of Wroclaw (electric) and Bumar-Fablok of Chrzanow (diesel-electric).

The Type 302 D main line diesel locomotive is an example of the family being manufactured by Cegielski. This locomotive is powered by a 3,000 hp engine, has electric transmission and incorporates an internal combustion engine to drive its electric heating generator. Maximum speed is 140 km/h. Its power unit is an air-cooled, supercharged Type 2116 SSF 16-cylinder engine, built under Fiat licence, and a synchronous 150 Hz AC main generator.

UPDATED

Kolomna

Kolomna Plant Joint Stock Company
Partizan Street, 140408 Kolomna, Moscow Region, Russian Federation
Tel: +7 095 38152   Fax: +7 095 203 2434

Key personnel
See entry in *Diesel engines, transmission and fuelling systems* section.

Products
Diesel-electric passenger locomotives.

Recent production includes the Co-Co TEP70 and Bo+Bo-Bo+Bo TEP80 types. Powered by four-cycle, 16-cylinder 2A-5D49 engine, the 2,942 kW TEP70 has a maximum speed of 160 km/h. The TEP80 is rated at 4,413 kW and is powered by a four-cycle, 20-cylinder 2-20DG engine. Maximum speed is 160 km/h.

VERIFIED

TEP80 diesel-electric locomotive
1996

Konstal

See GEC Alsthom

Krauss-Maffei

Krauss-Maffei Verkehrstechnik GmbH
PO Box 500340, Krauss-Maffei Strasse 2, D-80973 Munich, Germany
Tel: +49 89 88990   Fax: +49 89 8899 3336

Key personnel
Managing Board: Dipl Ing Werner Görlitz, Walter Tichy

Corporate developments
A minority shareholding in Krauss-Maffei Verkehrstechnik GmbH is owned by Siemens AG.

Products
Electric locomotives, diesel-electric and diesel-hydraulic locomotives for all duties, gauges, speeds and for both main line and industrial service. Power units for high-speed trainsets.

Krauss-Maffei Series 152 electric locomotive with DB Germany
1997

Krauss-Maffei diesel locomotives

Railway/ customer	Type	Axle arrangement	Transmission	Rated power (kW)	Max speed (km/h)	Total weight (t)	Total units (under licence)	Years built	Builders Diesel engine	Transmission
Various	ME 05	Co	electric	500-560	60	60-75	23	1981-88	MTU	ABB
Various	MH 05	C	hydraulic	500-560	45	60-66	23	1984-98	MTU/Cat	Voith
Turkish State Railway	ME 07	Bo-Bo	electric	700	90	68	85 (35)	1984-90	MTU	ABB/GEC
Mobarakeh Steel Complex, Iran	ME 10	Bo-Bo	electric	1,000	100	76	13 (6)	1991-93	MTU	ABB
NISCO Iran	ME 10	Bo-Bo	electric	1,000	100	76	2 (2)	1993	MTU	ABB

Krauss-Maffei electric locomotives

Railway's own designation	Axle arrangement	Line voltage	Rated output continuous (kW)	Max speed (km/h)	Weight (t)	Overall length (mm)	Total units (under licence)	Years built	Builders		Remarks
									Mechanical parts	Electric equipment	
DB, Class 111	Bo-Bo	15 kV 16⅔ Hz	3,700	160	83	16,750	226	1974-84	Krauss-Maffei[1] Krupp ABB-Henschel	Siemens[1] ABB AEG	Single-phase commutator motors
DB, Class 120	Bo-Bo	15 kV 16⅔ Hz	5,600	200	84	19,200	65	1980-88	Krauss-Maffei[2] Krupp ABB-Henschel	Siemens ABB AEG	
DB, Class 410 Intercity-Experimental power unit	Bo-Bo	15 kV 16⅔ Hz	3,640	350[3]	78	20,810	2	1985	Krauss-Maffei Krupp ABB-Henschel	Siemens ABB AEG	
DB, Class 401 Intercity-Express power units	Bo-Bo	15 kV 16⅔ Hz	4,800	280	80	20,560	120	1989-92	Krauss-Maffei Krupp ABB-Henschel	Siemens ABB AEG	Three-phase propulsion system
RENFE, Spain Class S 252	Bo-Bo	3 kV 25 kV 50 Hz	5,600	220	86	20,380	75 (60)	1991-94	Krauss-Maffei[1] ABB-Henschel Spanish Industries	Siemens[1] ABB	
CP, Portugal Class LE 5600	Bo-Bo	25 kV 50 Hz	5,600	220	88	20,380	(30)	1992-96	Krauss-Maffei[1] Portuguese Industries	Siemens[1]	
DB, Class 127	Bo-Bo	15 kV 16⅔ Hz	7,000	230[4]	86	19,580	1	1992	Krauss-Maffei	Siemens	
DB, Class 402 Intercity-Express power units	Bo-Bo	15 kV 16⅔ Hz	4,800	300	80	20,560	48	1995-97	Krauss-Maffei Siemens	Siemens	
OSE, Greece	Bo-Bo	25 kV 50 Hz	5,000	200	80	19,580	6	1997	Krauss-Maffei	Siemens	
DB, Class 152	Bo-Bo	15 kV 16⅔ Hz	6,400	140	88	19,580	195	1997-2001	Krauss-Maffei[5] Siemens	Siemens	

1 Design: Krauss-Maffei/Siemens
2 Consortium leadership: Krauss-Maffei
3 Max speed reached: 406.7 km/h
4 Max speed reached: 310 km/h
5 General contractor

UPDATED

LHB

See GEC Alsthom

Luganskteplovozstroj

Lugansk Diesel Locomotive Works
ulica Frunze 107, 348 002 Lugansk, Ukraine

Products
Diesel locomotives.

VERIFIED

Lyudinovo Locomotive Works JSC

1 K Liebknecht Street, Lyudinovo, Kaluga region 249400, Russian Federation
Tel: +7 084 44 20120/25259
Fax: +7 084 44 20120/25259

Key personnel
General Director: Oleg V Buzyun
Deputy General Director, Finance: Leonid A Abramov
Chief Engineer: Sergey M Fomin
Head of Import and Export Department:
  Yuriy K Marinichenko

Products
Diesel-hydraulic and diesel-electric locomotives (800 to 2,000 hp) for industrial, shunting and main line applications. Spare parts for locomotives.

VERIFIED

Mafersa

Mafersa SA
Av Raimundo Pereira de Magalhães 230, CEP 05092-901, São Paulo, SP, Brazil
Tel: +55 11 261 8911   Fax: +55 11 260 0224

Key personnel
President: José Gustavo de Carvalho

Products
Passenger cars in carbon and stainless steel for metro, suburban and long-distance·services; light rail vehicles; all-purpose freight cars; carbody shells, underframes, rolled and forged monobloc wheels for rail vehicles.

Mafersa has supplied 132 passenger cars to the São Paulo Metro; 38 stainless steel push-pull passenger cars to Northern Virginia Transit Commission, USA; 40 carbody shells to the Mitsui Corporation of Japan; 256 carbody shells to Chicago Transit Authority (CTA); and 48 carbody shells for Metro North M6 cars.

Recent contracts include the supply of 80 stainless steel cars to the Brasilia Metro and the refurbishment of Series 101 and Series 200 trainsets for CBTU, Brazil.

In 1996 Mafersa signed a contract with CMRJ Rio de Janeiro for the refurbishment of 28 metrocars for Line 1 of the metro system. In 1997 Mafersa implemented a contract with CPTM São Paulo for the refurbishment of 18 Series 700 commuter cars.

UPDATED

Brasilia Metro trainset

Materfer

Materfer SA
Juan Bautista Alberdi 1001, 1678 Caseros, Buenos Aires, Argentina
Tel: +54 1 750 7854/7072   Fax: +54 1 750 1476

Works
Fábrica Materfer SA
Ruta 9, Km 695, 5123 Ferreyra, Córdoba, Argentina
Tel: +54 51 97 2489/2941   Fax: +54 51 972980

Key personnel
President: Dr Guillermo Scarsoglio
General Manager: Eng Enzo Filipelli
Commercial Director: Eng Antonio Maltana

Group companies
Centro de Actividades Termomécanicas SA (CAT)
Grandes Motores Diésel SA (GMD)

Products
Diesel-electric locomotives, rotating electrical equipment.

VERIFIED

Matra Transport

Matra Transport International SA
PO Box 531, 48-56 rue Barbès, F-92542 Montrouge Cedex, France
Tel: +33 1 49 65 70 00   Fax: +33 1 49 65 70 93

Key personnel
Chairman and Chief Executive Officer: Frédéric d'Allest
President: Bernard Sillion
Financial Director: M François Azières
Senior Vice-President and Chief Financial Director:
   M François Azières
Vice-President Communications: M Benoît Parayre

Corporate developments
Matra Transport International is a joint company consisting of Matra (Lagardère Group) and Siemens.

Products
For more than 25 years, Matra Transport International has produced automatic transport systems, including VAL, Maggaly and Meteor.

VAL: Automated light transit system, using rubber-tyred light alloy vehicles, capable of running in varied train configurations, on a dedicated right of way, with high speeds and short headways. The system uses 750 V DC traction power with reduced energy consumption.

VAL 206 has a capacity for 160 to 208 passengers. VAL 208 cars carry 140 to 240 passengers and VAL 258 cars carry 85 to 140 passengers.

Automatic train control ensures safety, monitors train movements and directs train operation. Collision avoidance is based on a fixed block system. Full automation achieves flexibility to respond easily to different demands. A headway of a train every minute, including a 25 second dwell time in stations, is achieved in Lille during the peak period.

Increased passenger security and comfort is achieved through communications, both onboard and at stations, directly with control centre staff.

Operating experience since 1983 on Line 1 in Lille shows VAL achieving 99.8 per cent availability and the high quality of service produced considerably increased ridership and revenues.

Orly Airport VAL system   *1996*

The VAL system in Lille has 62 stations and is 50 km in length. Other VAL systems are operating in Toulouse and are under construction in Rennes. In Toulouse, which opened in 1993, ridership has increased by more than 40 per cent during the first two years of service. In 1991 a VAL system opened between Antony and Paris-Orly Airport. Called OrlyVAL, it links the airport with the RATP metro.

In USA a VAL system entered service at Chicago's O'Hare airport and operates 24 hours a day.

The Mucha line opened in Taipei in 1996 and carried two million passengers in the first month of operation.

Fully automatic train control (ATC) has been in operation in Lyon (Maggaly Line D) since 1992 and is shortly to start in Paris (Meteor Line 14).

Automatic train control systems include the PA135 system in Paris, Lyon, Budapest, Mexico and Caracas. Being built in 1997 is a PA135 system in Prague.

Another ATC system is SACEM, which is in use on Paris RER Line A, Mexico lines A and 8 and being built for San Juan, Mexico.

The Antares ATC system is being installed on Paris RER Lines B and C.

Matra is also offering extended maintenance and support services to railway operators and is marketing Siemens railway equipment, including tramways.

UPDATED

Mecanoexportimport

Mecanoexportimport SA
30 Dacia Blvd, Bucharest, Romania
Tel: +40 1 211 9855   Fax: +40 1 210 7894

Key personnel
Managing Director: Cornel Anghel
Technical Manager: Mahitar Dolmanian

Financial Manager: Ion Capatina
Head of Marketing Department: Ioana Rogoveanu

Products
Electric, diesel-electric and diesel-hydraulic locomotives, diesel railcars, emus, passenger coaches, multifunction road/rail vehicles, rotary snow-ploughs, axles, wheelsets and bogies.

Mecanoexportimport is the export sales company for the Romanian railway supply industry. For the majority of the locomotive designs available see the entries for Electroputere and Faur.

UPDATED

Metrowagonmash

Metrowagonmash Joint Stock Company
4 Kolontsov str, Mytishchi, 141009 Moscow, Russian Federation
Tel: +7 095 582 5651   Fax: +7 095 581 1256

Key personnel
General Manager: J A Goulko
Technical Director: J P Soldatov
Deputy General Manager: A A Andreyev

Subsidiaries
Spola Spare Parts Production Co (Ukraine),
Vyshnevolotski Machine Building Plant

Products
Metro cars and bogies.

VERIFIED

Michurinsk Locomotive Works

ulica Privokzalnaya 1, 393 740 Michurinsk, Tambov region, Russian Federation

Products
Locomotives.

VERIFIED

Mitsubishi Electric

Mitsubishi Electric Corporation
Mitsubishi Denki Building, 2-3 Marunouchi 2-chome,
Chiyoda-ku, Tokyo 100, Japan
Tel: +81 3 3218 3430   Fax: +81 3 3218 2895

Key personnel
President: Takashi Kitaoka

General Manager, Overseas Marketing Division,
Public Use and Buildings: Kenji Kimura

Products
Complete electric locomotives, diesel-electric
locomotives.

Recent sales have included: 30 Series 251 B-B-B
chopper-controlled locomotives with a rated output of
4,650 kW at 3 kV DC; 169 Series 269, 279, 289 B-B

locomotives; and four Series 269 B-B chopper-controlled
locomotives for Spanish National Railways (RENFE)
with rated output of 3,100 kW at 3 kV DC, maximum speed
160 km/h, weight 88 tonnes; traction and auxiliary
electrical equipment for 56 diesel-electric locomotives
and 64 electric locomotives for NSW SRA of Australia,
with advanced features such as large-capacity thyristor
technology and microcomputer digital control.

Electric locomotives equipped by Mitsubishi Electric since 1985

Class	Railway	Wheel arrangement	Line voltage	Rated output (kW) continuous	Max speed (km/h)	Weight (t)	No in service	Year first built	Builders Mechanical parts	Electrical equipment
EF 500	JR Freight	Bo-Bo-Bo	20 kV AC 1.5 kV DC	6,000	120	100.8	1	1990	Kawasaki Heavy Industry	Mitsubishi Electric
EF-210	JR Freight	Bo-Bo-Bo	1.5 kV DC	3,390	110	100.8	1	1995	Kawasaki Heavy Industry	Mitsubishi Electric

UPDATED

Moës

Moteurs Moës SA
62 Rue de Huy, B-4300 Waremme, Belgium
Tel: +32 19 322352   Fax: +32 19 323448

Key personnel
Chairman: C Froidbise
Managing Director: R Thirion
Sales Director: J Antoine

Products
Narrow-gauge diesel-hydraulic and diesel-mechanical
locomotives (3 to 30 tonnes, 10 to 190 kW) for mine
railways.

VERIFIED

MotivePower Industries

MotivePower Industries
1200 Reedsdale Street, Pittsburgh, Pennsylvania 15233,
USA
Tel: +1 412 237 2250   Fax: +1 412 321 7756
Web: www.motivepower.com

Works
USA: Boise Idaho, Braddock Pennsylvania, Latham New
York, Jackson Tennessee, Gilman Illinois, Elk Grove
Village Illinois.
Mexico: San Luis Potosi, Acambaro

Key personnel
Chairman: John C (Jack) Pope
President and Chief Executive Officer: Michael Wolf
Senior Vice-President and Chief Financial Officer:
William F Fabrizio
Vice-Presidents
General Counsel and Secretary:
Jeanette Fisher-Garber

Controller and Principal Accounting Officer:
William D Grab
Treasurer: Thomas P Lyons
Human Resources and Administration:
Scott E Wahlstrom
Investor and Public Relations: Timothy R Wesley

Operating Group Management
Components Group
Engine Systems Company Inc
President: James E Lindsay

Motor Coils Manufacturing Company
President: J Lynn Young

Power Parts Company
Executive Vice-President: David M Cullen

Touchstone Company
President: Theodore E Nelson

Locomotive Group
Boise Locomotive Company
President: Joseph S Crawford
Vice-President and General Manager: Francis X Larkin

MPI de Mexico SA de CV
Director-General: Carlos Vidaurreta

Products
Through its subsidiaries, MPI specialises in the
manufacturing and distribution of engineered locomotive
components and parts; provides locomotive fleet
maintenance, remanufacturing and overhauls and
manufactures environmentally friendly switcher, commuter and mid-range locomotives up to 4,000 hp (2,985
kW).

The company's main customers are freight and
passenger railways including every Class 1 railroad in
North America.

UPDATED

MSV

Moravskoslezská Vagónka as
Butovická ul, 74213 Studénka, Czech Republic
Tel: +42 655 47 1111/2201   Fax: +42 655 47 2000/2204
Email: jvyoralek@oasanet.cz

Key personnel
General Manager: Ivan Heczko
Production Manager: Aleš Musil
Commercial Manager: Tomáš Hrabal
Commercial Manager: Pavel Kožuch

Products
Diesel-electric and diesel-hydraulic railcars and multiple-
units, railcar trailers, double-deck electric multiple-units.

Deliveries include double-deck Class 471 emus and
Class 843 diesel railcars. MSV is part of the consortium
(along with Siemens, Fiat and ČKD) building Class 680
tilting trains for ČD for the Berlin—Prague—Vienna
corridor.

UPDATED

MSV Class 843 diesel railcar

1997

Muromteplovoz

Murom Diesel Locomotive Works
ulica Filatova 10, 602 200 Murom, Vladimir region,
Russian Federation

Products
Diesel locomotives.

VERIFIED

National Railway Equipment Company

14400 South Robey Street, PO Box 2270, Dixmoor, Ilinois 60426, USA
Tel: +1 708 388 6002   Fax: +1 708 388 2487

Key personnel
President: Lawrence J Beal
Vice-Presidents: Wilfred A Burrows, Patrick C Frangella

Products
Supply and remanufacture of diesel-electric locomotives; remanufacture of locomotive components including diesel engines, rotating electrical equipment, high-voltage cabinets, traction motors, cooling fans and power assemblies.

Recent contracts include the remanufacture of eight General Motors SD39-2M diesel-electric locomotives for Fepasa, Chile.

VERIFIED

NEVZ

Novocherkassk Electric Locomotive Works
346 413 Novocherkassk, Rostov region, Russian Federation
Tel: +7 86352 33800   Fax: +7 86352 34446

Key personnel
General Director: Misichenko Anatoly Pavlovich
Marketing Director: Noskov Alexander Leonidovich
Chief, Foreign Department: Budkov Alexander Markovich

Products
Electric locomotives.

VERIFIED

Newag

Newag GmbH & Co KG
Ripshorster Strasse 321, D-46117 Oberhausen 12, Germany
Tel: +49 208 865030   Fax: +49 208 865 0320

Key personnel
Managing Director: C Kohl

Technical Director: W Kern
Sales Director: G Halfmann

Products
Diesel-hydraulic locomotives from 150 to 900 kW for gauges 750 to 1,676 mm. The remanufacture of diesel-electric and diesel-hydraulic locomotives of 20 to 2,240 kW.

UPDATED

Newag shunting locomotive
1995

Niigata

Niigata Engineering Co Ltd
1-9-3 Kamata-Honchou, Ota-ku, Tokyo 144, Japan
Tel: +81 3 3739 6721   Fax: +81 3 3739 8115

Works
Ohyama Works, 1-2-1, Akiba, Niigata City, 950 Japan

Key personnel
President: Yoshihiro Muramatsu
General Manager: Toshio Sato
Sales Manager, Trans-Con Systems Division:
  Eiichi Kobayashi
Technical Director: Naoaki Okada

Subsidiary
Niigata Converter Co Ltd
5-27-9 Sendagaya, Shibuya-ku, Tokyo 151, Japan
Tel: +81 3 3354 7111   Fax: +81 3 3341 5365

Products
Diesel and electric railcars; passenger coaches; rotary snow-ploughs; work cars. Diesel locomotives.

Niigata type HK100 electric railcar for Hokuetsu Railway   **1997**

Niigata diesel railcars (typical examples)

Class	Cars per unit	Motor cars per unit	Motored axles per motor car	Transmission	Rated power (kW) per motor	Max speed (km/h)	Weight (tonnes) per car	Total seating capacity	Length per car (m)	No in service	Year first built	Builders Mechanical parts	Builders Engine and type	Builders Transmission
NDC	1	1	2	hydraulic torque converter	188	95	26.2	52	16.3	64	1988	Niigata	Niigata DMF13HS	Niigata Converter TACN-22-1100
KIHA 1,000	1	1	2	hydraulic torque converter	340	110	31.5	70	21.3	48	1990	Niigata	Komatsu DMF11HZ	Niigata Converter DW14C
KIHA 200	2	2	2	hydraulic torque converter	340	110	34.5	52	21.3	28	1991	Niigata	Niigata DMF13HZA	Niigata Converter R-DW4
KIHA 111	2	2	2	hydraulic torque converter	320	100	39.8	60	20.0	81	1991	Niigata	Niigata DMF13HZA	Niigata Converter DW14A-B
KIHA 125	1	1	2	hydraulic torque converter	250	95	29.5	59	18.5	27	1993	Niigata	Niigata DMF13HZ	Niigata Converter TACN22-1600
MRT300	2	2	2	hydraulic torque converter	250	95	33.2	66	21.3	4	1994	Niigata	Niigata DMF13HZ	Niigata converter TACN22-1600

Niigata electric railcars

Class	Cars per unit	Line voltage	Motor cars per unit	Motored axles per motor car	Rated output (kW) per motor	Max speed (km/h)	Weight (tonnes) per car	Total seating capacity	Length per car (m)	No ordered	Year first built	Builders Mechanical parts	Builders Electrical equipment
HK 100	1	1.5 kV DC	1	1	95	110	36.5	61	20.5	9	1996	Niigata	Mitsubishi

UPDATED

Nippon Sharyo

Nippon Sharyo Ltd
Riverside Yomiuri Building, 11th Floor, 36-2 Nihombashi-
Hakozaki-cho, Chuo-ku, Tokyo 103, Japan
Tel: +81 3 3668 3330   Fax: +81 3 3669 0238

Works
Toyokawa Plant, 2-20 Honohara,
Toyokawa, Aichi 442, Japan

Subsidiary company
Nippon Sharyo USA Inc.
375 Park Avenue, Suite 2806, New York, New York 10152,
USA
Tel: +1 212 755 2150   Fax: +1 212 755 2257

Key personnel
President: Yasuo Shimizu
Senior Vice-President and General Manager, Rolling
    Stock Division: Takashi Itoh
General Manager, Overseas Department, Rolling Stock
    Division: Tomiji Ogawa

Products
High-speed trains, electric and diesel railcars, light rail
vehicles, automated guideway transit vehicles. Diesel-
electric, diesel-hydraulic locomotives.
Bogies for transit vehicles.

5300 series emu for Tokyo Metro   *1996*

Recent Nippon Sharyo electric railcars or multiple-units

Railway	Cars per unit	Line voltage	Motor cars per unit	Motored axles per motor car	Rated output (kW) per motor	Max speed (km/h)	Weight (t) per car (M-motor T-trailer)		Total seating capacity per car	Length per car (mm)	Rate of accele-ration (m/s²)	Year first built	Builders Mechanical parts	Builders Electrical equipment
East Japan Railway (JR East) E2 series for for Shinkansen	8	25 kV AC	6	4	300	275	M T	46.7 44.0	630/unit	25,000 25,700	0.44	1995	Nippon Sharyo	Hitachi Mitsubishi Toshiba
Central Japan Railway (JR Tokai) 383 series for limited express (tilting)	6	1.5 kV DC	3	4	155	130	M Tsc	37.9 36.5	355/unit	21,300	0.58	1994	Nippon Sharyo	Mitsubishi Toshiba
Central Japan Railway (JR Tokai) 373 series for limited express	3	1.5 kV DC	1	4	170	120	Mc Tc	37.9 31.7	179/unit	21,300	0.58	1995	Nippon Sharyo	Mitsubishi Toshiba
Odakyu Japan Railway 30000 series for limited express	10	1.5 kV DC	4	4	195	120	M T	40.0 34.0	590/unit	20,000 19,900	0.56	1995	Nippon Sharyo	Toshiba
Housing and Urban Development Corporation series 9100 (C-Flyer) for commuter	8	1.5 kV DC	6	4	130	120	M T	34.0 30.0	382/unit	18,000	0.97	1995	Nippon Sharyo	Toyo Denki
Tokyo Metropolitan Government series 5300 for subway	8	1.5 kV DC	4	4	165	110	Mc M T T	34.5 34.0 26.5 26.0	390/unit	18,000	0.92	1990	Nippon Sharyo	Hitachi

Recent Nippon Sharyo diesel railcars or multiple-units

Railway	Cars per unit	Motor cars per unit	Motored axles per motor car	Trans-mission	Rated power (hp) per motor	Max speed (km/h)	Weight (t) per car (M-motor) (T-trailer)		Total seating capacity per car	Length per car (mm)	Year first built	Builders Mechanical parts	Builders Engine and type	Builders Trans-mission
Central Japan Railway (JR Tokai) 85 Series for limited express	4	4	2	Torque converter	2 × 350 259	120	Mc	41.5	244/unit	21,300	1989	Nippon Sharyo	Cummins NTA885-R1	Niigata C-DW14A
Central Japan Railway (JR Tokai) 75 series for suburban service	2	2	2	Torque converter	2 × 350 259	120	Mc	40.2	108/unit	21,300	1993	Nippon Sharyo	Cummins C-DMF14HZ	Niigata C-DW14A
Hokkaido Railway (JR Hokkaido) 281 series for limited express (tilting)	7	7	2	Torque converter	2 × 350 259	130	Mc Ms	43.2 43.0	353/unit	21,300 21,300	1993	Nippon Sharyo	Komatsu DMF11HZ	Niigata N-DW15
Kyushu Railway (JR Kyushu) 200 series for suburban service	2	2	2	Torque converter	450 333	110	Mc	32.5	108/unit	21,300	1991	Nippon Sharyo	Niigata DMF13HZA	Niigata RDW14
Kashima Rinkai 7000 series for excursion service	2	2	2	Torque converter	230 170	95	Mc1 Mc2	38.0 37.5	86/unit	21,000 21,000	1991	Nippon Sharyo	Niigata 6L13AS	Niigata DB115

VERIFIED

Pafawag

See Adtranz

PEC

The Projects & Equipment Corporation of India Ltd
A Government of India Enterprise
Hansalaya, 15 Barakhamba Road, New Delhi 110 001,
India
Tel: +91 11 331 6372/3619/5508/3351/5763
Fax: +91 11 331 5279/4797/3664

Key personnel
Chairman: S M Dewan
Director: T P S Narang
Chief General Manager: R K Gupta
General Manager, Railway Equipment Division:
  S M Gupta

Products
Diesel-electric, diesel-hydraulic, electric, industrial and
mining locomotives; spares for locomotives.
  Diesel-electric locomotives and spares have been
exported to Tanzania and to Vietnam.

VERIFIED

Peoria Locomotive Works

Peoria Locomotive Works
301 Wesley Road, Creve Coeur, Illinois 61610, USA
Tel: +1 309 694 8662   Fax: +1 309 694 8627

Key personnel
Manager - Engineer/Sales: Thomas L Derry

Products
Switching locomotives powered by Caterpillar diesel
engines.
  PLW also makes dual-mode (electro-diesel)
locomotives for maintenance trains on transit railroads. It
has built one such locomotive for the PATH metro system
in New York which is used for ballast trains, snow-

ploughing duties and for hauling passenger trains in the
event of power cuts.

NEW ENTRY

Plymouth

Plymouth Locomotive International Inc
607 Bell Street, Plymouth, Ohio 44865, USA
Tel: +1 419 687 4641   Fax: +1 419 687 8112

Key personnel
President: David Egner
Export Manager: Wiltrude Shull

Products
Diesel-hydraulic locomotives for industrial, rapid transit

and mining/tunnelling applications in standard form, or
custom-manufactured to detailed specifications.
  Industrial locomotives are available in sizes from small
(5 short tons) to large (120 short tons), 70 to 1,200 hp, in a
wide variety of track gauges. The customer can choose
from Caterpillar, Cummins, Detroit Diesel or Deutz
engines.
  Rapid transit models are available for maintenance
purposes as well as for towing a disabled transit train. The
locomotives can be equipped with snow-ploughs on the
bumpers, and an auxiliary diesel-powered snow blower

can be coupled with the locomotive for heavy snow
removal.
  Recent contracts include the supply of shunting
locomotives to Thailand, Korea (South), USA; six
tunnelling locomotives to P R China, and a mining
locomotive for Mexico.

UPDATED

Precision National

908 Shawnee Street, Mount Vernon, Illinois 62864, USA
Tel: +1 618 244 0405   Fax: +1 618 244 0405

Key personnel
President: Dean Manes
Vice-President, Operations: Bill Fesler
Purchasing Manager: Ken Bradley
Customer Service/Sales: Carol Rudofski

Products
Locomotive remanufacture, locomotive sales and hire,
parts, mobile service and repairs.

VERIFIED

Qishuyan

Qishuyan Locomotive and Rolling Stock Works
Qishuyan, Changzhou City, Jiangsu Province,
People's Republic of China
Tel: +86 519 877 1711   Fax: +86 519 877 0358

Key personnel
President: Yang Weishu
Export Director: Xu Jun
Export Manager: Wang Jiazhen

Products
Diesel-electric locomotive manufacture, overhaul and
repair; component manufacture for locomotives and
rolling stock; rolling stock manufacture and repair.

In addition to meeting domestic needs, Qishuyan
products have been exported to more than 30 countries in
Europe, America, Asia and Africa. A major product is the
3,310 kW Dong Feng 8 freight diesel locomotive with
AC/DC electric transmission, first built in 1984. It is
powered by a single Vee-type, four-stroke diesel engine
(Type 16V280ZJ) of 16 cylinders, each of 280 mm bore
diameter and 285 mm piston stroke. The separately
excited AC traction generator has a rated capacity of
3,330 kVA at 1,000 rpm. The 480 kW traction motors are
series-excited DC. The cooling system comprises a plate-
fin water radiator and static hydraulic-driven cooling fan.
The two three-axle bogies, which are interchangeable, are
pedestal-less, with no centre plate or balance beam.
  The first Dong Feng 9 diesel locomotive with AC/DC
transmission was manufactured in 1990. It is equipped

with a 16V280ZJA diesel engine, similar to the Dong Feng
8, producing a maximum power of 3,610 kW. The
synchronous TQFR-3000-1 traction alternator has a rated
power of 3,500 kVa when running at a speed of
1,000 rpm. The 480 kW traction motors are series-excited
DC units. New copper pipe radiators with double flowing
channels are used for the cooling system and the cooling
fans are driven by the static hydraulic system. The two-
stage suspension bogies are fitted with highly flexible
round springs; the axle boxes are positioned with traction
links and the traction motors are fully suspended with
hollow axles, to meet the needs of high-speed running.
The locomotive is equipped with dynamic braking.
  The latest development is the Dong Feng 11, a
3,040 kW diesel-electric passenger locomotive with a
maximum speed of 170 km/h, designed for main line
express duties. Powered by a 16V280ZJA engine, the
Dong Feng 11 is equipped with a synchronous alternator
and six ZD106A traction motors and features
microprocessor control and dynamic braking.
  Recent contracts include the supply of 27 Dong Feng
11 locomotives to Ministry of Railways, People's Republic
of China.

Dong Feng 11
Track gauge: 1,435 mm
Wheel arrangement: Co-Co
Maximum speed: 170 km/h
Axle load: 23 t
Maximum starting tractive effort: 245 kN
Continuous tractive effort: 160 kN
Min curvature radius: 145 m
Max height (rail surface to top end): 4,736 mm
Max width: 3,304 mm
Length over couplers: 21,250 mm

VERIFIED

*Dong Feng 11 diesel-electric passenger
locomotive*
1996

Qualter Hall

Qualter Hall & Co Ltd
Johnson Street, Barnsley S75 2BY, UK
Tel: +44 1226 205761   Fax: +44 1226 286269

Key personnel
Managing Director: G Hobson
Commercial Director: G Orton
Works Director: K Richardson

Sales Manager, Mining and Tunnelling: C Hope
Manufacturing Sales Manager: A Thompson

Corporate structure
Qualter Hall is a part of Wagner-Biro, a member of Auricon AG Group of Austria.

Products
Locomotive superstructures; mining and tunnelling locomotives; passenger and freight vehicles; narrow-

gauge underground transportation systems. The company built 36 locomotive superstructures for the Channel Tunnel shuttle operation. The structures are approximately 33 tonnes in weight and are of advanced monocoque design conceived using computer-aided design techniques.

VERIFIED

Railcare

Railcare Ltd
3 Ibstock Road, Coventry CV6 6NL, UK
Tel: +44 1203 644066/364897   Fax: +44 1203 644074/644074
Email: marketing.railcare@dial.pipex.com

Works addresses
Wolverton Depot, Stratford Road, Wolverton, Milton Keynes MK12 5NT

Springburn Depot, 79 Charles Street, Glasgow G21 2PS

3 Ibstock Road, Coventry CV6 6NL

Key personnel
Managing Director: Barry Turnbull
Business Development Director: Paul L Robinson
Finance Director: Eric McDonnell
Engineering Director: Dave Furlong

Products
Rail vehicle maintenance, refurbishment, modification and overhaul; painting, crash and damage repairs, including bogies, wheelsets, brake cylinders and AC modules; diesel engine and equipment overhaul including in-field support; vehicle exterior and interior design, including design and supply of seats, toilets, lighting systems and partitions; light rail vehicles; specialist conversions.

Contracts include design and refurbishment of seven four-car Class 319 sets for Connex South Central; repair and overhaul of 22 three-car Class 320 emus for Eversholt Leasing; repainting of GNER fleet of Mark IV fleet (345 coaches. Delivery by December 1998); repair and refurbishment of 76 GNER HST power cars and coaches (completion 1998); repair/refurbishment of 287 HST power cars and coaches for Great Western Trains.

UPDATED

Rautaruukki

Rautaruukki Engineering Division — Transtech
PO Box 217, FIN-90101 Oulu, Finland
Tel: +358 8 88360   Fax: +358 8 883 6960

Key personnel
See entry in *Freight vehicles and equipment* section.

Products
Electric locomotives, diesel-hydraulic and diesel-electric locomotives.
Rautaruukki is making the locomotive bodies and providing the final assembly of the 20 electric locomotives that the Swiss consortium Adtranz/SLM is supplying to VR over the period 1995-98.

Rautaruukki has reached an agreement with HKL Helsinki and Adtranz to supply 20 low-floor tramcars based on the Variotram concept. Delivery is expected between 1998 and 2000.

UPDATED

Reggiane

Officine Meccaniche Italiano SpA
PO Box 431, 27 Via Agosti, I-42100 Reggio Emilia, Italy
Tel: +39 522 5881   Fax: +39 522 588243

Key personnel
Managing Director: F Squadrelli Saraceno
Sales Director: O Chierci

Products
Electric, diesel-electric, diesel-hydraulic and diesel-mechanical locomotives; railcars; rolling stock components.

The company also manufactures mechanical subassemblies for other companies, such as bogies for locomotives complete with quill drive or toothed gearing.

VERIFIED

Relco

Relco Locomotives Inc
113 Industrial Avenue, Minooka, Illinois 60447-0058, USA
Tel: +1 815 467 3030   Fax: +1 815 467 6060

Key personnel
Vice-President, Marketing: Gene Copeland

Products
Remanufacture of diesel-electric locomotives and components, including upgrade of braking equipment and installation of remote control, microprocessor excitation and monitoring systems; diesel-electric locomotives (600 to 2,000 hp) for sale or lease with full contract maintenance.
Recent contracts include the supply of locomotives to 15 industrial and short-line operators.

UPDATED

Diesel-electric locomotive remanufactured by Relco
1996

Republic Locomotive

Republic Transportation Systems Incorporated
Suite 101, 131 Falls Street, Greenville, South Carolina 29601-2825, USA
Tel: +1 864 271 4000   Fax: +1 864 233 2103

Works
1861 West Washington Road, Greenville, South Carolina 29601, USA

Key personnel
President and Chief Executive Officer:
   Hugh B Hamilton Jr
Manufacturing Manager: Mike Dixon
Director of Engineering: Tim Armstrong

Principal affiliates
Republic Locomotive Works Inc
Republic Group Inc
Republic Raileasing Inc

Products
New or remanufactured locomotives for railway, industrial and passenger applications.
Republic has successfully tested the RD20 model diesel-electric locomotive, which is the first of a new series of locomotives developed by Republic and Detroit Diesel. A new product is a switching locomotive with AC traction motors.

UPDATED

RFS (E) Ltd

PO Box 400, Doncaster Works, Hexthorpe Road, Doncaster DN1 1SL, UK
Tel: +44 1302 340700   Fax: +44 1302 790058

Key personnel
Head of Engineering: Michael Roe

Ruhrthaler

Ruhrthaler Maschinenfabrik GmbH & Co KG
PO Box 10 16 54, D-45416 Mülheim Ruhr, Germany
Tel: +49 208 445131   Fax: +49 208 479041

RVR

Riga Carriage Building Works
201 Brivibas Gatve, Riga LV-1039, Latvia
Tel: +371 365 440   Fax: +371 755 5219/782 8396

Key personnel
President: Janis Anderson
Vice-President, Financial Director: Velerij Novarro
Vice-President, Technical Director: Robert Reingardt
Commercial Director: Sergey Chigorin
Sales and Marketing Manager: Vadim Maximov

Saalasti

Saalasti Transport Machinery Ltd
Arinatie 6, FIN-00370 Helsinki, Finland
Tel: +358 9 557775   Fax: +358 9 550780
email: info@salaasti.fi/teijo.salaasti@saalasti.fi

Key personnel
Managing Director: Teijo Saalasti

Products
Diesel shunting locomotives; automatic shunting yard systems road/rail vehicles for shunting; permanent way train crane tractors; shunting couplings; snow-ploughs.

The Saalasti range includes the NALLE road/rail shunting locomotive, especially suited for congested railway yards, and the OTSO 4 two-axle shunting locomotive. Suitable for railway and industrial operators, the OTSO 4 can be equipped with radio remote control.

The OTSO range of shunting locomotives features the patented OTSO control system, where a single control wheel combines starting, speed control, change of direction and braking functions. If the handwheel or the drive lever of the radio control apparatus is inadvertently released, the brakes are applied, the locomotive stops and the engine idles. The latest OTSO engines are equipped with Voith turbohydraulic transmission and Caterpillar engines. The locomotives can be equipped with an anti-slip device and radio control, shunting couplers and a snow-plough.

The OTSO-robot is a radio-controlled unmanned shunting vehicle that can can move trains up to 4,000 tonnes in weight. Available in two- and four-axle models, the OTSO-robot is designed for use on industrial systems and at freight terminals and similar installations.

Recent contracts include the supply of an automatic shunting system to Outokumpu Polarit steel factory, Tornio, Finland. The system consists of an unmanned, four axle OTSO-Robot 100 shunting locomotive and a control system. The control system can automatically move the train from siding to loading track and it controls the railway switches and doors of the depot/building. A built-in security system prevents collision with doors and other obstructions.

Commercial Director: John Meehan
Fleetcare Director: Martin Pridmore
Operations Director: Mick Bostock

Products
Manufacture, overhaul, repair and conversion of rolling stock, locomotives and ancillary equipment; operational maintenance.

Key personnel
General Managers: Manfred Opp,
   Hilmar Rudolph Kuppe
Export Manager: Mrs Jutta Dudda

Corporate Development
The Latvian government sold a 50.1 per cent stake in RVR to Latek, a joint venture of Latvian and Ukrainian companies.

Products
1,435 mm and 1,529 mm gauge diesel and electric (AC and DC) multiple-units for local services.

Recent 1,520 mm gauge dmu production includes the Type DR1B, comprising two power cars (modified Type M62 Co-Co diesel-electric locomotives) and 10 trailers,

Locomotives have been supplied to Tilcon, a UK stone company.

UPDATED

Products
Diesel-hydraulic narrow-gauge mining locomotives; suspended monorail diesel locomotives for underground transport of personnel and materials.

VERIFIED

and the Type DR8. A development of the Type DR1A, the DR8 comprises two power cars with cabs and four trailers. Each power car has two 736 kW M787BR diesel engines driving GDP1000M hydraulic transmissions, with a maximum speed of 120 km/h. Driving trailer cars for DR1A and DR1B dmus are also available.

Recent contracts include the supply of Type DR1B dmus to Belarussian Railways.

A new articulated LRV, the TR-2, is in production.

UPDATED

Saalasti OTSO-robot 100 shunting locomotive   **1997**

Saalasti diesel shunting locomotives

	OTSO-robot 50	OTSO-robot 100	NALLE	OTSO 4	OTSO 8 & 10
Weight (t)	50	100	14	40-44	80-90
Power (hp)	147	320	120	400	750-1,000
Drawbar pull (kN)	125	250	130	240-270	
Speed (km/h)	3 or 6	3	20	25	35/70
Overall length (mm)	5,360	10,090	5,200	600	11,580
Overall height (mm)	3,250	3,250	4,000	3,850	4,300
Max width (mm)	3,000	3,000	3,300	3,100	3,200
Axle arrangement	B	B+B	B	B	B'B'
Rail gauge (mm)		1,435/1,524			

UPDATED

SAN

SAN Engineering & Locomotive Co Ltd
PO Box 4802, Whitefield Road, Bangalore 560048, India
Tel: +91 80 845 2271   Fax: +91 80 227 3700

Key personnel
Managing Director: Milind S Thakker
Senior Vice-President: R S Sarma

Principal subsidiary
Engineering Products Division
Plots 1 & 10, Hebbal Industrial Area, Belwadi Post, Mysore 571 106, India

Products
Diesel-hydraulic and diesel-electric locomotives, transmissions for locomotives and industrial applications,

gears and gearboxes. Locomotives manufactured are used by industries such as cement plants, oil refineries, petrochemical complexes, steel plants, fertiliser plants, thermal plants, construction sites and so on. Locomotives are tailored to customer needs.

The company also manufactures flameproof locomotives for underground coal mines.

VERIFIED

Santa Matilde

Cia Industrial Santa Matilde
Rua Frei Caneca 784, Sao Paulo, Cep 01307-000, Brazil

Works
Rua Isaltino Silveira 768, Cep 25804-020, Três Rios, Rio de Janeiro, Brazil
Tel: +55 242 521662   Fax: +55 242 52 1276

Key personnel
President: Octávio Henrique Ilha Campos
Marketing and Export Director:
  Eduardo Hubert K Monteiro

Products
Emus; passenger coaches.

Recent contracts include refurbishment of Series 160 and Series 401/431 stainless steel emus for CPTM, and refurbishment of two Series 500 and five Series 800 stainless steel emus for Flumitrens.

VERIFIED

Schindler

Schindler Waggon AG
CH-4133 Pratteln, Switzerland
Tel: +41 61 825 9111   Fax: +41 61 825 9205

Key personnel
Managing Director: Pierino Piffaretti
Manager, Development and Production: H-R Käser
Marketing Manager: Reinhard Christeller

Corporate developments
Schindler Waggon withdrew from the maintenance and refitting business centred at Altenrhein in 1997. This business was taken over by Stadler Altenrhein AG (qv).

In late 1997, agreement was reached that in January 1998 Adtranz Switzerland would take over Schindler's new-build works at Pratteln, with Schindler taking shares in Adtranz Switzerland in exchange.

Products
Powered and trailer cars for urban and suburban services; low-floor light rail vehicles (LRVs); high-speed cars.

LRVs have been supplied to various Swiss private railways, manufactured in aluminium with a low-floor section between the bogies. The railcar formation, which features two identical units, can be driven from both ends. The all-electric design uses modern frequency converter technology with a high-acceleration capability, due to an advanced AC traction system and a lightweight design.

The Cobra low-floor LRV features an ultra-low-floor arrangement without steps. It is designed specially for small track radii and steep gradients. The carbody shells are made of composites. Lightweight in design, it is fitted with large entrance doors. Fault-diagnostic and data-logging systems are available.

A total of 120 cars were delivered in 1996. The main customer was Swiss Federal Railways, which took 12 EuroCity cars, four NPZ suburban shuttle power cars and three driving trailers, 16 power cars and 32 non-driving trailers for Zürich S-Bahn services together with 29 IC Bt driving cars.

Delivery continues of the IC2000 double-deck cars for SBB's Bahn 2000 services.

Schindler has also built 27 carbodies for Fiat Ferroviaria Pendolino sets. Schindler has won an order to develop and build the Swiss InterCity tilting train fleet. Lead partner is Adtranz, in association with Schindler and Fiat-SIG.

VBZ Zürich has decided to buy the new-generation Cobra LRV. The LRV has an ultra-low-floor and steerable Fiat-SIG bodies. The first six Cobras go into service in 1999 and there are confirmed orders for 11 more. By 2013 it is expected that 75 Cobra LRVs will be in service.

Schindler double-decker vehicle for the Zurich S-Bahn

UPDATED

Schöma

Christoph Schöttler Maschinenfabrik GmbH
PO Box 1509, D-49345 Diepholz, Germany
Tel: +49 5441 9970   Fax: +49 5441 99744

Key personnel
Chairman: Ing Fritz Schöttler
General Manager: Ing C Schlöttler
Sales Manager: Ing L Niermeyer

Products
Standard and narrow-gauge diesel-hydraulic locomotives for shunting duties and mining, works and tunnel construction systems. Gang trolleys and inspection cars.

The company has extended its product range to locomotives of 70 tonnes weight and 600 kW output.

Recent sales have included: 14 CFL-500 VR works locomotives for London Underground Ltd's Jubilee Line Extension; 28 CFL-200 DCL tunnel locomotives for the Pingling Project, Taiwan; two CFL-500 DCL BB shunting locomotives for China Steel, Taiwan; five CFL-180 DCL tunnel locomotives for Doukkala, Morocco; and eight CFL-200 DCL-R service locomotives for MTRC, Hong Kong.

VERIFIED

Schöma locomotive for Jubilee Line Extension project in London
1996

SEMAF

Société Générale Egyptienne de Matériel des Chemins de Fer
Ein Helwan, Cairo, Egypt
Tel: +20 2 782358/782177/782716   Fax: +20 2 788413

Key personnel
Chairman: Eng T El-Maghraby
Technical Manager: Eng A Rahik
Commercial/Financial Manager: A Farid
Works Manager, Coach and Metro: Dr Eng L Melek
Works Manager, Wagon and Bogie: Eng El-Sherbini

Products
Power cars, passenger cars, railcar/trailers, trams and metro cars.

VERIFIED

Paxman, Ruston, Mirrlees Blackstone

The driving force in rail traction

For proven performance choose heavy duty medium speed Mirrlees Blackstone, medium speed Ruston or high speed Paxman diesel traction engines. From 715 - 6875 kWb, our engines offer low fuel consumption, dependable performance and extended service intervals, backed by worldwide customer support.

GEC ALSTHOM Diesels - a leader in diesel technology.

GEC ALSTHOM

GEC ALSTHOM Mirrlees Blackstone Limited, Bramhall Moor Lane, Hazel Grove, Stockport, Cheshire, SK7 5AH, England.
Telephone UK + 44 161 483 1000 Fax UK + 44 161 487 1465
GEC ALSTHOM Paxman Diesels Limited, Paxman Works, Hythe Hill, Colchester, Essex CO1 2HW, England.
Telephone UK + 44 1206 795151 Fax UK + 44 1206 797869
GEC ALSTHOM Ruston Diesels Limited, Vulcan Works, Newton-le-Willows, Merseyside WA12 8RU, England.
Telephone UK + 44 1925 225151 Fax UK + 44 1925 222055

Engine	Maximum rating		Continuous traction rating		Displacement litres (in³)	Bore and stroke mm (in)	Number of cylinders	Aspiration	Net weight kg (lb)
	hp	rpm	hp	rpm					
Railcar engines									
N-855-R2	235	2,100	210	2,100	14 (855)	140 × 152 (5.5 × 6)	6	N	1,185 (2,600)
NT-855-R5	335	2,100	285	2,100	14 (855)	140 × 152 (5.5 × 6)	6	T	1,200 (2,700)
NTA-855-R1	400	2,100	340	2,100	14 (855)	140 × 152 (5.5 × 6)	6	T/A	1,255 (2,800)
NTA-855-R3	430	2,100	365	2,100	14 (855)	140 × 152 (5.5 × 6)	6	T/A	1,335 (2,944)
KTA-19-R	600	2,100	510	2,100	19 (1,150)	159 × 159 (6.25 × 6.25)	6	T/A	1,770 (3,900)
KTA-19-R2	650	2,100	550	2,100	19 (1,150)	159 × 159 (6.25 × 6.25)	6	T/A	1,850 (4,080)

Key personnel
Rail Manager: Dave Peters

Products
Cummins Engine Company manufactures a range of diesel engines from 76 to 2,000 hp for a wide variety of rail-associated applications.

Aftercooler: Large-capacity aftercooler results in cooler, denser intake air for more efficient combustion and reduced internal stresses for longer life. Aftercooler is located in the engine coolant system eliminating the need for special plumbing.

Cooling system: Gear-driven centrifugal water pump. Large-volume water passages provide even flow of coolant around cylinder liners, valves and injectors. A total of four modulating bypass thermostats regulate coolant temperature. Spin-on corrosion resistors check rust and corrosion, control acidity and remove impurities.

Cylinder block: Alloy cast-iron with removable wet liners. Cross-bolt support to main bearing cap provides extra strength and stability.

Cylinder heads: Alloy cast-iron. Each head serves one cylinder. Valve seats are replaceable corrosion-resistant inserts. Valve guides and crosshead guides are replaceable inserts.

Cylinder liners: Replaceable wet liners dissipate heat faster than dry liners and are easily replaced without reboring the block.

Fuel system: Cummins exclusive low-pressure PT system with wear compensating pump and integral dual-flyball governor. Camshaft-actuated fuel injectors give accurate metering and timing. Spin-on fuel filters.

Lubrication: Large-capacity gear pump provides pressure lubrication to all bearings and oil supply for piston cooling. All pressure lines are internal drilled passages in block and heads. Oil cooler, full flow filters and bypass filters maintain oil condition and maximise oil and engine life.

Turbocharger: Two AiResearch exhaust gas-driven turbochargers mounted at top of engine. Turbocharging provides more power, improved fuel economy, altitude compensation and lower smoke and noise levels.

Developments
The QSK19 is an underfloor diesel engine rated at 410–560 kW and is intended for high-speed dmus.

UPDATED

Dalian

Dalian Locomotive & Rolling Stock Works
51 Zhong Chang Street, Dalian, Liaoning, People's Republic of China
Tel: +86 411 460 2043   Fax: +86 411 460 6447

Key personnel
See entry in *Locomotives and powered passenger vehicles* section

Products
Diesel engines and diesel generating sets. The 240ZJ diesel engine series features a cast welded engine block, an alloy modular cast-iron crankshaft, steel-backed aluminium alloy bearing shells, parallel connecting rods, wet cylinder liners, thin-walled nodular iron pistons (or steel-crowned, aluminium-skirted or steel-crowned, iron-skirted pistons), cylinder heads with double bottom decks, individual injection pumps, closed-type injection equipment, gas turbochargers and a constant speed and constant power hydraulic governor. This series of engine can be equipped with various kinds of governors, fuel injectors, turbochargers and generators according to the number of cylinders and cylinder arrangement to provide a range of power outputs to meet various applications.

The model 16V240ZJC is a development of the 16V240ZJB which has been in production for many years. The hp rating of the new engine has been increased by improvements to the design and materials of the crankshaft, connecting rods and cylinder liners. The 16V240ZJD diesel engine has been developed in association with Ricardo Consulting Engineers of the UK. Many of the main components, such as the crankshaft and cylinder head, have been improved. New parts include the ABB VTC 254-13 turbochargers, Bryce FCVAB fuel injection pumps, NTDLB injectors and NOVA-Swiss high-pressure pipes. Glacier main journal and connecting rod bearing shells and a Woodward PGEV governor have been introduced.

To date, some 5,000 units of the 240ZJ series of engines have been produced.

UPDATED

Detroit Diesel

Detroit Diesel Corporation
13400 Outer Drive West, Detroit, Michigan 48239-4001, USA
Tel: +1 313 592 5000   Fax: +1 313 592 7580

Key personnel
Chief Executive Officer and Chairman:
  Roger S Penske
President and Chief Operating Officer: Ludvik F Koci
Vice-President, International: Paul A Moreton
Vice-President, Construction and Industrial Sales:
  Jeffrey Sylvester

Products
Diesel and alternative fuel engines from 5 to 10,000 hp. Generator sets.

VERIFIED

EMG

Elektro-Mechanik GmbH
Industriestrasse 1, D-57482 Wenden, Germany
Tel: +49 2762 6120   Fax: +49 2762 612331

Key personnel
Sales Director: E Greiner

Products
Cardan shaft axledrives for diesel railcars.

VERIFIED

Eminox

Eminox Ltd
North Warren Road, Gainsborough DN21 2TU, UK
Tel: +44 1427 810088   Fax: +44 1427 810061

Associated companies
Eminox BV, Hendrik Ido Ambacht, Netherlands
Connectors Ltd, Keighley, UK

Key personnel
Sales Director: M H Galey
Commercial Director: G A Richards

Products
Eminox stainless steel exhaust systems for use on diesel multiple-units, railcars and locomotives.

Eminox Greencat exhaust products incorporate Johnson Matthey pollution-control technology. The range comprises a catalyst, catalyst/silencer, particulate filter and the CRT combined catalyst and filter.

Eminox provides design, development and manufacturing services to manufacturers of rolling stock and engines and railway operators for exhaust systems and ancillary products such as cooling systems, air intake systems and toilet discharge pipes. The Eminox range of insulation products is designed for use where the surface temperature of pipes and silencers has to be kept to a minimum.

VERIFIED

An Eminox stainless steel exhaust on Class 166 dmu

Faur

Faur SA
B-dul Basarabia 256, Bucharest 3, R-73249, Romania
Tel: +40 1 627 6275   Fax: +40 1 312 8070

Key personnel
See entry in *Locomotives and powered passenger vehicles* section

Products
Cardan shafts for high-torque applications and diesel engines for rail traction from 220 to 1,050 kW, suitable for a wide variety of uses in both diesel-electric and diesel-hydraulic locomotives; axledrives; two-motor driving bogies (with GEC Alsthom traction motors).

The Types 6, 8, and 12 four-stroke turbocharged engines feature charge air cooling with direct injection; bore is 165 mm and stroke 185 mm.

Types 6, 8 and 12 V 396 engines

Type designation	Speed	Rated output	Weight	Dimensions mm		
	rpm	kW/hp	kg	Length	Width	Height
6V396TC12	1,800	525/715	1,900	1,501	1,424	1,345
8V396TC12	1,800	700/950	2,400	1,721	1,442	1,345
12V396TC12	1,800	1,050/1,430	3,350	2,251	1,522	1,405

UPDATED

Fiat

Fiat Ferroviaria SpA
Piazza Galateri 4, I-12038 Savigliano (CN), Italy
Tel: +39 172 718333   Fax: +39 172 718306

Key personnel
See entry in *Locomotives and powered passenger vehicles* section

Products
Diesel engines for rail applications derived directly from Iveco large-volume power plants for road trucks.

Design and manufacture of components and transmission for rail vehicles, in particular diesel railcar transmissions, output ratings 147 to 205 kW (200 to 280 hp), both hydromechanical (hydraulic coupling and five-speed gearbox) and hydraulic (torque converter); recently, the mechanical version has been improved by introducing a microprocessor device for automatic control of transmission. Also drives for locomotives, metro car tractive units and tramcars in monomotor and twin-motor versions with traction motors mounted longitudinally or transversally. Drives for high-speed (up to 300 km/h) motor bogies are now in service after five years of development and trials.

VERIFIED

Freudenberg

Freudenberg Dichtungs und Schwingungstechnik KG
Boxhanger Strasse 79/82, D-10245 Berlin, Germany
Tel: +49 30 293 70374   Fax: +49 30 293 70286

Key personnel
Chairman: Jorg Sost

Management Board
  Herbert Fehrecke
  Norbert Schebesta
  Jorg Sost
Sales Manager, Railcar Industry, Europe: Erik Reule

Associate companies in Austria, Belgium, Brazil, Denmark, Finland, India, Japan, Luxembourg, Mexico, Netherlands, Norway, Poland, Russia, Singapore, Spain, Sweden, Switzerland, UK and USA.

Products
Resilient couplings linking motor, gearbox and axle, resilient mountings.

NEW ENTRY

Ganz-David Brown

Ganz-David Brown Transmissions Kft
Orczy út 46-48, H-1089 Budapest, Hungary
Tel: +36 1 210 2583/1150   Fax: +36 1 334 0364

Key personnel
General Manager: Tamás Fodor

Marketing and Technical Manager: József Fáy
Chief Designer: Károly Fóti
Quality Assurance Manager: Istvan Lorincz
Engineering Manager: Laszlo Meszaros

Products
Hydrodynamic and hydromechanical power transmissions for diesel railcars and locomotives.

Axledrive units with helical and bevel gears for railcars, locomotives and light rail vehicles. Wholly suspended axledrive units for monomotor bogies for metro trainsets. Helical gear pairs for high-speed locomotives and railcars, spiral bevel gear pairs for locomotives, railcars and light rail vehicles.

UPDATED

Gardner

L Gardner & Sons Ltd
Barton Hall Engine Works, Patricroft, Eccles,
Manchester M30 7WA, UK
Tel: +44 161 789 2201   Fax: +44 161 787 7549

Key personnel
Managing Director: Stan Lawrenson
Sales and Marketing Director: Gareth Williams

Products
Horizontal and vertical engines from 180 to 350 bhp featuring high torque, low weight and low fuel consumption. The engines are proven in rail applications as well as truck, bus, coach and marine operation throughout the world.

UPDATED

Model		6LXB	6HLXB	6LXCT	6HLXCT	6LXDT	6LYT	LG1200
No of cylinders		6	6	6	6	6	6	6
Max bhp		180	180	230	230	290	350	300
Engine speed	rpm	1,850	1,850	1,900	1,900	1,900	1,800	1,900
Weight approx	kg	707.6	774.3	858	858	858	1,091	838
	(lb)	(1,560)	(1,707)	(1,892)	(1,892)	(1,892)	(2,407)	(1,848)
Length	mm	1,397	1,397	1,536	1,566	1,569	1,585	1,580
	(in)	(55)	(55)	(60½)	(61½)	(62)	(63)	(62.2)
Width	mm	667	1,397	608	1,706	706	754	716
	(in)	(26¼)	(55)	(24)	(67)	(28)	(30)	(28.2)
Height	mm	1,149	660	948	687	1,140	1,283	1,150
	(in)	(45¼)	(26)	(37¼)	(27)	(45)	(51)	(45.3)

GE

General Electric Transportation Systems
2910 East Lake Road, Erie, Pennsylvania 16531, USA
Tel: +1 814 875 5385   Fax: +1 814 875 6487

Key personnel
See entry in *Locomotives* section

Products
Diesel engines and complete electric transmissions.

Series FDL (8-, 12- and 16-cylinder 45° Vee) engines
Type: 4-cycle turbocharged with water-cooled charge air cooler.
Cylinders: Bore 229 mm (9 in). Stroke 267 mm (10½ in). Swept volume 668 in³ per cylinder. Individual unitised cast cylinder with renewable liner and head. Compression ratio 12.7:1.
Fuel injection: Individual injectors and fuel pumps.
Turbocharger: One, exhaust-driven (no gear drive to crankshaft).

Lubrication: Forced full flow filtered oil to all bearings and pistons, gear-type engine-driven pump.

Cooling system: Forced circulation water cooling of cylinders, turbocharger and intercoolers. The water passages are external of the crankcase and mainframe.

Current engine specifications

Model	7FDL8	7FDL12	7FDL16	7HDL16
No of cylinders	8	12	16	16
Output (U/C) standard	2,000	3,300	4,100	6,250
Stroke cycle	4	4	4	4
Cylinder arrangement	45° Vee	45° Vee	45° Vee	45° Vee
Bore	228.6 mm (9 in)	228.6 mm (9 in)	228.6 mm (9 in)	250 mm (9.84 in)
Stroke	266.7 mm (10½ in)	266.7 mm (10½ in)	266.7 mm (10½ in)	320 mm (12.60 in)
Compression ratio	12:7:1	12:7:1	12:7:1	15.5:1
Idle speed	385 rpm	385 rpm	385 rpm	350 rpm
Full-rated speed	1,050 rpm	1,050 rpm	1,050 rpm	1,050 rpm
Firing order	1R-1L-2R-2L-4R-4L-3R-3L	1R-1L-5R-5L-3R-3L-6R 6L-2R-2L-4R-4L	1R-1L-3R-3L-7R-7L-4R-4L 8R-8L-6R-6L-2R-2L-5R-5L	1R-1L-3R-3L-7R-7L-5R-5L 8R-8L-6R-6L-2R-2L-4R-4L
Turbocharger	Single	Single	Single	Dual
Engine dimensions				
Height (excluding stack)	2,191 mm (86¼ in)	2,289 mm (90⅛ in)*	2,289 mm (90⅛ in)	2,611 mm (102.80 in)
Length (overall)	3,264 mm (128½ in)	4,051 mm (159½ in)	4,902 mm (193 in)	4,984 mm (196.24 in)
Width (overall)	1,734 mm (68¼ in)	1,740 mm (68⅜ in)	1,740 mm (68⅜ in)	1,700 mm (66.93 in)
Weight (dry)	12,200 kg (27,000 lb)	15,900 kg (35,000 lb)	19,700 kg (43,500 lb)	20,700 kg (45,600 lb)

* Note: Domestic (USA) type engines only. The export model has a lower water header (86¼ in, 2,191 mm)

UPDATED

GEC Alsthom

GEC Alsthom Transport Division
48 rue Albert Dhalenne, F-93482 Saint-Ouen Cedex, Paris, France
Tel: +33 1 41 66 90 00   Fax: +33 1 41 78 77 55
Web: http://www.gecalsthom.com

GEC Alsthom Ltd
PO Box 70, Mill Road, Rugby CV21 1TB
Tel: +44 1788 546600   Fax: +44 1788 546440

GEC Alsthom Traction
PO Box 134, Manchester M60 1AH
Tel: +44 161 872 2431   Fax: +44 161 875 2131

For full list of companies in the group, see GEC Alsthom entry in *Locomotives and powered passenger vehicles* section.

Products
Full range of electric transmissions and gearboxes.
GEC Alsthom's gears factory at Rugby has secured an order from Hanjin Heavy Industries, Korea, for 680 gearboxes for trains on Pusan Transit Authority's Line 2. The order is shared with a Korean partner and all gear rotating parts are built at Rugby, where new facilities have been introduced. GEC Alsthom is already supplying traction gearboxes to another Korean train builder, Hyundai Precision Industries, for Malaysian Railways.

UPDATED

GEC Alsthom ACEC Transport

GEC Alsthom ACEC Transport
Rue Cambier Dupret 50-52, PO Box 4211,
B-6001 Charleroi, Belgium
Tel: +32 71 445411   Fax: +32 71 445778

Key personnel
Managing Director: C Jauquet

Products
Electric transmissions for diesel-electric locomotives.

UPDATED

GEC Alsthom Paxman Diesels

GEC Alsthom Paxman Diesels Ltd
A management company of GEC Alsthom Diesels Ltd
Paxman Works, Hythe Hill, Colchester CO1 2HW, UK
Tel: +44 1206 795151   Fax: +44 1206 797869

Key personnel
Commercial Director: D Brooks
General Sales Manager: J G Hill

Products
Lightweight compact high-speed diesel engines in the 840 to 2,520 kW power range, for rail traction applications.

The Valenta 12CL engine has now amassed over 18 million running hours in High Speed Train (HST) power cars in the UK, and the State Railway Authority of New South Wales' XPT fleet is powered by a similar unit.

Engine type	Turbocharged or turbocharged/intercooled	No of cylinders	Cont traction rating kW (bhp)	Engine speed rpm	BMEP bar (lbf/in²)	Piston speed m/s (ft/min)	Full load fuel consumption g/bhp/h (lb/bhp/h)	Bore mm (in)	Stroke mm (in)	Displacement litres (ins²)	Compression ratio	Approx dimensions mm (in)			Crankcase centre line height	Approx dry weight kg (lb)
												Length	Width	Height		
Valenta 6CL	TC/I	6	840 (1,126)	1,500	17 (247)	10.8 (2,125)	170 (0.376)	197 (7.75)	216 (8.5)	39.4 (2,405)	13.0:1	2,780 (109.5)	1,200 (47.25)	1,850 (72.8)	635 (25)	5,175 (11,385)
Valenta 8CL	TC/I	8	1,120 (1,500)	1,500	17 (247)	10.8 (2,125)	170 (0.376)	197 (7.75)	216 (8.5)	52.6 (3,207)	13.0:1	2,010 (79.14)	1,580 (62.2)	1,850 (72.8)	740 (29)	5,690 (12,518)
Valenta 12CL	TC/I	12	1,790 (2,399)	1,500	17 (247)	10.8 (2,125)	170 (0.376)	197 (7.75)	216 (8.5)	78.9 (4,811)	13.0:1	2,600 (102.3)	1,580 (62.2)	1,850 (72.8)	740 (29)	8,117 (13,596)
Valenta 16CL	TC/I	16	2,240 (3,003)	1,500	17 (247)	10.8 (2,125)	170 (0.376)	197 (7.75)	216 (8.5)	105.1 (6,415)	13.0:1	2,950 (116)	1,580 (62.2)	2,300 (90.5)	740 (29)	10,220 (22,484)
Valenta 18CL	TC/I	18	2,520 (3,380)	1,500	17 (247)	10.8 (2,125)	170 (0.376)	197 (7.75)	216 (8.5)	118.3 (7,217)	13.0:1	3,350 (131.9)	1,580 (62.2)	2,500 (98.4)	740 (29)	11,147 (24,523)
Vega 12V(JL)	TC/I	12	890 (1,193)	1,500/1,800	16.27 (236)	9.5/11.4 (1,869/2,243)	164 (0.362)	160 (6.3)	190 (7.5)	45.8 (2,795)	13.8:1	2,350 (92.5)	1,400 (55.1)	1,960 (77.1)	646 (25.4)	4,924 (10,832)
Vega 12V(CL)	TC/I	12	1,005 (1,347)	1,500/1,800	16.27 (236)	9.5/11.4 (1,869/2,243)	164 (0.362)	160 (6.3)	190 (7.5)	45.8 (2,795)	13.8:1	2,350 (92.5)	1,400 (55.1)	1,960 (77.1)	646 (25.4)	4,924 (10,832)
Vega 16V(JL)	TC/I	16	1,190 (1,595)	1,500/1,800	16.2 (235)	9.5/11.4 (1,869/2,243)	164 (0.362)	160 (6.3)	190 (7.5)	61.1 (3,729)	13.8:1	3,115 (122.6)	1,400 (55.1)	1,960 (77.1)	646 (25.4)	6,001 (13,215)
Vega 16V(CL)	TC/I	16	1,345 (1,803)	1,500/1,800	16.2 (235)	9.5/11.4 (1,869/2,243)	164 (0.362)	160 (6.3)	190 (7.5)	61.1 (3,729)	13.8:1	3,115 (122.6)	1,400 (55.1)	1,960 (77.1)	646 (25.4)	6,001 (13,215)
12VP185	TC/I	12	1,860 (2,493)	1,500/1,800	19.6 (284)	9.79/11.76 (1,926/2,314)	—	185 (7.28)	196 (7.71)	63.21 (3,856)	13.1:1	3,142 (123.7)	1,441 (56.7)	2,004 (78.9)	656 (25.8)	7,400 (16,280)
18VP185	TC/I	18	2,790/3,090 (3,742/4,144)	1,500/1,800	19.6 (284)	9.79/11.76 (1,926/2,314)	—	185 (7.28)	196 (7.71)	94.8 (5,784)	13.1:1	3,840 (151.2)	1,480 (58.2)	2,200 (86.6)	820 (32.3)	11,400 (25,080)

Engine ratings: Continuous traction rating corrected for altitude of 150 m (500 ft), air temperature of 30°C (85°F) and water temperature to intercooler 45°C (113°F).
Dimensions: These are for engines with standard equipment.
Engine weights: These are for complete engines ready for installation and may vary slightly, depending on customer requirements.

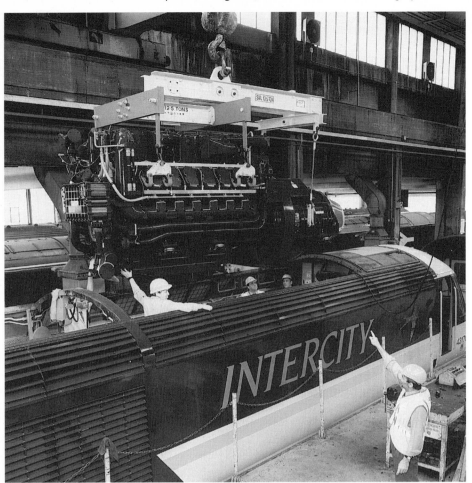

Recent contracts include the supply of 12VP185 engines for HST power cars, UK, and four Valenta units for Sri Lanka.

A contract for another five 12VP185 high-speed diesel engines for Angel Train Contracts has been won by Paxman. The engines are equipped with Viking 22 electronic governors and controls are being supplied by Regulateurs Europa.

UPDATED

Paxman 12VP185 engine being lowered into an InterCity 125 power car
1996

GEC Alsthom Ruston Diesels

GEC Alsthom Ruston Diesels Ltd
A management company of GEC Alsthom Diesels Ltd
Vulcan Works, Newton-le-Willows, Merseyside
WA1 28RU, UK
Tel: +44 1925 225151   Fax: +44 1925 222055

Key personnel
Managing Director: J M MacKinnon
Commercial Director: C B Foulkes
Customer Services Director: M Whattam

Products
Medium-speed diesel engines for rail traction within a power range of 920 to 6,875 kW.

The RK series of diesel engines first entered railway service in a six-cylinder in-line form in 1934. Since the introduction of higher-powered Vee form models in 1948, the RK range of engines has undergone a continuous programme of evolutionary development to achieve higher output, longer component life, improved overhaul periodicity and lower fuel consumption across a wide range of climates, geographical locations and customer operating and maintenance practices.

The 270 mm bore RK270 combines proven features of the RK series with design improvements for increased performance and a higher standard of reliability. The RK270 provides a maximum output of 344 kW per cylinder at 1,000 rpm and is manufactured in six- and eight-cylinder in-line and 12-, 16-, and 20-cylinder Vee forms.

The 215 mm bore RK215 is a recent addition to the Ruston range, featuring low weight and a high power-to-weight ratio. The RK215 provides a maximum output of 180 kW at 1,000 rpm and is manufactured in six-cylinder in-line and eight- and 12-cylinder Vee forms.

| Engine type | Speed rpm | No of cylinders | Standard power kW | Dimensions | | | Approx dry weight of engine with flywheel kg |
				Length mm	Width mm	Height mm	
6RK215T	850	6(L)	920	2,597	1,480	2,145	6,606
	900	6(L)	970				
	950	6(L)	1,030				
	1,000	6(L)	1,080				
8RK215T	850	8(V)	1,220	2,422	1,707	2,695	8,800
	900	8(V)	1,300				
	950	8(V)	1,370				
	1,000	8(V)	1,440				
12RK215T	850	12(V)	1,840	3,315	1,707	2,746	11,700
	900	12(V)	1,940				
	950	12(V)	2,060				
	1,000	12(V)	2,160				
6RK270T	850	6(L)	1,770	4,020	1,990	2,800	13,000
	900	6(L)	1,875				
	950	6(L)	1,970				
	1,000	6(L)	2,065				
8RK270T	850	8(L)	2,360	5,300	1,700	3,050	17,500
	900	8(L)	2,500				
	950	8(L)	2,605				
	1,000	8(L)	2,750				
12RK270T	850	12(V)	3,540	5,010	1,810	2,580	22,000
	900	12(V)	3,750				
	950	12(V)	3,940				
	1,000	12(V)	4,125				
16RK270T	850	16(V)	4,720	5,075	1,830	2,820	27,000
	900	16(V)	5,000				
	950	16(V)	5,250				
	1,000	16(V)	5,500				
20RK270T	850	20(V)	5,900	5,965	1,940	2,820	33,000
	900	20(V)	6,250				
	950	20(V)	6,560				
	1,000	20(V)	6,875				

UPDATED

General Motors Corporation

Electro-Motive Division
9301 West 55th Street, LaGrange, Illinois 60525, USA
Tel: +1 708 387 5293　Fax: +1 708 387 3944

Key personnel
See entry in *Locomotives and powered passenger vehicles* section

Products
Electro-Motive Division first developed the Model 567 diesel engine in 1938 when it began locomotive manufacture at LaGrange, Illinois, USA.

To provide increased hp and greater efficiency, the Model 645 engine was introduced in mid-1965. The major change in the Model 645 over the 567 was the increase in cylinder liner bore from 216 mm (8½ in) to 230 mm (9⅛ in), the stroke remaining at 254 mm (10 in).

The turbocharged 645E3B engine introduced in 1979 and the turbocharged 645F3 engine introduced in 1981 were a result of the search for increased product reliability, performance and fuel economy. With increased hp and fuel economy these engines could haul more tonnage at the same speed or the same tonnage at a higher speed than their predecessors.

The 710G series of engines is an evolutionary development of GM/EMD's turbocharged, uniflow-scavenged, two-stroke cycle engine. The 16-cylinder 710G3B is rated at 4,250 hp at 900 rpm for locomotive applications and has a displacement of 710 in³ per cylinder. This series is the result of a succession of improvements to the engine. From 1989 to 1991, for example, the fuel efficiency of the 710G was increased by 1.5 per cent. Greater displacement and an advanced turbocharger give the 710G the capacity for significant increases in hp.

Full load fuel consumption of the model 710G3B engine is down 11.5 per cent from the 1980 model and 4.9 per cent from the 1983 model in the 645 range. Among the ways fuel efficiency has been increased is improved turbocharger aftercoolers and fuel injectors, and low-restriction liner intake ports.

As compared to the 645 series engines, the 710 features a longer stroke and added displacement which led to these structural improvements in the engine: Model G crankcase; larger diameter plunger injectors; larger diameter crankshaft; new camshaft; longer cylinder liner; and longer piston and rod assembly. The 710G design also increased the overall dimensions: the new engine is 1⅝ in higher and 4⅝ in longer.

The increase in length is the result of a larger, more efficient turbocharger. Entry to the turbine was streamlined to improve gas flow. An improved exhaust diffuser also reduces flow restriction. The turbocharger is deeper to accommodate a larger annulus for a smoother and less restrictive discharge of exhaust gases. This new state-of-the-art G turbocharger provides a 15 per cent increase in air flow for reduced thermal loading of critical engine components. This higher air flow, in combination with an increased injection rate from the new ⁹⁄₁₆ in plunger injector, accounts for the increase in fuel economy at rated output with no increase in engine mechanical loading.

A key concern in the development of a large displacement engine has been reliability. Throughout the development of the 710G, GM/EMD used advanced laboratory techniques to analyse stress and predict performance. Finite element analysis and comprehensive strain-gauge testing were used extensively.

GM/EMD has recently broken with decades of US tradition by developing a four-stroke diesel engine for rail use.

Model		16-645FB	16-710G
Bore	in	9.06	9.06
Stroke	in	10	11
Displacement	in³	645	710
Cylinder spacing	in	16⅝	16⅝
Bank angle		45	45
Compression ratio		16.0:1	16.0:1
Engine speed	rpm	950	900
bhp		3,800	4,250

VERIFIED

Giro

Giro Engineering Ltd
Talisman, Duncan Road, Park Gate, Southampton
SO31 7GA, UK
Tel: +44 1489 885288　Fax: +44 1489 885199
Email: giro@dial.pipex.com

Key personnel
Managing Director: J P Williams
Commercial Director: C R Galley

Products
Design and manufacture of diesel engine sheathed and unsheathed fuel injection pipes.

Unsheathed fuel injection pipes were supplied to Dalian Locomotive Works in 1996; unsheathed Alco fuel injection pipes were supplied to Indian Railways in 1996 and sheathed Mirrlees fuel injection pipes were sent to Mirrlees for railway applications in May 1996.

UPDATED

GMD

Grandes Motores Diesel SA
Av Juan Bautista Alberdi 1001, 1678 Caseros,
Buenos Aires, Argentina
Tel: +54 1 750 4209/9019/2251　Fax: +54 1 750 1476

Works
Ruta 9, Km 694, 5123 Ferreyra, Córdoba, Argentina
Tel: +54 51 972212/2106　Fax: +54 51 972309

Key personnel
President: Dr Guillermo Scarsoglio
Vice-President and General Manager:
　Ing Enzo N Filipelli
Commercial Manager: Ing Antonio Maltana

Group Companies
Materfer SA
Centro de Actividades Termomécanicas (CAT) SA

Products
GMD manufactures the Alco 251 engine under General Electric licence.

Together with CAT, the company manufactures spares for Fiat GMT engines.

VERIFIED

Grandi Motori Trieste

Cantieri Navali Italiani SpA
Diesel Engines Division, Bagnoli della Rosandra 334,
I-34018 Trieste, Italy
Tel: +39 40 319 3111　Fax: +39 40 382 7371

Key personnel
Managing Director: G R Lami
Technical Director: F Bartoli

Products
Diesel engines for railway traction, marine and industrial applications. Hydraulic and mechanical transmissions for locomotives and railcars. Axledrives for electric and diesel-powered vehicles. For rail traction, the Fincantieri locomotive engine range includes Series A210 and BL230 from 620 to 4,400 kW, and the 1700 Series from 225 to 2,000 kW.

In addition, Sulzer slow-speed engines are produced for the Italian market and a cross-licensing agreement exists with Sulzer for medium-speed engines of the A 32 and ZA 40 S types.

UPDATED

Hidromecanica

Hidromecanica SA
78 Boulevard 15 November, R-2200 Brasov, Romania
Tel: +40 68 134082　Fax: +40 68 310461
Email: hidro@starnets.ro

Key personnel
General Manager: Lucian Florea

Production Manager: Vasile Toma
Technical Manager: Andrei Mihăilă
Commercial Manager: Marian Stefan
Head of Marketing Department: Petru Gârbacea
Head of Sales Department: Constantin Belu

Products
VTR series (350 to 1,500 hp) and TS series (1,200 to 4,000 hp) turbochargers for railway applications; torque converters and power shift transmissions (60 to 1,000 hp) for shunting locomotives and other applications; and hydraulic transmissions and inverter-reducers (136 to 1,500 hp) for diesel-hydraulic locomotives.

Customers include railway operators in Canada, Egypt, Greece, Hungary, Pakistan, Poland and Turkey.

UPDATED

Hitachi

Hitachi Ltd
6 Kanda Surugadai 4-chome, Chiyoda-ku,
Tokyo 101, Japan
Tel: +81 3 3258 1111　Fax: +81 3 3258 5212

Key personnel
See entry in *Locomotives and powered passenger vehicles* section

Products
Complete control equipment, electric transmissions and hydraulic transmissions.

VERIFIED

Hygate Transmissions

Hygate Transmissions Ltd
A member of the David Brown Rail Equipment Ltd
Lower Bristol Road, Bath BA2 3EB, UK
Tel: +44 1225 334000   Fax: +44 1225 318582

Key personnel
Director and General Manager: R Bailey
Sales & Marketing Director: N Crossley
Technical Sales Manager: N Antrobus
Technical Manager: J A Falkner

Products
Design and manufacture of all types of gear drives for urban railway and mass transit systems. Single and double reduction parallel shaft gearboxes and spiral bevel gearboxes. Double engagement gear couplings for all rail applications. Redesign and upgrading of existing transmissions. Consultancy, maintenance, overhaul and repair services.

Recent contracts include the supply of 400 gearboxes and couplings for Inchcon Subway Line 1, South Korea. This brings the total number of gearboxes supplied to South Korea for metro applications in Seoul, Taegu and Inchcon in the last few years to over 2,000. In December 1996 the company was awarded a contract for the supply of 696 LRV gearboxes for Eurotram vehicles operating in Strasbourg and Milan.

UPDATED

Hygate single-reduction emu gearbox

Jenbacher

Jenbacher Energiesysteme AG
Achenseestrasse 1-3, A-6200 Jenbach, Austria
Tel: +43 5244 6000   Fax: +43 5244 63255
Web: http//www.jenbacher.com

Key personnel
See entry in *Locomotives and powered passenger vehicles* section

Products
Diesel engines for rail vehicles.

UPDATED

Kim Hotstart

Kim Hotstart Mfg Company
PO Box 11245, Spokane, Washington 99211-0245, USA
Tel: +1 509 534 6171   Fax: +1 509 534 4216

Key personnel
Vice-President and General Manager: Rick Robinson
Director, Sales and Marketing: John R Schratz
Manager, Industrial Products: Rick Cargill

Products
Layover protection systems for diesel engines, coolant only; coolant and lube oil; and lube oil, coolant and diesel fuel.

Preheating systems for locomotives are available in models from 15,000 to 72,000 W at 240 or 480 V. Other specific voltages can be provided.

VERIFIED

Kolomna

Kolomna Plant Joint Stock Company
Partizan Street, 140408 Kolomna, Moscow Region, Russian Federation
Tel: +7 095 38152   Fax: +7 095 203 2434

Key personnel
Director: V A Berezhkov
Chief Engineer: V V Maslov
Marketing Director: V A Nefyedov

Products
D49 series of diesel locomotive engines. The D49 series comprises four-stroke, turbocharged engines with four or six cylinders arranged in-line or eight, 12, 16 and 20 cylinders in Vee-versions.

The D49 series is built on a modular concept basis providing high manufacturing, operational and maintenance efficiency.

The main modules are:
Cast-welded cylinder block: the crankcase portion of the cylinder block is formed by a series of standard elements with steel uprights depending on the number of cylinders;
Cylinder set (including cylinder head with an underslung cylinder liner with piston and connecting rod);
Tray (housing) with a camshaft and drive unit for valves of both cylinder rows;
Drive units of valve timing and attached devices formed by a box-like double-walled housing with built-in gear mechanisms mounted on cylinder block ends in assembled and adjusted state.

D49 diesel engines and generating sets are in service in Europe and countries in Southeast Asia, Africa, South America as well as northern regions of Russia. Recent contracts include the supply of diesel engines to Germany, Latvia, Lithuania and Estonia.

D49 diesel locomotive engines
Bore: 260 mm
Stroke: 260 mm
Speed: min 750-1,000 rpm
Mean effective pressure: MPa 1.1-1.96
Mean piston speed: 6.8-8.6 m/s
Specific fuel consumption: g/kW/h 190 +5%

VERIFIED

Engine type	Output		Dimensions mm			Weight kg	Type of locomotive
	kW	hp	Length	Width	Height	Diesel engine	
4 LD49	300-750	—	3,030	1,580	2,300	9,000	—
6 LD49	1,031	1,402	3,929	1,577	2,313	11,000	Shunting
8 VD49	590-1,620	800-2,200	3,370	1,665	2,330	10,070	TGM 6V, TGM 8
12 VD49	1,100-2,650	1,500-3,600	4,030	1,665	3,030	14,390	2TE 116, TEM 7A
16 VD49	1,840-3,520	2,500-4,800	4,900	1,655	3,070	17,460	2TE 116, 2TE 121, TEP 70
20 VD49	3,700-4,770	5,000-6,500	6,270	1,665	3,190	20,880	2TE 136, TEP 80

Output, specific fuel consumption and weight values are for ISO standard reference conditions.

L & M Radiator, Inc

1414 East 37th Street, Hibbing, Minnesota 55746, USA
Tel: +1 218 263 8993

Key personnel
President: Alex Chisholm
Vice-President: Richard Braun

Products
Radiators and radiator cores.

VERIFIED

MAN

MAN Nutzfahrzeuge Aktiengesellschaft
Dachauer Strasse 667, D-808995 Munich, Germany
Tel: +49 911 420 2002   Fax: +49 911 420 1932

Works
Nuremberg Works, Vogelweiherstrasse 33, D-90441 Nuremberg

Key personnel
Director, Engine & Components Division: Kurt Heuser
General Sales Manager: Günter Knohsalla
Sales Manager: Wolfgang Kuntze
Service Manager: Gerhard Schneider

Products
Four-stroke direct-injection water-cooled six-cylinder diesel engines, rated at 160-300 kW at 2,100 rpm. A V-12 engine is available, rated at 305-529 kW at 2,100 rpm.

For auxiliary drives MAN produces six-cylinder in-line engines for generator sets, rated at 47-313 kW, V-8, V-10 and V12 cylinder engines from 325 to 587 kW at 1,500-1,800 rpm.

Both engine applications are based on MAN's truck range.

Recent contracts include 400 type D2866 LUE602 engines for SNCF, rated at 300 kW at 2,100 rpm. This six-cylinder engine meets Euro-2 regulations.

MAN has received an order for more than 200 engines from RENFE for existing MACOSA trains. These engines are rated at 230 kW at 2,100 rpm. MAN is also supplying the engines for the Spanish IC3 trainsets.

NEW ENTRY

The perfect drive system for rail vehicles.
Economical, ecological, comfortable, safe.

Voith, the specialist for demanding tasks in power transmission technology is particularly committed to developing innovative drive systems for rail vehicles.

For metros and city rail vehicles:
Voith Hydrolock self-locking limited slip differentials for decoupled single-wheel or single axle drives
- sinusoidal running on straight track
- low torque between driving wheels when negotiating curves
- better adhesion utilisation.

For light rail vehicles in commuter trains with high acceleration:
Voith power packs
- suitable for low-floor applications
- flanged to the engine or in free installation
- proven and cost-effective.

For high-performance diesel railcars with high final speeds:
Voith turbo transmissions
- high tractive effort
- high degree of efficiency in the main operating range
- wear-free retarder.

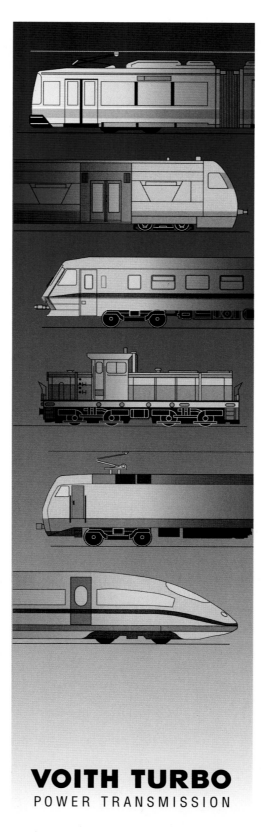

For shunting and multipurpose locomotives:
Turbo-reversing transmissions
- high availability and reliability
- long service life
- low maintenance costs.

For electric locomotives and railcars:
Axle drive gearboxes, quill-shaft final drives, tripode shafts and cooling systems.

Reference deliveries:

Turbo transmission for diesel railcars
- VT 611 of Deutsche Bahn AG
- X-TER of SNCF France
- DM 90 of Nederlandse Sporwegen
- CDC of Korean National Railways
- TRD of RENFE built by CAF

Automatic transmission or turbo transmission for light rail vehicles
- Regio Shuttle built by ADtranz
- LVT/S built by DWA
- INTEGRAL built by Jenbach BR
- 640/641 of DB AG (LHB)
- TER of SNCF (De Dietrich)

Cooling units for electrical rail vehicles
- BR 145 of Deutsche Bahn AG
- S-Bahn Brisbane Australia

Self-locking limited slip differential for metros and city rail vehicles
- Underground RATP Paris
- Municipal railway Berlin
- Municipal railway Stuttgart

Axle drive gearbox for electrical rail vehicles
- E 152 of Deutsche Bahn AG
- Underground Valencia
- Underground Taipeh
- S-Bahn Taiwan
- ICE 3 of Deutsche Bahn AG

Further informations:

Voith Turbo GmbH & Co. KG
P.O. Box 1930
D-89509 Heidenheim
Tel. (07321) 37-4479
Fax (07321) 37 76 03

VOITH TURBO
POWER TRANSMISSION

at 035.1e

Mirrlees

Mirrlees Blackstone Ltd
Hazel Grove, Stockport SK7 5AH, UK
Tel: +44 161 483 1000　Fax: +44 161 487 1465

Key personnel
Managing Director: R Kington

Products
Diesel engines.

VERIFIED

M & J Diesel Locomotive Filter

805 Golf Lane, Bemsenville, Illinois 60106, USA
Tel: +1 630 595 4560　Fax: +1 630 595 0646

Key personnel
President and Chairman of the Board: Harold O'Connor
Vice President, Sales: Robert S Grandy
Executive Vice-President, Financial: Robert Holden

Products
Lube oil, fuel and air filters for diesel locomotives.

NEW ENTRY

MTU

Motoren- und Turbinen-Union
Friedrichshafen GmbH
D-88040 Friedrichshafen, Germany
Tel: +49 7541 900　Fax: +49 7541 902247/903918

Key personnel
Chairman: Dr Rolf A Hanssen
Senior Vice-President of Operations:
　Dr Gerd-Michael Wolters
Director of Sales & Technology: Hermann Amrein

Products
MTU produces diesel engines for marine propulsion, railway, electric power generation and heavy vehicular applications. To date, more than 64,000 MTU diesels have come off the assembly line, of which about 10,000 units are in railway shunting and mainline service with hydraulic or electric power transmission. By virtue of their compactness and favourable power/volume ratios, MTU engines are also suitable for electric power generation to provide train heating and air conditioning, as well as for locomotive repowering.

MTU diesels are liquid-cooled, direct injection, four-stroke engines with turbocharging and intercooling.

The first 12-cylinder engine of MTU's new 4000 series was installed in an 80 tonne locomotive of Verkehrsbetriebe Peine-Salzgitter GmbH for transporting ore. The locomotive is operating on some 370 km of track belonging to VPS, in addition to DB track. The engine is rated at 1,500 kW and was specified because of its capability to fit in the limited space available.

The new Series 2000 and 4000 engines have been developed jointly by MTU and Detroit Diesel Corporation.

VPS diesel-hydraulic industrial locomotive powered by MTU 12V 4000 engine　　　**1997**

Train electricity generation

Engine	Speed rpm	Output (UIC) kW	Weight kg	Length mm	Width mm	Height mm
6R 183* AA12G	1,500	129	815	1,325	820	1,165
	1,800	152				
6R 183* TA12G	1,500	180	835	1,325	820	1,165
	1,800	195				
8V 183* TA12G	1,500	240	930	1,450	1,060	1,060
	1,800	255				
8V 183* TE12G	1,500	255	950	1,520	1,075	1,135
	1,800	295				
12 183* TA12G	1,500	360	1,300	1,645	1,215	1,095
	1,800	382				
12 183* TE12G	1,500	407	1,380	1,575	1,215	1,175
	1,800	459				
12 183* TB12G	1,500	441	1,385	1,645	1,215	1,175
	1,800	529				

* MTU Series 099 and 183, based on Mercedes-Benz Series 300 and 400

Rail traction

Engine	Speed rpm	Output (UIC) kW	Output (UIC) hp	Weight kg	Length mm	Width mm	Height mm
Underfloor installation							
6R 183* AA13H	2,200	157	214	820	1,315	1,110	670
6R 183* TD13H	2,200	220	299	950	1,425	1,265	660
6R 183* TD13H	2,100	320	374	950	1,425	1,265	660
8V 183* TC13	2,100	323	439	950	1,390	1,200	1,135
8V 183* TD13	2,100	370	503	950	1,390	1,200	1,135
12V 183* TC13	2,100	485	660	1,465	1,610	1,285	870
12V 183* TD13	2,100	550	748	1,440	1,690	1,305	870
Above floor installation							
6R 099* TA11	2,400	126	171	450	965	735	915
6R 183* AA12	2,100	162	220	815	1,325	820	1,165
6V 183* TD13	2,100	250	340	765	960	1,040	1,130
8V 183* TA12	2,100	267	363	930	1,320	970	1,035
8V 183* TC13	2,100	323	439	950	1,390	1,200	1,135
8V 183* TD13	2,100	370	503	950	1,390	1,200	1,135
12V 183* TA12	2,100	400	544	1,300	1,515	1,350	895

Engine	Speed rpm	Output (UIC) kW	Output (UIC) hp	Weight kg	Length mm	Width mm	Height mm
Above floor installation *continued*							
12V 183* TC13	2,100	485	660	1,465	1,610	1,285	870
12V 183* TD13	2,100	550	748	1,440	1,690	1,305	870
6V 396 TC14	1,800	590	802	2,010	1,690	1,460	1,340
8V 396 TC14	1,800	785	1,068	2,520	1,920	1,490	1,340
12V 396 TC14	1,800	1,180	1,605	3,510	2,430	1,540	1,400
16V 396 TC14	1,800	1,570	2,135	4,700	2,890	1,560	1,630
8V 396 TB14	1,800	920	1,251	3,010	2,220	1,580	1,400
12V 396 TB14	1,800	1,380	1,877	4,040	2,680	1,540	1,550
16V 396 TB14	1,800	1,840	2,502	5,150	3,080	1,580	1,610
12V 595 TC10	1,650	2,250	3,060	8,810	3,410	1,500	2,465
16V 595 TC10	1,650	3,000	4,080	11,350	4,000	1,500	2,510
12V 595 TF10	1,650	2,400	3,264	8,810	3,410	1,500	2,465
16V 595 TF10	1,650	3,200	4,352	11,350	4,000	1,500	2,510
12V 1163 TB12	1,200	2,460	3,346	11,400	3,430	1,660	2,370
16V 1163 TB12	1,200	3,280	4,461	14,350	4,120	1,660	2,420
20V 1163 TB12	1,200	4,100	5,576	17,050	5,000	1,660	2,420

UPDATED

MWM

MWM
Motoren-Werke Mannheim AG
A Klöckner-Humboldt-Deutz company
PO Box 102263, D-68140 Mannheim, Germany
Tel: +49 621 3840　Fax: +49 621 384328

Products
Diesel engines for rail vehicles up to 2,000 kW

NEW ENTRY

NICO

Niigata Converter Company Ltd
Asano Sinjuku Building, 27-9 Sendagaya 5-chome,
Shibuya-ku, Tokyo 151, Japan
Tel: +81 3 3354 6931   Fax: +81 3 3341 5365

Main works
Kamo plant: Gejobo 405, Oaza Kamo, Niigata 959-13,
Japan
Omiya plant: 405-3 Yoshinocho 1-chome, Omiya, Saitama
330, Japan

Key personnel
President: S Takagi

Niigata

Niigata Engineering Company Ltd
1-10-1 Kamata-Honchou, Ota-ku, Tokyo 144, Japan
Tel: +81 3 5710 7731   Fax: +81 3 5710 4752

Key personnel
See entry in *Locomotives and powered passenger
vehicles* section

Products
Diesel engines for rail traction use up to 2,000 hp.

OMT

OMT SpA
Via Ferrero 67/A, I-10090 Casine Vica, Rivoli (TO), Italy
Tel: +39 11 957 5354   Fax: +39 11 957 5474

Paulstra

Paulstra
61 rue Marius Aufan, F-92305 Levallois-Perret, France
Tel: +33 1 40 89 53 87   Fax: +33 1 47 57 44 20

Perkins Engines

Varity Perkins
Eastfield, Peterborough PE1 5NA, UK
Tel: +44 1733 67474   Fax: +44 1733 582240

Main works
Perkins Engines (Shrewsbury) Ltd
Sentinel Works, Shrewsbury SY1 4DP, UK
Tel: +44 1743 212000   Fax: +44 1743 369911

Key personnel
Managing Director: Brian J Willmott
Director of Sales and Marketing: Peter W Baker

PSI

Peaker Services Inc
8080 Kensington Court, Brighton, Michigan 48116-8591,
USA
Tel: +1 810 437 4174   Fax: +1 810 437 8280

Key personnel
President: Richard R Steele
Marketing and Sales: Vance Shoger, Frank Boatwright
Sales Engineers: Kim Stone, Terry Warrick

Remy-Barrere-Engrenages

PO Box 210, 62 rue Eugène Muller, F-42005 Saint
Etienne, France
Tel: +33 4 77 43 08 70   Fax: +33 4 77 41 30 38

Key personnel
General Manager: Christian Toulouse

Managing Directors: Y Kasuya, A Shima
General Manager, International Operations:
  M Kubota

Principal subsidiaries
NICO Transmission (Singapore) Pte Ltd
46 Gul Crescent, Jurong Town, Singapore 2262
Tel: +65 862 1332   Fax: +65 862 1762

Products
Single-stage torque converters, three-stage torque
converters, power shift transmissions, hydraulic
couplings for engines rated from 50 to 1,400 hp.
  Recent products include:
Model TACN-22-1600 two-speed forward, two-speed

12V16FX
Type: 12-cylinder Vee, water-cooled, four-stroke
turbocharged and charge air-cooled.
Cylinders: Bore 165 mm. Stroke 185 mm. Swept volume
3.96 litres per cylinder.

DMF18HZ
Type: 6-cylinder horizontal in-line, water-cooled, four-
stroke turbocharged and charge air-cooled.
Cylinders: Bore 150 mm. Stroke 165 mm. Swept volume
2.92 litres per cylinder.

Products
Diesel fuel injection equipment.

VERIFIED

Products
Tetraflex coupling of 4,000 Nm torque capacity, part of a
family of power transmission couplings developed by
Paulstra. Used between electric motors and gearboxes,
they are characterised by a reduced axial thickness and a

Products
Perkins Engines manufactures diesel engines for all
applications from 45 to 1,500 bhp.
  The smaller Perkins engines are supplied to the rail
industry for specialised applications and general support
equipment. Latest ranges from Perkins Engines
(Shrewsbury), where the company builds its larger
engines, are the 2000 Series of six-cylinder engines and
the 8- and 12-cylinder Vee-configuration 3000 Series.
Included in the 2000 Series range is the 2006-TWH, a
horizontal engine capable of powering 145 km/h railcars.
This engine, developing between 186 kW (250 bhp) at
1,900 rpm and 260 kW (350 bhp) at 2,100 rpm, has been
designed for high-speed intercity and urban operations by

Products
Diesel engine rebuilding and maintenance; exchange
service for diesel engine components and personnel
training.
  PSI is an independently owned company specialising in
medium-speed, large diesel engines manufactured by the
Electro-Motive Division of General Motors Corporation.
Services include engine conversions and upgrading, unit
exchange components, engine overhaul (including repair
of case and pan sections, power assemblies, pumps and
governors), field repairs, service contracts, application

Products
Design and manufacture of traction gears. Awarded ISO
3002 certification since 1984.
  Contracts include supply of gears for TGV trainsets.

NEW ENTRY

---

reverse power shift transmission with Type 8 single-stage
torque converter for 330 hp diesel railcars;
Model DW 14 two-speed forward, two-speed reverse
power shift transmission with three-stage torque
converter for 420 hp express diesel railcars.
Model DW 17 three-speed forward, three-speed reverse
power shift transmission with Type 8 single-stage torque
converter for 660 hp express diesel railcars.
  Contracts include power shift transmissions for South
Korea.

VERIFIED

General specifications for both models
Cylinders: Monobloc cast-iron cylinder block and
crankcase, removable cast-iron liners with integral water
jacket. Cast-iron cylinder heads secured by studs.
Fuel injection: Bosch-type injectors and Bosch pump.
Lubrication: Forced feed.
Starting: Electric starter.

VERIFIED

---

radial misalignment capacity of several millimetres. The
torque range available is between 2,000 and 8,000 Nm
with a maximum speed of 3,000 to 3,500 rpm.

UPDATED

---

cars carrying around 80 passengers. The 2006-TWH
powers the Class 158 railcars and the Class 165 railcars in
the UK.

VERIFIED

---

studies, crankcase line boring and repairs, locomotive
inspections and evaluations and personnel training in
locomotive maintenance and repair.
  PSI has developed expertise in redesigning the
electrical systems of EMD locomotives for greater
efficiency, prolonged service life of the unit, and
convenient access and repair.

UPDATED

SACM

SACM
Wartsila SACM Diesel
40 rue du Moulin des Bruyères, F-92400 Courbevoie,
France
Tel: +33 1 47 17 11 11   Fax +33 1 43 34 93 21

Products
Diesel engines for rail vehicles from 600 kW to 4,000 kW.

NEW ENTRY

Scania

S-151 87 Södertälje, Sweden
Tel: +46 8 553 81000   Fax: +46 8 553 82993

Key personnel
Head of Industrial and Marine Engine Division: A Bexell
Sales Manager: L Eriksson

Products
The company, which produced its first internal combustion engine in 1897 and its first diesel engine in 1936, specialises in high-speed engines.

Scania's industrial engine programme now comprises engines with outputs ranging from 142 to 441 kW. The programme is in part a preparedness for future demands for reduced emission levels in industrial engines. Here charge air-cooling is a distinct advantage in optimising the engines to meet more stringent regulations without loss of fuel economy.

The engines are specially adapted for operation with high average output. To reduce the danger of piston ringstick in extremely heavy operation, a keystone-ring is fitted as upper compression ring on the piston. A feature of Scania engines is a cylinder ring preventing coke build-up on the piston.

Generator drive engines for power generation

Model	Engine output gross	Prime duty*		Limited time power**		Emergency standby power***	
		50 Hz	60 Hz	50 Hz	60 Hz	50 Hz	60 Hz
DS9	kW	146	156	146	156	161	178
DS9	kW	154	178	154	178	176	200
DS9	kW	—	200	176	212	199	222
DSC9	kW	208	228	229	248	264	287
DS11	kW	202	231	223	249	246	269
DSI11	kW	227	249	250	275	271	296
DSC11	kW	228	249	244	268	301	330
DSC11	kW	244	268	272	299	309	334
DSC11	kW	264	296	287	309	330	352
DSC11	kW	287	313	309	334	352	377
DSI14	kW	285	341	314	361	366	419
DSI14	kW	316	—	342	—	398	—
DSC14	kW	317	362	342	362	408	420
DSC14	kW	334	—	351	380	441	—
DSC14	kW	351	—	376	—	—	—

* Prime duty: Rated power overloadable by 10% 1h/12h.
** Limited time power: Continuous operation according to ISO 8528.
*** Emergency standby power: 300 h/year service.
Standards: ISO 3046, ISO 8528 and DIN 6280.

Generating set engines have been specially adapted for generator speeds of 1,500 and 1,800 rpm. The injection pump and single-speed Bosch RQ governor provides faster and more precise governing of engine speed. With this governor the requirements for Class A1 (high requirements of governing accuracy) in ISO 3046 are fulfilled. The new governor is also particularly well suited in parallel operation of multi-engine installations.

Industrial engines

Model	DS9	DSI9	DSC9	DS11	DSI11	DSC11	DS14	DSI14	DSC14
Output* kW (hp)	157 (213)-216 (294)	170 (231)-231 (314)	243 (330)	244 (332)	270 (367)	278 (378)	320 (435)	353 (480)	376 (511)
No of cylinders	6 in-line	6 in-line	6 in-line	6 in-line	6 in-line	6 in-line	V8	V8	V8
Cylinder volume, dm³	9	9	9	11	11	11	14.2	14.2	14.2
Max torque Nm	780-1,020	865-1,085	1,313	1,335	1,497	1,551	1,668	1,903	2,066
Specific fuel consumption at 1,500 rpm g/kWh	202-203	199	193	204	204	198	204	199	198
Weight (dry) kg	825	835	910**	930	950	1,020**	1,160	1,180	1,256**

* Full power 1h/6h. No limitation on running hours. Standards: ISO 3046.
** Weight including radiator and expansion tank.

UPDATED

SEMT Pielstick

2 quai de Seine, PO Box 75, F-93202 Saint-Denis Cedex,
France
Tel: +33 1 48 09 76 00   Fax: +33 1 48 09 78 78

Key personnel
Commercial Director: Pierre Bousseau
Sales Director: Alain Malbrancq

Products
High- and medium-speed diesel engines for mainline passenger and freight locomotives, including the PA4 (8 to 16 cylinders, 1,350 to 3,600 hp) and PA6 (6 to 16 cylinders, 2,820 to 7,520 hp) series.

PA4-185 Series
Type: 8, 12 and 16 Vee (90°), 4-cycle, water-cooled.
Cylinders: Bore 185 mm. Stroke 210 mm. Swept volume 5.65 litres per cylinder. Wet liners, individual cast-iron cylinder heads. Central precombustion chamber fitted with pintle-type injectors.
Fuel injection: Pintle-type injectors fitted to precombustion chambers. Monobloc injection pump located inside Vee, controlled by hydraulic governor.
Superchargers: Exhaust gas turbochargers, one for 6- and 8-cylinder engines, one for 12 cylinders and two for 16 and 18 cylinders, between cylinder banks. Air coolers arranged on timing gear side.
Cooling: Water pumps fitted on timing gear end of frame.
Starting: Either electrically or by compressed air.

PA4-200 Series
Type: 8, 12 and 16 Vee (90°), 4-cycle, water-cooled.
Two models:
VG: Variable geometry precombustion chamber
VGA: High-ratio turbocharging
Cylinders: Bore 200 mm. Stroke 210 mm. Swept volume

	PA4-185 VG		
No of cylinders	8(V)	12(V)	16(V)
Turbocharged	Yes	Yes	Yes
Charge air-cooled	Yes	Yes	Yes
Power rating (hp)	1,340	2,000	2,680
Engine speed (rpm)	1,500	1,500	1,500
Piston speed (m/s)	10.5	10.5	10.5
Bmep (bar)	17.3	17.3	17.3
Weight (dry) (kg)	3,900	5,600	7,100
Length (mm)	1,940	2,540	3,140
Width (mm)	1,450	1,450	1,450
Height (mm)	1,865	1,865	1,865

	PA4-200 VG			PA4-200 VGA		
No of cylinders	8(V)	12(V)	16(V)	8(V)	12(V)	16(V)
Turbocharged	Yes	Yes	Yes	Yes	Yes	Yes
Charge air-cooled	Yes	Yes	Yes	Yes	Yes	Yes
Power rating (hp)	1,600	2,400	3,200	1,800	2,700	3,600
Engine speed (rpm)	1,500	1,500	1,500	1,500	1,500	1,500
Piston speed (m/s)	10.5	10.5	10.5	10.5	10.5	10.5
Bmep (bar)	17.8	17.8	17.8	20.5	20.5	20.5
Weight (dry) (kg)	4,400	6,000	7,720	5,500	8,000	10,000
Length (mm)	1,925	2,525	3,125	2,185	2,805	3,504
Width (mm)	1,575	1,450	1,700	1,575	1,680	1,740
Height (mm)	1,865	1,865	1,865	1,810	1,940	1,940

	PA5-255			
No of cylinders	6(L)	8(L)	12(V)	16(V)
Turbocharged	Yes	Yes	Yes	Yes
Charge air-cooled	Yes	Yes	Yes	Yes
Power rating (UIC) (hp)	1,955	2,610	3,915	5,220
Engine speed (rpm)	1,000	1,000	1,000	1,000
Piston speed (m/s)	9	9	9	9
Bmep (bar)	19	19	19	19
Weight (dry) (kg)	10,500	13,500	17,000	22,200
Length (mm)	3,590	4,400	4,060	5,140
Width (mm)	1,300	1,310	1,980	2,070
Height (mm)	2,255	2,440	2,620	2,870

	PA6B-280		
No of cylinders	6(L)	8(L)	12(V)
Supercharged	Yes	Yes	Yes
Charge air-cooled	Yes	Yes	Yes
Power rating (UIC) (hp)	2,820	3,760	5,640
Engine speed (rpm)	1,000	1,000	1,000
Piston speed (m/s)	11	11	11
Weight (dry) (kg)	14,000	18,000	22,000
Length (mm)	3,900	4,820	4,690
Width (mm)	1,450	1,450	2,150
Height (mm)	2,580	2,755	3,225

6.6 litres per cylinder. Wet liners, individual cast-iron cylinder heads.

Pistons: Cast-iron pistons cooled by pressure lubricating oil fed through connecting rod and piston pin into an annular chamber level with top compression ring.

Fuel injection: Monobloc injection pump inside the Vee, controlled by hydraulic governor.

Superchargers: Exhaust gas turbochargers, one for 8-cylinder engine, two for 12 and 16 cylinders, between cylinder banks. Air coolers arranged on timing gear side.

Cooling: Water pumps fitted on timing gear end of frame.

Starting: Either electrically or by compressed air.

PA5-255 Series

Type: 6 and 8 cylinders in-line, 12 and 16 cylinders Vee, supercharged, water-cooled.

Cylinders: Bore 255 mm. Stroke 270 mm. Swept volume 13.79 litres per cylinder. Wet liners directly mounted in the crankcase, without cooling jackets. Individual cast-iron cylinder heads. Single combustion chamber. Direct injection.

Fuel injection: Direct injection by means of injectors of the multihole type. Individual injecting pump housed in the crankcase, directly controlled by the camshafts. Injection controlled by hydraulic speed governor.

Turbochargers: Two per engine, driven by a turbine on the exhaust gas, and housed in the centreline of the engine above each end of the crankcase. Air cooler at supercharger outlets, housed above the middle of the crankcase, and crossed by a special waterline.

The PA5 engine has successfully run 100 hours UIC tests (12 PA5 V).

PA6B-280 Series

Type: 6 and 8 cylinders in-line, 12 cylinders Vee, supercharged, water-cooled.

Cylinders: Bore 280 mm. Stroke 330 mm. Swept volume 20.3 litres per cylinder. Wet liners directly mounted in the crankcase, with cooling jackets. Individual cast-iron cylinder heads. Single combustion chamber. Direct injection.

Fuel injection: Direct injection by means of injectors of the multihole type. Individual injecting pump housed in the crankcase, directly controlled by the camshafts. Injection controlled by hydraulic speed governor.

Turbochargers: Driven by a turbine on the exhaust gas, and housed above the end of the crankcase.

Air cooler at supercharger outlets, housed above the middle of the crankcase and crossed by a special waterline.

Cooling: Two water pumps of the centrifugal type, driven by the timing train, one for jacket and cylinder head line, the other for air cooler and lube oil line.

360 hour UIC test

The 12-cylinder 12PA6V-280 engine has officially run its 360 hour UIC locomotive test in accordance with ORE regulations.

UPDATED

SM

Strömungsmaschinen GmbH
Power Transmission Division
Königsbrücker Strasse 96, PO Box 100508, D-01075 Dresden, Germany
Tel: +49 351 599 3413   Fax: +49 351 599 3207

Key personnel
Managing Director: Dr Ing Carl Woebeken
Managing Director, Power Transmission Division: Jürgen Theimer

Manager, Rail Systems Division:
Dr Ing Reinhard Kernchen

Products
Hydrodynamic power transmissions for diesel locomotives and diesel railcars. Over 8,800 units are installed in 16 countries. Features of the transmissions are: fully automatic working; infinitely variable torque and speed adjustment; vibration damping and shock reduction; and hydrodynamic braking for hydrodynamic reversing transmissions.

SM offers a wide range of transmissions with a nominal output of between 100 and 1,050 kW. The company has recently specialised in the repair and overhaul of hydrodynamic locomotive transmissions produced by other manufacturers.

SM offers an international servicing and technical consultancy service for retrofit programmes for diesel locomotive and railcar drive systems.

VERIFIED

TSM

Technical Service and Marketing Inc
10765 Ambassador Drive, Kansas City, Missouri 64153, USA
Tel: +1 816 891 6544   Fax: +1 816 891 9329

Key personnel
Vice-President & General Manager: Albert C Lundstrom

President: Douglas D Klink
Vice-President, Sales: John H Chionchio
Administrator, Marketing & Sales: Mark W Heinz

Corporate developments
In 1996 TSM was acquired by Rockwell International. TSM remains an independent company within the Railroad Electronics Division of Rockwell International.

Products
Microprocessor-based control and monitoring systems for diesel locomotives including temperature sensing and cooling control systems, electronic fuel gauges and fuel-management monitors. Distributed power locomotive control systems.

UPDATED

Tülomsas

The Locomotive and Motor Corporation of Turkey
Ahmet Kanatli Cad, TR-26490 Eskisehir, Turkey
Tel: +90 222 234 8130   Fax: +90 222 231 7944

Key personnel
See entry in *Locomotives and powered passenger vehicles* section

Products
Diesel engines with outputs of 1,865, 2,200 and 2,400 hp.

VERIFIED

Turbomeca

F-64511 Bordes, France
Tel: +33 5 59 12 50 00   Fax: +33 5 59 53 15 12

Key personnel
President: Sonia Meton
Executive Vice-President: Jean-Bernard Cocheteux
Executive Vice-President: Jean-Louis Chenard

Subsidiary
Turbomeca Engine Corporation
2709 Forum Drive, Grand Prairie, Texas 75052, USA
Tel: +1 214 641 6645

Products
There are two turbines currently being marketed for railway use. The first is the Makila TM-1600. This engine is used for both traction motor drive as well as direct propulsion. The TM-1600 has a speed of 6,500 rpm and a power output of 1,050 kW (1,600 hp). It is a two-shaft engine and weighs 410 kg with a length of 1,850 mm.

The Astazou is a single-shaft 1,500 rpm engine with an output of 450 hp and 330 kW. It measures 1,500 mm and weighs 300 kg. It is used for running hotel power.

VERIFIED

Twiflex

Twiflex Ltd
104 The Green, Twickenham TW2 5AQ, UK
Tel: +44 181 894 1161   Fax: +44 181 894 6056

Key personnel
Managing Director: John Starbuck
Sales Director: Alan Hughes

Products
Layrub and Laylink flexible shafts and couplings; industrial and marine disc brakes and Flexi-clutch couplings.

Both Layrub and Laylink couplings incorporate compressed cylindrical rubber blocks. The Laylink coupling carries these blocks in links, while the Layrub coupling carries them in a carrying plate. The use of these couplings and flexible shafts allows large amounts of angular and axial misalignment to be accommodated; it also absorbs shock, controls vibrations and simplifies close coupling in confined spaces. The units need no servicing or lubrication and can cater for very high operating speeds and transmission of high power without loss.

Recent contracts include the supply of Layrub double couplings for light rail vehicles for MTA Baltimore, USA; Layrub shafts for Thailand State Railways railbuses; and centrifugal clutch couplings and airstart clutches for Plasser track maintenance machines.

VERIFIED

Twin Disc

Twin Disc Incorporated
1328 Racine Street, Racine, Wisconsin 53403, USA
Tel: +1 414 638 4000   Fax: +1 414 638 4482

Key personnel
Sales Manager: J Kearney
Vice-President, Europe (Belgium): Ph Pecriaux

Principal subsidiaries
Twin Disc International SA, Chaussée de Namur 54, B-1400 Nivelles, Belgium

Tel: +1 32 67 887211   Fax: +1 32 67 887333

Twin Disc (Pacific) Pty Ltd, PO Box 442, Virginia, Queensland 4014, Australia
Tel: +61 7 265 1200   Fax: +61 7 865 1371

Twin Disc (South Africa) Pty Ltd, PO Box 40542, Cleveland 2022, South Africa
Tel: +27 11 626 2714   Fax: +27 11 626 2717

Twin Disc (Far East) Ltd, PO Box 155, Jurong Town Post Office, Singapore 9161
Tel: +65 261 8909   Fax: +65 264 2080

Products
Universal joints; hydraulic torque converters, power shift transmissions and controls suitable for locomotives and railcars.

VERIFIED

UCM Resita

Uzina de Constructii de Masini Resita SA
1 Golului Street, R-1700 Resita, Romania
Tel: +40 55 211577   Fax: +40 55 220113

Key personnel
General Manager: Enache Barbu
Commercial Manager: Emil Toth

Products
High-speed diesel engines from 500 to 4,500 hp per unit; spare parts for R251, LDS/LDSR and Alco 251 engines; refurbishment of R251 and Alco 251 engines.

Recent contracts include the overhaul of 50 diesel engines for Romanian National Railways and the supply of spare parts. Spares for R251 engines have been supplied to Iranian Railways.

LDS/LDSR series engines

	6	12	12
No of cylinders	6	12	12
Compression ratio		11.25 to 1	
rpm range		350 - 750	
Max, full load (HP)	1,250	2,100	2,500
Bore & stroke (mm)		280 × 360	
Displacement (dm³)	133	266	266
Turbocharged	Yes	Yes	Yes
Aftercooled	Yes	No	Yes
Fuel system type	Mech.	Mech.	Mech.
Heat dissipation rate			
Oil (kcal/Hp.min)	1.3	1.8	1.3
Water (kcal/Hp.min)	5.6	4.4	5.6
Starting system	*	**	**
Cum/start, average	7	7	7
Pressure range (bar)		6-10	
Weight - dry (tons)	10.5	28.0	29.3
- wet (tons)	11.3	29.5	30.8

Notes: * Based on Sulzer licence. External, traction generator or dyna-starter. Air motor on special request. ** DC generator included. Engine start by DC generator. Air motor on special request.

R 251 series engines

No of cylinders	4	6	8	12	16	18
rpm range	400-1,100	400-1,100	400-1,000	400-1,100	400-1,100	400-1,100
Max, full load (HP)	500-750	700-1,520	1,000-1,720	1,500-3,040	1,900-3,960	2,600-4,560
Compression ratio			(12.5) 11.5 to 1			
Bore & stroke (mm)			228 × 267			
Displacement (dm³)	43.8	65.7	87.6	131.4	175.2	197.1
Turbocharged	Yes	Yes	Yes	Yes	Yes	Yes
Aftercooled	Yes	Yes	Yes	Yes	Yes	Yes
Fuel system type	Mech	Mech	Mech	Mech	Mech	Mech
Heat dissipation rate						
Oil (kcal/Hp.min)	1.2	1.2	1.2	1.2	1.2	1.2
Water (kcal/Hp.min)	5.5	5.5	5.5	5.5	5.5	5.5
Starting system		air motor	—		air motor	
Cum/start, average	7	7	7	7	7	7
Pressure range (bar)			6-10			
Weight - dry (tons)	8.6	11.2	12.0	14.7	19.3	22.2
- wet (tons)	9.4	12.0	12.7	15.5	21.0	24.5

Note: Based on Alco licence. MDO operation also available.

UPDATED

Unipar

Unipar Inc
7210 Polson Lane, Hazelwood, Missouri 63042, USA
Tel: +1 314 521 8100   Fax: +1 314 521 8052

Key personnel
Executive Vice-President: Dennis McClure
Sales Manager: Mark Cleveland

Products
New and remanufactured replacement power assemblies for GM/EMD locomotives. Component parts for Alco, GE and GM locomotives.

Recent contracts include the supply of parts to CN North America (Grand Trunk), Union Pacific, Conrail, Southern Pacific, CSX Transportation, Wisconsin Central, Pakistan Railways and Egyptian Railways.

UPDATED

Voith Turbo

Voith Turbo GmbH
PO Box 1940, D-89509 Heidenheim/Brenz, Germany
Tel: +49 7321 370   Fax: +49 7321 37 7603

Key personnel
Managing Director:
  Dr Günter Armbruster
Railway Division Manager:
  Dr Hermann Bruns
Sales and Application Manager:
  Karl-Otto Dahler

UK Subsidiary
Voith Engineering Ltd
6 Beddington Farm Road, Croydon CR0 4XB, UK
Tel: +44 181 667 0333   Fax: +44 181 667 0403
Manager, Rail Products: A L Morris

Products
Hydrodynamic transmissions and retarders, torque converters and automatic hydromechanical transmissions. Final drive reduction gearboxes for mechanical or electrical drives in locomotives, metro cars and light rail vehicles. DIWA hydromechanical transmissions for light rail vehicles. Limited-slip differential device for metro cars and light rail vehicles.

Voith automatic hydrodynamic transmissions are designed specifically for installation in rail vehicles. The basic components are drainable hydraulic torque converters and fluid couplings, which in combination provide tractive effort over a wide speed range in an efficient and cost-effective manner. The filling characteristics ensure wear-free, smooth shifting without interruption of tractive effort. Turbo-reversing transmissions used in shunting locomotives extend the principle to allow direction shifting in a similar manner. All non-reversing turbo transmissions can be fitted with a wear-free retarder.

Voith final drives are available in bevel and spur gear configurations, from axle-hung drives to bogie or body-suspended quill-shaft drives, with single or double reduction.

Voith is offering a new type of cardan shaft specially designed for high-performance rail and mechanical engineering applications. The new shaft is designated SM and is available with flange diameters of 225, 250, 285, 315 and 350 mm.

Recent contracts include the supply of T312br transmissions for Class VT612 tilting diesel trainsets for DB AG; T311r transmissions for the new Finnish railcars as well as orders for the T211rzze transmissions and KB190 retarders for the new IC2 railcars for RENFE Spain. Other contracts include 20 L2r4seU2 turbo reversing transmissions for DSB shunting locos; 10 L3r4 turbo-reversing transmissions supplied to Krauss-Maffei for locos operated by Eisenbahn and Hafen, Duisburg. Orders have been received for final drive reduction units for ET425 and 426 S-Bahn emus, IC3 power cars and LRVs for Salt Lake City, and transformer and inverter oil cooling units for Class BR145 locomotives for DB AG.

UPDATED

Volvo Penta

Volvo Penta AB
S-405 08 Gothenburg, Sweden
Tel: +46 31 235460   Fax: +46 31 510597

Key personnel
Managing Director: J Walldorf
Railway Manager: L Ahlberg

Products
Diesel engines and transmissions.

Volvo Penta engines are the power units in the 'Cargosprinter' Windhoff freight dmu, now in operation with DB Germany. Each power car has two Rail Pac engines, the front one driving the rear axle of the front powered bogie and the engine at the rear driving the front axle of the rear bogie. Each Rail Pac comprises a Volvo DH10A360 engine rated at 265 kW, at 2,050 rpm, and meeting Euro-2 regulations. The drive is through a Volvo Powertronic Pt 1650 five-speed automatic gearbox which includes converter and retarder as well as electronic torque limiter.

UPDATED

Volvo Penta DH10A-360 diesel engine, four of which power each freight dmu   **1997**

ZF

ZF Friedrichshafen AG
D-88038 Friedrichshafen, Germany
Tel: +49 7541 770   Fax: +49 7541 772948

Key personnel
Chief Executive Officer, Marketing: Dr Klaus Bleyer

Subsidiaries
ZF Hurth Bahntechnik GmbH
Adelheidstrasse 40, D-88046 Freidrichschafen, Germany
Tel: +49 7541 30601   Fax: +49 7541 306400

ZF Great Britain Ltd
Abbeyfield Road, Lenton, Nottingham NG7 2SX, UK
Tel: +44 115 986 9211   Fax: +44 115 986 9261

Products
Drives for rail vehicles.

UPDATED

ZF Padova

ZF Padova SpA
Via Penghe N 48, I-35030 Caselle di Selvazzano Dentro, Padua, Italy
Tel: +39 49 829 9311   Fax: +39 49 829 9550/9560/9570

Key personnel
President: H G Harter
Managing Director: Ing Francesco Petilli
Product Manager: Adriano Giuriati

Parent company
ZF AG, Germany

Products
Traction gears, special gearboxes. ZF Padova designs and manufactures case-hardened ground gears for rail transmissions with profile correction for long life and smooth running.

The company has developed computer programs for calculation and projecting custom-engineered gears. ZF Padova is currently supplying traction gears for Class

E444, E633, E652 and E656 locomotives for Italian Railways; traction gears for ETR 500 high-speed trains for Italian Railways; and ground bevel gears for ETR 460 (Italian Railways) and IC NeiTec (DB AG) tilting trainsets.

UPDATED

ELECTRIC TRACTION EQUIPMENT

Alphabetical Listing

3M Germany
Adtranz
A K Fans
Ansaldo Trasporti
BHEL
Brecknell, Willis
Brush
Cenemesa
ČKD
Clyde
Daewoo
EAO
EFACEC
EG & G
Elin

Entrelec
Faiveley Transport
Ferraz
FIREMA Trasporti
Fuji Electric
Ganz Ansaldo
GEC Alsthom
GEC Plessey
Hamworthy
Hitachi
Holec Ridderkerk
Hyundai
Kiepe Elektrik
Merlin Gerin Brasil
Mitsubishi Electric
Morio Denki
National

Normalair-Garrett Limited
Pafawag
Parizzi
Permali
RDS Technology Ltd
Sécheron
Siemens
Siemens Electric
Siemens Transportation
SMC
SPII
Stemmann
Toshiba
Toyo Denki
Transportation Products
Tülomsas
Westinghouse Electric

Classified Listing

CONTROL EQUIPMENT, CONVERTERS AND TRANSFORMERS

Adtranz
Ansaldo Trasporti
BHEL
Brush
ČKD
Daewoo
EAO
EFACEC
Elin
Entrelec
FIREMA Trasporti
Fuji Electric
Ganz Ansaldo
GEC Alsthom
GEC Plessey
Hitachi
Holec Ridderkerk
Hyundai
Kiepe Elektrik
Merlin Gerin Brasil
Mitsubishi Electric
Morio Denki
Normalair-Garrett Limited
Parizzi
Sécheron

Siemens
Siemens Electric
Siemens Transportation
SPII
Toshiba
Toyo Denki
Transportation Products
Tülomsas
Westinghouse Electric

COOLING SYSTEMS

3M Germany
A K Fans
EG & G

CURRENT COLLECTION EQUIPMENT

Brecknell, Willis
Faiveley Transport
Ferraz
Fuji Electric
Hamworthy
Normalair-Garrett Limited
Pafawag
Permali
Siemens
SMC
Stemmann
Toyo Denki

TRACTION MOTORS AND TRANSMISSIONS

Adtranz Ansaldo Trasporti
BHEL
Brush
Cenemesa
ČKD
Clyde
Daewoo
EFACEC
EG & G
Elin
FIREMA Trasporti
Fuji Electric
Ganz Ansaldo
GEC Alsthom
Holec Ridderkerk
Hyundai
Mitsubishi Electric
National
Siemens
Siemens Transportation
Toshiba
Toyo Denki
Tülomsas
Westinghouse Electric

LOOK CAREFULLY, ONE PREMIER PARTNER
CAN HIDE ANOTHER

A global concept of programmed protection for a traction network's integrated management

This other partner is never seen. But he is there alright, protecting fixed and mobile rail installations and guaranteeing the safety and comfort of their passengers and operators.

Sécheron is this iron partner in a velvet glove, present on railways throughout the world.

- *Traction components and their electronic peripherals*
- *Measuring and recording systems*
- *DC traction substations.*

And if Sécheron has become the partner of choice of the largest manufacturers of electric public-transport vehicles on the five continents it is also because exactitude does not exclude flexibility. Sécheron responds rapidly and unerringly to every challenge, so that any problem is transformed into progress.

Technology Designed for Performance

Head Office:
Sécheron Ltd. PO Box 116
CH- 1211 Geneva 21
Switzerland

Tel: +4122 / 739 41 11
Fax: +4122 / 738 73 05
Telex: 412 268 sech ch

Key personnel

See entry in *Locomotives and powered passenger vehicles* section

Products

Passenger cars. Recent contracts have included 22 couchette cars for Spanish National Railways (RENFE).

VERIFIED

BEML

Bharat Earth Movers Ltd
BEML Soudha, 23/1 4th Main, SR Nagar,
Bangalore 560 027, India
Tel: +91 80 222 4141   Fax: +91 80 222 6883

Works

Bangalore Complex, New Thippasandra, Bangalore 560 075, India
Tel: +91 80 222 2414   Fax: +91 80 222 5545

Key personnel

Chairman and Managing Director: Dr K Aprameyan
Chief General Manager: A Maruthachalam
General Manager, Research and Development:
   T Prabhakar Rao

Products

Lightweight passenger coaches of integral welded steel construction of all types including sleeper coaches, day travel coaches, postal vans, parcel vans, brake and luggage vans and motor-cum-parcel vans.

The division has supplied over 12,000 coaches of different types for Indian Railways. Coaches have also been exported to Bangladesh and Sri Lanka.

UPDATED

BN

BN Division of Bombardier Eurorail
Avenue Louise 65, B-1050 Brussels, Belgium
Tel: +32 2 535 5511   Fax: +32 2 539 0428

Key personnel

See entry in *Locomotives and powered passenger vehicles* section

Products

Passenger coaches (single- and double-deck), trailer vehicles for high-speed trainsets.

Recent contracts include 163 Type I11 coaches for SNCB; and assembly and testing of 85 trailers for THALYS (Paris–Brussels–Cologne–Amsterdam) high-speed trainsets.

UPDATED

Bombardier

Bombardier Inc
Transportation Equipment Group — North America
1101 Parent Street, Saint-Bruno, ,
Québec J3V 6E6, Canada
Tel: +1 514 441 2020   Fax: +1 514 441 1515

Bi-level commuter car for Coaster Line in San Diego by Bombardier   1997

Push-pull commuter Comet IV car for New Jersey Transit by Bombardier   1997

Key personnel

See entry in *Locomotives and powered passenger vehicles* section

Products

Passenger coaches for suburban and intercity applications.

Orders include 67 Comet IV push-pull commuter cars for New Jersey Transit, USA; 26 bi-level commuter cars for the SCRRA Metrolink in Los Angeles, California, USA; five bi-level commuter cars for Tri-Rail, Florida, USA; 34 push-pull commuter cars for Metro-North, New York, USA; bi-level commuter cars for the Vancouver West Coast Express service; bi-level commuter car for Coaster Line in San Diego and 195 bi-level Superliner II Cars for Amtrak, USA.

UPDATED

Bi-level commuter car for Vancouver West Coast Express by Bombardier   1997

Breda

Breda Costruzioni Ferroviarie SpA
Via Ciliegiole 110b, I-51100 Pistoia, Italy
Tel: +39 573 3701   Fax: + 39 573 370292

Key personnel

See entry in *Locomotives and powered passenger vehicles* section

Products

Stainless steel, carbon steel and aluminium alloy passenger coaches.

Contracts include Z1-type coaches for Italian Railways (FS); amenity coaches for Eurotunnel; panoramic coaches for BVZ, FO and MOB, Switzerland; trailer vehicles for ETR 500 high-speed trainsets for FS; and double-deck emu trailer cars for FS and North Milan Railway.

VERIFIED

BN Type I11 coach for SNCB   1995

CAF

Construcciones y Auxiliar de Ferrocarriles SA
Padilla 17, E-28006 Madrid, Spain
Tel: +34 1 435 2500   Fax: +34 1 276 6263

Key personnel
See entry in *Locomotives and powered passenger vehicles* section

Products
Passenger coaches, including saloon and compartment vehicles, sleeper cars and restaurant cars. Equipped with GC-type bogies, coaches feature air conditioning, public address systems, fire detection systems, showers and vacuum toilets.
    Contracts include supply of coaches for the Heathrow Express project, UK.

VERIFIED

CFC

Costruzioni Ferroviarie Colleferro SpA
A member of the Fiat Group
Via Sabotino, I-00034 Colleferro, Rome, Italy
Tel: +39 6 978 1280   Fax: +39 6 978 2746

Key personnel
President: Dr C Giancarlo
Delegate Administrator: Ing L Basta
Technical Director: Ing V Travaglini
Project Officer: Ing G Clementi
Production Officer: PI F Cherubini
Production Officer: Ing A Rigon
Import/Export Officer: Rag V Nobilio

Products
Passenger cars, freight cars, refrigerated wagons and containers.

VERIFIED

Changchun Railway Car Works

5 Qingyin Road, Changchun, Jilin, People's Republic of China
Tel: +86 431 790 2380   Fax: +86 431 293 8740

Key personnel
See entry in *Locomotives and powered passenger vehicles* section

Products
Single- and double-deck passenger coaches; lightweight coaches for high-speed (160 km/h) operation, sleeping cars. Passenger coach repairs.

VERIFIED

China National Railway Locomotive & Rolling Stock Industry Corporation (LORIC)

10 Fu Xing Road, Beijing,
10844 People's Republic of China
Tel: +86 10 6351 1620/6351 7766
Fax: +86 10 6351 1614/6326 0830

Other works addresses
Changchun Railway Car Works (qv)

Tangshan Locomotive & Rolling Stock Works
3 Changqian Road, Tangshan New District, Tangshan 063035, Hebei, China
Tel: +86 315 324 1912   Fax: +86 315 324 2939

Sifang Locomotive & Rolling Stock Works (see *Locomotives and powered passenger vehicles* section)

Nanjing Puzhen Rolling Stock Works
5 Longhu Lane, Puzhen, Nanjing 210032, China
Tel: +86 25 885 2424   Fax: +86 25 885 2655

Key personnel
See entry in *Locomotives and powered passenger vehicles* section

LORIC RW25G soft sleeping car   *1997*

LORIC double-deck soft seating car   *1997*

Products
Passenger, sleeping, dining and double-deck car design, production and refurbishment.
    Production figures from 1986 to 1995 for China Railways are put at 18,362, most for 1,435 mm gauge. Metre-gauge coaches have been supplied to Myanmar and Malaysia and 30 1,067 mm coaches have been supplied to Tanzania. Myanmar received 40, ten being first-class.
    Other contracts include 48 double-deck passenger cars for Iran and 50 second-class cars for Nigeria.

UPDATED

Costamasnaga

Costamasnaga SpA
Viale IV Novembre 2, I-22041 Costamasnaga Como, Italy
Tel: +39 31 869411   Fax: +39 31 855330

Key personnel
General Manager: Fabio Magni
Technical Director: Sandro Maluta
Commercial Director: Giuliano Felten

Corporate developments
A new company, Costaferroviaria SpA, has been formed to carry on the railway activity of Costamasnaga SpA.

Products
Passenger coaches.
    Recent contracts include delivery of 20 Type A sleeping cars for FS Italy. The cars have innovative features including onboard diagnostics, security cameras and passenger-conductor phones. They are mounted on FW bogies, fitted with a third disc brake and are suitable for 200 km/h running.
    FS has also ordered 35 UIC-Zi driving trailers for delivery starting in 1998.
    Other contracts have included supply of three amenity coaches for Eurotunnel, UK.

UPDATED

Daewoo

Daewoo Heavy Industries Ltd
PO Box 7955, Daewoo Centre Building 23rd Fl, 541, 5-GA, Namdaemun-Ro, Jung-Gu, Seoul, South Korea
Tel: +82 2 726 3181
Fax: +82 2 726 3186/726 3307

Key personnel
See entry in *Locomotives and powered passenger vehicles* section

Products
Passenger coaches.
    Recent deliveries include 196 passenger coaches for Korean National Railroad in 1996/7 and 40 day and night coaches to SRT Thailand.

UPDATED

Stainless steel coaches for State Railway of Thailand from Daewoo   *1996*

De Dietrich Ferroviaire

PO Box 35, F-67891 Niederbronn Cedex, France
Tel: +33 3 88 80 25 00   Fax: +33 3 88 80 25 12
Email: ddf@dx-net.fr.

Key personnel
See entry in *Locomotives and powered passenger vehicles* section

Products
Passenger coaches in high-yield strength steel or aluminium.

Recent contracts include the supply of TGV-Réseau trailers to SNCF; Eurostar passenger saloons with powered bogies for EPS/SNCB/SNCF; 34 end trailers for TGV high-speed trainsets for Korea (South), with technology transfer; double-deck TGV-Duplex trailers in aluminium with shock-absorbing structures for SNCF; 28 passenger coaches for Northern Ireland Railways/Iarnród Éireann.

Astra (qv) has delivered the first 200 km/h coaches to SNCFR Romania. They have been constructed within a technology transfer contract for which De Dietrich has adapted Corail coaches and supplied other expertise.

UPDATED

Duro Daković

Duro Daković Industries
(Railway Vehicles Factory Ltd)
PO Box 94, 55102 Slavonski Brod, Croatia
Tel: +385 55 241926/232189   Fax: +385 55 232454

Key personnel
See entry in *Locomotives and powered passenger vehicles* section

Products
Passenger coaches.

VERIFIED

DWA

Deutsche Waggonbau Aktiengesellschaft
Kablower Weg 89, D-12526 Berlin, Germany
Tel +49 30 67930   Fax: +49 30 674 4560

Key personnel
Board Chairman: Peter Witt
Board Members: Christian Göbel, Walter Grawenhoff, Siegfried Möbius, Harald Pahl

Works
Ammendorf (Halle), Bautzen, Görlitz, Niesky and Vetschau, Germany

Principal subsidiary
Fahrzeugausrüstung Berlin GmbH
Wolfener Strasse 23, D-12681 Berlin, Germany
Tel: +49 30 936420   Fax: +49 30 936 42302

Research and Development
Institut für Schienenfahrzeuge GmbH
Adlergestell 598, D-12527 Berlin, Germany
Tel: +49 30 6793 2200   Fax: +49 30 6793 2222

Corporate structure
Advent International, an investment firm based in Boston (USA), is a shareholder in DWA.

Products
Non-powered passenger vehicles.

Deliveries include 63 new and 15 reconditioned passenger coaches for the Russian Federation; 31 passenger coaches for Mongolia; 40 trailer vehicles for ICE-2.1 high-speed trainsets for DB AG; 63 double-deck coaches and 51 double-deck driving trailers for DB AG; 34 trailer cars for BR611 regional tilting dmus for DB AG and three RIC sleeping cars for Ukraine.

Recent contracts include an additional order for 30 trailer cars for DB ICE-2 trainsets; 142 cars for ET481 emus for S Bahn Berlin; an additional order for 60 trailers for BR611 regional tilting dmus; three second-class passenger coaches for DB; 142 double-deck coaches; 53 double-deck driving trailers for DB; 10 RIC sleeping cars for ZSR Slovakia and 18 ICT tilting trainsets for DB.

UPDATED

First class interior of coach for Ireland, by De Dietrich Ferroviaire   **1997**

TGV Thalys end trailer by De Dietrich Ferroviaire   **1997**

DWA double-deck train with driving trailer in service with DB   **1997**

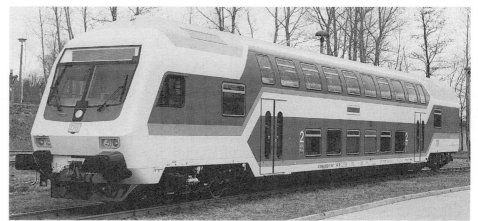

DWA double-deck driving trailer for DB AG   **1995**

Energomachexport

25A Protopopovsky per, 129010 Moscow, Russian Federation
Tel: +7 095 288 8456/6983   Fax: +7 095 288 7990/6983
Email: in@eme.tsr.ru

Key personnel
See entry in *Bogies and suspensions, wheels and axles* section

Products
Metro cars

UPDATED

Ferrostaal

Ferrostaal AG
PO Box, Hohenzollernstrasse 24,
D-45116 Essen, Germany
Tel: +49 201 81801   Fax: +49 201 818 2822

Key personnel
See entry in *Locomotives and powered passenger vehicles* section

Products
Passenger coaches including special designs; inspection and service trolleys for track and overhead maintenance and track installation; motor and trailer bogies for freight wagons, passenger coaches, locomotives, railcars; rolling stock components such as wheels, axles, assembled wheelsets, bearings, suspensions, couplers and electrical equipment.

VERIFIED

Fiat

Fiat Ferroviaria SpA
Piazza Galateri 4, I-12038 Savigliano (CN), Italy
Tel: +39 172 718333   Fax: +39 172 718306

Key personnel
See entry in *Locomotives and powered passenger vehicles* section

Products
Passenger coaches (sleeping cars, self-service cars, restaurant coaches, saloon cars, TEE coaches).

VERIFIED

FIREMA

FIREMA Trasporti SpA
Viale Edison 110, I-20099 Sesto S Giovanni (Milano), Italy
Tel: +39 2 249 4396   Fax: +39 2 248 3508

Key personnel
See entry in *Locomotives and powered passenger vehicles* section

Products
Passenger coaches.

Recent orders for Italian Railways (FS) include 23 Type UICZ second-class passenger coaches, 171 trailer vehicles in light alloy for ETR 500 high-speed trainsets and 32 double-deck emu trailers in light alloy.

UPDATED

Fuji Car

Fuji Car Manufacturing Company Ltd
3 Shoho Building, 2-2-3 Nishishinsaibashi, Chuo-ku, Osaka 542, Japan
Tel: +81 6 213 2711   Fax: +81 6 213 4071

Key personnel
See entry in *Locomotives and powered passenger vehicles* section

Products
Passenger cars.

VERIFIED

Fuji Heavy Industries

Fuji Heavy Industries Ltd
Transport Equipment Division
7-2 Subaru Building, Nishishinjuku 1-chome, Shinjyuku-ku, Tokyo 160, Japan
Tel: +81 3 3347 2436   Fax: +81 3 3347 2117

Key personnel
See entry in *Locomotives and powered passenger vehicles* section

Products
Passenger coaches; works vehicles.

VERIFIED

Ganz-Hunslet

Ganz-Hunslet Részvénytársaság
PO Box 29, H-1430 Budapest, Hungary
Tel: +36 1 210 1177/313 0887   Fax: +36 1 210 1175/210 1180
Sales office: +36 1 210 1173

Key personnel
See entry in *Locomotives and powered passenger vehicles* section

Products
Passenger coaches, trailer vehicles for electric multiple-units.

Recent contracts include the supply of a total of 40 commuter coaches to Hungarian State Railways (MÁV), for operation as locomotive-hauled stock or as part of an electric trainset.

UPDATED

Ganz-Hunslet commuter car for MÁV

GEC Alsthom

GEC Alsthom Transport Division
48 rue Albert Dhalenne, F-93482
Saint Ouen Cedex, France
Tel: +33 1 41 66 90 00   Fax: +33 1 41 66 96 66

Key personnel
See entry in *Locomotives and powered passenger vehicles* section

Products
All types of passenger rolling stock and related equipment, including metro cars, suburban and interurban trainsets, double-deck coaches.

UPDATED

GEC Alsthom

GEC Alsthom Metro-Cammell Limited
PO Box 248, Leigh Road, Washwood Heath, Birmingham B8 2YJ, UK
Tel: +44 121 328 5455   Fax: +44 121 327 6430

Key personnel
Managing Director: P J Murray

Products
Main contracting and engineering for the supply of high-speed trainsets, multiple-units, rapid transit and metro cars and passenger coaches.

VERIFIED

GEC Alsthom

GEC Alsthom Transporte SA
Via de las Dos Castillas 33, Edificio 7 2a Planta,
E-28224 Pozuelo de Alarcón, Madrid, Spain
Tel: +34 1 352 8640   Fax: +34 1 352 9978

Key personnel
See entry in *Locomotives and powered passenger vehicles* section

Products
Passenger coaches.

Contracts include a second order to supply Israeli Ports & Railways Authority with a further order for 17 coaches. The two orders cover 31 coaches and six power cars. The trains are for the Tel Aviv to Haifa line and will run at a commercial speed of 160 km/h. Each coach will carry up to 86 passengers. The coaches, of stainless-steel construction, will come from the Barcelona factory and the bodies will be assembled at Valencia.

UPDATED

Goninan

A Goninan & Co Ltd
PO Box 3300, Hamilton,
New South Wales 2303, Australia
Tel: +61 49 235000   Fax: +61 49 238501

Key personnel
See entry in *Locomotives and powered passenger vehicles* section

Products
Passenger coaches and passenger coach refurbishment.

Recent contracts include the refurbishment of 408 double-deck passenger coaches for State Railway Authority of New South Wales, Australia and conversion of 472 tramcars to driver-only operation (including installation of automatic fare collection equipment) for Victoria Public Transport Corporation and the refurbishment of 115 trams for VPTC Melbourne.

UPDATED

Hanjin

Hanjin Heavy Industries Co Ltd
118 Namdaemun ro-2-Ga, Chung-Ku, Seoul, South Korea
Tel: +82 2 728 5441/5420
Fax: +82 2 755 0928/756 5455

Hanjin high-speed passenger coach for China **1997**

Key personnel

See entry in *Locomotives and powered passenger vehicles* section

Products

Passenger coaches including sleeping cars, dining cars and generator vans.

Recent contracts include the supply of 30 high-speed passenger coaches for P R China on the Guangzhou to Hong Kong line, up to 200 km/h. Over the past five years 135 coaches have been delivered to Korean National Railroad.

UPDATED

Hoogovens-VAW

VAW Aluminium AG
Georg-von-Boeselager-Strasse 25,
D-53117 Bonn 1, Germany
Tel: +49 228 55202   Fax: +49 228 552 2268

Key personnel

See entry in *Locomotives and powered passenger vehicles* section

Products

More than 30 years of experience in designing lightweight aluminium extrusions for short- and long-distance passenger traffic rolling stock. Production of large aluminium extrusions up to 650 mm wide as well as fully automatic MIG-welding of extrusions up to 30 m long and 2.8 m wide.

VERIFIED

Hyundai

Hyundai Precision & Ind Company Ltd
Hyundai Building, 140-2, Gye-Dong, Chongro-ku,
Seoul, South Korea
Tel: +82 2 719 0649   Fax: +82 2 719 0741

Works

85 Daewon-Dong, Changwon, Kyungnam, South Korea
Tel: +82 551 82 1341

Key personnel

See entry in *Locomotives and powered passenger vehicles* section

Products

Passenger coaches.

VERIFIED

ICF

The Integral Coach Factory
Perambur, Madras 600 038, India
Tel: +91 44 661091   Fax: +91 44 6261829

Key personnel

See entry in *Locomotives and powered passenger vehicles* section

Products

Air conditioned sleeper and chair cars; pantry cars; metro cars; tourist cars; coaches for intercity express trains; track recording cars; power cars; and double-deckers.

VERIFIED

Jenbacher

Jenbacher Energiesysteme AG
Achenseestrasse 1-3, A-6200 Jenbach, Austria
Tel: +43 5244 6000   Fax: +43 5244 63255
Web: http//www.jenbacher.com

Key personnel

See entry in *Locomotives and powered passenger vehicles* section

Products

Development, design, production and sales of passenger coaches for long- and short-distance traffic. Airtight, air conditioned second-class open saloon coaches equipped with enclosed vacuum lavatories and designed for a maximum speed of 200 km/h have been delivered to Austrian Federal Railways.

UPDATED

Jessop

Jessop & Company Ltd, Calcutta
63 Netaji Subhas Road, Calcutta 700,001, India
Tel: +91 33 243 2041/3420   Fax: +91 33 243 1610

Key personnel

See entry in *Locomotives and powered passenger vehicles* section

Products

Passenger coaches.

Contracts include nine first-class tourist coaches for DSVN Vietnam delivered in January 1996 and 72 bogie coaches for Vietnam in 1996.

UPDATED

Kawasaki

Kawasaki Heavy Industries Ltd
World Trade Center Building, 4-1 Hamamatsu-cho
2-chome, Minato-ku, Tokyo 105, Japan
Tel: +81 3 3435 2588   Fax: +81 3 3435 2157/3436 3037

Key personnel

See entry in *Locomotives and powered passenger vehicles* section

Products

Passenger coaches.

Recent contracts include 114 bi-level coaches for Long Island Rail Road Co, 50 for Maryland Mass Transit Administration and 17 bi-level coaches for Massachusetts Bay Transportation Authority, USA. Delivery is expected to be completed by 1998

UPDATED

Keller

Keller SpA
Via Francesco Guardione 3, I-90139 Palermo, Italy
Tel: +39 91 586322   Fax: +39 91 582784/6114967

Key personnel

Chairman: Dr Ing Giovanni Salatiello
Managing Directors: Dr Maurizio Salatiello,
   Dr Alfonso De Simone, Dr Graziella Viale

Main works

Via Maltese 147/149, Palermo, Italy
Via della Ferrovia 2/A, Palermo, Italy
Via Ugo La Malfa 6, Palermo, Italy

Associated company

Keller Meccanica SpA, Villacidro, Cagliari, Italy

Products

Passenger coaches.

VERIFIED

Kinki Sharyo

The Kinki Sharyo Co Ltd
Kinki Rolling Stock Manufacturing Co Ltd
3-9-60 Inada-Shinmachi, Higashi-Osaka City,
Osaka 577, Japan
Tel: +81 6 746 5240   Fax: +81 6 745 5135
Email: krstan@kinsha.dp.u-netsurf.orjp

Key personnel

See entry in *Locomotives and powered passenger vehicles* section

Interior of Kinki Sharyo Series 283 driving trailer **1997**

Products

Passenger coaches.

Recent contracts include the supply of 12 double-deck passenger coaches to Kowloon—Canton Railway Corporation, Hong Kong.

UPDATED

Kolmex

Kolmex SA
Grzybowska 80/82, PL-00-844 Warsaw, Poland
Tel: +48 22 661 5000   Fax: +48 22 620 9381

Key personnel

See entry in *Locomotives and powered passenger vehicles* section

Products

Type Z1 and Type Z2 passenger coaches for operation up to 200 km/h and 160 km/h and railbuses, manufactured by Cegielski of Poznan and Pafawag of Wroclaw.

UPDATED

Linke-Hofmann-Busch

Linke-Hofmann-Busch GmbH
PO Box 411160, D-38233 Salzgitter, Germany
Tel: +49 5341 2105   Fax: +49 5341 213943

Key personnel

See entry in *Locomotives and powered passenger vehicles* section

Products

Passenger coaches.

Contracts include the supply of Bvmz 802 trailer cars for ICE high-speed trainsets and Bvmz 185 long-distance passenger coaches for DB AG.

VERIFIED

Materfer

Materfer SA
Juan Bautista Alberdi 1001, 1678 Caseros,
Provincia de Buenos Aires, Argentina
Tel: +54 1 750 4209/2251   Fax: +54 1 750 1476

Key personnel

See entry in *Locomotives and powered passenger vehicles* section

Products

Passenger coaches (with or without air conditioning); metro cars; mail vans.

VERIFIED

Mecanoexportimport

30 Dacia Boulevard, Bucharest, Romania
Tel: +40 1 211 9855   Fax: +40 1 210 7894

Key personnel

See entry in *Locomotives and powered passenger vehicles* section

Products

Passenger coaches.

VERIFIED

MSV

Moravskoslezská Vagónka as
Butovická ul, 74213 Studénka, Czech Republic
Tel: +42 655 47 1111/2201   Fax: +42 655 47 2000/2204
Email: jvyoralek@oasanet.cz

Key personnel

See entry in *Locomotives and powered passenger vehicles* section

Products

Passenger cars, trailers for railcars and multiple-units.

In co-operation with Siemens SGP, MSV is building high-speed coaches and dining cars. Other orders received include trailers and driving cabs for dmus and emus and refurbishment of trailers.

UPDATED

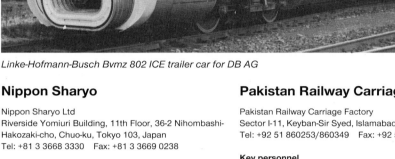

Linke-Hofmann-Busch Bvmz 802 ICE trailer car for DB AG

Nippon Sharyo

Nippon Sharyo Ltd
Riverside Yomiuri Building, 11th Floor, 36-2 Nihombashi-Hakozaki-cho, Chuo-ku, Tokyo 103, Japan
Tel: +81 3 3668 3330   Fax: +81 3 3669 0238

Key personnel

See entry in *Locomotives and powered passenger vehicles* section

Products

Passenger coaches.   *VERIFIED*

NWRZ

Novorossiysk Carriage Repair Works
Mihailova 1, 353906 Novorossiysk, Russian Federation
Tel: +7 861 345 2021   Fax: +7 861 342 4396

Key personnel

Director: Nikolai V Maltsev

Products

Passenger coach refurbishment, including catering vehicles and air conditioning systems. Spare parts manufacture.

Recent contracts include the refurbishment of passenger coaches in conjunction with DWA, Germany, and the retrofitting of lighting systems to passenger coaches in conjunction with FAGA, Germany.

VERIFIED

OFV

Officine Ferroviarie Veronesi SpA
Lungadige A Galtarossa 21, I-37133 Verona, Italy
Tel: +39 45 806 4111   Fax: +39 45 803 2876

Key personnel

President: Paolo Biasi
Technical Manager: Massimo Toniato
Sales Manager: Paolo Galbier

Products

Passenger coaches.

Recent contracts include medium-distance, long-distance and suburban passenger coaches for German Railways (DB AG) and Italian Railways (FS).

VERIFIED

Pafawag

Fabryka Wagonów Pafawag SP ZOO
ul Fabryczna 12, PL-53-609 Wroclaw, Poland
Tel: +48 71 552258/562111   Fax: +48 71 551289/554881

Key personnel

See entry in *Locomotives and powered passenger vehicles* section

Products

Passenger coaches.   *VERIFIED*

Pakistan Railway Carriage

Pakistan Railway Carriage Factory
Sector I-11, Keyban-Sir Syed, Islamabad, Pakistan
Tel: +92 51 860253/860349   Fax: +92 51 861550

Key personnel

Chairman: Mehboob Ahmed
Railway Board Member, Mechanical Engineering: Zia Ullah
Managing Director, Mechanical Works: B A Khan
Deputy Chief Mechanical Engineer: Asad Ahsan

Products

Passenger coaches.

The factory has produced over 1,600 passenger coaches, including 223 exported to Bangladesh.

VERIFIED

PEC

The Projects & Equipment Corporation of India Ltd
A Government of India Enterprise
Hansalaya, 15 Barakhamba Road,
New Delhi 110 001, India
Tel: +91 11 331 6372/3619/5508/3351/5763
Fax: +91 11 331 5279/4797/3664

Key personnel

See entry in *Locomotives and powered passenger vehicles* section

Products

Passenger coaches of any type and design for various gauges; spares for coaches. Over 480 coaches manufactured in India are currently operating in Taiwan, Zambia, Philippines, Myanmar, Bangladesh, Mozambique, Nepal, Nigeria, Sri Lanka, Tanzania, Uganda and Vietnam.

Recent contracts include nine 1,000 mm gauge coaches and 63 bogies for Vietnam Railways.

VERIFIED

PFA

Partner für Fahrzeug-Ausstattung GmbH
A member of the Schaltbau Group
Zur Centralwerkstätte 11, D-92637 Weiden, Germany
Tel: +49 961 38880   Fax: +49 961 3888 992/997/999

Key personnel

Commercial Manager: Hans Kurllacek
Technical Manager: D Günther
Logistics Manager: G Nehls
Export Manager: H Kleinschmidt

Products

Passenger coach refurbishment.

Recent contracts include redesign of intercity coaches, conversion of 30 passenger coaches to driving trailers for push-pull operation on intercity routes.

UPDATED

schaltbau

railway engineering
munich
tel. 089/9 30 05-0
fax   /9 30 05-3 50

bode

mobile railway
engineering
kassel
tel. 05 61/50 09-0
fax   /5 59 56

brose

information and
display systems
wuppertal
tel. 02 02/70 95-0
fax   /70 95-102

gez

mobile railway
engineering
frankfort
tel. 069/42 09 06-0
fax   /42 09 06-13

krueger

information and
display systems
schenefeld
tel. 040/8 30 39-0
fax   /8 30 39-115

NEW TARGETS

FOR RAILWAYS

pfa

rebuilding and
modernization of rail cars
weiden
tel. 09 61/38 88-0
fax   /38 88-9 92

pintsch bamag

stationary and mobile
railway engineering
dinslaken
tel. 02064/6 02-0
fax   /6 02-2 66

protec

mobile railway
engineering
weiden
tel. 09 61/67 00 60
fax   /6 70 06 20

wandel &
goltermann

information and
communication systems
eningen
tel. 071 21/9 86-0
fax   /9 86-100

Luwa – THE Specialist for Air Conditioning and Shock Wave Protection Systems in High Speed Trains

Railway companies all over the world rely on the experience and know-how of Luwa.
The proof: More than 3,500 coaches in all continents are equipped by Luwa.
Luwa's diagnostic systems lead to considerable savings in maintenance and repair.

Come to Luwa for comfort, reliability and savings

Luwa Fahrzeugklimatechnik GmbH
Hanauer Landstrasse 200 · D-60314 Frankfurt/Main
Tel.069-40351-200 · Fax.069-40351-385

DATA RECORDERS, FIRE PROTECTION AND TRAIN MANAGEMENT SYSTEMS continued
SEPSA
Siemens
TBA
Wood Group Fire Systems
XP

DOOR SYSTEMS AND COMPONENTS
Bircher
Bode
Conbrako
ContiTech
Deans Powered Doors
Dewhurst
EAO Highland
Faiveley Transport
Ferro International
Geze
HP
IFE
Kiekert
KV
LM Glassfiber
Morio Denki
MSV
NABCO
Narita
Nippon Signal
Parker Pneumatic
Phoenix
Pimatic
Pintsch Bamag
SAB WABCO
Schindler
SMC
Toyo Denki
Transintech
Vapor
Widney Transport Components

GANGWAYS
Adams & Westlake
Faiveley Transport
Fiat-SIG
Hübner
Narita
Northern Rubber
Woodville Polymer Engineering

INTERIOR FITTINGS AND SEATING
Aim Aviation (Henshalls)
Alna Koki
Bosch Telecom
BTR Permali RP
Callow & Maddox
Chapman
Cole
Compin
Concar
ContiTech
Deans Powered Doors
Deco Seating
Desso
FAINSA
Ferro
Fiberite
Grammer
Halais
Hexcel
Hübner
Hunting
IRAUSA LOIRE
KAB Rail
Kiel
Percy Lane
LM Glassfiber
MSV
Lazzerini
Narita
Parker Pneumatic
People Seating
Permali

Phoenix
Protec
Sanivac
Railcare
RG Manufacturing
Schindler
Sütrak
Temoinsa
Transintech
TriCon
Unicel
VBK

LIGHTING SYSTEMS AND COMPONENTS
Adtranz
Angst+Pfister
Atlas International
Dialight
Excil
GEZ
Morio Denki
SBF
Specialty Bulb
Teknoware
Thorn Transport Lighting
Toshiba

TOILET SYSTEMS AND COMPONENTS
Aim Aviation (Henshalls)
Bayham
EVAC
Microphor
Monogram Sanitation
NIF
Parker Pneumatic
Protec
Sanivac
Schindler
Semco
SERINOX
Temoinsa

UNDERFLOOR EQUIPMENT
Angst+Pfister
Bayham
Carrier Khéops Bac
Compair Hydrovane
Electro Wire
Ellcon National
Freudenberg
GMT
LPA

Mechan
Narita
Phoenix

WINDOWS AND WINDSCREENS
Alna Koki
Cleff
Conbrako
ContiTech
Deans Powered Doors

Geze
Klein
Percy Lane
Morio Denki
MSV
Phoenix
Pilkington Aerospace
Westberga
Widney Transport Components

Company Listing by Country

AUSTRALIA
Sigma Industries
SMC

AUSTRIA
IFE

BELGIUM
GEC Alsthom ACEC Transport

CZECH REPUBLIC
MSV

DENMARK
Ferro International
LM Glassfiber
Semco

FINLAND
EKE Electronics
Finnyards
NIF
Pimatic
Teknoware

FRANCE
Carrier Khéops Bac
Cegelec
Compin
ELNO
Faiveley Transport
Ferraz
Halais
IRAUSA LOIRE
Klein
Neu Systems Ferroviaires
SAFT
SERINOX

GERMANY
Adtranz
Bode
Bosch Telecom
Cleff
ContiTech
FAGA
Freudenberg
GEZ
GMT
Grammer
HFG
Hübner
Kiekert
Kiel
Kuckuck
Luwa
Phoenix
Pintsch Bamag
Protec
SBF
Schaltbau
Siemens
SMA
Sütrak
Transtechnik
TriCon

INDIA
Stone India

ITALY
Connei
Elettromeccanica
FIREMA Trasporti
HP
Lazzerini

JAPAN
Alna Koki
Hitachi
Morio Denki
NABCO
Narita
Nippon Signal
Toshiba
Toyo Denki

NETHERLANDS
Deco Seating
Desso
Nieaf-Smitt

NORWAY
VBK

PORTUGAL
EFACEC

SOUTH AFRICA
Conbrako
Widney Transport Components

SPAIN
FAINSA
SEPSA
Stone International
Stone UK
Temoinsa

SWEDEN
SAB WABCO
EVAC

SWITZERLAND
Adtranz
Angst+Pfister
Bircher
Ebo
Fiat-SIG
Schindler

UK
Aim Aviation (Henshalls)
Airscrew Howden
A K Fans
Atlas International
Bayham
BTR Permali RP
Callow & Maddox
Chapman
Cole
Compair Hydrovane
Concar

Craig & Derricott
Cressal Resistors
Deans Powered Doors
Dewhurst
Dialight
EAO Highland
Ebac
Excil
Ferranti Technologies
Ferro
GEC-Marconi Aerospace
GEC-Marconi Avionics
GEC-Marconi Defence
Hexcel
Howden Buffalo
Hunting
KAB Rail
Kidde
KV
Percy Lane
Litton
LPA
Mechan
Normalair-Garrett Limited
Northern Rubber
Parker Pneumatic
People Seating
Permali
Pilkington Aerospace
Powertron
Railcare
RG Manufacturing
Sanivac
Siemens
SMC
Stone UK
TBA
Thorn Automation
Thorn Transport Lighting
Transintech
Westberga
Wood Group Fire Systems
Woodville Polymer Engineering
XP

USA
Adams & Westlake
Adtranz
Deutsch Relays
Electro Wire
Ellcon National
Fiberite
Microphor
Monogram Sanitation
Reidler Decal
Specialty Bulb
Stone International
Transit Control Systems
Unicel
Vapor

Adams & Westlake

Adams and Westlake Ltd
940 North Michigan Street, Elkhart, Indiana 46514, USA
Tel: +1 219 264 1141   Fax: +1 219 264 1146

Key personnel
President: L F Ott
General Sales Manager: P E Gingerich

Products
End diaphragms and custom-manufactured parts.

VERIFIED

Adtranz

ABB Daimler-Benz Transportation GmbH
Saatwinkler Damm 42-43, D-13627 Berlin, Germany
Tel: +49 30 38320   Fax: +49 30 3832 2000

Key personnel
See entry in *Locomotives and powered passenger vehicles* section

Products
Development, design, engineering, sales, production, installation, maintenance and after-sales service of rolling stock systems and equipment for all railway types, systems and track gauges; electrical equipment, electrical subsystems and climate-control equipment for rail vehicles; customer support services for passenger coach equipment including commissioning and warranty, supply of spare parts, refurbishment and repair, servicing and maintenance; project management for major projects and consultancy work.

Included are also train control and communication with fault diagnosis as well as room climate HVAC systems (Heading, Ventilation, Air Conditioning) for traction vehicle driver cabs. These Adtranz products are also being used by other railway manufacturers and in the support of railway operators for repairs and refurbishment of their rolling stock and systems.

UPDATED

Aim Aviation (Henshalls)

Aim Aviation (Henshalls) Ltd
Abbot Close, Oyster Lane, Byfleet KT14 7JT, UK
Tel: +44 1932 351011   Fax: +44 1932 352792

Key personnel
Chairman and Chief Executive: J C Smith
Directors
 Managing: B P Jarlett
 Financial: M J Davis
 Technical: A Morrell
 Production: G Bass

Products
Catering equipment for rolling stock, products for carriage interiors.

Recent contracts include the supply of wall-mounted grilles for the Channel Tunnel trains, and the supply of toilet cubicles for the Channel Tunnel nightstock.

VERIFIED

Airscrew Howden

Airscrew Howden Ltd
111 Windmill Road, Sunbury-on-Thames TW16 7EF, UK
Tel: +44 1932 765822   Fax: +44 1932 761098

Key personnel
Head of Sales, Fans and Motors: Gwyn Jones

Products
Ventilation fans and supply inverters. Pressure ventilation heaters for passenger saloons and cabs.

Recent contracts include the supply of fans for Class 465 emus in the UK.

VERIFIED

A K Fans

A K Fans Ltd
32-34 Park Royal Road, London NW10 7LN, UK
Tel: +181 961 6888   Fax: +181 965 0601

Key personnel
See entry in *Electric traction equipment* section

Products
Fans and allied equipment for rail traction applications; axial, centrifugal, mixed flow and crossflow fans.

Contracts include the supply of cab heaters, cab air handling units and saloon heaters for metro trainsets for London Underground Ltd's Jubilee and Northern lines.

UPDATED

Alna Koki

Alna Koki Co Ltd
4-5 Higashi Naniwa-cho 1-chome, Amagasaki 660, Japan
Tel: +81 6 401 7283   Fax: +81 6 401 6168

Key personnel
See entry in *Locomotives and powered passenger vehicles* section

Products
Various types of aluminium windows and window sashes; power windows; honeycomb sandwich doors and panels for railcars and passenger coaches.

UPDATED

Angst+Pfister

Angst+Pfister AG
Thurgauerstrasse 66, CH-8052 Zürich, Switzerland
Tel: +41 1 306 6111   Fax: +41 1 302 1871

UK subsidiary
Angst+Pfister Ltd
20 Rufford Court, Hardwick Grange, Woolston, Warrington WA1 4RF
Tel: +44 1925 852688   Fax: +44 1925 852687

Key personnel
Marketing Director: Andreas Ferrari

Products
Components for rail vehicles including plastics mouldings, washers, seals, valves and ducting.

NEW ENTRY

Atlas International

Atlas International Ltd
Merrington Lane, Spennymoor DL16 7UR, UK
Tel: +44 191 301 3115   Fax: +44 191 301 3110

Associate company
Thorn Transport Lighting

Key personnel
Logistics Manager: T Burton

Products
Lighting components for rail vehicles; inverter ballasts for fluorescent lighting 24, 36, 52, 70/72, 110 V DC, AC; ballasts for various voltages; lampholders and other lighting accessories including luminaires and subassemblies of standard or special types; AC and DC converters for low-voltage tungsten halogen lamps for 12 V reading lights and locomotive headlights; inverter ballasts for fluorescent lamps to the European standard, and luminaires using compact fluorescent lamps.

An extended range of Atlas brand electronic lighting inverter ballasts has been introduced to operate at 15 W to 40 W 26-38 mm tubes. Advances in production technology have enabled them to offer these compact electronic inverters in voltages covering 24-110 V DC. They meet RIA, European (EN), French (NF), International (UIC) and associated standards for rolling stock.

NEW ENTRY

Bayham

Bayham Ltd
Daneshill West Industrial Estate, Basingstoke RG24 0PG, UK
Tel: +44 1256 464911   Fax: +44 1256 464366

Key personnel
Chairman: J J Boulcott
Managing Director: E A Salter
Export Sales: A J Bowman

Subsidiary
The Ranger Instrument Company Ltd

Products
R & G direct and remote reading fuel and coolant tank gauges, together with those for drinking water and lavatory flush tanks on passenger carriages; combination level indicators and switches on a single mounting flange give continuous level indication plus warning of low/high liquid level with optional automatic shutdown in the event of catastrophic coolant losses.

VERIFIED

Bircher

Bircher AG
CH-8222 Beringen, Switzerland
Tel: +41 52 687 1111   Fax: +41 52 687 1210

Key personnel
President and Chief Executive Officer: Giorgio Behr
Executive Directors: Max Bircher, Otto Stehle
Managing Directors: Rémy Höhener, Ernst Bührer, Roland Kaufmann
Sales and Marketing Manager: Rémy Höhener

Principal subsidiaries
Bircher America Inc
1865 Hicks Road, Suite C/D, Rolling Meadows, Illinois 60008, USA
President: Rémy Höhener

Bircher Asia Pacific Sdn Bhd
278 Jalan Simbang, Taman Perling, 812000 Johor Bahru, Malaysia
General Manager: Hanspeter Ritzmann

Bircher Deutschland GmbH
Leonberger Strasse 28, D-71063 Sindelfingen, Germany
General Manager: Erich Maier

Products

Safety edges for train doors; safety mats for train entrances; switch mats for gangway doors between coaches; time delay relays for general control purposes; safety equipment for station platforms.

Contracts include the supply of door safety edges for the refurbishment of SBB rolling stock for local services; switch mats for gangway doors on refurbished SNCF TGV-SE high-speed trainsets; and switch mats for station doors for RATP, France.

UPDATED

Bode

Gebrüder Bode & Co GmbH
Ochshäuserstrasse 14, D-34123 Kassel, Germany
Tel: +49 561 50090   Fax: +49 561 55956
Email: 106 433.633@compuserv.com

Key personnel
Technical Director: Siegfried Heinrich
Commercial Director: Rainer Wicke
Sales Manager: Jürgen Holz

Products

Electric and pneumatic sliding doors, sliding plug doors, pressure-sealed doors for high-speed vehicles, outswing plug doors and inswing plug doors; ramp systems; step systems; door controls.

Recent contracts include components for trains for DB AG (ICE 2/1), Berlin S-Bahn, MTRC Hong Kong, Kuala Lumpur Metro, ICT Germany, Bombardier Talent, USTRA Hanover, MBTA Boston and Amsterdam.

UPDATED

Bosch Telecom

Bosch Telecom Öffentliche Vermittlungstechnik GmbH
Kölnerstrasse 5, D-65760 Eschborn am Taunus, Germany
Tel: +49 61 96 979640   Fax: +49 61 96 979613

Head office
Robert Bosch GmbH
PO Box 106050, D-70049 Stuttgart
Tel: +49 711 8110   Fax: +49 711 811 6630

Key personnel
Marketing: Norbert Kayser
Product Management: Heinz-Peter Schönberg

Products

The Ökart-Zug system is a card-operated telephone for trains. The machine, which is resistant to vandalism, scratching and graffiti, accepts a telephone card instead of money. The card can be either the equivalent of a prepaid number of charge units, or it can be used to debit the user's bank account protected by a PIN code. The Ökart-Zug system is installed on the ICE high-speed train operated by the German Federal Railway. Its modular design enables it to meet new requirements such as the digital GSM standard, accepted worldwide.

UPDATED

BTR Permali RP

BTR Permali RP Ltd
Bristol Road, Gloucester GL1 5TT, UK
Tel: +44 1452 52867   Fax: +44 1452 304215

See also *Permanent way equipment*

Key personnel
Managing Director: M W Mallorie
Sales and Marketing Manager: C Mason

Products
GRP compression-moulded shells

NEW ENTRY

Callow & Maddox

Sibree Road, Baginton, Coventry CV3 4FD, UK
Tel: +44 1203 639393   Fax: +44 1203 639712

Key personnel
Director: A S Wotherspoon
Business Manager: T J Rogers

Products
Seating for passenger vehicles.
Recent contracts include the supply of seats for refurbished metro trainsets for London Underground Ltd's Circle and Piccadilly lines.

VERIFIED

Carrier Khéops Bac

PO Box 3, boulevard Pierre Lefaucheux,
F-72024 Le Mans Cedex, France
Tel: +33 2 43 61 45 45   Fax: +33 2 43 61 45 00

Key personnel
Managing Director: D Plantey
Railway Product Manager: P Roseleur

Products

Electrical plugs and sockets; cable couplers for high power and signal train lines, onboard equipment connections, shielded connectors, databus, video, coax or twinax; power shore supply connectors; rack-mounted connectors for battery drawers, air conditioning units and high-voltage units; public address connectors according to UIC 568; heating couplers according to UIC 552; European electropneumatic brake connectors; connectors according to the new fire and smoke standards NFF 16-101 and NFF 16-102 used for metro trains and Channel Tunnel rolling stock; and emergency disconnection connectors used in the Channel Tunnel Eurostar trainsets (low and high voltage).

A new Series CMC range of connectors to meet NFCC61030 standard has been developed for extreme mechanical and climatic conditions for fixed equipment and rolling stock.

UPDATED

Cegelec

Cegelec Soprano
Parc Technologique de l'Isle d'Abeau, 40 rue Condorcet, F-38090 Vaulx Milieu, France
Tel: +33 4 74 82 27 27   Fax: +33 4 74 82 27 04

Key personnel
Manager: Michel Favre

Products

Air conditioners for passenger vehicles and locomotive, trainset and LRV cabs.

Recent contracts include the supply of cab air conditioners for SNCF TGV-Atlantique high-speed trainsets, RATP MP89 metro trainsets and LRVs for Grenoble.

VERIFIED

Chapman

AW Chapman Ltd
Rodd Industrial Estate, Govett Avenue, Shepperton TW17 8AE, UK
Part of the Rodd Group of companies.
Tel: +44 1932 220551   Fax: +44 1932 246257

Key personnel
Managing Director: J Harvey
Sales Director: S I Smith

Associate company
Chapman Seating Ltd
79 Miles Road, Mitcham CR4 3YL
Tel: +44 181 640 6011   Fax: +44 181 640 1050

Key personnel
General Manager: M Traynor

Products
Passenger and crew seating.
Customers include Adtranz, GEC Alsthom, Volvo, Brush, Hunslet and Australian Railway Corporation.

UPDATED

Cleff

C W Cleff GmbH & Co, Postfach 260180, D-42243 Wuppertal, Germany
Tel: +49 2026 47990   Fax: +49 2026 479988

Products
Windows.

NEW ENTRY

Cole

Malcolm Cole Ltd
10 Chantry Park, Cowley Road, Nuffield Industrial Estate, Poole BH17 7UJ, UK
Tel: +44 1202 682830   Fax: +44 1202 665572

Key personnel
Engineer: Max Dales

Products

Oval 316 stainless steel tube as used for grab handles and commode handles.

Recent contracts include the supply of tube for metro trainsets for London Underground Ltd and for rolling stock for Channel Tunnel overnight services.

VERIFIED

Bosch radio terminal for Thalys   **1997**

Carrier Khéops CMC series of connectors   **1997**

Compair Hydrovane

Compair Hydrovane
Claybrook Drive, Washford Industrial Estate,
Redditch B98 0DS, UK
Tel: +44 1527 525522 Fax: +44 1527 521140

Key personnel
Managing Director: Malcolm G Quarterman
Business Development Manager: Andrew J Fennell

Products
Trackair range of rotary compressors specially designed for mobile railway applications. There are 12 basic models available for any working pressure required between 7 and 10 bar.

Hydrovane range of rotary vane railway compressors for stationary applications. Range extends from 1.98 litres/s to 207 litres/s up to 10 bar.

Recent contracts include delivery of 26 TA20 units for Mexico City metro.

UPDATED

Compin

Etablissements Compin
59/61 rue La Fayette, F-75009 Paris, France
Tel: +33 1 49 70 55 66 Fax: +33 1 49 70 55 69

Works
59 rue Lemarrois, F-27800 Brionne, France

Key personnel
President: Jean-Louis Danton
Chief Executive Officer: Jean-Marc Courtade
Export and Marketing Manager: Gilles Vacher

Subsidiaries
Belgium, USA

Products
Seats for passenger vehicles including high-speed, regional and metro trainsets and light rail vehicles. Vandal-resistant seat coverings.

Recent contracts include supply of seats for KCRC Hong Kong trains.

Other contracts include supply of seating for Eurostar; AVE; TGV-Duplex; Channel Tunnel Nightstock; Berlin S-Bahn; Paris Metro (Météor); Narita Express, Japan; ÖBB.

UPDATED

Conbrako

Conbrako (Pty) Ltd
PO Box 4018, Luipaardsviei 1743, Transvaal, South Africa
Tel: +27 11 762 2421 Fax: +27 11 762 6535

Products
Sliding doors; electropneumatic door mechanisms; coach windows.

VERIFIED

Concar

Concar Co Ltd
Old Mixon Crescent, Weston Super Mare BS24 9AH, UK
Tel: +44 1934 628221 Fax: +44 1934 417623

Key personnel
Sales & Marketing Manager: Tim Roper

Products
Glass reinforced plastics components including side panels, window surrounds, skirts, ceiling panels, third-rail covers, seats, consoles, cab fronts. Materials include phenolic Class 1 ARC barrier material.

Contracts include mouldings for London Underground Jubilee and Northern Line trains, closed moulded litter bins for LUL night stock; supply of phenolic stand backs to LUL.

NEW ENTRY

Connei

Connei SpA
Via Pillea 14-16, I-16153 Genoa, Italy
Tel: +39 10 600821 Fax: +39 10 650 8573/1256

Key personnel
General Manager: Giuseppe Lancella
Export Sales Manager: Mauro Gramaccioni

Products
Electrical connectors (rectangular, rack and panel).

Recent contracts include the supply of connectors for ETR 402, ETR 450, ETR 460, ETR 470, ETR 480 and ETR 500 trainsets for Italian Railways; Class 465 and Class 466 emus for British operators; and Eurostar high-speed trainsets for EPS/SNCB/SNCF.

VERIFIED

ContiTech

ContiTech Holding GmbH
PO Box 169, D-30001 Hannover, Germany
Tel: +49 511 93802 Fax: +49 511 938 2766

Key personnel
Customer Management, Rolling Stock: Manfred Hunze

Products
Door and window sealing profiles; gaiter materials; upholstered units for seats; vinyl-coated seating fabrics.

UPDATED

Craig & Derricott

Craig & Derricott Ltd
Hall Lane, Walsall Wood, Walsall WS9 9DP, UK
Tel: +44 1543 375541 Fax: +44 1543 452610

Key personnel
Managing Director: Rod Pettit
Rolling Stock Co-ordinator: Lionel Collins
Field Sales Manager: Mike Ingram
Marketing Manager: Richard Kennedy

Products
A comprehensive range of switchgear and custom-designed control panels adapted to meet the control and safety requirements of the rail industry. Specifically including: shunting control panels; customised rotary switches and isolators; rotary switches featuring high-security key locks; and mushroom-headed push-buttons used as both emergency stops and passenger alarm switches. Also supplied is a full range of limit and reed switches suitable for mounting in or around all rail equipment.

Recent contracts include the supply of push-button controls for Channel Tunnel Nightstock; master control panels and passenger communication switches for trainsets for London Underground Ltd's Jubilee Line Extension; and Train Monitoring System switches and display panels for London Underground Ltd's refurbished D78 trainsets.

VERIFIED

Cressal Resistors

Standard Cressal Ltd
Evington Valley Road, Leicester LE5 5LZ, UK
Tel: +44 116 273 7911 Fax: +44 116 273 3633

Key personnel
Director: Peter Duncan

Products
Electric heaters and fans.

Recent contracts include 126 custom-built heaters for GVBA Amsterdam. Each heater provides 14 kW output while fitting into the same space as the 9 kW units they replace. The heaters withstand surges from 600 V to 750 V DC.

NEW ENTRY

Deans Powered Doors

PO Box 8, Grovehill, Beverley HU17 0JL, UK
Tel: +44 1482 868111 Fax: +44 1482 881890

Key personnel
Managing Director: D Skidmore

Sales and Marketing Director: M Phillips
Technical Director: P Spencer

Products

Powered doors (electric and pneumatic) and door-operating mechanisms; seating stanchions, handrails and windows; aluminium sand and gravity die castings for rail and bus applications.

Recent developments include aluminium honeycomb-based hot-bonded door leaves designed specifically for railway applications.

Recent contracts include door leaves for: London Underground Ltd's Central Line, Docklands Light Railway (London), Strathclyde PTE and Beijing Metro. Also bodyside skirts for GEC Alsthom Class 465/466 trainsets for British operators.

VERIFIED

Desso

Desso Hotel Aero-Marine Carpets International
Molenweg 81, NL-5349 AC Oss, Netherlands
Tel: + 31 4126 67911   Fax: +31 4126 35165

Products
Carpets.

NEW ENTRY

Deutsch Relays

Deutsch Relays Inc
65 Daly Road, East Northport, New York 11731 USA
Tel: +1 516 499 6000   Fax: +1 516 499 6086

Key personnel
President: Jean-Marie Painvin
Vice-President and General Manager, Technology:
    Tom Sadusky
Marketing Director: James Bedell

Overseas offices
Relais Electroniques Deutsch
St Jean de la Ruelle, France

Products
Special relays designed for reliable operation under severe environmental conditions. The technology

Deutsch Relays hermetically sealed six-pole relay package in a 1.5 in³ metal enclosure

features miniaturised design of power switching electromechanical relays and time delay which are packaged in hermetically sealed, corrosion-resistant metal enclosures. Deutsch also produces mating relay sockets or bases, as well as other mounting systems. PCB and racking assembly design and production are now available.

Recent contracts include the supply of components for emu cars for STCUM, Canada, by Bombardier; light rail vehicles for Dallas, USA, by Kinki Sharyo; TGV high-speed trainsets for SNCF, France, by GEC Alsthom; and metro cars for SEPTA, USA, by Adtranz.

UPDATED

Dewhurst

Dewhurst plc
Inverness Road, Hounslow TW3 3LT, UK
Tel: +44 181 570 7791   Fax: +44 181 572 5986

Key personnel
Director, New Business Division (Hounslow):
    Keith Bossard
New Business Manager (Birmingham): John Nicholds

Products
Push-button controls to meet the new UK rolling stock requirements. Standard ranges of vandal-resistant push-buttons, keypads and push-button control panels for external passenger doors, vestibule doors, emergency call panels, drivers' cab controls, guard stations and crew access.

Contracts for British operators include push-button controls and indicators for Class 158, InterCity 225, Class 323, mainline trains 165, 166, and 465 rolling stock. Other contracts include London Underground Ltd's Central Line, Manchester Metrolink, SL Stockholm and the Lantau Airport extension, Hong Kong.

UPDATED

Dialight

Exning Road, Newmarket CB8 0AX, UK
Tel: +44 1638 662317   Fax: +44 1638 560455

Key personnel
Vice-President, Sales and Marketing: Gary Durgin
European Business Manager: Gareth Eaton

Products
External LED indicator lights.

VERIFIED

EAO Highland

EAO Highland Electronics
Albert Drive, Burgess Hill RH15 9TN, UK
Tel: +44 1444 245021   Fax: +44 1444 236641

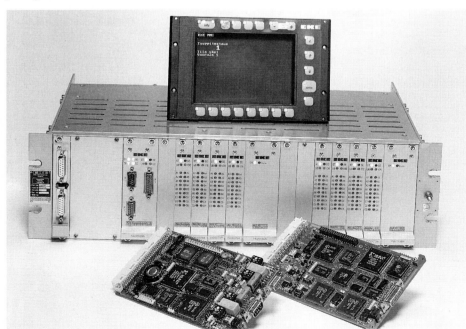

EKE-Trainnet® equipment including computer, coach display and WTB gateway boards   1997

Key personnel
Managing Director: Nick Williams
Marketing Director: Sue Fisher

Subsidiary company
Elektro Apparateban Olten
Tannwaldstrasse 88, CH-4601, Olten, Switzerland

Products
Vehicle power supply units, driver's cab switches, door open-close actuators, cab circuit breakers.

Recent contracts include units for London Underground Northern Line, Berlin U Bahn, DB Germany, NS Netherlands, Zagreb local tram undertaking, Malaysian Railways, Red Line Boston, SBB Switzerland and NSB Norway.

Other contracts have included supply of equipment to London Underground Jubilee Line and SNCB Belgium.

NEW ENTRY

Ebac

Ebac Ltd
St Helen Trading Estate, Bishop Auckland,
County Durham DL14 9AL, UK
Tel: +44 1388 605061   Fax: +44 1388 609845

Key personnel
Managing Director: John Elliott MBE
Executive Director: Graham Higgs
Projects Managers (Sales): Alan LePatourel,
    Mark Mason

Principal subsidiaries
Ebac Systems Inc
106 John Jefferson Road, Suite 102, Williamsburg,
Virginia 23185, USA
Tel: +1 804 229 3038   Fax: +1 804 229 3321

Ebac Deutschland GmbH
Romerring 7, D-74821, Mosbach-Diedesheim, Germany
Tel: +49 6261 60057   Fax: +49 6261 64206

Products
Design, manufacture and supply of air conditioning, heating and ventilation systems for all types of rail vehicles. Heat pump technology; microprocessor-based controls and diagnostics; chilled water systems; low refrigerant content, R134a systems; roof-mounted, underframe-mounted and split systems.

Recent contracts include Channel Tunnel Nightstock passenger car heating, ventilation and air conditioning systems; cab air conditioning, saloon heating and ventilation systems for London Underground Ltd's Jubilee Line cars.

VERIFIED

Ebo

Ebo AG
Zürichstrasse 103, CH-8134 Adliswil, Switzerland
Tel: +41 1 487 2211   Fax: +41 1 487 2277

Key personnel
Managing Director: Heinz B Fischer
Export Sales: Mrs Ilse Wedel

Products
Cable management and support systems, (trays, ducts and ladders in glass-reinforced polyester).

VERIFIED

EFACEC

EFACEC Sistemas de Electrónica, SA
PO Box 31, P-4470 Maia, Portugal
Tel: +351 2 941 3666   Fax: +351 2 948 5428

Products
Static converters. Recent contracts include supply of static converters for Corail-type coaches for CP.

VERIFIED

EKE Electronics

Piispanportti 7, FIN-02240 Espoo, Finland
Tel: +358 9 6130 3308   Fax: +358 9 6130 3300
email: electronics@eke.fi
Website: www.eke.fi

Are you looking for an easy-to-install Train Management System that is tailored to your needs?

Easy and secure to install

The EKE-Trainnet® Train Management System can be used when building new trains or when refurbishing coaches.

Its modular and distributed construction combined with a modern data bus structure makes the installation work easy.

The EKE-Trainnet® system's interface modules can be located near signal sources, which minimises the wiring work.

The interfaces are designed to be connectable with the wide variety of signal standards.

The application programming of the EKE-Trainnet® system is carried out by a Computer Aided SW Engineering tool which makes system design and testing simple and flexible.

Saving your costs

The EKE-Trainnet® Train Management System provides detailed information on incidents which have occurred.

In addition to the normal fault log downloading at the depot, monitoring and diagnostics information can be delivered to the depot even before the train's arrival. The EKE-Trainnet® Maintenance Support System is used for evaluating this monitoring and diagnostics information for preventative maintenance purposes.

In cases where the reason for failure is not apparent, the EKE-Trainnet® System gives your maintenance staff tools to investigate stored signals in the depot or even to make real time inspections during normal service. A Windows based graphical tool for signal analysis is included in the supporting products.

Flexible and modular

EKE-Trainnet® family products are highly modular and based on an open system design. Our approach offers you tailored and cost effective solutions for each application.

For detailed information on our EKE-Trainnet® Train Management System, Registering Device and Speedometer products please contact:

ELECTRONICS

EKE-ELECTRONICS LTD
Piispanportti 7, FIN-02240 Espoo, FINLAND
Tel. +358 9 6130 3308, Telefax +358 9 6130 3300
e-mail: electronics@eke.fi, web: www.eke.fi

Key personnel
Managing Director Export Sales: Timo Kataja
System Design Manager: Anssi Laakkonen
Production Manager: Ari Lokka
Service and Technical Support: Mika Lindén

Products
Railway electronics including EKE-Trainnet® train management system and its components, including WTB gateways, EKE-TDR registration devices (black boxes) and EKE-NMI ATC speedometers.

EKE-Trainnet products are in use on London Underground Central Line stock, Channel Tunnel shuttle trains, VR Finland passenger coaches, VR Finland locomotives and Pendolino high-speed trainsets.

UPDATED

Electro Wire

Electro Wire Inc
1000 Touhy Avenue
Elk Grove Village
Illinois 60007
Tel: +1 847 593 2500   Fax: +1 847 593 2501

Key personnel
See entry in *Fixed electrification equipment* section

Products
Wires and cables for use in rolling stock and power transmission purposes. Available in conventional insulation or with low smoke, zero halogen jackets.

VERIFIED

Elettromeccanica

Elettromeccanica CM
Via IV Novembre 29, Loc Cantagrillo, I-51034 Serravalle P SE, Pistoia, Italy
Tel: +39 573 527395/6   Fax: +39 573 526392

Products
Electrical systems for passenger vehicles, including converters, for roof or underfloor mounting.

VERIFIED

Ellcon National

Ellcon National Inc
50 Beechtree Boulevard, PO Box 9377, Greenville, South Carolina 29604-9377, USA
Tel: +1 803 277 5000   Fax: +1 803 277 5207

Key personnel
Chairman: E P Kondra
President: Douglas E Kondra
Executive Vice-President: R A Nitsch
Treasurer: L F D'Alessio

Licensees
Gregg Company Ltd
15 Dyatt Place, PO Box 430, Hackensack, New Jersey 07602-0430, USA

Sales Representatives
Canada
Pandrol Canada Ltd
8310 Cote de Liesse Road, Suite 100, Montreal, Quebec H4T 1G7

Mexico
Dinamica SA, Avenida Madero 40, Mexico 1, DF

Products
Handbrakes, bogie-mounted brakes, empty load brakes, pneumatic discharge gates, slack adjusters, Magor Rail Car parts.

VERIFIED

ELNO

ELNO SN
17 rue Jean Pierre Timbaud, F-95100 Argenteuil, France
Tel: +33 1 39 98 44 44   Fax: +33 1 39 98 44 46

Key personnel
Chairman: Philippe Bertin
General Manager: Jacques Fedon
Export Manager: Gabriel Grosjean

Products
Audio and video systems for passenger vehicles. Audio components including driver/guard handsets and microphones, loudspeakers, power amplifiers, passenger alarm units and remote/central communications and alarm management units.

ELNO has supplied systems and components for use in Eurostar, TGV-Atlantique and SNCF/RATP MI2N trainsets.

VERIFIED

Deco Seating

Deco Seating BV
Oude Baan 75, NL-4825 BL Breda, Netherlands
Tel: +31 76 571 6006   Fax: +31 76 587 5951

Key personnel
Managing Director: Bob Scholte
Product Development Manager: Bram van Lieshout
Industrial Manager: Ad Bastiaansen

Products
Passenger seats for rail vehicles. Vandal-resistant upholstery for new or refurbished seating.

Recent contracts include second-class seats for DD-IRM emus for NS; first- and second-class seats for AM96 coaches for SNCB; first- and second-class seats for DM90 dmus for NS; and passenger seating for GEC Alsthom metro trainsets for Santiago.

VERIFIED

EVAC

EVAC AB
S-295 39 Bromölla, Sweden
Tel: +46 456 28500   Fax: +46 456 27972

Key personnel
Managing Director: Harry Blomster
Business Area Manager, Train Systems: Nils Andersson

Subsidiaries
EVAC Oy
Purotie 1, FIN-00380 Helsinki, Finland
Tel: +358 0 506761   Fax: +358 0 5067 6333

Envirovac Inc
1260 Turret Drive, Rockford, Illinois 61115-1486, USA
Tel: +1 815 654 8300   Fax: +1 815 654 8306

EVAC SA
Zac de Bellevues, PO Box 98, F-95613 Cergy-Pontoise, France
Tel: +33 1 34 21 99 88   Fax: +33 1 34 64 39 00

EVAC GmbH
Lederstrasse 15, D-22525 Hamburg, Germany
Tel: +49 40 540 0980   Fax: +49 40 5400 9811

EVAC Srl
Via San Terenziano 7, I-16040 Leivi (GE), Italy
Tel: +39 185 324700   Fax: +39 185 324780

Products
Vacuum toilet and sewage handling systems.

VERIFIED

Excil

Excil Electronics Ltd
Ripley Drive, Normanton WF6 1QT, UK
Tel: +44 1924 224100   Fax: +44 1924 224111

Key personnel
Managing Director: Phil Burns
Technical Director: Jonathan Rees
Commercial Manager (Sales): Mike Fitzgerald

Products
Passenger vehicle interior lighting systems; electronic lighting inverters; control and monitoring equipment.

Recent contracts include interior lighting for Arlanda Airport cars, Sweden.

Other contracts include metro cars for London Underground Ltd's Northern, Jubilee and Piccadilly lines; secondary door locking control panels for HST trailer vehicles in the UK; and voltage and DC current detectors for Class 465 electric multiple-units in the UK.

UPDATED

FAGA

Fahrzeugausrüstung Berlin GmbH
A subsidiary of Deutsche Waggonbau AG
Wolfener Strasse 23, D-12681 Berlin, Germany
Tel: +49 30 936420   Fax: +49 30 936 42302

Key personnel
Managing Director: Reinhard Schwarzenau

Products
Power supply systems, DC and AC generators, rectifiers, inverters, high-voltage equipment boxes in single and multitension design, switch cabinets, transistorised fluorescent ballasts, train/vehicle control systems, controlling and regulating and diagnostic devices.

UPDATED

FAINSA

Fabricación Asientos Vehículos Industriales SA
Calle Horta s/n, 08107 Martorelles (Barcelona), Spain
Tel: +34 3 570 5900   Fax: +34 3 570 1838

Key personnel
President: J Singla
Managing Director: Rafaél Roldán
Export Manager: Aurelio Gómez
Plant Manager: Aleix Singla

Products
Passenger seating for railway vehicles, LRVs and metro cars, including berths for sleeping cars.

Recent contracts include the supply of seating to RENFE (Spain), former British Railways (1988–1995), Amtrak USA, MAV Hungary, Cuba (1989), Thailand, KTM (Malaysia), ENR (Egypt), CP (Portugal) and DB AG (Germany).

UPDATED

Faiveley Transport

Faiveley Transport SA
143 boulevard Anatole France, F-93285 Saint Denis Cedex, France
Tel: +33 1 48 13 65 00   Fax: +33 1 48 13 65 66

Main works
Electromechanical Division
Les Yvaudières, avenue Yves Farge, F-37700 Saint-Pierre-des-Corps, France
Tel: +33 2 47 32 55 55   Fax: +33 2 47 44 80 24

Air Conditioning Division
ZI, 1 rue des Grands Mortiers, F-37700 Saint-Pierre-des-Corps, France
Tel: +33 2 47 32 55 55   Fax: +33 2 47 63 19 31

Electronics Division
rue Amélia Earhart, ZI du Bois de Plante, PO Box 43, F-37700 La-Ville-Aux-Dames, France
Tel: +33 2 47 32 55 55   Fax: +33 2 47 32 56 61

Key personnel
Chairman: Alain Bodel
General Manager: Bruno Challamel
Director, International Division: Jean-Jacques Maillard
Marketing Manager: E Oudman

Subsidiaries

Faiveley Española SA
Autovia Reus Km 5, Apartado 525, E-43080 Tarragona, Spain
Tel: +34 77 548506   Fax: +34 77 5479

Faiveley Italia SpA
Via della Meccanica N 21, Zona Industriale de Bassone, I-37139 Verona, Italy
Tel: +39 45 851 0011   Fax: +39 45 851 0020

Faiveley do Brazil Ltda
Equipfer Ltda
Rua Achilles Orlando, Curtolo 636, Barra Funda, 01139 São Paulo, Brazil
Tel: +55 11 825 0200   Fax: +55 11 662532

Nabco-Faiveley Ltd
9-18 Kaigan 1-chome, Minato-ku, Tokyo 105, Japan
Tel: +81 3 5470 2427   Fax: +81 3 5472 5080

Faiveley UK Ltd
Unit 10, Ninian Industrial Park, Ninian Way, Tame Valley Industrial Estate, Wilnecote, Tamworth B77 5DE, UK

Products

Onboard equipment and systems comprising door systems (electric and pneumatic operators, automatic external doors and steps, interior doors, automatic platform screen doors); electronics (onboard data processing, speed control and monitoring equipment, event recorders, anti-slip and anti-skid protection, multiplexing, power converters); air conditioning; and gangways.

Recent contracts include the supply of external doors for British Class 323 emus and LRVs for Rouen; speed monitoring equipment for Eurotunnel shuttle trains and SNCF TGV-Réseau high-speed trainsets; air conditioning for FS ETR 500 and EPS/SNCB/SNCF Eurostar trainsets; and intercar gangways for the metros of Barcelona, Paris (MF88) and Valencia.

VERIFIED

Ferranti Technologies

Ferranti Technologies Ltd
Cairo Mill, Waterhead, Oldham OL4 3JA, UK
Tel: +44 161 624 0281   Fax: +44 161 624 5244

Key personnel

Managing Director: T R Tuckley
Finance Director: F Brinksman
Commercial Director: P Davies
Manufacturing Director: D J Platt

Products

Power conversion components for auxiliary functions such as heating, ventilation and interior lighting, including: inverters (0.5-1.0 kVA), transformer rectifier units, static converters, power supply units, battery chargers, AC under-voltage monitors, AC and DC current detectors. Doppler radar, non-contact, distance/velocity measurement device (DVMD) with possible applications for speed measurement, traction control and automatic train protection/control. Video monitoring equipment including cameras, multiplexers and digital video recorders. Overhaul and repair of power conversion

Ferranti Technologies distance/velocity measurement device **1997**

equipment and electronic assemblies, subsystems and components.

Ferranti Technologies inverters are in use with London Underground Ltd.

UPDATED

Ferraz SA

PO Box 3025, F-69391 Lyon Cedex 03, France
Tel: +33 4 72 22 66 11   Fax: +33 4 72 22 67 13

Key personnel

See entry in *Electric traction equipment* section

Products

Earth return current units and associated resistors to prevent current flowing through bearing of axleboxes and associated resistors; fuses with very high breaking capacity for DC/AC converter protection and for heating circuits protection.

VERIFIED

Ferro

Ferro (Great Britain) Ltd, Powder Coatings Division
Westgate, Redhouse Industrial Estate, Aldridge WS9 8YH, UK
Tel: +44 1922 58300   Fax: +44 1922 59802

Key personnel

UK Sales and Marketing Director: Tony Pitchford

Products

Powder coatings for passenger coach interiors, including Bonalux AG Series fire-resistant and graffiti-resistant coatings and RVP 491 Series (polyester) and 4620 Series (epoxy) fire-resistant coatings.

Ferro coatings have been supplied for rolling stock for London Underground Ltd's Piccadilly, Northern and Jubilee lines.

VERIFIED

Ferro International

Ferro International A/S
Tirsbækvej 15, DK-7120 Vejle Ø, Denmark
Tel: +45 75 895611   Fax: +45 75 895937

Key personnel

Managing Director: Erik Sørensen
Export Manager: Finn Bach Laursen

Products

Sliding interior doors for passenger vehicles, including electric and pneumatic doors operated by push-buttons or automatically by sensors; manually operated doors with spring return.

Recent contracts include the supply of partition walls with automatic doors to Adtranz, TGOJ Sweden and PFA Germany.

UPDATED

Fiat-SIG

Fiat-SIG Schienenfahrzeuge AG
CH-8212 Neuhausen am Rheinfall, Switzerland
Tel: +41 52 674 7206   Fax: +41 52 674 6431

Key personnel

Managing Director: Peter Gsell
Sales and Marketing Manager: Peter Huber

Corporate developments

SIG's rail vehicle business unit became Fiat-SIG Schienenfahrzeuge AG in 1996. The new company is owned by Fiat (60 per cent) and SIG (40 per cent).

Products

Completely closed, airtight and noise damping intercar gangways, suitable for rolling stock with screw, semi-permanent or automatic couplers.

Fiat-SIG has developed a new extra-wide intercar gangway with high standing passenger capacity for metro and suburban railway applications. With room for up to 10 standing passengers, the gangway is completely airtight and features good sound and thermal insulation. The floor is completely level, facilitating passenger movement, and both halves of the gangway are easily coupled from the outside.

VERIFIED

Fiberite

Fiberite Inc
2055 East Technology Circle, Tempe, Arizona 85284, USA
Tel: +1 602 730 2000   Fax: +1 602 730 2190
Email: info@fiberite.com

Key personnel
Chief Executive Officer: Dr James Ashton
President: Carl Smith
Treasurer: Ron Miller

Products
Composite materials, including resin systems, mainly epoxies and phenolics, prepegged on to a variety of fabrics such as graphite, glass, aramid and hybrids of these fabrics. These composites are used for the interiors of coaches for sidewall panels, ceilings, overhead storage bins and bulkheads, and conform to specific requirements for low smoke, flame and toxicity.

Recent contracts include BART in San Francisco and other mass transit systems.

UPDATED

Fiat-SIG extra-wide intercar gangway   **1996**

multilingual announcements. Finnish State Railways has been operating the system since 1995 and has over 225 modules in service.

UPDATED

and onboard supervision systems; diagnostic and maintenance support systems; train communication networks to the new UIC standards.

UPDATED

Finnyards

Finnyards Ltd Electronics
Naulakatu 3, FIN-33100 Tampere, Finland
Tel: +358 3 245 0111   Fax: +358 3 213 0188

Key personnel
Product Line Manager: Kalevi Poukkula
Sales Manager: Reijo Niittynen

Products
On-train automatic public address system which uses a Global Positioning System receiver to make announcements at predetermined locations. The system uses a CD-ROM for extra capacity in the recorded

FIREMA

FIREMA Trasporti SpA, Ercole Marelli Trazione Business Unit
Viale Edison 110, I-20099 Sesto S Giovanni (Milano), Italy
Tel: +39 2 24941   Fax: +39 2 248 3508

Key personnel
See entry in *Locomotives and powered passenger vehicles* section

Products
DC/DC and DC/AC static converting equipment for onboard auxiliary services; battery chargers; automation

Freudenberg

Freudenberg Dichtungs und Schwingungstechnik KG
Boxhanger Strasse 79/82, 10245 Berlin, Germany
Tel: +49 30 293 70374   Fax: +49 30 293 70286

Key personnel
Chairman: Jorg Sost
Management Board
  Herbert Fehrecke
  Norbert Schebesta
  Jorg Sost
Sales Manager, Railcar Industry, Europe: Erik Reule

Associate companies in Austria, Belgium, Brazil, Denmark, Finland, India, Japan, Luxembourg, Mexico, Netherlands, Norway, Poland, Russia, Singapore, Spain, Sweden, Switzerland, UK and USA.

Products
Rubber/metal elastic materials, resilient mountings.

NEW ENTRY

GEC Alsthom ACEC Transport

Rue Cambier Dupret 50-52, PO Box 4211, B-6001 Charleroi, Belgium
Tel: +32 71 44 54 11   Fax: +32 71 44 57 78

Key personnel
See entry in *Locomotives and powered passenger vehicles* section

Products
DC, AC and multivoltage static converters designed for the supply of rolling stock auxiliaries (AC and DC), such as air conditioning, heating and ventilation units, battery chargers and power-equipment cooling.

VERIFIED

GEC-Marconi

GEC-Marconi Aerospace Ltd
Abbey Works, Titchfield, Fareham, Hants PO14 4QA, UK
Tel: +44 1329 853000   Fax: +44 1329 853797

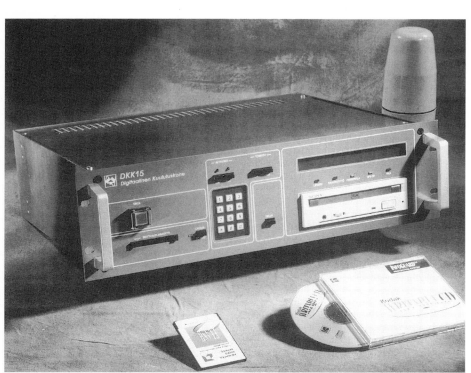

The Finnyards automatic on-train public address system uses a CD-ROM for the announcements   **1996**

Some
like it hot,
or cold, or...

air-conditioned.

We specialize in air-conditioning systems for rail vehicles. HFG has a comprehensive standard range of products offering you a number of different designs to meet your needs. Our engineers would also be happy to address your needs and specific requirements. Thanks to our know-how and years of successful experience, our team can turn your requirements into top quality, reliable systems all over the world. You get everything from the same source – from design and development through to manufacture – fast

It all depends on the conditioning –

and at competitive prices. We will provide you with whichever system functions best – no matter what the climate.

HFG

HAGENUK FAIVELEY GmbH

Germany: Industriestraße 60, D-04435 Schkeuditz, Tel.: 49 (34204) 85-300, Fax: 49 (34204) 85-302,
Westring 431, D-24118 Kiel, Tel.: 49 (431) 8001-300, Fax: 49 (431) 8001-302
UK: 17 Indus Acre, Avro Way Bowerhill, Melksham Wiltshire SN12 6TP, Tel.: 44 (1225) 70 27 40, Fax: 44 (1225) 70 27 50
China: Shanghai Hagenuk Refrigerating Machine Co. Ltd., 1481 Gong He Xin Road, Shanghai 20 00 72,
Tel.: 86 -21-56 62 58 04, Fax: 86 -21-56 62 55 00

Key personnel
Managing Director: C West
Sales & Marketing Director: P S Bradshaw

Products
Train management systems. GEC-Marconi supplies a databus-based system for the control and monitoring of subsystems and components throughout the train; status information is collated to provide diagnostic data for train maintenance. The company manufactures monitoring and diagnostic equipment for maintenance of way machinery.

GEC-Marconi is supplying its train management systems for London Underground Ltd's new Jubilee Line trains.

UPDATED

GEC-Marconi

GEC-Marconi Avionics Ltd, Navigation & Electro-Optic Systems Division
Silverknowes, Edinburgh EH4 4AD, UK
Tel: +44 131 343 5754   Fax: +44 131 343 5729

Key personnel
See entry in *Passenger information systems* section

Products
Electronic seat reservation systems; train monitoring and control systems; high-density DC/DC converters.

VERIFIED

GEC-Marconi

GEC-Marconi Defence Systems Ltd, Electronic Systems Division
The Grove, Warren Lane, Stanmore HA7 4LY, UK
Tel: +44 181 954 2311   Fax: +44 181 954 4909

Main works
The Airport, Portsmouth PO3 5PH, UK
Tel: +44 1705 675232   Fax: +44 1705 674041

Key personnel
Business Manager, Data Systems: D Gorshkov
Marketing Manager, Data Systems: D Abbott

Products
Design and manufacture of rail 'black box' accident data recorders, maintenance data recorders, and data replay systems using analysis software.

GEC-Marconi has supplied Vehicle Data Logging System (VDLS) units for Manchester Metrolink LRVs. The VDLS is used as an incident and accident data recording system, and is also configured to include maintenance and operational data monitoring and recording functions.

VERIFIED

GEC-Marconi Defence Systems VDLS unit   1995

GEZ

GEZ Gesellschaft für Elektrische Zugausrüstung mbH
Flinschstrasse 20, D-60388 Frankfurt/Main, Germany
A member of the Schaltbau group
Tel: +49 69 420 9060   Fax: +49 69 420 90613

Key personnel
Export Manager: F Vasel

GEC-Marconi Aerospace's cab-mounted wall display and driver's keypad wall display mounted in cab
1996

Products
Low-voltage equipment and electrical components for coaches, especially train lighting equipment, control panels, alternators, inverters.

UPDATED

Geze

Geze GmbH PO Box 1363, D-71226 Leonberg, Germany
Tel: +49 7152 203264   Fax: +49 7152 203514

UK subsidiary
Geze UK
4 Northumberland Court, Dukes Industrial Park, Chelmsford CM2 6UW
Tel: +44 1245 451093   Fax: +44 1245 451108

Key Personnel:
Marketing Services Manager: M Zeigler
Traffic Engineering Manager: Joachim Zimmerman
Project Management and Marketing: Manfred Wöhler

Products
Window and door systems (single, double and telescopic); closing mechanisms, electromechanical or electropneumatic drives for single- and double-leaf doors; actuators.

NEW ENTRY

GMT

Gummi Metall Technik GmbH
Liechtersmatten 5, D-77815 Bühl, Germany
Tel: +49 7223 8040   Fax: +49 7223 21075

Key personnel
Manager: Mrs S Engstler

UK Sales Office
GMT Rubber Metal Tecnic Ltd
The Sidings, Station Road, Guiseley, Leeds LS20 8BX
Tel: +44 1943 870670   Fax: +44 1943 870631

Products
Resilient components for rail vehicles.

UPDATED

Grammer

Grammer AG
PO Box 1454, 92204 Amberg, Germany
Tel: +49 9621 8800   Fax: +49 9621 880130

Products
Seating; seat belts.

NEW ENTRY

Halais

Georges Halais SA
6-10 rue Jean-Jacques Rousseau, F-93100
Montreuil-sous-Bois, France
Tel: +33 1 48 51 75 80   Fax: +33 1 48 51 73 39

Key personnel
Chief Executive Officer: M Cyril Josset

Products
Components for passenger car interiors including: stainless steel fittings, ceilings, interior doors and walls, table lamps, water heaters, lighting fixtures, handles and handrails, hinges, luggage racks, blinds, locks, slots for seat reservation cards, litter bins, ashtrays, picture frames, tables and folding tables.

Recent contracts include TGV Duplex (SNCF), MP89 (RATP), AVE (RENFE), MI2N (SNCF/RATP) and Eurostar (EPS/SNCB/SNCF).

VERIFIED

Hexcel Composites

Duxford, Cambridge CB2 4QD, UK
Tel: +44 1223 833141   Fax: +44 1223 838808

Key personnel
Head of Sales & Marketing: Sabine Preston
Marketing: Richard Roberts
Regional Sales Manager: Georges Soccal

Products
Hexlite® sandwich panels for interiors and structures; honeycomb cores (metallic and non-metallic); honeycomb energy absorbers; epoxy and phenolic prepregs; reinforcement fabrics, redux film adhesives.

Recent contracts include structural flooring for Schindler Wagon (IC2000), sandwich panels for Fiat Ferroviaria Pendolino interiors, energy absorbers for TGV trainsets and prepregs for SNCF.

UPDATED

HFG

Hagenuk Faiveley GmbH
Industriestrasse 60, D-04435 Schkeuditz, Germany
Tel: +49 34204 85300   Fax: +49 34204 85302

Key personnel
General Manager: W D Karneboge
Engineering Director: H Schmerler
Sales Manager, Northern Europe:
  B Lehmann-Matthaei
Sales Manager, Southern Europe & Overseas: S Net
Sales Manager, Eastern Europe: J Kreutzmann

Products
Heating and ventilation, air conditioning, heaters for hot water supply and refrigeration systems; microcomputer-controlled temperature control systems; pressure protection systems.

Newly developed is the Air-Cycle air conditioning system for rail vehicles

Air-Cycle and air conditioning equipment has been supplied to DB for ICE3 and ICT trainsets; air conditioning equipment has been supplied to Metro Bangkok and Norway for the Gardemoen line (Oslo airport-city centre shuttle).

UPDATED

Products

Gangway diaphragms, inter-car gap protection systems and other fabric-reinforced rubber products.

Contracts include inter-car gap protection mouldings for GEC Alsthom rolling stock for London Underground Northern and Jubilee Lines; fire-resistant kick strips on WCL ticket gates for London Underground.

UPDATED

Parker Pneumatic

Parker Hannifin plc
Pneumatic Division, Walkmill Lane, Bridgtown, Cannock, Staffordshire WS11 3LR, UK
Tel: +44 1543 456000   Fax: +44 1543 456001

Key personnel

Application manager: Brian Umney

Products

Parker manufactures pneumatic systems with a range of applications in rolling stock, including seat adjustment cylinders (Italian ETR 500 high-speed train), pneumatic circuit blocks for onboard toilet flush (French TGV), door opening control panel (ETR 500), valves and cylinders for heating and ventilating (Channel Tunnel Nightstock).

UPDATED

People Seating

People Seating Ltd
Unit 9, Washington Street Industrial Estate, Netherton, Dudley DY2 9RE, UK
Tel: +44 1384 257124   Fax: +44 1384 242106

Key personnel

Managing Director: David J Poston
Engineering Director: Robert L Scott

Products

Passenger and driver seating, interior trim components.

People Seating has supplied seating for Class 166 and Class 465 multiple-unit trainsets in the UK, and to Kowloon—Canton Railway.

VERIFIED

Permali

Permali Gloucester Ltd
Bristol Road, Gloucester GL1 5TT, UK
Tel: +44 1452 528282   Fax: +44 1452 507409

Key personnel

Managing Director: G King
Sales Manager, Transport: A Rogers

Products

Decorative phenolic laminates for passenger coach interiors (draught screens, side panels, end walls). Resin transfer moulded phenolic items for interior shapes.

Recent contracts include the supply of laminates (end walls and draught screens) to London Underground Ltd and phenolic foam to GEC Alsthom Metro-Cammell for use as core material in Channel Tunnel Nightstock gangways.

VERIFIED

Phoenix

Phoenix AG
PO Box 900854, 88 Hannoversche Strasse, D-21048 Hamburg, Germany
Tel: +49 40 7667 2277   Fax: +49 40 7667 2211

Key personnel

See entry in *Bogies and suspensions, wheels and axles* section

Products

Doorseals and windowseals.

VERIFIED

Northern Rubber inter-car protection mouldings for London Underground rolling stock **1997**

Pilkington Aerospace

Pilkington Aerospace Ltd
Eckersall Road, Kings Norton, Birmingham B38 8SR, UK
Tel: +44 121 606 4100   Fax: +44 121 458 6880
Email: 106321.1047@compuserv.com

Key personnel

Directors
   Sales & Marketing: R A Harper
   Technical: M Burgess
   Manufacturing: C J Woodhouse
   Managing: P Molineux
Sales & Marketing Manager: N L Stringer

Products

Design and manufacture of heated/unheated, curved/flat, framed/unframed impact-resistant transparencies for railway and transit industries.

Among the company's products are multilaminate glass/plastic windscreen assemblies for locomotives and rolling stock, incorporating high impact-resistant performance, integral electrical de-icing system and fully bonded aluminium alloy frames.

UPDATED

Pimatic

Pimatic Oy
Klaavolantie 1, PO Box 21, FIN-32701 Huittinen, Finland
Tel: +358 32 566721   Fax: +358 32 568501

Key personnel

Managing Director: Martti Pulli
Export Manager: Paul Nileleu

Corporate development

Pimatic has become part of Sophus Berensden International.

Products

Door systems and pneumatic components for railway vehicles.

Recent contracts include the supply of interior and gangway doors for X2000 trainsets for Swedish State Railways.

UPDATED

Pintsch Bamag

Pintsch Bamag Antriebs- und Verkehrstechnik GmbH
A member of the Schaltbau Group
PO Box 10 04 20, D-46524 Dinslaken, Germany
Tel: +49 2064 6020   Fax: +49 2064 602266

Products

Power supply equipment, inverters for train lighting, electronic door controls and air conditioning equipment, tail lights.

Recent developments include a new system for the control and supervision of folding, hinged and sliding coach doors which features fault diagnosis and is adaptable to all types of car.

UPDATED

Powertron

Powertron Ltd
Ainsworth Place, Cambridge CB1 2PQ, UK
Tel: +44 1223 327627   Fax: +44 1223 314069

Key personnel

Managing Director: Miles Rackowe
Technical Director: Andy Dickeson
Financial Controller & Quality Assurance Manager:
   Sue Benham
Production Manager: Richard Mainwaring
Quality Manager: John Short
Commercial Manager: Mike Carter

Products

High-reliability switch mode power supplies and DC-DC converters in the power range 10 W-2 kW. A principle area of activity is DC-DC converters for use on railway rolling stock. Applications include lighting, communications, brake monitoring equipment, fire protection equipment and train management systems.

UPDATED

Protec

Partner fur Umweittechnick GmbH
A member of the Schaltbau Group
Parksteiner Strasse 51, D-92637 Weiden, Germany
Tel: +49 961 670060   Fax: +49 961 670 0620

Products

Bio toilet system

NEW ENTRY

Railcare

Railcare Ltd
3 Ibstock Road, Coventry CV6 6NL, UK
Tel: +44 1203 364897   Fax: +44 1203 644074

Key personnel

See entry in *Locomotives and powered passenger vehicles* section

Products

Passenger coach equipment overhaul; vehicle exterior and interior design.

VERIFIED

Reidler Decal

The Reidler Decal Corporation
1 Reidler Road, Industrial Park, St Clair, Pennsylvania 17970, USA
Tel: +1 717 429 1812   Fax: +1 717 429 1528

Key personnel

President: Richard Reidler
Vice-President, Operations: Barry Frey

Products

Rail-Cal™ decals for rail vehicles, featuring heavy adhesive for pitted surfaces and a double-baking process for chemical and solvent protection; prismatic delineators to make rail vehicles more visible in poor light conditions.

VERIFIED

RG Manufacturing

RG Manufacturing Ltd
Brakey Road, Weldon Industrial Estate North, Corby NN17 5LU, UK
Tel: +44 1536 263691   Fax: +44 1536 203428

Key personnel

Managing Director: C J Ayrton
Technical Director and General Manager: E R Clark
Sales Executive: D C Baker

Products

Passenger seating, including the Networker and Weldon models. Tube bending and fabrication.

Recent contracts include the supply of Networker seats for Class 165, 166, 365 and 465 multiple-units in the UK and luggage stacks for Eurostar high-speed trainsets for EPS/SNCB/SNCF.

VERIFIED

SAB WABCO

Cardo Railway AB
Roskildevägen 1B, PO Box 193, S-201 21 Malmö, Sweden
Tel: +46 40 350460　Fax: +46 40 303803

Key personnel
See main entry in *Brakes and drawgear* section

Products
Air-operated and electric swing plug doors for mainline vehicles, noise reducing V wheels for LRVs; windscreen wiper systems; pantograph control units; complete control units for pneumatic and electropneumatic systems for rolling stock applications.

VERIFIED

SAFT

156 avenue de Metz, F-93230 Romainville, France
Tel: +33 1 49 15 36 00　Fax: +33 1 49 15 34 00
Email (Railway Product Manager):
　michael.lippert@saft.alcatel-alsthom.fr

Key personnel
Managing Director, Industrial Battery Group:
　Jean-Claude Dutailly
Marketing and Sales Director, Industrial Battery Group:
　Pascal Moinon
Railway Product Manager: Michael Lippert

Subsidiaries
Argentina, Australia, Austria, Belgium, Brazil, Canada, Cyprus, Finland, Germany, Hong Kong, Italy, Korea, Malaysia, Mexico, Netherlands, Norway, Singapore, Spain, Sweden, UK and USA.

Products
SAFT Nife Ni-Cd batteries, pocket plates or sintered/pbe types for starting diesel railcars, emergency supply, security and so on. The company supplies railways in 56 countries.
　Recent contracts include supply of units for the Pendolino tilting trainsets, passenger coaches for SNCB, AM96 and I11 trains, Stockholm metro, Kuala Lumpur LRVs and London Heathrow Express.

UPDATED

Sanivac

Sanivac Vakuumtechnik GmbH
Hafenstrasse 32a, D-22880, Wedel, Germany
Tel: +49 4103 91680　Fax: +49 4103 916890

Key personnel
Sales: Ian F Goodwin

Products
Toilet compartments, vacuum toilets, retention tanks.

NEW ENTRY

SBF

SBF Spezialleuchten Wurzen GmbH
Badergraben 16, D-04808 Wurzen, Germany
Tel: +49 3425 920181　Fax: +49 3425 920178

Key personnel
Managing Director: Hans D Sehn
Sales Manager: Fritz Strobelt

Products
Light fittings for passenger car interiors and exteriors.
　Recent contracts include the supply of light fittings to DB AG, DWA and Adtranz.

VERIFIED

Schaltbau

Schaltbau AG
PO Box 801540, D-81615 Munich, Germany
Tel: +49 89 930050　Fax: +49 89 9300 5352

Works
Industrie Strasse 12, D-84149 Velden/Vils, Germany
Dietmar-von-Ayst Strasse 10, D-94501 Aldersbach, Germany

Key personnel
Chairman: Heinzwerner Feusser
Board Members: Albert Johannes Jonker, Manfred John
Manager, Rail Division: Albrecht Rudolph
Export Manager: Siegfried Hohm
Marketing: Wolf Dieter Bloch

Products
High-voltage equipment for passenger coaches; electrical equipment for diesel-hydraulic railcars; electrical components for locomotives and metro trainsets.

UPDATED

Schindler

Schindler Waggon AG
CH-4133 Pratteln, Switzerland
Tel: +41 61 825 9111　Fax: +41 61 825 9205

Key personnel
See entry in *Locomotives and powered passenger vehicles* section

Products
Seats; interior fittings including luggage racks and wall-mounted tables; interior doors and external door systems; self-contained submodules for passenger coaches, including toilet modules incorporating compartment walls, toilet and water tanks; walls, ceilings and other interior components.
　Recent contracts include the supply of lighweight seats for Swiss Federal Railways (SBB), featuring wooden frames and other biodegradable/recyclable components.

VERIFIED

Semco

Semco Odense A/S
PO Box 120, Svendborgvej 226, DK-5260 Odense S, Denmark
Tel: +45 65 683300　Fax: +45 65 957374

Key personnel
Department Manager: Horst Kirchner
Sales Engineer: John Christensen

Products
Vacuum toilet systems; complete toilet compartments; toilet system components, including tanks and sensors.

UPDATED

SEPSA

Sistemas Electrónicos de Potencia SA
Albatros 7 and 9, (Pol Ind) La Estación, E-28320 Pinto, Madrid, Spain
Tel: +34 1 691 5261　Fax: +34 1 691 3977

Key personnel
President: Nicolas Fuster
General Manager: Felix Ramos
Commercial Director: Antonio Sosa
Technical Director: Carlos de la Viesca

Products
Static converters (DC, AC and multivoltage), microprocessor-controlled, for the supply of rail auxiliary equipment (air conditioning, heating, compressors and lighting), converters, inverters, choppers, rectifiers and battery chargers.
　Passenger information systems, public address, station announcers, displays. PLC systems to control both the auxiliary equipment and traction. Crash event recording equipment. ATP systems.
　Recent orders include provision of both static converters and information/control systems for MTRC Hong Kong, and static converters rated at 400 kVA, UIC multivoltage, for DB Germany.

UPDATED

SERINOX

route de Sainte Marguerite, PO Box 70, F-63307 Thiers Cedex
Tel: +33 4 73 80 22 01　Fax: +33 4 73 80 72 85

Key personnel
General Manager: Philippe Furodet

Products
Steel components for toilet systems and toilet compartments, including retention tanks, toilet bowls, litter bins, door handles and wash basins.
　Recent contracts include the supply of retention tanks for ICE-2 high-speed trainsets for DB AG and stainless steel seats for metro trainsets for Guangzhou (China) and Hong Kong.

VERIFIED

Lightweight seat for SBB by Schindler　1996

SEPSA 400 kVA multivoltage static converter for DB Germany Talgo trains　1997

Siemens

Siemens Aktiengesellschaft, Transportation
Systems Group
Mainline Rolling Stock Division (VT6)
PO Box 3240, D-91050 Erlangen, Germany
Tel: +49 9131 724157   Fax: +49 9131 726840

Key personnel

See entry in *Locomotives and powered passenger
vehicles* section

Products

Electrical components for passenger coaches; electrical
power supply systems for passenger coach auxiliaries;
inverters, single and multivoltage power supply units,
choppers and battery chargers.

Power supply systems have recently been supplied to
DACH Hotelzug AG, DB AG, Eurotunnel and ÖBB.

VERIFIED

Siemens

Siemens Schienenfahrzeugtechnik GmbH
PO Box 9293, D-24152 Kiel, Germany
Tel: +49 431 399503   Fax: +49 431 399 5562

Key personnel

See entry in *Locomotives and powered passenger
vehicles* section

Products

DC, AC and multivoltage solid-state converter systems for
LRVs, emus, locomotives, railcars and coaches for supply
of AC and DC auxiliary power for air conditioning units,
heating and ventilation units. Power converter systems for
locomotives for power supply of a complete train
consisting of air conditioned passenger coaches. Battery-
charging systems. Design and installation of switching
cabinets for coaches. Commissioning and installation of
electrical components in passenger coaches and
locomotives.

VERIFIED

Siemens

Siemens Transportation Systems Ltd
Sopers Lane, Poole BH17 7ER, UK
Tel: +44 1202 782067   Fax: +44 1202 782838

Key personnel

General Manager: P C Lavars
Sales Manager: A J Rose
Marketing Manager: S Heron

Products

On-train communications networks for control and
monitoring of equipment on locomotive-hauled coaches
and multiple-unit cars. Associated passenger information,
alarm and communications equipment, both audio and
visual, using LED and flat-screen TV technology.
Complete integrated systems with train position, radio
and data transfer capability and system components.

Siemens on-train systems have been supplied to a
number of European main line operators.

VERIFIED

Sigma Industries

Sigma Industries Pty Ltd
4 Bachell Avenue, Lidcombe, New South Wales 2141,
Australia
Tel: +61 2 330 7100   Fax: +61 2 330 7199

Key personnel

General Manager: Keith Allen
Business Development Manager: Geoff Rule

Subsidiary

Sigma Air-Conditioning Inc
321 South Fairbank, Addison, Illinois 60101, USA
Tel: +1 708 628 3244   Fax: +1 708 628 6623

Key personnel

President: Robert Darling

Products

Air conditioning equipment for all types of rolling stock,
LRVs and locomotives, including heating and emergency
ventilation facilities.

Sigma features integrated modular roof-mounted
package systems, split systems with underfloor
condenser as required, or wall-mounted systems for
fitment to locomotive cabs. The cooling capacity of air
conditioning units ranges from 5 kW for cab air
conditioning up to 56 kW for air conditioning of large
capacity double-deck cars. System control is offered via
programmable logic control or by relay logic, with plug-in
diagnostic facility as required.

Sigma air conditioning is widely used in Australia and
Japan. Recent contracts include Eastern & Oriental
Express (Singapore—Bangkok); LRVs for Kuala Lumpur,
Malaysia; and diesel railcars for State Railway of Thailand.

VERIFIED

SMA

SMA Regelsysteme GmbH
Hannoversche Strasse 1-5, D-34266 Niestetal, Germany
Tel: +49 561 95220   Fax: +49 561 9522 100

Key personnel

Managing Director Power Engineering: Günther Cramer
Sales Managers: Birgit Wilde-Velasco, Uwe Kleinkauf

Products

Single- and multi-voltage power supply systems for
passenger coaches; power electronics and
microprocessor systems for railway applications; battery
chargers; battery converters; diagnostic systems.

More than 1,000 battery chargers and power supply
systems have been supplied since 1990 to railways in
Europe, mainly to DB.

UPDATED

SMC

SMC Transit International (Australia)
18 Hudson Avenue, Castle Hill, New South Wales 2154,
Australia
Tel: +61 2 680 3222   Fax: +61 2 634 7764

Key personnel

See entry in *Electric traction equipment* section

Products

Pneumatic and electric door systems for passenger
vehicles.

VERIFIED

SMC

SMC Transit International (UK)
4-5 Clarendon Drive, Wymbush, Milton Keynes MK8 8DA,
UK
Tel: +44 1908 568791   Fax: +44 1908 569163

Key personnel

Managing Director: E H H Mason
Division Manager: G Bruce
Commercial Manager: L Seward

Corporate structure

SMC Transit International has four sector headquarters in
UK, USA, Australia and Japan. As part of the SMC
Corporation, SMC Transit International provides after-
sales and local site support in over 40 countries
worldwide.

Products

Pneumatic and electric door systems and control
equipment, including sliding, plug and bifolding door
systems, gangway doors, emergency detrainment doors
and ramps for disabled passengers. Platform door
equipment, secondary air suspension systems and
pneumatic components including actuators and solenoid
valves.

Recent contracts include the supply of equipment and components for the Manchester Metrolink, Kowloon—Canton Railway Corporation, Hong Kong MTRC, Jacksonville and Boston, USA, and Malaysia.

VERIFIED

Specialty Bulb

The Specialty Bulb Co Inc
80 Orville Drive, Bohemia, New York 11716, USA
Tel: +1 516 589 3393   Fax: +1 516 563 3089

Key personnel
Manager: Victor Beja

Products
Light bulbs for passenger coaches.

VERIFIED

Stone India

Stone India Ltd
16 Taratalla Road, Calcutta 700 088, India
Tel: +91 33 478 4661   Fax: +91 33 478 4886

Key personnel
See entry in *Brakes and drawgear* section

Products
Train lighting alternators, air conditioning equipment, pantographs and rubber components.

VERIFIED

Stone International

Stone International
A member of Vapor Group
10655 Henri Bourassa West, Montreal, Quebec H4S 1A1, Canada

Stone UK Limited (Stone International)
Unit 9, Crossways Business Park, Stone Marshes, Dartford DA2 6QG, UK
Tel: +44 1322 289323   Fax: +44 1322 289282
Managing Director: Anthony J Walsh

Stone Safety Service
240 South Main Street, South Hackensack, New Jersey 07606, USA
Tel: +1 201 489 0200   Fax: +1 201 489 9362
Vice-President: Vincent Mirandi

Products
Air conditioning, heating, pressure ventilation and temperature control equipment, static inverters, battery chargers, alternators, DC motors.

UPDATED

Stone UK

Stone UK Limited
A member of Vapor Group of Westinghouse Air Brake Company
Crossways Business Park, Stone Marshes, Dartford DA2 6QG, UK
Tel: +44 1322 289323   Fax: +44 1322 289282

Key personnel
Managing Director: Anthony J Walsh
Commercial Manager: Lynne Smith
Sales and Marketing Director: Nigel Twort

Products
Air conditioning, lighting and ventilation equipment, train lighting and temperature control equipment, auxiliary/power generation equipment including alternators, inverters and connectors.
Contracts include: Singapore and Taipei; Thailand and Indonesian Railways sleeping and executive coaches; cab air conditioning systems for Singapore, Hong Kong and London Transport cars; KCRC emus; refurbishment of MTR and KCRC air conditioning systems in Hong Kong.

NEW ENTRY

Sütrak

Sütrak Transportkälte GmbH
Heinkelstrasse 5, D-71272 Renningen, Germany
Tel: +49 7159 9230   Fax: +49 7159 6362

Products
Air conditioning systems for passenger vehicles, available in roof-mounted, modular and compact configurations. All systems are available with environmentally friendly refrigerant. Route number and destination display systems, audio/video units, mini-galley equipment.

VERIFIED

TBA

TBA Textiles Ltd
PO Box 40, Rochdale OL12 7EQ, UK
Tel: +44 1706 47422   Fax: +44 1706 354295

Key personnel
Managing Director: Dr A V Ruddy
Managers
  Business: Ron Bartram
  Sales: Alan Schofield
  Marketing: Ellen Archer
  European Sales: Norman Wolf

Products
Fireblocking and anti-vandal fabrics for passenger transport seating. Fire resisting/insulating liners for use within the bodywork. Moulded fire-resistant seat pans.
Recent contracts include work for London Underground Ltd and work on Eurostar and Nightstar stock used on Channel Tunnel services.

VERIFIED

Teknoware

Teknoware Oy
Ilmarisentie 8, FIN-15200 Lahti, Finland
Tel: +358 3 883020   Fax: +358 3 883 0240

Key personnel
European Export Manager: Leif Damstén
Overseas Export Manager: Esa Melkko

Products
Inverters/ballasts and fluorescent lighting systems for LRVs and passenger coaches.
Recent developments include UIC 555.1 standard inverters for railway use, protected against radio interference up to EN55015 level and certified to ISO 9001 standard.

VERIFIED

Temoinsa

Técnicas Modulares e Industriales SA
Poligono Industrial Congost, Avenida San Julián 100, E-08400 Granollers, Barcelona, Spain
Tel: +34 3 846 6835   Fax: +34 3 846 6486

Key personnel
Chairman: Alvaro Colomer
Chief Executive Officer: Miguel de Sagarra
General Manager: Jose M Pedret
Commercial Manager: Antonio Fábregas

Interior of coach after refurbishment by Temoinsa
1997

Products
Design, manufacture, engineering and technical assistance of components for fitting out passenger coach interiors with fully developed modular systems, including air conditioning, heating and ventilation, vacuum toilet systems; high-technology composites, control systems, passenger information systems and electric panels.
Turnkey projects for complete interiors of new vehicles and refurbishment.

UPDATED

Thorn Automation

Thorn Automation Ltd
Armitage Road, Rugeley, Staffordshire WS15 1DR, UK
Tel: +44 1889 585151   Fax: +44 1889 577324

Key personnel
See entry in *Signalling and telecommunications* section.

Products
Vehicle-mounted auxiliary power supplies. DC to AC inverters; single-phase AC to three-phase AC inverters; DC to DC converters; battery chargers.

VERIFIED

Thorn Transport Lighting

Thorn Transport Lighting Ltd
Elstree Way, Borehamwood WD6 1HZ, UK
Tel: +44 181 905 1313/967 6336
Fax: +44 181 967 6337/6343

Associate company
Atlas International (qv)

Main works address
Merrington Trading Estate, Spennymoor, UK

Key personnel
General Manager: R A Richardson

Products
Lighting components for rail vehicles; inverter ballasts for fluorescent lighting 24, 36, 52, 70/72, 110 V DC, AC; ballasts for various voltages; lampholders and other lighting accessories including luminaires and subassemblies of standard or special types; AC and DC converters for low-voltage tungsten halogen lamps for 12 V reading lights and locomotive headlights.
Recent developments include a range of new inverter ballasts for fluorescent lamps to the European standard.
The company has equipped the former British Rail, London Underground and Swedish State Railways and has supplied equipment to many European and Asian countries.

UPDATED

Toshiba

Toshiba Corporation
Railway Projects Department
Toshiba Building, 1-1 Shibaura 1-chome, Minato-ku, Tokyo 105, Japan
Tel: +81 3 3457 4924   Fax: +81 3 3457 8385

Key personnel
See entry in *Locomotives and powered passenger vehicles* section

Club car interior for Canada fitted out by Temoinsa
1997

Company Listing by Country

ARGENTINA
Callegari
Cometarsa
SABB

AUSTRALIA
Adtranz
ANI Railway Transportation Group
Gemco
Goninan
Perry

AUSTRIA
Jenbacher
Siemens SGP

BELGIUM
BREC

BRAZIL
CCC
Engesa-FNV
Mafersa
Santa Matilde
Soma

CANADA
AMF
Innotermodal
National Steel Car
Procor
Trenton Works

CHINA
China National Railway Locomotive and Rolling Stock
Industry Corporation (LORIC)
Dalian Locomotive
Qiqihar
Qishuyan

CROATIA
Duro Daković

CZECH REPUBLIC
MSV

DENMARK
Adtranz

EGYPT
SEMAF

FINLAND
Rautaruukki

FRANCE
ABRF Industries
Arbel
Marrel
Orval
RE.MA.FER
Sambre et Meuse

GERMANY
Adtranz
DWA
Ferrostaal
Graaff
Haacon
Hoogovens
Linke-Hofmann-Busch
Talbot
Windhoff

HUNGARY
Ganz-Hunslet
MÁV

INDIA
Bharat Wagon & Engineering
Braithwaite
Burn Standard
Cimmco International
HDC
Jessop
KT Steel
PEC
Texmaco

INDONESIA
INKA

IRAN
Wagon Pars

ITALY
Breda
CFC
Costamasnaga
Fiat
FIREMA
Keller
OFV
Reggiane
SGI

JAPAN
Alna Koki
Fuji Car
Kawasaki
Kinki Sharyo
Nippon Sharyo
Wakamatsu Sharyo

KOREA, SOUTH
Daewoo
Hanjin
Hyundai

MOROCCO
SCIF

MOZAMBIQUE
Cometal

NEW ZEALAND
Price

NORWAY
Adtranz
Finsam

PAKISTAN
Pakistan Railways Carriage

POLAND
Kolmex
Konstal
Zastal

PORTUGAL
Adtranz

ROMANIA
Astra
Meva
Mecanoexportimport

RUSSIAN FEDERATION
BMZ
Energomachexport
Lyudinovo Locomotive Works
NWRZ
Uralvagonzavod

SERBIA
Goša

SLOVAKIA
Tatravagónka

SOUTH AFRICA
Dorbyl

SPAIN
Babcock & Wilcox
CAF
GEC Alsthom Transporte SA
Intamodal-Eimar
Tafesa

SWEDEN
Adtranz

SWITZERLAND
Adtranz
Cattaneo
Stag
Tuchschmid

TURKEY
Tülomsas

UK
Bombardier Prorail
Cromweld Steels
Davis
EKA
Hunslet-Barclay
Oleo
Powell Duffryn Rail Projects
Railcare
RFS Engineering
Ray Smith

USA
ACF
Amherst
Anbel
Difco
Dorsey
The Gregg Company
Gunderson
Johnstown America
Portec
SEEC
Strick
Thrall
Transcisco Industries Inc
Transcisco Rail Services Co
Trinity Industries
Union Tank
Unity
Wabash National

ZIMBABWE
More Wear
Zeco

ABRF Industries

Ateliers Bretons de Réalisations Ferroviaires Industries
PO Box 19, ZI rue Lafayette, F-44141 Châteaubriant Cedex, France
Tel: +33 2 40 81 19 20   Fax: +33 2 40 28 02 02

Key personnel
General Manager: Jean-Luc Remondeau
Commercial and Technical Director: Gérard Gueguin
Commercial Engineer: Jean-Pierre Cadiou

Products
Freight wagons, including 'Easiloader' curtain hood wagon for general merchandise, tank and hopper wagons.

VERIFIED

ACF

ACF Industries Inc
620 North Second Street, St Charles, Missouri 63301, USA
Tel: +1 314 940 5000   Fax: +1 314 940 5020

Key personnel
President: Roger Wynkoop
Vice-President, Sales and Leasing: George Sullivan

Products
Specialised covered hopper and tank wagons, including the Pressureaide® pressure differential covered hopper capable of operating with internal pressure up to 14.5 lb/in^2, for fast and efficient unloading of dry bulk products to remote silos. Freight wagon components, outlets, valves and trailer hitches.

VERIFIED

Adtranz

ABB Daimler-Benz Transportation GmbH
Saatwinkler Damm 42-43, D-13627 Berlin, Germany
Tel: +49 30 38320   Fax: +49 30 3832 2000

Key personnel
See entry in *Locomotives and powered passenger vehicles* section

Products
Development, design, engineering, sales and production of all types of freight vehicles, systems and equipment for all railway types, systems and track gauges; customer support services for freight vehicles including commissioning and warranty, supply of spare parts, refurbishment and repair, servicing and maintenance.
    Recent contracts include the maintenance of 412 tank wagons for Esso by Adtranz Customer Support Ltd, UK.

VERIFIED

Alna Koki

Alna Koki Company Ltd
4-5 Higashi Naniwa-cho 1-chome, Amagasaki 660, Japan
Tel: +81 6 401 7283   Fax: +81 6 401 6168

Key personnel
See entry in *Locomotives and powered passenger vehicles* section

Products
General purpose freight wagons; low-floor wagons; tank wagons; dump wagons.

VERIFIED

AMF

AMF
1830 Le Ber Street, Montréal, Québec H3K 2A4, Canada
Tel: +1 514 925 3826   Fax: +1 514 925 3828

Key personnel
See entry in *Non-powered passenger vehicles* section

Products
Manufacture, remanufacture and repair of freight wagons and component parts.
    Recent contracts include the design and supply of 75 ore hopper wagons for Québec Iron and Titanium Inc, and 24 flat cars for CTA New York and the remanufacture of six flat cars for Staten Island Railroad.

UPDATED

Amherst

Amherst Industries, Inc
Port Amherst, Charleston, West Virginia 25306, USA
Tel: +1 304 926 1122   Fax: +1 304 926 1136

Key personnel
President: Charles T Jones

Products
Freight wagons; interior linings for tank and hopper wagons.

VERIFIED

Anbel

The Anbel Group
PO Box 19775, Houston, Texas 77224-9775, USA
Tel: +1 713 447 0303   Fax: +1 713 447 0505

Key personnel
President: Kenneth Roy Nichols

Products
Freight wagons.

VERIFIED

ANI Railway Transportation Group

ANI Railway Transportation Group
PO Box 105, Maud Street, Waratah, New South Wales 2298, Australia
Tel: +61 49 412600   Fax: +61 49 412661
Email: bkcad@anibradken.com.au

Key personnel
See entry in *Brakes and drawgear* section

Products
Freight wagons, including container, cement, coal and grain wagons. Bogies for wagons, locomotives and passenger cars. Drawgear sets, including couplers, draftgear and yokes. Spare parts for freight wagons, locomotives and passenger cars. Service, maintenance and refurbishment of freight wagons, locomotives and passenger cars.
    Recent contracts include the supply of 40 cement wagons to Siam Cement, Thailand, 500 container wagons for KTMB Malaysia, prototype slab wagon for NRC Australia, 864 bogies for QR, 200 bogies for CRA Australia, 200 drawgear sets for tandem coal wagons for QR Australia, reconditioning and upgrading of 500 wagons for NRC and upgrading of 26 five-pack stand-alone well wagon sets for NRC.

UPDATED

Arbel

Arbel Fauvet Rail
40 blvd Henri Sellier, F-92156 Suresnes Cedex, France
Tel: +33 1 41 18 11 00   Fax: +33 1 47 28 71 39

Works
140 rue du Paradis, F-59500 Douai, France

Key personnel
President: Jean-Marc Blanc
Commercial Director: Georges Carbonnières

Corporate developments
In September 1995, Arbel invested US$15 million in a joint venture with Ludinovski Teplovozostroitelny Zavod (LTZ),

a Russian diesel locomotive builder, to produce wagons in the Russian Federation. The new venture, Arbel-Ludinovo-Wagons (ALW) is owned 51 per cent by Arbel, 49 per cent by LTZ. ALW was producing a gauge-changing design that would be able to run between the rail systems of the Russian Federation and Western Europe without any need for transhipping goods at the border point.

Products
Design, manufacture and refurbishment of all types of freight wagons and tank containers.
    Recent contracts include 450 intermodal wagons and 350 fully enclosed car-carrying wagons for freight services through the Channel Tunnel; 150 double-deck car-carrying wagons; 250 heavy-duty flat wagons for the transport of tracked tanks and other heavy loads; 200 covered wagons; and over 300 tank wagons for the transport of chemicals and liquefied gases.

VERIFIED

Astra

Societatea Comerciala Astra Vagoane Arad SA
Calea Aurel Vlaicu 41-43, R-2900 Arad, Romania
Tel: +40 57 231255/235379
Fax: +40 57 250169/233988

Key personnel
See entry in *Locomotives and powered passenger vehicles* section

Products
Freight wagons, including open, flat and covered wagons, tipping and dump wagons, gondolas, grain and ore wagons and 4, 6, 10, 12, or 20-axle vehicles for the transport of heavy cargoes. Specialised wagons for the iron and steel industry, for transport of coke, hot ingots, molten steel and other products.
    Recent contracts include construction of side-tipping 105 tonne wagons for 1,520 mm gauge; gondola wagons; coal wagons; 120 tonne ore wagons for 1,435 mm gauge; flat wagons for banana and sugar cane crops; tank wagons (40, 93 and 95 cu m capacity); grain wagons; trucks for transport of containers and trucks; 72 tonne grain hopper wagons for 1,520 mm.

UPDATED

Babcock & Wilcox

Babcock & Wilcox Española
PO Box 294, Alameda Recalde 27, E-48009 Bilbao, Spain
Tel: +34 4 424 1761   Fax: +34 4 423 7092

Key personnel
See entry in *Locomotives and powered passenger vehicles* section

Products
Freight wagons, rolling stock for the steel industry, railway slewing cranes.

VERIFIED

Fully enclosed car-carrying wagon by Arbel   1995

Braithwaite 24-wheel special-purpose wagon with 182 tonnes payload **1997**

Bharat Wagon & Engineering

Bharat Wagon & Engineering Company Ltd
(A Government of India undertaking)
C Block, 5th Floor, Maurya Lok, Dak Bungalow Road,
Patna 800 001, India
Tel: +91 612 226699   Fax: +91 612 222147

Key personnel
General Manager: S P Singh

Products
Freight wagons.

VERIFIED

BMZ

JSC Bryansk Engineering Works
ulica Ulyanova 26, 241 015 Bryansk, Russian Federation
Tel: +7 832 55 8673/0030   Fax: +7 95 203 3395

Key personnel
See entry in *Locomotives and powered passenger vehicles* section

Products
Freight wagons, including grain hoppers and refrigerated wagons. Specialised wagons for the iron and steel industry. Refrigerated containers.

VERIFIED

Bombardier Prorail Ltd

A member of the Bombardier Transportation Group
Horbury, Wakefield WF4 5QH, UK
Tel: +44 1924 271881   Fax: +44 1924 274650

Key personnel
See entry in *Locomotives and powered passenger vehicles* section

Products
Design and manufacture of freight wagons, including bogie petroleum tank wagons, bogie hopper wagons, nuclear flask wagons and wagons for engineering and works trains.
Recent contracts include the supply of 60 90 tonne petroleum tank wagons, 22 bogie hopper wagons, 23 wagons for the construction of London Underground Ltd's Jubilee Line Extension and six 170 tonne nuclear flask wagons.
Recent export orders for Bombardier Prorail include the supply of LPG wagons to Ianrodd Eirann and works wagons for the Ankara metro, Turkey. The company has undertaken conversion and modification work on over 250 wagons.

UPDATED

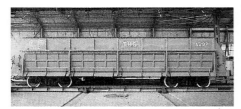

Braithwaite coal hopper wagon for Vietnam Railways **1997**

Bottom-discharge hopper wagon for the transport of copper concentrates for Gécamines-Exploitation, Zaïre, by BREC

Braithwaite

Braithwaite & Company Ltd
(A Government of India undertaking and subsidiary of BBUNL)
5 Hide Road, Calcutta 700 043, India
Tel: +91 33 49 7962/7996/6727/6613
Fax: +91 33 49 5607

Branch Office
74 Janpath, New Delhi 110 001
Tel: +91 11 372 3144   Fax: +91 11 332 3734

Works
Clive Works, 5 Hide Road, Calcutta 700 043
Angus Works, PO Angus, Dist Hooghly, West Bengal
Fax: +91 33 836208
Victoria Works, P-61, CGR Road, Calcutta 700 043
Tel: +91 33 495705

Marketing and Projects Office
59B Chowringhee Road (6th Floor), Calcutta 700 020
Tel: +91 33 247 0695/240 2573   Fax: +91 33 240 0767

Key personnel
Managing Director: Satish C Gupta
Deputy General Manager (Marketing & Projects):
  A K Battacharyya
Deputy Manager (Marketing): M K Chakraborty
Assistant Manager (Projects): S K Basu

Products
Railway wagons, fabricated steel structures for railway bridges, cast steel bogies and components for couplers and bogies.
Recent contracts include LPG tank wagons, oil tank wagons and caustic soda wagons for Indian Railways.

UPDATED

BREC

BREC NV
Mol Cy NV, Diksmuidesteenweg 63, B-8830 Hooglede, Belgium
Tel: +32 51 701681   Fax: +32 51 703038

Works
Huysmanslaan 53, B-1651 Lot (Beersel), Belgium
Tel: +32 2 378 0510   Fax: +32 2 378 1109

Key personnel
General Manager: M Mol
Sales and Logistics: R Brohee

Products
Freight wagons, bogies for freight wagons and passenger coaches.
Contracts include the supply of 100 Type Fals coal wagons and 100 Type Sgss container flat wagons to SNCB, Belgium; 25 air-dump wagons, 200 bottom-discharge hopper wagons and 75 tipping wagons for Gécamines-Exploitation, Zaïre; and 12 tank wagons for Tanzanian Railways Corporation.

UPDATED

Breda

Breda Costruzioni Ferroviarie SpA
Via Ciliegiole 110b, I-51100 Pistoia, Italy
Tel: +39 573 3701   Fax: +39 573 370292

Key personnel
See entry in *Locomotives and powered passenger vehicles* section

Products
Freight wagons in aluminium, stainless and carbon steel, including bimodal vehicles.

Breda shuttle wagon for Eurotunnel

CAF pocket wagon 1995

Recent contracts include supply of freight vehicle shuttle wagons for Eurotunnel; and Type Habillnss covered wagons, Type Tadns hopper wagons, Type Sggnss container flat wagons, Type Saadknns low-floor wagons for intermodal traffic and bimodal road/rail trailers for Italian Railways (FS).

VERIFIED

Burn Standard Co Ltd

A subsidiary of Bharat Bhari Udyog Nigam Ltd
(A Government of India undertaking)
10-C Hungerford Street, Calcutta 700 017, India
Tel: +91 33 247 1067/1762/1772   Fax: +91 33 247 1788

Works
20-22 Nityadhan Mukherjee Road, Howrah 711 101
Burnpur Works, Burnpur 713 325
Tel: +91 33 660 2601/5   Fax: +91 341 20 8530

Key personnel
Chairman: Shri A K Mohapatra
Managing Director: R P Singh
Director, Engineering: I C Sinha

Principal subsidiaries
Bharat Brakes & Valves Ltd
22 Gobra Road, Calcutta 700 014

Reyrolle Burn Ltd
99 Dr Abani Dutta Road, Howrah 711 101

Products
Freight wagons.

VERIFIED

CAF

Construcciones y Auxiliar de Ferrocarriles SA
Padilla 17, E-28006 Madrid, Spain
Tel: +34 1 435 2500   Fax: +34 1 576 6263

Key personnel
See entry in *Locomotives and powered passenger vehicles* section

Products
Full range of freight wagons tailored to clients' requirements. Designs according to UIC, AAR or individual specifications.
Recent contracts include 200 pocket wagons and 223 container wagons for Intercontainer and 53 hopper wagons for Israel.

VERIFIED

Callegari

José Callegari e Hijos
Rivadavia y Peru, 2800 Zarate, Prov Buenos Aires, Argentina
Tel: +54 1 328 228800   Fax: +54 1 325 0645

Key personnel
President: Pablo A A Callegari
Director-General: Clara Mandelli Vda de Callegari
Sales and Export Director: Eduardo Rivas

Products
Freight wagons.

VERIFIED

Cattaneo

Ferriere Cattaneo SA
CH-6512 Giubiasco, Switzerland
Tel: +41 91 857 3131   Fax: +41 91 857 6955

Key personnel
Managing Director: Aleardo Cattaneo
Engineering Director: M Fregni

Products
Freight wagons, carbon and alloy steel die forgings.
Product range includes the Mega Double-Waggon for the transport of intermodal loads up to 92 tonnes in weight, such as two craneable 41-tonne semi-trailers (Jumbo and Megatrailer types included) or four swapbodies or containers (Types 20, 30 and 40).

UPDATED

Cattaneo Mega Double-Waggon

CCC

Companhia Comércio e Construções
Av Rio Branco 156/22°, Salas 2234-5, Centro, Rio de Janeiro CEP 20043, Brazil
Tel: +55 21 282 1343   Fax: +55 21 262 1439

Key personnel
See entry in *Non-powered passenger vehicles* section

Products
Manufacture and repair of passenger cars and freight wagons. The company's two freight manufacturing plants, in Deodoro and Cruzeiro (São Paulo state), can produce 1,500 vehicles annually.

VERIFIED

CFC

Costruzioni Ferroviarie Colleferro SpA
A member of the Fiat Group
Via Sabotino, I-00034 Colleferro Rome, Italy
Tel: +39 6 978 1280   Fax: +39 6 978 2746

Key personnel
See entry in *Non-powered passenger vehicles* section

Products
Freight wagons, refrigerated wagons with glass fibre-reinforced polyester resin bodies and refrigerated containers.

VERIFIED

China National Railway Locomotive and Rolling Stock Industry Corporation (LORIC)

10 Fuxing Road, Beijing 100844 People's Republic of China
Tel: +86 10 6351 1620/7766
Fax: +86 10 6351 1614/6326 0830

Works addresses
Qiqihar Rolling Stock Works
10 Zhonghua East Road, Qiqihar 161002, Heilongjiang, PR China
Tel: +86 452 251 2981   Fax: +86 452 251 4464

Zhuzhou Rolling Stock Works
Zuzhou 412003, Hunan, P R China
Tel: +86 733 840 3551   Fax: +86 733 840 3134

Meishen Rolling Stock Works
Habin Rolling Stock Works
Shenyang Rolling Stock Works
Dalian Rolling Stock Works
Beijing February 7th Rolling Stock Works
Taiyuan Rolling Stock Works

Jinan Rolling Stock Works
Qishuyan Rolling Stock Works
Wuhan Rolling Stock Works
Wuchang Rolling Stock Works
Guiyang Rolling Stock Works
Xian Rolling Stock Works

Key personnel

See entry in *Locomotives and powered passenger vehicles* section

Products

Freight wagons. Examples include gondolas, covered wagons, flat wagons, double-deck flat wagons, container wagons, hopper wagons, tank wagons, special wagons for transporting extra-long and heavy loads and refrigerated wagons.

LORIC has supplied 232.926 freight wagons over the period 1986 to 1995 for China Railways, most of them 1,435 mm gauge. Other countries supplied include Botswana, Thailand, Bangladesh, Malaysia, Myanmar, Tanzania, Zambia, Sri Lanka, Vietnam, Albania and Cuba.

Recent deliveries include 12 flat wagons for East Asia, 152 cement wagons for Thailand and 22 wagons for Myanmar.

Recent orders include two 60 tonne diesel cranes for Myanmar, 180 cement wagons for Thailand; 20 covered wagons, 80 flat wagons and 100 ballast hopper wagons to Nigeria.

UPDATED

Cimmco International

A division of Cimmco Birla Ltd
Prakash Deep, 7 Tolstoy Marg, New Delhi 110 001, India
Tel: +91 11 331 4383/84/85
Fax: +91 11 332 0777/372 3520

Main works

Wagon Division, Bharatpur 321 001, Rajasthan, India

Key personnel

Chairman: S Birla
President: R Upadhaya
General Manager: M P Gupta
Marketing Manager: G Sodhi

Products

Design and manufacture of freight wagons. The company manufactures wagons to meet special material handling applications and has supplied over 30,000 wagons in India and abroad. The range includes: covered wagons; bottom and side discharge wagons; tank wagons with heating arrangements for transport of all types of liquid.

Recent contracts include 30 covered wagons for Cambodia Railways, and 60 petrol tank wagons for Sri Lanka government Railway.

UPDATED

Cometal

Cometal-Mometal Sarl
PO Box 1401, Maputo, Mozambique
Tel: +258 752124/5/6/7/8

Key personnel

General Director: Ldos A Kanji Simão

Products

Freight wagons; baggage vans; inspection cars; harbour and overhead cranes.

VERIFIED

Cometarsa

Cometarsa SAIC
LN Alem 1067, Piso 24, 1001 Buenos Aires, Argentina
Tel: +54 1 313 8968

Key personnel

See entry in *Locomotives and powered passenger vehicles* section

Products

Freight wagons.

VERIFIED

LORIC covered hopper wagon for Botswana Railways   **1997**

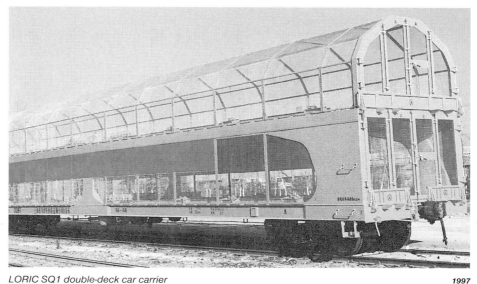

LORIC SQ1 double-deck car carrier   **1997**

Costamasnaga

Costamasnaga SpA
Viale 4 Novembre, I-22041 Costamasnaga, Como, Italy
Tel: +39 31 869411 Fax: +39 31 855330

Key personnel

See entry in *Non-powered passenger vehicles* section

Products

Freight wagons of all types.

Delivery has been completed of 70 articulated wagons with Y25 LSS bogies for transport of swap bodies and containers. Costamasnaga has also designed and is producing 500 container wagons for DB and SNCB freight services. Recent orders include delivery of 15 wagons for Athens metro.

UPDATED

Cromweld Steels Ltd

The Old Vicarage, Tittensor, Stoke-on-Trent ST12 9HY, UK
Tel: +44 1782 374139 Fax: +44 1782 373388

Key personnel

Commercial Director: Chris Beckitt
Technical Director: Ian Warrington
Financial Director: John Vickers
Marketing Manager: Jacqueline Redman

Products

Suppliers of 3CR12, a low-cost stainless steel (for wagon construction) with an 11 to 12 per cent chromium content.

VERIFIED

Daewoo

Daewoo Heavy Industries Ltd
PO Box 7955, Daewoo Centre Building 23rd Floor, 541, 5-Ga, Namdaemun-ro, Jung-gu, Seoul, South Korea
Tel: +82 2 726 3181 Fax: +82 2 726 3186/3307

Key personnel

See entry in *Locomotives and powered passenger vehicles* section

Products

Freight wagons.

Daewoo has supplied more than 10,000 freight wagons to operators in over 30 countries.

Recent contracts include the supply of 100 freight wagons for KNR Korea and 50 container flat wagons for Samik Transportation.

UPDATED

Dalian Locomotive and Rolling Stock Works

51 Zhong Chang Street, Dalian 116022, People's Republic of China
Tel: +86 411 419 9386/460 2043 Fax: +86 411 460 3064

Key personnel

See entry in *Locomotives and powered passenger vehicles* section

Products

Freight wagons, including Type C64 and C62B gondola wagons.

Recent contracts include the supply of 900 C64 and 100 C62B gondola wagons for Sino Railways Construction Development Centre, People's Republic of China.

VERIFIED

Dalian C64 gondola wagon   *1996*

Key personnel
See entry in *Locomotives and powered passenger vehicles* section

Associate company
Vagonka, Czech Republic

Products
Freight vehicles including open and covered wagons; flat wagons of all types; double-deck auto-carrier wagons; special purpose wagons for the iron and steel industry; tank wagons; wagons with sliding walls and roofs; bogies and components; and wagon inspection and maintenance.

Recent deliveries include 460 four-axle Type Habbinns two-axle sliding wall wagons for AAE, Switzerland and 19 Type Laaiss two-axle twin-wagon units with expanding hoods and sliding walls for Nordwagon.

Contracts in hand include an order for 400 four-axle and 220 two-axle sliding wall wagons for AAE; 115 Type Hbbi(ll)nss two-axle large-capacity wagons with sliding walls for PLES Hungary. The Type Hbbi(ll)nss wagon is designed for large-volume or pallet loads. It can be used as a sliding wall wagon or sliding hood wagon. Load capacity is increased by up to 30 per cent compared with a 15.5 m standard wagon.

UPDATED

Davis

W H Davis Ltd
PO Box 3, Langwith Junction, Mansfield NG20 9SA, UK
Tel: +44 1623 742621   Fax: +44 1623 744474

Key personnel
Chairman: D Sharpe
Sales Director, Wagons: M S Burge
Managing Director and Sales Director, Containers:
    D G Bradley
Financial Director and Company Secretary:
    M A Jackson
Commercial Director: G A Wardle

Products
Freight wagons; containers.
Recent contracts include the supply of rolling stock to Kenya Railways, Bardon London Ltd, Cleveland Potash, Marcon Topmix and Indonesia.

UPDATED

Difco

Difco Inc
PO Box 238, Findlay, Ohio 45839, USA
Tel: +1 419 422 0525   Fax: +1 419 422 1275

Key personnel
President and Managing Director: Wayne S Westlake
Executive Vice-President, Sales: Robert J Ward

Products
Air-operated side-dump wagons, air-operated drop-end side-dump wagons, heavy-duty wagons, Ballaster and Auto-Ballaster systems.
Contracts include 108 automated coal hoppers for Burlington Northern, 91 Auto-Ballasters ballast cars for BN and Santa Fe with a further 55 for Consolidated Rail and 55 ton flat cars for Inland Steel.

UPDATED

Dorbyl

Dorbyl Transport Products (Pty) Ltd
PO Box 229, Boksburg East 1460, Transvaal, South Africa
Tel: +27 11 914 1400   Fax: +27 11 914 1884

Key personnel
See entry in *Locomotives and powered passenger vehicles* section

Products
Freight wagons, guards' vans, steam heat vehicles.

VERIFIED

Dorsey

Dorsey Trailers, Inc
100 Paces West, Suite 1200, 2727 Paces Ferry Road, Atlanta, Georgia 30339, USA
Tel: +1 770 438 9595   Fax: +1 770 438 8190

Key personnel
President and Chief Executive Officer: Marilyn R Marks
Executive Vice-President, Sales: Hank Carter

Products
Trailers, piggyback trailers, platform trailers, reefers, dump, and drop-frame vans.

UPDATED

Duro Daković

Railway Vehicles Factory Ltd
PO Box 94, 55102 Slavonski Brod, Croatia
Tel: +385 55 241926/232189   Fax: +385 55 232454

Products
Freight wagons.
Recent contracts include the supply of freight wagons to SLZ Ljubljana and HZ Zagreb.

VERIFIED

DWA

Deutsche Waggonbau Aktiengesellschaft
Kablower Weg 89, D-12526 Berlin, Germany
Tel: +49 30 67930   Fax: +49 30 674 4560

EKA

EKA Ltd
Valkyrie House, 38 Packhorse Road, Gerrards Cross SL9 8EB, UK
Tel: +44 1753 889818   Fax: +44 1753 880004

Key personnel
Managing Director: W O Forster
Sales Liaison Manager: J E Fadelle

Products
The EKA 'Stevedore' side-loading semi-trailer is ideally suited to handling ISO containers at lightly used road/rail transfer yards where the cost of expensive fixed gantries or heavy forklift trucks cannot be justified. There is also no need for separate vehicles for transporting containers by road. With the 'Stevedore', one man can collect a container at a transfer yard and deliver to a destination where it can be grounded for emptying or stacked for storage. Individually controlled hydraulic stabilisers ensure total stability and ease of levelling. There are versions for 20 and 40 ft long ISO containers weighing up to 28 tonnes.

EKA Simple Rail Transfer Equipment (SRTE), comprises a demountable sideloader which unloads 20 ft, ISO containers/flatracks from rail wagons alongside. EKA has supplied 24 SRTE units to the Ministry of Defence, UK.

VERIFIED

Energomachexport

25A Protopopovsky per, 129010 Moscow, Russian Federation

DWA Type Hbbi(ll)nss sliding wall wagon   *1997*

Tatravagónka

Tatravagónka as
Štefánikova 887/53, SK-058 01 Poprad, Slovakia
Tel: +421 92 723275   Fax: +421 92 721732
Email: vagontei@pp.sinet.sk

Key personnel
General Manager: František Králik
Sales Manager: Rudolf Fabian

Products
Freight wagons, including open, covered, tank, bulk powder, hopper, intermodal, car transporters, coil steel and specialised types including ladle wagons for transporting molten metal.

Contracts in 1997 include 370 four-axle wagons and 155 two-axle wagons for DWA Niesky Germany; 47 four-axle tank wagons for EVA Düsseldorf and 50 more for VTG, Hamburg; 106 four-axle container flat wagons for ACTS Utrecht, Netherlands and 50 more for PRA Israel (delivered in 1996).

UPDATED

Texmaco

Texmaco Ltd
6th Floor, Birla Building, 9/1 RN Mukherjee Road, Calcutta 700 001, India
Tel: +91 33 280135/248 9101/220 1680
Fax: +91 33 220 5833

Main works
Belgahria, Calcutta 700 056, India
Tel: +91 33 553 1672/553 1202/553 1713
Fax: +91 33 553 2448

Key personnel
President: R Maheshwari
Vice-Presidents: S K Agrawal, R C Chopra
Vice-President, Marketing: A K Sinha

Products
Freight wagons of all kinds, bogies and couplers.

VERIFIED

Thrall

Thrall Car Manufacturing Co
2521 State Street, Chicago Heights, Illinois 60411, USA
Tel: +1 708 757 2214   Fax: +1 708 757 4112

Key personnel
Vice-President, Marketing: Chris Schmalbruch
Vice-President, Business Development:
   Charles Magolske
Vice-President, Automotive Products: Robert Ortner

Principal subsidiaries
Transportation Corporation of America
Service Parts
Thrall Europa

Works addresses
Chicago Heights and Clinton, Illinois
Cartersville and Winder, Georgia
York, UK

Corporate development
A wagon building facility is opening in 1998 at the former rail vehicle manufacturing plant at York, UK, for the supply of wagons to English, Welsh and Scottish Railway.

Products
Thrall designs and manufactures a wide variety of freight wagons, leases equipment and supplies parts for freight wagons.

UPDATED

Transcisco Industries Inc

601 California Street, Suite 1301, San Francisco, California 94108, USA
Tel: +1 415 477 9700   Fax: +1 415 788 0583

Key personnel
President and Chief Executive Officer: Steven L Pease
Chief Financial Officer: Greg Saunders

TrentonWorks high cube covered hopper wagon for carrying grain   *1997*

Senior Vice-President, Marketing and Sales:
   George A Tedesco

Principal subsidiaries
Transcisco Rail Services Company
Transcisco Trading Company
Transcisco Leasing Company

Products
UNITEMP heating element for tank wagons; UNIFLO unloading device for high-density dry bulk products; freight wagon maintenance and repair.

Recent and continuing contracts include a 23.5 per cent interest in SFAT, Russian Federation's largest private rail transport company. This Moscow-based joint stock company owns and leases a fleet of more than 5,500 tank wagons, of which over 1,500 are equipped with Transcisco's UNITEMP heating system. Other SFAT shareholders include the former Ministry of Petrochemicals and the Russian Ministry of Railways.

Transcisco also offers full-service wagon leasing packages to railways and major utilities.

VERIFIED

Transcisco Rail Services Company

A subsidiary of Transcisco Industries Inc
601 California Street, Suite 1301, San Francisco, California 94108, USA
Tel: +1 415 397 1010   Fax: +1 415 433 7531

Key personnel
President: Robert A Jahnke
Senior Vice-President, Sales and Marketing:
   Brian Comstock
Vice-President, Engineering: Paul G Hayes

Products
Transcisco Industries is a railcar services company engaged in the maintenance, retrofitting and leasing of

freight wagons. Transcisco Rail Services Company operates a network of full-service wagon maintenance workshops across the USA.

VERIFIED

TrentonWorks

TrentonWorks Ltd
PO Box 130, Trenton, Nova Scotia B0K 1X0, Canada
Tel: +1 902 752 1541   Fax: +1 902 752 7190

Key personnel
President and Chief Executive Officer: Richard McKay
Vice-President, Marketing: Gary W MacGillivray
Manager, Export Sales: Mike Sood

Products
Freight wagons.

Recent contracts include supply of 1,075 covered wagons and 1,850 covered hopper wagons. Orders have been received for 200 gondola wagons and 600 covered hopper wagons.

UPDATED

Trinity Industries

Trinity Industries Inc
2525 Stemmons Freeway, PO Box 568887, Dallas, Texas 75356-8887, USA
Tel: +1 214 631 4420   Fax: +1 214 589 8171

Main works
Bessemer, Alabama
Greenville, Pennsylvania
Mount Orab, Ohio
Oklahoma City and Tulsa, Oklahoma
Beaumont, Dallas, Fort Worth and Longview, Texas

Key personnel
President and Chief Executive Officer: W Ray Wallace
Senior Vice-President and Chairman, Railcar Division:
   Tim Wallace

Trinity Industries aluminium RD II open hopper for coal

Vice-President, Freight Car Sales and Marketing:
  Duncan Gillies
General Manager, Freight Car Sales: Clay Howard
Vice-President, Tank Car Sales: Tim Schitter

Products
Freight wagons, including covered hoppers for
transporting grain, cement, plastic pellets and chemicals;
pressure discharge wagons for transporting dry free-
flowing materials; intermodal wagons including spine
wagons and well wagons for transporting trailers or
double-stack containers; steel and aluminium gondolas
for transporting coal, ore, forest products, steel products
or scrap; open hoppers including steel or aluminium
conventional and rapid discharge wagons for coal,
aggregates, woodchips and ore; covered wagons,
including insulated wagons constructed from composite
materials; tank wagons for chemicals, corn syrup, clay
slurry, liquid gases, crude oil and alcohol.
  Trinity Industries also has a repair and parts division
based in Asheville, NC, specialising in rebody kits and
replacement parts for freight wagons.

VERIFIED

Tuchschmid

Tuchschmid Enterprises AG
Kehlhofstrasse 54, CH-8501 Frauenfeld, Switzerland
Tel: +41 52 728 8111   Fax: +41 52 728 8100

Key personnel
Manager: Richard Nägeli
Manager, Intermodal Transport Systems: Daniel Erni
Manager, High Rack Storage: Urs Kern

Products
ACTS system of container transfer, developed in
conjunction with Swiss Federal Railways and road
hauliers. The system dispenses with independent transfer
machines and enables the driver of a road vehicle to
achieve a road-rail transfer or vice-versa on his own. The
system employs special flat wagons equipped with
rotating guideways and road chassis equipped with a
tilting frame and chain mechanism to slide the containers
on and off the wagons.

UPDATED

Tülomsas

The Locomotive and Motor Corporation of Turkey
Ahmet Kanatli Cad, TR-26490 Eskisehir, Turkey
Tel: +90 222 234 8130   Fax: +90 222 231 7944

Key personnel
See entry in *Locomotives and powered passenger
vehicles* section

Products
Various types of special purpose freight wagons including
tank wagons, refrigerated hopper wagons and wagons for
the transport of ore, tracked tanks and containers.

VERIFIED

Union Tank

Union Tank Car Co
A member of The Marmon Group of companies
111 West Jackson Boulevard, Chicago, Illinois 60604,
USA
Tel: +1 312 431 3111   Fax: +1 312 431 5003

Key personnel
President: Kenneth P Fischl
Senior Vice-President, Marketing and Sales:
  William L Snelgrove
Senior Vice-President and Controller: Mark J Garrette
Operations: Louis A Kulekowskis
Vice-President, Fleet Management:
  Wiliam R Constantino

Products
Steel, stainless steel and aluminium tank wagons for
liquids and compressed gases; covered hopper wagons
for plastic pellets and resins.

UPDATED

Tuchschmid ACTS container transfer system   1995

5,800 ft³ capacity covered hopper wagon for plastic pellets and powders by Union Tank Car

23,000 gallon capacity tank wagon by Union Tank Car for general purpose service   1997

Unity

Unity Railway Supply Co Inc
805 Golf Lane, Bensenville, Illinois 60106, USA
Tel: +1 708 595 4560   Fax: +1 708 595 0646

Key personnel
President and Chairman: Harold R O'Connor
Vice-President, Sales: Robert S Grandy
Executive Vice-President, Financial: Robert Holden

Products
Components for freight wagons including IKG grating kits, Camcar fasteners, AAR gauges, journal lubricators; safety warning lights; brake steps, end platforms and running boards; slack adjusters, angle cocks and retaining valves; reusable shipping containers; and batten bars.

UPDATED

Uralvagonzavod

Uralvagonzavod
622006, Nizhny Tagil, Russian Federation
Tel: +7 83435 231774/230197
Fax: +7 83435 233492/230357

Products
Freight wagons.

VERIFIED

Wabash National Corporation

Wabash National Corporation
RoadRailer Division
PO Box 6129, Lafayette, Indiana 47903, USA
Tel: +1 317 448 1591   Fax: +1 317 449 5474

Key personnel
Chairman, President and Chief Executive Officer, Wabash National: Donald J Ehrlich
President, RoadRailer and Vice-President, Marketing, Wabash National: Lawrence J Gross
Vice-President, International Marketing, Wabash National: Billy L Hedrick
Vice-President, Engineering: Rodney Ehrlich

European Office
RoadRailer Europa
PO Box 1342, D-85505 Ottobrunn, Germany
Tel: +49 89 609 7025   Fax: +49 89 609 5000
Manager: Peter Bange

Products
Design, production, licensing, marketing and sales of the RoadRailer Mark V intermodal system for both North America and international markets through the RoadRailer division.

Wabash has also entered the railcar market with the AllRailer.

The RoadRailer Mark V system consists of a detachable two- or three-axle rail bogie supporting specially designed truck trailers. All Mark V rail bogies can be used to carry any RoadRailer trailer, no matter what the length, height or type. All RoadRailer trailers use their air suspension to lower and raise the road wheels, eliminating the need for terminal cranes. RoadRailer trailers are joined together with special couplers to form

Wabash National RoadRailer trailer with CouplerMate interface bogie for operation with conventional wagons

Swift 53 ft high cube plate van Wabash National RoadRailer trailer. The unit is riding on a Mark V intermediate bogie
1997

trains (up to 125 units in length or 4,800 short tons in trailing weight), or at the end of conventional trains. RoadRailer trains are coupled to conventional wagons by means of the CouplerMate bogie.

For the North American market, plate wall dry vans are available in 48-, 53-, and 57-foot lengths, in both standard and high cube versions. The high cube van uses smaller tyres to provide an interior height of up to 118 in at the nose and 121 in at the rear of the trailer. The AutoRailer® van is a special type of high cube trailer that has a raisable deck for carrying up to six full-size cars; A new variant of the AutoRailer has a split deck design making it possible to carry trucks and cars or light commercial vehicles. Other dry vans are the 48- and 28-foot sheet and post trailers. The 48 ft van is for mail service and has large side doors. The 28 ft van is called a PupRailer® trailer, has a single axle, pintle hook and roll-up door.

The ReeferRailer® trailer is a refrigerated RoadRailer and is available in 48 and 53 ft lengths. For the international market RoadRailer trailers are available in a wide range of configurations and all trailers built for Europe are compatible with each other permitting co-ordinated service.

The AllRailer® multilevel vehicle is designed for the transport of finished cars, in bi-level or tri-level configurations. It is 57 ft long and 19 ft high and carries nine cars or six light trucks. designed to operate principally in rail mode and featuring a single road axle.

Current RoadRailer operators include Triple Crown, Swift Transportation, Schneider National, Amtrak and Burlington Northern Santa Fe. Over 5,000 units are in service in the USA. RoadRailer trailers are also in operation in Germany, France, Italy and Australia, and prototypes have been tested in the UK, Thailand, China and India.

UPDATED

Wagon Pars

Wagon Pars Company
10 Azarshar Street, South Kheradmand Avenue, Tehran, 15846, Iran
Tel: +98 21 884 8330/8339   Fax: +98 21 884 8338

Key personnel
Marketing Executive: Reza Esfahlani

Works address
Km 4, Tehran Rd Arak
Tel: +98 861 330 4650   Fax: +98 861 33999

Corporate development
Wagon Pars Company has been in full production since 1984.

Products
Freight wagons including cement and powder wagon, LPG tank wagon, hopper wagon, covered wagon and four-axle wagon.

Also produces non-powered passenger vehicles (See *Non-powered passenger vehicles* section) and locomotives (See *Locomotives and powered passenger vehicles* section).

Three-unit set of Santa Fe Wabash National AllRailer multilevel wagons
1997

NEW ENTRY

Wakamatsu Sharyo

Wakamatsu Sharyo Co Ltd
1 Kitaminato machi 6-chome, Wakamatsu-ku,
Kitakyushu 808, Japan
Tel: +81 93 761 2331   Fax: +81 93 761 2335

Products
Freight wagons, specialised steelworks vehicles.

VERIFIED

Windhoff

PO Box 1963, D-48409 Rheine, Germany
Tel: +49 5971 580   Fax: +49 5971 58209
Email: windhoff-ag@t-online.de

Works
Hoverstrasse 10, D-48431 Rheine

Subsidiary company
Windhoff Technik GmbH, PO Box 1110, D-48482
Neuenkirchen

Key personnel
Chairman: Dr Bernd Windhoff
Board Member: Dipl Ing Heinz Lörfing
Managers: Dipl Ing Günter Knieper,
Dipl Ing Franz-Josef Cramer, Dipl Ing Christoph Wessels
Export Manager: Dipl Ing Helmut Pühs

Products
Standard types of shunting vehicle; Windhoff Tele-Trac
with tractive forces up to 40,000 daN, diesel or
electrohydraulically driven with control of shunting and
coupling operations by radio or by interlinking with the
loading program; shunting equipment for railway
connections and sidings.

Developments
The CargoSprinter is a self-propelled container freight
dmu, produced in association with Talbot. It is 90.36 m
long and weighs 120 tonnes unladen. It can carry 160
tonnes at up to 120 km/h and is powered by two 265 kw
Volvo diesel engines. Three went into service with DB
Germany in 1997.

NEW ENTRY

Zastal

Zastal SA Holding
ul Sulechowska 4a, PL-65-119 Zielona Góra, Poland
Tel: +48 68 263984/253091/272926
Fax: +48 68 202869/272926

Key personnel
President: Adam Lezański
Director, International Trade: Janina Król

Products
Freight wagons manufactured according to UIC
standards, including: four- and eight-wheel covered and
flat wagons, eight-wheel high-sided coal wagons, eight-

Windhoff CargoSprinter with Volvo engines and transmissions (Bill Godwin)   *1997*

Zastal Type 449 R 96 m³ tank wagon

wheel open self-dumping wagons, and eight-wheel self-
dumping wagons for the transport of cereals. Freight
wagons for operation on 1,520 mm (CIS) gauge, including
12-wheel open self-dumping wagons, eight-wheel self-
dumping cereal wagons and eight-wheel covered
wagons. Wagon spare parts and refurbishment, steel
structures and technological equipment.

UPDATED

Zeco

Zimbabwe Engineering Ltd
PO Box 1874, Bulawayo, Zimbabwe
Tel: +263 9 78931   Fax: +263 9 72259
Email: zeco@acacia.samara.co.zw

Key personnel
See entry in *Locomotives and powered passenger
vehicles* section

Products
Construction, overhaul and rebuilding of freight wagons.
Supply of complete bogies, bogie components and all
spares for freight wagons.

UPDATED

BRAKES AND DRAWGEAR

Alphabetical Listing

ABC
Abex Rail
Acieries de Ploërmel
Adtranz
Allied Signal Bremsbelag
Amsted
Anchor Brake Shoe
ANI Railway Transportation Group
ASF
Atlas Copco
Avon
BBA Friction
Bharat
Blair Catton
Bremskerl
BSI
Buckeye
Buffalo Brake Beam
Buhlmann
Cardwell Westinghouse
Cimmco International
Cobra Brake Shoes
Cobreq
Comet
Cometna
Compair Hydrovane
Conbrako
Couplomatic
Davies & Metcalfe
De Dietrich Ferroviaire
Dellner Couplers
Delta Rail
Dominion Castings
Dr Techn Josef Zelisko GesmbH*
Ellcon-National
Escorts

Faur
FMI
Forges de Fresnes
Freinrail SA*
Frenos Calefaccion y Señales
Frensistemi Sri*
Freudenberg
Futuris
GEC Alsthom Transporte SA
General Standard
Graham-White
Greysham
Hanning & Kahl
ICER
Industria Freios Knorr Ltda*
Jarret
Karl Georg
Keystone
Knorr Brake Australia Pty Ltd*
Knorr Brake Corporation*
Knorr Brake Ltd*
Knorr-Bremse
Knorr-Bremse (Far East) Ltd*
Knorr-Bremse GesmbH*
Knorr-Bremse Rail Systems India Pvt Ltd*
Knorr-Bremse Rail Systems Korea Ltd*
Knorr-Bremse SA (Pty) Ltd*
Koshin-Knorr Ltd*
Kolmex
LAF
Lloyd ABC Couplers
Miner
Mitsubishi Electric
MSV
Multi-Service Supply
MZT

NABCO
Newag
New York Air Brake Corporation*
Nippon Signal
Oerlikon-Knorr Eisenbahntechnik AG*
OKE
Oleo
Paulstra
Poli
Radenton
Railway Products
Réservoir, Le
RFS (E)
Ringfeder
Saalasti
SAB WABCO
Sambre et Meuse
Scharfenbergkupplung
SEE
SMC
Stabeg
Standard
Stone India
Sumitomo
Textar
Tokyu Car
Triax
TSM
Ueda
WABCO
Westinghouse Brakes

*See Knorr-Bremse

Classified Listing

BRAKE PADS AND SHOES
ABC
Abex Rail
Acieries de Ploërmel
Allied Signal Bremsbelag
Anchor Brake Shoe
BBA Friction
Bremskerl
BSI
Cobra Brake Shoes
Cobreq
Futuris
ICER
NABCO
Newag
Nippon Signal
Standard
Textar
Ueda

BRAKE SYSTEMS AND COMPONENTS
Atlas Copco
Bharat
Blair Catton
BSI
Buffalo Brake Beam
Buhlmann
Cardwell Westinghouse
Cimmco International
Comet
Compair Hydrovane
Conbrako
Davies & Metcalfe
Dr Techn Joseph Zelisko GesmbH*
Ellcon-National
Escorts
Faur
Forges de Fresnes
Freinrail SA*
Frenos Calefaccion y Señales
Frensistemi Sri*

Freudenberg
General Standard
Graham-White
Greysham
Hanning & Kahl
Industria Freios Knorr Ltda*
Knorr Brake Australia Pty Ltd*
Knorr Brake Corporation*
Knorr Brake Ltd*
Knorr-Bremse
Knorr-Bremse (Far East) Ltd*
Knorr-Bremse GesmbH*
Knorr-Bremse Rail Systems India Pvt Ltd*
Knorr-Bremse Rail Systems Korea Ltd*
Knorr-Bremse SA (Pty) Ltd*
Kolmex
Koshin-Knorr Ltd*
Mitsubishi Electric
Multi-Service Supply
MZT
NABCO
New York Air Brake Corporation*
Oerlikon-Knorr Eisenbahntechnik AG*
OKE
Poli
Railway Products
Réservoir, Le
RFS (E)
SAB WABCO
SEE
SMC
Stabeg
Stone India
Suecobras
Tokyu Car
Triax
TSM
WABCO
Westinghouse Brakes

COUPLERS AND DRAWGEAR
Acieries de Ploërmel
Adtranz

ANI Railway Transportation Group
ASF
Avon
Blair Catton
BSI
Buckeye
Buhlmann
Cardwell Westinghouse
Cimmco International
Cometna
Conbrako
Couplomatic
Davies & Metcalfe
De Dietrich Ferroviaire
Dellner Couplers
Delta Rail
Dominion Castings
Escorts
Faur
FMI
GEC Alsthom Transporte SA
Jarret
Karl Georg
Keystone
LAF
Lloyd ABC Couplers
Miner
MSV
Oleo
Paulstra
Radenton
RFS (E)
Ringfeder
Saalasti
Sambre et Meuse
Scharfenbergkupplung
Stabeg
Sumitomo
Textar
WABCO

*See Knorr-Bremse

Company Listing by Country

AUSTRALIA
ANI Railway Transportation Group
Knorr Brake Australia Pty Ltd*
Futuris
SMC

AUSTRIA
Dr Techn Josef Zelisko GesmbH*
Knorr-Bremse GesmbH*
Stabeg

BELGIUM
Buhlmann
SAB WABCO

BRAZIL
Cobreq
Industria Freios Knorr Ltda*
SAB WABCO do Brasil
Suecobras

CANADA
Dominion Castings
Knorr Brake Ltd*

CZECH REPUBLIC
MSV

FINLAND
Saalasti

FRANCE
Acieries de Ploërmel
Couplomatic
Delta Rail
Forges de Fresnes
Freinrail SA*
ICER
Jarret
LAF
Paulstra
Réservoir, Le
Sambre et Meuse
SEE

GERMANY
Abex Rail
Adtranz
Allied Signal Bremsbelag
Bremskerl
BSI
Freudenberg

Hanning & Kahl
Karl Georg
Knorr-Bremse
Newag
Ringfeder
Scharfenbergkupplung
Textar

HONG KONG
Knorr-Bremse (Far East) Ltd*

INDIA
Bharat
Cimmco International
Escorts
Greysham
Knorr-Bremse Rail Systems India Pvt Ltd*
Railway Products
Stone India

ITALY
Frensistemi Sri*
Poli

JAPAN
Koshin-Knorr Ltd*
Mitsubishi Electric
NABCO
Nippon Signal
Sumitomo
Tokyu Car
Ueda

KOREA, SOUTH
Knorr-Bremse Rail Systems Korea Ltd*

MACEDONIA
MZT

POLAND
Kolmex

PORTUGAL
Cometna

ROMANIA
Faur

SOUTH AFRICA
Knorr-Bremse SA (Pty) Ltd*
Conbrako

SPAIN
Frenos Calefaccion y Señales
GEC Alsthom Transporte SA

SWITZERLAND
Oerlikon-Knorr Eisenbahntechnik AG*
OKE

SWEDEN
Dellner Couplers
SAB WABCO

UK
Atlas Copco
Avon
BBA Friction
Blair Catton
Compair Hydrovane
Davies & Metcalfe
Lloyd ABC Couplers
Oleo
Radenton
RFS (E)
Westinghouse Brakes

USA
ABC
Amsted
Anchor Brake Shoe
ASF
Buckeye
Buffalo Brake Beam
Cardwell Westinghouse
Cobra Brake Shoes
Comet
Ellcon-National
FMI
General Standard
Graham-White
Keystone
Knorr Brake Corporation*
Miner
Multi-Service Supply
New York Air Brake Corporation*
Standard
Triax
TSM
WABCO

*See Knorr-Bremse Germany

ABC

ABC Rail Products Corporation
Mechanical Products Division
200 South Michigan Avenue, Chicago, Illinois 60604, USA
Tel: +1 312 322 0360   Fax: +1 312 322 0377

Key personnel
Chairman and Chief Executive Officer: Donald W Grinter
Vice-President, Planning and Investor Relations:
   Paul E Dunn
Vice-President, Export Sales: David G Kleeshulte

Products
Normal and high-phosphorus cast-iron brake shoes.

VERIFIED

Abex Rail

Lütticher Strasse 565, D-52074 Aachen, Germany
Tel: +49 2417 1283   Fax: +49 2417 1252

Key personnel
Sales Manager: K W Kever

Main works
FrenDo, Avellino, Italy
Cosid Rail, Coswig, Germany
Piret SA, Gilly, Belgium

Products
Normal and high-phosphorus (patented) cast-iron brake shoes. Composition and sintered brake shoes and disc brake pads.

VERIFIED

Acieries de Ploërmel

Acieries de Ploërmel
PO Box 103, F-56804 Ploërmel, France
Tel: +33 2 97 73 24 70   Fax: +33 2 97 74 03 90

Key personnel
Managing Director: Jean-Luc Lancelot
Sales Manager: Alain Noblet
Product Manager, Railway: Bertrand Jolinel

Products
Brake block holders, buffers.

VERIFIED

Adtranz

ABB Daimler-Benz Transportation GmbH
Saatwinkler Damm 42-43, D-13627 Berlin, Germany
Tel: +49 30 38320   Fax: +49 30 3832 2000

Key personnel
See entry in *Locomotives and powered passenger vehicles* section

Products
Coupler components.

VERIFIED

Allied Signal Bremsbelag

Allied Signal Bremsbelag GmbH (Jurid Products)
PO Box 1201, D-21504 Glinde, Germany
Tel: +49 40 72710   Fax: +49 40 7271 2408

Main works
Glinder Weg 1, D-21509 Glinde/Hamburg, Germany

Key personnel
Chairman: Dr Ing R W Müller
Managing Director: Dipl Ing C-H Glanz
Sales Director: S Hackländer

Products
Composition brake blocks; disc brake pads; friction plates; sintered brake blocks and disc brake pads for

heavy-duty rail brakes; data acquisition equipment and complete test and measurement instrumentation for rail brake system evaluation; opto-electronic laser systems for engineering measurement.

VERIFIED

Amsted

Amsted Industries International
A division of Amsted Industries Inc
200 West Monroe Street, Chicago, Illinois 60606, USA
Tel: +1 312 372 5384   Fax: +1 312 372 8230

Key personnel
President: Michael T Gallagher
Manager, Marketing: D J Jarvis

Products
Amsted Industries International handles all business, licensing and sales of American Steel Foundries (ASF) and Griffin Wheel Company (see *Bogies and Suspensions, Wheels and Axles* section), which are divisions of Amsted Industries Inc.

UPDATED

Anchor Brake Shoe, LLC

Anchor Brake Shoe, LLC
1920 Downes Drive, West Chicago, IL 60185, USA
Tel: +1 630 293 1110   Fax: +1 630 293 7188

Key personnel
Chairman: Richard A Mathes
President: Jack M Payne
Plant Manager: James Quattrone
Field Service Manager: Joseph H Samolowicz
Quality Control Supervisor: Michael Tatera

Products
Composition brake shoes for locomotives and freight cars.

NEW ENTRY

ANI Railway Transportation Group

ANI Railway Transportation Group
PO Box 105, Maud Street, Waratah, New South Wales 2298, Australia
Tel: +61 49 412600   Fax: +61 49 412661
Email: bkcad@anibradken.com.au

Key personnel
See entry in *Brakes and drawgear* section

Products
Drawgear sets, including couplers, draftgear and yokes.
   Recent contracts include the supply of 200 drawgear sets for tandem coal wagons for QR Australia and 150 drawgear sets for five-pack container wagons for NRC.

UPDATED

ASF

American Steel Foundries
200 West Monroe Street, Suite 2301, Chicago, Illinois 60606, USA
Tel: +1 312 372 5384   Fax: +1 312 372 8230

See also *Bogies and suspensions, wheels and axles* section

Key personnel
President: Michael T Gallagher
Manager, Marketing: David J Jarvis

Products
Cast steel freight car components; hot-wound coils; yokes; articulated couplers; snubbing packages; friction shoes. Automatic couplers and yokes. ASF's Articulated Connector provides a means to fully exploit the articulated wagon or train principle.

UPDATED

Atlas Copco

Atlas Copco Compressors Ltd
PO Box 79, Swallowdale Lane, Hemel Hempstead HP2 7HA, UK
Tel: +44 1442 61201   Fax: +44 1442 234791

Key personnel
Managing Director: Michael Tatum

Products
GA series of rotary screw brake compressors for electric and diesel locomotives, railcars, LRVs and tramcars.

VERIFIED

Avon

Avon Technical Products Division
Melksham SN12 8AA, UK
Tel: +44 1221 63911   Fax: +44 1221 63780

Key personnel
Sales Manager: Pat Grace
Engineering Manager: David Boast

Principal subsidiary
Avon Spencer Moulton
rue de la Gare, F-45330 Malesherbes, France
Tel: +33 2 38 32 72 28   Fax: +33 2 38 34 73 42
Product Manager: Guy Joly

Products
Draftgear, drawgear, buffers, rubber-to-metal bonded components and suspension systems.

VERIFIED

BBA Friction

BBA Friction Ltd
Railway Product Group, Hendham Vale, Manchester M9 5SX, UK
Tel: +44 161 205 2371   Fax: +44 161 205 5501

Key personnel
Business Manager, Railway Products: S Morris
Principal Engineer, Rail: N J Hughes

Products
Asbestos-free low- and high-friction composition brake blocks for passenger and freight applications. Asbestos-free disc pads for a variety of applications.
   Contracts include the supply of brake blocks for metro cars for Ankara, Turkey, and for metro cars for London Underground Ltd's Jubilee and Northern lines.

UPDATED

Bharat

Bharat Brakes & Valves Ltd
A Government of India undertaking
22 Gobra Road, Calcutta 700 014, India
Tel: +91 33 244 4803/1756/0857/0858
Fax: +91 33 244 0855

Key personnel
Managing Director: Benu Munshi
Chief Manager, Finance: G C Bardhan
Manager (Works): B Guha
Manager (Commercial): S Das

Products
Vacuum brake equipment for wagons and coaches; Northey-rotary positive air-cooled high-vacuum locomotive exhausters; airbrake equipment including distributor valves for wagons; and brake regulators comprising slack adjuster, empty load device and changeover gear for wagons; air compressors.
   Regular supplier to Indian Railways and to manufacturers of locomotives, coaches and wagons in India. Vacuum brake equipment also supplied to Bangladesh Railways, the UK and to several countries in Africa and Southeast Asia.

UPDATED

Blair Catton

A division of William Cook plc
Cross Green, Leeds LS9 0SG, UK
Tel: +44 113 249 6363   Fax: +44 113 249 1376

Key personnel
Product Development Director: P Hagger

Products
Steel brake discs. Couplers and coupler assemblies, including Drophead Buckeye, Alliance and Tightlock types.

VERIFIED

Bremskerl

Bremskerl Reibbelagwerke Emerling & Co Kg
Brakenhof 7, D-31629 Estorf/Weser, Germany
Tel: +49 5025 8823   Fax: +49 5025 8810

Key personnel
Managing Director: Hartmut Emmerling

UK Office
Bremskerl (UK) Ltd, Unit 2, Stable Yard, Windsor Bridge Road, Bath BA2 3AY, UK
Tel: +44 1225 442895   Fax: +44 1225 442896

Key personnel
General Manager: Chris Prior

Products
Brake linings, disc brake pads, brake blocks.

VERIFIED

BSI

Bergische Stahl-Industrie
Papenberger Strasse 38, D-42859 Remscheid, Germany
Tel: +49 2191 3670   Fax: +49 2191 367215

Key personnel
See entry in *Diesel engines, transmission and fuelling systems* section

Corporate development
BSI and its subsidiary Davies & Metcalfe are now part of Cargo BSI Rail, a Cargo-Thyssen joint venture.

Products
A large range of special components for all classes of rail vehicles: railway brake systems and equipment: disc brakes with high reliability, low wear and high capacity; different designs of wheel-, axle- or flange-mounted brake discs meeting all demands with enforced recooling by self-ventilation, special low-energy ventilation for use at very high speeds; complete disc brake rigging including brake pads and actuators for pneumatic, electrohydraulic or spring force application, spare parts and incomplete components; BSI or SAB brakes; brake indicator devices; BSI electromagnetic brakes and their supporting devices, actuator cylinders, switching devices and auxiliary equipment; automatic centre-buffer couplers of the COMPACT type and semi-permanent couplers for commuter trains, metro, rapid transit and tramway vehicles; special semi-permanent couplers for high-speed ICE trains, automatic shunting couplers for UIC drawgear equipment of Type RK 900; resilient SAB-V-wheels; railway axle drives for longitudinal and parallel-arranged motors in a large range of power classes and different executions; fully integrated drives including motor bearings and brake systems; special arrangements of drives and brakes for low-floor mass transit vehicles; elastic shaft couplings.

UPDATED

Buckeye

Buckeye Steel Castings Co
A subsidiary of Worthington Industries Inc
2211 Parsons Avenue, Columbus, Ohio 43207, USA
Tel: +1 614 444 2121   Fax: +1 614 445 2084/2209

Key personnel
Vice-President and General Manager: Joe W Harden
Vice-President, Sales: Jeffrey E Laird
Director, Product Engineering and Mass Transit:
   J R Downes

Principal subsidiary company
GSI Engineering Inc

Products
Reduced slack drawbar system. Automatic couplers, draft yokes, centre plates, sill centrebraces and draft sill ends.

VERIFIED

Buffalo Brake Beam

Buffalo Brake Beam Co
400 Ingham Avenue, Lackawanna, New York 14218-2536, USA
Tel: +1 716 823 4200   Fax: +1 716 822 3823
Email: bbb@brakebeam.com
Web: http://www.brakebeam.com

Key personnel
Chairman and Chief Executive Officer: Richard G Adams
President and Chief Operating Officer: Garold L Stone Jr
Vice-President, Sales: Christopher F Adams
Director of Engineering: Louis E Bobsein
Director of Sales: Christopher F Adams

Products
Wagon brake beams, unit side-frame wear plates (steel or plastic), brake rod connectors, brake shoe keys and coupler carrier wear plates.

UPDATED

Buhlmann

Buhlmann SA
Rue des Coteaux 249, B-1030 Brussels, Belgium
Tel: +32 2 216 2030   Fax: +32 2 241 9602

Key personnel
Chairman: Walter Buhlmann
Rolling Stock Department: Paul Dequidt

Products
Railway and mass transit brake equipment: electric and electromagnetic; automatic couplers.

VERIFIED

Cardwell Westinghouse WABCO

8400 South Stewart Avenue, Chicago, Illinois 60620-1794, USA
Tel: +1 708 655 5200   Fax: +1 708 655 5202

Corporate developments
Cardwell Westinghouse has become a subsidiary of WABCO (qv)

Key personnel
Vice-President and General Manager: Mark Van Cleave

Products
Friction, rubber-friction and hydraulic friction draftgear; handbrakes; automatic slack adjusters. Vacuum brake equipment and components, Alliance couplers, AAR standard-type Alliance couplers, MCA couplers, automatic centre buffer couplers, enhanced screw couplers, screw couplings.

UPDATED

Cimmco International

A division of Cimmco Birla Ltd
Prakash Deep, 7 Tolstoy Marg, New Delhi 110 001, India
Tel: +91 11 331 4383/84/85
Fax: +91 11 332 0777/372 3520

Key personnel
See entry in *Freight vehicles and equipment* section

Products
Vacuum brake equipment and components; automatic centre-buffer couplers, including AAR types E and F, Alliance II and high-tensile couplers; enhanced centre-buffer couplers for freight wagons; ABC couplers for locomotives; and MCA and PH type couplers for coaches.
   Recent contracts include the supply of coupler components to Sudan Railway Corporation; coach and wagon spares to Myanmar Railways; locomotive and coach spares to Vietnam Railways; and couplers to KTM, Malaysia.

VERIFIED

Cobra Brake Shoes

Railroad Friction Products Corporation
PO Box 1349, Laurinburg, North Carolina 28353, USA
Tel: +1 910 844 9710   Fax: +1 910 844 9733

Key personnel
Vice-President and General Manager: F J Grejda
Director, Sales and Marketing: L R Charity
Product Manager: Michael F Griffin

Products
Composition brake shoes and disc pads.

VERIFIED

Cobreq

Cia Brasileira de Equipamentos
Praia do Flamengo 200, 9° Andar, Flamengo 22210, Rio de Janeiro, Brazil
Tel: +55 21 285 2233   Fax: +55 21 285 7060

Main works
Rua Tupi 293, Caixa Postal 54, Vila Maria, Indaiatuba, 13300-001 São Paulo, Brazil
Tel: +55 192 753133   Fax: +55 192 757129

Key personnel
Sales Director: R Darigo

Products
Non-metallic composition brake shoes and brake pads for railroad vehicles.

VERIFIED

Comet

Comet Industries Inc
4800 Deramus Avenue, Kansas City, Missouri 64120,
USA
Tel: +1 816 245 9400   Fax: +1 816 245 9460

Main works
4504 Macks Drive, Bossier City, Louisiana 71111
5401 Mills Road, Carson City, Nevada 89706

Key personnel
President: E A Johnson
Vice-President, Finance: L J Pagel
Exports Sales Representative: J B Killian

Products
Reconditioning of locomotive and freight wagon airbrake
systems.

VERIFIED

Cometna

Copanhia Metalurgica Nacionel
Rua Marechel Gomes Dacosta, Famoes P-2675 Odivelas,
Lisbon, Portugal
Tel: +351 1 933 3139   Fax: +351 1 933 3143

Key personnel
President: Jose Bissaia Barreto

Products
Knuckle-type couplers for locomotives and rolling stock.

VERIFIED

Compair Hydrovane

Compair Hydrovane Ltd
Claybrook Drive, Washford Industrial Estate, Redditch
B98 0DS, UK
Tel: +44 1527 525522   Fax: +44 1527 521140

Key personnel
See entry in *Passenger coach equipment* section

Products
Trackair range of rotary compressors specially designed
for mobile railway applications. There are 12 basic
models available for any working pressure required
between 7 and 10 bar.
Hydrovane range of rotary vane railway compressors
for stationary applications. Range extends from 1.98
litres/s to 207 litres/s up to 10.3 bar.
Recent contracts include delivery of 26 TA20 units for
Mexico City metro.

UPDATED

Conbrako

Conbrako (Pty) Ltd
PO Box 4018, Luipaardsvlei 1743, Transvaal, South Africa
Tel: +27 11 762 2421   Fax: +27 11 762 6535

Key personnel
Managing Director: R G Child

Products
Air and vacuum brakes; drawgear; snubbers.

VERIFIED

Couplomatic

25 rue des Bateliers, PO Box 165, F-93404 Saint-Ouen
Cedex, France
Tel: +33 1 40 10 63 43   Fax: +33 1 40 10 66 53

Key personnel
Managing Director: J Larroumets
Commercial Director: B Longueville

Products
Automatic multifunction couplers and semi-permanent
couplers for trams, light rail vehicles, rapid transit and
metro vehicles, multiple-unit power cars, passenger
coaches, locomotives and high-speed trainsets. Special
and transition couplers.

Recent contracts include the supply of automatic
couplers for Eurostar and TGV Duplex high-speed
trainsets.

VERIFIED

Davies & Metcalfe

Davies & Metcalfe plc
Injector Works, Stockport Road, Romiley, Stockport
SK6 3AE, UK
Tel: +44 161 430 4272   Fax: +44 161 494 2828

Key personnel
Managing Director: K W Pennington
Technical Manager: M J Leigh
Sales Manager: J O Boyle
Commercial Manager: M L Taylor

Principal subsidiaries
Davies & Metcalfe (Repairs & Overhauls Division) Ltd,
Leek, UK
Davies & Metcalfe Engineering Ltd, Sydney, Australia
Davies & Metcalfe (India) Pvt Ltd, New Delhi, India

Products
Electronic, pneumatic and electropneumatic brake
control systems; air compressors and accessories; air
dryers; electronic overspeed protection equipment;
electronic and electromechanical vigilance systems;
wheelslip detection and correction equipment; disc
brakes; automatic couplers; brake rigging regulators;
brake cylinders; distributor valves; load proportional
brake equipment; spring and hydraulic parking brakes;
transmission gearboxes; sanding equipment; passenger
emergency systems; driver's consoles and equipment
cases; and point setting equipment. Complete range of
equipment designed specifically for mass transit rail
systems.
Recent contracts obtained include: automatic airbrake
equipment for 67 tank wagons for the Tanzanian Railway
Corporation built by Cometal, Mozambique; automatic
couplers to Brush Traction for 22 locomotives for MTRC,
Hong Kong; 21 sets of vacuum brake equipment for
passenger coaches built by Adtranz for Bangladesh
Railways; brake controls, disc brakes, couplers and
magnetic track brakes to GEC Alsthom Metro-Cammell
Ltd for 139 coaches for Channel Tunnel overnight
services; supply of automatic and semi-permanent
couplers and air compressors to GEC Alsthom Metro-
Cammell Ltd for 88 emus for MTRC, Hong Kong; brake
control, disc brake and WSP equipment to Tokyu Car
Corporation for 17 dmus for Iarnród Éireann, Ireland;
brake control and coupling equipment to Jenbacher for
18 emus for KTM, Malaysia; brake control equipment to
De Dietrich Ferroviaire for 28 coaches for Iarnród Éireann,
Ireland; 88 automatic couplers for Lantau Airport civil
engineering wagons for MTRC, Hong Kong; 64 sets of
brake control equipment to Adtranz for emus for Royal
Mail, UK; and brake control and air supply equipment to
Adtranz for electric locomotives for Indian Railways.

VERIFIED

De Dietrich Ferroviaire

PO Box 35, F-67891 Niederbronn Cedex, France
Tel: +33 3 88 80 25 00   Fax: +33 3 88 80 25 12
Email: ddf@dx-net.fr.

Key personnel
See entry in *Powered passenger vehicles* section

Products
Anti-climbing buffer with shock-absorber and vertical
maintenance of coupled vehicles.

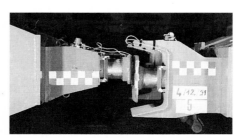

De Dietrich anti-climbing buffer   **1997**

Contracts include supply of anti-climbing buffers for
double-deck TGV Duplex vehicles and for TGV vehicles of
Korean National Railways.

NEW ENTRY

Dellner Couplers

Dellner Couplers AB
Vikavägen 144, S-791 95 Falun, Sweden
Tel: +46 23 765400   Fax: +46 23 765410
Email: info@dellner.se

Key personnel
President: Hans R Yngvesson
President, Coupler Division: Dieter F Ernst
Marketing Director, Coupler Division: A Philip Pastouna
General Manager, USA: Thomas G Tarantino
Marketing Director, Nordic Countries: Tomas Westbom
Manager Sales Support: Roger Danielsson

Principal subsidiaries
Dellner Kupplungen GmbH
Stahlstrasse 4a, D-42281 Wuppertal, Germany
Tel: +49 202 504026   Fax: +49 202 506021

Dellner Couplers Inc
8334-H Arrowridge Blvd, Charlotte, North Carolina 28273,
USA
Tel: +1 704 527 2121   Fax: +1 704 527 2125

Dellner Couplers UK
Tel: +44 151 342 3852   Fax: +44 151 342 7040

Products
Fully automatic and semi-automatic couplers for high-
speed and intercity trains, commuter, metro, light rail and
rapid transit vehicles.
Dellner products have recently been supplied for SJ
X2000, VR SM200 and DB AG VT612, VT644, DSB IR4,
NSB Gardermoen trainsets, Czech and CP Pendolino
tilting trainsets; for LRVs for the cities of Manchester, San
Diego, Baltimore, San Francisco, Leipzig, Kuala Lumpur,
Boston, Izmir, Halle, Chicago and New Jersey.
Also for metro cars in the cities of Lisbon, Oslo, KTM
Berhad, Stockholm, Prague and Tren Urbano.

UPDATED

Delta Rail

17-19 rue Fernand Drouilly, F-92250 La Garenne
Colombes, France
Tel: +33 1 42 42 11 44   Fax: +33 1 42 42 11 16

Key personnel
President: Yves Daunas
Marketing: Maire Collins

Products
Rolling stock buffers, shock-absorbers, suspension air
springs, platform buffers.

VERIFIED

Dominion Castings

Dominion Casting Limited
A Naco Inc Company
100 Depew Street, PO Box 5010, Hamilton, Ontario
L8L 8G1, Canada
Tel: +1 905 544 5000   Fax: +1 905 544 1225

Key personnel
Vice-President, Locomotive Group: Andy Mikalauskas
General Manager: Dale Harper
Sales and Marketing Manager: Dennis Chiarot

See also *Bogies and suspensions, wheels and axles*
section

Products
Coupler systems; associated parts and drawbars; custom
coupler components for manufacturers of automatic
couplers for transit systems.

UPDATED

BOGIES AND SUSPENSIONS, WHEELS AND AXLES

Alphabetical Listing

ABC
Acieries de Ploërmel
Adtranz
AMSU
Amurrio Ferrocarril
ANF-Industrie
ANI Bradken
ASF
Astra
Ateliers de Braine-le-Comte
Avon
Beall
BHEL
Blair Catton
Bombardier
Bombardier Prorail
Breda
Buckeye
CAF
CFD
Cimmco International
ČKD
Cockerill Forges & Ringmill
Cometna
Comsteel
ContiTech
De Dietrich Ferroviaire
Delta Rail
Dominion Castings
Dorbyl
DWA
Energomachexport
Ferraz

Ferrostaal
Fiat
Fiat-SIG
FIREMA Trasporti
Freedom Forge
Freudenberg
Fuchs Lubricants
Ganz-Hunslet
GEC Alsthom
GMT
Goninan
Griffin
HDA Forgings
HDC
IBG
IMS (UK)
Invar
Koni
Krupp Brüninghaus
Langen & Sondermann
Linke-Hofmann-Busch
Lord
Lucchini Group
Mafersa
Mecanoexportimport
Metalastik
OFV
ORX
Pafawag
Penn
Phoenix
Poli
Powell Duffryn Rail Projects

Qishuyan
Rafil
Railx
Ringrollers
R W Mac
SAB WABCO
Sambre et Meuse
Siemens SGP
SLM
Standard
Steel Authority of India
Stork RMO
Stucki
Sumitomo
Superior Graphite
Swasap
Tafesa
Talbot
Talgo
Tatravagónka
Techni-Industrie
TSM
Tülomsas
Uralvagonzavod
Valdunes
Vevey
Vibratech
VSG
Walkers
Wheel & Axle
Woodhead Shock Absorbers
ŽDB
Zeco

Classified Listing

AXLES, TYRES, WHEELS AND WHEELSETS
ABC
Adtranz
CAF
Cockerill Forges & Ringmill
Comsteel
Energomachexport
Ferrostaal
Freedom Forge
Fuchs Lubricants
GMT
Griffin
IMS (UK)
Lucchini Group
Mafersa
Mecanoexportimport
ORX
Penn
Poli
Rafil
Railx
Ringrollers
SAB WABCO
Steel Authority of India
Swasap
TSM
Valdunes
Vevey
VSG
Wheel & Axle
ŽDB

BOGIES
Acieries de Ploërmel
Adtranz
Amurrio Ferrocarril
ANF-Industrie
ANI Bradken
ASF
Astra

Ateliers de Braine-le-Comte
BHEL
Blair Catton
Bombardier
Bombardier Prorail
Breda
Buckeye
CAF
CFD
Cimmco International
ČKD
Cometna
De Dietrich Ferroviaire
Dominion Castings
Dorbyl
DWA
Energomachexport
Ferrostaal
Fiat
Fiat-SIG
FIREMA Trasporti
Ganz-Hunslet
GEC Alsthom
Goninan
HDA Forgings
HDC
Invar
Linke-Hofmann-Busch
OFV
ORX
Pafawag
Powell Duffryn
Qishuyan
Railx
R W Mac
Sambre et Meuse
Siemens SGP
SLM
Standard
Stork RMO

Stucki
Sumitomo
Tafesa
Talbot
Tatravagónka
Techni-Industrie
Tülomsas
Uralvagonzavod
Vevey
Walkers
Zeco

SUSPENSION SYSTEMS AND COMPONENTS
Adtranz
AMSU
Avon
Beall
ContiTech
Delta Rail
Energomachexport
Ferraz
Ferrostaal
Freudenberg
IBG
Koni
Krupp Brüninghaus
Langen & Sondermann
Lord
Metalastik
Phoenix
R W Mac
SAB WABCO
Standard
Stucki
Superior Graphite
Talgo
Vibratech
Woodhead Shock Absorbers

Company Listing by Country

AUSTRIA
Siemens SGP

AUSTRALIA
Adtranz
ANI Bradken
Comsteel
Goninan
Walkers

BELGIUM
Ateliers de Braine-le-Comte
Cockerill Forges & Ringmill

BRAZIL
Mafersa

CANADA
Bombardier
Dominion Castings
Invar

CHINA
Qishuyan

CZECH REPUBLIC
ČKD
ŽDB

FRANCE
Acieries de Ploërmel
AMSU
ANF-Industrie
CFD
De Dietrich Ferroviaire
Delta Rail
Ferraz
GEC Alsthom
Sambre et Meuse
Techni-Industrie
Valdunes

GERMANY
Adtranz
ContiTech
DWA
Ferrostaal
Freudenberg
GMT
IBG
Krupp Brüninghaus
Langen & Sondermann
Linke-Hofmann-Busch
Phoenix

Rafil
Talbot
VSG

HUNGARY
Ganz-Hunslet

INDIA
BHEL
Cimmco International
HDC
Steel Authority of India
Wheel & Axle

ITALY
Adtranz
Breda
Fiat
FIREMA Trasporti
Lucchini Group
OFV
Poli

JAPAN
Sumitomo

NETHERLANDS
Koni
Stork RMO

POLAND
Pafawag

PORTUGAL
Cometna

ROMANIA
Astra
Mecanoexportimport

RUSSIAN FEDERATION
Energomachexport
Uralvagonzavod

SLOVAKIA
Tatravagónka

SOUTH AFRICA
Dorbyl
Ringrollers
Swasap

SPAIN
Amurrio Ferrocarril
CAF
Tafesa
Talgo

SWEDEN
Adtranz
SAB WABCO

SWITZERLAND
Adtranz
Fiat-SIG
SLM
Vevey

TURKEY
Tülomsas

UK
Adtranz
Avon
Blair Catton
Bombardier Prorail
Fuchs Lubricants
HDA Forgings
IMS (UK)
Metalastik
Powell Duffryn
Woodhead Shock Absorbers

USA
ABC
ASF
Beall
Buckeye
Freedom Forge
Griffin
Lord
ORX
Penn
Railx
R W Mac
Standard
Stork RMO
Stucki
Superior Graphite
TSM
Vibratech

ZIMBABWE
Zeco

When it's got to be right the first time.

ABC

ABC Rail Products Corporation
Mechanical Products Division
100 River Point Corporate Center, Suite 220,
Birmingham, Alabama 35243, USA
Tel: +1 205 972 1245   Fax: +1 205 972 1386

Key personnel
See entry in *Brakes and drawgear* section

Products
Cast-steel wheels, wheelsets and metal brake shoes.

VERIFIED

Acieries de Ploërmel

Acieries de Ploërmel
PO Box 103, F-56804 Ploërmel, France
Tel: +33 2 97 73 24 70   Fax: +33 2 97 74 03 90

Key personnel
See entry in *Brakes and drawgear* section

Products
Bogie components. Recent contracts include parts for
bogies for the Jubilee Line Extension trains for London
Underground Ltd, UK, and the TER trains in France.

VERIFIED

Adtranz

ABB Daimler-Benz Transportation GmbH
Saatwinkler Damm 43, D-13627 Berlin, Germany
Tel: +49 30 38320   Fax: +49 30 3832 2000

Key personnel
See entry in *Locomotives and powered passenger
vehicles* section

Products
Development, design, engineering, sales and production
of rolling stock systems and equipment for all railway
types, systems and track gauges including: motor bogies
for locomotives and power cars; passenger coach and
freight wagon bogies; bogie components; radial steering
bogies; wheelsets, suspensions, coupler components,
axles and tyres. Customer support services for bogies
and suspensions, wheels and axles, including
commissioning and warranty, supply of spare parts,
refurbishment and repair, servicing and maintenance.

Adtranz has established System Lead Centres (SLC)
which manage worldwide all design and production
activities for a specific system with its subassemblies and
components. SLC Bogies is at Siegen, Germany.

Contracts include supply by Adtranz Australia of bogie
frames for 222 emu cars for SEPTA, USA; supply by
Adtranz Australia of bogies for 33 locomotives for Indian
Railways; supply by Adtranz Germany of Flexifloat motor
bogies for DB AG ICE high-speed trainsets; supply by
Adtranz Italy of motor and trailer bogies for FS and other
Italian railway companies; supply by Adtranz Sweden of
specialised soft suspension bogies for SJ X2000 high-
speed tilting trainsets; and supply by Adtranz Customer
Support Ltd, UK, of wheelsets for Class 365 emus and for
electric locomotives for Eurotunnel.

UPDATED

AMSU

AMSU SA
6-8 avenue Salvador Allende, F-93804 Epinay-sur-Seine
Cedex, France
Tel: +33 1 42 35 75 60   Fax: +33 1 42 35 47 56

Key personnel
General Manager: E Bosio
Marketing Manager: A Dupon
Industrial Manager: A Bricout
Research and Development Manager: M Tissot

Products
Suspension coil springs, precision springs, torsion bars.

VERIFIED

Amurrio Ferrocarril

Amurrio Ferrocarrill y Equipos SA
Maskuribai 10, E-014709 Amurrio, Alava, Spain
Tel: +34 45 891600   Fax: +34 45 892480

Key personnel
General Manager: J M de Lapatza
Foundry Director: L M de Lapatza
Director of Engineering: V Ruiz
Technical Manager: R Sanabria
Sales Manager: J M Gutierrez
Commercial Manager: M González
Quality Manager: M Alonso

Products
Bearings and axleboxes for locomotives and wagons;
adaptors; wheelsets, bogies, centre pivots; buffing gear,
traction motor yokes and frames; frames and bolsters for
bogies and other rolling stock parts.

UPDATED

ANF-Industrie

A subsidiary of Bombardier Eurorail
1 place des Ateliers, F-59154 Crespin, France
Tel: +33 3 27 23 53 00   Fax: +33 3 27 35 16 24

Key personnel
See entry in *Locomotives and powered passenger
vehicles* section

Products
Motor and trailer bogies of all types for passenger
vehicles.

Recent developments include tilting technology and
the innovative steerable-axle system as fitted to the MF88
trainsets supplied to RATP, featuring independent wheels
and activated and de-activated differential.

Recent contracts include 304 bogies for two-car
double-deck emus for SNCF; 288 Type Y401 motor
bogies for Z2N double-deck power cars for SNCF; 300
Type Y36P2A trailer bogies for double-deck trailer cars for

SNCF; 500 trailer bogies for TGV-Réseau high-speed trainsets for SNCF; 265 bogies for TGV-Duplex double-deck high-speed trainsets for SNCF; 212 motor and 56 trailer bogies for trainsets for Caracas Metro; and 806 bogies for AM96 emus and I11 passenger coaches for SNCB.

VERIFIED

ANI Bradken

Railway Transportation Group
PO Box 105, Maud Street, Waratah, New South Wales 2298, Australia
Tel: +61 49 412600   Fax: +61 49 412661

Key personnel
See entry in *Brakes and drawgear* section

Products
Bogies for locomotives, passenger coaches and freight wagons. Spare parts.
   Recent contracts include the supply of 100 steering bogies for State Railway Authority of New South Wales, Australia; and 700 bogies for National Rail Corporation, Australia.

VERIFIED

ASF

American Steel Foundries
A division of Amsted Industries Inc
200 West Monroe Street, Suite 2301, Chicago, Illinois 60606, USA
Tel: +1 312 372 5384   Fax: +1 312 372 8230

Key personnel
See entry in *Brakes and drawgear* section

Products
ASF designs, tests, manufactures and markets cast steel components and hot-wound coil products for both the rail and road industry. Freight car components include side frames, bolsters, bogies, draft sill end castings, couplers, rotary couplers, yokes, articulated connectors, slack-free drawbars, AAR and low-profile centre plates, snubbing packages (Ride Control, Super Service Ride Control, Ridemaster, Super Service Ridemaster), AR-1 self-steering trucks, strikers, draft lugs, AAR coils and control coils.

UPDATED

Astra

Societatea Comerciala Astra Vagoane Arad SA
Calea Aurel Vlaicu 41-43, R-2900 Arad, Romania
Tel: +40 57 231255/235379
Fax: +40 57 250169/233988

Key personnel
See entry in *Non-powered passenger vehicles* section

Products
Bogies for metro cars, passenger coaches, freight wagons and special purpose vehicles.
   Helical and leaf springs for bogies.

UPDATED

Ateliers de Braine-le-Comte

Ateliers de Braine-le-Comte et Thiriau Réunis SA
Rue des Frères Dulait 14, B-7090 Braine-le-Comte, Belgium
Tel: +32 67 560211   Fax: +32 67 561217

Key personnel
Commercial Manager: A Lejeune
Commercial Manager, Railway Division: R Brohée

Products
Welded bogies, three-axle bogies.

VERIFIED

Bogie for SNCB I11 passenger coach by ANF-Industrie   *1996*

Avon

Avon Technical Products Division
Melksham SN12 8AA, UK
Tel: +44 1221 63911   Fax: +44 1221 63780

Key personnel
See entry in *Brakes and drawgear* section

Products
Suspension systems, including air springs, chevrons and primary/secondary suspension bondings; sealing sections; drawgear packs/buffing springs and special requirement rail pads.

VERIFIED

Beall

Beall Manufacturing Inc
112 North Shamrock, PO Box 70, East Alton, Illinois 62024, USA
Tel: +1 618 259 8154   Fax: +1 618 259 7953

Key personnel
President: M Speciale
Sales Manager: A Rahn
Engineering Manager: C Jorgenson

Products
Elliptic leaf springs for locomotives and cabooses; trackwashers.

VERIFIED

BHEL

Bharat Heavy Electricals Ltd
Jhansi, India 284129
Tel: +91 0517 440240/440615/440944
Fax: +91 910517 443108/444366

Key personnel
See entry in *Locomotives and powered passenger vehicles* section

Products
Fabricated steel bogies for freight and passenger locomotives.
   BHEL is currently manufacturing 150 fabricated bogies for Indian Railways.

UPDATED

Blair Catton

A division of William Cook plc
Cross Green, Leeds LS9 0SG, UK
Tel: +44 113 249 6363   Fax: +44 113 249 1376

Key personnel
See entry in *Brakes and drawgear* section

Products
Bogie castings, including frame castings, centre castings, brackets, axleboxes, traction motor casings and suspension parts.

Recent contracts include the supply of bogie castings for Class 323 and 465 emus and Class 92 locomotives in the UK, Central LIne metro trainsets for London Underground Ltd, and Channel Tunnel Nightstock in the UK.

VERIFIED

Bombardier

Bombardier Inc
Transportation Equipment Group - North America
1101 Parent Street, Saint-Bruno, Quebec J3V 6E6, Canada
Tel: +1 514 441 2020   Fax: +1 514 441 1515

Key personnel
See entry in *Locomotives and powered passenger vehicles* section

Products
Welded, frame-braced and steerable axle bogies.
   Designed for increased passenger comfort on commuter and intercity coaches, the B55H bogie is configured for ease of inspection and maintenance. It is based on a welded, H-structure frame with a helicoil spring primary suspension using an axlebox frame rod link and helicoil spring secondary suspension with a filtering pad. The dampers operate vertically and laterally in the secondary suspension and vertically in the primary suspension. Connection from the bogie to the carbody is by drag rods attached to the bolster under secondary suspension with king pin and side bearing between the bogie frame and the bolster. Four tread and four disc brakes are fitted.
   Main characteristics are: wheelbase 2.64 m; wheel diameter 0.91 m; bogie weight 7,350 kg, capacity 29,484 kg; maximum operating speed 200 km/h (125 mph).

VERIFIED

Bombardier B55H bogie

Bombardier Prorail

Bombardier Prorail Ltd
A member of the Bombardier Transportation Group
Horbury, Wakefield WF4 5QH, UK
Tel: +44 1924 271881   Fax: +44 1924 274650

Key personnel
See entry in *Locomotives and powered passenger vehicles* section

Products
Motor and trailer bogies for electric multiple-units, including the BT13 suburban bogie and the B5000 bogie. The B5000 has been tested in powered (AC motors) and trailer versions under former British Rail Class 466 suburban emus. In addition B5000 bogies have been on trial in Norway and Germany, where they have successfully run at up to 250 km/h.
   Recent contracts include the supply of bogies for Class 323 suburban emus in the UK.

UPDATED

B5000 bogie by Bombardier Prorail 1996

Breda

Breda Costruzioni Ferroviarie SpA
Via Ciliegiole 110/b, I-51100 Pistoia, Italy
Tel: +39 573 3701   Fax: +39 573 370292

Key personnel
See entry in *Locomotives and powered passenger vehicles* section

Products
Motor and trailer bogies for locomotives, high-speed trainsets, metro trainsets, light rail vehicles, passenger coaches and freight wagons.
   Contracts include motor and trailer bogies for light rail vehicles for San Francisco and Boston; motor and trailer bogies for metro trainsets for Los Angeles; bogies for freight wagons; motor and trailer bogies for double-deck emus for Italian Railways (FS); motor and trailer bogies for ETR 500 high-speed trainsets for FS; and motor bogies for E 402B electric locomotives for FS.

VERIFIED

Bogie for Los Angeles metro trainset by Breda 1996

Buckeye

Buckeye Steel Castings Co
A subsidiary of Worthington Industries Inc
2211 Parsons Avenue, Columbus, Ohio 43207, USA
Tel: +1 614 444 2121   Fax: +1 614 445 2084/2209

Key personnel
See entry in *Brakes and drawgear* section

Products
Cast-steel four-wheel bogie side frames, bogie bolsters, wagon couplers, draft yokes, centre plates, sill centre braces, draft sill ends, six-wheel bogies, span bolsters, and other castings for railroad wagons. Undercarriages for railroad passenger cars and mass transit rail vehicles. Buckeye Steel Castings is a major supplier to railroads, railcar builders, and railcar repair shops.
   Recent developments include the XCR freight car bogie; this unit is less prone to hunting than the conventional three-piece bogie and is subject to less wear.
   Recent contracts include the supply of passenger bogies to Amtrak and Caltrans.

VERIFIED

GC5 bogie by CAF 1995

CAF

Construcciones y Auxiliar de Ferrocarriles SA
Padilla 17, E-28006 Madrid, Spain
Tel: +34 1 435 2500   Fax: +34 1 576 6263

Key personnel
See entry in *Locomotives and powered passenger vehicles* section

Products
Bogies, axles and wheel assemblies.
   Recent contracts include GC5 passenger coach bogies for operation at up to 200 km/h on 1,435 mm and 1,668 mm gauge; bogies for light rail vehicles and railcars; 17,450 wheels for Algeria; 60 wheels and 150 axles for Morocco; 3,376 wheels for Tunisia; and 4,770 wheels for Mauritania.

VERIFIED

CFD

CFD Industrie
9-11 rue Benoît Malon, F-92150 Suresnes, France
Tel: +33 1 45 06 44 00   Fax: +33 1 47 28 48 84

Key personnel
See entry in *Locomotives and powered passenger vehicles* section

Products
Locomotive bogies for axleloads up to 22 tonnes and speeds up to 120 km/h. Passenger-coach bogies for speeds up to 140 km/h.

VERIFIED

Cimmco International

A Division of Cimmco Birla Ltd
Prakash Deep (6th Floor), 7 Tolstoy Marg, New Delhi 110,001, India
Tel: +91 11 331 4383/84/85
Fax: +91 11 332 0777/372 3520

Key personnel
See entry in *Freight vehicles and equipment* section

Products
Cast-steel bogies for passenger and freight wagons.
   Recent contracts include the supply of passenger coach bogies to Vietnam.

VERIFIED

ČKD

ČKD Dopravnı Systémi AS
Ringhofferova 115/1, 15500 Praha 5, Czech Republic

Commercial department
Českomoravská 205, 19005 Prague 9
Tel: +42 2 6603 8200   Fax: +42 2 6603 8801

Key personnel
See entry in *Locomotives and powered passenger vehicles* section

Products
Bogies for trams, LRVs, locomotives and other powered passenger vehicles.

UPDATED

Cockerill Forges & Ringmill SA

PO Box 65, B-4100 Seraing 1, Belgium
Tel: +32 43 377777/377888/369090
Fax: +32 43 377902/377904

Works
Main Cockerill Site, Seraing, Belgium

Key personnel
Chief Executive Officer: Fred Godard
Executive Vice-President, Marketing and Sales:
　Urbain Roggen

Products
Steel tyres for all types of railway, light rail, tramway and metro rolling stock.

UPDATED

Cometna

Companhia Metalurgica Nacionel
Rua Marechal Gomes Dacosta, Famoes P-2675 Odivelas, Lisbon, Portugal
Tel: +351 1 933 3139   Fax: +351 1 933 3143

Key personnel
President: Jose Bissaia Barreto

Products
Cast-steel bogies for locomotives and freight wagons.

VERIFIED

Comsteel

Commonwealth Steel Company Limited
PO Box 14, Maud Street, Waratah, New South Wales 2298, Australia
Tel: +61 49 680411   Fax: +61 49 601799

Key personnel
Chief Executive: Wilton Ainsworth
Sales and Product Manager, Railway Products:
　Lindsay Reid

Products
Rolled-steel wheels and tyres; axles; and assembled sets. The company is a major supplier to all Australian rail systems and to export markets, especially India.
　Recent contracts include SRA of NSW: wheels and axles; and New Zealand Railways: wheels.

VERIFIED

ContiTech

ContiTech Holding GmbH
PO Box 169 D-30001, D-30165 Hannover, Germany
Tel: +49 511 93802   Fax: +49 511 938 2766

Key personnel
See entry in *Passenger coach equipment* section

Products
Elastomer and plastic suspension products for rail vehicles including primary springs; rubber metal conical springs with integrated hydraulic damping system; rubber metal layer springs; rolling rubber springs for axle suspension; secondary airbags; air spring suspension systems.

ContiTech products have been supplied for TGV high-speed trainsets for SNCF and Korea (South); Eurostar high-speed trainsets for EPS/SNCB/SNCF; AVE high-speed trainsets for RENFE; ICE-2 high-speed trainsets and VT611 tilting dmus for DB AG; hotel train cars for DB AG/ÖBB/SBB; IC/3 dmus for DSB; and light rail vehicles and suburban and metro trainsets.

UPDATED

De Dietrich Ferroviaire

PO Box 35, F-67891 Niederbronn Cedex, France
Tel: +33 3 88 80 25 00   Fax: +33 3 88 80 25 12
Email: ddf(CA}dx-net.fr.

Key personnel
See entry in *Locomotives and powered passenger vehicles* section

Products
Y32 series bogies, available in all rail gauges, with steel or air secondary suspension springs; C80 series narrow-gauge (950 to 1,067 mm) bogies with steel coil or air secondary suspension.
　De Dietrich Ferroviaire has manufactured over 5,000 Y32 bogies, of which approximately 1,000 have been exported to Belgium, Netherlands, Portugal, Morocco and Gabon. De Dietrich Ferroviaire has also granted manufacturing licences to manufacturers in other countries, such as Belgium and Portugal (in this latter country the bogie has been adapted to 1,668 mm gauge, with adaptation facilitated by the bogie chassis concept). Licensing agreements have recently been signed with Turkish Railways (TCDD) and SCIF in Morocco for manufacture of Type Y32 bogies.
　De Dietrich has entered into a technology transfer agreement with Romania for Corail-type coaches and Type Y32 steel-spring bogies.
　Other contracts include the supply of two protoype 1,524 mm gauge Y32 prototype bogies to Ukraine; and 1,600 mm gauge Y32 bogies with air suspension as fitted to the cross-border trainsets for Iarnród Éireann/Northern Ireland Railways.

UPDATED

Delta Rail

17-19 rue Fernand Drouilly, F-92250 La Garenne Colombes, France
Tel: +33 1 42 42 11 44   Fax: +33 1 42 42 11 16

Key personnel
See entry in *Brakes and drawgear* section

Products
Shock-absorbers, suspension air springs.

VERIFIED

Dominion Castings

Dominion Castings Limited
A Naco Inc company
100 Depew Street, PO Box 5010, Hamilton, Ontario L8L 8G1, Canada
Tel: +1 905 544 5000   Fax: +1 905 544 1225

Key personnel
See entry in *Brakes and drawgear* section

Products
Standard and high-speed two-axle bogies for AAR 50, 70 or 100 short ton freight applications. Cast-steel locomotive and passenger vehicle bogies.

VERIFIED

Dorbyl

Dorbyl Ltd
PO Box 229, Boksburg 1460, South Africa
Tel: +27 52 8276   Fax: +27 52 5714

Key personnel
See entry in *Locomotives and powered passenger vehicles* section

Products
Various types of bogies under licence, including the Scheffel High Stability bogie.
　HS bogies are used on Spoornet's ore line between Sishen and the harbour at Saldanha Bay.

VERIFIED

DWA

Deutsche Waggonbau Aktiengesellschaft
Kablower Weg 89, D-12526 Berlin, Germany
Tel: +49 30 67930   Fax: +49 30 6744560
Email: info@dwa.de
Web: http://www.dwa.de

Key personnel
See entry in *Non-powered passenger vehicles* section

Products
Passenger coach bogies of various types for various gauges; general overhaul and refurbishment of tramcar bogies. Bogies are produced by DWA's Görlitz and Vetschau works.
　The GP 210 bogie is designed for running up to 250 km/h. Gauge is 1,435 or 1,520 mm; load carrying capacity 20.5, 23.5, 25 or 28 tonnes; and tare weight 6.8 tonnes.
　Recent developments include the Görlitz VIII Do bogie for standard gauge double-deck rolling stock. Air sprung, it has a load-carrying capacity of 29 tonnes, three brake discs per axle and a tare weight of 6.75 tonnes. Service speed is 140 km/h.
　Vetsdrau works is building the SGP400 high-speed bogie for ICE-2 trainsets for DB under licence from Siemens.

UPDATED

Energomachexport

25A Protopopovsky per, 129010 Moscow, Russian Federation
Tel: +7 095 288 8456/6983   Fax: +7 095 288 7990/6983
Email: in(CA}eme.tsr.ru

Main works
Altai Wagon Works, Russian Federation
Bezhitsk Steel Manufacturing Works, Russian Federation
Kalinin Wagon Plant, Russian Federation
Krementchug Wagon Plant, Ukraine

1,524 mm gauge Y32 bogie by De Dietrich Ferroviaire for Ukraine

Key personnel
General Director: M Nosanov
Director, Transenergo Department: G Stepnov

Products
Full range of bogies for passenger and freight vehicles; primary and secondary suspension units; rolled-steel wheels, tyres; axles and wheelsets; and Type SA-3 automatic coupling devices.

VERIFIED

Ferraz SA

PO Box 3025, F-69391 Lyon Cedex 03, France
Tel: +33 4 72 22 66 11   Fax: +33 4 72 22 67 13

Key personnel
See entry in *Electric traction equipment* section

Products
Earth current units to prevent current flowing through bearings of axleboxes, and associated resistors; current collecting device on live rail and its associated shoe fuse box.
    Recent contracts include earth return current units for TGV-Atlantique (SNCF), ICE (DB AG) and AVE (RENFE) high-speed trainsets; current collecting devices for SEPTA, MRTC Singapore and Paris; and current collecting devices for VAL vehicles for Orly Airport and Toulouse, France, and Jacksonville and Chicago, USA.

VERIFIED

Ferrostaal

Ferrostaal AG
PO Box, Hohenzollernstrasse 24, D-45116 Essen, Germany
Tel: +49 201 81801   Fax: +49 201 818 2822

Key personnel
See entry in *Locomotives and powered passenger vehicles* section

Products
Motor and trailer bogies for all types of rolling stock; wheels, axles, assembled wheelsets, bearings and suspensions.

VERIFIED

Fiat

Fiat Ferroviaria SpA
Piazza Galateri 4, I-12038 Savigliano (CN), Italy
Tel: +39 172 718111   Fax: +39 172 718306

Key personnel
See entry in *Locomotives and powered passenger vehicles* section

Products
Bogies for tractive units and hauled vehicles. All bogies incorporate integral flexicoil suspension designed to eliminate friction and permit simplified construction with consequent reduced maintenance. This solution has been adopted for the various types of suspensions,

including coil spring, air spring and rubber spring versions.
    Contracts include 522 bogies for the Channel Tunnel shuttle trains; high-speed bogies for the ETR 500; bogies and tilting components for VT610 diesel-electric railcars for DB AG, manufactured by a German consortium; high-speed trailer and motor bogies for the third generation of tilting 'Pendolino' trainsets.

UPDATED

Fiat-SIG

Fiat-SIG Schienenfahrzeuge AG
CH-8212 Neuhausen am Rheinfall, Switzerland
Tel: +41 52 674 7206   Fax: +41 52 674 6431

Key personnel
See entry in *Passenger coach equipment* section

Products
Motor and trailer bogies for a wide range of applications.
    Recent contracts include the supply of motor bogies for mDDM double-deck motor cars for NS Netherlands.

UPDATED

FIREMA

FIREMA Trasporti SpA
Viale Edison 110, I-20099 Sesto S Giovanni (Milano), Italy
Tel: +39 2 249 4396   Fax: +39 2 262 25380

Key personnel
See entry in *Locomotives and powered passenger vehicles* section

Products
Motor and trailer bogies for locomotives and high-speed trainsets.
    Recent contracts for Italian Railways include the supply of 70 motor bogies for E402 locomotives; 194 trailer bogies for ETR 500 high-speed trainsets; and 30 motor bogies for ETR 500 trainsets.

VERIFIED

Freedom Forge

Freedom Forge Corporation
500 N Walnut Street, Burnham, Pennsylvania 17009, USA
Tel: +1 717 248 4911   Fax: +1 717 248 8050

Key personnel
Chairman and Chief Executive Officer: Herbert C Graves
President and Chief Financial Officer: James A Spendiff
Vice-Presidents
    Operations: John O Parke
    Sales and Marketing: John M Hilton
    Quality and Technology: Larry A Niemond

Principal subsidiaries
Standard Steel, Burnham and Latrobe, Pennsylvania, USA

American Welding & Manufacturing Co, Warren, Ohio, USA
Gentz Industries, Warren, Michigan, USA
Marston Ring Division, Wolverhampton, UK

Products
Various types of wheels, axles and mounted assemblies (freight, diesel and transit). Box lids.

VERIFIED

Freudenberg

Freudenberg Dichtungs und Schwingungstechnik KG
Boxhanger Strasse 79/82, D-10245 Berlin, Germany
Tel: +49 30 293 70374   Fax: +49 30 293 70286

Key personnel
Chairman: Jorg Sost
Management Board:
    Herbert Fehrecke
    Norbert Schebesta
    Jorg Sost
Sales Manager, Railcar Industry, Europe: Erik Reule

Associate companies in Austria, Belgium, Brazil, Denmark, Finland, India, Japan, Luxembourg, Mexico, Netherlands, Norway, Poland, Russia, Singapore, Spain, Sweden, Switzerland, UK and USA.

Products
O-rings, seals, rubber/metal elastic materials for brake components, resilient couplings linking motor, gearbox and axle, resilient mountings.

NEW ENTRY

Fuchs Lubricants

Fuchs Lubricants (UK) plc
Hanley Plant, New Century Street, Hanley, Stoke-on-Trent ST1 5HU, UK
Tel: +44 1782 202521   Fax: +44 1782 202470

Key personnel
Sales Manager: Peter Baker

Products
Centrac range of dry solid stick friction modifiers to reduce wheel/rail noise and wear, applied continuously to the wheel tread or flange by means of vehicle-mounted equipment.

VERIFIED

Ganz-Hunslet

Ganz-Hunslet Részvénytársaság
PO Box 29, H-1430 Budapest, Hungary
Tel: +36 1 210 1177/313 0887
Fax: +36 1 210 1175/210 1180
Sales office: +36 1 210 1173

Key personnel
See entry in *Locomotives and powered passenger vehicles* section

Products
Two- and three-axle bogies for locomotives, powered and non-powered bogies for dmus and emus, bogies for passenger vehicles.
    The standard GH-250 bogies by Ganz-Hunslet are characterised by the combination of flexicoil steel springs and laminated rubber springs (chevrons) in the secondary

NS mDDM motor car with three Fiat-SIG motor bogies   1997

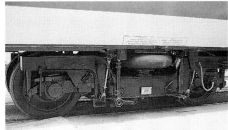

Ganz-Hunslet bogie under KTMB Class 8200 emu built by UCW   1997

Ganz-Hunslet emu motor bogie for 160 km/h operation   **1995**

Locomotive bogie for Queensland Rail, Australia, by Goninan   **1996**

suspension system and in the pivot structure, to eliminate the traditional bolster mechanism. The GH-250 bogies are designed for 250 km/h maximum speed and have tested successfully at the DB Rollprüfstand in Munich Freimann. GH-250 bogies are in service under the new Ganz-Hunslet designed and produced Intercity and commuter emu sets both as powered and trailer bogies, and under the Z1 and Z2 passenger coaches of the Hungarian State Railways.

Recent deliveries include motor and trailers bogies for commuter and intercity emus for MÁV for speeds up to 160 km/h. 144 have been delivered for Z2 passenger cars up to 160 km/h and 102 for Z1 passenger cars, for speeds up to 200 km/h.

A special derivative of the standard bogie is the 11 sets of light railcar bogies with propeller shaft axledrive and a shorter wheelbase, supplied in 1995 to the Turkish coach builder TUVASAS for its Sakariya railcars.

KTMB's new Class 8200 emu sets, ordered from Union Carriage and Wagon (UCW) of South Africa, are running 92 air sprung motor and 48 trailer bogies. An additional 86 motor and 48 trailer bogies were due to be delivered by the end of 1997.

Some 40 metre-gauge bogies with air-sprung secondary suspension have been ordered for refurbished passenger coaches of Malaysian Railways (KTMB). An option exists for a further 40.

UPDATED

GEC Alsthom

GEC Alsthom Transport
Villeurbanne 11/13 Avenue, Bel Air, 69627 Villeurbanne, France
Tel: +33 04 72 35 52 00   Fax: +33 04 72 35 52 87

Key personnel
Managing Director: J B Patin

Products
Bogies, including the Type Y21 Rse for 20-tonne axleload wagons running at up to 100 km/h, and with special devices for quick axle change at break of gauge; Type Y27 for 16-tonne axleload wagons on metre-gauge; a three-axle bogie for 25- to 30-tonne axleload vehicles for use in the iron and steel industry; the Y25 Rst/Lst bogie standardised by the UIC for 20 to 22.5-tonne axleload wagons; and the Y32B helical-spring, disc-braked bogie for 16-tonne maximum axleload passenger cars running at up to 200 km/h.

UPDATED

GMT

Gummi Metall Technik GmbH
Liechtersmatten 5, D-77185 Bühl, Germany
Tel: +49 72 238040   Fax: +49 72 232 1075

Key personnel
Marketing Manager: Susanne Engstler

Products
Rubber and rubber-metal elements, such as axle springs, rolling rubber springs, bushes, cone mountings, ball joints and bonded springs.

VERIFIED

Goninan

A Goninan & Co Ltd
PO Box 3300, Hamilton, New South Wales 2303, Australia
Tel: +61 49 235000   Fax: +61 49 238501

Key personnel
See entry in *Locomotives and powered passenger vehicles* section

Products
Bogies for locomotives, passenger vehicles and freight wagons.

Recent contracts include the supply of 80 locomotive bogies for State Railway of Thailand; 54 bogies for cement wagons for State Railway Authority of New South Wales, Australia; 240 locomotive bogies for National Rail Corporation, Australia; 850 bogies for coal wagons for State Railway Authority of New South Wales; and 80 locomotive bogies for Queensland Rail.

UPDATED

Griffin

Griffin Wheel Co
A division of Amsted Industries Inc
200 West Monroe Street, Chicago, Illinois 60606, USA
Tel: +1 312 372 5384   Fax: +1 312 372 8230

Key personnel
President: Michael T Gallagher
Marketing Manager: David J Jarvis

Products
Steel wheels using the unique controlled-pressure pouring system into graphite moulds. These wheels are AAR-approved for locomotive, passenger and freight applications.

UPDATED

HDA Forgings

HDA Forgings Ltd
Windsor Road, Redditch B97 6EF, UK
Tel: +44 1527 64211   Fax: +44 1527 591760
Email: pjrm(CA}hdaf.co.uk

Key personnel
Managing Director: Dr A J Scanlon
Sales and Marketing Director: P J R Masters
Commercial Director: D W Smith
Director and General Manager: Paul R Langston

Subsidiary company
BTR plc

Products
Forged components in aluminium alloys for railway rolling stock.

Contracts include the supply of aluminium alloy bolster forgings produced on a 12,000 tonne press, for London Underground Northern Line GEC Alsthom trains.

UPDATED

HDC

Hindustan Development Corporation Ltd
Mody Building, 27 Sir RN Mukherjee Road, Calcutta 700 001, India
Tel: +91 33 280 166/67/68   Fax: +91 33 281922/202607

Works
Bumunari Plant, National Highway No 2, Bumunari 712 205, District Hooghly, West Bengal, India

Key personnel
See entry in *Freight vehicles and equipment* section

Products
Cast steel two- and three-axle bogies and locomotive bogies fitted with suspension arrangements and axleboxes, high-tensile coupler and high-capacity draft gear. Production is approximately 30,000 units annually. Supplied bogies, axleboxes, couplers to various countries.

VERIFIED

IBG

IBG Monforts GmbH & Co
An der Waldesruh 23, D-41238 Mönchengladbach, Germany
Tel: +49 2166 86820   Fax: +49 2166 868244

Products
Slide bearing systems for applications such as bogie air springs.

Recent contracts include the supply of bearing systems for ICE-2 high-speed trainsets, VT611 tilting dmus and double-deck coaches for DB AG.

NEW ENTRY

IMS

IMS Special Steels
7 Hill Street, Birmingham B5 4UP, UK
Tel: +44 121 632 4252   Fax: +44 121 643 8762

Key personnel
Managing Director: H Smith
Director: J Symes
Manager, Railway Materials: A Hance

Products
Supply of wheelsets, wheelset components, couplers and draftgear as exclusive agent in the UK and Ireland for Valdunes (France); Cockerill Forges & Ringmill (Belgium); Forcast (Belgium); and LAF (France).

VERIFIED

Invar

Invar Manufacturing Ltd
A subsidiary of Linamar Corporation
1 Parry Drive, Batawa, Ontario K0K 1E0, Canada
Tel: +1 613 398 6106   Fax: +1 613 966 7932

Key personnel
General Manager: E McGregor
Technical Sales Manager: James Burns
Sales Manager: Frank Brazda
Regional Sales Manager: Cam Nardocchio

Products
Bogie components, wheelsets and assemblies for urban
transit vehicles.
  Recent contracts include an order for 32 bogie
assemblies for UTDC/Lavalin.

VERIFIED

Koni

Koni BV
Langeweg 1, PO Box 1014, NL-3260AA Oud-Beijerland,
Netherlands
Tel: +31 186 635500   Fax: +31 186 612322
Email: koniis@euronet.nl

Key personnel
Chairman and Managing Director: C R van der Heyden
Marketing and Sales Director: P A Maarleveld

Subsidiary company
Koni-Jim Vance
15279 Alphin Lane, Culpeper, VA 22701, USA

Products
Primary and secondary dampers; shock-absorber testing
equipment.
  In addition to the normal range of vertical and horizontal
dampers, Koni has developed a yaw damper which is
designed to control small amplitude sinusoidal rotational
movements and enable vehicles to operate at higher
speeds.
  Recent contracts include the supply of dampers for
ICE-2 high-speed trainsets for German Railways (DB AG)
and dampers for 324 coaches for CPPR China.

UPDATED

Krupp Brüninghaus

Krupp Brüninghaus GmbH
PO Box 1760/1780, D-58777 Werdohl, Germany
Tel: +49 239 2560   Fax: +49 2392 56919

Key personnel
Board Members
  Marketing/Sales: Klaus Bölling
  Technical/Engineering/Personnel: Manfred Lebang

Products
Parabolic springs for freight wagons. R & D partner and
supplier to railways in Europe, North America and Asia.

VERIFIED

Langen & Sondermann

Langen & Sondermann Ferdenwerk
PO Box 1626, D-44506 Lünen
Tel: +49 2306 750750   Fax: +49 2306 57672

Key personnel
Managing Director: J Kohl
Sales Director: K H Hauschopp

Products
Leaf springs, conical springs, spiral springs.

VERIFIED

Linke-Hofmann-Busch

Linke-Hofmann-Busch GmbH
PO Box 411160, D-38233 Salzgitter, Germany
Tel: +49 5341 2105   Fax: +49 5341 213943

Key personnel
See entry in *Locomotives and powered passenger
vehicles* section

Products
Bogies for passenger vehicles and freight wagons.

VERIFIED

Lord

Lord Corporation
Mechanical Products Division
2000 West Grandview Boulevard, PO Box 10040, Erie,
Pennsylvania 16514-0040, USA
Tel: +1 814 868 5424   Fax: +1 814 868 3109

Key personnel
President: Charles Hora
Director, International Business: Larry Bindseil
Manager, International Business Development:
  Eric Ravinowich

Principal subsidiary
Lord GmbH
Im Niederfeld 4, D-64293 Darmstadt, Germany
Tel: +49 6151 897151   Fax: +49 6151 897155

Products
LC-Pads for roller bearing adaptors, designed to reduce
lateral forces, accommodate motion without wear, reduce
rail wear and eliminate adaptor crown wear on self-
steering bogies.
  V Springs (chevron springs) for the primary suspension
system. Applications include primary suspension for
rapid transit bogies, locomotive bogies, mining cars and
maintenance equipment.

Bolster mounts to accommodate lateral movement of locomotive bolsters.

Dyna-Deck for loading-shock protection. Designed to absorb longitudinal shocks and movements up to 12 in.

VERIFIED

Lucchini Group

Lucchini Siderurgica SpA
Via Oberdan 1/A, 25127 Brescia, Italy
Tel: +39 30 39921   Fax: +39 30 3384065

Key personnel
President: Luigi Lucchini
Managing Directors:
 Giuseppe Lucchini
 Michele Bajetti
Commercial Director: Giovanni Bajetti
Sales Manager, Railway Products: Roberto Forcella

Piombino Works
Products
Rails from 27 to 60 kg/m

Lovere Works
Products
Design, manufacture and assembly of wheels, tyres, axles and wheelsets complete with axleboxes, brake discs and drive units.

Lovere Meccanica Ferroviaria SpA
Via G Paglia 94, 24065 Lovere (BG), Italy
Tel: +39 35 983331   Fax: +39 35 983647

Key personnel
President and Managing Director: Pier Luigi Scetti
Technical Manager: Zaverio Tignonsini
Sales Manager: Roberto Forcella

Products
Overhaul and full refurbishment of wheelsets including axleboxes, bearings, brake discs and drive units.

TMC SpA
Via Jucker 19, 21053 Castellanza (VA), Italy
Tel: +39 331 501350   Fax: +39 331 505189

Key personnel
President: Aldo Gagliardi
Managing Director: Pier L Scetti

Products
Axleboxes and bearings for railway and mass transit systems.

UPDATED

Mafersa

Sociedade Anönima Mafersa
Ave Raimundo Pereira de Magalhães 230, CEP 05092-901, São Paulo, SP, Brazil
Tel: +55 11 261 8911   Fax: +55 11 260 0224

Key personnel
See entry in *Locomotives and powered passenger vehicles* section

Products
Forged and rolled carbon steel railway wheels.

Recent contracts include 26,000 wheels for China, 7,000 wheels for Mexico and 30,000 wheels for the USA.

UPDATED

Mecanoexportimport

Mecanoexportimport SA
30 Dacia Boulevard, Bucharest, Romania
Tel: +40 1 211 9855   Fax: +40 1 210 7894

Key personnel
See entry in *Locomotives and powered passenger vehicles* section

Products
Wheels, axles, wheelsets and bogies (including Y25 types) for locomotives, passenger coaches and freight wagons.

VERIFIED

Metalastik

Metalastik Vibration Control Systems, Dunlop Ltd
PO Box 98, Evington Valley Road, Leicester LE5 5LY, UK
Tel: +44 116 273 0281   Fax: +44 116 273 5698

Key personnel
Business Manager, Rail and Marine: W J Mortel
Sales and Overseas Development Manager: D Weston

Products
Rubber-bonded-to-metal springs for primary and secondary suspension systems; air spring systems; anti-vibration mountings; flexible bearings.

VERIFIED

OFV

Officine Ferroviarie Veronesi SpA
Lungadige A Galtarossa 21, I-37133 Verona, Italy
Tel: +39 45 8064111   Fax: +39 45 8032876

Products
Bogies for freight wagons.
 Recent contracts include the supply of 628 Y25 bogies to German Railways (DB AG).

VERIFIED

ORX

ORX Railway Corporation
1 Park Avenue, Tipton, Pennsylvania 16684, USA
Tel: +1 814 684 8484   Fax: +1 814 684 8400

Key personnel
President: Glenn Brandimarte
General Manager: Don Boore
Sales Manager: Rocco Pacifico

Products
Axles, wheelsets and bogies.

VERIFIED

Pafawag

Fabryka Wagonów Pafawag Sp ZOO
ul Fabryczna 12, PL-53-609 Wroclaw, Poland
Tel: +48 71 562111/552258
Fax: +48 71 551289/554881

Key personnel
See entry in *Locomotives and powered passenger vehicles* section

Products
The UIC/ORE Type Y25Lsd standard bogie which has the following parameters: wheelbase 1,800 mm; wheel diameter 920 mm; maximum loading per axle 22.5 tonnes; maximum speed 100 to 120 km/h (depending on weight).

VERIFIED

Penn

Penn Machine Company
A member of the Marmon Group
106 Station Street, Johnstown, Pennsylvania 15905, USA
Tel: +1 814 288 1547   Fax: +1 814 288 2260
Email: richt@internetmci.com

Key personnel
Vice-President and General Manager: H Karl Wiegand
Vice-President, Manufacturing and Engineering:
 Thomas Redvay
Vice-President, Transportation Sales: Richard E Trail
Sales Engineer, Transportation and Export Sales:
 Paul V Campbell
Sales Engineer, Transportation and Export Sales: Jaideep
 S Luthra

Principal subsidiary
Penn Locomotive Gear Company
470 Roberts Avenue, Louisville, Kentucky 40214, USA
Tel: +1 502 367 4858   Fax: +1 502 367 4911

Sales Office
210 Pine Street, Carnegie, PA 15106, USA
Tel: +1 412 279 4460   Fax: +1 412 279 4465

Licensing agreements
Penn Machine Company has agreements with ZF Hurth and VSG of Germany to manufacture passenger vehicle gearboxes and resilient wheels in the USA.

Products
Resilient wheels; axles; pinions; gears; journal boxes; complete gearboxes; gearbox components; pinions, gears and shafts for diesel-electric locomotives, primarily General Motors, GE Transportation Systems and Alco types.

Contracts include the supply of resilient wheels and axles to Siemens for LRVs for San Diego, St Louis, Portland and Denver; to Breda for LRVs for San Francisco; and to Kinki Sharyo for LRVs for Dallas and Boston.

UPDATED

Phoenix

Phoenix AG
PO Box 900854, Hannoversche Strasse 88, D-21048 Hamburg, Germany
Tel: +49 40 7667 2277   Fax: +49 40 7667 2211

Key personnel
Chief Engineers: Peter Eckworth/Dirk Lambrecht
Export Sales: Angela Büttner
Sales Manager: J Eggers

Subsidiary companies
Phoenix (GB) Ltd
Timothy Bridge House, Timothy Bridge Road, Stratford upon Avon CV37 9NQ, UK
Tel: +44 1789 205090   Fax: +44 1789 298638

Phoenix North America Inc
1 Minue Street, Carteret, NJ 07008-1198, USA
Tel: +1 908 969 0319   Fax: +1 908 969 3751

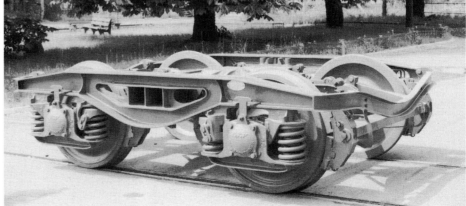

Type Y25Lsd bogie from Pafawag

Products

Suspensions for bogies, axle springs, mouldings, primary springs, secondary spring system, air spring bellows.

Primary suspension contracts include layer springs, bushes and buffers for the Adtranz Variotram and primary spring silent blocks for ICEII, DB, and Taiwan metro.

Secondary spring systems have been supplied to Kuala Lumpur, Malaysia, Chicago, USA, Los Angeles, USA and SEPTA Philadelphia, USA.

UPDATED

Poli

Poli Officine Meccaniche SpA
Via Marconi 3, I-26014 Romanengro (CR), Italy
Tel: +39 373 270126   Fax: +39 373 729097

Key personnel
See entry in *Brakes and drawgear* section.

Products
Gear reductors, resilient wheels, tyres, manufacture and overhaul of complete wheelsets for traction units and trailers.

Recent contracts include the supply of the above products to Netherlands Railways (NS) and to metros and railway companies in Italy.

VERIFIED

Powell Duffryn Rail Projects

Powell Duffryn Standard Ltd
Celtic House, Riverside Court, Taffs Wells, Cardiff
CF4 8SS, UK
Tel: +44 1222 813333   Fax: +44 1222 813337

Key personnel
See entry in *Freight vehicles and equipment* section

Products
Bogies for freight wagons. Wheels, axles and wheelsets for freight and passenger stock.

UPDATED

Qishuyan

Qishuyan Locomotive and Rolling Stock Works
Qishuyan, Changzhou City, Jiangsu Province, People's Republic of China
Tel: +86 519 877 1711   Fax: +86 519 877 0358

Key personnel
See entry in *Locomotives and powered passenger vehicles* section

Products
Bogies for locomotives and freight wagons.

VERIFIED

Rafil

Radsatzfabrik Ilsenburg GmbH
PSF 480, D-38866 Ilsenburg, Germany
Tel: +49 39452 930   Fax: +49 39452 93205

Key personnel
General Managers: Dr Ing Jendricke, Dr Ing Döing
Sales Manager: H Böhme

Products
Wheelsets with monobloc and tyred wheels for motive power, passenger cars and freight wagons. A special development is a lightweight monobloc wheel, proved in German Railways (DB AG) service. It has an axleload from 22.5 tonnes to 25 t and is capable of a maximum speed of 350 km/h.

A new development is a wheelset that can change gauge from 1,475 mm to 1,524 mm. Other special products are brake pulleys (divided and undivided).

Recent contracts include the supply of wheelsets to DWA, Adtranz, ZF Hurth, Preuss AG and DB AG.

UPDATED

Railx

1661 Dixon Airline Road, Augusta, Georgia 30906, USA
Tel: +1 706 793 8792   Fax: +1 706 793 9385

Key personnel
President: Loren D Perry
Vice-President, Operations: Steven Faulkner

Products
Wheelsets and axles for locomotives, passenger vehicles and freight wagons. Wheel and axle repair.

VERIFIED

Ringrollers

Ringrollers
A division of Dorbyl Ltd
PO Box 504, Springs, 1560 Gauteng, South Africa
Tel: +27 11 362 6670   Fax: +27 11 815 2805

Works address
11 Pienaar Road, Springs, 1560 Gauteng, South Africa

Key personnel
General Manager: S Nel
Export Sales Manager (Europe, Middle East, Australasia, Asia): P Myburgh
Export Sales Manager (Africa, South America, North America): F Venter

Products
Forged steel tyres for locomotives, passenger coaches and freight wagons. Gibson retaining rings.

Recent contracts include the supply of tyres to Hong Kong, Sudan, Denmark, UK, USA, Chile, Ghana, Mozambique, Zimbabwe, Zaire, Sri Lanka, Bangladesh, Pakistan and Philippines.

UPDATED

R W Mac

R W Mac Co
PO Box 56, Crete, Illinois 60417, USA
Tel: +1 708 672 6376/81

Key personnel
President: R W MacDonnell
Vice-President, Sales and Exports: J K MacDonnell

Products
Car-safe freight wagon bolster supports; locomotive bogie bolster supports; EMD and GE Journal box wear plates (steel); custom-made locomotive and freight wagon parts.

VERIFIED

SAB WABCO

Cardo Railway AB
Roskildevägen 1B, PO Box 193, S-201 21 Malmö, Sweden
Tel: +46 40 350460   Fax: +46 40 303803

Key personnel
See main entry in *Brakes and drawgear* section

Products
Air suspension control equipment; resillient wheels for main line vehicles, noise reducing V wheels for LRVs.

VERIFIED

Sambre et Meuse

Immeuble Le Volta, 17-19 rue Jeanne Braconnier,
F-92366 Meudon-la-Forêt, France
Tel: +33 1 46 32 23 00   Fax: +33 1 46 31 81 61

Key personnel
See entry in *Freight vehicles and equipment* section

Products
Design, testing and manufacture of three-piece bogies for 1,000 mm gauge; rigid cast-steel bogies Types Y25, Y33, Y39 and VNH for 1,435 mm and other European gauges, for speeds up to 160 km/h and 22.5 tonne axleloads. Parts for welded bogies including spring supports, pivots and suspension caps.

VERIFIED

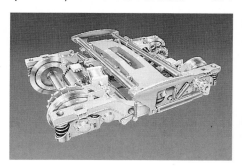

SF600 tilting bogie by Siemens SGP   1997

Siemens SGP Verkehrstechnik

Siemens SGP Verkehrstechnik GmbH
Bogie Division
Eggenburger Strasse 31, A-8021 Graz, Austria
Tel: +43 316 594 60511   Fax: +43 316 594 53511

Key personnel
Bogie Division
Director: Dipl Ing Hans M Schabert
Sales Manager: Dipl Ing Alf Windeck
Engineering Manager: Dipl Ing Hans Hoedl

Products
Bogie development, design and construction for mass transit and main line rolling stock; bogies for electric main line and shunting locomotives and for diesel-electric locomotives; bogies for diesel and electric railcars and multiple-units for standard and low-floor applications; motor and trailer bogies for high-speed applications, such as the German ICE2 and ICE3 trains.

The bogie division of Siemens SGP Verkehrstechnik has developed and delivered SGP400 trailer bogies for the ICE2 trains for speeds up to 300 km/h. Development of the SGP500 motor and trailer bogies for the German ICE3 high-speed trainsets has been completed and series production has been started.

The double-deck cars for OBB are fitted with SGP400 bogies and 480 have been delivered so far. RIC type SF300 trailer bogies have been delivered for passenger coaches for Czech Railways.

SF600 tilting bogies are being delivered for the German VT605 tilting train. New SF5000-D bogies in driven and shared (Jacobs type) bogie configuration have been developed for the German LVT642 dmus.

Locomotive bogie production includes delivery of 390 SF2 bogies for the German Class 152 electric locomotive.

The bogie division of Siemens SGP Verkehrstechnik also designs and manufactures bogies for other mass transit vehicles including standard and low-floor tramcars.

NEW ENTRY

SLM

Schweizerische Lokomotiv- und Maschinenfabrik AG
Swiss Locomotive and Machine Works Ltd
CH-8401 Winterthur, Switzerland
Tel: +41 52 264 1010   Fax: +41 52 213 8765

Key personnel
See entry in *Locomotives and powered passenger vehicles* section

Products
Bogies for locomotives, emus, dmus and LRVs for all gauges, rack or rack/adhesion.

SLM traction bogie for articulated railcars   1997

Radial self-steering bogies, wheelsets and suspensions. Customer support services for bogies and suspensions, wheels and axles, including commissioning, supply of spare parts, refurbishment and repair, servicing and maintenance.

Recent deliveries include 13 sets of frameless traction units (one per set) and trailer bogies (two per set) for 11 low-floor articulated railcars for the Biel—Täuffelen—Ins—Bahn (BTI) and for the Chemin de fer Electriques Veveysans, both metre-gauge railways in Switzerland and 24 traction and trailer bogies for MC/SNCF metre-gauge rack railways.

UPDATED

Standard Car Truck frame brake retrofit design
1997

Standard Car Truck frame brake integral cast design
1997

Standard

Standard Car Truck Co
865 Busse Highway, Park Ridge, Illinois 60068, USA
Tel: +1 847 692 6050   Fax: +1 847 692 6299

Key personnel
Chief Executive Officer/President: Richard A Mathes
Vice-President, Technological Resources:
 Robert L Bullock
Vice-President, International Operations:
 Robert P Geyer
Vice-President, Marketing, Sales & Service: Jack M Payne
Secretary/Treasurer: Donald J Popernik

Subsidiary company
Standard Car Truck—Asia
54 Jalam SS 2/67, Potaling Jaya, Malaysia 47300
Tel: +603 773 0186   Fax: +603 773 0166
Vice-President, International Marketing: David J Watson

Products
Complete cast steel bogies incorporating load-sensitive Barber Stabilized suspension and control elements.

The Barber Stabilized bogie utilises vertical damping forces directly related to the vehicle's load. A wide range of capacities and track gauges can be accommodated.

The same damping features are offered in self-steering radial bogies. The advantages of self-steering can also be enjoyed with existing bogies through the use of the Barber Frame Bracing retrofit.

UPDATED

Steel Authority of India

Steel Authority of India Ltd
Durgapur Steel Plant, Durgapur, West Bengal, India
Tel: +91 343 83000   Fax: +91 343 82317

Key personnel
See entry in *Permanent way equipment* section.

Products
Wheels and wheelsets.

VERIFIED

Wheelsets produced for coaches for Indian Railways by the Durgapur Steel Plant, India   *1996*

Stork RMO

Stork RMO BV
PO Box 1250, NL-1000 BG Amsterdam, Netherlands
Tel: +31 20 523 3700   Fax: +31 20 622 0617

Key personnel
General Manager: Ing J A Pijnappels
Project Co-ordinator: Ir J A Verwer
Chief Engineer: Prof Ir C P Keizer

Works
Oostenburgervoorstraat 181, NL-1018 MP Amsterdam, Netherlands

Products
Motor and trailer bogies for emus, trainsets, LRVs, metro trainsets and tram cars; motor and trailer bogies with radial adjustable wheelsets for passenger trainsets; overhaul of bogies and components; automatic retractable interconnecting gangways for passenger trainsets.

Recent contracts include the supply of high-speed bogies to GEC Alsthom for TGV Thalys trainsets, and bogies to Bombardier for RET Rotterdam metrocars.

UPDATED

Stucki

A Stucki Company
2600 Neville Road, Pittsburgh, Pennsylvania 15225-1480, USA
Tel: +1 412 771 7300   Fax: +1 412 771 7308
Email: jfaryniak@stucki.com

Key personnel
Chairman: W S Hansen
President: J G Faryniak
Vice-President, Engineering: J F Wright
Manager, Sales and Service Engineering: D Rhen

Products
Hydraulic bogie stabilisers, HS-7, HS-7-100 and HS-10, designed to control harmonic rocking and vertical bounce in 50, 70 and 100 short ton freight wagons; single and double roller steel bogie side bearings, resilient constant contact side bearings (conventional and metal-capped), to control light bogie hunting; body side bearing wear plates and wedges for 50, 70 and 100 short ton wagons; resilient-padded friction wedges for elimination of bolster wear in Ride Control or Barber bogies.

New for 1997 is a hydraulic yaw damper for freight wagons to control hunting. It is a double-acting hydraulic stabiliser mounted horizontally between the bogie and wagon body to control bogie hunting at high speeds. Another new development is a locomotive air dryer, using a membrane drying system to remove moisture in the train air supply.

UPDATED

Sumitomo

Sumitomo Metal Industries Ltd
Ote Center Building, 1-1-3 Otemachi, Chiyoda-ku, Tokyo 100, Japan
Tel: +81 3 3282 6111   Fax: +81 3 3282 6764/6680
Email: ooizumi-ytk@aw.sumikin.co.jp

Stork RMO motor bogie for NS DD-IRM   *1996*

Key personnel
See entry in *Brakes and drawgear* section

Products
Bogies, bogie components, wheels and wheelsets, axles and gearboxes.

UPDATED

Superior Graphite

Superior Graphite Co
120 S Riverside Plaza, Suite 970, Chicago, IL 60606, USA
Tel: +1 312 559 2999   Fax: +1 312 559 9064
Web: http//www.graphitesgc.com

Key personnel
International Sales Manager: Des Baker

Overseas offices
Sweden
PO Box 1300, Sundsvall
Tel: +46 60 134188   Fax: +46 60 134128

Canada
PO Box 20015, John Galt Postal Station, Cambridge, Ontario N1R 8C8
Tel: +1 519 650 1608   Fax: +1 519 650 1803

Products
Graphite-based rail lubricants.
    Lubricants have been supplied to Indian Railways and rail systems in USA including Burlington Northern Railroad.

NEW ENTRY

Swasap

Swasap Works
PO Box 566, Germiston 1400, South Africa
Tel: +27 11 825 3110   Fax: +27 11 873 1825/825 4675
Email: swasap@pipex.co.za

Main works
Rinkhals Street, Industries East, Germiston, Transvaal, South Africa

Key personnel
Managing Director: R C Duff
General Manager: D W Anderson
Export Manager: P B A Montgomery

Products
Axles and wheelsets.
    Recent contracts include supply of 2000 axles to Bradford Kendal, Australia, for 500 freight wagons for Malaysia Railways.

UPDATED

Tafesa

Tafesa SA
Carretera de Andalucía Km 9, E-28021 Madrid, Spain
Tel: +34 1 798 0550   Fax: +34 1 798 0961

Key personnel
See entry in *Non-powered passenger vehicles* section

Products
Design, testing and manufacture of bogies.

VERIFIED

Talbot

Waggonfabrik Talbot GmbH & Co KG
A subsidiary of Bombardier Eurorail
Jülicher Strasse 213-237, D-52070 Aachen, Germany
Tel: +49 241 18210   Fax: +49 241 1821214

Key personnel
See entry in *Locomotives and powered passenger vehicles* section

Products
Bogies for passenger vehicles and freight wagons. Passenger bogies are produced with torsionally flexible frames; other designs are available, ranging from

standard bogies to specialised designs such as 160 km/h freight bogies and two- to four-axle bogies with small wheels.
    Recent developments include the ContRoll tilting system, which can be retrofitted to powered and non-powered passenger vehicles, as well as incorporated in new designs. The mechanically simple ContRoll system employs bogies equipped with stabilisers, and is suitable for low-floor vehicles and vehicles equipped with Jacobs-type bogies. The tilting technology has been successfully tested on a DB VT614 dmu.

UPDATED

Talgo

Patentes Talgo SA
Montalbán 14, E-28014 Madrid, Spain
Tel: +34 1 522 2848   Fax: +34 1 522 8347

Key personnel
See entry in *Non-powered passenger vehicles* section

Products
The Talgo suspension and wheel guidance system for lightweight low centre of gravity high-speed equipment. The latest Talgo designs include equipment with automatically adjustable axles for through running between Spain and France, and equipment with pendular suspension.

VERIFIED

Tatravagónka

Tatravagónka as
Štefánikova 887/53, SK-058 01 Poprad, Slovakia
Tel: +421 92 723275   Fax: +421 92 721732

Key personnel
See entry in *Freight vehicles and equipment* section

Products
Y25-type bogies for freight wagons.

VERIFIED

Techni-Industrie

Techni-Industrie SA
ZI de la Chambrouillère, F-53960 Bonchamp-lès-Laval, France
Tel: +33 2 43 59 23 80   Fax: +33 2 43 59 23 89

Key personnel
See entry in *Powered passenger vehicles* section

Products
Bogies for metro trainsets and freight wagons.

VERIFIED

TSM

Technical Service and Marketing Inc
10765 Ambassador Drive, Kansas City, Missouri 64153, USA
Tel: +1 816 891 6544   Fax: +1 816 891 9329

Key personnel
See entry in *Diesel engines, transmission and fuelling systems* section

Products
Onboard flange lubricator systems with electronic control.
    Recent contracts include the supply of flange lubricator systems to Burlington Northern Santa Fe, USA, maintained and serviced by TSM Services.

VERIFIED

Tülomsas

The Locomotive & Motor Corporation of Turkey
Ahmet Kanatli Cad, TR-26490 Eskisehir, Turkey
Tel: +90 222 234 8130   Fax: +90 222 231 7944

Key personnel
See entry in *Locomotives and powered passenger vehicles* section

Products
Bogies for locomotives and freight wagons.

VERIFIED

Uralvagonzavod

Uralvagonzavod
622006 Nizhny Tagil, Russian Federation
Tel: +7 83435 231774/230197   Fax: +7 83435 233492/230357

Products
Bogies.

VERIFIED

Valdunes

Immeuble Pacific, TSA 40004, 13 Cours Valmy, F-92070 La Défense Cedex, France
Tel: +33 1 41 25 91 17   Fax: +33 1 41 25 91 11

Key personnel
Managing Director: Jean-Pierre Auger
Commercial Manager: Christian Pignerol
Deputy Commercial Manager: François Raymond

Talbot DRRS motor bogie with disc brakes

Trailer wheelset with brake discs by Valdunes   *1996*

Products

Forged wheels, including sound-dampening wheels and wheels for light rail vehicles and heavy-haul applications; axles; powered and trailer wheelsets; brake discs; gear blanks.

Recent contracts include the supply of wheels and wheelsets to operators, manufacturers and private owners in over 60 countries, principally in Europe, Asia and North America.

UPDATED

Vevey

Vevey Technologies SA
PO Box 32, CH-1844 Villeneuve, Switzerland
Tel: +41 21 967 0505   Fax: +41 21 967 0500

Products

Motor and trailer bogies.

UPDATED

Vibratech

Vibratech Inc
11980 Walden Avenue, Alden, New York 14004-9790, USA
A Unit of the Idex Corporation
Tel: +1 716 937 7903   Fax: +1 716 937 4632

Key personnel

Marketing Co-ordinator: Rosemary J Sheehan

Products

Vibration and motion damping systems.

Customers include General Electric, Kawasaki, Siemens, Sumitomo and Bombardier.

NEW ENTRY

VSG

VSG Verkehrstechnik GmbH
Alleestrasse 70, D-44793 Bochum, Germany
Tel: +49 234 68910   Fax: +49 234 689 1580

Key personnel

General Manager: K H Berneiser
Sales Manager: W Deimel

Products

Wheel and axle sets and components for light rail, metro and main line railway systems. Rolled steel wheels, tyres and wheel centres. Rubber-cushioned single-ring wheels, vibration absorbers to reduce running noise and curve squeal.

VERIFIED

Walkers

Walkers Ltd
A member of the Evans Deakin Industries Group
23 Bowen Street, Maryborough, Queensland 4650, Australia
Tel: +61 71 208100   Fax: +61 71 224400

Key personnel

See entry in *Locomotives and powered passenger vehicles* section

Products

Bogies for freight wagons.

VERIFIED

Wheel & Axle

Wheel & Axle Plant (Indian Railways)
Yelahanka, Bangalore 560 064, India
Tel: +91 80 846 0349/2045   Fax: +91 80 846 0367

Key personnel

General Manager: Gopal Krishna Malhotra
Chief Mechanical Engineer: Rajneesh Dubey

Products

Cast-steel wheels, axles and wheelsets.

Recent contracts include the supply of 948 wheels and 200 axles to Progress Rail Services, USA.

VERIFIED

Woodhead Shock Absorbers

Church Street, Ossett WF5 9DL, UK
Tel: +44 1924 273521   Fax: +44 1924 276157

Key personnel

Chairman: S Beyazit
Sales Manager: A C Kart

Products

Shock-absorbers and dampers for bogies and door systems.

Recent contracts include the supply of shock-absorbers and dampers to Vapor Canada, London Underground Ltd and Taiwan Railway Administration.

VERIFIED

ŽDB

ŽDB AS
Wheelsets Division
Bezručova 300, CZ-735 93 Bohumín, Czech Republic
Tel: +42 69 608 2304   Fax: +42 69 608 2805

Key personnel

General Director: Jakub Tomšej
Managing Director, Wheelsets Division: Richard Bonček
Commercial Director, Wheelsets Division:
    Jaroslav Sedlák

Products

Wheelsets, solid wheels, axles, tyres and wheel centres for locomotives, powered and non-powered passenger vehicles and freight wagons.

ŽDB products have been supplied to rolling stock manufacturers in 35 countries worldwide.

UPDATED

Zeco

Zimbabwe Engineering Ltd
PO Box 1874, Bulawayo, Zimbabwe
Tel: +263 9 78931   Fax: +263 9 72259

Key personnel

See entry in *Locomotives and powered passenger vehicles* section

Products

Bogies, bogie components and spares for freight wagons.

VERIFIED

BEARINGS

Alphabetical Listing

American Koyo Corporation
AWS
Brenco
Comet
Devol
FAG
Glacier Clevite
IBG
KLF-ZVL

Koyo Seiko
Magnus/Farley
MIBA
Molykote
Multi-Service Supply
NSK
NSK-RHP
NTN Toyo
Puzhen

Railko
Railx
SKF
Stucki
Tenmat
Timken
TMC

Company Listing by Country

CHINA
Puzhen

GERMANY
AWS
FAG
IBG

ITALY
TMC

JAPAN
Koyo Seiko
NSK
NTN Toyo

SLOVAKIA
KLF-ZVL

SWEDEN
SKF

UK
Devol
Molykote
NSK-RHP
Railko
Tenmat
Timken

USA
American Koyo Corporation
Brenco
Comet
Glacier Clevite
Magnus/Farley
MIBA
Multi-Service Supply
Railx
Stucki

American Koyo Corporation

Division of KCU Corporation of USA
29570 Clemens Road, Westlake, Ohio 44145, USA
Tel: +1 216 835 1000   Fax: +1 216 835 9347

Key personnel
General Manager: Yoshio Yabuno
Vice-President, Sales: Ray Normandin
OEM Sales Manager: Roger Lewis
After-Sales Manager: Don Kishton
OE Industrial Marketing Manager: Dale Neumann

Products
ABU-type journal roller bearings.

VERIFIED

AWS

Achslagerwerk Stassfurt GmbH
An der Liethe 5, D-39418 Stassfurt, Germany
Tel: +49 3925 9603   Fax: +49 3925 960405

Key personnel
Managing Director: Heinz-Jürgen Luig

Products
Roller axle bearings for locomotives, railcars, passenger cars and freight wagons according to UIC and GOST specifications. Roller bearings for the standard Type Y25 freight bogie.

VERIFIED

Brenco

Brenco International
One Park West Circle, Suite 201, Midlothian,
Virginia 23113, USA
Tel: +1 804 794 1436   Fax: +1 804 379 4668

Works
PO Box 389, Petersburg Industrial Park, Petersburg,
Virginia 23804
Tel: +1 804 732 0202   Fax: +1 804 732 2531

Key personnel
Chairman and Chief Executive Officer: N B Whitfield
President: J Craig Rice
Vice-President, Marketing and Sales: Howard J Bush
Director of International and Industrial Market
  Development: Arun Dhir

Principal subsidiaries
Quality Bearing Service (QBS)
SealTech Inc
Full Steam Ahead (FSA)
Rail Link Inc

Products
Locomotive and freight wagon bearings and components; forgings.

VERIFIED

Comet

Comet Industries Inc
4800 Deramus Avenue, Kansas City, Missouri 64120,
USA
Tel: +1 816 245 9400   Fax: +1 816 245 9461

Key personnel
See entry in *Brakes and drawgear* section

Products
Rail-associated bearings and components.

VERIFIED

Devol

Devol Engineering Limited
Clarence Street, Greenock PA15 1LR, UK
Tel: +44 1475 725320   Fax: +44 1475 787873

Key personnel
Sales/Technical Director: Graham Adair
Rail Products Engineer: M Wainwright
Customer Service: Mitchell Farquhar
Operations Director: G Stark

Subsidiary company
Devol Moulding Services Ltd

Products
Polymer bearing materials and components for bearings and bushes applied to disc caliper and clasp brake gear; anti-rollbar spherical and plain bearings; axlebox guides; gangway fascias; drawbar and side bearer pads; coupler support wear plates; dry slide wear plates for turnouts.

UPDATED

FAG

FAG OEM und Handel Aktiengesellschaft
PO Box 1260, D-97419 Schweinfurt, Germany
Tel: +49 97 21 913548   Fax: +49 97 21 913113
A member of the FAG Kugelfischer Group

Key personnel
Division Manager: Dr Raimund Abele

Production facilities in
Austria, Brazil, Canada, Germany, India, Italy, Portugal, UK and USA

Products
Axleboxes (cast steel, ductile iron, light metal); journal roller bearings and package units (AAR standard and metric); gearbox and transmission bearings; traction motor bearings; complete suspension units; mounting and dismounting equipment; instruments for bearing diagnosis; lubricants for rail vehicles.

UPDATED

Glacier Clevite

Glacier Clevite Heavywall Bearings
5037 North State Route 60, McConnelsville, Ohio 43756, USA
Tel: +1 614 962 4242   Fax: +1 614 962 8202

Key personnel
President: David E Norris
Director of Marketing: Joseph J Vauter
Sales Manager, Railroad Replacement: David A Comer

Products
Main, con-rod and flanged main journal bearings, thrust washers, cam bearings and various other shapes for accessory applications. Company innovations include tri-metal steel-backed cast-copper lead bearings, precision-plated overlays, nickel dam and the delta wall which allows the loading capacity to be raised without increasing the size of the bearing. An OE supplier to the world's locomotive engine manufacturers, Clevite also produces bearings for other large engine, compressor and aircraft applications.

VERIFIED

IBG

IBG Monforts GmbH & Co
An der Waldesruh 23, D-41238 Mönchengladbach, Germany
Tel: +49 2166 86820   Fax: +49 2166 868244

Products
Slide bearing systems for applications such as bogie air springs.
  Recent contracts include the supply of bearing systems for ICE-2 high-speed trainsets, VT611 tilting dmus and double-deck coaches for DB AG.

VERIFIED

KLF-ZVL A/S

024 11 Kysucké Nové Mesto, Slovakia
Tel: +42 826 212603/213086
Fax: +42 826 212519/212307
Email: klfzvl@netlab.sk

Key personnel
Managing Director: Anton Ježık
Commercial and Technical Director: Joseph Polčica
Marketing Director: Anton Imrišek

Products
Single row cylindrical roller bearings for railway axles.
  KLF-ZVL bearings have been supplied to Slovakia, Czech Republic, Hungary, Poland, Germany, Russia, Austria and Netherlands.

UPDATED

Koyo Seiko

Koyo Seiko Co Ltd
5-8 Minamisemba 3-chome, Chuo-ku, Osaka 542, Japan
Tel: +81 6 245 6087   Fax: +81 6 244 0814

Key personnel
Chairman: Uzuhiko Tsuboi
President: Hiroshi Inoue
Senior Executive Director: Takatoyo Uematsu

Principal subsidiaries
Australia, Brazil, Canada, France, Germany, Italy, Japan, Mexico, Netherlands, Panama, Singapore, Spain, Sweden, Thailand, UK and USA.

Products
Axlebox cartridge-type sealed journal roller bearings (ABU type); roller bearings, ball-bearings, needle roller bearings, pillow blocks.
  Koyo tapered roller bearings, cylindrical and spherical roller bearings and ball-bearings are produced with a patented hardening process known as 'upset rolling and forging' which makes for continuous metal grain flow. Available in all standard types and sizes, Koyo ABU-type journal bearings need no relubrication for eight years or 800,000 km. Koyo bearings have been approved for use by the Association of American Railroads after undergoing a series of rigorous tests. They are fully interchangeable with other AAR-approved makes. Koyo journal tapered roller bearings have been adopted for metro cars of the New York City Transit Authority.

VERIFIED

Magnus/Farley

Magnus/Farley Inc
PO Box 1029, Fremont, Nebraska 68026-1029, USA
Tel: +1 402 721 9540   Fax: +1 402 721 2377

Key personnel
President: S S Coleman
Vice-President: J E Macklin

Products
High-leaded bronze bearings for traction motor application; tin bronze bearings and special analysis; solid journal bearings; proprietary centrifugal castings, horizontal and vertical; babbitt bearing linings, centrifugal, static and plated; Statistical Process Control (SPC); robotic material handling and integrated machining; electric induction furnaces and spectrographic analysis.

VERIFIED

MIBA

Miba American Corporation
PO Box 369, Clinton, IN 47842, USA
Tel: +1 317 832 7751   Fax: +1 317 832 7756

Products
Engine bearings and locomotive bushings.

NEW ENTRY

and external (LED or electromagnetic) information display units.

Recent orders include provision of equipment for MTRC Hong Kong, Mexico metro and Madrid metro.

UPDATED

Siemens

Siemens Aktiengesellschaft
Transportation Systems Group
Control Systems Division
Ackerstrasse 22, D-38126 Braunschweig, Germany
Tel: +49 531 226 2723   Fax: +49 531 226 4309

Key personnel
Division Manager: Dr Hagermeyer
Subdivision Manager: R Grolms
Subdivision Commercial Manager: L Heinicke

Products
Scaleable passenger information systems for main line railways and public rail traffic with LCD, LED, flap displays and public address capability, beginning with a single PC up to a client/server network, using reasonable hardware and software.

UPDATED

Siemens Austria

Siemens AG, Österreich
Audio and Video Systems Division
Erdberger Lände 26, A-1030 Vienna, Austria
Tel: +43 1 17070   Fax: +43 1 1707 56510

Key personnel
Chairman, Siemens Audio Video Group: Dr A Wais
Head of Audio Systems Division: Dipl Ing M Kerman
Sales Director: Dipl Ing R Duerholz
Product Managers: Dipl Ing F Woschitz, Dipl Ing L Reuter

Products
Public address systems for stations, office buildings and workshops; complex audio solutions including networks and remote-control facilities; public address for rolling stock; on-train audio/video entertainment and information systems.

UPDATED

Silec

Société Industrielle de Liaisons Electriques
69 rue Ampère, F-75017 Paris, France
Tel: +33 1 40 53 66 00   Fax: +33 1 46 22 89 08

Key personnel
See entry in *Signalling and telecommunications* section

Products
On-train message synthesiser, for automatic announcement to passengers at the appropriate juncture of a journey of such items as: the next stop; arrival at a station; connections; arrival at the terminus; and procedure in the event of an incident.

VERIFIED

Solari

Solari di Udine SpA
Via Gino Pieri 29, I-33100 Udine, Italy
Tel: +39 432 4971   Fax: +39 432 480160

Key personnel
President: Massimo Paniccia
Systems Sales Manager: Marco Zoratti
Products Sales Manager: Roberto Fidel

Products
Passenger and staff information display systems using monitors and display boards (LED, VEDS, dots and flaps); master and slave clocks; automatic announcement systems; time and attendance recording systems;

advertising display systems; automatic information systems; access control systems. Provision of systems on a turnkey basis; staff training and organisation of maintenance.

Recent contracts include the supply of systems for Poznan, Poland; Brno and Prague, Czech Republic; Graz and Salzburg, Austria; Namur, Belgium; Hamburg and Dortmund, Germany; 20 stations in France; Sopron, Hungary; and Brescia, Rome, Cremona, Pavia-Casalpusterlengo and the Milan Metro, Italy.

VERIFIED

Techspan Systems

Techspan Systems plc
Church Lane, Chalfont St Peter SL9 9RF, UK
Tel: +44 1753 889911   Fax: +44 1753 887496

Key personnel
Managing Director: Edward Terris
Commercial Manager: Alistair Chirnside
Sales Executive: Russell Hartwell
Technical Manager: B Whitnall

Corporate development
Techspan is part of the Streamline Holdings group of companies.

Products
Design, supply, installation and maintenance of passenger information systems, including LCD boards for interior and exterior use; video monitor systems; stand-alone and networked control systems; digital clocks; and electronic signs (LED, LCD, VFD, back-lit and electromechanical).

Recent contracts include a complete passenger information display system, including video displays and a recorded announcement system, at Ashford International station, UK; passenger information display systems for Argyle Street, Central Low Level stations in Glasgow, UK, Northallerton, London Victoria, London Liverpool Street, and LED safety information displays featuring animated graphics at Waterloo International Terminal, UK.

UPDATED

Vaughan

Vaughan Harmon Systems Ltd
The Maltings, Hoe Lane, Ware SG12 9LR, UK
Tel: +44 1920 462282   Fax: +44 1920 460702

Key personnel
See entry in *Signalling and telecommunications* section

Products
Passenger information systems; train reporting systems; staff information systems; timetable creation and control systems; network management systems.

VERIFIED

Velec

Velec SA
278 chaussée Fernand Forest, PO Box 6303, F-59203 Tourcoing, France
Tel: +33 3 20 25 77 00   Fax: +33 3 20 25 77 55

Key personnel
Commercial Director: J Apruzzese
Marketing Manager: D Knockaert
Railway Sales Manager: M A Balut

Products
Onboard public address systems, destination indicators, digital announcement systems, LCD and LED signs, video monitoring systems, alarm and service intercoms. Track-to-train transmission by leaky feeder cable. Station video

and audio information systems for passengers, platform surveillance video equipment.

Recent contracts include the supply of the video and public address systems for RENFE, Spain; and public address systems for TGV-R high-speed trainsets for SNCF, France.

VERIFIED

Vultron

Vultron International Ltd
City Park Industrial Estate, Gelderd Road, Leeds
LS12 6DR, UK
Tel: +44 113 263 0323   Fax: +44 113 279 4127
Email: vultronint@aol.com

Key personnel
Managing Director: John Moorhouse
Project Manager: Paul Kiley

Products
Passenger information display systems, including 'Clearsign' Liquid Crystal Displays (LCD), LCDs, Digi-Dot electromechanical reflective disc displays. These displays are used to provide passenger information as departure boards, platform indicators, special noticeboards, onboard destination and next stop displays.

Recent contracts include a Digi-Dot car park summary departures board at Bristol Parkway, UK; Clearsign LCD special noticeboard system at Marylebone station, London and Edinburgh Waverley, Scotland.

UPDATED

Wandel & Goltermann

A memeber of the Schaltbau Group
Wandel & Goltermann Kommunikationstechnik GmbH
PO Box 1361, 72796 Eningen, Germany
Tel: +49 7121 9860   Fax: +49 7121 986100

Key personnel
Managing Director: Fariborz Khavand
Director, Public Transportation Systems:
   Karl-Heinz Bahnmuller
Director, Public Safety Systems: Alex Treffers

Products
Onboard computers, next-stop displays, digital announcement equipment, public address systems with integrated passenger alarm intercom for buses and trains.

Contracts include supply of equipment for Netherlands Railways, Berlin S-Bahn and Munich transport; also for low-floor trams in Dusseldorf and Munich.

NEW ENTRY

Westinghouse Cubic

Westinghouse Cubic Ltd
177 Nutfield Road, Merstham RH1 3HH, UK
Tel: +44 1737 644921   Fax: +44 1737 643693

Key personnel
See entry in *Automatic fare systems* section

Products
Passenger information systems, help points and security systems.

Recent contracts include passenger security and information systems for London Underground Ltd's Piccadilly Line; customer information systems and maintenance support for Thameslink.

UPDATED

AUTOMATIC FARE SYSTEMS AND STATION EQUIPMENT

Alphabetical Listing

Abberfield Technology Pty Ltd
Adtranz
AES
Almex
Ascom
Ascom Monétel
Atron Electronic
Automatic Systems
Bemrose
Burle Industries
BZA
Casas
Cegelec CGA
Cubic
Dassault Automatismes et Télécommunications
Elgeba
FG
FIREMA Trasporti
GFI-Genfare
GPT Card Technology
Gunnebo

Höft & Wessel
Howe Green
ICL
IER
Indra
Intec
Italdis
Klein
Klüssendorf
Laakmann
Logibag
Loksafe
MAEL
Mars
MicroTouch Systems
Mobile Data Processing
Narita
Newbury Data
Nippon Signal
NKI
Norprint

O&K
Omron
Philips Semiconductors
Rand McNally
Russet
Sadamel
Scanpoint
Scheidt & Bachmann
Schlumberger
Siemens
Sony
Strategic Imaging Systems
Takamisawa Cybernetics
Tecnotour-Eltec
Thorn Transit Systems
Toshiba
Toyo Denki
Westinghouse Brakes
Westinghouse Cubic
Zelisko

Classified Listing

ACCESS CONTROL EQUIPMENT
Ascom Monétel
Atron Electronic
Automatic Systems
Burle Industries
Cegelec CGA
Cubic
Dassault Automatismes et Télécommunications
GFI-Genfare
Gunnebo
ICL
Indra
Intec
Italdis
Klein
Nippon Signal
Omron
Siemens
Takamisawa Cybernetics
Thorn Transit Systems
Toshiba
Toyo Denki
Westinghouse Cubic
Zelisko

STATION EQUIPMENT
Casas
Howe Green
Logibag
Loksafe

Narita
Newbury Data
NKI
O&K
Westinghouse Brakes

TICKET ISSUING EQUIPMENT
Abberfield Technology Pty Ltd
Adtranz
AES
Almex
Ascom
Ascom Monétel
Atron Electronic
Automatic Systems
Cegelec CGA
Cubic
Dassault Automatismes et Télécommunications
Elgeba
FIREMA Trasporti
GFI-Genfare
Höft & Wessel
IER
Intec
Klüssendorf
MAEL
Mars
MicroTouch Systems
Nippon Signal
Omron

Russet
Sadamel
Scanpoint
Scheidt & Bachmann
Schlumberger
Siemens
Tecnotour-Eltec
Thorn Transit Systems
Toshiba
Toyo Denki
Westinghouse Cubic
Zelisko

TICKETS AND SMARTCARDS
AES
Bemrose
BZA
Elgeba
FG
GPT Card Technology
Intec
Laakmann
Mobile Data Processing
Norprint
Philips Semiconductors
Rand McNally
Scanpoint
Sony
Strategic Imaging Systems
Westinghouse Cubic

Company Listing by Country

AUSTRALIA
Abberfield Technology Pty Ltd
AES

AUSTRIA
Philips Semiconductors
Zelisko

BELGIUM
AES Prodata
Automatic Systems

DENMARK
Scanpoint

FRANCE
Ascom Monétel
Cegelec CGA
Dassault Automatismes et Télécommunications
IER
Klein
Logibag
Schlumberger

GERMANY
Adtranz
Atron Electronic
Elgeba
FG
Höft & Wessel
Klüssendorf

Laakmann
O&K
Scheidt & Bachmann
Siemens

ITALY
FIREMA Trasporti
Italdis
MAEL
Mobile Data Processing
Tecnotour

JAPAN
Narita
Nippon Signal
Omron
Sony
Takamisawa Cybernetics
Toshiba
Toyo Denki

NETHERLANDS
NKI

SOUTH KOREA
Intec

SPAIN
Casas
Indra

SWEDEN
Gunnebo

SWITZERLAND
Ascom
Mars
Sadamel

UK
Almex
Bemrose
GPT Card Technology
Howe Green
ICL
Loksafe
Newbury Data
Norprint
Russet
Strategic Imaging Systems
Thorn Transit Systems
Westinghouse Brakes
Westinghouse Cubic

USA
Burle Industries
Cubic
BZA
GFI-Genfare
MicroTouch Systems
Rand McNally

Abberfield Technology Pty Ltd

32 Cross Street, Brookvale, NSW 2100, Australia
Tel: +61 2 9939 2844   Fax: +61 2 9938 3462

Key personnel
Managing Director: John M Colyer
Finance Director: John J James

UK Technical Support Office
Abberfield (Europe) Ltd
4 Andover Street, Sheffield S3 9EG
Tel: +44 114 272 7108   Fax: +44 114 272 7108

Products
Ticket vending machines and ticket validators; design and manufacture of ticketing systems.

Recent contracts include the provision of ticket vending and validating equipment for the South Yorkshire Supertram system, UK; and ticketing equipment for the Oasis Monorail, Gold Coast, Queensland, Australia.

VERIFIED

Adtranz

ABB Daimler-Benz Transportation GmbH
Saatwinklër Damm 42-43, D-13627 Berlin, Germany
Tel: +49 30 38320   Fax: +49 30 3832 2000

Head Office, Fixed Installations
ABB Daimler-Benz Transportation Bahnfahrwegsysteme
Mainzer Landstrasse 351, D-60326 Frankfurt-am-Main, Germany
Tel: +49 69 75070   Fax: +49 69 750 7584

Key personnel
See entry in *Fixed electrification equipment* section

Products
Ticket printers and automatic ticket vending machines; ticket cancellers; onboard and stationary computers for ticket issuing and collection of accounting sales data.

Adtranz has moved into smartcard technology with electronic payment and smartcards for urban transport systems.

The ACT 400 is a new smartcard terminal, designed for contact or proximity cards. ANDY is a new hand-held ticket printer for paper tickets with an option for electronic payment with smartcards.

UPDATED

AES

AES Prodata Holdings Ltd
A subsidiary of ERG Ltd
247-249 Balcatta Road, Balcatta, Western Australia 6021, Australia
Tel: +61 9 273 1100   Fax: +61 9 344 3686
Email:jfarrer@aesprodata.com.au
101661.21@compuserv.com

Key personnel
Chief Executive Officer, AES Prodata (Belgium):
    Franky Carbonez
Marketing Manager (Europe): Torben Nielson
Sales & Marketing Manager (Asia Pacific): John Farrer

Principal subsidiary
AES Prodata (Belgium) SA
Leuvensesteenweg 540B.2, 1930 Zaventum
Tel: +32 2 722 8911   Fax: +32 2 725 0448

Overseas offices
Canada, France, Hong Kong, Sweden, UK

Products
Automatic fare collection products and systems using smartcards or magnetic stripe card tickets, including station processors, ticket vending machines, barrier gates and ticket validators.

Contracts include the supply of a contactless smartcard system for Hong Kong; magnetic stripe/contactless smartcard system for Melbourne; contactless smartcard system for Gothenburg; and a magnetic stripe system for Carinthia, Austria.

An AFC system is being supplied for the Moscow Metro. It includes the new V3000 combined magnetic and contactless smartcard system.

UPDATED

Almex

Metric Group, Metric House, Love Lane,
Cirencester GL7 1YG, UK
Tel: +44 1285 651441   Fax: +44 1285 650633

Key personnel
General Manager: Steve Foster
International Sales Manager: Kevin Aspin
Business Development Manager: Tony Emery

Principal subsidiaries
Metric Inc
2540 Route 130, Suite 110, Cranbury, New Jersey, USA
Tel: +1 609 655 7755   Fax: +1 609 655 7711
General Manager: James Meany

Metric GmbH
Langenhorner Chaussée 4, D-22335 Hamburg 63, Germany
Tel: +49 40 5328 8203   Fax: +49 40 5328 8299
Managing Director: Klaus Schiering

Products
Automatic revenue collection systems for railway and light rail applications; ticket issuing machines, portable ticket issuing machines, magnetic ticket validators, automatic vending machines; contact and contactless smartcards.

Recent contracts include the supply of ticket issuing equipment to Maryland Mass Transit Administration, USA.

VERIFIED

Ascom

Ascom Autelca Ltd
Vendomation Division
Worbstrasse 201, CH-3073 Gümlingen-Berne, Switzerland
Tel: +41 31 999 6111   Fax: +41 31 999 6405

Key personnel
Head of Vendomation Division: Roland Greuter
Head of Strategic Marketing: Christian Schmid
Head of Sales: Leo Muff

Products
Automatic revenue collection and information systems; automatic ticket vending machines, portable ticket issuing machines, agent-operated ticket printers and information systems for open or closed solution systems.

Recent contracts include the supply of ticketing equipment to Hamburger Hochbahn; VAG, Nuremburg; Rhein-Main-Verbund, Frankfurt; MTRC, Hong Kong; NSB, Oslo; and Tri-County Commuter Rail Authority, USA.

VERIFIED

Ascom Monétel

Ascom Monétel SA
rue Claude Chappe, PO Box 348, F-07503 Guilherand-Granges, France
Tel: +33 4 75 81 41 41   Fax: +33 4 75 81 42 00

Key personnel
General Manager, Fare Collection Systems Department:
    Yves Peuriere
Sales and Marketing Manager: Gabriel Hanis

Products
Automatic fare collection systems (software and hardware) including: automatic ticket vending machines with payment by coins, banknotes, multiservice card or credit card: user dialogue by keyboard and display unit; small- and large-capacity booking office machines for ticket sales; access controllers with turnstile or with onboard or fixed-ticket validator; built-in circuit board for processing statistical and accounting data.

Monétel's fare collection systems are designed for use with magnetic tickets of Edmondson (30 × 60 mm) or credit card formats or with integrated contactless circuit cards. The systems are capable of handling any type of fare structure and ticket (single ride, prepaid/stored value cards, multiride tickets, time-based tickets) and a wide variety of user categories including season ticket holders, occasional users, students and reduced rates. Data transfer can be effected either by portable memory units or infrared datalink.

Contracts include the supply of equipment for the Paris, Lille, Marseilles, Toulouse, Mexico City, Rio de Janeiro, Seoul, Baltimore, Glasgow, Tyne & Wear, Barcelona and Medellín Metros; RER and St Denis–Bobigny tramway (Paris); SNCF; Iarnród Éireann, Ireland; Vevey-Montreux, Switzerland; and Portugal, Brasilia and Kuala Lumpur.

VERIFIED

Atron Electronic

Atron Electronic GmbH
Landsberger Strasse 509, 81241 Munich, Germany
Tel: +49 8121 5071   Fax: +49 8121 40333
Web: http://www.atron.de

Products
Smartcard terminals; AFC systems; stationary and mobile ticket machines.

NEW ENTRY

Automatic Systems

Automatic Systems SA
Avenue Mercator 5, B-1300 Wavre, Belgium
Tel: +32 10 230211   Fax: +32 10 230202

Key personnel
Managing Director: Yves Le Clercq
General Manager: Michel Coenraets
Export Manager: Michel Meli
Market Development Manager: Daniel Wautrecht

Products
Design and manufacture of vehicle and pedestrian access control equipment, including automatic rising barriers, tripod turnstiles, automatic gates type NO or NC, safety rotating drums, ticket vending machines.

VERIFIED

Bemrose

Bemrose Security Printing
PO Box 18, Wayzgoose Drive, Derby DE21 6XG, UK
Tel: +44 1332 294242   Fax: +44 1332 290366

Key personnel
Sales Director: Colin Harrison
Sales Manager: Trevor Willis
Export Sales Manager: Anne-Marie Mourer

Principal subsidiaries
Henry Booth (Hull) Ltd
ESP Security Print

Products
Vouchers, warrants, season tickets and magnetic tickets.

Recent contracts include the supply of a new combined bus/rail travel card called Centrocard for West Midlands Passenger Transport Executive, UK.

VERIFIED

Burle Industries

Robot Access Control Hardware
7041 Orchard Street, Dearborn, Michigan 48126, USA
Tel: +1 313 846 2623   Fax: +1 313 846 3569

Keeping people on the move

Satisfying your customers relies on moving them from A to B – fast. Rapid ticketing is an essential part of keeping them on the move. Every day more than 100 million people worldwide rely on Mars Electronics International cash management systems for convenient and secure payments. So if you need banknote, coin and card systems that enable your customers to make fast and reliable ticket purchases, talk to us about your specific needs.

Please contact me to discuss my requirements.

Name_____ Title_____

Company_____

Address_____

_____

Tel_____ Fax_____

Return to: Serge Guillod, Mars Electronics International, Case Postale 2650, CH-1211 Geneva 2, Switzerland. Tel: (+41) 22 884 0505 Fax: (+41) 22 884 0504

**Switzerland (+41) 22 884 0505 Japan (+81) 44 712 1315
UK (+44) 1189 446255 USA (+1) 914 722 4075**

Helping you deliver.

SODECO™
CASH MANAGEMENT SYSTEMS

**MARS
ELECTRONICS
INTERNATIONAL**

 Mars Electronics International manufacturing, and sales are ISO 9002 approved.

A division of the worldwide Mars, Incorporated group.

Newbury Data

Newbury Data Recording Ltd
Premier Park, Road 1 Industrial Estate, Winsford,
Cheshire CW7 3PT, UK
Tel: +44 1606 593424   Fax: +44 1606 556969

Key personnel

Managing Director: Alan J Phillips
Product General Manager: Ashley Bailey
Marketing Executive: Philippa Molyneux

Products

Flexstore — a hand-held AB ticket reader, designed to
read and display information held on magnetic stripe
tickets, and to download that data into a central computer
for passenger and ticket analysis purposes. Currently
supplied to European Passenger Services for that
company's Eurostar trains.

Flexfare — a modular booking office ticketing system,
comprising a terminal, receipt printer and ISO-sized card
ticket issuer. Fully configurable to customer's
requirements.

VERIFIED

Nippon Signal

The Nippon Signal Co Ltd
3-1 Marunouchi 3-chome, Chiyoda-ku, Tokyo, Japan
Tel: +81 3 3287 4500   Fax: +81 3 3287 4649
Email:nr9t-fry@asahi-net.or.jp

Works

Yono Factory, 13-8 Kamikizaki 1-chome, Urawa City
Utsunomiya Factory, 11-2 Hiraide Kougyo Danchi,
Utsunomiya City

Key personnel

See entry in *Signalling and telecommunications* section

Products

Automatic fare collection equipment such as bill changer,
ticket vending machine, gate controller, passenger gate,
automatic fare adjusting machine, season ticket issuing
machine, multifunction booking office machine, ticket
issuing machine for station staff, data processing
machine, visual display, visual magnetic card system
(VISMAC); prepaid card systems.

UPDATED

NKI

Nederlandse Kunststof Industrie BV
PO Box 222, 3-5 Industriestraat, NL-5100 AE Dongen,
Netherlands
Tel: +31 1623 17200   Fax: +31 1623 15657
Email: nki-b.v.-holland.net

US office

NKI Inc
Riverwood Building, 3350 Cumberland Circle, Suite 1900,
Atlanta, Georgia 30339, USA
Tel: +1 770 984 5404   Fax: +1 770 984 5401

Key personnel

Managing Directors: G E E Aerts
Sales Manager: H A J J Janssens
Sales Support Manager: Loran A H Janssens

Products

NKI offers a total service in design, manufacture and
installation of the working environment in passenger
terminals. NKI provides basic information, design
concepts, layout projections and engineering details prior
to production. The company offers station ticket counter
systems which meet the latest ergonomic and technical
requirements.

UPDATED

Norprint

Norprint International Ltd
Norfolk Street, Boston PE21 6AF, UK
Tel: +44 1205 591473   Fax: +44 1205 591639
Email: magnordata@ukbusiness.com

Key personnel

Director: Mike Ward

Sales and Marketing Manager: Mark Newton
Product Manager: Elaine Hubbert

Overseas Sales Offices

Norprint USA Inc
1827 Powers Ferry Road, Building 4, Suite 150, Atlanta,
Georgia 30339, USA
Tel: +1 770 952 3305   Fax: +1 770 952 4409
Sales Manager: Allen Davidson

Norprint Holland BV
Planetenweg 61A, NL-2132 HM Hoofddorp, Netherlands
Tel: +31 23 563 1431   Fax: +31 23 564 1264
Sales Manager: Arnoud Luttikhuis

Products

Magnetic stripe tickets for automatic fare collection
systems. These can be supplied in a number of formats
(cut single, fan-folded, reel to dimensional requirement)
on a variety of materials (paper, plastic, paper/plastic
sandwich), including thermally coated materials. Both
low- and high-coercivity magnetic striped tickets can be
supplied. Numerous security features can be
incorporated into the ticket design, including anti-
photocopying inks, UV inks and security backgrounds.
Norprint also manufactures ATB tickets, and can supply
plastic thermal material for medium- and long-term
magnetic transport tickets.

Norprint has supplied tickets to Iarnród Éireann,
Ireland, SNCF and Cityrail, Australia.

UPDATED

O&K

O&K Rolltrepen GmbH
Nierenhofer Strasse 10, D-45525 Hattingen/Ruhr,
Germany
Tel: +49 2324 2050   Fax: +49 2324 205215

Products

Escalators and autowalks.

NEW ENTRY

Omron

Omron Corporation
Omron Tokyo Building, 3-4-10 Toranomon, Minato-ku,
Tokyo 105, Japan
Tel: +81 3 3436 7083   Fax: +81 3 3436 7056

Key personnel

Managing Director, Public Systems Division: I Minami
Manager, Overseas Business Promotion Department,
    Public Systems Division: T Iwakata

Principal subsidiaries

Omron Systems Inc, USA
Omron Systems Management GmbH, Germany
Omron Systems UK Ltd
Omron Business Systems Singapore (Pte) Ltd

Products

Automatic fare collection systems including ticket
vending machines, gate machines, ticket printers and
station computers.

Recent contracts include the supply of an automatic
fare collection system for Teito Rapid Transit Authority;
and ticket vending machines for Nagoya Municipal
Transportation Bureau.

VERIFIED

Philips Semiconductors

Philips Semiconductors (Mikron) GmbH
Mikron-Weg 1, A-8101 Gratkorn, Austria
Tel: +43 3124 299760   Fax: +43 3124 299270

Key personnel

General Manager: Günter Schlatte
Marketing Manager, Contactless Smartcards:
    Alexander Harrer

Corporate developments

Mikron was purchased by Philips, Netherlands, in June
1995 and is now part of Philips Semiconductors.

Products

Contactless smartcards; radio frequency identification
components. The Mifare® contactless smartcard for
automatic fare collection systems and other applications
is in use in 50 installations worldwide.

A new development is the Mifare-Plus combi-card and
Mifare-Light small memory chip for cost-sensitive high-
volume applications, such as electronic 10-trip tickets or
phone cards.

UPDATED

Rand McNally

Rand McNally & Co
8255 North Central Park Avenue, Skokie, Illinois 60076,
USA
Tel: +1 847 329 8100   Fax: +1 847 673 8143

Key personnel

Vice-President, Sales: M Dawson

Principal subsidiary

Rand McNally International
McNally House, Tring Business Park, Tring HP23 4JX, UK
Tel +44 1442 824011   Fax: +44 1442 828531
Sales Director: A Heseltine

Products

Magnetically striped and bar-coded tickets and cards,
and other security printed products.

VERIFIED

Russet

Russet Ltd
Unit 2, Rose Kiln Lane, Reading RG2 OHP, UK
Tel: +44 1734 868147   Fax: +44 1734 755853

Key personnel

Managing Director: Paul Cooper
Business Development Manager: David Leggett

Products

R240 matrix ticket printer for credit card size (54 × 85 mm)
tickets; privilege plastic card printer with colour and
magnetic encoding.

VERIFIED

Sadamel

Sadamel SA
Rue du Collège 73, CH-2300 La Chaux-de-Fonds,
Switzerland
Tel: +41 32 968 0770   Fax: +41 32 968 0885
Email: sadamel@sadamel.ch

Key personnel

General Director: Roger Cattin
Development Director: Jerôme Froidevaux
Production Director: Bertrand Hochart
Commercial and Marketing Manager:
    Werner Frei

Products

Automatic ticket vending machines suitable for paper and
magnetic tickets with payment by coins, and a device for
recycling the coins; magnetic and smartcard readers;
banknote readers, systems for accounting and statistics.
Onboard or counter-based automatic ticket vending
machines, portable ticket machines and ticket cancelling
units.

Recent contracts include Swiss Federal Railways
(SBB): 120 ticket vending machines (counter-based with
touchscreen facility); Transports Publics de Genève
(TPG): 210 ticket vending machines (payment with
magnetic card); and Verkehrsbetrieb Luzern (VBL): 230
stationary ticket vending machines and vending
machines for 55 buses and six sales points, all with the
AES Prodata-type magnetic ticketing system.

UPDATED

Scanpoint portable fare computer   **1996**

Scanpoint

Scanpoint Technology A/S
Vibeholms Allé 22, DK-2605 Brøndby, Denmark
Tel: +45 43 433999   Fax: +45 43 433488

Key personnel
Managing Director: Yuris Nora

Corporate development
In 1997, Thorn Transit Systems International (qv) became part of the Cubic Automatic Revenue Group (qv) which owns WCL (qv) and Scanpoint.

Products
Electronic fare collection systems based on the use of magnetic stripe plastic cards (high- or low-coercivity) or smartcards (contact/contactless) complying with ISO standards, employing hands-free or paper cards. Mobile, stationary and portable fare computers.
Recent contracts include the supply of a contactless smartcard system to NSB, Norway.

UPDATED

Scheidt & Bachmann

Scheidt & Bachmann GmbH
Breite Strasse 132, D-41238 Mönchengladbach, Germany
Tel: +49 21 662660   Fax: +49 21 6626 6699

Key personnel
Marketing Manager, Europe: Manfred Feiter

Products
Automatic fare collection and ticket vending machines for stationary and mobile applications; electronic ticket printers for vehicles and ticket offices; central computer systems for accounting and data provision.

UPDATED

Schlumberger

Schlumberger Technology
Urban Terminals and Systems
PO Box 62004, 50 avenue Jean Jaurès, F-92542 Montrouge Cedex, France
Tel: +33 1 47 46 60 00   Fax: +33 1 47 46 67 82

Schlumberger Electronic Transactions
PO Box 620-12, 50 Avenue Jean Jaurès, F-92542, Montrouge Cedex, France

Main works
Parc la Fayette, 6 rue Isaac Newton, PO Box 2079, F-25051 Besançon Cedex, France
Tel: +33 3 81 54 56 00   Fax: +33 3 81 52 76 38

Key personnel
General Manager: Jacques Brault
Commercial/Sales Director: Jean-Claude Grüner
Technical Director: Jean-Louis Bezin
Marketing Director: Paul Lenfant
Communications Director: Helene Myngers

Products
The range comprises smartcard systems and the Addams, DAC, Discobb and TVM ticket dispensers.

Addams: A multidestination ticket dispenser with an emphasis on security, since it automatically prints a financial control ticket and will not allow any ticket to be issued with the door open. Modular, it provides a choice of destination, 30 possible fare structures and choice of class.

DAC: An automatic ticket book dispenser with a dual application. It receives money which is deposited by drivers (coins, notes and cheques) and also supplies them with tickets 24 hours a day. Security is an important feature as a receipt is issued for each transaction which is performed.

Discobb: A dispenser and validator for single tickets. All parameters can be modified (ticket type, display, fares).

TVM: A ticket vending machine which is fully automated for ticketing and fare collection.

Up to 1,500 Discobb and 1,200 Addams models have been supplied to SNCF.

Schlumberger Electronic Transactions is installing 22 new multifunction vending machines in Lille which will supply tickets for both the SNCF railway network and the city's metro and bus services from a single purchase. The machine is based on the DBR automatic ticket dispenser produced by Schlumberger for SNCF, and currently installed at 500 sites throughout France. The new ticket machines accept payments by coins and bank cards, including smartcards.

Schlumberger Electronic Transactions is also refurbishing Paris metro kiosks with 900 advanced ticket sales terminals. SNCF is also taking delivery of 150 fast service ticket dispensers for the Paris urban transport network.

UPDATED

Siemens

Siemens Aktiengesellschaft
Transportation Systems Group (VT)
Automatic Fare Collection Division (VT FGM)
PO Box 65, D-12414 Berlin, Germany
Tel: +49 30 6174 1292   Fax: +49 30 6174 1032

Key personnel
General Managers: A Hoerder, V Rind
Sales and Marketing: J Janssen, K Koenen

Products
Automatic fare collection systems; complete turnkey systems for integrated ticketing and fare collection, based on magnetic cards and contact and contactless smartcards; system components, including smartcard readers, ticket vending machines, ticket gates and ticket office machines.

Schlumberger Discobb ticket dispenser

Recent contracts include trials in Oldenburg, Germany for contactless chipcards and an order for a complete elevated rail system, including a closed ATC system.

VERIFIED

Sony

Sony Corporation
Card Systems Development Department
6-7-35 Kitashinagawa, Shinagawa-ku, Tokyo 141, Japan
Tel: +81 3 5448 6832   Fax: +81 3 5448 6833

Products
Smartcard systems.
Recent developments include the Felica contactless smartcard system.

VERIFIED

Strategic Imaging Systems

8 St Peters Road, Poole BH14 0PA, UK
Tel: +44 1202 716100   Fax: +44 1202 716140

Key personnel
Managing Director: G A Douglas
Technical Director: C J Leatherbarrow

Products
Systems for issue and personalisation (with ID) of all types of smartcards as well as thin pvc magnetic barrier tickets. A fully integrated central control system is also available to monitor and audit utilisation of travel passes.
Current contracts include smartcard projects for London Transport, Merseytravel, West Yorkshire Passenger Transport Executive and Kent and Surrey county councils.

UPDATED

Takamisawa Cybernetics

Takamisawa Cybernetics Co Ltd
Nakano Heiwa Building, 2-48-5 Chuo, Nakano-ku, Tokyo 164, Japan
Tel: +81 3 3227 3371   Fax: +81 3 3227 3396

Key personnel
Managing Director: S Kozeki
Managing Director, Sales Division: S Nejime
Manager, Trading Department: T Hisada

Works
Nagano Factory No 1
525 Kitagawa, Usada-machi, Minami-saku-gun, Nagano-ken, 384-03, Japan

Products
Design and manufacture of automatic fare collection systems and equipment, including ticket vending machines, ticket gates, fare adjustment machines and ticket printers; AFC-related currency and card handling unit.

UPDATED

Tecnotour-Eltec

Tecnotour-Eltec SpA
A member of the Olivetti-Tecnost Group
Via T Tasso 19, I-25080 Molinetto di Mazzano (BS), Italy
Tel: +39 30 212 1111   Fax: +39 30 262 9631

Key personnel
Managing Director: A Portesi

Products
Automatic fare collection systems; ticket vending machines for onboard and stationary applications; cancelling machines; booking office machines.
Contracts include the supply of equipment to Italian Railways (FS) and many public and private transit companies.

UPDATED

Thorn Transit Systems International Ltd

EMI Group plc
Wookey Hole Road, Wells BA5 1AA, UK
Tel: +44 1749 670222   Fax: +44 1749 679363

Key personnel

Managing Director: J Slater
Sales and Marketing Director: K Thorpe
Technical Director: L Adams
Operations Director: B R Harris
European Marketing Manager: J O'Donnell
Business Development Manager: D Croker

Products

Complete fare collection systems for mass transit and intermodal applications, including central computer systems, secure software, station monitoring systems, ticket vending machines, bus and rail validators, portable and desktop ticket machines, magnetic validator assemblies, automatic gates (flap and tripod), proximity card systems.

Contracts: TTSI has a significant share of the AFC market with contracts to supply equipment to mass transit systems in Europe and Asia Pacific.

Recent projects include supply of a complete AFC system for the second phase of the Kuala Lumpur LRT, following on from the new airport express line in Hong Kong and the Seoul Subway, South Korea. Current European projects include both light rail and metro lines in Ankara, Izmir, Stockholm, Manchester and London Docklands. In addition, TTSI is continuing its maintenance and upgrade support of the ticketing system for the rail network in Britain.

UPDATED

Toshiba

Toshiba Corporation
Automation Systems Group: Electronic Systems Department
1-1 Shibaura 1-chome, Minato-ku, Tokyo 105, Japan
Tel: +81 3 3457 2545   Fax: +81 3 5444 9409

Key personnel

Senior Manager: M Okada
Assistant Senior Manager: T Imamura

Products

Automatic fare collection systems.

Products include season ticket renewal machine, which is operated by a passenger by inserting the old season ticket; a ticket-vending machine, including change dispenser; multifunction booking office machine; Automatic flap door-type gate, available in three models: entry, exit, and reversible.

A new portable ticket issuing machine replaces the time-consuming process of issuing train tickets by hand.

VERIFIED

Toyo Denki

Toyo Denki Seizo KK
Toyo Electric Manufacturing Co Ltd
Yaesu Mitsui Building, 7-2 Yaesu 2-chome, Chuo-ku, Tokyo 104, Japan
Tel: +81 3 3271 6374   Fax: +81 3 3271 4693

Key personnel

See entry in *Electric traction equipment* section

Products

Ticket issuing systems for suburban and rapid transit railway systems; automatic ticket issuing machines, fare adjusting equipment.

Toyo Denki's ticket issuing system for suburban and rapid transit systems can issue magnetic tickets for automatic gates. It can also calculate fares for complex urban networks where different routeings are possible and there is much interline traffic between different operators.

VERIFIED

Market Street station, Manchester, showing AFC machines supplied by TTSI for Manchester Metrolink
1997

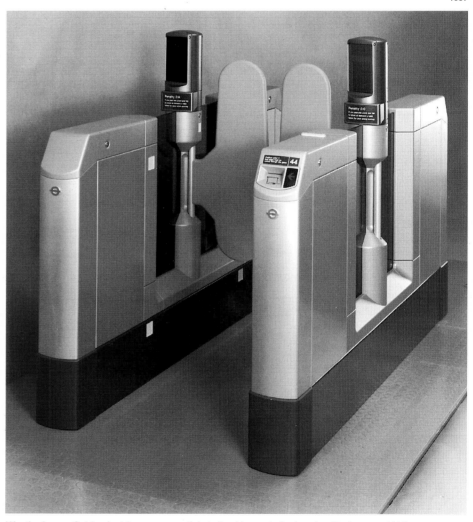

Westinghouse Cubic electric passenger ticket checking gate for London Undergound Ltd   *1995*

Westinghouse Brakes Ltd

PO Box 74, Foundry Lane, Chippenham SN15 1HY, UK
Tel: +44 1249 442000   Fax: +44 1249 655040

Key personnel

See entry in *Brakes and drawgear* section

Products

Platform screen door systems.

Recent contracts include the supply of platform screen door systems for London Underground Ltd's Jubilee Line Extension; Kuala Lumpur LRT System 2; and a people mover system at Hong Kong Airport.

VERIFIED

WCL

Westinghouse Cubic Ltd
177 Nutfield Road, Merstham RH1 3HH, UK
Tel: +44 1737 644921   Fax: +44 1737 643693

Key personnel

General Manager: S Harris
Operations Director: Nigel Bryant
Finance Director: Simon Edgington
Marketing Manager: Terry Hill

Corporate development

In 1997, Thorn Transit Systems International (qv) became part of the Cubic Automatic Revenue Group which owns WCL and Scanpoint (qv).

Products

Automatic fare collection systems (design and manufacture); passenger information systems (design and supply); security systems including CCTV, passenger help points and radio clocks; electrical works, including power and data cables, lighting and power supplies; facilities management, including maintenance, 24hr fault desk, management reporting and system monitoring.

Recent contracts include the supply of an automatic fare collection system for London Underground Ltd's Jubilee Line Extension, Heathrow Express and Connex South Central; security systems for LUL Northern and Piccadilly Lines, customer information systems for Thameslink and British Airports Authority; trackside cabling for Railtrack.

UPDATED

Zelisko

Steinfeldergasse 12, A-2340 Mödling, Austria
Tel: +43 2236 406290   Fax: +43 2236 406299

Products

Ticket issuing machines and cancellers for smartcard, magnetic and other tickets.

NEW ENTRY

FIXED ELECTRIFICATION EQUIPMENT

Alphabetical Listing

Adtranz
Alcatel Siette
Allied Insulators
Ampcontrol
Ansaldo Trasporti
Balfour Beatty Rail Projects
Barclay Mowlem
BEML
BICC
Brecknell, Willis
Cegelec Projects
Cembre
Contransimex
Costamasnaga
Delta
DWA
Ebo
EFACEC
Electric Rails
Electro Wire
Elektrim

Elpro
Ferraz
FIREMA Trasporti
Flury
Fuji Electric
Furrer + Frey
Ganz Ansaldo
GEC Alsthom ACEC Transport
GEC Plessey
Geismar
Greysham
HDC
Hitachi Cable
Holec Projects
Hyundai
Jacques Galland
Kaufmann
Kummler + Matter
Lerc
Merlin Gerin Brasil
Permali

Pfisterer
Pirelli
Powernetics
SAE (India)
SAFT
Sasib Railway Electrification
SDCEM
Sécheron
Sefag
Sekko
Siemens
SMC
SPIE Enertrans
Thorn Automation
Toshiba
Transmitton
Trend
Westinghouse Cubic
Whipp & Bourne
Wild & Grunder

Classified Listing

MAINTENANCE VEHICLES AND EQUIPMENT
BEML
Costamasnaga
DWA
Geismar

OVERHEAD LINE AND THIRD RAIL EQUIPMENT
Allied Insulators
BHEL
Brecknell, Willis
Cembre
EFACEC
Elektrim
Elpro
Flury
Geismar
Greysham
HDC
Hitachi Cable
Jacques Galland
Kaufmann
Kummler + Matter
Lerc
Permali
Pfisterer
Sasib Railway Electrification
SDCEM
Sefag
Sekko

Siemens
SMC
Wild & Grunder

POWER SUPPLY EQUIPMENT
Adtranz
Ampcontrol
Ansaldo Trasporti
BICC
Cegelec Projects
Cembre
Delta
Ebo
EFACEC
Electric Rails
Electro Wire
Elektrim
Elpro
Ferraz
FIREMA Trasporti
Fuji Electric
Ganz Ansaldo
GEC Alsthom ACEC Transport
GEC Plessey
Hitachi Cable
Holec Projects
Hyundai
Merlin Gerin Brasil
Powernetics

SAE (India)
SAFT
Sasib Railway Electrification
SDCEM
Sécheron
Thorn Automation
Toshiba
Transmitton
Trend
Whipp & Bourne

TURNKEY RAILWAY ELECTRIFICATION
Alcatel Siette
Ansaldo Trasporti
Balfour Beatty Rail Projects
Barclay
Contransimex
Electric Rails
Furrer + Frey
Holec Projects
Pirelli
SAE (India)
Sasib Railway Electrification
Siemens
SPIE Enertrans
Westinghouse Cubic

Company Listing by Country

AUSTRALIA
Adtranz
Ampcontrol
Barclay
SMC

AUSTRIA
Adtranz

BELGIUM
GEC Alsthom ACEC Transport

BRAZIL
Merlin Gerin Brasil

FINLAND
Electric Rails
Sekko

FRANCE
Ferraz
Geismar
Jacques Galland
Lerc
SAFT
SDCEM
SPIE Enertrans

GERMANY
Adtranz
DWA
Elpro
Siemens

HUNGARY
Ganz Ansaldo

INDIA
BEML
Greysham
HDC
SAE (India)

ITALY
Adtranz
Alcatel Siette
Ansaldo Trasporti
Cembre
Costamasnaga
FIREMA Trasporti
Pfisterer
Sasib Railway Electrification

JAPAN
Fuji Electric
Hitachi Cable
Toshiba

KOREA, SOUTH
Hyundai

NETHERLANDS
Holec Projects

POLAND
Elektrim

PORTUGAL
EFACEC

ROMANIA
Contransimex

SWITZERLAND
Ebo
Flury
Furrer + Frey
Kaufmann
Kummler + Matter
Sécheron
Sefag
Wild & Grunder

UK
Allied Insulators
Balfour Beatty Rail Projects
BICC
Brecknell, Willis
Cegelec Projects
Delta
GEC Plessey
Permali
Pirelli
Powernetics
Thorn Automation
Transmitton
Trend
Westinghouse Cubic
Whipp & Bourne

USA
Electro Wire

Adtranz

ABB Daimler-Benz Transportation GmbH
Group Holding Headquarters and Group Corporate
Centre
Saatwinkler Damm 43, D-13627 Berlin
Tel: +49 303 8320   Fax +49 303 832 2000

Head Office, Fixed Installations Group
ABB Daimler-Benz Transportation (Deutschland) GmbH
Mainzer Landstrasse 349-351, D-60326 Frankfurt,
Germany
Tel: +49 69 750 7551   Fax +49 69 750 7584

Key personnel
Executive, Fixed Installations Group: Anders Larsson

UK member company
ABB Daimler-Benz Transportation (Signal) Ltd
Apex Plaza, Atrium Court, Reading RG1 1AX
Tel: +44 1734 579757   Fax: +44 1734 579452

Products
Design, supply and installation of AC/AC, AC/DC stations
and low- or industrial frequency applications for railways,
including mobile stations.

Design, supply and installation of catenaries and third
rail systems and their related components.

Design, supply and installation of complete feeder
systems.

Contracts include 25 kV 50 Hz AC electrification of
Kuala Lumpur suburban routes for KTM, Malaysia; supply
of five DC substations for SL Tag AB's Roslagbanan,
Sweden; DC substations for Dallas Area Rapid Transit,
USA; frequency converter station for Amtrak, USA;
electrification of Line 1 of the Shanghai Metro, China
(People's Republic), including DC power supply and
catenary; extension and modernisation of existing
catenary on Cairo suburban routes for Egyptian National
Railways; power supply and catenary systems for
DB AG's Hannover—Würzburg and Mannheim—Stuttgart
high-speed lines, Germany; static converter for DB AG's
Jübek station, Germany; electrification of Lines 2 and 3 of
the Athens Metro, Greece, including DC substations and
third rail equipment; Encants substation for Barcelona
Metro, Spain; supply of four substations and
refurbishment of two substations for Bilbao Metro, Spain;
electrification of Saarbrücken LRT system, Germany;
electrification of Gardermoen airport railway, Norway; and
supply of static power converters for Banverket, Sweden.

UPDATED

Alcatel Siette

A division of Alcatel Italia SpA
Via Provinciale Lucchese 33, I-550019 Osmannoro, Sesto
Fiorentino, Florence, Italy
Tel: +39 55 30631   Fax: +39 55 306 3391

Key personnel
Transportation Manager: Giuseppe Celli

Products
Signalling and automation systems for railways and metro
systems; telecommunication systems; electrification;
technologies for high-speed systems.

VERIFIED

Allied Insulators

Allied Insulators Ltd
PO Box 17, Milton, Stoke-on-Trent ST2 7EE, UK
Tel: +44 1782 534321   Fax: +44 1782 545804

Key personnel
Managing Director: M B Page
Commercial Director: R G Shenton
Technical Director: F Liptrop
Sales Director: T B Lee

Products
Insulator assemblies for feeder transmission, tracked

overhead transmission, third rail systems, pantograph
support and switching apparatus.

Recent contracts include the supply of overhead
catenary insulators for the electrification system within the
Channel Tunnel and for Heathrow Express, London
Paddington to Heathrow Airport.

UPDATED

Ampcontrol

Ampcontrol Pty Ltd
250 Macquarie Road, Warners Bay, New South Wales
2282, Australia
Tel: +61 49 565899   Fax: +61 49 565985
Email: ampcsm@ozemail.com.au

Key personnel
Sales Director: N Sawyer
Engineering Director: P Cockbain

Products
Traction control switchgear and resistors; traction power
control systems; traction substation switchrooms (DC and
AC); transformers and switchgear.

Recent contracts include the supply of the electrical
distribution control and protection equipment between
the 132 kV switchboard and the 25 kV overhead electrical
system for the extension of the Perth suburban rail
network.

UPDATED

Ansaldo Trasporti

Ansaldo Trasporti SpA
425 Via Argine, I-80147 Naples, Italy
Tel: +39 81 565 0111   Fax: +39 81 565 0638-9

Key personnel
See entry in *Locomotives and powered passenger
vehicles* section

Products
AC and DC electrification systems with centralised
control; high-speed circuit breakers; rectifiers; static
converters for AC and DC substations; design, supply and
erection of feeder lines and substations; electronic
converters and controls, auxiliary apparatus; sales,
installation, start-up and servicing.

VERIFIED

Balfour Beatty Rail Projects

Balfour Beatty Rail Projects Ltd
Railway Electrification
PO Box 12, Acornfield Road, Kirkby, Liverpool
L33 7TY, UK
Tel: +44 151 548 5000   Fax: +44 151 548 5320

Key personnel
Business Manager: P Kehoe
Commercial Manager: K F Bennet

Products
Consultancy, engineering studies, design, supply,
installation and maintenance for electrification schemes
worldwide. Turnkey projects covering a wide variety of
transport systems.

Balfour Rail Projects is a member of the BICC group
and has electrified well over 25,000 km of rail systems,
undertaking design, supply and installation contracts
throughout the world.

Recent contracts include electrification of the
Guangzhou Metro, China; re-electrification of the North
London Line for Railtrack, UK; upgrading of the Beijing
Metro, China; MTRC Lantau and Airport Railway, Hong
Kong; and electrification of the New Haven—Boston route
for Amtrak, USA.

UPDATED

Barclay Mowlem

Barclay Mowlem Construction
20 Bridge Street, Pymble, New South Wales 2073
Tel: +61 2 9481 1333   Fax: +61 2 9481 1369

Key personnel
Managing Director: D C Hudson
General Manager, Railway Engineering & Construction
  Group: P W Welley
Business Procurement Manager, Railway Engineering &
  Construction Group: H J Tarrant

Subsidiary company
Austrak Pty Ltd

Products
Main line and LRT electrification schemes, AC or DC;
manufacture of pre-stressed concrete poles.

UPDATED

BEML

Bharat Earth Movers Ltd
BEML Soudha, 23/1 4th Main, SR Nagar, Bangalore 560
027, India
Tel: +91 80 222 4141   Fax: +91 80 222 6883

Key personnel
See entry in *Non-powered passenger vehicles* section

Products
Overhead equipment inspection car, a self-propelled,
eight-wheeled vehicle for periodic inspection and
maintenance of overhead equipment on electrified rail
routes. The car is self-contained with workshop, storage
facilities, staff cabins and elevating platform and is fully
equipped for repairs to overhead equipment and erecting
catenary and contact wires. It is available in both single-
and twin-engine versions.

Recent contracts include the supply of 26 single-engine
and four twin-engine cars (1,676 mm gauge) for Indian
Railways.

UPDATED

BEML overhead equipment inspection car

BICC

BICC Cables Ltd
Chester Business Park, Chester CH4 9PZ, UK
Tel: +44 1244 688400   Fax: +44 1244 688401

Key personnel
See entry in *Signalling and telecommunications* section

Products
Power cables.

VERIFIED

Brecknell, Willis

Brecknell, Willis & Co Ltd
Member of the Fandstan Electric Group
PO Box 10, Chard TA20 2DE, UK
Tel: +44 1460 64941   Fax: +44 1460 66122

Key personnel
See entry in *Electric traction equipment* section

Products
Current collection and power distribution equipment for the transportation sector.

Includes supply of complete overhead contact and third rail systems for railway and metro applications covering design, manufacture, supply and installation.

Gas tensioning equipment, spring boxes and ground return units for railways, metro, light rail systems and tramways.

Projects include systems for LUL Jubilee Line Extension and Northern Line improvement programmes, Ankara and Taipei Metro systems; overhead contact systems for the Midland Metro LRT system and third rail system for Merseyrail.

UPDATED

Cegelec Projects

Cegelec Projects Ltd
Boughton Road, Rugby CV21 1BU, UK
Tel: +44 1788 563563   Fax: +44 1788 563765
Email: bc2@cegelecproj.co.uk

Key personnel
Managing Director: J A Davies
Division Manager, Transportation and Industrial Power
  Supplies: H J Thorpe
Commercial Manager, Transportation and Industrial
  Power Supplies: B Carr

Products
Comprehensive AC and DC traction power supply systems comprising indoor and outdoor substations embracing rectifiers, transformers, AC and DC switchgear, battery chargers, low-voltage distribution equipment, stray current control equipment, over-voltage protection systems and cabling. Contact rail systems, signalling power supplies, DC power system studies and computer simulation; and SCADA equipment.

Recent contracts include Manchester Metrolink, London Underground Ltd (Central Line and Jubilee Line Extension), Hong Kong MTRC (Lantau and Airport Railway), Docklands Light Railway, Caracas Metro, and Ankara Metro.

UPDATED

Cembre

Cembre SpA
Via Serenissima 9, I-25135 Brescia, Italy
Tel: +30 36921   Fax: +30 336 5766

UK subsidiary
Cembre Ltd
Fairview Industrial Estate, Kingsbury Road, Curdworth, Sutton Coldfield B76 9EE
Tel: +44 1675 470440   Fax: +44 1675 470220

Brecknell, Willis high-conductivity aluminium third rail with stainless steel head (left), compared to conventional third rail. The new design reduces the number of substations required   **1996**

Other associate companies in Paris, Madrid and Holmestrand, Norway

Products
Electrical connectors and installation tools.

NEW ENTRY

Contransimex

Contransimex SA
PO Box 2006, 38 Dinicu Golescu Boulevard, R-77113 Bucharest, Romania
Tel: +40 1 618 0526, 638 7094/7132
Fax: +40 1 618 0042

Key personnel
Chairman: Alfons Irinescu
Manager: Liviu Vasiliu
Deputy Manager, Construction Supervision:
  Daniel Vladescu
Chief Executive, Tendering Department:
  Constantin Ciobanu
Chief Executive, Marketing: Andrei Niculescu

Products
Railway construction and complete electrifications, metros.

VERIFIED

Costamasnaga

Costamasnaga SpA
Viale 4 Novembre, I-22041 Costamasnaga, Italy
Tel: +39 31 869411   Fax: +39 31 855330

Key personnel
See entry in *Non-powered passenger vehicles* section

Products
ASTRIDE road/rail vehicle which is suitable for maintenance of electric overhead lines and is equipped with a platform fitted to a crane providing a wide range of access. The vehicle has a railway system which takes the power from the engine of the road vehicle (modified Iveco 150). The front axle is driven and the rear axle is trailing. The wheels are 500 mm in diameter and are fitted with leaf springs and shock-absorbers in order to obtain good contact with the rail even at high speeds. Traction is hydromechanical and the braking system utilises disc brakes. Also, the vehicle is provided with service, emergency and parking brakes.

Maximum speed is more than 50 km/h while at low speeds it is possible to use a remote control from the inspection basket.

ASTRIDE, fitted by Permaquip, is in service in the UK.

VERIFIED

Delta

Delta Crompton Cables Ltd
Mill Marsh Lane, Brimsdown, Enfield EN3 7QD, UK
Tel: +44 181 804 2468   Fax: +44 181 804 7505

Works
Alfreton Road, Derby DE2 4AE, UK

Key personnel
Commercial Manager: G Battle
Project Manager: J Rickman

Products
Railway signalling and track feeder cables, power, control and instrumentation cables insulated with a variety of insulants.

VERIFIED

Costamasnaga ASTRIDE road/rail vehicle operating in the UK

DWA

Deutsche Waggonbau Aktiengesellschaft
Kablower Weg 89, D-12526 Berlin, Germany
Tel: +49 30 67930   Fax: +49 30 674 4560
Email: info@dwa.de
Web: http://www.dwa.de

Key personnel
See entry in *Non-powered passenger vehicles* section

Products
ORT railcar for regular inspection and servicing of overhead lines and repair work. The vehicle is provided with a diesel-hydraulic drive unit rated for a maximum running speed of 100 km/h, and contains a workshop and rest area. The ORT railcar is equipped with a fixed and a swivelling working platform which can be lifted hydraulically. Operations at the catenary suspension in heights ranging from 8 to 18 m are achieved by means of a telescopic ladder. The glazed dome arranged on the roof ensures a good all-round view of the contact wire system and working platform.

UPDATED

Ebo

Ebo AG
Zürichstrasse 103, CH-8134 Adliswil, Switzerland
Tel: +41 1 487 2211   Fax: +41 1 487 2277

Key personnel
Managing Director: Heinz B Fischer

Products
GRP cable support systems; cable trays, ground ducts, cable ladders; supports for trays, ducts and ladders.

VERIFIED

EFACEC

EFACEC — Sistemas de Electrónica SA
Av Eng Frederico Ulrich, PO Box 31, P-4470 Maia, Portugal
Tel: +351 2 941 3666   Fax: +351 2 948 5428

Products
Electrification equipment, including traction substations (1,500 V DC and 25 kV 50 Hz AC) and associated telecontrol systems, catenary systems.

VERIFIED

Electric Rails

Electric Rails Ltd
Rajatorpantie 8, Vantaa, FIN-01019 Ivo, Finland
Tel: +358 9 856 1580   Fax: +358 9 507 1163

Key personnel
Managing Director: Pekka Salo
Technical Director: Seppo Taskinen
Marketing Manager: Raimo Mättö

Products
Design, supply, installation and commissioning of fixed installations for rail electrification systems (overhead systems and feeder stations); delivery and installation of power lines and cables; delivery and erection of antenna masts for mobile communications.

UPDATED

Electro Wire

Electro Wire Inc
1000 Touhy Avenue
Elk Grove Village
Illinois 60007
Tel: +1 847 593 2500   Fax: +1 847 593 2501

Key personnel
President: Micky M Hamano
Senior Vice-President: Richard A A Hall
Senior Vice-President: Kevin E McNamara
Regional Vice-President: Michael Schmidt
Chief Financial Officer: James F Hogan

Products
Wires and cables for use in rolling stock and power transmission purposes. Available in conventional insulation or with low-smoke, zero halogen jackets.

VERIFIED

Elektrim

Elektrim SA
PO Box 638, Chalubinskiego 8, PL-00-950
Warsaw, Poland
Tel: +48 22 301000/302000
Fax: +48 22 300841/301218

Products
Substations, overhead line equipment, DC switchgear, high-speed circuit breakers, signalling and telecommunications equipment, engineering and commissioning of signalling and telecommunications projects.

VERIFIED

Elpro

Elpro Leit- und Energietechnik GmbH
Marzahner Strasse 34, D-13053 Berlin, Germany
Tel: +49 30 9861 2571   Fax: +49 30 9861 2572

Products
Equipment for AC and DC electrification systems, including substations, switchgear, overhead lines, control and distribution systems.

UPDATED

Ferraz SA

PO Box 3025, F-69391 Lyon Cedex 3, France
Tel: +33 4 72 22 66 11   Fax: +33 4 72 22 67 13

Key personnel
See entry in *Electric traction equipment* section

Products
AC protistor fuses for the internal protection of the AC/DC and/or AC/DC/AC substation converters, large power filters and auxiliary circuits; disconnectors to isolate substation converters; automatic fast-acting earthing device with large short-circuit capability, which can be either bi- or unidirectional.

VERIFIED

FIREMA

FIREMA Trasporti SpA
Ercole Marelli Trazione business unit
Viale Edison 110, I-20099 Sesto S Giovanni (Milano), Italy
Tel: +39 2 24941   Fax: +39 2 248 3508

Key personnel
See entry in *Locomotives and powered passenger vehicles* section

Products
Converters and feeder substations.
   Recent orders include substations for the Rome Metro Line A extension and MV/LV equipment for Rome layover areas A Cornelia and Laurentina.

UPDATED

Flury

Arthur Flury AG
Fabrikstrasse 4, CH-4543 Deitingen, Switzerland
Tel: +41 32 613 3366   Fax: +41 32 613 3368

Key personnel
President: Adrian Flury
Managing Director: Jürg Zwahlen

Products
Components for overhead electrification systems, including section insulators and phase breaks; messenger wire and contact wire insulators; earthing equipment; terminals, suspension clamps, connecting clamps and feeder clamps.

UPDATED

Fuji Electric

Fuji Electric Co Ltd
New Yurakucho Building 12-1, Yurakucho 1-chome, Chiyoda-ku, Tokyo 100, Japan
Tel: +81 3 3211 7111   Fax: +81 3 5388 7803

Key personnel
See entry in *Diesel engines and transmission systems* section

Products
Power supply equipment: computer-based remote supervisory control equipment; fluorocarbon cooling silicon rectifiers, SF6 gas circuit breakers and mini high-speed circuit breakers; moulded transformers; total control systems including electric power management, station office apparatus control, data management and disaster prevention management.

VERIFIED

Furrer + Frey

Furrer + Frey AG
Thunstrasse 35, CH-3000 Berne 6, Switzerland
Tel: +41 31 351 6111   Fax: +41 31 351 6235

Works
PO Box, Stationsstrasse 17, CH-3645 Gwatt-Thun

Key personnel
Chief Executive Officer, Export and Marketing: B Furrer
Executive Officer, Light Rail and Trolleybus: E P Bichsel
Executive Officer, Electrification Projects: F Friedli
Executive Officer, Export Department: R D Brodbek

Products
Design, manufacture and installation of overhead current supply equipment for electrification of railway lines, up to 25 kV AC. Aerial surveys for electrification projects.
   Specialist equipment includes overhead contact lines for rack railways, tram and light rail systems; overhead conductor rails; movable conductor rail for depots and maintenance facilities and software for electrification projects.
   Newly developed is the Liracos light rail system with insulated synthetic cantilevers.
   Recent contracts include conductor rail (74 km) for Korean National Railroad; complete reconstruction of Spiez station for BLS, Switzerland; conductor rail installation in three tunnels (1 km) for ÖBB, Austria; conductor rail installation at North Pole depot for Powertrack, UK; catenary adjustment for Pendolino traffic and catenary planning for the Gotthard base tunnel for SBB, Switzerland and design, engineering and installation of new catenary for piggy-back traffic through the Simplon tunnel, for SBB.

UPDATED

Ganz Ansaldo

Ganz Ansaldo Electric Ltd
Lövöház utca 39, H-1024 Budapest, Hungary
Tel: +36 1 175 3322   Fax: +36 1 156 2989

Key personnel
See entry in *Locomotives and powered passenger vehicles* section

Products
Power stations for railway electrification with output of 25 kV single-phase. Power and booster transformers for electrification with 2 × 25 kV 50 Hz. Signalling and interlocking equipment, complete traffic control systems.

VERIFIED

GEC Alsthom ACEC Transport

Rue Cambier Dupret 50-52, PO Box 4211, B-6001 Charleroi, Belgium
Tel: +32 71 445411   Fax: +32 71 445775

Key personnel
See entry in *Locomotives and powered passenger vehicles* section

Products
Ultra-fast DHR circuit breakers.
    The DHR is a new type of DC circuit breaker combining a precision mechanism with power electronics. It operates quickly and can be used in conjunction with microprocessors, fault-recording systems and remote control.

VERIFIED

GEC Plessey

Plessey Semiconductors Ltd, Power Division
Carholme Road, Lincoln LN1 1SG
Tel: +44 1522 510500   Fax: +44 1522 510550

Key personnel
See entry in *Electric traction equipment* section

Products
Power semiconductor devices: thyristors, diodes, transistors, IGBTs, gate turn-off thyristors, power modules, and air, oil, water and phase change cooling assemblies. These products may be used for onboard or trackside applications.

VERIFIED

Geismar

Société des Anciens Etablissements L Geismar
113 bis avenue Charles-de-Gaulle, F-92200 Neuilly sur Seine, France
Tel: +33 1 41 43 40 40   Fax: +33 1 46 40 71 70

Products
Geismar provides equipment to build or maintain 25 kV AC and 750 V, 1,500 V and 3,000 V DC catenary lines, including contact wire and catenary suspension grips and clips; contact wire splice clamps; ending sleeves; splice sleeves; feeder suspension clamps; electric power supply terminal plugs; automatic tension equipment; section insulators; ceramic insulators; composite insulators; disconnectors; overhead line erection trains; maintenance and servicing vehicles; catenary inspection gang cars; catenary inspection trailers; and overhead line unrolling trainsets.

VERIFIED

Greysham

Greysham (International) Pvt Ltd
2/81 Roop Nagar, Delhi 110 007, India
Tel: +91 11 251 5260/252 1785/293 6673
Fax: +91 11 292 3782/575 716008

Key personnel
See entry in *Brakes and drawgear* section

Products
Overhead fittings for railway electrification projects.

UPDATED

HDC

Hindusthan Development Corporation Ltd
Mody Building, 27 Sir RN Mukherjee Road, Calcutta 700 001, India
Tel: +91 33 248 0166/67/68
Fax: +91 33 248 1922/220 2607

Works
Insulators & Electrical Company (IEC)
1/8 New Industrial Area, Mandideep 462,046, District Raisen, Madhya Pradesh, India

Key personnel
See entry in *Freight vehicles and equipment* section

Products
Manufacture and supply of 25 kV solid core insulators.

VERIFIED

Hitachi Cable

Hitachi Cable Ltd
Chiyoda Building, 2-1-2 Marunouchi, Chiyoda-ku, Tokyo 100, Japan
Tel: +81 3 5252 3452   Fax: +81 3 3213 0402/0445

Main works
5-1 Hitaka-Machi, Hitachi City, Ibaraki 319-14, Japan

Key personnel
President: Seiji Hara
Executive Vice-President: Yasuaki Watanabe
Director, Overseas Division: Keisuke Izumi
General Manager, Opto-Electronics & Telecommunications Group, Overseas Division:
    Yasuhito Mitomi

Subsidiaries
Singapore, Hong Kong, UK, USA and Thailand

Products
Trolley wires; high-voltage, low-impedance coaxial feeders for AC electrification; leaky coaxial cable for train radio systems; fibre optic cables for use in monitoring and control systems in electric passenger vehicles; superconducting wires for magnetic levitation vehicles; rubber pads, buffers and vibration isolators.
    Recent overseas contracts include 24 km of leaky coaxial cable for Australia; 11 km of leaky coaxial cable for Hong Kong; and leaky coaxial cable for Caracas Metro, Venezuela.

UPDATED

Holec Projects

Holec Projects BV
PO Box 258, NL-7550 AG Hengelo, Netherlands
Tel: +31 74 355 8800   Fax: +31 74 355 8801

Products
Installation and supply of electricity generation, conversion and distribution systems including power stations, DC power supplies, inverters, signal guides and complete electrical systems for railways. Central traffic control systems.

VERIFIED

Hyundai

Hyundai Electrical Engineering Co Ltd
Hyundai Building, 140-2 Kye-Dong, Chongro-ku, Seoul, South Korea
Tel: +82 2 741 4151/60

Products
Transformers, generators, motors and circuit breakers.

VERIFIED

Jacques Galland

Matériel Pour Lignes Electriques de Traction
20 rue de l'Insurrection Parisienne, F-94600 Choisy-le-Roi, France
Tel: +33 1 46 80 25 72   Fax: +33 1 46 80 83 42

Key personnel
Managing Director: Denis Galland

Products
Overhead line equipment.

VERIFIED

Kaufmann

A Kaufmann AG
Zaystrasse 3, CH-6410 Goldau, Switzerland
Tel: +41 41 711 6700   Fax: +41 41 855 1704

Key personnel
Managing Director: Alois Kaufmann-von Dach

Products
KAGO rail clamps for electrical connections and for fixing all types of ropes, cables or wires up to 20 mm in diameter.

UPDATED

Kummler + Matter

Kummler + Matter AG
Hohlstrasse 176, CH-8026 Zürich, Switzerland
Tel: +41 1 247 4747   Fax: +41 1 291 0262

Kaufmann KAGO rail clamp (inset) and cable connection in progress

Key personnel
Vice-President: Daniel Steiner
Export Sales Manager: Rodolfo Middelmann

Principal subsidiaries
Kummler + Matter, Netherlands
Kummler + Matter, Hungary

Products
Overhead contact line equipment for light rail, branch lines, suburban and main line railways, and trolleybuses. Engineering and feasibility studies.

UPDATED

Lerc

Lerc SA
Chemin des Hamaïdes, PO Box 119, F-59732 Saint Amand les Eaux Cedex, France
Tel: +33 3 27 22 85 50   Fax: +33 3 27 22 85 55

Key personnel
Export Manager: F Romet

Products
A range of insulators with silicon shed shells for railway, tram and metro lines.

VERIFIED

Merlin Gerin Brasil

Merlin Gerin Brasil SA
Av Brigadeiro Faria Lima 2003, 14th andar, 01451-001 São Paulo SP, Brazil
Tel: +55 11 816 4500   Fax: +55 11 813 0943

Main works
Av da Saudade s/n, 13171-320, Sumaré, SP, Brazil

Key personnel
See entry in *Electric traction equipment* section

Products
Traction chopper control system; high- and low-voltage switchboards; self-inductive coils, resistors and static converters, traction rectifiers; control boards; auxiliary switchboards and low-voltage rectifiers; track circuits; power and signalling mimic panels; relay racks; data transmission; boards; low-, medium- and high-tension equipment.
Recent contracts include rolling stock modifications for São Paulo's east-west metro; installation of the electrification system on São Paulo's Paulista metro (substation and auxiliary supplies); Metro Belo Horizonte: installation, test and commission of the signalling system including computerised data transmission; renovation of the CTC system for FEPASA, Amador Bueno-Iperó including renewing all signalling cables, renovating lineside equipment, and control centre; VLT Campinas, São Paulo: level crossings and automatic block control; installation and testing of 376 track circuits for FEPASA São Paulo; and the supply of medium-tension substation power panels to Coboce, Bolivia.

VERIFIED

Permali

Permali Gloucester Ltd
Bristol Road, Gloucester GL1 5TT, UK
Tel: +44 1452 528282   Fax: +44 1452 507409

Key personnel
See entry in *Passenger coach equipment* section

Products
High-tension cable terminations, tension insulators, third rail and post insulators, SRBP trackside bushings to 52 kV.

VERIFIED

Pfisterer

Pfisterer Srl
Via A Pacinotti 31, I-20094 Corsico, Milan, Italy
Tel: +39 2 4510 0213   Fax: +39 2 447 9008

Key personnel
Managing Director: Dr Ing Osvaldo Nannini
Export Manager: Dip Ing Paolo Zorzan

Products
Silicon rubber composite insulators for railway, tram and metro lines; clamps, voltage detectors and earthing devices.
Pfisterer has recently developed an equipotential reversible cable hanger for use on FS high-speed lines electrified at 25 kV 50 Hz AC.
Recent contracts include the supply of overhead line equipment for the Milan metro, and of silicon rubber arm and tension insulators to SNCB.

VERIFIED

Pirelli

Pirelli Cables Ltd
PO Box 6, Leigh Road, Eastleigh SO50 9YE, UK
Tel: +44 1703 295400   Fax: +44 1703 295111

Head Office
11 Berkeley Street, London W1X 6BU, UK

Key personnel
Managing Director: Geraint Anderson
Business Director, Utilities: R J W Barrett
Operations Director, Energy Cables: S Ford
Chief Engineer: S R Norman

Products
Design, provision and erection of railway overhead and third rail electrification equipment; provision and installation of all types of power, signalling and communication cables; design and provision of specialised installation plant; design, provision and erection of towers for floodlights, radio, and TV surveillance; civil and electrical engineering.

UPDATED

Powernetics Ltd

Jason Works, Clarence Street, Loughborough LE11 1DX, UK
Tel: +44 1509 214153   Fax: +44 1509 262460

Key personnel
Managing Director: Satish Chada
Marketing Manager: Jim Goddard
Projects Manager: Kevin Pateman

Products
DC-DC converters, switch mode power supplies for trackside railborne and tunnel applications, battery chargers; Uninterruptible Power Supply (UPS) systems; static inverters; frequency changers.
Contracts include coach ventilation converters for NS Netherlands and Bombardier Prorail (London Underground Ltd), heating/ventilation converters for Ramseyer and Jenser, Switzerland, and catering car converters for Adtranz (express trains).

UPDATED

SAE (India)

SAE (India) Limited
29-30 Community Commercial Centre, Basant Lok, Vasant Vihar, New Delhi 110 057, India
Tel: +91 11 688 2655/5801
Fax: +91 11 611 1190/688 5958

Main works
PO Box 96, Jabalpur 482001, India

Key personnel
President: Dr R K Dwivedi
Vice-President, Finance: Y L Madan
General Manager: P Varma
General Manager, Marketing: D Luthra
Chief Manager, Projects: A K Das

Products
Design, supply and erection of 3 kV DC and 25 kV 50 Hz AC overhead equipment; substations; booster transformer stations; telecommunications cabling for railway electrification.
Contracts include electrification of 300 track-km at 25 kV 50 Hz AC for Indian Railways.

UPDATED

SAFT

156 avenue de Metz, F-93230 Romainville, France
Tel: +33 1 49 15 36 00   Fax: +33 1 49 15 34 00

Key personnel
See entry in *Passenger coach equipment* section

Products
Saft Nife Ni-Cd batteries, with pocket or sintered and plastic bonded electrodes for supplying energy to all fixed electrification equipment.
Recent contracts include the supply of batteries to Singapore metro, Pakistan Railways, CP Rail, Canada, and DB AG, Germany.

VERIFIED

Sasib Railway Electrification

Sasib Railway Electrification SpA
A company of Sasib Railway Business Area
Via Lago dei Tartari 10, I-00012 Guidonia, Rome, Italy
Tel: +39 774 37741   Fax: +39 774 353430
Email: sasib—re@ainet.it

Key personnel
Managing Director: Giuseppe Bonfigli
Sales Manager: Roberto Tazzioli
Marketing: Enrico Dolfi

Products
Complete 3 kV DC and 25 kV 50 Hz AC railway electrification; low-, medium- and high-tension lines; exterior lighting; outdoor transformer stations; overhead line construction equipment; steel structures; signalling (see also Sasib Railway entry in *Signalling and telecommunications systems* section).

VERIFIED

SDCEM

Société Dauphinoise de Constructions Electro Mécaniques
10 allée de La Grange, F-38450 Vif, France
Tel: +33 4 76 72 76 72   Fax: +33 4 76 72 46 26

Key personnel
Managers: Claude Yvetot; Alain Plirai; François Mees; Gérard Dubois

Products
Catenary and switch disconnectors for 1.5/3 kV DC, 25 kV and 15 kV 16⅔ Hz AC with manual and electrical operating mechanisms; 25 to 330 kV disconnectors for substations.

VERIFIED

Sécheron

Sécheron Ltd
14 Avenue de Sécheron, CH-1211 Geneva 21, Switzerland
Tel: +41 22 739 4111   Fax: +41 22 738 7305

Key personnel
See entry in *Electric traction equipment* section

Products
DC traction power substations and ancillary equipment including system engineering and network computer simulation; solid-state rectifiers and inverters; harmonic filters; DC switchgear; DC high-speed circuit breakers, isolating and changeover switches; electronic protection relays; microprocessor-based remote-control and protection systems.

Contracts include DC switchgear for Line 6 and the extension of Lines 7 and 8 of Seoul metro as well as Line 1 of Incheon metro and Line 2 of Pusan metro.

See entry in *Signalling and Telecommunications Systems* section.

UPDATED

Sefag

Sefag AG
Werkstrasse 7, CH-6102 Malters, Switzerland
Tel: +41 41 497 1991   Fax: +41 41 497 2269

Key personnel
Managing Director: Dr K O Papailiou
Technical Director: W Fluri
Sales Director: W Bachmann
Works Director: W Wipfli
Commercial Director: P Wunderlin
Export Director: M Peter

Products
SILCOSIL composite insulators with silicon sheds as suspension, dead-end and post insulators, and as special insulators for tunnels and high-speed routes.

Contracts include the supply of insulators to Swiss Federal Railways, Austrian Railways, Bern—Lötschberg—Simplon Railway, and other railways in Switzerland and abroad.

VERIFIED

Sekko

Oy Sekko AB
An Ensto company
PO Box 51, FIN-06101 Porvoo, Finland
Tel: +358 204 7621   Fax: +358 204 762515
Email: ensto@ensto.fi

Key personnel
Managing Director: Matti Kuvaja
Product Manager: Veijo Vilenius

Products
Aluminium cantilevers and components; composite, ceramic and glass insulators; crimp- and screw-type fittings; hot-dipped galvanised steel parts.

Recent contracts include VR, Finland; Banverket, Sweden; NSB, Norway; DSB, Denmark and SNCB, Belgium.

UPDATED

Siemens

Siemens AG
Traction Power Supplies
PO Box 3240, D-91050 Erlangen, Germany
Tel: +49 9131 724621   Fax: +49 9131 727969

Key personnel
Divisional Technical Manager: H Habermann
Divisional Commercial Manager: L Zagel

Products
Catenaries for main line and rapid transit applications at 3 kV DC and 15 kV 16⅔ Hz and 25 kV 50 Hz AC; specialised equipment for tunnels; transmission lines; project engineering; supply of materials, erection of systems, training, commissioning and maintenance; supply of components for contact line systems.

Contracts include Madrid—Seville high-speed line, RENFE, Spain; Hannover—Würzburg high-speed line, Magdeburg—Berlin and Mannheim—Stuttgart, DB AG, Germany; Hudiksvall—Sundsvall, Banverket, Sweden; and Helsinki area, VR, Finland.

UPDATED

Siemens

Siemens Transportation Systems Inc
186 Wood Avenue South Iselin, NJ 08830, USA
Tel: +1 908 205 2200   Fax: +1 908 603 7379

Mass Transit Division, 7464 French Road, Sacramento, CA 95828
Tel: +1 916 688 5014   Fax: +1 916 688 3513

Key personnel
President & Chief Executive Officer: Jimmy Morrison
Vice-President and Chief Financial Officer:
   George F Dohanue
Vice-President & General Manager: George Ernst

Products
Static frequency converters, catenary equipment, components for traction power substations.
(see also Locomotives & Powered Passenger Vehicles and Signalling sections)

NEW ENTRY

SMC

SMC Transit International (Australia)
18 Hudson Avenue, Castle Hill, New South Wales 2154, Australia
Tel: +61 2 680 3222   Fax: +61 2 634 7764

Key personnel
See entry in *Electric traction equipment* section

Products
Current collection pantographs and carbon wear strips for AC and DC power supply.

VERIFIED

SPIE Enertrans

Parc Saint-Cristophe, F-95861 Cergy-Pontoise Cedex, France
Tel: +33 1 34 22 56 08   Fax: +33 1 34 22 62 76

Key personnel
Operations Director: M Chagnas
Business Development Manager: B Atkinson

Products
Design, construction and maintenance of railway infrastructure including: trackwork, catenary systems, power supplies and electromechanical systems for railways including high-speed rail, metros, tramways and other transport systems.

Recent contracts include Channel Tunnel, RATP (Paris metro), TGV Atlantique, TGV Nord, Cairo metro and Heathrow Express.

VERIFIED

Thorn Automation

Armitage Road, Rugeley WS15 1DR, UK
Tel: +44 1889 585151   Fax: +44 1889 577324

Key personnel
See entry in *Signalling and telecommunications* section

Products
Traction rectifier equipment and onboard auxiliary power converters. Turnkey projects including AC/DC switchgear and associated power distribution networks.

Much equipment is supplied as part of a comprehensive contract involving transformers, rectifiers, AC and DC switchgear, supervisory control and auxiliary equipment. Modernisation with silicon rectifier replacements for ageing mercury arc equipment has also been undertaken.

VERIFIED

Toshiba

Toshiba Corporation
Railway Projects Department
Toshiba Building, 1-1 Shibaura 1-chome, Minato-ku, Tokyo 105, Japan
Tel: +81 3 3457 4924   Fax: +81 3 3457 8385

Products
DC and AC railway substation equipment; supervisory control systems; transformers; rectifiers; circuit breakers; arresters.

VERIFIED

Transmitton

Transmitton Ltd
Ashby Park, Ashby-de-la-Zouch LE65 1JD, UK
Tel: +44 1530 415941   Fax: +44 1530 258005
Email: rail@transmitton.co.uk

Key personnel
Managing Director: D Moore
Transport Sales Director: R Burdis
Transport Accounts Manager: E Turnock

Products
The Transmitton Cromos SCADA system provides comprehensive control and monitoring featuring a real-time computer master station with high-resolution, full workstation graphics.

Fastflex intelligent electronic control and data gathering services. Supply and system integration for traction power control, communication networks, passenger information systems, public address, passenger help points, fare collection and other intelligent equipment used in rail and mass transit systems.

UPDATED

Trend

Trend Installation Tooling
Unit 11, Brindley Road, St Helens WA9 4HY, UK
Tel: +44 1744 851100   Fax: +44 1744 851122

Key personnel
Managing Director: Jack Taylor

Products
Railway electrification products and light engineering.

NEW ENTRY

Westinghouse Cubic

Westinghouse Cubic Ltd
177 Nutfield Road, Merstham RH1 3HH, UK
Tel: +44 1737 644921   Fax: +44 1737 643693

Key personnel
See entry in *Automatic fare systems* section

Products
Electrical installation, cabling, maintenance.

Recent contracts include power transformer installation and tunnel relighting for London Underground Ltd, and data cabling and routeing for Railtrack Northwest.

UPDATED

Whipp & Bourne

Whipp & Bourne
A division of FKI Engineering Group
Switchgear Works, Castleton, Rochdale OL11 2SS, UK
Tel: +44 1706 32051   Fax: +44 1706 345896

Key personnel
Managing Director: B S Bullock
Sales and Marketing Director: L C Toma

Products
High-speed DC circuit breakers with ratings up to 3 kV, 12,000 A, 255 kA (short-circuit); semi-high-speed DC circuit breakers with ratings up to 1,000 V, 3,150 A, 80 kA (short-circuit); microprocessor-based multifunction overcurrent and impedance/undervoltage protection relays for DC traction systems.

Recent contracts include the supply of components for London Underground Ltd's Jubilee and Northern Lines; Blackpool Tramway refurbishment; Airport Line, Oslo Sporveier, Norway; Lantau and Airport Line, Hong Kong; and Kuala Lumpur metro.

VERIFIED

Wild & Grunder

Wild & Grunder AG
Kelamttstrasse 10, CH-6403 Küssnacht, Switzerland
Tel: +41 41 850 6020   Fax: +41 850 6026

Key personnel
Engineer: Roland Ferrari

Products
Computer system for mapping information on lineside structures, such as location of overhead support poles and the date at which they were installed.

NEW ENTRY

PERMANENT WAY EQUIPMENT AND SERVICES

Alphabetical Listing

Abetong Teknik
ABC
Abtus
A & K
A I Welders
Akzo Nobel
Aldon
Allegheny
Aluminothermique
AMEC Rail Ltd
Americ
American Railroad Curvelining Corporation
Amey Railways
Amurrio
Angle Plant
Apcarom
Arbil
Aspen Aerials
Atlantic Track
Atlas Copco
Atlas Copco Berema
Atlas Hydraulic Loaders
Atlas Weyhausen
Austrack
Balfour Beatty
Balfour Beatty Rail Projects
Ballast Nedam
Bance
Banverket
Barclay Mowlem
BBR
Beilhack
BEML
Bethlehem Steel
BHP Steel
Bomag
British Steel Track Products
BTR Permali
Burn Standard Co
BWG
BWS
Caltronic
Cemafer
Cembre
Cementation Railways
Central Track Renewals
Century Precast
CF&I Steel
Chemetron
Chemgrate
Chipman Rail (see entry for Nomix-Chipman)
Cimmco
Clouth
Cogifer
Colebrand
Collis Engineering
Compair Hydrovane
Conbrako
ContiTech
Cooper & Turner
Cowans Sheldon
CSR Humes
CXT
Daido
Danieli Centro Maskin
Darcy
Davy British Rail International
Delachaux
Delkor
Desec
Desquenne et Giral
D'Huart
Difco
Donelli
Drouard
Eastern Infrastructure Maintenance Co
EBS
Edgar Allen
Edilon
Electrologic
Elektro-Thermit
Energomachexport
Esab
EWEM

Exel Oy
EXIM
FAB-RA-CAST
Fairmont Tamper
Fairmont Tamper (Australia)
Fassetta
Fastline
Faur
Ferotrack
Ferrostaal
Ferrostaal Corporation
Findlay, Irvine
First Engineering
Foster
Framafer
Geismar
Gemco
Getzner
Grant Lyon Eagre
GrantRail
Grinaker Duraset
Grove Worldwide
GT Railway Maintenance Ltd
Gummiwerk Kraiburg Elastik
Hanning & Kahl
HDC
Hi-Force Hydraulics
Holland
Holland Co
Huck
HWD
IBM
Infra Safety Services
Instant Zip-Up
Interep
International Track Systems
IPA
JAFCO
Jakem
Jaraguá
Jarvis Facilities
Jenbacher
Kalyn Siebert
Kango
Kaufmann
KIHN
Kirow
Kloos Railway Systems
Knox Kershaw
Krautkrämer
Künzler
Laser Rail
Lindapter
Linsinger
Loram
Lord
Lucchini
Lukas
Lyudinovo Locomotive Works JSC
Mannesmann
Manoir Industries
Matériel de Voie
Matisa
Matisa SpA
Matix Saferail
McGregor
Mecanoexportimport
Mer Mec
Millbrook Proving Ground
Mitchell Equipment Corporation
Mitsukawa
Modern Track Machinery
Monterrey
Moore & Steele
Moss Systems
MTH Praha
NARSTCO
Newag
Nippon Kido Kogyo
NKK
Nomix-Chipman
Noord-Ned
Nordco
NRS

NS Materieel
Oleo
OLMI
ORTEC
Orton/McCullough
Osmose
Palfinger
Pandrol Jackson
Pandrol Rail Fastenings
Permali
Permaquip
Pettibone
Phoenix
Pintsch Bamag
Plasser
Pohl
Portec Inc
Portec (UK)
Pouget
Premesa
P. S. Corporation
Quest
Racine
Railpro
Rails Co
Railtech
Ranalah
Rawie
Raychem
Relayfast
Response Environmental Services
Richardson & Cruddas
RMC Concrete Products
Robel
Rolba
Rotabroach
Rotamag
SaarGummi
Salient
Sateba
Schlatter
Schramm
Schwihag
Semperit
SICFA
Sigmaform
Sika
SILF
H J Skelton & Co Ltd
SMIS
Sola
Somafel
Sonatest
Sonit
South East Infrastructure Maintenance Co Ltd
Southern Track Renewals Co
Spefaka
Speno
Sperry
Spie Batignolles
SRS
Starfer
Stedef
Steel Authority of India
Strukton Railinfra
Swingmaster Corporation
Sydney Steel
Tarmac
Tectran
Tempered Spring Co
Templeton
Tetsudo Kiki
Thebra
Thermit Australia
Thermit Welding
Thompsons, Kelly & Lewis
Thyssen
Tiefenbach
Tiflex
Tipco
Tokimec
Tooltract
True Temper
TSO

The world's fastest trains...

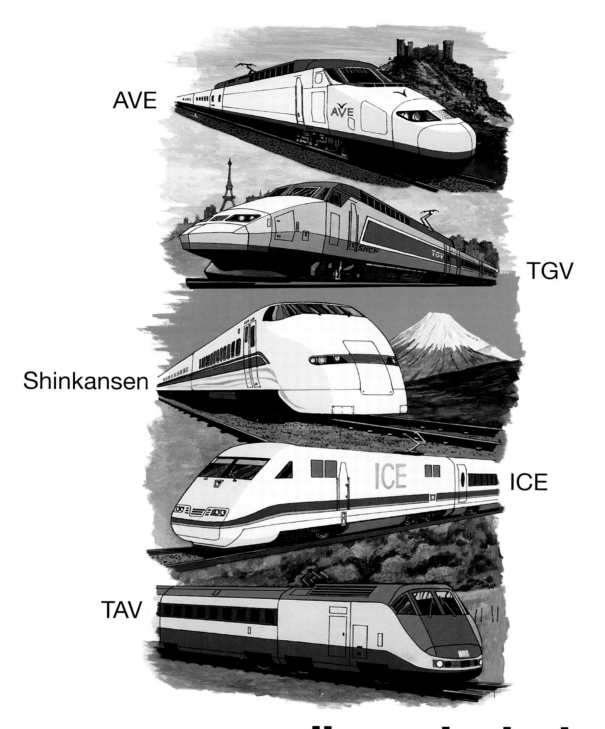

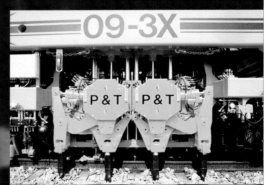

Tülomsas
Türk + Hillinger
Turkington Precast
Unit Rail Anchor
UniTrac Systems
VAE
VAE Nortrak

Von Roll
Vortok
Vossloh Rail Systems
Walter Bau-Aktiengesellschaft
Western-Cullen-Hayes
Wickham
Wieland

Windhoff
Yamato Kogyo
Zweiweg Schneider
Zwicky

Classified Listing

TRACK COMPONENTS

Abetong Teknik
ABC
A & K
Akzo Nobel
Allegheny
Amurrio
Apcarom
Austrack
Atlantic Track
Balfour Beatty
Bance
Barclay Mowlem
BBR
Bethlehem Steel
BHP Steel
British Steel Track Products
BTR Permali
Burn Standard Co
BWG
Caltronic
Cembre
Cementation Railways
Century Precast
CF&I Steel
Chemgrate
Cimmco
Clouth
Cogifer
Colebrand
Collis Engineering
ContiTech
Cooper & Turner
CSR Humes
CXT
Daido
Darcy
Delkor
D'Huart
Drouard
Edgar Allen
Edilon
EWEM
Exel Oy
EXIM
FAB-RA-CAST
Fassetta
Ferotrack
Ferrostaal
Ferrostaal Corporation
Findlay, Irvine
Foster
Getzner
Grant Lyon Eagre
GrantRail
Grinaker Duraset
Gummiwerk Kraiburg Elastik
Hanning & Kahl
HDC
Holland
Huck
HWD
Interep
International Track Systems
IPA
Jakem
Jaraguá
Kaufmann
KIHN
Kloos Railway Systems
Lindapter
Lord
Lucchini
Lukas
Manoir Industries
Matériel de Voie
McGregor
Mecanoexportimport

Mitchell Equipment Corporation
Mitsukawa
Monterrey
Moore & Steele
NARSTCO
Nippon Kido Kogyo
NKK
NRS
Oleo
OLMI
ORTEC
Osmose
Pandrol Rail Fastenings
Permali
Pettibone
Phoenix
Pintsch Bamag
Pohl
Portec Inc
Portec (UK)
Pouget
Premesa
P.S. Corporation
Railpro
Rails Co
Ranalah
Rawie
Raychem
Response Environmental Services
Richardson & Cruddas
RMC Concrete Products
SaarGummi
Salient
Sateba
Schwihag
Semperit
SICFA
Sigmaform
Sika
SILF
H J Skelton & Co Ltd
Sonit
Sperry
SRS
Stedef
Steel Authority of India
Sydney Steel
Tarmac
Tempered Spring Co
Tetsudo Kiki
Thompsons, Kelly & Lewis
Thyssen
Tiefenbach
Tiflex
Tipco
Türk + Hillinger
Turkington Precast
Unit Rail Anchor
UniTrac Systems
VAE
VAE Nortrak
Von Roll
Vortok
Vossloh Rail Systems
Walter Bau-Aktiengesellschaft
Yamato Kogyo

TRACK CONSTRUCTION AND MAINTENANCE EQUIPMENT

Abtus
A & K
A I Welders
Aldon
Aluminothermique
Americ
American Railroad Curvelining Corporation
Angle Plant
Arbil

Aspen Aerials
Atlas Copco
Atlas Copco Berema
Atlas Hydraulic Loaders Ltd
Atlas Weyhausen
Balfour Beatty Rail Projects
Ballast Nedam
Bance
Banverket
Barclay Mowlem
Beilhack
BEML
Bomag
BWS
Cemafer
Chemetron
Chipman Rail (see entry for Nomix-Chipman)
Compair Hydrovane
Conbrako
Cowans Sheldon
Danieli Centro Maskin
Darcy
Delachaux
Desec
Desquenne et Giral
Difco
Donelli
EBS
Electrologic
Elektro-Thermit
Energomachexport
Esab
EXIM
Fairmont Tamper
Fairmont Tamper (Australia)
Fassetta
Faur
Framafer
Geismar
Gemco
Grove Worldwide
Hi-Force Hydraulics
Holland Co
HWD
Instant Zip-Up
JAFCO
Jenbacher
Kalyn Siebert
Kango
Kirow
Knox Kershaw
Krautkrämer
Künzler
Laser Rail
Linsinger
Loram
Lord
Lukas
Lyudinovo Locomotive Works JSC
Mannesmann
Matisa
Matisa SpA
Matix Saferail
Mer Mec
Millbrook Proving Ground
Mitchell Equipment Corporation
Modern Track Machinery
Moss Systems
MTH Praha
Newag
NKK
Nomix-Chipman
Noord-Ned
Nordco
NS Materieel
Orton/McCullough
Palfinger
Pandrol Jackson

TRACK CONSTRUCTION AND MAINTENANCE EQUIPMENT continued

Permaquip
Pettibone
Plasser
Pouget
Quest
Racine
Railpro
Rails Co
Railtech
Robel
Rolba
Rotabroach
Rotamag
Schlatter
Schramm
SMIS
Sola
Sonatest
Spefaka
Speno
Spie Batignolles
SRS
Starfer
Swingmaster Corporation
Templeton
Tetsudo Kiki
Thebra
Thermit Australia
Thermit Welding
Thompsons, Kelly & Lewis

Tokimec
Tooltract
True Temper
TSO
Tülomsas
Unit Rail Anchor
VAE Nortrak
Von Roll
Western-Cullen-Hayes
Wickham
Wieland
Windhoff
Zweiweg Schneider
Zwicky

TRACK CONSTRUCTION AND MAINTENANCE SERVICES

AMEC Rail Ltd
American Railroad Curvelining Corporation
Amey Railways Ltd
Balfour Beatty
Balfour Beatty Rail Projects
Ballast Nedam
Banverket
Central Track Renewals
Chemetron
Chipman Rail (see entry for Nomix-Chipman)
Cogifer
Davy British Rail International
Desquenne et Giral
Drouard
Eastern Infrastructure Maintenance Co

Fairmont Tamper
Fastline
First Engineering
Grant Lyon Eagre
GrantRail
GT Railway Maintenance Ltd
Holland Co
IBM
Jarvis Facilities
Laser Rail
Millbrook Proving Ground
NKK
Nomix-Chipman
OLMI
Osmose
Pandrol Jackson
Permaquip
P. S. Corporation
Railpro
Relayfast
Somafel
South East Infrastructure Maintenance Co Ltd
Southern Track Renewals Co
Speno
Sperry
Spie Batignolles
SRS
Strukton Railinfra
Tectran
TSO

Company Listing by Country

AUSTRALIA
Austrack
Barclay Mowlem
BHP Steel
CSR Humes
Delkor
Electrologic
Fairmont Tamper (Australia)
Gemco
Holland
Mitchell Equipment Corporation
Sonit
Thermit Australia
Thompsons, Kelly & Lewis

AUSTRIA
BWS
Getzner
Jenbacher
Linsinger
Palfinger
Plasser
Semperit
Sola
VAE

BRAZIL
Jaraguá
Premesa
Tectran
Thebra

CANADA
Modern Track Machinery
Sydney Steel
Tipco
VAE Nortrak

CZECH REPUBLIC
MTH Praha

DENMARK
Caltronic

FINLAND
Desec
Exel Oy

FRANCE
Aluminothermique
Cogifer
Delachaux

Desquenne et Giral
D'Huart
Drouard
Fassetta
Framafer
Geismar
Interep
Manoir Industries
Matériel de Voie
Pouget
Railtech
Sateba
Spie Batignolles
Stedef
TSO

GERMANY
Atlas Weyhausen
Beilhack
Bomag
BWG
Cemafer
Clouth
ContiTech
Elektro-Thermit
EXIM
Ferrostaal
Gummiwerk Kraiburg Elastik
Hanning & Kahl
Kirow
Krautkrämer
Lukas
Mannesmann
Newag
ORTEC
Phoenix
Pintsch Bamag
Rawie
Robel
SaarGummi
Spefaka
Tiefenbach
Thyssen
Türk + Hillinger
Vossloh Rail Systems
Walter Bau-Aktiengesellschaft
Wieland
Windhoff
Zweiweg Schneider

INDIA
BEML

Burn Standard Co
Cimmco
HDC
Richardson & Cruddas
Steel Authority of India

ITALY
Cembre
Donelli
IPA
Lucchini
Matisa SpA
Mer Mec
Olmi
SICFA
SILF
Starfer

JAPAN
Daido
Mitsukawa
Nippon Kido Kogyo
NKK
P. S. Corporation
Tetsudo Kiki
Tokimec
Yamato Kogyo

LUXEMBOURG
KIHN

MEXICO
Monterrey

NETHERLANDS
Akzo Nobel
Ballast Nedam
Edilon
Infra Safety Services
Kloos Railway Systems
Noord-Ned
NS Materieel
Railpro
Strukton Railinfra

PORTUGAL
Somafel

ROMANIA
Apcarom
Faur
Mecanoexportimport

RUSSIAN FEDERATION
Energomachexport
Lyudinovo Locomotive Works JSC

SOUTH AFRICA
Cementation Railways
Conbrako
Grinaker Duraset

SPAIN
Amurrio

SWEDEN
Abetong Teknik
Atlas Copco Berema
Banverket
Danieli Centro Maskin
Esab
SRS

SWITZERLAND
BBR
EBS
EWEM
Kaufmann
Künzler
Matisa
Matix Saferail
Rolba
Schlatter
Schwihag
Sika
Speno
Von Roll

TURKEY
Tülomsas

UK
Abtus
A I Welders
AMEC Rail Ltd
Amey Railways
Angle Plant
Arbil
Atlas Copco
Atlas Hydraulic Loaders Ltd
Balfour Beatty
Balfour Beatty Rail Projects
Bance
British Steel Track Products
BTR Permali
Central Track Renewals
Chipman Rail (see entry for Nomix-Chipman)
Colebrand
Collis Engineering
Compair Hydrovane
Cooper & Turner
Cowans Sheldon
Darcy
Davy British Rail International
Eastern Infrastructure Maintenance Co
Edgar Allen
Ferotrack
Fastline
Findlay, Irvine
First Engineering
Grant Lyon Eagre
GrantRail
Grove Worldwide
GT Railway Maintenance Ltd
Hi-Force Hydraulics
HWD
IBM
Instant Zip-Up
JAFCO
Jakem
Jarvis Facilities
Kango
Laser Rail
Lindapter
McGregor

Millbrook Proving Ground
Moss Systems
Nomix-Chipman
NRS
Oleo
Pandrol Rail Fastenings
Permali
Permaquip
Portec (UK)
Ranalah
Relayfast
Response Environmental Services
RMC Concrete Products
Rotabroach
Rotamag
Sigmaform
H J Skelton & Co Ltd
SMIS
Sonatest
South East Infrastructure Maintenance Co Ltd
Southern Track Renewals Co
Tarmac
Tempered Spring Co
Thermit Welding
Tiflex
Tooltract
Turkington Precast
Vortok
Wickham
Wieland
Zwicky

USA
ABC
A & K
Aldon
Allegheny
Americ
American Railroad Curvelining Corporation
Aspen Aerials
Atlantic Track
Bethlehem Steel
CF&I Steel
Century Precast
Chemetron
Chemgrate
CXT
Difco
FAB-RA-CAST
Fairmont Tamper
Ferrostaal Corporation
Foster
Holland Co
Huck
International Track Systems
Kalyn Siebert
Knox Kershaw
Loram
Lord
Moore & Steele
NARSTCO
Nordco
Orton/McCullough
Osmose
Pandrol Jackson
Pettibone
Pohl
Portec Inc
Quest
Racine
Rails Co
Raychem
Salient
Schramm
Sperry
Swingmaster Corporation
Templeton
True Temper
Unit Rail Anchor
UniTrac Systems
Western-Cullen-Hayes

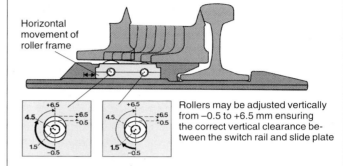

Abetong Teknik

Abetong Teknik AB
PO Box 24, S-351 03 Växjö, Sweden
Tel: +46 470 96500   Fax: +46 470 16081

Main works
Vislanda

Key personnel
Managing Director: Stefan Westberg
Marketing Director: Stig Thim

Principal subsidiary
Swedish Rail System AB SRS

Products
Concrete sleepers for main lines and turnouts in main lines and sidings; LRT sleepers; grade crossings; technical services for manufacture and design of concrete sleepers.

Some 350,000 main line sleepers per year are made for Swedish National Rail Administration (Banverket) at Vislanda, as well as sleepers for turnouts, prefabricated crane tracks and concrete elements for level crossing systems. The present plant produces prestressed reinforced monolithic sleepers designed for 22-tonne axleloads at 200 km/h. The company has supplied its know-how to some 21 different factories worldwide; together these plants have now produced over 35 million sleepers.

The company has designed concrete sleepers for the Hamersley Iron Ore Railway and Robe River Railroad of Western Australia, Queensland Railways, Canadian National Railways, Conrail, CSX, UP and Amtrak, for heavy-duty turnouts to suit traffic specifications of 37 tonnes maximum and 30 tonnes nominal axleloads at up to 80 km/h, and annual gross train tonnages of more than 50 million. Abetong has also developed special sleepers for high-speed turnouts.

VERIFIED

ABC

ABC Rail Products Corporation
Track Products Division
200 South Michigan Avenue, Chicago, Illinois 60604, USA
Tel: +1 312 322 0360   Fax: +1 312 322 0377

Key personnel
See entry in *Brakes and drawgear* section

Products
Trackwork products including frogs, switches, points, crossings, guardrails, switch stands, turnouts and turnout components.

VERIFIED

Abtus

Abtus Ltd
Falconer Road, Haverhill CB9 7XU, UK
Tel: +44 1440 702938   Fax: +44 1440 702961

Key personnel
Managing Director: Russell Owen
Technical Manager: Alan Overall

Products
Sighting, measured shovel packing, void detection and measurement, bond drilling and track slewing equipment; self-powered track maintenance vehicles; design, consultancy, full repair and recalibration.

Recent contracts include the supply of standard and purpose-made equipment to Railtrack, London Underground Ltd, Docklands Light Railway, British Rail Infrastructure Services, all major European railway systems and Hong Kong.

VERIFIED

A & K

A & K Railroad Materials Inc
1505 South Redwood Road, Salt Lake City, Utah 84104, USA
Tel: +1 801 974 5484   Fax: +1 801 972 2041

International Office
5206 FM 1960 West Suite 103, Houston, Texas 77069, USA
Tel: +1 281 893 3908   Fax: +1 281 893 8371
Web: http://www.akrailroad.com

Key personnel
Chairman: K W Schumacher
President: M H Kulmer
Vice-President, International: Julian Polit
Manager, International Sales: Alfredo Sansores

Products
Rail (new and used), rail accessories, track tools, trackwork materials, welding, continuous welded rail, complete switches, frogs, anchors, bolts, spikes, lockwashers, gauge rods, ties, sleepers, hand track tools and other track materials.

UPDATED

A I Welders

A I Welders Ltd
Seafield Road, Longman Industrial Estate, Inverness IV1 1LZ, UK
Tel: +44 1463 239381   Fax: +44 1463 225445
Email: 101364.453@compuserv.com

Key personnel
Managing Director: A J Hunter
Production Director: H Cossar
Applications Engineer, Sales: N Sherriffs

Products

Rail welding machines for continuous welded rail, switches and crossings; static and mobile rail straightening presses; complete rail welding depot installations, including conveyor systems and gantry cranes; reconditioning and upgrading of rail welding machines and depots.

UPDATED

Akzo Nobel

Akzo Nobel Geosynthetics
PO Box 9300, Westervoortsedijk 73, NL-6800 SB Arnhem, Netherlands
Tel: +31 26 366 4600   Fax: +31 26 366 4830

Key personnel
General Manager: Jan van Boldrick
Sales Manager: Blair Rawes
Marketing Manager: Wim Voskamp

Products
Enkadrain TP and Colbonddrain, track components.

UPDATED

Aldon

The Aldon Co
3410 Sunset Avenue, Waukegan, Illinois 60087, USA
Tel: +1 847 623 8800   Fax: +1 847 623 6139

Key personnel
President: J R Ornig
General Manager: J A Shelton

Products
Railway safety and maintenance equipment, including lightweight straddle-type rerailers; track levellers; track gauges; track jacks; safety derailers; rail benders; and track carts.

VERIFIED

Allegheny

Allegheny Rail Products
A division of L B Foster Co
415 Holiday Drive, Pittsburgh, Pennsylvania 15220-2793, USA
Tel: +1 412 928 3500   Fax: +1 412 928 3510

Key personnel
President: Henry M Ortwein Jr
Engineering: Sidney A Shue
Technology: W Barry Collins
Finance: Dennis E Koehler
Sales: Michelle C Chapin

Products
Insulated rail joints, epoxy bonded and 'Toughcoat'. Micro-alloy steel and polyurethane-coated joint bars.

VERIFIED

Aluminothermique

L'Aluminothermique
ZI du Bas Pré, F-59590 Raismes, France
Tel: +33 3 27 25 55 55   Fax: +33 3 27 36 73 98

Key personnel
Division Manager: Didier Bourdon

Products
Rail welding equipment. The company specialises in the Boutet processes of aluminothermic welding for all rail profiles, and for manganese switch diamonds. Other speciality: fixed and mobile welding yard.

VERIFIED

AMEC Rail Ltd

Floor 5, Bay A, Stephenson House, 2 Cherry Orchard Road, Croydon CR9 6JB, UK
Tel: +44 181 667 2600   Fax: +44 181 667 2703

Key personnel
Managing Director: William Hill

Corporate development
As part of the British Rail sell-off, South West Infrastructure Maintenance Co was sold to the construction group AMEC plc in April 1996.

Services
Infrastructure and track maintenance and upgrading.

VERIFIED

Americ

Americ Corporation
925 Estes Avenue, Elk Grove Village, Illinois 60007-4905, USA
Tel: +1 847 364 4646   Fax: +1 847 364 4695

Key personnel
Sales and Marketing Manager: Tony Calcopietro

Overseas Distributors
Australia, France, Germany, Greece, Israel, Italy, Hong Kong, Mexico, Netherlands, New Zealand, Spain, Sweden, Switzerland, Taiwan and UK.

Products
Alumi-Cart, a lightweight railway inspection vehicle. It is constructed of tubular aluminium and powered by a 4 hp engine. It can be used for transporting workers and equipment for spot repairs and inspection. A trailer is available.

VERIFIED

American Railroad Curvelining Corporation

American Railroad Curvelining Corporation
137 Hollywood Avenue, Douglaston, Long Island, New York 11363-1110, USA
Tel: +1 718 224 1135   Fax: +1 718 631 3304
Email: zicraf@aol.com

Key personnel
Chief Executive Officer: R A Fichter
President: J M Flechter

Subsidiaries
Bondarc Division
Marine Division

Products
Track geometry analysis; curve lining computers; roll ordinators; Trakchek; Trakanalyzer. Recent products include the Archimedes high-memory graphic display curveliner. Archimedes stores practically unlimited volumes of information. Using the latest video technology, it displays the middle ordinate diagram in full size, while identifying the diagram of original ordinates in one colour, the corrected diagram in another and the superelevation in a third colour. The system automatically highlights the area currently being worked on in a fourth colour. It can be supplied in a set of separate components, and can be interfaced with IBM-PC and other systems. The high-capacity built-in memory can give the engineer complete control of all maintenance work. Data is fed directly from the Model ATB Roll-Ordinator to Archimedes or to Archimedes program on PC.

VERIFIED

Amey Railways Ltd

Amey Railways Ltd
Gloucester Wing, 125 House, 1 Gloucester Street, Swindon SN1 1SU, UK
Tel: +44 1793 515532   Fax: +44 1793 515564

Corporate development
Amey Railways, a division of the Amey Construction Group, bought the Western Infrastructure Maintenance Co for £15 million in 1995.

Key personnel
Managing Director: Richard Entwhistle

Services
Amey Railways operates in three main areas — infrastructure maintenance, construction and engineering, and signalling installation/commissioning. The company's skills are also integrated with other parts of the Amey Group to carry out large multidisciplinary projects.
    Amey and Desquenne et Giral of France have formed an association between their respective railway companies, Amey Railways and SECO/DGC, to undertake track-laying works in the UK and in other areas of the world.

UPDATED

Amurrio

Amurrio Ferrocarril y Equipos SA
Maskuribai 10, E-01470 Amurrio, Alava, Spain
Tel: +34 45 891600   Fax: +34 45 892480

Key personnel
See entry in *Bogies and suspensions, wheels and axles* section

Products
Points, crossings, movable-frog crossings for high-speed crossovers, turnouts, manganese steel frogs, expansion joints, insulated rail joints, turntables, buffers, height gauges, rerailers.
    Recent contracts include the supply of turnouts for the Medellín and Bilbao Metros; turnouts and points for the Madrid and Barcelona Metros; turnouts and points for the Valencia Tramway; turnouts for CP, Portugal; and track components for RENFE including movable-frog crossings for the Madrid — Seville high-speed line.

VERIFIED

Angle Plant

Angle Plant (UK) Ltd
The Mount Buildings, Tunnel Hill, Upton-upon-Severn WR8 0QS, UK
Tel: +44 1684 593052   Fax: +44 1684 592249

Products
PowerTilt TT-10 allows bucket of a road-rail excavator to be turned at an angle.

NEW ENTRY

Apcarom

SC Apcarom SA
2 Soseaua Brailei, Buzau R-5100, Romania
Tel: +40 38 710511   Fax: +40 38 710218

Key personnel
General Manager: Vintila Mocanu
Technical Manager: Ion Matei

Products
Design and manufacture of points and crossings for railway and metro systems; track compensating devices for bridges; speed regulators; transition rails; glued insulating rail joints.
    Recent contracts include the supply of track products to MT Eisenbahnbedarf, Austria; and SNCFR, Romania.

VERIFIED

Arbil

Arbil Ltd
Lifting Gear Centre
Foundry Lane, Fishponds Trading Estate, Bristol BS5 7XH, UK
A member of the Raymond Bills group of companies
Tel: +44 117 965 3143   Fax: +44 117 965 8607

Key personnel
Manager: Dave Vale

Products:
Rail thimbles. Four standard models are available with fixed or swivel eye, manual or hydraulically operated.
    The latest model is the MK2 with a working load limit of 3 tonnes on lifting points of vertical roller pins. Features include improved design of tapered rolling pins for ease of replacement, hydraulic cylinder fitted with safety valve in case of hose failure as part of standard specification and heat-treated wearing parts.

NEW ENTRY

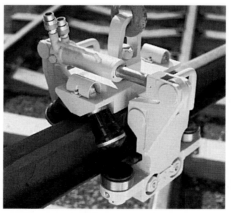

Arbil MK2 rail thimble   *1997*

Aspen Aerials

Aspen Aerials Inc
4303 West 1st Street, PO Box 16958, Duluth, Minnesota 55816-0958, USA
Tel: +1 218 624 1111   Fax: +1 218 624 1714

Key personnel
Vice-President: John W Stubenvoll

Angle Plant PowerTilt fitted to dipper of road-rail excavator   *1997*

Products
UB30 truck-mounted bridge inspection unit. An aerial platform, it operates either side of the truck, within a 2.4 m width when rotated, and does not require outriggers. It features an articulating fourth boom and interchangeable platforms. These can be either a three-person inspection platform with a 272 kg capacity, or a 5.18 m long, 454 kg capacity maintenance platform.

VERIFIED

Atlantic Track

Atlantic Track and Turnout Co
270 Broad Street, PO Box 1589, Bloomfield, New Jersey 07003, USA
Tel: +1 201 748 5885   Fax: +1 201 748 4520

Main works
St Clair Industrial Park, RD No 3, PO Box 360, Pottsville, Pennsylvania 17901, USA

Key personnel
President and Chief Executive Officer: R H Dreesen
Export Sales Director: P A Hughes
Domestic Sales Director: T R Jones

Products
All new ASCE, AREA, ARA-A, ARA-B rail sections produced; full line of relay rail and special trackwork; track accessories including switch materials, maintenance tools and insulating material. Third-rail transit products including fibreglass insulators, coverboard and brackets.

VERIFIED

Atlas Copco

Atlas Copco Compressors
Atlas Copco Construction & Mining Ltd
PO Box 79, Swallowdale Lane, Hemel Hempstead HP2 7HA, UK
Tel: +44 1442 61201   Fax: +44 1442 234467

Key personnel
Executive: P Haddow

Products
Self-contained power tamper/drill and pneumatic equipment, pumps, tampers. Hydraulic breakers. Portable and stationary compressors.

VERIFIED

Atlas Copco Berema

Atlas Copco Berema AB
PO Box 767, S-131 24 Nacka, Sweden
Tel: +46 8 743 9600   Fax: +46 8 743 9650

Works
Kalmar Works, PO Box 703, S-391 27 Kalmar, Sweden

Key personnel
Managing Director: Jörgen Krook
Marketing Manager: Peo Sollerud
Manager, Rail Department: Derek McCool

Principal subsidiaries
Atlas Copco Berema Inc, USA
Atlas Copco Berema A/S, Norway

Products
Pionjär and Cobra self-contained petrol-powered combination drill, breaker and ballast tamper for construction, maintenance and permanent way work.

A wide range of pneumatic breakers and rock drills is available, as well as heavy-duty boom-mounted hydraulic hammers for bridge deck demolition and pile driving, compressors and pneumatic accessories.

VERIFIED

Atlas Hydraulic Loaders

Atlas Hydraulic Loaders Ltd
Wharfedale Road, Euroway Estate, Bradford BD4 6SE, UK
Tel: +44 1274 686827   Fax: +44 1274 687889

Key personnel
General Manager: Ulrich Weter
Sales Manager: Martin Stafford

Products
Road/rail excavators.

VERIFIED

Atlas Weyhausen

Atlas Weyhausen GmbH
PO Box 1844, Stedinger Strasse 324, D-27747 Delmenhorst, Germany
Tel: +49 42 214910   Fax: +49 42 2149 1213

Key personnel
Chairman: Dipl Ing Günter Weyhausen
Marketing Director: Gerhard Brünjes

Products
Road/rail excavators and loading cranes.

VERIFIED

Austrack

Austrack Pty Ltd
973 Fairfield Road, Moorooka, Queensland 4105, Australia
Tel: +61 7 3892 9247   Fax: +61 7 3892 9389

Key personnel
Managing Director: D C Hudson
General Manager: S G Douglas

Products
Manufacture of prestressed concrete sleepers, turnout ties and concrete poles.

NEW ENTRY

Balfour Beatty

Balfour Beatty Railway Engineering Ltd
Osmaston Street, Sandiacre, Nottingham NG10 5AN, UK
Tel: +44 115 939 0125   Fax: +44 115 939 0000
Part of BICC Group

Key personnel
General Manager/Director: D M Ingham
Commercial Director: N J Duffy
Finance Director: N Potts
Managing Director: Bob Somerville
General Manager Designate: Keith Churn
UK Client Account Manager: Gary Elliott
Marketing Director: Phil Bean
Sales & Marketing Administrator: Katherine Marriott

Products
Supply of spheroidal graphite and grey iron castings; lever boxes; fabricated crossings; shallow-depth switches; friction buffer stops; high-speed points.

A contract was issued in 1996 by PATH New York for tunnel network junction renewals at Hoboken and Grove Street, New Jersey, and 33rd Street, Manhattan. From 1996, Balfour Beatty has been responsible for the construction of trackwork for the Lantau Airport Railway, Hong Kong. High-speed points systems have been supplied to Amtrak for its North East Corridor.

Developments: A gantry mill machine was installed in 1996. Designed and built by Forest Liné Albert, France, it can accommodate 38 m rails and is capable of machining operations throughout the entire length of rail, including web drilling. Twin 50 kW vertical cutting heads are serviced by ten-position auto-tool changers for the vertical heads, and five-position auto-tool changers for the horizontal drilling attachments. It is controlled by a Siemens 840C computer serviced by CAD/CAM programming. Completely finished machined rails are unloaded from the machine automatically.

UPDATED

Balfour Beatty Rail Projects

Balfour Beatty Rail Projects
Southern Track Renewals
PO Box 272, Croydon CR0 1YW, UK
Tel: +44 181 666 6633   Fax: +44 181 666 6615

Key personnel
Managing Director: Bob Somerville
Commercial Director: Tony Smith
Production Director: Bob Crease
Finance Director: Paul Lake
Personnel Director: Denis Parsons

Corporate development
Southern Track Renewals Co was one of the British Rail Infrastructure Services units sold off as part of the British Rail privatisation. The company was sold to Balfour Beatty in 1996.

Services:
Track maintenance, construction and associated services.

The Railway Engineering Contracting Division has been awarded a Dutch compliance certificate for the design, installation and maintenance of rail track. Balfour Beatty has formed a joint venture with Ballast Nedam, a Dutch construction company, to carry out rail infrastructure projects in Holland.

UPDATED

Ballast Nedam

Ballast Nedam Grond en Wegen BV
PO Box 2268, NL-1180 EG Amstelveen, Netherlands
Tel: +31 20 545 3907   Fax: +31 20 545 3935

Key personnel
Project Manager: H J C Masselink

Services
Implementation and construction of rail infrastructure projects.

Ballast Nedam and Balfour Beatty (qv) have formed a joint venture for carrying out rail infrastructure projects in Holland.

NEW ENTRY

Bance

R Bance & Co Ltd
Cockcrow Hill House, St Mary's Road, Surbiton KT6 5HE, UK
Tel: +44 181 398 7141   Fax: +44 181 398 4765
Email: sales@bance.co.uk

Key personnel
Managing Director: R Bance
Marketing & Sales: Kit Marshall

Products
Tapered rail joint shims for maintaining jointed track; self-powered impact wrenches and auger; rail disc cutters; rechargeable work lights; emergency standby lights; single rail trolleys; cross level gauges and other track measuring gauges; Alumi-Cart portable rail inspection vehicle and trailer; tie tampers; ultrasonic rail flaw detection vehicle.

UPDATED

Bance ultrasonic rail flaw detection vehicle   1997

Balfour Beatty gantry mill machine   1997

Banverket rail-laying machine at work in Norway
1997

Banverket

Banverket Industrial Division, S-78185 Borlänge, Sweden
Tel: +46 243 45000   Fax: +46 243 5009

Key personnel
General Manager: Claes Sandgren

Services
Banverket Industrial Division is an offshoot of the Swedish National Rail Administration (see *Systems* section) set up to tender for contract work. It has had some success in obtaining contracts outside its parent company, having undertaken work for NSB Norway.

NEW ENTRY

Barclay Mowlem

Barclay Mowlem Construction
20 Bridge Street, Pymble, New South Wales 2073, Australia
Tel: +61 2 9481 1333   Fax: +61 2 9481 1369

Key personnel
Managing Director: D C Hudson
General Manager, Railway Engineering & Construction Group: P W Welley
Business Procurement Manager, Railway Engineering & Construction Group: H J Tarrant

Subsidiary company
Austrak Pty Ltd (qv)

Products
Design and construction of track layouts; track upgrading and maintenance; manufacture of prestressed sleepers.

NEW ENTRY

BBR

Bureau BBR Ltd
Florastrasse 44, CH-8034, Zurich, Switzerland
Tel: +41 1 383 1910   Fax: +41 1 383 9930

Key personnel
Chairman: P Ing F Speck
General Manager: P Ing U Brunner

Products
BBR-THOSTI and BBR-Hibond prestressed concrete sleeper systems.
Recent contracts include orders from Germany, India, Indonesia, Sri Lanka and South Africa.

UPDATED

Beilhack

Beilhack Systemtechnik GmbH
PO Box 100155, D-83001 Rosenheim, Germany
Tel: +49 80 31 18060   Fax: +49 80 31 180612

Key personnel
Managing Partner: W Beilhack
Managing Director: W Grübler

Products
Production and supply of self-propelled, propelled and vehicle-mounted snow-clearing equipment and vehicles, including blowers, ploughs, rail sweeping equipment, flangers and ice cutters; multipurpose infrastructure maintenance vehicles, including self-propelled units with tipper, crane and mower equipment; feasibility studies and consultancy.

VERIFIED

BEML

Bharat Earth Movers Ltd
BEML Soudha, 23/1 4th Main, SR Nagar, Bangalore 560 027, India
Tel: +91 80 222 4141   Fax: +91 80 222 6883

Key personnel
See entry in *Non-powered passenger vehicles* section

Products
Tracklaying equipment, including tracklayers and spoil disposal units. The BEML self-propelled diesel-hydraulic tracklayer is designed to move on an auxiliary track. It has hydraulically operated grippers for handling concrete sleepers and rails from wagons and panel assemblies of concrete sleepers and rails. Maximum lifting capacity is 9 tonnes.
BEML's spoil disposal unit is designed for use with ballast cleaning machines for the reception, storage and unloading of spoil generated during ballast screening. Equipped with a hydraulically operated horizontal conveyor inside its hopper and a slew conveyor at one end, the spoil disposal unit can unload itself into similar units coupled together, wagons on an adjacent track or on to the slope of the formation.
Recent contracts include the supply of 29 tracklayers and five spoil disposal units to Indian Railways.

UPDATED

Bethlehem Steel

Bethlehem Steel Corporation
Pennsylvania Steel Technologies Inc
215 South Front Street, Steelton, Pennsylvania 17113, USA
Tel: +1 717 986 2276   Fax: +1 717 986 2700

Key personnel
Chairman and Chief Executive Officer: Curtis H Barnette

President: Andrew R Futchko
Vice-President, Sales and Marketing: Tim Demma

Corporate development
Pennsylvania Steel Technologies Inc is a subsidiary of Bethlehem Steel Corporation.

Products
Rail, including 80 ft long rail in four grades (in-line head hardened, fully heat-treated, medium hardness and standard; T-rail, contact rail and crane rail sections.

UPDATED

BHP Steel

BHP Steel, Long Products Division
PO Box , 196B, Newcastle, NSW 2300, Australia
Tel: +61 49 402411   Fax: +61 49 402505

Key personnel
Manager, Export Market: Greg Booth

Sales offices
Taiwan
Tel: +886 7 333 6900   Fax: +886 7 333 6907
General Manager: John Hunt

China/Hong Kong
Tel: +852 284 0233   Fax: +852 284 0244
General Manager: Manzar Iqbal

Philippines
Tel: +632 894 0121   Fax: +632 894 7832
General Manager: Mauro Cervames

Singapore/Malaysia
Tel: +65 535 0622   Fax: +65 532 7182
General Manager: Harold Quek

India/Sri Lanka/Bangladesh/Middle East
Tel: +971 4 314848   Fax: +971 4 310886
General Manager: Barry Gallagher

Products
Rolled steel rail (standard carbon and head hardened to UIC and Australian standards), steel sleeper bar, structural steel sections.

UPDATED

Bomag

Bomag GmbH
PO Box 1155, D-56135 Boppard, Germany
Tel: +49 6742 1000   Fax: +49 6742 3090

Key personnel
President: Anton Schwarzinger
Senior Vice-Presidents
  Finance: Wilfried Reinelt

BEML spoil disposal unit
1995

Manufacturing: Lothar Wahl
Engineering: Gülertan Vural
Vice-President, Sales: Dr Arnd Julius

Principal subsidiaries
In Austria, Canada, France, Japan, Jordan, Singapore, UK and USA.

Products
Tampers, vibrating plates (single direction and reversible), single and double drum rollers (hand guided), trench compactors, tandem rollers, combi rollers, single drum rollers (including asphalt versions), pneumatic tyred rollers, towed vibratory rollers, sanitary landfill compactors, asphalt surface recycler, soil stabiliser, hardware and software for compaction control of permanent way including data processing of all measured data.

VERIFIED

British Steel Track Products

British Steel Track Products
Moss Bay, Derwent Howe, Workington CA14 5AE, UK
Tel: +44 1900 64321   Fax: +44 1900 64800

Key personnel
Managing Director: Tony Williams
General Manager: Kerry Hill
Commercial Manager: Stuart W Askew
Sales Managers
UK: Geoff Suitor
Europe: George Thompson
Rest of World: Bob Docherty

Corporate development
BS Track Products and Royal Volker Stevin formed a jointly owned company GrantRail Ltd (qv) in 1996. It was formed from the track-laying division of British Steel subsidiary, Grant Lyon Eagre Ltd (qv), and Royal Volker Stevin's railway engineering company Railbouw (UK) Ltd.

Products
Heavy and light railway track rail from 9.88 to 67.57 kg/m; steel sleepers; rolled steel baseplates; fishplates; bridge and crane rail; electric conductor rail; special turnout rail.
A full range of rail grades is manufactured from 800 N/mm² tensile strength. High-strength rail is produced by an online heat treatment process.
Recent contracts include the supply of rail to Railtrack and London Underground Ltd, (UK); Canadian National; Indian Railways; Egypt, Sudan, Sri Lanka, Peru and Norway.

UPDATED

BTR Permali

BTR Permali RP Ltd
Bristol Road, Gloucester GL1 5TT, UK
Tel: +44 1452 528671   Fax: +44 1452 304215

Key personnel
Managing Director: M W Mallorie
Sales and Marketing Manager: C Mason

Products
GRP track baseplates; and GRP detector box covers.
Contracts include the supply of seat shells for UK railway coaches.

UPDATED

BWS trackbed and tunnel cleaning machine

Burn Standard Co

Burn Standard Co
A subsidiary of Bharat Bhari Udyog Nigam Ltd
10-C Hungerford Street, Calcutta 700 017 India
Tel: +91 33 247 1067/1762/1772   Fax: +91 33 247 1788

Key personnel
See *Freight vehicles and equipment* section

Products
Points and crossings, sleepers, fishplates, bridge girders.

VERIFIED

BWG

Butzbacher Weichenbau GmbH
PO Box 305, D-35503 Butzbach, Germany
Tel: +49 6033 8920   Fax: +49 6033 892123

Key personnel
Chief Executive Officer: E Bittel
Marketing and Engineering Executive: H Höhne
Export Manager: D Schluck

Works
PO Box 305, Wetzlarer Strasse 101, Industriegebiet Nord, D-35510 Butzbach

Products
Points and crossings (semi-welded and monoblock), carbon steel crossings, swing-nose crossings and expansion joints.
Contracts include Amtrak/NJT; DORTS, Taipei; Konkan Railway, India; DB AG, NSB Norway and VR Finland.

UPDATED

BWS

Bombardier-Wien Schienenfahrzeuge AG
A subsidiary of Bombardier Eurorail
Donaufelderstrasse 73-79, A-1210 Vienna, Austria
Tel: +43 1 259 46100   Fax: +43 1 259 46107

Key personnel
See entry in *Locomotives and powered passenger vehicles* section

Products
Trackbed cleaning machines for underground railways. These provide a solution to safety problems arising from dust and wear in tunnels (causing failures in electric and electronic systems) by using a wet cleaning vacuum method. This eliminates the danger of dust explosions. BWS cleaning machines feature a compact modular configuration which can be adapted to special profiles, conditions and requirements.

VERIFIED

Caltronic

Caltronic A/S
Sortedam Dossering 83, DK-2100 Copenhagen Ø, Denmark
Tel: +45 3526 6011   Fax: +45 3526 5018

Key personnel
Managing Director: Ulrik Danneskiold-Samsøe

Caltronic wheel monitoring system

Product
Wheel monitoring system for online detection of wheel defects. The detection of wheel flats operates as a modular system which can be combined with proprietary equipment for identification of wagons.
The system has been installed in Scandinavian and other European countries and the USA for both freight traffic and metro applications. It detects wheel flats by means of an array of accelerometers clamped to the rail foot. This principle makes it possible to identify wheel flats independently.

VERIFIED

Cemafer

Cemafer Gleisbaumaschinen und Geräte GmbH
Ihringer Landstrasse 3, PO Box 1327, D-79206 Breisach, Germany
Tel: +49 76 67582   Fax: +49 76 671008

Key personnel
General Manager: A Wagner

Products
Power wrenches, coach-screwing machines, rail drills, rail saws, sleeper drills, sleeper adzing and drilling machines, rail grinding equipment, rail benders, light tampers, inspection trolleys, trailers, portal cranes, hand tools, electric generators (portable), gauges, jacks, rail cutting machines, rail stripping machines, sleeper boring machines, sleeper placing machines, spanners, spike drivers and extractors, and tracklaying equipment.

VERIFIED

Cembre

Cembre SpA
Via Serenissima 9, I-25135 Brescia, Italy
Tel: +30 36921   Fax: +30 336 5766

UK subsidiary
Cembre Ltd Fairview Industrial Estate
Kingsbury Road, Curdworth, Sutton Coldfield B76 9EE
Tel: +44 1675 470440   Fax: +44 1675 470220

Other associate companies in Paris, Madrid and Holmestrand, Norway

Products
Rail drilling equipment.

NEW ENTRY

Cementation Railways

Cementation Railways
A division of Cementation (Africa Contracts Pty) Ltd
50 Booysens Road, Selby, Johannesburg, South Africa
Tel: +27 11 974 1566   Fax: +27 11 974 5049/7880

Works
4 Anvil Road, PO Box 21, Isando 1600, South Africa

Key personnel
Managing Director: M D Mack
General Manager: W C Ebersohn
Export Manager: P Vorster
Sales Manager: C R Jaggs

Principal subsidiaries
William Bain
Railway Track Supplies
Moirs Railway Engineering

Products
Railway turnouts, steel sleepers and accessories for narrow- (underground and surface) and broad-gauge applications.

Recent contracts include products for the railways of Botswana, Mozambique, Namibia and Zambia, Iscor Steel Works and Highveld Steel & Vanadium.

VERIFIED

Central Track Renewals

Central Track Renewals Co Ltd
3rd Floor, Quayside Tower, 252-260 Broad Street, Birmingham B1 2HF
Tel: +44 121 654 8309   Fax: +44 121 654 8318

Key personnel
Managing Director: John Russell
Managers
   Commercial: Richard Brown
   Production: Derek Wolfendale

Corporate development
Central Track Renewals Co was one of the British Rail Infrastructure Services units sold off as part of the British Rail privatisation. The company was sold in March 1996 to Tarmac Construction Ltd.

Services
Infrastructure and track maintenance and upgrading.

Central Track Renewals has contracts for track work on the important West Coast main line, on which a major modernisation project is planned.

VERIFIED

Century Precast

PO Box 228, Sulphur, LA 70664-0228, USA
Tel: +1 318 527 5266
Email: cengrp1@maas.net
Web: www.century.com

Key personnel
Secretary/treasurer: Jon Russ Vincent
National Director/Sales & Marketing (Railroad Products Division): Robert W Goodner
Vice-President/Sales & Marketing (Railroad Products Division): Jerry McCoombs

Products
Full-depth grade crossings for curves, turnouts, diamond crossings and straight track. Century Precast offers its elastomeric flangeway filler with its crossings to ensure safety for pedestrian and vehicular traffic.

Crossings have been installed by DART Dallas, Port of Houston, Port of New Orleans and BART San Francisco.

NEW ENTRY

CF&I Steel

CF&I Steel LP
PO Box 1830, Pueblo, Colorado 81002, USA
Tel: +1 719 561 7505   Fax: +1 719 561 7256

Key personnel
Vice-President, Sales and Marketing: J E Dionisio
Sales Manager, Railroad Products: M C McLean

Products
Rails, including T-rails.

VERIFIED

VERIFIED   Century Precast crossing   *1997*

Chemetron

Chemetron Railway Products Inc
177 West Hintz Road, Wheeling, Illinois 60090, USA
Tel: +1 847 520 5454   Fax: +1 847 520 6373
Email: cttsales@aol.com

Key personnel
President: P J Cunningham
Vice-President, Sales and Marketing: R N Madderom

Principal subsidiary
True Temper Railway Appliances
177 West Hintz Road, Wheeling, Illinois 60090, USA

Products
Electric flash-butt rail welding plants including rail welders, rail end polishers, base grinders, rail saws, automatic rail straighteners and rail pushers. Rail trains, rail wagons and miscellaneous rail handling equipment including turnkey design of rail welding plants. Contract welding service of rail into continuous welded rail in any of standard, alloy or head-hardened rails. Ergonomically safe manually operated switch stands.

Chemetron rail welding machines operate using AC or DC power. Systems are solid-state and can be controlled with various levels of automation. Production capabilities are in excess of 25 welds/h for all rail sizes. Transportable/mobile flash-butt rail welding plants are also available, including truck-mounted road/rail in-track units.

Chemetron operates plants in the USA and Canada and provides equipment and technical advice to Mexico, Asia, South America and Australia.

True Temper Railway Appliances is a leading manufacturer of rail anchors and fastening systems in the USA. Anchors available for all rail sizes to North and South America, Australia, Europe, Asia and Africa.

UPDATED

Chemgrate

Chemgrate Corporation
4115 Keller Springs Road, Suite 218 Addison, TX 75244-3024, USA
Tel: +1 75244 3024   Fax: +1 972 732 8070

Products
Anti-slip and corrosion-resistant grating, stair treads and floor plates for rail systems.

NEW ENTRY

Cimmco

Cimmco International
A division of Cimmco Birla Ltd
Prakash Deep, 7 Tolstoy Marg, New Delhi 110,001, India
Tel: +91 11 331 4383/84/85
Fax: +91 11 332 077/372 3520

Key personnel
See entry in *Freight vehicles and equipment* section

Products
Permanent way materials including: cast-iron, pressed steel and concrete sleepers; elastic rail fastening system; rigid fasteners; points and crossings; rail anchors; fishplates, nuts and bolts; track tools and various types of spikes.

UPDATED

Clouth

Clouth Gummiwerke AG
Conveyor Belt Division
PO Box 600229, Niehler Strasse, D-50682 Cologne, Germany
Tel: +49 221 777 3624/3593   Fax: +49 221 777 3700

Key personnel
Executive: Norbert Martin
Technical Manager: Dr Wilhelm Engst
Manager, Marketing & Sales: Michael Kottmann

Products
Elastic rail fasteners (DFF®); SBM® sub-ballast matting and trackbed matting; RRS resilient primary suspension; MFS® elastomeric bearings for floating slab systems; ASM® protective matting for waterproof coatings of bridges and structures; insulation matting and Oil-EX® oil absorption mats.

UPDATED

Cogifer

Compagnie Générale d'Installations Ferroviaires
40 quai de l'Ecluse, F-78290 Croissy-sur-Seine, France
Tel: +33 1 34 80 45 00   Fax: +33 1 34 80 03 31

Key personnel
President: Régis Bello
Presidents of subsidiary companies
Henri Dehe (Cogifer TF)
Claude Schwartz (Cogifer Industries)
Louis Wagner (Cogifer Sicatelec)

Principal subsidiaries
Cogifer TF
40 quai de l'Ecluse, F-78290 Croissy-sur-Seine, France
Tel: +33 1 39 76 53 54   Fax: +33 1 39 76 16 33

Cogifer Industries
40 quai de l'Ecluse, F-78290 Croissy-sur-Seine, France
Tel: +33 1 34 80 45 00   Fax: +33 1 34 80 03 31

Cogifer Sicatelec
40 quai de l'Ecluse, F-78290 Croissy-sur-Seine, France
Tel: +33 1 34 80 45 00   Fax: +33 1 34 80 03 31

Products
Cogifer TF specialises in tracklaying and civil engineering, such as the supply and laying of new tracks for high-speed lines (TGV), metros (steel wheel or rubber tyres), tramways, and Matra VAL systems; mechanised renewal of tracks (ballast clearing, screening, dismantling of existing tracks and laying of new ones, ballasting, tamping, levelling); and the maintenance of national and private railways and sidings.

Cogifer Industries manufactures turnouts and Cogifer Sicatelec specialises in signalling and catenary.

UPDATED

Colebrand

Colebrand Ltd
Colebrand House, 18-20 Warwick Street, London W1R 6BE, UK
Tel: +44 171 439 1000   Fax: +44 171 734 3358/287 1544

Key personnel
Managing Director: K N Tusch
Chief Executive: Rear Admiral R I T Hogg
Sales Manager: J R Harrison

Main works
CXL Factory, Goodshawfold Road, Rossendale BB4 8QF, UK

Colebrand LUD on Docklands Light Railway

Products
The Colebrand Lock Up Device (LUD) is fitted to structures such as bridges that must resist the braking and traction forces from rail traffic, while allowing for thermal expansion/contraction as well as possible shrinkage and creepage. Colebrand LUDs have recently been successfully incorporated into the Docklands Light Railway where they have been used to strengthen the overhead sections carrying the existing track. The LUD is ideal for use in earthquake zones.

Recent contracts include the supply of LUDs to: Indonesia for three rail bridges; to London Underground Ltd; and the Kuala Lumpur LRT system.

VERIFIED

Collis Engineering

Collis Engineering Ltd
Salcombe Road, Meadow Lane Industrial Estate, Alfreton DE5 7EZ, UK
Tel: +44 1773 833255   Fax: +44 1773 520693

Key personnel
See entry in *Signalling and telecommunications systems* section

Products
Point fittings, sitework tents for trackside maintenance and cable jointers, rail drilling jigs, permanent way equipment and services and structural steelwork.

VERIFIED

Compair Hydrovane

Compair Hydrovane
Claybrook Drive, Washford Industrial Estate, Redditch B98 0DS, UK
Tel: +44 1527 525522   Fax: +44 1527 521140

Key personnel
See *Passenger coach equipment* section

Products
Trackair range of rotary compressors specially designed for mobile railway applications. There are 12 basic models available for any working pressure required between 7 and 10 bar.

Hydrovane range of rotary vane railway compressors for stationary applications. Range extends from 1.98 litres/s to 207 litres/s up to 10 bar.

Recent contracts include delivery of 26 TA20 units for Mexico City metro.

NEW ENTRY

Conbrako

Conbrako (Pty) Ltd
PO Box 4018, Luipaardsvlei 1743, Transvaal, South Africa
Tel: +27 11 762 2421   Fax: +27 11 762 6535

Products
Track jacks.

VERIFIED

Stoneblower

The Stoneblower . . . employs the time tested process called measured shovel packing to correct surface and line deviations. Stone is carried on board and is pneumatically blown under the ties (sleepers) in areas where needed. Ballast savings, longer tamping cycles and immediate removal slow orders are only a few of the benefits associated with this new and unique method of surfacing track.

Pandrol Jackson's Stoneblower is truly a machine of the future. The technology found in this machine will serve our industry well into the 21st century.

ContiTech

ContiTech Holding GmbH
Büttnerstrasse 9, D-30165 Hannover, Germany
Tel: +49 511 93802   Fax: +49 511 938 2766

Key personnel
See entry in *Passenger coach equipment* section

Products
Rubber metal suspension systems for ballastless track (such as on bridges and in tunnels). Sub-ballast rubber mats; oil-absorbing rubber mats.

VERIFIED

Cooper & Turner

Cooper & Turner
Sheffield Road, Sheffield S9 1RS, UK
Tel: +44 114 256 0057   Fax: +44 114 244 5529

Key personnel
Director: P N Cook
Sales Manager: P A White

Products
Fish-bolts, track-bolts, screwspikes, crossing-bolts, Renlok locknut, insulated fishplates.

VERIFIED

Cowans Sheldon

Clarke Chapman Ltd
PO Box 9, James Street, Carlisle CA2 5BJ, UK
Tel: +44 1228 24196   Fax: +44 1228 24795

Key personnel
Product Sales Manager, Railway Equipment: P Fraser

Products
Track maintenance equipment, including long-welded rail trains for laying continuously welded rail, twin-line tracklaying machines, single-line track panel-laying cranes, side-mounted rail loading cranes, heavy diesel breakdown cranes, ballast regulating machines, lightweight hydraulic rerailing equipment. Workshop equipment including traversers and turntables.

Recent contracts include the supply of a twin jib tracklaying machine for London Underground Ltd.

VERIFIED

CSR Humes

CSR Humes Pty Ltd
Building D, 4th Floor, World Trade Centre, Corner of Flinders and Spencer Streets, Melbourne 3005, Australia
Tel: +61 39 286 2666   Fax: +61 39 286 2671

Key personnel
Technical Services Manager: M Kiefel

Products
Prestressed concrete railway sleepers, box culverts and pipes.

VERIFIED

CXT

CXT Incorporated
North 2420 Sullivan Road, PO Box 14918, Spokane, Washington 99214, USA
Tel: +1 509 924 6300   Fax: +1 509 927 0299

Key personnel
President: John G White
Vice-President Railroad Division: Derek Firth

Products
Prestressed concrete sleepers for both track and turnouts. CXT designs and manufactures sleepers for specific applications, as well as level crossings and other concrete products for railways and rapid transit.

Recent contracts include the manufacture of sleepers for various customers in two locations in the USA. A mobile manufacturing plant to supply export customers is also available.

VERIFIED

Daido

Daido Steel Co Ltd
Kogin Building 11-18 Nishiki 1-chome, Naka-ku, Nagoya, Japan
Tel: +81 52 201 5111   Fax: +81 52 221 9268

Key personnel
Manager, Castings Sales Division: Takao Ohi

Products
High-manganese cast-steel frogs and crossings.

Recent developments include a movable nose frog for slab track.

VERIFIED

Danieli Centro Maskin

Danieli Centro Maskin SpA
Swedish branch office
PO Box 17067, Lilla Munkebäcksg 4, S-402 61 Gothenburg, Sweden
Tel: +46 31 250340   Fax: +46 31 250711

Key personnel
Managing and Marketing: Ove Lein

Products
Carbide-tipped saws and carbide-tipped drill units for cutting rail to length.

VERIFIED

Darcy Products Track Mat with Track Grip laid on top to provide a non-slip surface **1997**

Darcy

Darcy Products Ltd
Invicta Works, East Malling, West Malling ME19 6BP, UK
Tel: +44 1732 843131   Fax: +44 1732 870016

Products

Track Mats, for protection of ballast and sleepers from oil, grease, grit and other rubbish. Darcy reports that the mats improve ballast formation and minimise the risk of run-off from the track flowing into nearby streams and watercourses or polluting ground water.

Track Mats consists of 4 m long 145 cm wide double thicknesses of high-tensile strength Drizit polypropylene oil-absorbent material with a backing to prevent splitting when laid over sharp ballast. They are fitted with tie ribbons for securing to rail holding clips. Sleeper ends can be protected in the same manner using sleeper end mats.

Track Grip is a lightweight plastic grid providing a non-slip surface for foot traffic and to protect the absorbent material from erosion by continual contact with fuel lines, power cables, hose couplings and similar equipment.

NEW ENTRY

Davy British Rail International

Ashmore House, Richardson Road, Stockton-on-Tees, TS18 3RE, UK
Tel: +44 1642 602221   Fax: +44 1642 341001

Corporate development

Jointly owned by Kvaerner Davy (60 per cent) and Halcrow Transmark (40 per cent). Kvaerner Davy is a subsidiary of Kvaerner ASEA, a Norwegian business group involved in ship building and the paper industry.

Services

Design, project management, construction engineering and training services for rail rehabilitation, including turnkey projects.

DBRI completed the rehabilitation of the 120 km PERUMKA rail link between Jakarta and Merak in 1996.

NEW ENTRY

Desec Tracklayer laying turnouts direct from wagons **1997**

Desec Tracklayer at work **1996**

Delachaux

C Delachaux SA, Welding Division
119 avenue Louis-Roche, F-92231 Gennevilliers, France
Tel: +33 1 47 90 61 20   Fax: +33 1 47 90 64 52

Products

Aluminothermic rail welding equipment and mechanised equipment for high-activity worksites.

VERIFIED

Delkor

Delkor Pty Ltd
75 Hutchinson Street, St Peters, New South Wales 2044, Australia
Tel: +61 2 550 5111   Fax: +61 2 550 5626

Key personnel

Managing Director: Kjell Blendulf
Technical Manager: Peter Schonstein
Sales Manager: Franz Rolinck

Products

Elastic rail fasteners, including noise-reducing fasteners for bridges and tunnels; ballast mats for ballasted track; floating slab systems. Delkor products are manufactured under licence from Clouth Gummiwerke AG, Germany.

Recent contracts include the supply of noise-reducing elastic rail fasteners for the Sydney Harbour Bridge, Australia; and rail fasteners for the Tsing Ma Bridge, Hong Kong.

VERIFIED

Desec

Desec Ltd
FIN-39700 Parkano, Finland
Tel: +358 3 448 3442/5 260 9550
Fax: +358 3 448 3443/5 260 9448

Key personnel

Managing Director: Seppo Koivisto
Sales Manager: Einari Venäläinen

Products

Track and turnout replacement machines; trolleys for turnout and track laying; lifting devices for track maintenance; supply of turnout transport wagons; design of railway cranes.

Desec Tracklayers are radio-controlled, straddle carrier-type multipurpose machines for carrying, lifting and assembling very long and heavy track and turnout elements. They are designed to work under catenary and in tunnels; tracklaying and replacement of turnout elements can be carried out without any additional lifting aid.

A Tracklayer unit is transported to the site on a conventional flat wagon or road trailer and is capable of loading and unloading itself using its crawler tracks and four supporting legs. The crawler tracks are driven by hydraulic motors and located on arms that can be horizontally and vertically telescoped in and out. When the crawler tracks are in their widest position, an element of 5 m in width, 32 m in length and 36 tonnes in weight

Station on the PERUMKA Jakarta—Merak link, rehabilitated by DBRI **1997**

can be lifted, moved and assembled by one TL 50 tracklayer.

Two Tracklayers can operate together by means of a connecting control cable to give almost double lifting capacity. The TL 70 Tracklayer can handle elements up to 40 m in length.

Recent contracts include the supply of three TL 50 units to VR Track Ltd, Finland; two TL 70 units to Banverket, Sweden; one TL 50 unit to ZS Praha AS, Czech Republic; one TL 50 unit to NNRA, Norway; one TL 50 unit to TSS Bratislava AS, Slovakia; lifting devices to VR Track Ltd, Finland and tracklaying trolleys to NNRA, Norway.

UPDATED

Desquenne et Giral

Desquenne et Giral Group
13 rue Le Sueur, F-75116 Paris, France
Tel: +33 1 46 69 60 60   Fax: +33 1 47 21 85 79

Works
15 rue Saint Maurice, F-92024 Nanterre Cedex, France

Key personnel
Chairman of the Board: J L Giral
General Manager: J C Guede

Principal subsidiary
SECO/Desquenne et Giral
15 rue Saint Maurice, F-92024 Nanterre Cedex, France

Products
Mechanised railway track construction and track maintenance work, supported by manufacture of specialised equipment. This machinery includes: SPRA *(Satellite Pour Rails et Attaches);* SPRO *(Satellite Pour Récupération Optimale du ballast);* ballast cleaning machines; ballast conveyors; twin crane assembly, tracklaying, gantry cranes; torque-controlled coach-screwing machines.

Recent contracts include mechanised renewal of 1,000 km of track; tracklaying on the TGV Nord high-speed line between Paris and the Channel Tunnel; and track maintenance and tracklaying on the Metro and RER systems in Paris.

VERIFIED

D'Huart

Jean D'Huart et Cie
3 rue de l'Industrie, F-57110 Yutz, France
Tel: +33 3 82 56 34 84

Products
Rail, steel and timber sleepers, fishplates, other track components.

VERIFIED

Difco

Difco Inc
PO Box 238, Findlay, Ohio 45839, USA
Tel: +1 419 422 0525   Fax: +1 419 422 1275

Key personnel
See entry in *Freight vehicles and equipment* section

Products
Rolling stock for permanent way construction and maintenance duties including air-operated side-dump wagons; air-operated drop-end side-dump wagons; and Ballaster and Auto-Ballaster systems.

The new Auto-Ballaster system provides automated ballasting using remote valves located at one end of the wagon to control the gate operation. Radio remote controls are available as an option. Ballast flow, which is adjustable, can be directed to the centre or either side of the track. Power comes from the locomotive air compressor; a separate line provides air to each car in the train. The gates, which open and close with enough power to shear limestone ballast, are made of heavy-steel plates with a shape and motion that tends to push the ballast back into the wagon when closing. The gates can also be operated manually.

VERIFIED

Donelli

Donelli DIMAF SpA
Via Romana 99, I-42028 Poviglio, Reggio Emilia, Italy
Tel: +39 522 969046/7/8   Fax: +39 522 969691

Key personnel
Managing Director: S Fitoussi

Products
Ballast regulators, hydraulic cranes, jacks, sleeper placing machines, track aligners, tracklaying equipment, track lining machines.

Other products: complete range of light and heavy-duty gang cars; brushwood cutters; workshop trailers; weedkiller-spreading trailers; overhead catenary line erection; maintenance and servicing vehicles; catenary inspection gang cars; catenary inspection trailers; rail/road loaders; hi-rail cranes.

VERIFIED

Drouard

Drouard
Parc Saint-Christophe, F-95865 Cergy-Pontoise Cedex, France
Tel: +33 1 34 22 50 00   Fax: +33 1 34 22 62 29

Key personnel
Director: D Mallet
General Manager: J Lemercier
Business Development Manager: B Atkinson

Products
Tracklaying and associated works (including TGV); manufacture of concrete sleepers; maintenance and renovation of track and ballast for rail, metros and tramways.

Recent contracts include trackwork for TGV North, France, maintenance of the Paris Metro network high-output renewals on major lines in France and non-ballasted trackwork in Germany.

UPDATED

Eastern Infrastructure Maintenance Co

Eastern Infrastructure Maintenance Co Ltd
Room B201, Midland House, Nelson Street, Derby DE1 2SA
Tel: +44 1332 263801   Fax: +44 1332 262965

Key personnel
Managing Director: David Swallow
Business Development Manager: Stephen Flewitt

Corporate development
As part of the British Rail sell-off, Eastern Infrastructure Maintenance Co was sold to the construction group Balfour Beatty in April 1996.

Services
Track and infrastructure maintenance and upgrading.

VERIFIED

EBS

Eisenbahn sicherung AG
Steinengraben 22, CH-4002 Basel, Switzerland
Tel: +41 61 285 1444   Fax: +41 61 285 1445

Key personnel
Sales Manager: Uwe Wunram

Products
Warning system for track maintenance teams which economises on look-out personnel. The approach of a train triggers flashing lights.

NEW ENTRY

Edgar Allen

Edgar Allen Engineering Limited
PO Box 42, Shepcote Lane, Sheffield S9 1QW, UK
Tel: +44 114 244 6621   Fax: +44 114 242 6826

Key personnel
Directors
Managing: S R Adams
Financial: C J Cantrill
Operational: T Cassidy
Sales: J Steele
Managers
Export Sales: S Needham
Sales: R Dibbe
Technical: T Grindle
Production: D Turner

Products
Design and manufacture of trackwork, switches and crossings for railways, mass transit, tramways, docks and harbours and steel works; manganese-steel wearing parts for locomotive and axlebox manufacturers and railway maintenance workshops.

The company is a major supplier to Railtrack of manganese steel switches and crossings. It also supplies trackwork to North America to AREA specifications and to other countries to UIC specifications.

UPDATED

Edilon

Edilon BV
Nijverheidsweg 23, NL-2031 CN Haarlem, Netherlands
Tel: +31 23 319519   Fax: +31 23 310751

Key personnel
Managing Director: R Vogelaar

Principal subsidiary
Edilon Corkelast SA, Spain

Products
Specialised adhesives and elastomers for permanent way applications: Edilon Corkelast, a resilient pourable elastomer for embedded rail and embedded single block support systems; Edilon Dex range, specialised epoxy-based products for timber sleeper preservation; and Edilon acoustic web blocks for noise reduction from track.

VERIFIED

Electrologic

Electrologic Pty Ltd
Unit 16, 43 College Street, Gladesville, New South Wales 2111, Australia
Tel: +61 2 9816 1515   Fax: +61 2 9816 5978
Email: eloaus@ozemail.com.au

Key personnel
Managing Director: B Heij

Products
Continuous non-contact optical track geometry measurement system; continuous non-contact optical rail-shape measurement system; portable track recording system; rail thermometers; survey database systems; non-contact wheel shape measurement; rail stress monitor; and non-contact overhead wire measurement system.

Recent contracts include non-contact optical track geometry recording car measurement system and overhead wire geometry measurement system for Queensland Railways; overhead geometry measurement system for SEPTA Philadelphia, USA; non-contact track geometry and third rail recording car for MRTC Singapore; non-contact track geometry for Iarnród Éireann, Ireland; and non-contact overhead and wire wear for China.

UPDATED

Products

The company manufactures switches and crossings to UIC and national standards for high-speed and heavy-load applications. Manufacturing facilities include rail machining shop, foundry, fabrication and assembly shops.

UPDATED

GrantRail

GrantRail Ltd
Scotter Road, Scunthorpe DN15 8EF, UK
Tel: +44 1724 295200   Fax: +44 1724 295220
Email: 101775,332@Compuserve,Com

Key personnel

Trackwork Manager: Ray Rogers
Marketing & Business Development: Graeme Ferguson

Corporate developnment

British Steel and Royal Volker Stevin formed GrantRail as a jointly owned company. It has been formed from the track-laying division of British Steel subsidiary, Grant Lyon Eagre Ltd (qv), and Royal Volker Stevin's railway engineering company Railbouw (UK) Ltd.

Products

Construction, renewal and maintenance of LRT, metro, underground and heavy rail systems.

Complete systems are offered for LRT projects, covering planning, supply of rail and installation.

Contracts

Major customers are Railtrack UK, London Underground and Midland Metro.

NEW ENTRY

Grinaker Duraset

Grinaker Duraset
A branch of Grinaker Construction Ltd
PO Box 365, Brakpan 1540, South Africa
Tel: +27 11 813 2340   Fax: +27 11 813 4222

Works

77 Lemmer Road, Vulcania, Brakpan 1540, South Africa

Key personnel

Chairman: R C MacMillan
Managing Director: J C Havinga

Products

Prestressed concrete railway products including sleepers, level crossing slabs, turnouts and electrification masts.

VERIFIED

Grove Worldwide

Grove Europe Limited
Crown Works
Pallion, Sunderland SR4 6TT, UK
Tel: +44 191 565 6281   Fax: +44 191 564 0442

Key personnel

Vice-President Crane Sales: W Lawson
General Manager, Marketing: N Day
UK Sales Manager: W N Green

Principal subsidiary

Grove Coles France SA
PO Box 203, F-95523 Cergy-Pontoise Cedex, France

Products

Grove mobile hydraulic telescopic cranes: truck-mounted, all-terrain and rough-terrain, lifting capacities from 0 to 250 tonnes; Grove Manlift self-propelled aerial work platforms: scissor-lift, telescopic boom and articulated telescopic boom.

UPDATED

GT Railway Maintenance Ltd

GT Railway Maintenance Ltd
252-260 Broad Street, Birmingham B1 2HF
Tel: +44 121 654 8200   Fax: +44 121 654 8651

Key personnel

Managing Director: Mike Casebourne
Commercial Director: John Hurrel
Business Development: Julian Garratt

Corporate development

Formerly known as Central Infrastructure Maintenance Co, GT Railway Maintenance Ltd was one of the British Rail Infrastructure Services units sold off as part of the British Rail privatisation. The company was sold in April 1996 to a joint venture between GEC Alsthom Ltd (a major supplier of signalling) and Tarmac Construction Ltd (a major civil engineering company).

Services

Track maintenance and upgrading; also inspection and renewal.

GT Railway Maintenance Ltd has continuing contracts for track maintenance work on the important West Coast main line, on which a major upgrading programme is planned.

UPDATED

Gummiwerk Kraiburg Elastik

Gummiwerk Kraiburg Elastik GmbH
Göllstrasse 8, D-84529 Tittmoning, Germany
Tel: +49 8683 7010   Fax: +49 8683 70126

Key personnel

President: Peter Schmidt
Administration: Horst Steidl
Sales and Marketing: H Pfriender
Technical Director: Uwe Dahlweg

Products

STRAIL level crossing system — a full-depth rubber crossing designed for use at locations which experience dense traffic. Also, miniSTRAIL level crossing system, a rubber/plastic crossing suitable for light traffic areas.

The company has supplied crossings to railway companies in Europe and throughout the world.

UPDATED

Hanning & Kahl tramway hand point setting mechanism **1997**

Hanning & Kahl

Hanning & Kahl GmbH & Co
PO Box 1342, 33806 Oerlinghausen, Germany
Tel: +49 5202 707600   Fax: +49 5202 707629

Key personnel

General Manager: Eckart Dümmer
Sales Director: Wolfgang Helas
Technical Director: Dr Carsten Kipp

Products

Points mechanisms for all gauges and types of rail with magnetic, motor or electrohydraulic drive; manual point setting mechanisms; point mechanism for grooved rail.

NEW ENTRY

HDC

Hindustan Development Corporation Ltd
Mody Building, 27 Sir RN Mukherjee Road, Calcutta 700 001, India
Tel: +91 33 248 0166/67/68
Fax: +91 33 248 1922/220 2607

Works

Tiljala Plant (TP)
38 Tiljala Road, Calcutta 700 039, India

GTRM track renewal in progress **1997**

HRTP125 power pack for rail stressing equipment by Hi-Force Hydraulics   **1996**

Bamunari Plant (BP)
National Highway No 2, Bamunari 712 205, District Hooghly, West Bengal, India

General Engineering Works (GEW)
Industrial Area, Bharatpur 31 001, Rajasthan, India

Key personnel
See entry in *Freight vehicles and equipment* section

Products
Rail; track components; cast-manganese crossings.

VERIFIED

Hi-Force Hydraulics

Hi-Force Hydraulics Ltd
Bentley Way, Daventry NN11 5QH, UK
Tel: +44 1327 77511   Fax: +44 1327 704466

Key personnel
Directors: Chris Jones, John Taylor
Managers
    Area Sales: Allan Webster, Bob Horton
    Export Sales: Richard Green
    Marketing: Karen Lintern

Products
HRTP petrol engine-driven power packs for hydraulic rail stressing equipment; hydraulic jacks and presses.
    Recent contracts include the supply of power packs to British Rail.

VERIFIED

Holland

John Holland Construction & Engineering Pty Ltd
PO Box 7181, Cloisters Square, Perth, Western Australia 6850, Australia
Tel: +61 9 221 2442   Fax: +61 9 325 7024

Key personnel
General Manager, Rail Division (Perth): David Tasker
Construction and Estimating Manager (Perth):
    Joe Angelucci
Project Manager, Infrastructure Maintenance and
    Construction (Melbourne): Wayne Donelly

Products
Manufacture of single-gauge and gauge-convertible concrete sleepers. Track design, construction, rehabilitation, gauge conversion and maintenance, including installation of concrete sleepers under traffic conditions or during temporary line closures.

UPDATED

Holland Co

Holland Co
1020 Washington Avenue, Chicago Heights, Illinois 60411, USA
Tel: +1 708 756 0650   Fax: +1 708 756 2641

Key personnel
President: Philip C Moeller
Senior Vice-President, Marketing and Sales:
    Joseph F Sloat
Vice-President, International Sales: E Parker
Engineering Manager: George K Clem
Secretary and Treasurer: Steven M Kuehn

Products
Sales and contracting of electric flash-butt welding personnel and equipment; rail and road mobile welders, portable on-site welding plants and fixed-plant management/production services. Holland can supply all support equipment or provide a turnkey operation.

VERIFIED

Huck

Huck International Inc
6 Thomas Drive, Irvine, California 92718, USA
Tel: +1 714 855 9000   Fax: +1 714 855 0398/8537

Key personnel
Executive Vice-President, International Operations:
    Robert S Levine

Products
Fastening systems, including lockbolts for use in rail joints and rolling stock.

VERIFIED

HWD

Henry Williams Darlington Limited
Dodsworth Street, Darlington DL1 2NJ, UK
Tel: +44 1325 462722   Fax: +44 1325 381744

Key personnel
Managing Director: R H S Dilley
Marketing Director: M Rowe

Products
Forged and fabricated railway equipment including forged, rolled and insulated fishplates; rail anchors and clips; switch clamps; lineside apparatus cases; signalling cranks and rods; switch levers; track tools and gauges; maintenance escalator trolleys; and specialist fabrications and machined parts.
    Recent contracts include the supply of escalator trolleys to London Underground Ltd; and fishplates to Railtrack, KCRC, SNCB, NS, Sweden and Malaysia.

VERIFIED

IBM

IBM Travel and Transportation
1 New Square, Bedfont Lakes, Feltham TW14 8HB, UK
Tel: +44 181 818 4020   Fax: +44 181 818 5291
Web: http://www.uk.ibm.com/travel

Key personnel
Solutions Manager, IBM: Steve Orman
Consultant, UP: Dan Faulkner

Malaysia office, Kuala Lumpur
Tel: +65 320 1835   Fax: +65 221 9697

Corporate development
IBM and Union Pacific Technologies formed an alliance in 1997 to enable IBM to market UP's Infrastructure Control Systems (ICS) around the world. The marketing is from IBM's base in USA.

Services
ICS, which integrates all the computer systems required by the engineering department at Union Pacific Railroad, USA. The service is available to railways worldwide.

NEW ENTRY

Infra Safety Services

PO Box 1075, NL-3300 BB Dordrecht, Netherlands
Tel: +31 78 654 0655   Fax: +31 78 651 4421

Key personnel
Director: C J de Graaff
General Manager: J F A M Weijtmans

Products
Infra Safety Services provides a total package for securing the work area. The company draws up and executes safety plans, and develops high-standard systems such as ARW 5/2 and Minimel 90 or PWA.

NEW ENTRY

Instant Zip-Up

Instant Zip-Up Ltd
Special Products Division
153 Newton Road, Lowton, Warrington WA3 1EZ, UK
Tel: +44 1942 680160   Fax: +44 1942 601984

Key personnel
Director: Alan Wilson
Sales Manager: Tony Horrocks

Products
Supply and rental of access equipment for infrastructure maintenance including road/rail vehicles (equipped with a rotating scissor-lift with extending deck or a rotating articulated boom arm) and rail-mounted alloy towers. Staff training in the use of work platforms and aluminium scaffold.

UPDATED

Interep

Interep SA
rue de l'Industrie, F-43110 Aurec-sur-Loire, France
Tel: +33 4 77 35 20 21   Fax: +33 4 77 35 26 17

Key personnel
Managing Director: Daniel Boffy
Sales and Marketing Director: Philippe Charbonnier

Products
Vibration-absorbing microcellular foam rubber for use in ballast/sleeper mats and rail/sleeper/slab pads.

VERIFIED

International Track Systems

International Track Systems Inc
Railroad Rubber Products
620 West 32nd Street, PO Box 857, Ashtabula, Ohio
44004, USA
Tel: +1 216 992 9206   Fax: +1 216 992 6752

Key personnel
Managing Director: Harold L Reiter
Sales Director: Benjamin F Baker

Products
Rubber products including tie pads, insulating rubber tie
plates, direct fixation fasteners, flangeway filler strips for
level crossings, and rubber tie boots. Window and door
glazings for passenger cars and rubber sand pipe nozzles
for locomotives. Polyethylene shims and tie pads, rubber
and plastic extrusions and mouldings.

VERIFIED

IPA

Industria Prefabbricati E Affini
Via Provinciale per Trescore, I-24050 Calcinate (BG), Italy
Tel: +39 35 442 3077   Fax: +39 35 442 3205

Works
Via Don P Bonetti 45, I-24060 Gorlago (BG), Italy
Tel: +39 35 951066   Fax: +39 35 952414

Key personnel
Executive: Enzo De Biasio

Principal subsidiary
Ipabras
Via Oswaldo Pinto Martins 260, 06900 Embû-Guacu, São
Paulo, Brazil

Products
Prestressed concrete sleepers for track and switches;
prestressed concrete slabs for track, switches, bridges,
level crossings and tramways; noise barriers.
  Recent contracts include the supply of products to
Italian Railways (FS), Milan Metro, North Milan Railway
(FNME), Barcelona Metro, and RFFSA, Brazil.

VERIFIED

JAFCO

JAFCO Tools Ltd
Queen Street, Darlaston, Wednesbury WS10 8XA, UK
Tel: +44 121 526 6363   Fax: +44 121 526 4173

Key personnel
Managing Director: Jane Anthill

Products
Track maintenance hand tools for use on electrified and
non-electrified rails; track gauges; train uncoupling bars.
  Customers include Railtrack UK and London
Underground.

NEW ENTRY

Jakem

Jakem Timbers Ltd
The Old Malt House, 125 High Street, Uckfield TN22 1EG,
UK
Tel: +44 1825 768555   Fax: +44 1825 768483

Key personnel
Director: R A Helyar

Products
Hardwood sleepers, crossing and bridge timbers.

VERIFIED

Jaraguá

Jaraguá SA, Indústrias Mecânicas
Av Mofarrej 706, 05311-903 Vila Leopoldina, São Paulo
SP, Brazil
Tel: +55 11 835 8355   Fax: +55 11 260 1581/2156

Works
Av Jaraguá 300, 18087-308 Aparecidinha, Sorocaba SP,
Brazil
Tel: +55 152 251800   Fax: +55 152 251568/1488

Jenbacher rail milling vehicle   *1997*

Key personnel
Managing Director: Hans H Klemm
Sales and Marketing Director: Irineu de Freitas
Sales Manager: Pedro Fernandes

Products
Turnouts, switches and crossings.

VERIFIED

Jarvis Facilities

Jarvis Facilities Ltd
Hudson House, Toft Green, York Y01 1HS, UK
Tel: +44 1904 522522   Fax: +44 1904 523271

Key personnel
Managing Director: Bob Clark
Director, Infrastructure: Noel Broadbent
Commercial Director: Rob Johnson
Director, Technical Services: David Painter
Director, Strategic Development: Peter Richardson
Finance Director: Steve Hurrell

Corporate development
Jarvis Facilities is the railway engineering and facilities
management arm of Jarvis plc. There are 12 regional
offices and 45 depots throughout the UK. Jarvis acquired
Fastline (qv) and Relayfast (qv) in 1997.

Services
Inspection, repair, installation and maintenance of
buildings, structures and infrastructure. A rapid-response
emergency service is available.

UPDATED

Jenbacher

Jenbacher Energiesysteme AG
Achenseestrasse 1-3, A-6200 Jenbach, Austria
Tel: +43 5244 6000   Fax: +43 5244 61101

Key personnel
See main entry in *Locomotives and powered passenger
vehicles* section

Products
Development, design, production and sales of testing and
recording cars, infrastructure testing cars, trackbed
(vacuum) cleaning cars and rail milling machines. The
infrastructure testing and recording car is an air
conditioned measuring vehicle developed and built in co-
operation with Plasser & Theurer, suitable for operation at
speeds up to 250 km/h.
  The trackbed cleaning car for metro and tram systems
is a four-axle diesel-powered bidirectional vehicle. A
cleaning car has been delivered to the Vienna Metro.
  Jenbacher's rail milling machine rides on six axles, is
diesel-powered and features a hydrostatic transmission. It
operates at a speed of 5 km/h.

VERIFIED

Kalyn Siebert

Kalyn Siebert Inc
PO Box 758, Gatesville, Texas 76528, USA
Tel: +1 817 865 7235   Fax: +1 817 865 7234
Email: john@kalyntx.com

Key personnel
Sales Manager: Wes Chandler
Advertising Manager: John Cope

Kalyn Siebert road trailer for the transport of rail vehicles   *1995*

Products

Road trailers for the transport of rail vehicles, with hydraulically operated folding goose-necks for loading and unloading.

Contracts include supply of 12 tonne tactical van semitrailers and tilt deck fork lift transport trailers to TACOM. A five-year contract with GSA has been signed for 75 tonne lowbed semitrailers.

UPDATED

Kango

Kango Ltd
12 Flag Business Exchange, Vicarage Farm Road, Peterborough PE1 5TX, UK
Tel: +44 1733 866200   Fax: +44 1733 866266

Key personnel

General Manager: G Torssell
Marketing and Export Sales Manager: A Bröms
UK Sales and Marketing Manager: B Smith
Quality and Technical Manager: V K Lilly

Products

Ballast tampers; petrol, diesel and LPG generators; hand-held stone blowers; electropneumatic hammers; petrol-driven hammers and cut-off saws.

VERIFIED

Kaufmann

A Kaufmann AG
Pilatusstrasse 2, CH-6300 Zug, Switzerland
Tel: +41 41 711 6700   Fax: +41 41 855 1704

Products

Specialist engineering products for railways, including a complete range of non-screwed rail clamps and rail connectors for various rail profiles and sections of 4 to 240 mm²; various fastenings for lineside cables and wires; special welding electrodes for copper welding; special earthing connectors; complete range of welding connectors in 35 and 50 mm². KAZU-type tunnel catenary supports.

UPDATED

KIHN

Ateliers de Constructions KIHN Sarl
17 rue de l'Usine, L-3701 Rumelange, Luxembourg
Tel: +352 56 47711   Fax: +352 56 5854

Key personnel

Manager: Jean Pierre Allegrucci
Export Sales Engineer: Jose Chartier

Products

Engineering and supply of turnouts, points and crossings, crossovers and junctions, trackwork combinations, monobloc and welded frogs, diamond crossings, expansion joints, glued insulated joints and special layouts for urban transport systems, main line railways and industrial network.

VERIFIED

Kirow

Kirow Leipzig GmbH
Spinnereistrasse 13, D-04179 Leipzig, Germany
Tel: +49 341 49530
Fax: +49 341 477 3274/495 3125

Key personnel

Managing Director: L Koehne
Technical Director: W Köllner
Marketing Director: J Kühn

Corporate development

In 1997 Kirow took over Kocks Krane International, which specialises in container cranes and heavy lift cranes. it also acquired Kranbau Eberswalde, which also manufactures cranes.

Kaufmann non-screwed rail clamp   1997

Products

Cranes for tracklaying, breakdowns and accidents. The latest model is the KRC 900 rail-based rescue crane.

Recent contracts include supply of 80 t breakdown cranes to Tanzania and Ghana, and a 200 t breakdown crane to Korea. Ghana is also taking delivery of a KRC 900 crane.

Cranes have also been supplied to SBB and to USA.

Within the last three years Kirow has delivered 50 railway cranes to countries within the CIS.

UPDATED

Kloos Railway Systems

Kloos Railway Systems BV
West Kinderdijk 24, NL-2953 XW Alblasserdam, Netherlands
Tel: +31 78 691 4000   Fax: +31 78 691 4542

Key personnel

Managing Director: J van Houwelingen

Products

Design, development, construction and delivery of standard and custom-built track materials for railways, tram systems, metros, cranes and heavy-duty systems including: turnouts, crossings, points, expansion joints and special constructions.

Recent contracts include the supply of track materials to operators in Egypt, Germany, Indonesia and the Netherlands.

VERIFIED

Knox Kershaw

Knox Kershaw Inc
PO Box 4100, Montgomery, Alabama 36103, USA
Tel: +1 262 0851   Fax: +1 263 1772

Main works

1650 North McDonough Street, Montgomery, Alabama 36104, USA

Key personnel

Chief Executive Officer: J Knox Kershaw
President: C David Wachs
Sales Manager: Thomas L Pair

Products

Ballast regulators, repair kits, improved performance kits, ballast undercutter/cleaners, railway cranes, equipment for sleeper and rail replacement, sand and snow removal, vegetation control and various other maintenance operations.

Sales are made to many USA railways.

UPDATED

Kirow rail-mounted KRC 900 rescue crane for Tanzania   1997

Krautkrämer

Krautkrämer GmbH & Co
Robert Bosch Strasse 3, D-50354 Hürth, Germany
Tel: +49 2233 6010   Fax: +49 2233 601402

Products

Stationary installations for non-destructive testing of rails and axles using ultrasonics; portable ultrasonic flaw detectors for manual inspection of rails, axles and wheels.

VERIFIED

Künzler

Künzler Jau AG, 3426 Aefligen, Switzerland
Tel: +41 34 445 14 84   Fax: +41 34 445 53 42

Key personnel

Sales Manager: Kurt Beck

Products

Inspection tower capable of running on rails or highways. The telescopic tower can be used for repairs to overhead catenary, lamps, tunnel roofs and bridges, both under and over the line.

NEW ENTRY

Laser Rail

Laser Rail Ltd
Jessop House, 39 Smedley Street East, Matlock DE4 3FQ
Tel: +44 1629 760750
Fax: +44 1629 760751

Key personnel

Director: David M Johnson

Corporate development

Laser Rail was established in 1989 by David Johnson in response to a rapidly growing need to manage the implementation of new technology into the commercial rail environment.

Products

Interactive track design gauging system software for gauging applications, including route enhancement. Computerised systems for designing track geometry, for both renewal and maintenance. Track geometry measurement and database systems for track assessment, redesign and monitoring of both track performance and maintenance machinery.

Laser Rail operates a range of computer facilities as part of its services. It also provides training and certification to various levels of competency and is available in-house and can be supplied as part of the overall support package.

UPDATED

Lindapter

Lindapter International
A member of the Steels and Engineering Division of Glynwed International
Lindsay House, Brackenbeck Road, Bradford BD7 2NF, UK
Tel: +44 1274 521444   Fax: +44 1274 521130
e-mail: lindapter@dial.pipex.com

Key personnel

Director: Gordon Browning
Marketing Manager: Neil Tilsley
Export Sales Manager: Malcolm Eastwood
Technical Support Manager: Michael Knight

Products

Holdfast adjustable rail clips, including 'soft' clips to hold the rail in precise alignment whilst accomodating rail wave; 'hard' clips to prevent vertical rail movement when used in slow-speed applications; and 'spring' clips to cater for rail wave whilst holding the rail down. Type BR clips for flat bottom and bridge rails on slopes up to 8°. Temporary support system to support and insulate running rails during repairs. Fixing products for catenary systems, bridge signage, station monitors and anti-vandal screens.

Contracts include Rome Metro, London Underground Ltd, Channel Tunnel and East Coast main line, UK.

UPDATED

Linsinger

Linsinger Maschinenbau GesmbH
Dr Linsinger Strasse 24, A-4662 Steyrermühl, Austria
Tel: +43 7613 24110   Fax: +43 7613 244138

Key personnel

Managing Director: Ing H Riepl
Technical Manager: D I Pomikacsek
Marketing: Hermann Pamminger

Products

Mobile rail milling machine with post grinding and measuring equipment.

VERIFIED

Loram

Loram Maintenance of Way, Inc
PO Box 188, 3900 Arrowhead Drive, Hamel, Minnesota 55340, USA
Tel: +1 612 478 6014   Fax: +1 612 478 6916

Key personnel

Vice-President, Worldwide Sales & Market Development:
  Don A Powell
Manager, International: T L Smith
General Manager (Australia): P S Sroba
General Manager (Europe): J Kuchler

Principal subsidiaries

Loram Rail Ltd, UK
Loram Pty Ltd, Australia
Loram Srl, Italy

Products

Manufacture of rail grinding, ditching, shoulder ballast cleaning, automatic wheel inspection and track profile measurement equipment. Contract services for railways, metros and LRT systems.

UPDATED

Lord

Lord Corporation
Mechanical Products Division
2000 West Grandview Blvd, PO Box 10040, Erie, Pennsylvania 16514-0040, USA
Tel: +1 814 868 5424   Fax: +1 814 868 3109

Key personnel

See entry in *Bogies and suspensions, wheels and axles* section

Products

Elastomeric direct fixation fasteners. Manufactured in a variety of designs for new and existing transit systems, they are installed at grade, below grade and on elevated structures, and are fully tested and qualified by user transit authorities. The mid-range direct fixation fastener vertical spring rate ranges from 100,000 to 300,000 lb/in^2, the low-range (soft) direct fixation fastener from 60,000 to 90,000 lb/in^2, and the mid-range special trackwork fastener's vertical spring rate is comparable to that of the mid-range direct fixation fastener. Rail clamping systems are available for aerial and rigid installations.

VERIFIED

Lucchini Group Railway Sector

Lucchini Siderurgica SpA
Via Oberdan 1/A, I-25127 Brescia, Italy
Tel: +39 30 39921   Fax: +39 30 3384065

Key personnel

See entry in *Bogies and suspensions, wheels and axles* section

Products (Piombino Works)

Rails from 27 to 60 kg/m.

UPDATED

Lukas

Lukas Hydraulic GmbH & Co Kg
A Unit of the Idex Corporation
Weinstrasse 39, D-91058, Erlangen, Germany
Tel: +49 91 31 6980   Fax: +49 91 31 698394

Key personnel

Sales Manager: Herr V Kirchner

Products

Development and manufacture of hydraulic rerailing equipment for rolling stock.

Lukas rerailing equipment allows for precise lifting and rerailing to within one milimetre. Lukas also makes equipment for uprighting overturned rolling stock. It also makes a pulling device for pulling apart rolling stock, either from each other or from tunnel/bridge walls.

Lukas rescue tools and pneumatic lifting bags are in worldwide use.

NEW ENTRY

Lyudinovo Locomotive Works JSC

Lyudinovo Locomotive Works JSC
1 K Liebknecht Street, Lyudinovo, Kaluga region 249400, Russia
Tel: +7 084 44 20120/25259   Fax: +7 084 44 20120/25259

Key personnel

See entry in *Locomotives and powered passenger vehicles* section

Products

Rail lubricating machines, rotary snow-ploughs, track maintenance cars.

VERIFIED

Mannesmann

Mannesmann Demag Fördertechnik AG Gottwald
PO Box 180343, D-40570 Düsseldorf, Germany
Tel: +49 211 71090   Fax: +49 211 7109651

Key personnel

Managing Director: Dr D V Kelp
Sales Manager: M Hoberg

Products

Railway cranes for any track and loading gauge. Designed in accordance with maximum permissible axle and wheel loads, they offer SWL ratings up to 300 tonnes, minimum tail radii, hauling speeds up to 120 km/h, self-propelled speeds up to 100 km/h and a range of brake systems and buffers or couplers to suit.

Recent contracts cover track maintenance cranes for private contractors as well as eight heavy breakdown cranes for India.

UPDATED

Manoir Industries

Manoir Industries
2 rue de St Petersbourg, F-75008 Paris, France
Tel: +33 1 44 69 88 10   Fax: +33 1 44 70 09 19

Main works

Outreau Plant, PO Box 119, F-62230 Outreau, France
Tel: +33 3 21 99 53 00   Fax: +33 3 21 99 53 03

Key personnel

Plant Manager: Daniel Pain
Sales Manager: Jean Viallon
Railway Department: Jean Viallon

Principal subsidiary

Socarec, France

Products

Cast monobloc, manganese steel crossings to AREA and UIC specifications; welded crossings; cast cradles for movable point crossings; cast bodies and tongues for tram systems; track components for metro systems.

VERIFIED

Matériel de Voie

Le Matériel de Voie SA
Le Parc du Saint Laurent, Immeuble Toronto,
54 route de Sartrouville, F-78230 Le Pecq, France
Tel: +33 1 30 15 24 24   Fax: +33 1 30 15 24 00

Key personnel
Communications Manager: D Fougeray

Products
Rails, fishplates, baseplates, steel sleepers.

VERIFIED

Matisa

Matisa Matériel Industriel SA
PO Box 58, CH-1023 Crissier, Switzerland
Tel: +41 21 631 2111   Fax: +41 21 631 2168

Key personnel
Managing Director: Rainer von Schack
Technical Director: Jörg Ganz
Director (Marketing): Yvan Caffari

Principal subsidiaries
In Italy, Germany, Spain, Japan, France

Products
Track construction and maintenance machinery, including tamper-leveller-liners (continuous, conventional, combined for points and crossings and plain track); regulators with and without hoppers; tracklaying and track renewal trains; ballast cleaners; track geometry recording and analysis vehicles; track service vehicles; on-track rail grinders.
A multipurpose self-propelled track measuring vehicle, the M2000, is able to record several parameters including track geometry, rail profile, rail corrugation and catenary position.

UPDATED

Matisa SpA

Matisa SpA
Via Ardeatina km 21, I-00040 Pomezia S Palomba Rome, Italy
Tel: +39 6 9198 4612   Fax: +39 6 9198 4574

Key personnel
Chairman: F Carboni Corner
Managing Director: R Naggar

Products
Light tamping and lining machines, ballast regulators, line and switch portal crane, service vehicles from 15 to 800 hp, mechanical and hydraulic coach-screwing machines, portable sleeper drill, sleeper drilling machine, rail drilling machine, double positioning rail drilling machine, rail cutting machine, rail grinding machine, light trolley, lightweight ballast tamping unit with vibrating blades, and portable tools and implements for railway track maintenance.

VERIFIED

Matix Saferail

Matix Saferail SA
2 Arc-en-Ciel, CH-1023 Crissier, Switzerland
Tel: +41 21 634 9934   Fax: +41 21 634 3572

Key personnel
Marketing Manager: V E Peter

Principal subsidiary
Matix Industries SA
Zone Industrielle des Sablons, F-89100 Sens, France

Products
Machines and equipment for stationary rail regeneration and long welded new rails, stationary ultrasonic flaw detection equipment, portable rail joint straightness measuring/recording equipment.

VERIFIED

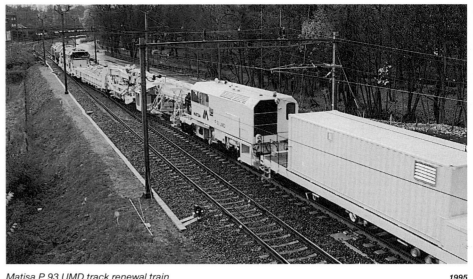

Matisa P 93 UMD track renewal train   **1995**

McGregor

McGregor Paving
A division of Norwest Holst Construction Ltd
Astral House, Imperial Way, Watford WD2 4YX, UK
Tel: +44 1923 233433   Fax: +44 1923 256481

Main works
87 New Square, Chesterfield S40 1AH, UK
Tel: +44 1246 276971   Fax: +44 1246 207680

Key personnel
Managing Director: D A L Joyce

Products
In collaboration with British Rail's Research Division, Robert McGregor developed PACT — the Paved Concrete Track system. PACT is an alternative to conventional ballasted track.
The system consists of a continuously reinforced concrete slab which provides a continuous support to the rails through a resilient rail pad. Main advantages of the system are its shallow depth of construction and that it ensures that the track geometry remains within tolerance over long periods. The PACT system has been in service for over 25 years throughout the world.
Contracts involved installation of PACT through the 14 km Rogers Pass Tunnel, the longest rail tunnel in North America; and in Sandling Tunnel, Kent as part of Channel Tunnel route clearance work for Railtrack.

UPDATED

Mecanoexportimport

Mecanoexportimport SA
30 Dacia Blvd, Bucharest, Romania
Tel: +40 1 211 9855   Fax: +40 1 210 7894

Key personnel
See entry in *Locomotives and powered passenger vehicles* section

Products
Permanent way materials including screws, fishplates, baseplates, steel sleepers, turnouts, switches, points and crossings, guardrails and rail clips.

VERIFIED

Mer Mec

Mer Mec SpA
Via Oberdan 70, I-70043 Monopoli (BA), Italy
Tel: +39 80 777977   Fax: +39 80 777085

Key personnel
General Manager: Vito Pertosa
Sales Manager: Mario Girolami
International Sales Manager: Stefano Cavicchia
Production Manager: Antonio Nitti

Products
Railway and road/rail vehicles for infrastructure maintenance; railway infrastructure analysis systems and vehicles.
Recent contracts include the supply of 30 road/rail excavators and 12 ladder trolleys to Italian Railways (FS).

VERIFIED

Millbrook Proving Ground

Millbrook Proving Ground Ltd
Millbrook, Near Ampthill, Bedford MK45 2JQ, UK
Tel: +44 1525 404242   Fax: +44 1525 403420
Web: http://www.millbrook.co.uk

Key personnel
Principal Rail Engineer: Vaughan Phillips

Products
Mobile and laboratory testing services for rail vehicles, including whole-vehicle crash testing, emissions development testing, system durability and refinement analysis.
Recent projects include diesel multiple-unit crash testing and Hyge Sled crash simulations on seats and occupants.

NEW ENTRY

Mitchell Equipment Corporation

Mitchell Equipment Corporation
16 Ballantyne Road, Kewdale, Western Australia 6105, Australia
Tel: +61 9 350 6363   Fax: +61 9 451 4516

Key personnel
Managing Director: A G Evans
Marketing Manager: G R Birkbeck
Sales Engineer: P A N Hayes

Principal subsidiary
Mitchell Equipment Corporation, Toledo, Ohio, USA

Products
All road/rail vehicular conversion equipment; insulated fishplate joints, switchblade slide pads; specialised track insulation.
Current contracts include vehicles for V/Line, Westrail Australia; New Zealand Rail and equipment for the State Railway of Thailand.

VERIFIED

Mitsukawa

Mitsukawa Metal Works Co Ltd
21 Harima-cho-nijima, Kako district, Hyogo Pref, Japan
Tel: +81 794 35 2288   Fax: +81 3 3284 0361

Key personnel
Sales Director: K Kukuda

Products
Rail fastenings, steel sleepers and forged crossings.

VERIFIED

Modern Track Machinery

Modern Track Machinery Canada Ltd
5926 Shawson Drive, Mississauga, Ontario L4W 3W5,
Canada
Tel: +1 905 546 1211　Fax: +1 905 564 1217

Key personnel
President: Claude Geismar
General Manager: B Pingel
International Sales Manager: M J Byrne

Principal subsidiary
Modern Track Machinery Inc
1415 Davis Road, Elgin, Illinois 60123-1375, USA
Tel: +1 847 697 7510　Fax: +1 847 697 0136
General Manager: John W Fox

Products
Track construction and maintenance machines and tools;
road/rail vehicles; motor trolleys.

UPDATED

Monterrey

Monterrey Industrial Ferroviaria SA de CV
Avenue Insurgentes Sur 2462, CO 01070 Villa Alvaro
Obregón, Mexico, DF
Tel: +52 5 550 4605/8377/616 2382
Fax: +52 5 550 6915
Email: meraco@internet.com.mx

Main works
Dia del Empresario 999, PO Box 1012, CP 67110, CD
Guadalupe, NL, Mexico
Phone: +52 64 9766/64 8888　Fax: +52 83 649717

Key personnel
President: Felipe Zirion Quijano
Vice-President, Marketing: Carlos López Patan
Sales Manager: Sergio Torres Loya
Plant Manager: Adolfo Pérez Murillo

Principal subsidiary
Cia Mexicana de Material para Ferrocarril, SA de CV
Miner y Mendez de Mexico, SA de CV

Products
Turnout sets for all rail sections, solid manganese or
assembled frogs, switch points, guardrails, plates, heel
plates and switch stands (to AREA and European
standards).

UPDATED

Moore & Steele

Moore & Steele Corporation
PO Box 189, Oswego, New York 13827, USA
Tel: +1 607 687 2751　Fax: +1 607 687 3914

Key personnel
President: S M Lounsberry III

Products
Rail lubrication systems including hydraulic and
electronic wayside lubricators, mobile lubricators
mounted on road/rail vehicles and bulk lubricant
dispensing systems.

VERIFIED

Moss Systems

Moss Systems Ltd
Moss House, North Heath Lane, Horsham, West Sussex,
RH12 5QE, UK
Tel: +44 1403 259511　Fax: +44 1403 217746
Email: mcl@moss.co.uk

Key personnel
Sales Manager: John Boyle
Group Marketing Communications Manager:
　Carol Heaton

Capabilities
Civil engineering 3-D modelling system. Gauging software
for accurate measurement of tunnels, bridges and other
structures.
　Introduced in 1996 was RailMOSS, a tailored package
for track design.

UPDATED

MTH Praha

MTH Praha as
Na Pankráci 58, CZ-140 00 Prague 4, Czech Republic
Tel: +42 2 61304 902　Fax: +42 2 61304 981/82/84

Key personnel
President: Petr Lukeš
General Director: Petr Wagenknecht
Director, Sales: Paval Türk
Vice-Director, Sales: Ladislav Novotný

Indian joint venture company
MTH Praha AS
Technip MTH-Strojexport India Private Ltd
212-215 Tolstoy House, 17 Tolstoy Marg, New Delhi
　110-001
Tel: +91 11 335 5618/5626/331 7800/4130
Fax: +91 11 372 1223/371 4463

Key personnel
Managing Director: S K Mandal

Products
Manufacture of permanent way maintenance machines
and equipment including ballast cleaners, ballast wagons
and ballast distribution systems; track stabilisers;
catenary maintenance vehicles; ballast compactors;
brush cutters; track recording cars; motor cars and power
units; hand tools.
　Contracts include the supply of maintenance
equipment to Russia, USA, Austria, India and Slovakia.

UPDATED

NARSTCO

North American Railway Steel Tie Corporation
39601 Galbraith Road, PO Box 1989, Squamish, BC
V0N 3G0 Canada
Tel: +1 604 590 0008　Fax: +1 604 590 9278

Key personnel
President & CEO: David Broadbent
Vice-President Marketing & Technical Services:
　Dino Piovesan
Vice-President, Operations & Engineering: Sean Keightley

Products
Design, manufacture and supply of steel track and turnout
sleepers. Steel sleepers are available in H10 and H12
heavy-haul steel sleeper sections, and M10 for lighter
traffic. Steel turnout sleeper sets are available as full,
partial and blank, all complete with fastenings. Insulated
and non-insulated packages are available to any custom
length. Also supply of steel sleeper fastening systems.
　Recent contracts include the supply of sleepers to
Union Pacific, Southern Pacific, BC Rail and Illinois
Central with steel track and turnout sleepers.

NEW ENTRY

Newag

Newag GmbH & Co KG
Ripshorster Strasse 321, D-46117 Oberhausen, Germany
Tel: +49 208 865030　Fax: +49 208 865 0320

Key personnel
See entry in *Locomotives and powered passenger
vehicles* section

Newag track maintenance vehicle　　　**1995**

Products
Track motor cars; personnel and platform trolleys;
multipurpose and custom-built cars and trolleys; special
purpose trains such as ballast and dirt handling trains for
ballast cleaners and wagon-mounted mobile concrete
plants for foundation work on bridges, tunnels, and for
electrification; hi-rail road/rail vehicles and cranes;
remanufacture of tampers, levellers and liners for all
gauges; ballast regulators and cleaners; gantries; rail
positioners; rail lifters and threaders.
　Newly developed is the MK Tool wear-resistant tamping
tines, reinforced with tungsten carbide.

UPDATED

Nippon Kido Kogyo

Nippon Kido Kogyo Co Ltd
Meiho Building 21-1 Nishi Shinjuku 1-chome, Shinjuku-ku,
Tokyo 160, Japan
Tel: +81 3 3343 8322　Fax: +81 3 3349 8705

Works
Tone Factory, PO 306, 77 Nakatashinden, Koga, Ibaraki,
Japan
Tel: +81 280 480 7335　Fax: +81 280 483184

Key personnel
Managing Director: A Nakano

Products
Precast concrete slab for level crossings, concrete
sleepers, rail fastenings.

VERIFIED

NKK

NKK Corporation
1-1-2 Marunouchi, Chiyoda-ku, Tokyo 100, Japan
Tel: +81 3 3217 2244　Fax: +81 3 3214 8417

Key personnel
President: Shunkichi Miyoshi
Export Director: Kiyoshi Kishi

Products
Rail to meet all internationally recognised specifications
including AREA, ASTM, UIC, BS, JIS and others.
　NKK produces two types of premium rail, the Thicker
Head-Hardened 370N (THH370N) and Thicker Head-
Hardened 370A (THH370A) with low alloy, by an online
typed heat treatment process. The top surfaces of these
rails feature Brinell hardness (H_B) values of 341 to 388,
and H_B 351 to 405, respectively. The steel is produced by
a continuous casting machine including a vacuum
degassing process. THH370N and THH370A rails have
been supplied to the USA, Canada and other countries.
For domestic users, NKK produces 50 m long standard
carbon rails.
　NKK also has extensive experience in providing rail
welding technology, both for hardware and software, and
welding services. The enclosed arc welding repair of high-
speed Shinkansen track is performed chiefly by NKK. The
company has developed an automatic rail welding
machine, the Rail Welding Robot, for field welding of rail.
This machine has been developed by applying the high-
speed rotating arc welding method to enclosed arc
welding.
　Recent contracts include the supply of rail to operators
in Japan, USA, Canada, China, Thailand, Taiwan, Korea,
Australia, Brazil and the Russian Federation.

VERIFIED

Nomix-Chipman

Chipman Rail plc
The Goods Yard, Horsham RH12 2NR, UK
Tel: +44 1403 260341　Fax: +44 1403 264799

Corporate developments
The company changed its name and moved premises in
September 1996.

Key personnel
Operations Manager: James Burgess
Head of Engineering: Steve Chambers
Safety Manager: Reg Weeks

Products
Equipment and technology for track weed control, drain
clearing, leaf jetting and sandite application.　*VERIFIED*

Noord-Ned

Noord-Nederlandsche Machinefabriek BV
St Vitusstraat 81, PO Box 171, NL-9670 AD Winschoten,
Netherlands
Tel: +31 5970 15225   Fax: +31 5970 54211

Key personnel
Sales Manager: P E A Nankmann

Products
The multipurpose Noord-Ned Railhopper for track and
overhead contact wire maintenance units.

The Railhopper is a self-powered rail vehicle fitted with
steel crawlers, which make it a cross-country vehicle
capable of moving itself on and off the rails. Once on the
rails it runs on four wheels. It moves up to the rails at right
angles. As soon as the vehicle starts crossing the first rail
a support comes out at the rear, which puts the vehicle in
a level position. At the front a slide arm is pushed across
the second rail to prevent the crawlers from dropping
between the rails. Two position hooks block the
railhopper as soon as its railwheels are in a position above
the rails. When the wheels are lowered the support, the
slide arm and the position hooks automatically return to
their original position. Maximum speed on rails is
40 km/h. When it is operated from its aerial platform,
however, its rail running speed is automatically limited to
5 km/h. The aerial platform can be raised to a maximum
height of 9 m above the rails without any extra support
being necessary. The assembly is insulated up to 1,500 V.
The diesel engine is 49 hp and the drive hydrostatic.

VERIFIED

Nordco

Nordco
182 W Oklahoma Avenue, Milwaukee, Wisconsin 53207,
USA
Tel: +1 414 769 4600   Fax: +1 414 481 3199

Key personnel
President: Don Himes
Marketing Manager: Steve Wiedenfeld

Products
Self-propelled adzers, rail drills, spike hammers, hydraulic
spike pullers, tie drills, gauging machines, hydra-spikers,
rail lifters, rail gang spikers, X-level indicators, track
inspectors, two-tie screw spacers, anchor removers,
anchor applicators.

UPDATED

NRS

National Railway Supplies
Gresty Road, Crewe CW2 6EH, UK
Tel: +44 1270 533000   Fax: +44 1270 533956

Key personnel
See entry in *Signalling and telecommunications systems*
section

Products
Manufacture, procurement, servicing, repair and
distribution of electronic, electromechanical and
engineering products for railway infrastructure.

Recent contracts include the supply of products to
Railtrack and the former British Rail Infrastructure
Maintenance and Track Renewal Units, UK.

UPDATED

NS Materieel

NS Materieel BV
PO Box 2025, NL-3500 Utrecht, Netherlands
Tel: +31 30 235 7772/4711   Fax: +31 30 235 4901/8541

Key personnel
Director: Kees Ahling

Products
Ultrasonic testing car, able to record at 140 km/h under
own power and at 200 km/h when towed by another
vehicle.

The measuring system was designed by NS, Holland
and based on a grill-express car from SNCF.

NEW ENTRY

Oleo fixed-stop energy absorbers   *1995*

Oleo

Oleo International Ltd
PO Box 216, Grovelands Estate, Longford Road, Exhall,
Coventry CV7 9NE, UK
Tel: +44 1203 645555   Fax: +44 1203 645777

Key personnel
See entry in *Freight vehicles and equipment* section

Products
Oleo produces a wide range of long-stroke hydraulic
buffers suitable for mounting on fixed or sliding end-
stops. Applications include freight yards, steelworks and
passenger terminals.

On sliding friction end-stops the need for continual
resetting of the friction elements is eliminated, and the
hydraulic buffers absorb all of the impact energy at low
speeds. Typically a 400 tonne train may be arrested by a
pair of 800 mm stroke buffers at 6 km/h without causing
the end-stop to slide. Initial and final jerk forces are also
eliminated. These buffer units are available for all types of
rail operation from LRVs to heavy freight.

VERIFIED

OLMI

OLMI SpA
Viale Europa 29, 24020 Suisio (Bg), Italy
Tel: +39 35 999 333   Fax: +39 35 999 261
Email: sleepers@olmi.it

Key personnel
Divisional Director: Andrea Montagni
Project Manager: Walter Cavadini

Products
Design, construction and installation and after-sales
service of concrete sleeper manufacturing systems, for
both main line and turnouts.

NS Materieel ultrasonic testing vehicle at Utrecht
rail station   *1997*

Recent contracts include supply of sleepers to railways
in Italy, Spain, Poland, Belgium, Czech Republic, Slovenia
and China.

To date, Olmi has designed and installed 14
manufacturing plants for rail sleepers and four for turnout
sleepers in Italy, Belgium, Slovenia, China, Poland and the
Czech Republic.

NEW ENTRY

ORTEC

ORTEC Gesellschaft für Schienentechnische Systeme
GmbH
Mühlenweg 25, D-51588 Nümbrecht, Germany
Tel: +49 2293 91040   Fax: +49 2293 910431

Key personnel
Managing Director: Hermann Ortwein

Products
Vibration-insulating rail fasteners, Whisper Rail
continuous elastic rail, noise insulation material.

UPDATED

Orton/McCullough

Orton/McCullough Crane Company
1244 East Market Street, PO Box 830, Huntington,
Indiana 46750, USA
Tel: +1 219 356 7900   Fax: +1 219 356 7902

Key personnel
President: J F McCullough

Products
Cranes and heavy lifting gear.

UPDATED

Osmose

Osmose Railroad Division
PO Box 8276, Madison, Wisconsin 53708, USA
Tel: +1 608 221 2292   Fax: +1 608 221 0618

Key personnel
Vice-President: Ken Norton
Products Manager: David Ostby

Products
ADZ-PAD® biodegradable preservative pads to prevent
decay of sleeper plate areas; NONFLAM® spray-on fire
retardant coating for use on creosote-treated wood;
Excalibur plugging system for open spike or boltholes in
timber sleepers.

UPDATED

Pandrol Jackson stoneblower   **1997**

Palfinger

Palfinger Hebetechnik
Moosmühlstrasse 1, A-5203 Köstendorf/Salzburg, Austria
Tel: +43 6216 7660   Fax: +43 6216 7763

Key personnel
Managing Director: Heinrich Gollegger

Products
Cranes (1 to 75 tonne lifting moment), aerial platforms for catenary inspection, positioning for overhead wires and carrying cable.

VERIFIED

Pandrol Jackson

Pandrol Jackson Inc
200 South Jackson Road, Ludington, Michigan 49431, USA
Tel: +1 616 843 3431   Fax: +1 616 843 4830

Pandrol Jackson Contract Services
309 Clark Street, East Syracuse, New York 13057, USA
Tel: +1 315 437 2547   Fax: +1 315 463 0180

Works
Pandrol Jackson Ultrasonic Development Centre
28 Eagle Road, Danbury, Connecticut 06810, USA
Tel: +1 203 778 6811   Fax: +1 203 778 8670

Key personnel
President: A R Zaydel
Executive Vice-President: R J Orrow
Senior Vice-President, Contracted Services, Marketing and International Sales: F Brady
Vice-President, North American Sales: P Brown

Associate company
Pandrol Jackson Ltd
63 Station Road, Addlestone KT15 2AR
Tel: +44 1932 834500   Fax: +44 1932 850858

Key personnel
Director: L P Hawker

Products
Design and manufacture of track maintenance machines including production grinders, point and crossing grinders and tamping machines and sleeper changers; ultrasonic equipment, including rail flaw detection cars; contract services for measurement of rail corrugation and for production and point and crossing grinding.

Developments include automatic rail flaw detection systems; laser systems for *in situ* measurement of rail profiles to provide data for the planning of rail maintenance; and a stone-blowing system for track levelling.

UPDATED

Pandrol Rail Fastenings

Pandrol Rail Fastenings Ltd
63 Station Road, Addlestone, Weybridge KT15 2AR, UK
Tel: +44 1932 834500   Fax: +44 1932 850858

Key personnel
Managing Director: G M Lodge
Marketing Director: J Beal-Preston

Principal subsidiaries
Pandrol Australia Pty Ltd, Blacktown, Australia
Pandrol Avaux SA, Anderlues, Belgium
Pandrol Canada Ltd, Montréal, Canada
Promorail SA, Paris, France
PT Pandrol Indonesia, Jakarta, Indonesia
Pandrol Italia SpA, Teramo, Italy
Pandrol Daewon Ltd, Seoul, Republic of Korea
Pandrol UK Ltd, Worksop, UK
Pandrol Incorporated, Bridgeport, USA
Vortok International Ltd, Addlestone, UK

Products
Design and manufacture of track fastening systems and associated installation equipment; resilient rail pads; Vortok Coils for restoring worn screwspike holes (see entry for Vortok International).

Pandrol Fastclip rail fastening system on turnouts installed on NSB's Gardermoen Airport rail link, Norway   **1997**

Pandrol continues its research into the dynamic behaviour of track to increase understanding of the relationship between forces in track and component performance, and of the generation of noise and vibration. Pandrol has developed a new range of fastening designs for specific applications, including the Pandrol Fastclip system, which is designed for low-cost installation and maintenance.

UPDATED

Permali

Permali Gloucester Ltd
Bristol Road, Gloucester GL1 5TT, UK
Tel: +44 1452 528282   Fax: +44 1452 507409
Email: @permali—gloucester.ltd.uk

Key personnel
See entry in *Passenger coach equipment* section

Product
Insulated rail joints and rail end posts in wood and glass composite.

Recent contracts include the supply of insulated rail joints to Perumka, Indonesia and OSE, Greece.

UPDATED

Permaquip

The permanent way equipment and services Co Ltd
1 Giltway, Giltbrook, Nottingham NG16 2GQ, UK
Tel: +44 115 938 7000/7005   Fax: +44 115 938 7001

Key personnel
Managing Director: Tony Withers
Divisional Technical Director: Bryce Randall
UK Area Sales Manager: Alan Leyland

Corporate development
Permaquip is part of Fairmont Tamper, a Harsco company.

Products
Design and manufacture of tools, plant and vehicles for infrastructure maintenance and construction. Products, including those of Fairmont Tamper, are available for sale, lease or hire.

Sleeper handling: hand tools and plant for moving, machining and changing wooden and concrete sleepers, including a portable sleeper squarer/spacer.

Rail handling: Ironman and powered rail pullers for the mechanised handling of rail and Continuously Welded Rail (CWR) within or outside track possessions; rail threaders, rail joint straighteners and specialised rail carrying vehicles.

Stressing CWR: hydraulic tensors for all-weather control of stressing CWR, including obstructionless types with lightweight power packs; weld trimmers for track

Permaquip high-capacity trolley supplied to New Jersey Transit   **1997**

Land Rover converted to road/rail by Permaquip   **1997**

welding and accessories; self-contained mobile welding workshops for CWR maintenance.

Track maintenance and construction: tampers, ballast regulators, maintenance grinders, complete track relaying trains; Permaclipper for production rate installation and removal of Pandrol fastenings, including the Mk V Permaclipper adaptable for use with Pandrol Fastclips; slewing machines, lightweight Ironman for manual movement of points and crossings; hydraulic spike extractors.

Materials and personnel transport: a wide range of vehicles ranging from manual trolleys to road/rail trucks; on-track vehicles including tug units and general purpose Tramms; specialist vehicles for metro systems and customised personnel carriers.

Structures and overhead line maintenance: access platforms mounted on road/rail or on-track vehicles, featuring cantilever extension, creep control for driving from the elevated platform, electrical/hydraulic Power Take Off (PTO) and auxiliary lighting.

Road/rail trucks: a wide range of road vehicles can be adapted for road/rail use with the Fairmont hi-rail system of bolt-on rail guidance wheels. Fittings for road/rail trucks include cranes, access platforms, tipper bodies, rail carrying frames, drum carriers, crew cabs and trailers. General purpose road/rail trucks available for hire in the UK, including a 17 tonne GVW unit with crane and rail carrying facility.

Contract support: spares and service support; operator and contract support for specialist contract work such as stressing, joint straightening, weed control, ballast cleaning and sleeper squaring.

Newly introduced is a road/rail Land Rover hire unit. The first railway contractor to use it was Right Track Construction, which bought two units. Both units were converted by Permaquip using Hy-Rail® bolt-on rail guidance wheels to give a road vehicle road/rail capability.

Other contracts include the leasing of a high-capacity trolley with scissor-lift to New Jersey Transit Authority, USA.

UPDATED

Pettibone

Pettibone Corporation
Railroad Products Group
5401 W Grand Avenue, Chicago, Illinois 60639, USA
Tel: +1 312 745 9496   Fax: +1 312 237 3763

Main works
Pettibone Ohio, 6917 Bessemer Avenue, Cleveland, Ohio 44127, USA

Key personnel
President: Larry Klumpp
General Manager: T E Hitesman

Products
Switches, switch-points, frogs, crossings, switch stands, guardrails, rail fasteners, compromise joints, switch plates, mobile maintenance-of-way and material handling equipment.

Phoenix

Phoenix AG
PO Box 900854, Hannoversche Strasse 88, D-21079 Hamburg, Germany
Tel: +49 40 2660/2508   Fax: +49 40 7667 2545

Key personnel
See entry in *Bogies and suspensions, wheels and axles* section

Products
Elastomer trackbed matting: CentriCon and Megiflex rail fasteners; rubber groove-sealing sections for safety of rails in workshops and other pedestrian areas; rubber boots with pads; continuous rail seating; and noise-absorbing material.

Phoenix has been concerned for several years with the problems of reducing vibration in machines and vehicles, and has developed a wide range of elastomer products for vibration and noise attenuation.

UPDATED

Pintsch Bamag

Pintsch Bamag Antriebs und Verkehrstechnik GmbH
PO Box 100420, D-46524 Dinslaken, Germany
Tel: +49 2064 6020   Fax: +49 2064 602266

Key personnel
See entry in *Signalling and telecommunications* section

Products
Automatic propane-fuelled infrared and electric point-heating equipment; solid-state snow detectors.

VERIFIED

Plasser

Plasser & Theurer
Johannesgasse 3, A-1010 Vienna, Austria
Tel: +43 1 515720   Fax: +43 1 513 1801

Main works
Pummererstrasse 5, A-4021 Linz/Donau

Principal subsidiaries
Australia, Brazil, Canada, Denmark, France, Germany, Hong Kong, India, Italy, Japan, Mexico, Poland, Spain, South Africa, UK and USA

Products
Automatic track levelling, lining and tamping machines; universal point and crossing tamping machines; dynamic track stabilisers; ballast consolidating machines; ballast regulators; ballast cleaning machines; ballast suction machines; formation rehabilitation machines; track laying and relaying machines; gantry cranes; rail grinding and planing machines; track recording cars; railway motor vehicles; catenary maintenance and inspection cars; catenary renewal trains; railway cranes; special machines and lightweight equipment for track maintenance.

The Plasser & Theurer 08 and 09 Series of tamping machines offers a range of equipment to meet the most varied conditions and requirements.

The 09-32 CSM machine offers continuous tamping motion, in which only 20 per cent of the total mass is accelerated and braked because only the lifting, lining and tamping units (32 tamping tines together), positioned on a separate underframe, are moved in work cycles from sleeper to sleeper. The main frame of the machine, which carries the operator's cabin, power supply and drive for the entire machine, moves forward continuously.

The 09-3X Tamping Express is the result of experience in operation and is based on the 09CSM Series. New features of the 09-3X are two 3-sleeper track tamping units which enable, for the first time, three sleepers to be tamped in one operation. Each tamping unit consists of two separate parts to be able to work on tracks with irregular sleeper spacing, if required.

The 09-90 and 09-Super CAT machines are integrated ploughing and sweeping machines. With a multifunctional design, they can create a ballast profile with exact track geometry in just one work cycle.

The 09-Dynamic is a continuous tamping machine with integrated ploughing, sweeping and dynamic track stabilising unit.

The UNIMAT 08-275 is a levelling, lining and tamping machine for plain track, switches and crossings. It is equipped with two heavy-duty, high-pressure, universal tamping units, carrying 16 tines each. When tamping plain track, all eight tines of the tamping unit are in action in their basic position. The ballast beneath each rail/sleeper intersection is tamped in one work cycle, that is, the sleeper is tamped both inside and outside the rail simultaneously. Most points and crossings can be tamped by the tines working in pairs. The pairs of tines

VERIFIED   *Plasser 09-3X 4S Tamping Express*   **1997**

Plasser FUM catenary renewal train 1997

Pohl

Pohl Corporation
PO Box 13613, Reading, Pennsylvania 19612, USA
Tel; +1 610 926 5400   Fax: +1 610 926 1897

Key personnel
President: Walter Pohl

Products
Rail from 12 lb ASCE to 175 Crane Rail and related accessories; special trackwork and switch components; spikes; steel sleepers (ties) for narrow-gauge track for the mining industry; New Century® switch stands and replacement parts.

NEW ENTRY

Portec Inc

RMP Division
PO Box 38250, Pittsburgh, Pennsylvania 15238-8250, USA
Tel: +1 412 782 6000   Fax: +1 412 781 1037

International Sales Office
300 Windsor Drive, Oak Brook, Illinois 60521, USA
Tel: +1 708 573 4600   Fax: +1 708 573 4604

Key personnel
Senior Vice-President: John S Cooper
Manager, Marketing, Sales and Service:
   Richard J Jarosinski
Manager, International Sales: Barbara Petkus

Products
Standard and insulated rail joints; rail joint insulation; rail and flange lubricators.

VERIFIED

Portec (UK)

Portec (UK) Ltd
Vauxhall Industrial Estate, Ruabon LL14 6UY, UK
Tel: +44 1978 820820   Fax: +44 1978 821439

Key personnel
Managing Director: Graham Tarbuck
Rail Divisional Manager : Chris Twigg
Finance Director: Malcolm Neal

Products
Track-mounted rail and flange lubricators, mechanical and electrical; rail and flange lubricant; insulated rail joints; rail anchors; switch protectors and switch guides; soil and ballast environmental protection.

UPDATED

Pouget

PO Box 69, 6 allée du Val du Moulin, F-93240 Stains, France
Tel: +33 1 48 26 62 12   Fax: +33 1 48 22 37 15
Web: http://www.asiaffairs.com—pouget

Key personnel
General Manager: Robert Pouget

Pouget D-120 ballast cleaner 1995

---

can be tilted up sideways and adapted to the particular configuration of the point or crossing.

A further development is the UNIMAT 08-275 3S, equipped with three-point lifting device for maintenance of heavy design points (for example, with concrete sleepers). The pivoting design of the tamping units permits complete treatment of slanting sleepers.

The latest development is the ability of the tamping units of the UNIMAT 08-475 4S to swing out 3.2 m from the centre of the machine. This means that the departing line at points can be processed simultaneously.

The UNIMAT 09-4S machines combine the advantages of a continuous action plain line tamping machine with the features of the latest generation of a switch tamping machine with three-rail lifting and four-rail tamping.

The range of ballast distributing and grading machines in the PSR, SSP and USP series is offered to cover every type of operation.

The BDS Ballast Distribution and Storage system consists of two units, a ploughing and ballast dosing unit and a sweeping and ballast transfer unit. MFS hopper and conveyor units can be coupled between them to increase storage capacity. The BDS can insert ballast precisely on plain track and in points and crossings and collects surplus ballast for added economy.

The DGS 62 N (Dynamic Track Stabiliser) produces stabilisation of the track following tamping work, ballast cleaning or tracklaying. Using controlled stabilisation it is possible to achieve the correct settlement of the track without altering the track geometry. In this way speed restrictions are eliminated. If required, the DGS can also be fitted with a two-axle measuring trailer that meets the stability requirements for a standard design railway vehicle. In combination with a six-channel recorder, it can record the parameters that are needed to document the work done.

The RM series offers different sizes of undercutter cleaner for plain track and points.

The VM 150 Jumbo vacuum scraper/excavator provides an alternative to conventional equipment for removing material such as ballast, soil and dust, particularly where obstacles may be present. Material picked up by the rotating suction nozzle passes through a material separator and a filter chamber, and then on to a transfer conveyor belt.

The EM series offers different sizes of track measuring and recording cars for the most varied working conditions. The EM 120 self-propelled track recording and analysing car works with electronic track measuring systems which have proved their reliability under the most severe conditions.

The EM 160 self-propelled track measuring car features a non-contact track geometry measurement system for operation at speeds up to 160 km/h. The EM 250 is a complete computer-supported non-contact track analysing and recording car for speeds up to 250 km/h. A laser-based non-contact catenary measuring system can also be provided for track measuring cars.

With the APT 500, flash-butt welding, previously restricted to stationary practice, has been mobilised and can now be carried out on track. Microprocessor control guarantees consistent welding quality, even for high-alloy rails. Plasser & Theurer welding machines have been built to many varied designs and combined with track maintenance machines (mobile, self-propelled, on-track welding machines, on-/off-track welding machines, stationary and pallet-mounted units). There is a correspondingly wide range of possible applications for these machines. With the 'Super Stretch' accessory, enough power is available for any duty, including final welding far below neutral rail temperature.

The SBM 250 rail rectification (planing) machine reprofiles side and head-worn rails *in situ*. The GWM 250 is a bogie-mounted rail grinding machine with two grinding units per rail and six grinding stones per unit; the GWM 550 is a six-axle machine with five grinding units. Both machines can work on plain track, points and crossings.

The PM 200 formation rehabilitation machine excavates old ballast by excavation chain and transports it to the area ahead of the machine via conveyor belts; inserts sand via conveyor belts; grades the surface of the sand with grading plate; consolidates the sand layer with plate consolidators; and inserts fresh ballast via conveyor belts and chutes. The AHM 800 R is a formation rehabilitation machine with ballast recycling.

Plasser & Theurer applied the assembly line principle to track relaying in 1968 with the development of the SUZ 2000 track relaying train. The SUM-SMD-SVM and HUZ Series (high-speed tracklaying and relaying machines of modular design) are the present day models, which can be adapted for any conditions. The WM system is designed for relaying points and crossings without auxiliary tools, while the WTW system can transport them directly from point of manufacture to the worksite without the need to dismantle them.

In recent years, a number of machines were built for catenary maintenance, inspection and renewal. These vehicles in the OBW, MSW, MTW and FUM series were specifically tailored and equipped to the customer's needs. For high output, continuous operation catenary renewal trains were built. Machines were also built for electrification.

To meet the demands of customers, a wide range of special machines (for example sand removal machines) for track maintenance and track work is available, including all kinds of motor vehicles and single or twin-jib heavy railway cranes as well as lightweight track maintenance equipment.

UPDATED

Products

Tracklaying gantry cranes, coach-screwing machines, fishplate-bolting machines, sleeper drills, rail saws, disc rail-cutting machines, rail drills, portable vibrating tampers, rail grinders, rail loaders, sleeper adzing/drilling machines, light ballast cleaners, ballast profiling and regulating equipment, lorries, jacks, hand tools and twin-bloc steel sleepers.

Recent products include the D-120 ballast cleaner which operates at a rate of 120 m/h, powered by a 250 hp diesel engine.

UPDATED

Premesa

Premesa SA Industrio e Comercio
Av Nossa Senhora do O 565, Limão, São Paulo, Brazil
Tel: +55 11 266 8188   Fax: +55 11 210 6031

Key personnel

General Manager: José Luiz Martins
Sales Superintendent: Luiz da Costa

Products

Turnouts, crossings, switches, points, frogs, track components.

VERIFIED

P. S. Corporation

P. S. Corporation
4-1 Marunouchi 3-chome, Chiyoda-ku, Tokyo 100, Japan
Tel: +81 3 3216 1981   Fax: +81 3 3284 0361

Key personnel

President: Akira Mogi
Executive Managing Director, Marketing:
    Tameaki Nakaoji
Executive Managing Director, Engineering:
    Giichi Tanaka
Managing Director, Export Sales: Matsuo Wajima

Subsidiaries

Japan Consultant Co, Ltd
Hatano Seisakusho Co, Ltd
New Tech Co, Ltd
Dairyo Co, Ltd
PT Komponindo Betonjaya (Indonesia)

Products

Prestressed concrete sleepers, track slabs and beams; construction of prestressed concrete railway bridges.

Recent contracts include the construction of a bridge on the Hokuriku Shinkansen high-speed line; construction of the Kansai new airport connection bridge, Osaka; construction of sections A4, B1 and C1 of the Jabotabek railway project, Indonesia.

UPDATED

Quest

Quest Corporation
950 Keynote Circle, Brooklyn Heights, Cleveland, Ohio 44131, USA
Tel: +1 216 398 9400   Fax: +1 216 398 7765

Key personnel

See entry in *Signalling and telecommunications systems* section

Products

Hand-held ultrasonic rail flaw detectors; electronic weighing systems and controls.

VERIFIED

Racine

Racine Railroad Products Inc
PO Box 4029, 1524 Frederick Street, Racine, Wisconsin 53404, USA
Tel: +1 414 637 9681   Fax: +1 414 637 9069

Key personnel

President: S J Birkholz
Chief Engineer: D Brenny
Plant Manager: G Christensen

Service Manager: R Rhodes
Controller: G Harmann
Sales Manager: R Turner
Customer Service: L Powell, P Degen

Products

Automatic anchor applicators; dual anchor spreaders and adjusters; dual clip applicators; Pandrol Fastclip applicators/removers; anchor removers; clip setters/applicators; abrasive saws; electric and petrol-driven profile grinders; reciprocating hacksaws; rail drills.

Recent contracts include the supply of anchor removers and applicators for Pandrol Fastclips, 'e' clips, Safeloc fasteners, anchor adjusters and anchor spreaders.

UPDATED

Railpro

Railpro BV
Nieuwe Crailoseweg 8, PO Box 888, 1200 AW Hilversum, Netherlands
Tel: +31 35 688 9600   Fax: +31 35 688 9666

Products

Railpro supplies all materials required in railway infrastructure work, acting as a stockist for contractors. The company can arrange transport to the worksite by road, water or rail; it operates a fleet of 2,200 rail wagons.

NEW ENTRY

Rails Co

The Rails Company
101 Newark Way, Maplewood, New Jersey 07040-3393, USA
Tel: +1 201 763 4320   Fax: +1 201 763 2585

Key personnel

President: G N Burwell
Vice-President: J Maldonado
Secretary/Treasurer: M Kinda

Products

Rail anchors, switch point locks, switch heaters (propane and natural gas), lubricators, compressors, track carts, controls, snow detectors, wheel stops and car retarders.

VERIFIED

Railtech

Railtech Schlatter Systems
PO Box 152, 119 avenue Louis Roche, F-92231 Gennevilliers Cedex, France
Tel: +33 1 46 88 17 30   Fax: +33 1 46 88 17 40

Key personnel

General Manager: Didier Bourdon
Sales Manager: Klaus Nebel

Products

Rail welding equipment.

VERIFIED

Ranalah

Ranalah Moulds Ltd
New Road, Newhaven BN9 0EH, UK
Tel: +44 1273 514676   Fax: +44 1273 516529

Key personnel

Directors: J H Layfield, P F Phillips
Technical Director: P F Phillips
Technical/Design Manager: S Orwin
Project Manager: E G Denton

Products

Design of prestressed concrete sleepers, moulds and equipment; design and manufacture of equipment to suit production of any type of sleeper; factory layout design, plant supply and commissioning; full operational training, initial management assistance. Turnkey service for supply of sleeper manufacturing plant.

Contracts include the supply of sleeper plants to Hong Kong, Philippines, Thailand and Malaysia.

UPDATED

Rawie

A Rawie GmbH & Co
Dornierstrasse 11, D-49090 Osnabrück, Germany
Tel: +49 541 912070   Fax: +49 541 912 0736

Key personnel

Managing Director, Marketing: J Fründ
Managing Director, Technical: R Roick
Export Co-ordinator: N L C Pratt
Senior Design Engineer: B Neehoff

Products

Fixed and friction buffer stops; fixed and/or friction buffer stops with hydraulic or elastomeric cylinders; friction, fixed and folding wheel stops; specialist track endings to customer requirements, including folding buffer stops and buffer stops with loading ramps.

Recent contracts include the supply of buffer stops to Lisbon Metro, Portugal; MTRC, Hong Kong; Boston USA; and Bielefeld, Germany.

VERIFIED

Raychem

Raychem Corporation
Transportation Division
300 Constitution Drive, Menlo Park, California 94025, USA
Tel: +1 415 361 3333   Fax: +1 415 361 2113

Key personnel

Chief Executive Officer: Richard Kashnow
Vice-President, Electronics: John McGraw
Electronics Sales Manager, Europe: Bernard Aunay
Electronics Sales Manager, UK: John Roberts

Electronics Division, Europe

Raychem Ltd
Edison Road, Dorcan, Swindon SN3 5JA, UK
Tel: +44 1793 528171   Fax: +44 1793 572516
Division Manager, Europe: John McGraw

Products

Electrical harnessing component systems including: low fire hazard wire and cable; heat-shrinkable zero-halogen tubing and moulded parts; wire making systems; electrical interconnection devices; harness sealing products; adaptors.

Recent contracts include the Channel Tunnel; STIB, Belgium; and BART, USA.

VERIFIED

Relayfast

Relayfast Ltd
8th Floor, Buchanan House, 58 Port Dundas Road, Glasgow G4 0HG, Scotland
Tel: +44 141 335 2422   Fax: +44 141 335 3468
Email: 101350.3166@compuserv.com

Key personnel

Chief Group Executive: Fred Saunders
Business Development Director: Hugh Harvie
Plant Director: Gordon Kay
Production Development Director: John Urquhart

Corporate development

Scotland Track Renewals Co was one of the British Rail Infrastructure Maintenance Services units sold off as part of the BR privatisation. The company was sold in 1996 to a management buyout team to become Relayfast Ltd. In 1996 Relayfast went on to purchase Western Track Renewals Co.

Services

Most of its work concerns renewal of track in Scotland but it has done other work in different parts of the UK.

UPDATED

Swingmaster Corporation

Swingmaster Corporation
11415 Melrose Avenue, Franklin Park, Illinois 60131, USA
Tel: +1 708 451 1224   Fax: +1 708 451 1247

Key personnel
President: Dan A Grammatis
Vice-President: Jerry Rakowski
General Manager, Manufacturing: John Noga

Products
On- and off-track, rough terrain loaders, excavators and cranes.

VERIFIED

Sydney Steel

Sydney Steel Corporation
PO Box 1450, Sydney, Nova Scotia B1P 6K5, Canada
Tel: +1 902 564 7900   Fax: +1 902 564 7903

Key personnel
Chairman: Zhang Xuewu
Acting President: J A Rudderham
Vice-President, Sales: Steve Didyk
Manager, Sales Administration: John Murphy

Products
A major supplier to Canadian railways and world markets of various steel rail sections.

Sydney Steel manufactures steel rails to all major national and international specifications, including AREA, ASTM, BS, CNR, CPR, ISO and UIC. Sydney Steel produces premium wear-resistant head-hardened rails, standard carbon, intermediate strength and premium alloy grades, all using clean steel practice. Sections range from 37 to 70 kg/m. Rail lengths can be produced up to 26 m.

UPDATED

Tarmac

Tarmac Precast Concrete Ltd
Tallington, Stamford PE9 4RL, UK
Tel: +44 1778 381000   Fax: +44 1778 348041

Key personnel
Managing Director: M J Saunders
Technical Director: Dr H P J Taylor
Commercial Director: N D Claxton
Commercial Manager, Rail: A B Moore

Principal subsidiaries
Dow Mac
Charcon Tunnels
S G Baldwin Ltd

Products
Dow Mac prestressed concrete monobloc sleepers, crossing bearers and other concrete track support structures; Charcon precast concrete tunnel linings; Bomac polymer concrete and reinforced concrete level crossing systems; Baldwin cast cable trough systems, cable covers, marker posts and blocks, oversail blocks, platform and steeple copings; manufacturing systems and technology.

Technical support and licence agreement for indigenous companies.

Recent contracts include Railtrack; London Underground Ltd, including the Jubilee Line Extension; Docklands Light Railway; Ankara Metro; and Polish State Railways; supply of prestressed concrete monobloc sleepers to SNCB Belgium and technical support and licence agreement, Malaysia.

UPDATED

Tectran

Tecnologia em Transporte
Rodovia Presidente Dutra, Km 155/156
São José dos Campos SP CEP 12240-420, Brazil
Tel: +55 12 331 8200
Fax: +55 12 322 9440/321 1820

Products
Road/rail vehicles including personnel carriers for up to 25 passengers, cranes and tractors.

NEW ENTRY

Tempered Spring Co

Tempered Spring Co
A unit of T & N plc
Park Works, Foley Street, Sheffield S47 W5, UK
Tel: +44 1742 720031   Fax: +44 1742 731413

Key personnel
Sales Manager: M L Martin

Products
Elastic rail fastenings, including BTREC system and CS-Springlock for concrete sleepers, KTG for K-type baseplates and KT for switches and crossings.

VERIFIED

Templeton

Templeton, Kenly & Co Inc
2525 Gardner Road, Broadview, Illinois 60153, USA
Tel: +1 708 865 1500   Fax: +1 708 865 0894

Key personnel
President: Robert Spath
Vice-President, Sales and Marketing: Bill Stephenson

Products
Mechanical trip/track jacks; hydraulic rail puller and expanders; hydraulic rerailing system; portable air/hydraulic jacks for car shop maintenance; hydraulic track jack.

VERIFIED

Tetsudo Kiki

Tetsudo Kiki Kaisha Ltd
1-5-5 Yaesu, Chuo-ku, Tokyo 103, Japan
Tel: +81 3 3271 5341   Fax: +81 3 3271 2174

Works
Fukuoka-Machi, Nishitonami-Gun,
Toyama Pref 939-01, Japan

Key personnel
President: Hiroshi Yoshida

Products
Points and crossings; expansion and glued insulated joints; movable set-off equipment (for work-car crossing over main track).

VERIFIED

Thebra

Thebra do Brasil
Rua Antonio Austregesilo 360, Rio de Janeiro GB, Brazil
Tel: +55 21 280473/260 4234

Products
Aluminothermic in-track welding equipment and rail grinders.

VERIFIED

Thermit Australia

Thermit Australia Pty
Lot 7-8 Somersby Falls Road, Somersby, NSW Australia 2250
Tel: +61 43 404988   Fax: +61 43 404004

Key personnel
General Manager: Ron Mouse
Commercial Manager: Kai Nitzsche
Marketing Manager: Bryan Pieper
Marketing Manager: David Harnot

Subsidiary company
Rail Track Maintenance, New Zealand

Products
Thermit brand welding materials; hydraulic rail shears; rail weld grinders; glued and mechanical insulated rail joints; training of Thermit welders; removable level crossing systems; Kryorit ballast stabilisation; waterproof bridge membranes.

Recent contracts include welding on the Chungho project, Taipei, Taiwan and ultrasonic training for MTR Hong Kong.

NEW ENTRY

Tectran 25-seat road/rail personnel carrier

1997

Thermit Welding

Thermit Welding (GB) Ltd
87 Ferry Lane, Rainham RM13 9YH, UK
Tel: +44 1708 522626   Fax: +44 1708 553806

Key personnel
Managing Director: A J Key
Works Manager: T C Clifton
Technical Manager: R S Johnson
Administration Manager: A R Sampson
Quality Manager: S R Foreman

Principal subsidiary
Thermitrex (Pty) Ltd, Boksburg, South Africa

Products
Aluminothermic rail welding equipment and consumables; insulated rail joints.
   Recent contracts include Ankara Metro, Manchester Metrolink and South Yorkshire Supertram.

VERIFIED

Thompsons, Kelly & Lewis

Thompsons, Kelly & Lewis Pty Ltd
26 Faigh Street, Mulgrave, Victoria 3170, Australia
Tel: +61 3 9562 0744   Fax: +61 3 9561 8912

Works
5 Parker Street, Castlemaine, Victoria 3450, Australia

Key personnel
Sales Manager, Railway Products: E A Smith
Manager, Railway Products: W G Kinscher
Manager, Sales & Marketing: A Grage
General Manager: W J Coulter

Principal subsidiary
Davies & Baird

Products
Trackwork, turnouts, points and crossings, switches; rail fastener system for concrete sleepers, steel turnout sleepers, insulated/non-insulated; and a range of accessories.
   Recent contracts include the supply of tramway trackwork for Hong Kong; crossings for MTRC, Hong Kong; turnouts for the Jabotabek track layout improvement project, Indonesia; turnouts for State Railway Authority of New South Wales, Australia; and points and crossings for Westrail and Victoria Public Transport Corporation, Australia; turnouts for the Sydney LRT system, turnouts for BHP Iron Ore Nelson Point yard and Jimblebar mine, Australia; five-year contract for tramway trackwork for Toronto Canada and turnouts for the State Railway of Thailand track rehabilitation, Phase 1.

UPDATED

Thyssen

Thyssen Stahl AG
D-47161 Duisburg, Germany
Tel: +49 203521   Fax: +49 203 522 5102

Key personnel
Chairman: Dr E Schulz

Products
Permanent way materials: flat-bottom rails, tongue rails, full web rails, guardrails, grooved rails, sleepers.

UPDATED

Tiefenbach

Tiefenbach GmbH
Nierenhofer Strasse 68, 45257 Essen, Germany
Tel: +49 201 48630   Fax: +49 201 486 3158

Key personnel
Technical Field Service Manager: Achim Weirather

Products
Microcomputer-controlled electrically operated point motors; level crossing systems; cable haulage systems.

NEW ENTRY

Tiflex

Tiflex Limited
Hipley Street, Old Woking GU22 9LL, UK
Tel: +44 1483 757757   Fax: +44 1483 757715/755374

Works
Treburgie Water, Liskeard PL14 4NB, UK

Key personnel
Managing Director: M P Fleming
Trackelast Product Manager: H M Kenyon
Trackelast Product Engineer: S C Barlow

Products
Rail pads, baseplate pads, undersleeper pads, ballast mats, floating slab track bearings, resilient bearings for noise and vibration isolation, height adjustment shims and continuous support strips.
   Recent contracts include the supply of bearings for the Tsing Ma bridge, Hong Kong and floating slab track bearings for the Jubilee Line Extension, London.

UPDATED

Tipco

Tipco Inc
1 Coventry Road, Bramalea, Ontario L6T 4B1, Canada
Tel: +1 905 791 9811   Fax: +1 905 791 4917

Key personnel
President: J J Tickins
Manager, Track Bit Department: B Crichton

Products
Flat beaded track bits.

VERIFIED

Tokimec

Tokimec Inc
2-16 Minami Kamata, Ota-ku, Tokyo, Japan

Sales Office
1-31 Nishi-Gotanda 1-chome, Shinagawa-ku, Tokyo 141, Japan
Tel: +81 3 3490 0821   Fax: +81 3 3490 1960

Principal subsidiary
Tokimec Europe BV
Beurs-World Trade Centre, Room 410-411, Beursplein 37, PO Box 30210, NL-3001 Rotterdam, Netherlands
Tel: +31 10 405 1260   Fax: +31 10 405 5042

Key personnel
Director and Division Manager: Tasuku Yoshida
General Sales Manager: Isamu Nakamura

Products
Ultrasonic flaw detectors, Models SM-101, SM-1, UM and SM series; portable rail flaw detectors, PRD series and ultrasonic thickness meters, Models UTM 101/201 and UTM-1. The company has also supplied an ultrasonic rail flaw detector car with rail damage detection systems to each JR company and to several private railway companies.

VERIFIED

Tooltract

Tooltract Ltd
A division of Magtron UK Ltd
43 Cateley Road, Darnall, Sheffield S9 5JF, UK
Tel: +44 114 261 1109   Fax: +44 114 261 8303

Key personnel
Technical Sales Manager: Brian Thomson

Products
Rail drilling machinery for all permanent way and signalling and telecommunications applications. Trackmajor 4000 point and crossing bondhole machine; Trackmajor baseplate conversion kit. Design and development capabilities.

VERIFIED

True Temper

True Temper Railway Appliances
177 West Hintz Road, Wheeling, Illinois 60090-6078, USA
Tel: +1 708 215 5253   Fax: +1 708 520 6373

Key personnel
President: P J Cunningham
Vice-President, Controller: P A Likus
Vice-President, General Manager, Sales: J A Schebo

Products
Channeloc rail anchors; True-loc spring anchors; Cliploc concrete tie fastener; Lineloc low-profile fastening system.
   Lineloc is specially designed for concrete cross-ties, providing a low-profile fastening system that is flush to the track. The shoulder has a back-off stop to ensure that the 'S' clip stays in place. A one-piece glass-reinforced nylon insulator distributes forces through a radius providing a large contact surface.

VERIFIED

TSO

Travaux du Sud-Ouest SA
Chemin du Corps de Garde, Zone Industrielle, PO Box 8, F-77501 Chelles Cedex, France
Tel: +33 1 64 72 72 00   Fax: +33 1 64 26 30 23

Key personnel
President of the Executive Board: Emmanuèle Perron
Export Manager: Claude Petit
Manager, France: Christian Boscher
Equipment: Jean-Marie Delpy

Products
Turnout laying cranes and equipment; track construction and maintenance for main line and metro systems; ballast mats for ballasted track in tunnel; and in-track flash-butt welding.
   Contracts include TGV tracklaying for French Railways; ballastless tracklaying for the Channel Tunnel; supply and installation of trackwork for Tamshui Line, Department of Rapid Transit Systems, Taiwan; and rehabilitation of the Boké Railway in Guinea.

UPDATED

TSO is involved in TGV tracklaying for SNCF

Tülomsas

The Locomotive and Motor Corporation of Turkey
Ahmet Kanatli Cad, TR-26490 Eskisehir, Turkey
Tel: +90 222 234 8130   Fax: +90 222 231 7944

Key personnel
See entry in *Locomotives* section

Products
Self-propelled rail vehicles for infrastructure maintenance duties. These include a maintenance car equipped with a hydraulic crane (lifting capacity 3,000 kg) and a catenary maintenance and inspection car with a hydraulic lifting platform.

VERIFIED

Türk + Hillinger

Türk + Hillinger GmbH
PO Box 242, D-78503 Tuttlingen, Germany
Tel: +49 7461 70140   Fax: +49 7461 78218

Key personnel
President: Erich Hillinger
Managing Director: Eberhard Härter

Principal subsidiaries
Türk + Hillinger, Elektrowärme GesmbH
Salzburgerstrasse 32b, PO Box 91, A-4820 Bad Ischl, Austria
Tel: +43 6132 25502   Fax: +43 6132 255024

Türk + Hillinger GmbH
Dorotheenstrasse 22, D-9102 Limbach/Oberfrohna, Germany
Tel: +49 3722 92354   Fax: +49 3722 92356

Türk + Hillinger Hungaria Kft
Arany J u 2, H-3350 Kal, Hungary
Tel: +36 36 487053   Fax: +36 36 487053

Products
Electric point-heating systems: these consist of flat, tubular heaters with a chrome-nickel-steel connection housing or a complete watertight connecting cable. All clamps and springs for installation at different rail profiles are available.
Recent contracts include the supply of point heaters for DB AG, SBB and SNCF.

VERIFIED

Turkington Precast

J H Turkington & Sons (Contractors) Ltd
Mahon Industrial Estate, Portadown, Co Armagh, Northern Ireland BT62 3EH, UK
Tel: +44 1762 332807   Fax: +44 1762 350276/361779

Key personnel
General Manager — Precast: Trevor Turkington

Products
Prestressed concrete railway sleepers.

UPDATED

Unit Rail Anchor

Unit Rail Anchor Company Inc
2604 Industrial Street, Atchison, Kansas 66002, USA
Tel: +1 913 367 7200   Fax: +1 913 367 0559
Web: http://www.unitrail.com

Key personnel
President: Paul T Ciolino
International Sales: Carol Hale

Products
Unit rail anchors, spring and drive-on; reclamation and remanufacture of rail anchors; E-Z Wrench spring anchor applicator tool.
Recent contracts include the supply of rail anchors to US railways including BNSF, CSX, Norfolk Southern, Illinois Central and Wisconsin Central. Unit rail anchors are also exported to Canada, Europe, South America, Australia and New Zealand.

UPDATED

UniTrac Systems

UniTrac Systems Inc
314 East Burnett Avenue, Louisville, Kentucky 40208-2701, USA
Tel: +1 502 634 9492   Fax: +1 502 634 9494

Key personnel
President and Chief Executive Officer: Curtis A Richards
Director, Project Services: Bernard Campbell
Director, Engineering Services: Kenneth Fitzgibbon

Products
Switch point and third rail heater controls; Calrod heater elements; electric switch machines and controls; overhead electrification equipment for LRT systems.
Recent contracts include the supply of equipment for Muni, San Francisco; TTC, Toronto; New Orleans Canal Street; Portland extension projects and Metro North Stamford Yard.

UPDATED

VAE

VAE Aktiengesellschaft
Rotenturmstrasse 5-9, A-1010 Vienna, Austria
Tel: +43 1 531180   Fax: +43 1 5311 8222

Works
Alpinestrasse 1, A-8740 Zeltweg, Austria

Key personnel
President: Edmund Auli

Principal subsidiaries
VAE Railway Systems Pty Ltd, Australia
VAE Nortrak Ltd, Canada
VAE Nortrak Inc, USA
VAE Nortrak Cheyenne Inc, USA
VAMAV Vasúti Berendezések Kft, Hungary
GERFER Ltda, Portugal
VAE Riga SIA, Latvia
UAB VAE Legetecha, Lithuania
JEZ Sistemas Ferroviarios SL, Spain
VAE Baileyfield Ltd, UK
VAE Italia Srl, Italy
VAE Murom LLC, Russia
VAE Sofia OOD, Bulgaria

Products
Turnouts and turnout components, crossings, fastening material, steel sleepers, plastic sleepers (Zeltweg patent), cast crossings (also welded, Zeltweg patent); VAE Roadmaster 2000 turnout monitoring system; 152000 non-contact monitoring system for tongues; and HOA 350 hot box detector for train speeds up to 350 km/h.

UPDATED

VAE Nortrak

16160 River Road, Richmond, British Columbia V6V 1L6, Canada
Tel: +1 604 273 3030   Fax: +1 604 273 8927

Key personnel
President: Al Tuningley
Vice-President, Sales: Gord Weatherly
Technical Director: Gary Click
Chief Financial Officer: Eduard Peinhopf
General Manager: Garry Brudziak

Subsidiary companies
3930 Valley East Industrial Drive, Birmingham, Alabama 35217, USA
Tel: +1 205 854 2884   Fax: +1 205 854 2885
Vice-President, Sales and Marketing: John Pit
General Manager: Jim Wilson

1740 Pacific Avenue, Cheyenne, Wyoming 82007, USA
Tel: +1 307 778 8700   Fax: +1 307 778 8777
Vice-President: Goro Weatherly
General Manager: Chuck Bresson

Products
Supply and manufacture of track materials including RBM, SSGM, welded heel manganese frogs, welded spring manganese frogs, jointless and boltless manganese frogs, movable point frogs and vario frogs; AREA and asymmetrical switches, guardrails, transition rails and related components; new relay rail, crane rail, tie plates and joint bars; screwspikes, cut spikes, track-bolts, frog and switch-bolts; track tools. Contract design and engineering services.

UPDATED

Von Roll

Von Roll Machinery and Handling Systems Ltd
PO Box 2701, CH-3001 Berne, Switzerland
Tel: +41 31 308 5111   Fax: +41 31 302 4946

Key personnel
Director: Rolf Mathis
Manager, Railway Maintenance: J Marfurt

Principal subsidiary
Arnold Neuweiler AG
PO Box 2701, CH-3001 Berne, Switzerland

Products
Rail fastenings, points, crossings; racks and rack turnouts for cog-wheel railways; turnouts; turntables and transfer tables.
Neuweiler specialises in rail welding and grinding and permanent way equipment.

VERIFIED

Vortok

Vortok International
Osprey House, 63 Station Road, Addlestone KT15 2AR, UK
Tel: +44 1932 828812   Fax: +44 1932 828691

Works
Units 6 & 7 Haxter Close, Belliver Industrial Estate, Roborough, Plymouth PL6 7DD, UK

Key personnel
Director and General Manager: J R Byles

Principal subsidiary
Multiclip Company Ltd

Products
Components for the rehabilitation and repair of timber sleepers. These include the Vortok Coil for loose screws, spikes and additives for wood preservation.
Recent contracts include the supply of coils to European railways.

UPDATED

Vossloh Rail Systems

Vossloh Rail Systems GmbH
PO Box 1860, D-58778 Werdohl, Germany
Tel: +49 2392 520   Fax: +49 2392 52375

Key personnel
Managing Director: Ulrich Rieger
Sales Manager: F G Heisler
Regional Sales Manager: J Spors

Overseas business office, Düsseldorf
Tel: +49 2102 49090   Fax: +49 2102 49094

Products
Rail fastening systems for concrete, timber and steel sleepers on ballasted and slab track; directly fixed rail fastenings; sleeper anchors for lateral track stabilisation; rehabilitation systems; noise reduction systems and vibration damping; absorption track mats and web cushioning.

UPDATED

Walter Bau-Aktiengesellschaft

Walter Bau-Aktiengesellschaft
PO Box 102547, Böeheimstrasse 8, D-86153 Augsburg,
Germany
Tel: +49 821 558 2180   Fax: +49 821 558 2363
Email: walterbau.na@augustanet.de

Key personnel
Director, International Division: Martin Lommatzsch
Head of Department, Railway Construction and
   Prestressed Concrete Sleepers: Lothar Geiger

Products
Prestressed concrete (monobloc) sleepers suitable for
any gauge and for any type of rail fastening.
   Licensed production has been agreed with customers
in Europe, Middle East, Far East, Australia, Africa and
South America.

UPDATED

Western-Cullen-Hayes

Western-Cullen-Hayes Inc
2700 West 36th Place, Chicago, Illinois 60632-1617, USA
Tel: +1 773 254 9600   Fax: +1 773 254 1110
Web: www.wch.com

Key personnel
President: Ronald L McDaniel
Vice-President: Barbara Gulick
Vice-President, Marketing: George S Sokulski
Customer Service Manager: Bill Crain
Systems Application: Rodney Yourist

Principal subsidiary
Hayes Plant Western Cullen-Hayes Inc
120 North 3rd Street, Box 756, Richmond, Indiana 47374,
USA

Products
Safety signals and accessories, gate arms, level crossing
warning systems, industrial crossing warning systems,
flashing light signals, switch lamps and targets, bumping
posts and accessories, wheel stops, chocks, switch-point
guards, track drills, rail benders, rail tongs, automatic
switch-point machines, journal and hydraulic jacks,
derails and accessories, blue flags, car rerailers,
locomotive revolving lights and warning bells, dragging
equipment detectors, and other custom-designed
equipment for railway and industrial applications.

UPDATED

Wickham

Wickham Rail Cars Parts and Service Centre
Unit 6, Court Farm Business Park, Bishops Frome
WR6 5AY, UK
Tel: +44 1885 490344   Fax: +44 1885 490633

Key personnel
Managing Director: M Kukla
General Manager: R Bowlcott

Products
Permanent way maintenance vehicles including
personnel cars, inspection platforms and rerailing
vehicles; road/rail shunting vehicles.

VERIFIED

Wieland

Wieland Lufttechnik GmbH
PO Box 3669, D-91024 Erlangen, Germany
Tel: +49 9131 60670   Fax: +49 9131 604401

Key personnel
Product Manager: Thomas Fenzel

Products:
ExcaVac attachment for hydraulic excavators and vehicle-
mounted loading booms, suitable for ballast removal,
refuse collection and light excavation.

NEW ENTRY

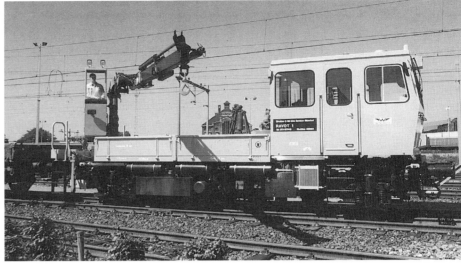

Windhoff OB 100 infrastructure vehicle for NS, Netherlands, with crane and tipping platform   **1996**

Windhoff BR 711 catenary maintenance vehicle for DB AG   **1996**

Windhoff

Windhoff AG
PO Box 1963, D-48409 Rheine, Germany
Tel: +49 5971 580   Fax: +49 5971 58209
Email: windhoff-ag@t-online.de

Key personnel
See entry in *Freight vehicles and equipment* section

Products
Repair, installation and maintenance vehicles,
multipurpose track maintenance machinery with a wide
range of attachments, such as tamping units, sleeper
changing units and shrub cutters.
   The BR 711 catenary maintenance vehicle is built for
DB AG (German Railways). It has a six-cylinder diesel
engine and a maximum speed of 120 km/h, working
platforms, a hydraulically adjustable catenary and
messenger wire unit for precise positioning, a video
recording facility, a measuring pantograph assessing
catenary height and stagger, an automatically operated
earthing isolation switch, an observation seat for
inspection of catenary and the measuring pantograph,
two driver cabins — front and back — with all control and
monitoring equipment, and a workshop area with work
bench and high-capacity storage facilities as well as a
spacious social room for the operating team, with kitchen
and sanitary facilities.

UPDATED

Yamato Kogyo

Yamato Kogyo Co Ltd
380 Kibi Otsu-ku, Himeji, Hyogo Pref, Japan
Tel: +81 792 731061

Key personnel
Manager: S Ichimura

Products
Rail, sleeper plates, fishplates, standard and special
turnouts, welded frogs, expansion joints, glued insulated
joints, compromise rail, rack rail and steel sleepers.

VERIFIED

Zweiweg Schneider

Zweiweg Schneider GmbH & Co KG
Oberbüscherhof, D-42799 Leichlingen, Germany
Tel: +49 2174 79095   Fax: +49 2174 79095

Key personnel
See entry in *Freight yard and terminal equipment* section

Products
Track-guidance rollers which convert a road vehicle into a
rail vehicle. Besides its use in creating a shunting unit (the
resultant tractive power equals about that of a 20 t
locomotive) the device also permits use of the Daimler-

Benz Unimog truck on rails as a working unit with various supplementary equipment.

A Zweiweg Unimog model ZW 82S provided with a steam-jet can be employed for points cleaning. For example, another unit equipped with a loading crane (and at the same time as a shunting unit) can haul up to 25 loaded wagons. For winter operation a rotary snow-plough or a drum-type snow-plough can be fitted, permitting effective snow removal on rails as well as on the road.

Two special units are available for the construction and maintenance of catenary: a Zweiweg Unimog with hydraulic lifting platform and the Zweiweg road-railer with working platform, which was initially constructed for the Netherlands Railways. The Zweiweg Unimog vehicles are also available for broad-gauge lines.

VERIFIED

Zwicky

Zwicky Engineering Ltd
Skyhi Division
A member of EIS Group plc
Molly Millars Lane, Wokingham RG11 2RY, UK
Tel: +44 1734 771331   Fax: +44 1734 774856

Key personnel
Managing Director: Anthony Wise
Sales Director: Graham Cornwall

Products
Track and wagon hydraulic jacks from 5 to 20 t; jack test rigs; rail benders; Track Aliner tools.

The Skyhi Track Aliner has been designed for the aligning and slewing of track, including points and crossings. When positioned in the ballast its low profile allows it to be used during traffic intervals and left in the track. Its horizontal action slides the sleepers through the ballast with minimum disturbance of the 'top' of the track.

Constructed in mild steel, it weighs 23 kg and has a safe working load of 8.128 t. There are two main parts, a hydraulic ram unit having a 152 mm stroke mounted on a base designed to provide a firm anchorage in the ballast. The swivel head has been designed so that it can be positioned against the web of any rail.

VERIFIED

FREIGHT YARD AND TERMINAL EQUIPMENT

Alphabetical Listing

ABC
Adtranz
Aldon
Ansaldo Trasporti
Babcock & Wilcox
Blatchford Transport Equipment
Bosch Telecom
BP-Battioni & Pagani
Caillard
Central Power Products
Control Chief
Cowans Sheldon
De Dietrich Ferroviaire
GRS
Hauhinco
Hegenscheidt-MFD
Herbert Pool (see Blatchford Transport Equipment)
Hyster

Jarret
Kalmar
Kershaw
KCI
Kyosan
LeTourneau
Liebherr
Mannesmann
Mitsubishi
Mors
Nelcon
Nippon Signal
Noell
Oleo
Rautaruükki
Rawie
Saalasti
Safetran
Siemens
Siemens Switzerland

Sika
Specialty Bulb
Steele
Stothert & Pitt
Strachan & Henshaw
Taylor
Teklite
Telemotive
Thyssen
Toshiba
Trackmobile®
Tuchschmid
Ultra Dynamics
Unilok
Vollert
Windhoff
YEC
ZAGRO
Zweiweg Schneider
Zwiehoff

Classified Listing

BUFFERSTOPS AND WHEEL CHOCKS
Aldon
Jarret
Oleo
Rawie

Rautaruükki
Stothert & Pitt
Strachan & Henshaw
Taylor
Tuchschmid

Strachan & Henshaw
Thyssen
Vollert
Windhoff

CRANES AND CARGO-HANDLING EQUIPMENT
Babcock & Wilcox
BP-Battioni & Pagani
Blatchford Transport Equipment
Caillard
Cowans Sheldon
Herbert Pool (see Blatchford Transport Equipment)
Hyster
Kalmar
Kershaw
KCI
LeTourneau
Liebherr
Mannesmann
Mitsubishi
Nelcon
Noell

ROAD/RAIL VEHICLES
Central Power Products
Hegenscheidt-MFD
Steele
Trackmobile®
Unilok
YEC
ZAGRO
Zweiweg Schneider
Zwiehoff

WAGON-HANDLING EQUIPMENT
Babcock & Wilcox
De Dietrich Ferroviaire
Hauhinco
Kyosan
Steele

YARD CONTROL EQUIPMENT
ABC
Adtranz
Ansaldo Trasporti
Bosch Telecom
Control Chief
GRS
Hauhinco
Nippon Signal
Safetran
Siemens
Siemens Switzerland
Telemotive
Thyssen
Toshiba
Ultra Dynamics

Company Listing by Country

FINLAND
KCI
Rautarüükki
Saalasti

FRANCE
Caillard
De Dietrich Ferroviaire
Jarret

GERMANY
Adtranz
Bosch Telecom
Hauhinco
Hegenscheidt-MFD
Mannesmann
Noell
Rawie
Siemens
Thyssen
Vollert
Windhoff
ZAGRO
Zweiweg Schneider
Zwiehoff

IRELAND
Liebherr
Unilok

ITALY
Ansaldo Trasporti
BP-Battioni & Pagani

JAPAN
Kyosan
Mitsubishi
Nippon Signal
Toshiba

NETHERLANDS
Nelcon

SPAIN
Babcock & Wilcox

SWEDEN
Adtranz
Kalmar

SWITZERLAND
Adtranz
Siemens Switzerland
Sika
Tuchschmid

UK
Blatchford Transport Equipment
Cowans Sheldon

Herbert Pool (see Blatchford Transport Equipment)
Hyster
Oleo
Steele
Stothert & Pitt
Strachan & Henshaw
Teklite
Ultra Dynamics
YEC

USA
ABC
Aldon
Central Power Products
Control Chief
GRS
Kershaw
LeTourneau
Safetran
Specialty Bulb
Taylor
Telemotive
Trackmobile®

ABC

ABC Rail Products Corporation
Track Products Division
200 S Michigan Avenue, Chicago, Illinois 60604, USA
Tel: +1 312 322 0360   Fax: +1 312 322 0377

Key personnel
See entry in *Brakes and drawgear* section

Products
Yard control systems.

VERIFIED

Adtranz

ABB Daimler-Benz Transportation GmbH
Saatwinkler Damm 42-43, D-13627 Berlin, Germany
Tel: +49 30 38320   Fax: +49 30 3832 2000

Head Office, Fixed Installations Group
ABB Daimler-Benz Transportation Bahnfahrwegsysteme
Mainzer Landstrasse 351, D-60326 Frankfurt-am-Main,
Germany
Tel: +49 69 75070   Fax: +49 69 7507 584

Key personnel
See entry in *Fixed electrification equipment* section

Products
Development, design, engineering, sales, production,
installation, maintenance and after-sales service of freight
yard and terminal systems and equipment including
mechanical systems and components for continuous
speed control of wagon movements in marshalling yards;
service, minor equipment and spare parts; project
management for major parts and consultancy work.

For continuous speed control of wagon movements in
marshalling yards, Adtranz has developed spiral-type
hydraulic retarders. These are mounted on the inside of
two rails to provide speed control within an ambient
temperature range from −40 to +40°C. When a wheel
passes it causes the brake cylinder of the retarder to
rotate one turn. This starts a fluid circulating inside the
retarder. When a wagon passes the retarder at a lower
than preset speed, the fluid circulates freely, and offers
little resistance to the passage of the wheel. At any higher
speed than the preset rate, the retarders execute full
braking power which remains constant as long as the
wagon exceeds the preset speed.

Retarders are available in fixed and remote-controlled
configurations and can be lowered to allow traction
vehicles or wagons with low clearances to pass. They
have been installed in a number of marshalling yards in
Sweden and other countries.

VERIFIED

Aldon

The Aldon Company
3410 Sunset Avenue, Waukegan, Illinois 60087, USA
Tel: +1 847 623 8800/1   Fax: +1 847 623 6139

Key personnel
See entry in *Permanent way equipment* section

Products
Wheel blocks, wheel chocks, warning signs, portable
friction rail skids, wagon stops, bumping posts, electric
and pneumatic wagon shakers, winch-type wagon
pullers, electric wagon haulers, power wagon movers,
wagon door wrenches and pullers, automatic bulk wagon
gate openers and retarders.

VERIFIED

Ansaldo Trasporti

Ansaldo Trasporti SpA
425 Via Argine, I-80147 Naples, Italy
Tel: +39 81 565 0111   Fax: +39 81 5650 6989

Key personnel
See entry in *Locomotives and powered passenger
vehicles* section

Products
Yard control equipment and yard layout design; power
signalling apparatus; geographic relay interlocking;
remote-control equipment; level crossing automation.

Blatchford rail-mounted self-propelled T-lift crane   1997

Ansaldo Trasporti marshalling yard control equipment at Marcianise, Italy

Recent contracts include the automation of the
Marcianise and Orbassano marshalling yards, Italy; and
supply of automation systems for two marshalling yards
on the new Beijing—Kowloon line, China.

VERIFIED

Babcock & Wilcox

Babcock & Wilcox Española SA
PO Box 294, Alameda Recalde 27, E-48009 Bilbao, Spain
Tel: +34 4 424 1761   Fax: +34 4 423 7092

Key personnel
See entry in *Locomotives and powered passenger
vehicles* section

Products
Mechanical handling equipment; container cranes; portal
cranes; dockside cranes; shipyard portal cranes; giant
shipyard portal cranes; polar cranes for nuclear power
facilities; overhead travelling cranes of all kinds; ingot
mould stripper and foundry ladle cranes; ship discharging
machinery; wagon tipplers.

VERIFIED

Blatchford Transport Equipment

Blatchford Transport Equipment
A Division of Herbert Pool Ltd
95 Fleet Road, Fleet GU13 8PJ, UK
Tel: +44 1252 620444   Fax: +44 1252 622292

Key personnel
Managing Director: Nigel Pool

Products
Mechanical handling systems for intermodal transport,
including truck/trailer-mounted side loaders; trailer and
rail-mounted cranes; self-propelled rail-mounted cranes;
heavy-duty cranes for terminal use.

The Blatchford side loader is available for fixed
mounting to vehicle chassis or sliding mounting to trailer
chassis for handling 20, 30 and 50 ft long ISO containers.

The Blatchford T-lift trailer and rail-mounted container
and swapbody cranes use a patented lifting and cross-
transfer system with capacities up to 35 t.

VERIFIED

Bosch Telecom

Robert Bosch GmbH
PO Box 106050, D-70049, Stuttgart, Germany
Tel: +49 711 8110   Fax: +49 711 811 6630

Bosch Telecom shunter's yard radio system   1997

Key personnel
See *Passenger coach equipment* section.

Products
Radio systems for shunting operations.

NEW ENTRY

BP-Battioni & Pagani

BP-Battioni & Pagani SpA
Località Croce, I-43058 Sorbolo (Parma), Italy
Tel: +39 521 604140/200   Fax: +39 521 604359

Key personnel
Chairman: Gianfranco Pagani
Vice-President: Amilcare Battioni

Products
Side loaders with capacity from two to 20 t; electric side
loaders with capacity from two to five tonnes; heavy-duty
forklift trucks with capacity from 4 to 38 t, including
machines fitted with spreader attachments for container
handling.

VERIFIED

Caillard

A subsidiary of Clarke Chapman Ltd
PO Box 1368, Place Caillard, F-76065 Le Havre Cedex,
France
Tel: +33 2 35 25 81 31   Fax: +33 2 35 25 11 41

Key personnel
Director: K Bayram
Sales Manager: A Beroule
Production Manager: B Bailly

Products
Breakdown cranes (up to 150 t capacity) for railways; rail
and pneumatic tyre-mounted gantries for container
handling; mobile cranes; all kinds of gantry cranes,
unloaders and jib cranes for general cargo, container or
bulk cargo; and mobile port cranes for ports and railways.
   Recent contracts include railway breakdown cranes for
Malawi (1) and for Bangladesh (3).

VERIFIED

Central Power Products

Central Manufacturing
4116 Dr Greaves Road, PO Box 777, Grandview, Missouri
64030, USA
Tel: +1 816 767 0300   Fax: +1 816 763 0705

Key personnel
President and Chief Executive Officer: John L Ying
Vice-President, Engineering and Product Development:
   Jack Highfill
Programme Manager, Shuttle Wagon Divsion: Tom
   Connel
Programme Manager, MTV: Richard Drukker
Customer Support: Joe Evans

Products
Shuttle Wagon road/rail wagon mover of 24,000 to
55,000 lb drawbar pull (eight models are available);
maintenance of way equipment; road-to-rail conversion
units.
   Multi-terrain track vehicles for maintenance of way
equipment; custom-design/build.

UPDATED

Control Chief

Control Chief Corporation
PO Box 141, Bradford, PA 16701, USA
Tel: +1 814 362 6811   Fax: +1 814 368 4133

De Dietrich Ferroviaire Autoloc shunter with radio remote control

Works address
14 Egbert Lane, Lewis Run, PA 16738, USA

Key personnel
Principal Officer: Robert Crofford

Products
Wireless remote-control system for locomotive using a
lightweight portable transmitter designed to reproduce
the controls inside the locomotive cab. The system comes
with two-way communication. An LCD display is used on
the hand-held transmitter to provide locomotive cab
gauge and meter readings.

NEW ENTRY

Cowans Sheldon

Clarke Chapman Ltd
PO Box 9, James Street, Carlisle CA2 5BJ, UK
Tel: +44 1228 24196   Fax: +44 1228 24795

Key personnel
See entry in *Permanent way equipment* section

Products
Cranes: diesel-hydraulic, diesel-electric and diesel-
mechanical railway breakdown and general purpose
cranes, capacity 5 to 250 t, with telescopic or lattice
booms; carriage designs to suit all rail gauges and all
wheel-loading conditions.

VERIFIED

De Dietrich Ferroviaire

De Dietrich Ferroviaire
PO Box 35, F-67891 Niederbronn Cedex, France
Tel: +33 3 88 80 25 00   Fax: +33 3 88 80 25 12
Email: ddf@dx-net.fr

Products
Autoloc shunters; stationary haulage systems.
   The Autoloc radio remote-controlled shunter is
designed to meet the wagon handling needs of industrial,
mining and port operators, and is constructed to full
railway standards. Powered by a diesel engine or electric
motors (from 30 to 400 kW), the Autoloc features
hydrostatic transmission on two or four axles and
operates at up to 20 km/h.
   De Dietrich semi-automatic and automatic stationary
haulage systems allow the movement of individual
wagons or complete trains weighing up to 5,000 short
tons. Based on steel ropes and capstan winches, they can
be operated by remote control.

UPDATED

GRS

General Railway Signal Co
A member of the SASIB Railway Business Area
150 Sawgrass Drive, PO Box 20600, Rochester, NY
14602-0600, USA
Tel: +1 716 783 2000   Fax: +1 716 783 2331
Web: http://www.sasib.com

Key personnel
See entry in *Signalling and telecommunications* section

Products
Design and manufacture of equipment and systems for
freight and passenger railways include switch machines,
signals, track circuits, wagon retarders and associated
hardware.
   Engineering services include design of central office,
communications and wayside systems for large and small
applications.
   Sasib Railway GRS also provides repair, field and
maintenance management services, and customer
training.

UPDATED

Hauhinco

Hauhinco Maschinenfabrik
G Hausherr Jochums GmbH & Co KG
PO Box 911320, D-45538 Sprockhövel, Germany
Tel: +49 2324 7050   Fax: +49 2324 705222

Key personnel
Managing Director: Peter Jochums
Sales Manager, Railway Technology: Gerd Schöler

Principal subsidiaries
Hauhinco Saar, Saarbrücken, Germany
Hauhinco India Ltd, Calcutta
Hauhinco Poland, Katowice
Hauhinco South Africa, Alrode
Hauhinco Trading, Warrendale Pennsylvania, USA

Products
Wagon shunting equipment for classification and sorting
tracks at marshalling yards and industrial sites.
   Recent contracts include a fully automated coal wagon
transfer facility for the Rybnick power complex in Poland.

VERIFIED

Hegenscheidt-MFD

Hegenscheidt-MFD GmbH
PO Box 1408, D-41804 Erkelenz, Germany
Tel: +49 243 1860   Fax: +49 243 186470

Key personnel
See entry in *Workshop, repair and maintenance equipment* section

Products
Portable hydraulic rerailing systems in aluminium alloy; hydraulic equipment for rapid track clearing after serious accidents; road/rail vehicle with rerailing equipment.

VERIFIED

Hyster

Hyster Europe Ltd
Berk House, Basing View, Basingstoke RG21 4HQ, UK
Tel: +44 1256 461171   Fax: +44 1256 56733
Email: sales@hyster.co.uk
Web: http://www.hyster.co.uk

Key personnel
Managing Director: Paolo De Chiara
Sales and Marketing Director: Terry Foreman
Area Business Director, North Eastern Europe, Africa, Middle East: Terry Foreman
Area Business Director, South Europe and Benelux: Timo Luukkainen

Principal subsidiaries
Hyster France SARL
Hyster GmbH, Germany
Hyster Italia SrL

Products
Forklift trucks and reach stackers for container and swapbody handling; counter-balanced forklift trucks, with capacities from 1 short ton upwards, for stuffing/stripping of containers and freight wagons.
   Recent contracts include the supply of intermodal handling ReachStacker to DSB Denmark for use at main Copenhagen terminal in 1996; H48.00C-16CH dedicated container handling lift truck for DB Berlin terminal.

UPDATED

Jarret

198 avenue des Grésillons, F-92600 Asnières Cedex, France
Tel: +33 1 46 88 46 20   Fax: +33 1 47 90 03 57

Key personnel
See entry in *Brakes and drawgear* section

Products
Shock-absorbers for end-of-track stops.

VERIFIED

Kalmar

Kalmar
S-341 81 Ljungby, Sweden
Tel: +46 372 26000   Fax: +46 372 26390

Key personnel
Managing Director: Jonas Suaufesson
Vice-President, Corporate Communications: S E Petterson

Subsidiary conmpanies in Austria, France, Germany, Netherlands, Norway, Spain, Singapore, Hong Kong and USA

UK Subsidiary
Kalmar UK Ltd
Siskin Drive, Coventry CV3 4FJ, UK
Tel: +44 1203 834500
Fax: +44 1203 834523

Key personnel
Managing Director: J Arkell
Financial Controller: E Pook
Parts and Service Director: Keith Snow

Hyster RS46-301H ReachStacker at the DSB railway container terminal in Copenhagen, Denmark **1997**

Products
IC engine and electric counterbalance lift-trucks up to 90 t capacity; IC engine and electric side loaders from 2 to 15 t capacity; IC engine reachstackers for container and intermodal handling.

UPDATED

Kershaw

Kershaw Manufacturing Co Inc
PO Box 244100, Montgomery, Alabama 36124-4100, USA
Tel: +1 205 271 1000   Fax: +1 205 277 6551

Key personnel
See entry in *Permanent way equipment* section

Products
Rubber-tyred/rail-mounted yard cleaners, track brooms, on/off track snow and sand removers; rubber-tyred and rail-mounted cranes equipped with lattice or hydraulic telescopic booms for handling locomotives, wagons or containers of up to 135 t; road/rail wagon movers with optional mounted crane.

VERIFIED

KCI

Konecranes VLC Corporation
PO Box 666, FIN-0580 Hyvinkää, Finland
Tel: +358 14 42711   Fax: +358 14 427 3100

Key personnel
President: Markku Leinonen
Regional Marketing Manager: Hannu Rossi

Products
Railway terminal gantry cranes, container-handling dockside cranes, multipurpose cranes, cargo and container-handling gantry cranes, container storage cranes, overhead travelling cranes for containers and other loads.

VERIFIED

Kyosan

Kyosan Electric Mfg Co Ltd
4-2 Marunouchi 3-chome, Chiyoda-ku, Tokyo 100, Japan
Tel: +81 3 3214 8136   Fax: +81 3 3211 2450

Main works
29-1 Heiancho 2-chome, Tsurumi-ku, Yokohama 230, Japan

Key personnel
See entry in *Signalling and telecommunications* section

Products
Automatic wagon haulage systems.

VERIFIED

LeTourneau

LeTourneau, Inc
PO Box 2307, Longview, Texas 75606, USA

Key personnel
President and Chief Executive Officer: Dan C Eckermann
Vice-President, Sales and Marketing: Dwight Baker

Products
Gantry cranes and side porters.
   Recent contracts include the supply of five SST-100 gantry cranes to CAST, Montreal.

UPDATED

Liebherr

Liebherr Container Cranes Ltd
Killarney, Co Kerry, Ireland
Tel: +353 64 31511   Fax: +353 64 31602/32735

UK Sales Office
Liebherr Great Britain Ltd, Travellers Lane, Welham Green, Hatfield AL9 7HW, UK
Tel: +44 1707 268161   Fax: +44 1707 261695

Key personnel
Directors: K Noelke, R Geiler
Secretary: H Brunner

Products
Liebherr manufactures rail-mounted container handling cranes for ship-to-shore terminals, railway and trucking terminals and storage yards. Sizes, speeds and safe working loads to meet all international tenders and customers' specific requirements.

VERIFIED

Mannesmann

Mannesmann Demag Fördertechnik AG Gottwald
PO Box 18 03 43, D-40570 Düsseldorf 13, Germany
Tel: +49 211 71020   Fax: +49 211 7102651

Key personnel
See entry in *Permanent way equipment* section

Products
Railway cranes. Available for any track and loading gauge and designed in accordance with the maximum permissible axle and wheel loads. The cranes offer SWL ratings up to 300 t, minimum tail radii, hauling speeds up to 120 km/h, a range of different brake systems and buffers or couplers to suit.

VERIFIED

Mitsubishi

Mitsubishi Heavy Industries Ltd
5-1 Marunouchi 2-chome, Chiyoda-ku, Tokyo 100, Japan
Tel: +81 3 3212 9607   Fax: +81 3 3212 9767

Key personnel
See entry in *Powered passenger vehicles* section

Products
Straddle carrier and gantry cranes.

VERIFIED

VERIFIED   *Nelcon container stacking crane for RSC, Rotterdam with AC trolley drives*

Nelcon

Nelcon BV
PO Box 5303, Doklaan 22, NL-3008 AH Rotterdam, Netherlands
Tel: +31 10 294 6666   Fax: +31 10 294 6777

Key personnel
Managing Director: T E M Kocken
Deputy Director: W G van Seters
Sales Manager: T R Stein

Products
Container (stacking) cranes; straddle carriers.
Recent contracts include the supply of container stacking cranes and straddle carriers for terminals in Rotterdam, Netherlands; and straddle carriers for terminals in Tilbury, UK, and Le Havre, France.

UPDATED

Nippon Signal

The Nippon Signal Co Ltd
3-1 Marunouchi, 3-chome, Chiyoda-ku, Tokyo, Japan
Tel: +81 3 3237 4500   Fax: +81 3 3237 4649

Works
Yono Factory, 13-8, Kamikizaki 1-chome, Urawa City
Utsunomiya Factory, 11-2, Hiraide Kougyo Danchi, Utsunomiya City

Key personnel
See entry in *Passenger coach equipment* section

Products
Automatic freight wagon control system for marshalling yards, automatic self-gravity wagon retarder equipment and various indication control boards for passengers.

VERIFIED

Noell

Noell GmbH
Port Equipment Division
PO Box 1640, D-30837 Langenhagen, Germany
Tel: +49 511 77040   Fax: +49 511 7704217

Key personnel
Sales and Marketing Director: V Schuessler

Principal subsidiaries
Noell Inc
2411 Dulles Corner Park, Suite 410, Herndorn, Virginia 22071, USA
Manager: Manfred Kohler

Peiner France
124 rue Nationale, Stiring Wendel, F-57600 Forbach, France
Manager: Roger Poliwoda

Products
Rail-mounted and rubber-tyred container gantry cranes, straddle carriers and bulk materials handling equipment.

Recent contracts include the supply of 10 rail-mounted gantry cranes for APL Los Angeles, USA; and additional rubber-tyred gantry crane for Rail Combi, Sweden; and straddle carriers for Portnet, South Africa, Schelde Terminal Noord Antwerpen, Belgium and Maersk, Taiwan.

VERIFIED

Oleo

Oleo International Ltd
PO Box 216, Grovelands Estate, Longford Road, Exhall, Coventry CV7 9NE, UK
Tel: +44 1203 645555   Fax: +44 1203 645777

Key personnel
See entry in *Freight vehicles and equipment* section

Products
50 Series, 70 Series and 700 Series long-stroke hydraulic buffers (250-2,400 mm stroke) available for mounting on either rigid or sliding stop structures, providing effective emergency impact protection for railway rolling stock.

VERIFIED

Rautarüükki

See entry in *Freight vehicles and equipment* section

Rawie

A Rawie GmbH & Co
Dornierstrasse 11, D-49090 Osnabrück, Germany
Tel: +49 541 912070   Fax: +49 541 912 0736

Key personnel
See entry in *Permanent way equipment* section

Products
Buffer stops with integral loading ramps; friction, fixed and folding (manual or motorised) wheel stops; fixed and friction buffer stops; specialist track endings to customer requirements.
Recent contracts include the supply of loading ramps for Hamburg, Germany.

VERIFIED

Saalasti

Saalasti Transport Machinery Ltd
Arinatie 6, FIN-00370 Helsinki 37, Finland
Tel: +358 9 557775   Fax: +358 9 550780

Key personnel
See entry in *Locomotives and powered passenger vehicles* section

Products
Snow-ploughs. The patented rolling snow-plough can be converted from the transport to the ploughing position in 2 minutes.
Recent contracts include the supply of snow-ploughs to private industry.

UPDATED

Safetran

Safetran Systems Corporation
4650 Main Street NE, Minneapolis, Minnesota 55421, USA
Tel: +1 612 572 1400   Fax: +1 612 572 0144

Key personnel
See entry in *Signalling and telecommunications* section

Products
Marshalling yard communication systems; dispatcher communication systems.

VERIFIED

Siemens

Siemens Aktiengesellschaft
Transportation Systems Group
Control Systems Division (VT 2)
Ackerstrasse 22, D-38126 Braunschweig, Germany
Tel: +49 531 226 2230   Fax: +49 531 226 4249

Key personnel
Divisional Technical Manager: Dr F W Hagermeyer
Divisional Commercial Manager: M F Duttenhofer

Products
Planning, control and monitoring of humping operations in marshalling yards; Automatic Vehicle Identification systems; electrically operated points; freight management and dispatching systems.
Multi-microcomputers, in hot standby operation, are used to acquire technical and operating data of arriving trains, and to plan, control and monitor train splitting and formation in accordance with the timetable. The MSR 32 multi-microcomputer system, employed for humping operation control, is of modular design, high reliability and easy handling. It is designed to suit individual operational demands, and guarantees a high rate of throughput in the distribution area and a target-accurate slowing-down even on curved classification tracks.
Client-server systems with standard relational databases to administer train, wagon and freight data, optimising yard or workshop operation and information management are also available.
Recent contracts include installation or modernisation of marshalling yard systems at Vienna (ÖBB); Bologna (FS); Nuremberg (DB AG); Villach (ÖBB); Ludwigshafen (BASF); Munich (DB AG); Frankfurt (DB AG); Antwerp (SNCB); Bologna (FS); Kornwestheim (DB AG); Hamburg Hohe Schaar and Hamburg South (private); Limmattal

(SBB); and Kijfhoek (NS). Recent contracts for freight management systems include Hamburg Maschen (DB AG); Limmattal (SBB); Vienna (ÖBB); Villach (ÖBB); Bologna (FS); and Chiasso (SBB).

VERIFIED

Siemens Switzerland

Siemens Switzerland Ltd
Industriestrasse 42, CH-8304 Wallisellen, Switzerland
Tel: +41 1 832 3232   Fax: +41 1 832 3600

Key personnel
See entry in *Signalling and telecommunications* section

Products
Domino mosaic panels for marshalling yard control systems; alphanumerical keyboard control.

UPDATED

Sika

Sika AG
Tüffenwies 16-22, PO Box, CH-8048 Zurich, Switzerland
Tel: +41 1 436 4040   Fax: +41 1 432 5600

Key personnel
See entry in *Permanent way equipment* section

Products
Sikarail KC330 elastic rail fixing system is a combination of an elastic durable reaction curing binder and compressible filler that absorbs vibration and redistributes eccentric loading ensuring that no compressive stresses are developed leading to edge failure.

Sika provides admixture designs for high-specification concrete mixes, jointing systems, mortars and grouts, adhesives and bonding agents, waterproofing, corrosion inhibitors, concrete repair and protective coatings for concrete, steel including industrial flooring.

UPDATED

Specialty Bulb

The Specialty Bulb Co Inc
80 Orville Drive, Bohemia, New York 11716, USA
Tel: +1 516 589 3393   Fax: +1 516 563 3089

Key personnel
See entry in *Passenger coach equipment* section

Products
Light bulbs for a wide range of specialist railway applications.

VERIFIED

Steele

E G Steele & Co Ltd
25 Dalziel Street, Hamilton ML3 9AU, UK
Tel: +44 1698 283765   Fax: +44 1698 891550

Key personnel
See entry in *Locomotives and powered passenger vehicles* section

Products
Locopulsor shunting machine, a single-wheel vehicle capable of moving wagons weighing 160 to 200 t on straight level track. It can also move wagons in curves, split a line of wagons and handle a wagon on a turntable.

The company is UK agent for Trackmobile road/rail shunting equipment. It offers a range of shunters capable of moving loads from 10 to 2,000 t.

VERIFIED

Stothert & Pitt

Stothert & Pitt
A subsidiary of Clarke Chapman Ltd
PO Box 25, Bath BA2 3DJ, UK
Tel: +44 1225 314400   Fax: +44 1225 332529

Key personnel
Director: J D Gittins
General Sales Manager: C Dowding

Strachan & Henshaw triple car dumper unloading iron ore at Port Hedland, Northwest Australia   **1997**

Strachan & Henshaw Rotaside XL dumper unloading a 24 m long, 5.48 m high woodchip car in the USA

Products
Telescopic spreader beams, twin-lift spreader beams, automatic or manual fixed-length spreader beams; bridge cranes for container marshalling and for loading on road/rail transport; quayside transporter cranes for loading container vessels; jib cranes for container handling.

VERIFIED

Strachan & Henshaw

Strachan & Henshaw Ltd
PO Box 103, Ashton House, Ashton Vale Road, Bristol BS99 7TJ, UK
Tel: +44 117 966 4677   Fax: +44 117 963 9515

Key personnel
Chairman: Kevin Gamble
Managing Director: Ken Grove
Director, Nuclear and Bulk Handling: P D Brooks
Marketing Manager: Ralph Starr

Subsidiaries
Strachan & Henshaw Australia Pty Ltd
Strachan & Henshaw Inc USA
Strachan & Henshaw Pty Ltd South Africa

Products
Wagon tipplers (dumpers) for random wagons or rotary-coupled unit trains; train movers (indexers, chargers, positioners) for use with wagon tipplers and at loadout stations; 'Beetle' haulage systems and wagon traversers.

Recent contracts include the supply of wagon tipplers and dumpers to China, Australia and USA; One Tripple car dumper for BHP Iron Ore, handling railcars at Port Hedland, Australia. A further order has been received for a two-car dumper system also at Port Hedland in

Australia in 1996/7; major refurbishment of a railcar hoist system for handling bauxite at Kamsar Guinea in Africa 1995-6.

UPDATED

Taylor

Taylor Machine Works Inc
Louisville, Mississippi 39339, USA
Tel: +1 601 773 3421   Fax: +1 601 773 9646

Products
Container and trailer handling trucks, offering a wide range of lift attachments: top pick; side pick; top and bottom pick; bayonet; twistlocks; fork-mounted; carriage-mounted or suspended by chains; for use with 7 to 13 m (20 to 44 ft) empty or laden containers, conventional or refrigerated. Attachments range from 5,670 to 40,820 kg (12,500 to 90,000 lb) capacity. The truck is designed specifically as a container or container/trailer handler.

VERIFIED

Teklite

Teklite UK Ltd
Chessingham Park, Common Road, Dunnington, York, YO1 5SE, UK
Tel: +44 1904 488880   Fax: +44 1904 488883

Key personnel
UK Sales Manager: Mark Smith

Products
Mobile, portable and emergency lighting products. Halogen (110 and 240 V AC) and high-pressure sodium,

metal halide lighting (12 and 24 V DC). Pneumatic and manual masts, tripod stands and hand-held portable lighting. Mobile trailer-mounted lighting provides 162,000 lumens of light with only a small 3.6 kVA generator.

VERIFIED

Telemotive

Telemotive Industrial Controls
Maxtec International Corporation, 6470 West Cortland Street, Chicago, IL 60635, USA
Tel: +1 773 889 9635   Fax: +1 773 889 2220
Email: kbird@telemotive.com
Web: www.telemotive.com

Key personnel
Marketing Manager: Ken Bird

Products
Radio remote-control systems for locomotives, wagon movers, cranes and other freight handling systems.

Recent contracts include the supply of radio remote-control systems for three gantry cranes at the Northeast Ohio Intermodal Terminal, Navarre, USA.

UPDATED

Thyssen

Thyssen Umformtechnik GmbH
Rangiertechnik
Werk Wanheim, Friemersheimer Strasse 40, D-47249 Duisburg, Germany
Tel: +49 203 7320   Fax: +49 203 732296

Foreign Sales Agency
Siemens Aktiengesellschaft
Transportation Systems Group
Goods Transport Division (VT 23)
Ackerstrasse 22, D-38126 Braunschweig, Germany
Tel: +49 531 226 2704   Fax: +49 531 226 4309

Products
Marshalling yard retarders and wagon-moving equipment. The company has supplied retarders for more than 60 German Railways' (DB AG) marshalling yards, and to German industry and railway companies abroad. The Hamburg Maschen shunting yard alone incorporates as many as 136 Thyssen retarders.

Recent contracts include the supply of eight primary two-rail beam retarders and 48 secondary single-rail beam retarders for Antwerp Noord marshalling yard, Belgium; and three primary two-rail beam retarders and 25 secondary single-rail beam retarders for Hamburg Alte Süderelbe marshalling yard, Germany.

VERIFIED

Toshiba

Toshiba Corporation
Railway Projects Department
1-1, Shibaura 1-chome, Minato-ku, Tokyo 105, Japan
Tel: +81 3 3457 4924   Fax: +81 3 3457 8385

Products
Yard control equipment including retarders; and Automatic Car Identification (ACI) systems employing vehicle-mounted transponders and track-mounted interrogators. Toshiba ACI showed reliability and performance in a field test at Hokkaido (northern Japan) conducted by JR with 60 transponders and an interrogator under severe environmental conditions such as low temperature (−30°C) and thick snow which covered the interrogator to a depth of 150 mm or more.

VERIFIED

Trackmobile®

Trackmobile®, Inc
1602 Executive Drive, La Grange, Georgia 30240-5751, USA
Tel: +1 706 884 6651   Fax: +1 706 884 0390

Key personnel
President: John J Vresics
Vice-President, Domestic Sales and Marketing:
   Jack W Kennedy
Vice-President, International Sales and Marketing:
   James R Codlin

Principal subsidiary
RSS/Railserve, Inc
Suite 120, 1590 Phoenix Boulevard, Atlanta, Georgia 30349, USA
Tel: +1 770 996 6838   Fax: +1 770 996 6830
Email: trackmobile@mindspring.com

Products
Manufacture of bimodal (road/rail) mobile rail vehicle movers. The Trackmobile® range comprises seven different models with tractive effort from 7,575 kg to 32,659 kg. Features include automatic weight transfer couplers. Various gauge and coupler configurations are available.

Recent developments include the MAX-TRAN automatic weight transfer system which ensures maximum weight transfer and tractive effort.

RSS/Railserve provides turnkey contract shunting services throughout the USA and Canada, using shunting locomotives and/or Trackmobile® vehicles.

VERIFIED

Tuchschmid

Tuchschmid Enterprises AG
Kehlhofstrasse 54, CH-8501 Frauenfeld, Switzerland
Tel: +41 52 728 8111   Fax: +41 52 728 8100

Key personnel
See entry in *Freight vehicles and equipment* section

Products
COMPACTTERMINAL low-cost intermodal terminal. The COMPACTTERMINAL system is modular in concept and suitable for all sizes of terminal, from installations for small throughputs to high-performance freight distribution centres.

VERIFIED

Ultra Dynamics

Ultra Dynamics Ltd
Anson Business Park, Cheltenham Road East, Staverton, Gloucester GL2 9QN, UK
Tel: +44 1452 857711   Fax: +44 1452 858222

Key personnel
Managing Director: D Burton
Sales Manager: C R G Ellis

Principal subsidiary
Ultra Dynamics Inc
1278 Research Road, Columbus, Ohio 43230-6625, USA
Tel: +1 614 759 9000   Fax: +1 614 759 9046
Email: 70414.1337@compuserve.com

Products
Ultra retarders are speed-sensitive units bolted to the inside of rails at strategic intervals along the track and these can be installed on the hump, in the switching area and in the classification tracks to provide the required wagon speed control.

Wagons are retarded accurately from the switching area to a safe buffing speed in the sidings. In the case of automatic couplers, wagon speeds are controlled between the specified bandwidth to ensure coupling takes place. The retarder units are pre-set during manufacture to the required speed control conditions of a particular marshalling yard. Noise levels are low and no exterior power source is required.

Retarders can be configured as High Capacity or as the new Trackmaster model. High-capacity retarders are available with a retraction facility for use in yards where the operations require considerable resorting of trains.

The company also manufactures emergency stopping systems and safety systems and is BS EN ISO9001 approved.

Recent contracts include installations in Copenhagen and Padborg marshalling yards (DSB); Keiyo Railways, Japan, Murata marshalling yard and several yards of the Union Pacific, CP and BNSF rail companies in North America.

UPDATED

Ultra Trackmaster retarder   **1997**

Ultra retarders in Vienna yard, Austria   **1997**

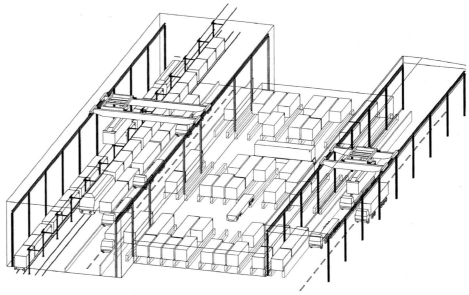

Tuchschmid COMPACTTERMINAL for intermodal transport   **1996**

Unilok

Unilokmotive Ireland Ltd
Deerpark Industrial Estate, Oranmore, Galway, Ireland
Tel: +353 91 790890   Fax: +353 91 790846

Key personnel
See entry in *Locomotives and powered passenger vehicles* section

Product
The Unilok range of road/rail wagon movers and shunting locomotives. Models are classified according to maximum drawbar pull up to 12,500 kg. A range of diesel engines may be fitted with outputs from 70 to 150 hp (52 to 112 kW) providing maximum speeds up to 30 km/h on road and rail. All machines are available with hydrostatic drive transmissions and a range of optional equipment including radio remote control, snow-plough, and hydraulic crane.

Uniloks are in service worldwide and are available in all gauges and coupler types.

Contracts include the supply of Unilok vehicles to Pakistan, Netherlands and Mexico.

VERIFIED

Vollert

Vollert GmbH & Co KG Maschinenfabrik
D-74185 Weinsberg, Germany
Tel: +49 7134 52228   Fax: +49 7134 52202

Products
Shunting equipment of various types; wagon transfer cars, radio-controlled diesel, battery or electric robot shunters of varying sizes and power including models capable of moving 5,000 t trains in temperatures as low as −15°C; remote-controlled functions include disengagement of couplings and an infinitely variable traction speed for accurate wagon positioning at discharge points.

VERIFIED

Windhoff

Windhoff AG
PO Box 1963, D-48409 Rheine, Germany
Tel: +49 5971 580   Fax: +49 5971 58209

Key personnel
See entry in *Freight and equipment* section

Products
Tele-Trac shunting vehicle, diesel or electrohydraulically driven, control of shunting course and coupling operations by radio or by interlinking with loading programme; marshalling yard equipment; turntables and traversers; screw-jacks for lifting locomotives, wagons and other heavy loads; lifting equipment for complete trains.

Recent contracts include the supply of a Tele-Trac shunter to Netherlands Railways (NS).

VERIFIED

Minilok DH100 four-axle road/rail vehicle from YEC   **1997**

YEC

Yorkshire Engine Co Ltd
PO Box 66, Rotherham S60 1DD, UK
Tel: +44 1709 820202   Fax: +44 1709 820206

Works
Unit A7, Meadowbank Industrial Estate, Rotherham, UK

Minilok works
Allrad-Rangiertechnik GmbH
D-5628 Heiligenhaus, Germany
Tel: +49 2056 68251

Key personnel
See entry in *Locomotives and powered passenger vehicles* section

Products
YEC is the UK agent for the Minilok road/rail locomotive range. The smallest is the two-axle DH30, which weighs 16 t and the range extends up to the DH340 six-axle vehicle which weighs 75 t.

NEW ENTRY

ZAGRO

ZAGRO Bahn- und Baumaschinen GmbH
Mühlstrasse 11-15, D-74906 Bad Rappenau-Grombach, Germany
Tel: +49 7266 91680   Fax: +49 7266 916825

Key personnel
Managing Director and Sales Manager:
  Wolfgang Zappel

Products
Road vehicles equipped with ZAGRO track guiding equipment for railway operation; Mini-Shunters for moving wagons on level track and over track pits; TP 100 suction sweeper for cleaning track and station platforms, snow removal and ballast spreading.

The range of road vehicles equipped with ZAGRO railway guide wheels includes the Mercedes-Benz Unimog for servicing, maintenance and transport duties on standard-, broad- and narrow-gauge systems; Mercedes-Benz 307-310 Sprinter for use as a personnel carrier and for servicing and maintenance duties; Renault Traffic 4 × 4 for duties including inspection and maintenance from the track or alongside; and forklift shunters for shunting railway wagons on standard-, broad- and narrow-gauge tracks with a hauling capacity of 300 t.

The ZAGRO Mini-Shunter has a tractive force of 150 t. The Mini-Shunter can be driven by a petrol or diesel engine. The required thrust force is transmitted from its wheel flanges to the wagon wheel. This and the continuously controlled hydraulic drive ensure safe braking of wagons. Wagons can be shunted in both directions without removing the machine.

The ZAGRO TP 100 track cleaning system features a suction sweeper equipped with a hand-actuated flexible suction pipe controlled via bypass openings. Speed can be adjusted from 5 to 40 km/h and maximum cleaning capacity is 500 m/h. The suction pipe operator drives the vehicle via remote control and a footboard, to accommodate two additional workers, is mounted on the platform.

UPDATED

Windhoff Tele-Trac shunters in operation at the Kaiserstuhl III plant, Dortmund

Unimog vehicle fitted with ZAGRO rail guiding equipment

Zweiweg Schneider

Zweiweg Schneider
Oberbüscherhof, D-42799 Leichlingen, Germany
Tel: +49 2174 79095   Fax: +49 2174 79095

Key personnel
Sales and Marketing Director: Walter Wagner

Products
Track-guidance rollers that convert a road vehicle into a rail vehicle. Besides its use in creating a shunting unit (the resultant tractive power equals about that of a 20 t locomotive), the device also permits use of the Mercedes-Benz Unimog on rails as a working unit with various supplementary equipment.

The Type 62S, 82S and 150S shunting vehicles for trailing loads of up to 1,200 t can be equipped for radio remote control. The portable transmitter operates via a 2 m band with a frequency range of 138 to 173 MHz. Transmitter performance is 50 to 5,000 MW. A Ni/Cd battery provides the power supply. The receiver is mounted in a stable, shock-resistant aluminium steel-cast housing in the vehicle. Test equipment is via light emitting diodes.

VERIFIED

Zwiehoff

Zwiehoff GmbH
PO Box 100845, Rosenheim 83008, Germany
Tel: +49 8031 219601   Fax: +49 8031 219603

Zwiehoff road/rail conversion on Unimog vehicle

1997

Key personnel
Managing Director: Gerd Zwiehoff

Products
Road/rail equipment including track-guidance rollers that convert a road vehicle into a rail vehicle.

NEW ENTRY

WORKSHOP, REPAIR AND MAINTENANCE EQUIPMENT

Alphabetical listing

Accent
Adtranz
Alzmetall
Atlas
CAM Industries
Casaire
Cattron
Chassijet
Chemirail
Cimmco International
Compair Hydrovane
Cragg Railcharger
Dawson-Aquamatic
EEC
Environmental Cleaning
Fergusson
GEC Alsthom
Hegenscheidt-MFD
Hi-Force Hydraulics
Hovair Systems

HYWEMA
INME
Instant Zip-Up
Instron Wolpert
Kambre i Täby
Kellenberger
Keller
Linsinger-Maschinenbau
Mechan
MTS
MTS Systems
Nencki
Neuero Technology
Nord Productique
Penetone
Pfaff-silberblau
Portec
Proceco
Progressive Engineering
Railquip

Railweight
Rescar
REW
Ross & White
SEFAC
Simmons
SMIS
Smith Bros & Webb
Somers Railway Engineering
Talgo
Toshiba
Tysol
Ultrasonic Sciences
Vanjax
Wagner
Wagons-Lits
Whiting
Windhoff
YEC

Classified Listing

CLEANING AND PAINTING EQUIPMENT
Accent
Chassijet
Chemirail
Compair Hydrovane
Dawson-Aquamatic
Environmental Cleaning
Fergusson
Kambre i Täby
Penétone
Proceco
Railquip
Ross & White
Smith Bros & Webb
Tysol

HEATING EQUIPMENT
Casaire

LIFTING GEAR AND ACCESS EQUIPMENT
Atlas
Cattron
Hi-Force Hydraulics
Hovair Systems
HYWEMA
INME

Instant Zip-Up
Mechan
Nencki
Neuero Technology
Pfaff-silberblau
Portec
Railquip
SEFAC
Somers Railway Engineering
Toshiba
Vanjax
Whiting
Windhoff

MAITENANCE AND REPAIR SERVICES
Adtranz
GEC Alsthom
Rescar
REW
Wagons-Lits

TESTING EQUIPMENT
Cragg Railcharger
ECC
Instron Wolpert
MTS

MTS Systems
Nencki
Proceco
Progressive Engineering
Railweight
SMIS
Toshiba
Ultrasonic Sciences

WHEEL LATHES AND MACHINE TOOLS
Alzmetall
Atlas
CAM Industries
Cimmco International
Hegenscheidt-MFD
Hi-Force Hydraulics
Kellenberger
Keller
Linsinger-Maschinenbau
Nord Productique
Proceco
Progressive Engineering
Railquip
Simmons
Talgo
Wagner

Company Listing by Country

AUSTRIA
Linsinger-Maschinenbau

FRANCE
Chemirail
Nord Productique
SEFAC
Wagons-Lits

GERMANY
Adtranz
Alzmetall
Hegenscheidt-MFD
HYWEMA
Instron Wolpert
MTS Systems
Neuero Technology
Pfaff-silberblau
Wagner
Windhoff

INDIA
Cimmco International
EEC
Vanjax

ITALY
Keller

JAPAN
Toshiba

SPAIN
INME
Talgo

SWEDEN
Kambre i Täby

SWITZERLAND
Kellenberger
Nencki

UK
Accent
Adtranz
Atlas
Casaire
Chassijet
Dawson-Aquamatic
Environmental Cleaning
GEC Alsthom
Hi-Force Hydraulics
Hovair Systems
Instant Zip-Up
Mechan
Progressive Engineering

Railweight
REW
SMIS
Smith Bros & Webb
Somers Railway Engineering
Ultrasonic Sciences
YEC

USA
CAM Industries
Cattron
Cragg Railcharger
Fergusson
MTS
Penetone
Portec
Proceco
Railquip
Rescar
Ross & White
Simmons
Tysol
Whiting

Accent

Accent Spray Booth Systems
Chadderton Industrial Estate, Greengate, Middleton, Manchester M24 1SW, UK
Tel: +44 161 655 3322   Fax: +44 161 655 3119

Key personnel
Marketing Manager: Barry Gregson

Products
Design, manufacture, installation and commissioning of Selspray booths, manufactured to meet British Standard BS 5750 Part 1 quality assurance benchmark. Features include full length, full width filtration for optimum air flow, colour-corrected lighting and a double-skinned construction.

Accent offers a complete turnkey package and a comprehensive maintenance agreement.

VERIFIED

Adtranz, Chart Leacon, maintenance workshops (Tony Pattison)   *1997*

Adtranz

ABB Daimler-Benz Transportation GmbH
Saatwinkler Damm 42-43, D-13627 Berlin, Germany
Tel: +49 30 38320   Fax: +49 30 3832 2000

Head Office, Fixed Installations Group
ABB Daimler-Benz Transportation Bahnfahrwegsysteme
Mainzer Landstrasse 351, D-60326 Frankfurt-am-Main, Germany
Tel: +49 69 75070   Fax: +49 69 7507 584

UK subsidiaries
ABB Daimler-Benz Transportation (Customer support) Ltd
Litchurch Lane, Derby DE 24 8AD
Tel: + 44 133 234 4666   Fax + 44 133 225 1884
Executive: Stig Svard
Other plants in: Crewe, Chart Leacon (Ashford, Kent), Doncaster, Ilford (London), Manchester, Swindon

Key personnel
See entry in *Fixed electrification equipment* section

Products
System logistics including design and construction of turnkey workshops and maintenance centres, computerised storage and retrieval of spare parts and documentation. Customer support for railway operators, including vehicle refurbishment and repair, field service and maintenance, commissioning and warranty and supply of spare parts.

UPDATED

Alzmetall

Alzmetall Werkzeugmaschinenfabrik und Giesserei Friedrich GmbH & Co
Steinerstrasse 2-8, D-83352 Altenmarkt/Alz, Germany
Tel: +49 8621 880   Fax: +49 8621 88213

Key personnel
Managing Director: A Friedmann
Export Director: J Reiter

Principal subsidiary
Bluthardt AG
Gerberstrasse 19, D-72622 Nürtingen, Germany

Products
Drilling machines; machining centres; special purpose machines.

VERIFIED

Atlas

Atlas Engineering Company
12 Croydon Road, Caterham CR3 6QB, UK
Tel: +44 1883 347635   Fax: +44 1883 345662

Key personnel
Sales Director: P J Hines

Products
Mobile railway lifting jack (up to 35 tonnes capacity); wheel profile trueing machines; crank axle turning machines; jacks; screwing machines; underfloor wheel trueing machines; double wheel lathes; hydraulic wheel presses.

VERIFIED

CAM Industries

CAM Industries Inc
Peerless Tool Division
215 Philadelphia Street, PO Box 227, Hanover, Pennsylvania 17331, USA
Tel: +1 717 637 5988   Fax: +1 717 637 9329

Key personnel
President: C A McGough Jr
Vice-President: C A McGough III

Products
Machinery and equipment for use in the manufacture and repair of DC motors and generators; electric traction motor and generator repair shops for railway workshops; engineering service for planning and equipping electric traction departments of railway workshops.

VERIFIED

Casaire

Casaire Ltd
Raebarn House, Northolt Road, Harrow HA2 0DY, UK
Tel: +44 181 423 2323   Fax: +44 181 864 2952

Works
Dashwood Avenue, High Wycombe HP12 3DP, UK

Key personnel
Chairman and Company Secretary: R T Roberts
Managing Director: M K Campbell
Technical and Sales Director: A S Mason

Products
Space heating systems.

Recent contracts include the supply of a direct-fired gas warm air space heating system for London Underground Ltd's Stratford Market depot.

VERIFIED

Cattron

Cattron Inc
58 West Shenango Street, Sharpsville, Pennsylvania 16150-1198, USA
Tel: +1 412 962 3571   Fax: +1 412 962 4310
Email: cattron.inc@industry.net

Key personnel
See entry in *Signalling and telecommunications systems* section

UK subsidiary
Cattron (UK) Ltd
Riverdene Industrial Estate, Molesey Road, Hersham, Walton on Thames KT12 4RY
Tel: 01932 247511   Fax: 01932 220937
Managing Director: Nigel P Day

Products
Radio and infrared cordless control systems for railway equipment including shunting locomotives, overhead cranes, wagon movers and ballast wagon doors.

UPDATED

Atlas ATG axle turning and grinding machine

Chassijet

Chassijet Ltd
6 Maubrook Road Industrial Estate, Birmingham Road,
Stratford-upon-Avon CV37 0BT, UK
Tel: +44 1789 415515   Fax: +44 1789 295942

Key personnel
Managing Director: C Scheffer
Marketing Executive: I Cleaver

Products
Vehicle cleaning systems.
Chassijet's Railjet 2000 system is designed for the removal of dirt, oil and grease from rail vehicles. Vehicle sides are cleaned by rail-mounted spray jets parallel to the track, and the underside is cleaned by a trolley system located between the running rails; the vehicle remains stationary whilst the mountings, holding high-pressure (130 bar) oscillating jets, move along. The jets are supplied by a 24 kVA pump unit delivering up to 90 litres per minute. Water can be heated up to 85°C if an oil or gas-fired module is selected, and can be recycled. Up to 100 programs can be stored in Railjet's microprocessor memory.

VERIFIED

Chemirail

Société des Établissements Roger Brillié SA
25 rue de la Victoire, PO Box 45, F-93155 Blanc Mesnil Cedex, France
Tel: +33 1 48 65 20 76   Fax: +33 1 48 67 30 18

Key personnel
Chief Executive Officer: M Vaniscotte
Director, Export Sales: J N Vassilopoulos
Technical Manager: M Lenaert
After-Sales Service: M Da Vinha

Products
Design, manufacture and installation of rolling stock washing machines to customer specification. Customers include SNCF (sole supplier, including special apparatus for TGV trainsets), RATP, DB AG, RENFE, SNCFT, CFCO and various metro and light rail systems.
Recent contracts include EPS, North Pole International Depot, London; DB AG, Munich and Hamburg; Shanghai metro; and SNCF, Le Landy TGV depot, Paris.

VERIFIED

Cimmco International

Cimmco International
A division of Cimmco Birla Ltd
Prakash Deep, 7 Tolstoy Marg, New Delhi 110001, India
Tel: +91 11 331 4383/384/385
Fax: +91 11 332 0777/372 3520

Key personnel
See entry in *Freight vehicles and equipment* section

Products
Machinery and equipment for manufacture and maintenance of rolling stock.
Contracts include the supply of welding materials and accessories, machine tools and hand tools to Myanmar Railways.

VERIFIED

Compair Hydrovane

Compair Hydrovane
Claybrook Drive, Washford Industrial Estate,
Redditch B98 0DS, UK
Tel: +44 1527 525522   Fax: +44 1527 521140

Key personnel
See entry in *Passenger coach equipment* section

Products
Trackair range of rotary compressors specially designed for mobile railway applications. There are 12 basic models available for any working pressure required between 7 and 10 bar.
Hydrovane range of rotary vane railway compressors for stationary applications. Range extends from 1.98 litres/s to 207 litres/s up to 10 bar.
Recent contracts include delivery of 26 TA20 units for Mexico City metro.

NEW ENTRY

Cragg Railcharger

2708 Summer Street North East, Minneapolis, Minnesota 55413, USA
Tel: +1 612 623 8804   Fax: +1 612 623 0847

Key personnel
See entry in *Signalling and telecommunications systems* section

Product
Cragg ST-2L, a digital display device to verify hot bearings and wheel defects, using a non-contact thermometer.

VERIFIED

Dawson-Aquamatic

Dawson-Aquamatic
A Barry-Wehmiller International Company
Gomersal Works, Gomersal, Cleckheaton BD19 4LQ, UK
Tel: +44 1274 873422   Fax: +44 1274 874930

Key personnel
Managing Director: B J Turner
Divisional Manager: P Barnett

Products
Design, manufacture and installation of drive-through washing and brushing systems for railcars, ranging from the simplest detergent/water wash-up to fully automatic installations for daily detergent washing and periodic removal of oxides and staining by acidic solutions; supporting control systems, water storage, effluent treatment and water recycling systems; railway workshop cleaning plant including bogie washing installations.

VERIFIED

EEC

Electronic & Engineering Company
EEC House, C-7 Dalia Industrial Estate, New Link Road,
Near Laxmi Industrial Estate, Andheri (West), Mumbai 400 053, India
Tel: +91 22 626 7148/626 7423   Fax: +91 22 626 9009

Key personnel
Managing Director: Ramesh Parikh
Research and Development Production Director: Nikhil Parikh
Sales and Marketing Director: Rajul Parikh

Products
Ultrasonic non-destructive testing equipment. The range includes an ultrasonic flaw detector for axles and general railway components; an ultrasonic rail tester, mounted on a trolley complete with probes and water container; a pocket ultrasonic rail tester with LED display for direct reading of defect location; and a multichannel multirail tester to test both rails simultaneously, provided with preset alarm functions and mounted on a lightweight, portable push trolley.

UPDATED

Environmental Cleaning

Environmental Cleaning Services Ltd
36-39 Westmoor Street, London SE7 8NR, UK
Tel: +44 181 858 8484   Fax: +41 181 858 1968

Key personnel
Managing Director: J I Charlton

Products
Graffiti removal and protection: chemical and mechanical cleaning of stone, concrete and floors, non-slip surfaces. Deep clean and cosmetics for buildings and rolling stock. Paint stripping and degreasing using safe bicarbonate of soda suitable for carriage renovation. Cleaning and protection of subways and stations. Odour destruction products, specialist odour-destroying cleaning products.

VERIFIED

Fergusson

Alex C Fergusson Inc
Spring Mill Drive, Frazer, Pennsylvania 19355, USA
Tel: +1 610 647 3300   Fax: +1 610 644 8240

Key personnel
Sales Manager: Joseph Woodring

Products
Aluminium and stainless-steel cleaners, sanitisers, degreasers and detergents.

VERIFIED

GEC Alsthom

GEC Alsthom Railway Maintenance Services Ltd
PO Box 3799, Washwood Heath Road, Birmingham B8 2UQ, UK
Tel: +44 121 695 3600   Fax: +44 121 695 3650

Key personnel
Director and General Manager: S J Ollier

Products
Maintenance, overhaul and refurbishment of railway rolling stock.
Recent contracts include mid-life refurbishment and technical upgrade of rolling stock for KCRC, Hong Kong; GEC Alsthom Railway Maintenance Services will be responsible for the maintenance of the fleet of Juniper emus for the London Victoria to Gatwick Airport line (Gatwick Express) during the 15 year franchise period.
As part of the company's involvement in whole-life maintenance of rolling stock, it has taken over existing depots both on London Underground (Northern Line) and Gatwick Express.

UPDATED

Hegenscheidt-MFD

Hegenscheidt-MFD GmbH
PO Box 1408, D-41804 Erkelenz, Germany
Tel: +49 243 1860   Fax: +49 243 186470

Key personnel
Managing Director: Klaus-Peter Schwarz
Sales Director: G Lades

Hegenscheidt-MFD CNC heavy-duty underfloor wheel lathe

Wagon door straightener by Hi-Force Hydraulics
                                                    1996

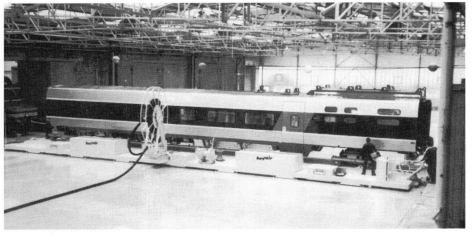

Hovair traverser and rotator unit supplied to De Dietrich Ferroviaire, France   *1995*

Corporate developments
In 1995, the activities of Wilhelm Hegenscheidt GmbH and Hoesch Maschinefabrik Deutschland GmbH were merged as Hegenscheidt-MFD GmbH, a subsidiary of Vossloh AG.

Products
Underfloor wheel lathes for machining wheelsets *in situ*; above-floor wheel lathes for universal machining of wheelsets; wheel presses for mounting and stripping wheels on to/off axles; hydraulic rerailing systems for lifting and repositioning vehicles; special equipment for machining engine crankshafts; wheelset diagnostic systems.

                                                    VERIFIED

Hi-Force Hydraulics

Hi-Force Hydraulics Ltd
Bentley Way, Daventry NN11 5QH, UK
Tel: +44 1327 77511   Fax: +44 1327 704466

Key personnel
See entry in *Permanent way equipment* section

Products
High-pressure hydraulic tools, including wagon door straighteners; jacks and presses; torque tools and accessories; pumps; crimping tools and nutsplitters.
   Recent contracts include the supply of hydraulic jacks to London Underground Ltd.

                                                    VERIFIED

Hovair Systems

Hovair Systems Ltd
North Lane, Aldershot GU12 4QH, UK
Tel: +44 1252 319922   Fax: +44 1252 334387

Key personnel
Managing Director: Andy Yates
Sales Manager: Danny Mercer

Products
Air film load-handling equipment. The system, which uses well-proven air bearing technology, has a multidirectional capability providing low resistance to motion and no damage to floors. It allows carriages to be moved within the workshop area unconstrained by rails. Complete carriages, with or without bogies, can be manoeuvred throughout the whole workshop, by only two men, allowing for removal of finished stock from a production or repair line. Carriages or trainsets can be rotated removing the need for turning facilities and, in manufacturing areas, can be used for movement between build, paint and fitting out. Complete carriages can be stored close together and, when required, taken to the single incoming rail for transfer to the rail network.
   Hovair systems are operating in Denmark, Sweden, Turkey and France, including a traverser and rotator unit at De Dietrich Ferroviaire.

                                                    UPDATED

HYWEMA

HYWEMA Lifting Systems
134-148 Wuppertaler Strasse, D-42653 Solingen, Germany
Tel: +49 212 25770   Fax: +49 212 592951

Key personnel
General Manager: D Paul
Sales Director: A Thomas

Products
Type FL/N mobile vehicle lift system for locomotives and for standard, articulated and multi-articulated railcars. Independent operation in all workshop areas. Synchronisation of all lifts is by a microprocessor-controlled electronic system.
   The Model FL/VN lift jack system is specially designed for changing bogies and wheelsets as well as welding and repair work on the carbody and the brakes.
   Various types are available with load capacities from 40,000 to 120,000 kg for locomotives, railcars and wagons.
   Recent contracts have been obtained from Plasser & Theurer, Linz, Austria; Hiroshima Tramway, Japan; and CFL, Luxembourg.

                                                    VERIFIED

INME

INME
Alameda de Urquijo 87, 48013 Bilbao, Spain
Tel: +34 4442 0448   Fax: +34 4442 1221

Key personnel
Marketing Manager: Pablo Diez
Engineering Manager: Jesus Ferro

Products
Mobile lifting columns, bogie platforms, overhead cranes, workshop haulage systems.

                                                    NEW ENTRY

Instant Zip-Up

Instant Zip-Up Ltd
Special Products Division
153 Newton Road, Lowton, Warrington WA3 1EZ, UK
Tel: +44 1942 680160   Fax: +44 1942 601984

Key personnel
See entry in *Permanent way equipment* section

Products
Supply and rental of access equipment for rolling stock maintenance including powered platforms, glass fibre towers and light-alloy scaffold systems; windscreen stands, passenger coach side access platforms, access steps; roof guardrail systems, guardrails for passenger coach doorways, pit bridges. Staff training in the use of work platforms and scaffold systems.

                                                    UPDATED

Instron Wolpert

Instron Wolpert GmbH
PO Box 21 14 80, D-67014 Ludwigshafen, Germany
Tel: +49 621 69070   Fax: +49 621 6907160

Key personnel
General Managers: Norman Smith, Gerhard Hoppner
Sales and Marketing Manager: Sergio Saggini
Marketing Manager: Brigitte Iffländer-Wiegmann
Technical Manager: Dr Jörg Meißner

Products
Testor hardness testing machines, spring testing machines, universal testing machines for tensile, compression, shear and bending tests; pendulum impact testing machines; special purpose testing machines to customer specification, automatic testing machines and installations.

                                                    UPDATED

Kambre i Täby

Kambre i Täby AB
PO Box 7221, S-183 07 Täby, Sweden
Tel: +46 8 630 0131   Fax: +46 8 630 0119

Key personnel
Chairman: Claes Johansson
Managing Director: Karl-Axel Kambre

Principal subsidiaries
Styrlogic Engineering AB, Täby, Sweden
Brövig A/S, Kristiansand, Norway

Products
Train washing machines, featuring brush and brushless washing equipment; specialised washing machines for cleaning the upper and lower surfaces of raked train noses; train interior cleaning systems.
   Recent contracts include the supply of a drive-through brush washer and an automatic washing machine to SJ, Sweden.

                                                    VERIFIED

Kellenberger

Kellenberger AG
Mittlerestrasse 13, CH-3600 Thun, Switzerland
Tel: +41 33 233923   Fax: +41 33 233926

Key personnel
Executive: Rudolf Kisslig

Products
Wheel-grinding machines.
   Recent contracts include the supply of underfloor grinding machines to SBB.

                                                    VERIFIED

Wagons-Lits

International Railway Management
31 rue du Colonel Avia, F-75904 Paris Cedex 15, France
Tel: +33 1 41 33 68 00   Fax: +33 1 41 33 68 02

Key personnel
Technical Manager: Jacques Strebelle
Finance Manager: Jose Ignacio Gonzalez
Study and Project Manager: Philippe Aloyol

Products
Wagons-Lits carries out maintenance, overhaul and major refurbishment of all kinds of rolling stock at its workshops in 26 European locations.

Wagon-Lits has signed maintenance contracts with CFF, DSB, FS, NS, ÖBB, SNCB and SNCF.

VERIFIED

Whiting

Whiting Corporation
15700 Lathrop Avenue, Harvey, Illinois 60426-5198, USA
Tel: +1 312 468 9400   Fax: +1 708 210 5030

Key personnel
President: J L Kahn
Vice-President, Sales and Marketing: C J Skorpinski
Manager, Product Systems and Transportation Sales:
  M N Milligan
Manager, Applications: Ron Koziel

Principal subsidiary
Whiting Equipment Canada Inc
PO Box 217, 350 Alexander Street, Welland, Ontario L3B 5P4, Canada
Tel: +1 905 732 7585   Fax: +1 905 732 2366
President: Rudi Kroeker

Products
Conventional/shallow pit car hoists, bogie repair hoists, body hoists/supports, portable electric jacks, wagon/train progression systems, transfer tables, bogie/vehicle turntables, drop tables, overhead and gantry cranes, rip jacks, sanding cranes.

Recent contracts include modernisation of facilities at Brentwood and Alexandria for Washington Metropolitan Area Transit Authority, USA.

VERIFIED

Windhoff

Windhoff AG
PO Box 1963, D-48409 Rheine, Germany
Tel: +49 5971 580   Fax: +49 5971 58209

Key personnel
See entry in *Freight vehicles and equipment* section

Products
Bogie lifting plants and rotation installations, transporters, air-cushion vehicles and lifting stands. Windhoff developed 70 vehicles with lifting work platforms for the inspection and maintenance of DB AG ICE high-speed trainsets; these were delivered to the ICE Maintenance and Service Centre in Hamburg-Eidelstedt. The complete eight-track installations mounted on supports, the lifting cars with guiding system and the air-cushion-type bogie and wheelset changing equipment were supplied by Windhoff.

The company has designed and installed a bogie maintenance installation at Haarlem, Netherlands. This enables wheelsets and bogies to be inspected and repaired on the combined lifting and turning plant, which has a 12 tonne capacity.

VERIFIED

Windhoff bogie measuring stand in the SGP factory at Graz   *1996*

Windhoff lifting installation for NS at Haarlem   *1996*

An SS2 Safety Scotch by YEC fitted to a driving wheel of a locomotive

YEC

Yorkshire Engine Company Ltd
PO Box 66, Rotherham, S60 1DD, UK
Tel: +44 114 242 3700   Fax: +44 114 275 1071

Key personnel
Executive: Peter Briddon

Products
Safety Scotch: a device for immobilising rail vehicles during maintenance or engineering work.

VERIFIED

TURNKEY SYSTEMS CONTRACTORS

Alphabetical Listing

Adtranz
Alcatel Canada
ANF-Industrie
Ansaldo Trasporti
Balfour Beatty Rail Projects
Bombardier
Chemetron
Davy British Rail International
Dimetronic
Fiat

GE
GEC Alsthom
GPT
Mecanoexportimport
Parsons Brinckerhoff Inc
Ranalah
SAIT-Devlonics
Sasib Hellas
Sasib Railway
Sasib Railway Iberica

SAT
Scitel Telematics
Sema Group
Siemens
Siemens Transportation Systems
Siemens Transportation Systems Inc
TCI
Telephone Cables
Temoinsa
Transintech Ltd

Company Listing by Country

BELGIUM
SAIT-Devlonics

CANADA
Alcatel Canada
Bombardier

FRANCE
ANF-Industrie
GEC Alsthom
SAT
Sema Group

GERMANY
Adtranz
Siemens

GREECE
Sasib Hellas

HUNGARY
Scitel Telematics

ITALY
Ansaldo Trasporti
Fiat
Sasib Railway

ROMANIA
Mecanoexportimport

SPAIN
Dimetronic
Sasib Railway Iberica
Temoinsa

UK
Balfour Beatty Rail Projects
Davy British Rail International

GPT
Ranalah
Siemens Transportation Systems
TCI
Telephone Cables
Transintech Ltd

USA
Chemetron
GE
Parsons Brinckerhoff Inc
Siemens Transportation Systems Inc

Adtranz

ABB Daimler-Benz Transportation GmbH
Group Holding Headquarters and Group Corporate
Centre
PO Box 130127, 13601 Berlin, Germany
Tel: +49 303 8320   Fax: +49 303 832 2000

Key personnel
See main entry in *Locomotives and powered passenger
vehicles* section

Projects
An Adtranz-led consortium has received the Shanghai
Metro Corporation (SMC) order for a total rail system
which involves development and building Line 2 of the
Shanghai Metro, running from East to West. The first part
is expected to start commercial service by the end of
2001. The contract includes installation of the catenary
system, telecommunications, remote control systems and
35 trains, each usually configured with six cars, but can be
extended to eight cars.

The Guangzhou Metro Corporation (GMC) contract
with the Adtranz/Siemens consortium to build a metro
system for the city of Guangzhou is in advanced
production. Adtranz is supplying 20 six-car trains (120
metrocars). The first train has already been handed over
to GMC and all should be delivered by early 1999 when
the first line is expected to open.

NEW ENTRY

Alcatel Canada

Alcatel Canada Inc
Transport Automation
1235 Ormont Drive, Weston, Ontario M9L 2W6, Canada
Tel: +1 416 742 3900   Fax: +1 416 742 1136

Key personnel
See main entry in *Passenger coach equipment* section

Projects
Turnkey signalling systems for tramcars, metros, light rail
transit, people movers and mainline railways.

Contracts include resignalling of the DLR, London, and
Newark Airport people mover train control system.

NEW ENTRY

ANF-Industrie

ANF-Industrie
PO Box 1, 59154 Crespin, France
Tel: +33 3 27 23 53 00   Fax: +33 3 27 35 16 24

Key personnel
See main entry in *Locomotives and powered passenger
vehicles* section

Projects
The first guided light transit vehicles (named TVR) for the
city of Caen are being built by ANF, which will also install
the system.

The GLT is a bimode vehicle operating on rubber tyres
but guided by a single rail; it is designed to offer the
capacity and image advantages of a light rail vehicle with
the flexibility of a bus. Propulsion is by electric motor,
supplied by either overhead line or diesel generator.

NEW ENTRY

Ansaldo Trasporti

Ansaldo Trasporti SpA
425 Via Argine, I-80147 Naples, Italy
Tel: +39 81 565 0111   Fax: +39 81 565 0698

Key personnel
Director, Turnkey Systems: Claudio Artusi
See also main entry in *Locomotives and powered
passenger vehicles* section

Projects
Ansaldo Trasporti has been selected to build the Bursa

light metro in Turkey as part of a consortium with
Siemens.

A contract has been won to build the Copenhagen
metro and covers, on a turnkey basis, the design,
construction, supply and installation of an automatic
urban metro system with 15 km of track and 15 stations. It
also covers the supply of 19 driverless vehicles with ATC.

NEW ENTRY

Balfour Beatty Rail Projects Ltd

Balfour Beatty Rail Projects Ltd
Railway Electrification
PO Box 12, Acornfield Road, Kirkby, Liverpool, L33 7TY,
UK
Tel: +44 151 548 5000   Fax: +44 151 548 5320

Key personnel
See main entry in *Fixed electrification equipment* section

Products
Turnkey projects covering a wide variety of transport
systems.

Balfour Rail Projects is a member of the BICC group
and has electrified well over 25,000 km of rail systems,
undertaking design, supply and installation contracts
throughout the world.

Recent contracts include electrification of the
Guangzhou Metro, China; re-electrification of the North
London Line for Railtrack, UK; upgrading of the Beijing
Metro, China; MTRC Lantau and Airport Railway, Hong
Kong; and electrification of the New Haven—Boston route
for Amtrak, USA.

NEW ENTRY

Bombardier Inc

Bombardier Inc
Transportation Equipment Group
1101 Parent Street, Saint-Bruno, Québec J3V 6E6,
Canada
Tel: +1 514 441 2020   Fax: +1 514 441 1515

Key personnel
See main entry in *Locomotives and powered passenger
vehicles* section

Projects
In March 1996, Amtrak announced the selection of the
Bombardier/GEC Alsthom consortium for supply of high-
speed equipment that will introduce high-speed rail
service on its Northeast Corridor (NEC) route from
Washington, DC to New York City and Boston. The
contract calls for the design and manufacture of up to 18
American Flyer trainsets, each consisting of two power
cars and six coaches, as well as 15 electric locomotives to
be used with other Amtrak equipment in the NEC fleet.
The contract also includes the design, construction and
installation of up to three maintenance facilities for the
rolling stock. The consortium partners will share the
power car and electric locomotive design. In addition to
being responsible for the complete design of the
coaches, Bombardier is also manufacturing the
locomotives, power cars and coaches, and is undertaking
the final assembly of the trainsets.

The Bombardier Consortium in Kuala Lumpur,
Malaysia, in co-operation with BC Transit of Vancouver, is
supplying all of the equipment, rolling stock and services
for the Advanced Rapid Transit (ART) system in Kuala
Lumpur. Under contract to PUTRA, Bombardier is
producing 70 Mark II LRVs. Phase 1 of the system is
opening in 1998.

The Ankara Metro Consortium of Bombardier, SNC-
Lavalin, and two Turkish construction and engineering
companies, Gama and Guris, is implementing the turnkey
contract for the design and construction of Phase 1 of the
Ankara Metro System for the Municipality of Greater
Ankara in Turkey. Bombardier is responsible for the
design and supply of 108 vehicles, automatic train
control, communications, and maintenance equipment,
as well as overall system integration, training, and system
commissioning. Based on the Toronto H6 cars, the
aluminium vehicles for Ankara incorporate changes and
improvements developed by Bombardier. With the

addition of an onboard microprocessor controller, the
vehicles can be operated in automatic mode, in-cab
signalling mode or manually.

Bombardier is part of the Tramtrack consortium
building the Croydon Tramlink network in south London.

NEW ENTRY

Chemetron

Chemetron Railway Products Inc
177 West Hintz Road, Wheeling, Illinois 60090, USA
Tel: +1 847 520 5454   Fax: +1 847 520 6373
Email: cttsales@aol.com

Key personnel
See main entry in *Permanent way equipment and services*
section

Projects
Turnkey design of rail welding plants. Contract welding
service of rail into continuous welded rail in any of
standard, alloy or head-hardened rails.

NEW ENTRY

Davy British Rail International

Davy British Rail International Ltd
Ashmore House, Richardson Road, Stockton-on-Tees
TS18 3RE
Tel: +44 1642 602221   Fax: +44 1642 341001

Key personnel
See main entry in *Permanent way equipment and services*
section

Projects
Design, project management, construction engineering
and training services for rail rehabilitation, including
turnkey projects.

DBRI completed the rehabilitation of the 120 km
PERUMKA rail link between Jakarta and Merak in 1996.

NEW ENTRY

Dimetronic

Dimetronic SA
Apartado 6, Parque Empresarial, E-28831 San Fernando
de Henares, Spain
Tel: +34 1 675 4212/4712   Fax: +34 1 656 2115

Key personnel
See main entry in *Locomotives and powered passenger
vehicles* section

Projects
Most of the projects contracted are of a turnkey nature.

Contracts include WESTRACE electronic interlocking
and CTC systems for the metros of Madrid and Lisbon,
SSI installations for 30 CP (Portugal) stations, signalling
for the Valencia Metro (including ATP) and WESTRACE
electronic interlocking for FGC (Spain).

NEW ENTRY

Fiat

Fiat Ferroviaria SpA
Piazza Galateri 4, I-12038 Savigliano (CN), Italy
Tel: +39 172 718111   Fax: +39 172 718306

Key personnel
See main entry in *Locomotives and powered passenger
vehicles* section

Projects
Sasib Railway has formed a consortium with Fiat called
Italrail for LRT turnkey projects.

NEW ENTRY

GE

GE Transportation Systems
2901 East Lake Road, Erie, Pennsylvania 16531, USA
Tel: +1 814 875 3457   Fax: +1 814 875 5911
Web: www.ge.com/transportation

Key personnel
See main entry in *Locomotives and powered passenger vehicles* section

Projects
GE Global locomotive maintenance service maintains over 2000 locomotives in comprehensive service programmes. GE Transportation Systems provides customised maintenance solutions ranging from field technical support to full, turnkey maintenance facility operations. These programmes feature high performance through reliability-centred maintenance programmes, continuous training, supply chain integration and dedicated engineering support.

NEW ENTRY

GEC Alsthom Systems Group

GEC Alsthom Transport
48 rue Albert Dhalenne, 93482 Saint-Ouen Cedex, Paris, France
Tel: +33 1 41 66 90 00   Fax: +33 1 41 66 96 66
Web: http://www.gecalsthom.com

Key personnel
See main entry in *Locomotives and powered passenger vehicles* section

Projects
Include the construction on a turnkey basis of the initial Docklands Light Railway, UK, and participation in the current extension to Lewisham; the design, construction, operation and maintenance of the Manchester Metrolink LRT system, UK, under a build, operate and transfer (BOT) contract (as a major participant in the concession company); undertaking, on a similar BOT basis, the Arlanda Airport Rail Link, Sweden, as the lead member of the A-Train AB consortium; as part of the KTGV consortium of the Seoul to Pusan High-Speed Railway in South Korea — provision of TGV Trainset, catenaries, sub-stations and signalling; the construction, as part of the Florida Fox consortium, of the high-speed Tampa to Miami Florida Overland Express system in the USA.

NEW ENTRY

GPT

GPT Limited
Strategic Communication Systems
PO Box 146, Coventry CV3 1LQ, UK
Tel: +44 1203 565000   Fax: +44 1203 565888
Email: support@scs.gpt.co.uk

Key personnel
See main entry in *Signalling and telecommunications* section

Projects
An example of integration capability is the development of a communications system, controlling telecommunications, public address, CCTV and passenger information displays via a single screen.
GPT TRACS (Transportation Communication Services) is a communications provision business which manages system obsolescence and enhances performance of communication systems.
GPT is providing communications for the Lantau Airport line, Hong Kong, and for Midland Metro Line 1.

NEW ENTRY

Mecanoexportimport

30 Dacia Boulevard, Bucharest, Romania
Tel: +40 1 211 9855   Fax: +40 1 210 7894

Key personnel
See entry in *Locomotives and powered passenger vehicles* section

Products
Construction on turnkey basis of industrial units and workshops.

NEW ENTRY

Parsons Brinckerhoff Inc

One Penn Plaza, New York, NY 10119-0061, USA
Tel: +1 212 465 5000   Fax: +1 212 465 5096

Key Personnel
See main entry in *Consultancy services* section

Projects
As a subcontractor for the Tren Urbano system, San Juan, Puerto Rico, Parsons Brinckerhoff is providing programme management and design services for the systems and test track turnkey contract.

NEW ENTRY

Ranalah

Ranalah Moulds Ltd
New Road, Newhaven BN9 0EH, UK
Tel: +44 1273 514676   Fax: +44 1273 516529

Key personnel
See main entry in *Permanent way equipment and services* section

Projects
Turnkey service for supply of sleeper manufacturing plant.
Contracts include the supply of sleeper plants to Hong Kong, Philippines, Thailand and Malaysia.

NEW ENTRY

SAIT-Devlonics

A member of the SAIT RadioHolland Group
Chaussée de Ruisbroek 66, B-1180 Brussels, Belgium
Tel: +32 2 370 5311   Fax: +32 2 370 5114

Key personnel
See main entry in *Signalling and telecommunications* section

Projects
Turnkey implementation of HF, VHF, UHF, SHF fixed and mobile telecommunication networks; communication and control systems for public transport, including use of radio in underground and other difficult environments; passenger information display systems under control of central processing units.

NEW ENTRY

Sasib Hellas

Sasib Hellas SA
A member of the Sasib Railway Business Area (see Sasib)
6 Parnassou, G-15124 Athens, Greece
Tel: +30 1 6143 1856   Fax: +30 1 6143 187

Key personnel
See main entry in *Signalling and telecommunications* section

Projects
Specialists in turnkey projects comprising design, supply, installation, commissioning and maintenance of signalling, telecommunications and vehicle identification systems; solid-state and relay-based interlocking; automatic block; Automatic Train Control (ATC) and Centralised Traffic Control (CTC) systems; automatic route setting; passenger information systems; central dispatching systems.

NEW ENTRY

Sasib Railway

Sasib Railway SpA
A company of Sasib Railway Business Area
Via di Corticella 87/89, I-40128 Bologna, Italy
Tel: +39 51 4191 111   Fax: +39 51 4191 594

Key personnel
See main entry in *Signalling and telecommunications* section

Products
Specialists in turnkey projects comprising design, supply, installation and commissioning of signalling and telecommunications systems.
Sasib Railway is involved in the Italian high-speed project with Consortium Saturno for signalling, telecommunications and electrification.
Also complete transport systems (including urban transport systems and automatic people mover systems) on a turnkey basis.

NEW ENTRY

Sasib Railway Iberica

Sasib Railway Iberica SA
A company of Sasib Railway Business Area (see Sasib)
c/Estudiantes 5, E-28040 Madrid, Spain
Tel: +34 1 535 2500   Fax: +34 1 554 9953
Email: !railiberica

Key personnel
See main entry in *Signalling and telecommunications* section

Projects
The company is involved in turnkey projects comprising design, supply, installation, commissioning and maintenance of signalling, telecommunications and vehicle identification systems.
Recent contracts include safety relay interlocking systems for RENFE's Oveido station and Ponteferrada—Montforte route and PLCs installed at Euskotren's Bilbao station.

NEW ENTRY

SAT

SAT
Part of the SAGEM Group
Network and Telecommunications Division
11 rue Watt, 75626 Paris Cedex 13, France
Tel: +33 1 55 75 75 75   Fax: +33 1 55 75 30 94

Key personnel
See also main entry in *Signalling and telecommunications* section

Projects
Engineering and network design and turnkey networks.

NEW ENTRY

Scitel Telematics

Scitel Telematics Ltd
A company of Sasib Railway Business Area (see Sasib)
Lehel út 3/b, 1st Floor, H-1062 Budapest, Hungary
Tel: +36 1 1299 048   Fax: +36 1 1401 735

Key personnel
See main entry in *Signalling and telecommunications* section

Projects
Turnkey projects comprising design, supply, installation, commissioning and maintenance of signalling, telecommunications and vehicle identification systems.

NEW ENTRY

Sema Group

Sema Group SA
56 rue Roger Salengro, F-94126 Fontenay sous Bois, France
Tel: +33 1 43 94 57 10   Fax: +33 1 43 94 27 12

Key personnel
See main entry in *Signalling and telecommunications* section

Projects
Turnkey supplier of integrated railway control systems combining traffic, power supply, communications, passenger information and environment and auxiliary systems functions.

Contracts include supply of train departure management systems for eight Metro lines and rail traffic management and time scheduling systems for RER Lines A and B for RATP, Paris; rail traffic management systems for Lines 1 and 2 of the Caracas Metro.

NEW ENTRY

Siemens

Siemens Transportation Systems Group
PO Box 3240, D-91050 Erlangen, Germany
Tel: +49 9131 724157   Fax: +49 9131 726840
Web: http://www.siemens.de

Key personnel
Managers, Turnkey systems: R V Ark, K Neubeck

See also main entry in *Locomotives and powered passenger vehicles* section

Projects
During 1996, Siemens won a turnkey order to build a new metro line in Puerto Rico and received the order for a second metro line in Shanghai, of which Siemens' share was DM 330 million.

Other major turnkey projects include the joint project for Puerto Rico metro and with Adtranz for BERTS Bangkok. In addition to the contract for the Valencia Metro, Venezuela, a letter of intent has been received for the Bursa metro project, Turkey.

Siemens also supplies complete turnkey systems for integrated ticketing and fare collection, based on magnetic cards and contact and contactless smartcards.

NEW ENTRY

Siemens Transportation Systems

Siemens Transportation Systems Ltd
Sopers Lane, Poole BH17 7ER, UK
Tel: +44 1202 782067   Fax: +44 1202 782838

Key personnel
See entry in *Passenger coach equipment* section

Projects
Turnkey services include radio coverage surveys and analysis of surface, building and underground requirements.

NEW ENTRY

Siemens

Siemens Transportation Systems Inc
186 Wood Avenue South Iselin, NJ 08830, USA
Tel: +1 908 205 2200   Fax: +1 908 603 7379

Key personnel
See main entry in *Locomotives and powered passenger vehicles* section

Products
Siemens is supplying 64 heavy-rail vehicles for the San Juan Tren Urbano turnkey rail project. Siemens is consortium leader for this project and is providing project management, rails and power system for the 17.2 km route and communications/train-control systems, in addition to the vehicles.

NEW ENTRY

TCI

Transportation Consultants International
1 Eversholt Street, London NW1 2DN, UK
Tel: +44 171 214 9380   Fax: +44 171 214 9389

Key personnel
See main entry in *Consultancy services* section

Projects
TCI will deliver projects on a turnkey basis or meet specific needs including risk assessment, safety case preparation, interface management, training, feasibility studies, project management, construction management, operational research and signalling and telecommunications.

NEW ENTRY

Telephone Cables

Telephone Cables Limited
A GPT Group company
Chequers Lane, Dagenham RM9 6QA, UK
Tel: +44 181 592 6611   Fax: +44 181 592 3876

Key personnel
See main entry in *Signalling and telecommunications* section

Projects
Turnkey project management, design and installation.

NEW ENTRY

Temoinsa

Técnicas Modulares e Industriales SA
Poligono Industrial Congost, Avenida San Julián 100, E-08400 Granollers, Barcelona, Spain
Tel: +34 3 846 6835   Fax: +34 3 846 6486

Key personnel
See main entry in *Passenger coach equipment* section

Projects
Turnkey projects for complete interiors of new vehicles and refurbishment.

NEW ENTRY

Transintech

Transintech Ltd
PO Box 201, Derby DE24 8AP, UK
Tel: +44 1332 257500   Fax: +44 1332 371950

Key personnel
See main entry in *Passenger coach equipment* section

Projects
Turnkey interior packages and components in advanced materials.

Contracts include refurbishment of a British Mark 2 coach interior, in conjunction with Eversholt Leasing and Adtranz. The work includes fitting of Compin seats and new toilet and baby changing facilities.

NEW ENTRY

ROLLING STOCK LEASING COMPANIES

ROLLING STOCK LEASING COMPANIES

EUROPE

AAE

Ahaus Alstätter Eisenbahn Holding AG
Alpentrasse 1, PO Box 4357, CH-6304 Zug, Switzerland
Tel: +41 711 9123   Fax: +41 711 9460

Key personnel
Managing Director: Andreas Goer
Deputy Managing Director, Operations: Markus Vaerst
Deputy Managing Director, Finance: Mark Stevenson
Technical Director: Dr Johannes Nicolin
Sales and Marketing: Ole Nygaard

Vehicles
AAE has over 86,000 freight wagons rented to state railway operators and private companies, including DB AG, SBB, NS, SNCB, SJ, DSB, NSB, CFL, ÖBB, ČD, MÁV, ŽSR, Intercontainer/Interfrigo, Hupac, Novotrans, Cemat and Nordwaggon. AAE is a member of UIC, RIV and BCC and its fleet includes covered wagons, flat wagons, pocket wagons and container wagons.

UPDATED

Algeco

Algeco SA
16 avenue de l'Opera, F-75040 Paris Cedex 01, France
Tel: +33 1 42 86 23 00   Fax: +33 1 42 97 41 59

Key personnel
Assistant Director, Exploitation: Michel Bernard

Vehicles
Tank and special purpose wagons; ISO tank containers for hazardous products.

UPDATED

Angel Trains

Angel Trains Contracts Ltd
14 Pentonville Road, London N1 9YZ
Tel: +44 171 728 0500   Fax: +44 171 728 0503

Key personnel
Chairman: Dr John Prideaux
Managing Director: Richard Wilkinson
Business Development Director: John Vale

Political background
Angel Trains Contracts is one of the three rolling stock leasing companies sold by the British government in November 1995. It was bought by GRS Holding Co Ltd, a consortium of the consultancy Prideaux & Associates, US brokers Babcock & Brown, and Japanese bank Nomura International for £672.5 million. This was the only rolling stock company to go to an outside bidder; the other two went to management buyout groups.

The company was sold with leases in place to the former British Rail train operating companies lasting from two to nine years.

Traction and rolling stock
Angel Trains owns a spread of passenger rolling stock, ranging from over 50 InterCity 125 trains and 150 Class 158 long-distance diesel multiple-unit vehicles to large quantities of 1960s-built electric multiple-unit vehicles at work on the 750 V DC network south of London.

Angel Train Contracts Ltd

Class	Train operating unit(s)	Number of vehicles in service April 1995
Locomotives		
43	GNER, West Coast, GNER, Great Western	115

Class	Train operating unit(s)	Number of vehicles in service April 1995
Multiple-units		
Various dmus and railcars	North West, Central, South Wales and West, North London, ScotRail	135
142	North East, North West	190
150/0	Central	6
150/1	North West, Central	100
150/2	North West, Central	40
153	North East, South Wales and West	30
156	ScotRail, North East	152
158	Central, South Wales and West	150
165	Chiltern	180
166	Central, Thames	63
303	ScotRail	141
305/1	North West	12
305/2	ScotRail, North West	47
308	North East, Central	72
309	North West	24
312	Great Eastern, London Tilbury, Southend, Central	180
314	ScotRail	48
317	West Anglia Great Northern	288
421	Connex South Central	336
423	Connex South Eastern	264
442	South West	120
465/2	Connex South Eastern	200
466	Connex South Eastern	86
507	Merseyrail	96
508	Merseyrail	81

UPDATED

Armita

Armita Nederland BV
Apollolaan 109, NL-1077 AN Amsterdam, Netherlands
Tel: +31 206 736117   Fax: +31 206 735857

Key personnel
Manager: H M Endstra

Vehicles
Tank cars: 420.

VERIFIED

ARR Rail Rent

Transportmittel Vermietungs GesmbH
Lohnsteinstrasse 36a, A-2380 Perchtoldsdorf, Austria
Tel: +43 1 865 6685   Fax: +43 1 865 66859

Key personnel
Managing Directors: Gernot Schwayer, Dr Brett

Vehicles
Short- and long-term leasing of freight wagons. The company owns a fleet of over 1,000 wagons.

VERIFIED

Brambles Italia

Brambles Italia Srl
Via Lanzone 29/31, I-20123 Milan, Italy
Tel: +39 2 8645 4488   Fax: +39 2 8645 5301

Key personnel
Managing Director: L Rampinelli
Financial Director: E F Pasqui
Technical Director: A Sangiorgi

Vehicles
1,700 wagons.

VERIFIED

CAIB

CAIB Benelux
A member of Brambles Europe SA
Uitbrieustrystraat 60, B-2600 Brussels
Tel: +32 2 663 7500   Fax: +32 2 663 7550

Key personnel
General Manager: A Margeus
Executive Directors: H Thoumyre, P G L Sudreau

Vehicles
Approximately 1,500, of which a quarter are for petroleum products, a quarter for chemicals, a quarter for dry bulk loads and the remainder comprise gas, high-cube and car transporter wagons.

The company belongs to the Brambles Group, a large European private wagon group which owns 35,000 wagons.

UPDATED

CAIB UK

CAIB UK Ltd
Imperial House, 350 Bournville Lane, Birmingham B30 1QZ
Tel: +44 121 478 0330   Fax: +44 121 477 8338

Key personnel
General Manager: L M G Harvey

Vehicles
CAIB UK offers a comprehensive rail freight service, including wagon hire, full maintenance package, and domestic and international transit management. The hire fleet numbers just over 2,200 wagons catering for all types of bulk liquids, solids and finished goods. The Marcroft Engineering subsidiary provides nationwide field maintenance service from 40 outstations supported by two principal workshops catering for overhaul, conversion and painting of all wagon types. Intermodal Repairs and Storage based at Widnes offers a similar range of engineering services to tank container users.

UPDATED

Cargowaggon

Cargowaggon GmbH
Röntgenstrasse 7-9, D-60388 Frankfurt am Main, Germany
Tel: +49 69 6109 7010   Fax: +49 69 6109 35002

Key personnel
Executive: Maximilian von Haller

Corporate developments
In 1997 Cargowaggon was purchased by General Electric of the USA.

Vehicles
Cargowaggon operates some 2,750 wagons, of which 1,000 are capable of running to and from the UK. The fleet includes covered (two- and four-axle) sliding-wall wagons, flat wagons and Debach-vit wagons with movable tarpaulins.

UPDATED

Convoy

Convoy-Contigas BV
Apollolaan 109, NL-1077 AN Amsterdam, Netherlands
Tel: +31 206 736117   Fax: +31 206 735857

Key personnel
Director: W Endstra

Vehicles
180 tank wagons.

VERIFIED

ERMEWA

ERMEWA Ltd
38 Station Road, Cambridge CB1 2JH, UK
Tel: +44 1223 324261   Fax: +44 1223 351784

Key personnel
Managing Director: R J Head

Vehicles
Tank wagons for transport of liquefied gases including cryogenics, liquid chemicals and powders, as well as a diversified fleet of specialised wagons for bulk commodities (grains), heavy industrial products (steel coils, steel profiles) and palletised goods.

VERIFIED

EVA

Eisenbahn-Verkehrsmittel GmbH
Schillerstrasse 20, D-40237 Dusseldorf, Germany
Tel: +49 211 67020   Fax: +49 211 670 2110

Key personnel
Managing Director: C van Eeden

Vehicles
Tank, powder and high-cube wagons: 9,993 owned and 2,190 managed.

VERIFIED

Eversholt

Eversholt Leasing Ltd
1 Eversholt Street, London NW1 1DN
Tel: +44 171 214 9040   Fax: +44 171 214 9326

Key personnel
Managing Director: Andrew Jukes
Directors
  Engineering: Roger Aylward
  Finance: Colin Habgood

Political background
Eversholt is one of three rolling stock companies sold by the British government in November 1995. It was bought by a management buyout group for £500 million, with an extra £80 million to follow when the Class 365 electric multiple-unit entered service.

The company was sold with leases in place to the former British Rail train operating companies lasting from two to nine years.

Traction and rolling stock
Eversholt's portfolio of stock is all-electric, and covers some of the more modern types in Britain. The company owns the InterCity 225 trains in service on the East Coast main line and the Class 86 locomotives in use on the West Coast main line, as well as over 2,400 electric multiple-unit vehicles.

Networker Expresses
The last order for passenger stock placed by the former British Rail was in late 1993, when 41 dual-voltage Class 365 outer suburban emus, tagged 'Networker Express', were ordered from Adtranz. These were the last trains built at York Works prior to its closure in 1995.

Due to the protracted period Railtrack required to give the new trains safety certification, the Class 365s were not able to enter service until late 1996. The fleet was divided between West Anglia Great Northern (25 trains) which would use them on 25 kV expresses between London Kings Cross and Cambridge, and South Eastern Trains (16 trains) which would use them on 750 V DC expresses between London and Canterbury.

Eversholt Train Leasing Co

Class	Train operating unit(s)	Number of vehicles in service April 1995
Locomotives		
86/2	West Coast, CrossCountry, Anglia	44
91	GNER	31
Multiple-units		
302	London Tilbury Southend	92
306	Great Eastern	3
310	Central, London Tilbury Southend	179
313	North London, West Anglia Great Northern	192
315	West Anglia Great Northern, Great Eastern	244
318	ScotRail	63
320	ScotRail	66
321	North London, Great Eastern	456
322	West Anglia Great Northern	20
365	WAGN, South Eastern	164
421	Connex South Eastern, South West	320
423	South West	308
455	Connex South Central	184
465/0	Connex South Eastern	368
483	Isle of Wight	16
Coaches		
Mark 2d/e/f	West Coast, Cross Country, Anglia, Great Western Trains, ScotRail	453
Mark 4	GNER	314
Mark 2a	NWRR	22
Mark 1	Anglia, NWRR, ScotRail	29

UPDATED

Invatra

Industrial de Vagones y Transportes SA
Poligono Industrial Alces, Alcazar de San Juan, Ciudad Real, Spain
Tel: +34 26 511113

Vehicles
58 tank wagons.

VERIFIED

KVG

KVG Kesselwagen Vermietgesellschaft mbH
Herrengraben 74, D-20459 Hamburg, Germany
Tel: +49 40 368040   Fax: +49 40 3680 4113

Key personnel
Executive Directors: Rainer Baumgarten, Gernot Schwayer
Managing Directors: Volker Grahl, Manfred Gürges

Subsidiary
Jungenthal-Waggon GmbH
Am Hafen 29, D-30629 Hannover, Germany
Tel: +49 511 958770   Fax: +49 511 9587715
Managing Directors: Volkmar Gassman/Volker Grahl

Associated Company
KVG Kesselwagen Vermietgesellschaft mbH
Lohnsteinstrasse 36a, A-2380 Perchtoldsdorf, Austria
Tel: +43 1 865 6685   Fax: +43 1 8656 6859
Executive Directors: Gernot Schwayer, Rainer Baumgarten

Vehicles
KVG hires privately owned tank wagons and other specialised vehicles. The company owns a fleet of approximately 10,000 vehicles transporting light and heavy oil products, liquefied petroleum gases, acids, alkalis, solvents and other chemicals, powdered or granular products as well as standard goods wagons.

UPDATED

OEVA

Oesterreichische Eisenbahn-Verkehrs-Anstalt GmbH
Volksgartenstrasse 3, A-1010 Vienna, Austria
Tel: +43 222 523 3621   Fax: +43 222 523 1555

Key personnel
Managing Director: Gerhard W Schwertmann

Vehicles
900 owned and 1,350 managed.

UPDATED

On Rail

Gesellschaft für Vermietung und Verwaltung von Eisenbahnwaggons mbH
Schwarzbachstrasse 30, D-40822 Mettmann, Germany
Tel: +49 2104 92970   Fax: +49 2104 25254

Key personnel
Directors: Charles Dill, Jean-Maurice Tastevin

Vehicles
On Rail manages and leases a fleet of some 1,400 private wagons, of which around 1,100 are tank wagons for the transport of light and heavy petroleum products, chemicals, pressurised gases and powders. On Rail also leases wagons for the transport of bulk goods, steel products and containers, as well as containers, tank containers and 7.15 m swapbodies.

VERIFIED

Porterbrook Leasing

Porterbrook Leasing Co Ltd
3rd Floor, Burdett House, Becket Street, Derby DE1 1JP
Tel: +44 1332 262293   Fax: +44 1332 262457

Networker Express dual-voltage emu on 25 kV lines north of London (David Percival)   **1995**

Key personnel
Managing Director: Sandy Anderson
Directors
  Finance: Ray Cork
  Commercial: Ian Cairns
  Engineering: Tim Gilbert

Political background
Porterbrook is one of three rolling stock companies sold by the British government in November 1995. It was bought by a management buyout group for £527 million.

The company was sold with leases in place to the former British Rail train operating companies lasting from two to nine years.

In 1996 Stagecoach Holdings, which owns the South West Trains franchise, acquired Porterbrook Leasing which valued the company at £825.5 million.

Traction and rolling stock
Porterbrook has a wide spread of stock, including InterCity 125 trains in use on the CrossCountry and Midland routes, electric Class 87 and 90 locomotives at work on the West Coast main line, and a large number of suburban diesel multiple-unit vehicles.

It has ordered 30 Juniper trainsets for SWT routes. The trains are being built at GEC Alsthom's Metro Cammell factory at Washwood Heath, Birmingham and will be deployed on the Reading to London Waterloo route. They will replace existing slam-door stock.

Porterbrook Leasing has a portfolio of 3,750 coaches and supplies 16 of the 25 UK train operating companies.

Porterbrook Leasing Co

Class	Train operating unit(s)	Number of vehicles in service April 1995
Locomotives		
43	CrossCountry, Midland	80
47/4	CrossCountry, Great Western	33
73/2	Gatwick Express	13
87/0	West Coast	35
90/0	West Coast	15
Multiple-units		
141	North East	38
143	South Wales and West, Cardiff Valleys	50
144	North East	56
150/2	ScotRail, South Wales and West, Cardiff Valleys, Anglia	126
153	North West, Central, Anglia	40
155	North East	14
156	North West, Central	76
158	ScotRail, North East, North West, CrossCountry	211
158/9	North East	20
159	South West	66
205	Connex South Eastern Connex South Central	29
207	Connex South Eastern	8
319	Connex South Central, Thameslink	344
321/9	North East	12
323	North West, Central	93
411	Connex South Eastern	416
412	South West	28
419	South Eastern	8
422	Connex South Central	92
423	Connex South Central	188
455	South West	364
456	Connex South Central	48

UPDATED

SGW

Société de Gerance de Wagons Grande Capacité
A subsidiary company of French National Railways
163 bis avenue de Clichy, F-75838 Paris Cedex 17, France
Tel: +33 1 40 25 37 00   Fax: +33 1 40 25 37 60

Key personnel
Chairman: Christian de Fournoux
General Manager: Alain Keck
Marketing Manager: Bernard Kail

Products
SGW caters exclusively for unit train movement of bulk freight suitable for open-wagon conveyance, such as coal, coke, ores, sand, stones and ballast, throughout Europe. It does not own wagons, but markets and manages the deployment of a pool of some 6,500 special purpose vehicles on behalf of wagon manufacturers, national and private industries, and private wagon leasing companies.

VERIFIED

Simotra SA

A member of Groupe CAIB
11 boulevard Pershing, F-75017 Paris, France
Tel: +33 1 44 09 13 13   Fax: +33 1 45 74 47 08

Key personnel
Managing Director: H Thoumyre
General Manager: P Boucheteil
Sales Director: P Charbonnier

Vehicles
11,230 rail wagons.

VERIFIED

Steele

E G Steele & Co Ltd
25 Dalziel Street, Hamilton ML3 9AU, UK
Tel: +44 1698 283765   Fax: +44 1698 891550

Key personnel
See entry in *Locomotives* section

Vehicles
Ninety-five 45 tonne tank wagons chiefly for petroleum products; seven 45 tonne stainless steel wagons for chemical products (mainly sulphuric and nitric acid).

VERIFIED

STVA

Société de Transports de Véhicules Automobiles
Immeuble Le Cardinet, PO Box 826, F-75828 Paris Cedex 17, France
Tel: +33 1 44 85 56 78   Fax: +33 1 44 85 57 00
Email: stva@stva.com
Web: www.stva.com

Key personnel
Commercial Director: J Henry

Vehicles
Automobile transporters; full service (predelivery inspection) throughout Europe.

UPDATED

Tiphook

Tiphook Rail Ltd
Linden House, 153-155 Masons Hill, Bromley BR2 9HB, UK
Tel: +44 181 466 9045   Fax: +44 181 466 9037

Key personnel
Managing Director: Stephen Goodwin
General Sales Manager: Ian Whelpton
Operations Manager: Jeff Rushforth

Vehicles
Short-, medium-, long-term rental of freight wagons in the United Kingdom and Continental Europe; intermodal and conventional wagons for international traffic.

Tiphook Rail's fleet is in excess of 2,200 wagons, of which half are suitable for international traffic. The fleet consists of container-carrying flat wagons, high-capacity covered wagons, covered flats, steel coil carriers, Class A and stainless steel tank wagons, aggregate hoppers and box wagons, bulk powder wagons and other tank wagons for various commodities.

VERIFIED

Tramesa

Transportes Mixtos Especiales SA
Avda Pablo Garnica 20, Torrelavega, Cantabria, Spain
Tel: +34 42 846100   Fax: +34 42 893831

Main works
Monte Esquinza, 41-6, E-28010, Madrid, Spain
Tel: +34 1 308 6875/308 6903
Fax: +34 1 308 6019/308 1299
General Manager: Andres Herbada Esteban

Subsidiary
Transportes Castellet San Miguel SA
Feixa Llarga 21, Sector F, Zona Franca, E-08040 Barcelona, Spain
Tel: +34 3 336 1111   Fax: +34 3 335 9551

Vehicles
256 chemical tank and hopper wagons.

VERIFIED

Transfesa

Transportes Ferroviarios Especiales SA
Musgo 1, Urbanizacion La Florida, Aravaca, E-28023 Madrid, Spain
Tel: +34 1 307 6585   Fax: +34 1 372 9059

Key personnel
President and Executive Director:
  Emilio Fernandez Fernandez
Managing Director: Luis Del Campo Villaplana

Products
The company is primarily engaged in activities covering the management of transport, distribution and warehousing of goods and logistic services.

Vehicles
The company owns a fleet of over 7,500 wagons, including vehicles with interchangeable axles to run between Spain and other European countries.

VERIFIED

VTG

VTG Vereinigte Tanklager und Transportmittel GmbH
Member of the Preussag Group
Nagelsweg 34, D-20097 Hamburg, Germany
Tel: +49 40 23540   Fax: +49 40 2354 1199

Key personnel
Managing Directors: Dr Klaus-Jürgen Juhnke, Heribert Becker, Michael Behrendt, Heinrich Sikora

Principal subsidiaries
VTG GmbH Vienna; VTG AG, Basel; VTG Benelux BV, Rotterdam; ALGECO SA, Paris; VTG Benelux BV, Brussels; VTG Hungaria Kft, Budapest; VTG Italia, Milan; Transpetrol GmbH; VTG France SA, Paris; VTG Finland Oy, Helsinki; VTG USA Inc, Philadelphia; Lehnkering Montan Transport AG, Duisberg; Transwaggon AG, Zug; ATG Autotransportlogistic GmbH, Eschborn.

Products
VTG is a leading European hiring company for tank wagons and special purpose freight wagons. VTG handles the products of the chemical and petrochemical industries, from liquid chemicals through pressurised gases to dry goods in bulk. VTG Tank-tainers are available for intermodal transportation of chemicals, gases or foodstuffs door-to-door.

VTG is an independent tank operator, with fully equipped installations at key positions and seaport terminals in Hamburg and Amsterdam. Facilities are available for the temporary or longer term storage of mineral oil and chemical products. The company offers a total service covering high security, product treatment, handling and local distribution.

The group has 16 inland tank terminals and four sea port terminals, 190 inland waterway barges, 269 lorries and 2,018 tank containers.

The activities of the VTG group also cover: forwarding services of tank wagons and special purpose wagons; international forwarding services for freight wagons;

inland waterway shipping of liquid and dry products as well as LPG; lorry transport.

Vehicles
22,000 tank and special purpose wagons; 5,000 automobile-carrying wagons; 7,000 general purpose freight wagons.

UPDATED

Wagonmarket

Wagonmarket Ltd
Ulica Rovná 594/5, 05,801 Poprad, Slovakia
Tel: +42 95 62996/65782   Fax: +42 95 23283/22142

Key personnel
Executive Manager: František Štupák

Commercial Manager: Michal Šmčák
Technical Manager: Ján Gavlák

Products
Freight wagon leasing. Marketing, purchase and sale of freight wagons, bogies and spare parts.

VERIFIED

NORTH AMERICA

American Refrigerator Transit Co

1416 Dodge Street, Omaha, New England 68179, USA
Tel: +1 402 271 5198

Key personnel
President: R J Dunne Jr

Vehicles
295.

VERIFIED

CGTX Inc

15th Floor, 1600 Boulevard René Lévesque Ouest, Montréal, Québec H3H 1P9, Canada
Tel: +1 514 931 7343   Fax: +1 514 931 5534

Key personnel
President and Chief Executive Officer: J C Leger
Vice-President and Treasurer: Jacques Poulin
Vice-President, Marketing and Sales: R A Podsiadlo
Vice-President, Engineering/Fleet Maintenance: G Sinclair
Director Fleet Maintenance: G Cooper

Products
Lessors of railway rolling stock in Canada: tank wagons and freight wagons. The company has maintenance workshops at Montréal, Red Deer and Moose Jaw.

Vehicles
8,300.

VERIFIED

Chicago Freight Car Leasing Co

1 O'Hare Centre, Suite 1000, 6250 N River Road, Rosemont, Illinois 60018, USA
Tel: +1 847 318 8000   Fax: +1 847 318 8045

Key personnel
President: F R Sasser
Senior Vice-President, Marketing and Sales: T F Kuklinski

Products
New and rebuilt freight wagons of all types; leasing services.

Vehicles
6,000.

UPDATED

FGE

Fruit Growers Express Co
1650 King Street, Suite 401, Alexandria, Virginia 22314, USA
Tel: +1 703 838 5560   Fax: +1 703 838 5599

Key personnel
President: Edward H Latchford
Vice-President, Marketing and Sales: John E Chapman
Vice-President, Operations: Clair E Smithers

Products
Insulated wagons and refrigerator wagons. Refrigerator wagon service on several railways.

Vehicles
3,000 RBL insulated wagons; 1,540 RPL-type wagons, mechanical refrigeration.

VERIFIED

First Union Rail

First Union Rail
6250 River Road, Suite 5000, Rosemont, Illinois 60018, USA
Tel: +1 847 318 7575   Fax: +1 847 318 7588

Key personnel
President: Jack Thomas

Products
Comprehensive fleet management service for wagon owners: approximately 3,800 freight wagons currently under management, for several Class I railroads as well as coal mining, public utility and other companies. Northbrook also manages and leases ISO liquid and dry-tank containers.

VERIFIED

GATX

General American Transportation Corp
A subsidiary of GATX Corporation
500 W Monroe Street, Chicago, Illinois 60661, USA
Tel: +1 312 621 6200   Fax: +1 312 621 6581

Key personnel
President: D Ward Fuller
Senior Vice-President: D Stephen Menzies
Vice-President and Chief Financial Officer: D J Schaffer

Products
Rail wagon leasing, repair, maintenance and fleet management services. GATX operates 65,000 wagons, 80 per cent of which are tank wagons. Over half of the tank wagon fleet is employed in chemicals traffic. The GATX tank wagon fleet includes the TankTrain system, a series of tank wagons interconnected with flexible hoses that allow the entire string to be loaded and unloaded from one connection.

GATX offers tank wagons of every size for handling any liquid commodity transported by rail. The tank wagon fleet includes general service, pressure, stainless steel, aluminium and commodity-specific tank.

The Airslide wagon is suitable for transporting and unloading finely divided bulk chemical and food products such as talc, flour, sugar, starch and carbon black. For shippers who require pneumatic unloading of their dry bulk commodities, GATX now complements its Airslide wagon by offering the Trinity-designed Power-Flo 15 lb/in^2, 5,125 ft^3 covered hopper wagon.

Recent additions to the GATX fleet include 3,000 ft^3 covered hopper wagons for the transport of cement and aggregates and jumbo covered hopper cars for grain.

Vehicles
65,000.

VERIFIED

GE Capital Railcar Services

GE Capital Railcar Services
A unit of General Electric Capital Corporation
33 West Monroe Street, Chicago, Illinois 60603, USA
Tel: +1 312 853 5000   Fax: +1 312 853 5447

Key personnel
President and Chief Executive Officer: R W Speetzen
Executive Vice-President, Sales: M R Powell
Senior Vice-President, Marketing: J A Lattanzio
Senior Vice-President, Fleet Operations: J Fenton

Executive Vice-President, Business Development: R H Tucker
Senior Vice-President, Government and Industry Relations: G D Birmingham

Corporate developments
GE Capital Services, USA, bought Cargowaggon (qv) in 1997. It has become part of GE Capital's Railcar Services business, based in Chicago, Illinois.

Products
Rail wagon leasing and repair services; 14 full-service and mobile repair facilities in North America.

Vehicles
143,000 wagons.

UPDATED

Procor Ltd

2001 Speers Road, Oakville, Ontario L6J 5E1, Canada
Tel: +1 905 827 4111   Fax: +1 905 827 0800
Web: http://www.procor.com

Key personnel
See entry in *Freight vehicles and equipment* section

Products
Leasing of tank and special purpose freight wagons.

Vehicles
Over 20,000.

UPDATED

Transcisco

Transcisco Industries Inc
601 California Street, Suite 1301, San Francisco, California 94108, USA
Tel: +1 415 477 9700   Fax: +1 415 788 0583/477 0599

Key personnel
Chief Executive Officer: Steven L Pease
Vice-President, Controller: Gregory S Saunders
Presidents
    Transcisco Rail Services: Robert A Jahnke
    Transcisco Trading: George A Tedesco
    Transcisco Leasing: William F Bryant

Products
Transcisco is engaged in the retrofitting and maintenance of rail wagons. Its rail wagon maintenance operation, Transcisco Rail Services Company, is one of the largest non-railway owned operations in the USA.

Transcisco Trading was formed to own and manage Transcisco's 23.5 per cent shareholding in SFAT, a Russian Federation private rail transport company. The other SFAT shareholders are the Russian Federation Ministries of Rail and Petrochemicals. Transcisco's patented and proprietary Uni-Temp heating system is the catalyst which brought about the formation of SFAT. All international activities will be conducted by Transcisco Trading Company.

VERIFIED

Trinity Industries Leasing Co

Trinity Industries Leasing Co
A subsidiary of Trinity Industries Inc
2525 Stemmons Freeway, PO Box 568887, Dallas, Texas
75356-8887, USA
Tel +1 214 631 4420   Fax: +1 214 589 8171

Key personnel
Vice-President and General Manager: Duncan Gillies

Products
Tank wagons are leased to companies in the chemical,
petroleum, food, mineral and fertiliser industries. Freight
wagons are leased to railways and chemical, food,
mineral and fertiliser companies. Trinity's tank wagons
are designed for the maximum load permitted on US
railways according to Department Of Transportation and
Association of American Railroads specifications.
Wagons are leased for varying periods of time from 1 to 20
years.

Vehicles
6,217.

VERIFIED

TTX

TTX Company
101 North Wacker Drive, Chicago, Illinois 60606, USA
Tel: +1 312 853 3223   Fax: +1 312 984 3790

Key personnel
President and Chief Executive Officer: R C Burton
Senior Vice-President, Fleet Management: H V Logan
Vice-President, Business and Market Planning: D C Cole

Products
TTX owns, maintains and rents to North American
railways a fleet of freight wagons, principally flat wagons
for the movement of containers and road trailers.

VERIFIED

Union Tank

Union Tank Car Co
A member of The Marmon Group of companies
111 West Jackson Boulevard, Chicago, Illinois 60604,
USA
Tel: +1 312 431 3111   Fax: +1 312 431 5003

Main works
151st and Railroad Avenue, East Chicago, IN 46312, USA

Key personnel
President: Kenneth P Fischl
Senior Vice-President, Marketing and Sales:
    William L Snelgrove
Senior Vice-President and Controller: Mark J Garrette
Senior Vice-President, Operations: Louis A Kulekowskis
Vice-President, Fleet Management:
    William R Constantino

Products
Steel, stainless steel and aluminium tank wagons for
carrying liquids and compressed gases. Covered hopper
wagons for bulk plastics.

Vehicles
49,000 for lease in the USA and Mexico.

UPDATED

OPERATORS OF INTERNATIONAL RAIL SERVICES IN EUROPE

OPERATORS OF INTERNATIONAL RAIL SERVICES IN EUROPE

PASSENGER

CityNightLine

DACH Hotelzug AG
Postfach 7377, Bahnhofplatz 15, CH-8023 Zurich, Switzerland
Tel: +41 1 225 75 75   Fax:+41 1 225 75 76

Key personnel
President: Hans-Peter Fagagnini
Marketing Manager: Bozidar Kojich

Organisation
DACH Hotelzug was set up by the national railways of Germany, Austria and Switzerland to operate luxury 'CityNightLine' sleeper services on international routes between the three countries. In the face of poor financial results, OBB pulled out of the consortium in 1996, leaving just DB AG of Germany (60 per cent) and SBB of Switzerland (40 per cent) as shareholders.

Services
CityNightLine services operate nightly on three routes: Hamburg–Zurich (the 'Komet'), Berlin–Zurich and Vienna–Dortmund (the 'Donau Kurier'). A fourth route, Vienna–Zurich (the 'Wiener Walzer'), was taken over by OBB when it left the consortium and is now run as a conventional EuroNight service.

CityNightLine services comprise three levels of accommodation. At the top end are 'A' class deluxe sleeping compartments, with toilet and shower in the compartment. 'B' class is similar to conventional sleepers, with beds and wash basins in the compartments. 'C' class features reclining seats. Continental breakfast is served to A and B class passengers.

Traction and rolling stock
The double-deck sleeping cars accommodating A and B class passengers were built new for CityNightLine services. Schindler of Switzerland, SGP of Austria and Bombardier Talbot of Germany built 18 cars each.

NEW ENTRY

VSOE

Venice Simplon-Orient-Express Ltd
A division of Orient-Express Hotels Inc
Sea Containers House, 20 Upper Ground, London SE1 9PF, UK
Tel: +44 171 805 5060   Fax: 44 171 805 5908

Key personnel
President: Simon M C Sherwood
Vice-President and Treasurer: Peter Parrott
Vice-President, Trains, Cruises and Retail Division: Nicholas R Varian
Vice-President of Public Relations: Nadia Stancioff

Services
VSOE operates the following services:
A luxury train between London, Paris, Düsseldorf and Venice, Florence, Rome and Prague.
A vintage Pullman train on day and weekend excursions within the UK.
A luxury train in the Far East between Singapore, Kuala Lumpur, Bangkok and Chiang Mai.
A deluxe river cruiser on the Ayerarwady river in Myanmar.

UPDATED

Wagons-Lits

International Railway Management
98 Gulledelle, B-1200 Brussels, Belgium
Tel: +32 2 778 1520   Fax: +32 2 778 1595

Key personnel
General Manager: Jean-Paul Camblain
Strategy and Development Manager: Ko van Heumen
Technical Manager: Jacques Strebelle
Finance and Administration Officer: Pierre Beysson

Services
Wagons-Lit operates cross-border restaurant and sleeping car services in western Europe.

UPDATED

FREIGHT

BTZ

Bayerische Trailerzuggesellschaft mbH
Poccistrasse 7, 83306 München, Germany
Tel: +49 89 609 7025   Fax: +49 89 609 5000

Key personnel
Managing Director: Dipl Volksw Heiner Rogge
Rail Operations: Dipl Ing Hartmut Thiele

Services
In June 1995, BTZ began operating RoadRailer bimodal vehicles on a trans-Alpine route from Munich, Germany, to Verona, Italy.

In October 1996 the service between Munich and Hamburg was added and in November 1996 a service between Munich and Cologne was begun.

Curtain-sided RoadRailer vehicles have been in operation between Munich and Verona since June 1995   *1996*

BTZ operates 60 curtain-sided trailers, 210 reefer trailers, 20 dry van (box) trailers, 166 tilt trailers and 20 container/swapbody chassis.

UPDATED

European Rail Shuttle

PO Box 299, NL-4760AG Zevenbergen, Netherlands
Tel: +31 168 385095   Fax: +31 168 385099

Key personnel
Managing Director: H Drent

Services
Operates intermodal services between Rotterdam, Italy and Germany.

UPDATED

Holland Rail Container

Holland Rail Container bv
PO Box 440, NL-3000 AK Rotterdam, Netherlands
Tel: +31 10 444 3444   Fax: +31 10 444 3400
e-mail: hrcal@euronet.nl

Key personnel
General Manager: Jan Hennink
Sales Manager: Rob Veltman
Marketing and Public Relations Manager: Ivo van Harmelen
Operations Manager: Chiel Boskamp

Services
Operates intermodal services between Rotterdam and central Europe.

VERIFIED

Intercontainer-Interfrigo

Intercontainer-Interfrigo (ICF) sc
Margarethenstrasse 38, CH-4008 Basel, Switzerland
Tel: +41 61 278 2525   Fax: +41 61 278 2445

Key personnel
Chairman: Dr Bernd Menzinger
Managing Director: Søren Rasmussen
Managers
    Marketing: Søøren Rasmussen
    Operational Services Combined Transport:
        Kell Robdrup
    Central Services: Mark William Smith

UK Joint Venture Company
ACI
Allied Continental Intermodal Services Ltd
33 Blagrave Street, Reading RG1 1PW
Tel: +44 1734 500030   Fax: +44 1734 500027
Managing Director: Jean Le Vot

Services
Intercontainer-Interfrigo operates cross-border intermodal and temperature-controlled services throughout western Europe. It is jointly owned by the major national railway administrations.

UPDATED

NDX Intermodal BV

Bavinckstaate, Prof J H Bavincklaan 5, 1183 AT Amstelveen, Netherlands
Tel: +31 20 347 5300   Fax: +31 20 347 5309

Key personnel
Commercial Director: W K Hancock

Services
NDX is a joint venture of the CSX Corporation of the USA, NS Cargo and DB AG (German Railways). NDX plans to have one of the most extensive intermodal transport networks in Europe. As the NDX network grows, all major

markets and ports will be connected. These include Antwerp, Hamburg, Bremerhaven, Munich, Milan and Rotterdam, and interior ports in eastern Europe.

UPDATED

STVA

Société de Transport de Véhicules Automobiles
Immeuble Le Cardinet, PO Box 826, F-75828 Paris Cedex 17, France
Tel: +33 1 44 85 56 78   Fax: +33 1 44 85 57 00

Key personnel
Commercial Director: J Henry

Services
Operates a fleet of automobile transporters and offers full service (predelivery inspection) throughout Europe.

VERIFIED

Trailstar

Trailstar NV
A Plesmanweg 151, NL-3088 GC Rotterdam, Netherlands
Tel: +31 10 495 2522   Fax: +31 10 428 0598

Key personnel
Sales Manager: Jos G de Zeeuw

Services
Operates intermodal services between Rotterdam and Austria.

UPDATED

Transfesa

Transportes Ferroviarios Especiales SA
Musgo 1, Urbanizacion La Florida, Aravaca, E-28023 Madrid, Spain
Tel: +34 1 307 6585   Fax: +34 1 372 9059

Key personnel
President and Executive Director:
   Emilio Fernández Fernández
Managing Director: Luis Del Campo Villaplana

Services
Operates cross-border rail services from Spain, including perishables traffic to northern Europe and car parts for Ford between Valencia, Spain, and Dagenham, UK, via the Channel Tunnel.

VERIFIED

UIRR SC

International Union of Road-Rail Transport Companies
100 Avenue du Port, Bte 3, B-1000 Brussels, Belgium
Tel: +32 2 425 4793   Fax: +32 2 425 3827

Key personnel
Chairman: Werner Külper
Director General: Rudy Colle

Member companies

Austria
Ökombi
Taborstrasse 95, A-1200 Vienna
Tel: +43 1 331 560   Fax: +43 1 331 56320

Belgium
TRW
100 Avenue du Port, Bte 1, B-1210 Brussels
Tel: +32 2 421 1210   Fax: +32 2 425 5959

Czech Republic
Bohemiakombi
Nekázanka 20, CZ-110 15 Prague 1
Tel: +42 2 2424 1575-1579   Fax: +42 2 2424 1580

Unilog wagon produced by Arbel-Fauvet   1997

Denmark
Kombi-Dan
Thorsvej 8, DK-6330 Padborg
Tel: +45 74 674181   Fax: +45 74 670898

France
Novatrans
21 rue du Rocher, F-75365 Paris Cédex 08
Tel: +33 1 53 42 54 54   Fax: +33 1 45 22 45 25

Germany
Kombiverkehr
PO Box 930105, D-60456 Frankfurt/Main
Tel: +49 69 795050   Fax: +49 69 79 505119

Hungary
Hungarokombi
Szilagyi Dezso tér 1, H-1011, Budapest
Tel: +36 1 266 0848   Fax: +36 1 266 0849

Italy
Cemat
Via Valtellina 5-7, I-20159 Milan
Tel: +39 2 6689 51   Fax: +39 2 6680 0755

Netherlands
Trailstar
Albert Plesmanweg 151, NL-3088 GC Rotterdam
Tel: +31 10 495 2522   Fax: +31 10 428 0598

Norway
Kombi-Nor
c/o Kombi-Dan, Thorsvej 8, DK-6330 Padborg, Denmark
Tel: +45 74 674181   Fax: +45 74 670898

Poland
Polkombi
ul Targowa 74, PL-03-734 Warsaw
Tel: +48 22 619 1369   Fax: +48 22 619 3218

Portugal
Portif
Avenue Sidono Pais, 4-4-P.3, P-1000 Lisbon
Tel: +351 1 52 3577   Fax: +351 1 315 3613

Slovenia
Adria Kombi
Tivolska 50, SLO-61000 Ljubljana
Tel: +386 61 1310157   Fax: +386 61 1310154

Spain
Combiberia
Rafael Herrera 11, 3° Pta 308, E-28036 Madrid
Tel: +34 1 314 9899   Fax: +34 1 314 9347

Sweden
Swe-Kombi
Hamntorget 3, S-252 21 Helsingborg
Tel: +46 42 126565   Fax: +46 42 138846

Switzerland
Hupac
Viale R Manzoni 6, CH-6830 Chiasso
Tel: +41 91 695 2900   Fax: +41 91 683 2661

United Kingdom
CTL
179/180 Piccadilly, London W1V 9DB
Tel: +44 171 355 4656   Fax: +44 171 629 5714

Services
The UIRR was founded in 1970 and its central objective is to ensure a more sustained development of rail transport of swapbodies and containers as well as of semi-trailers and lorries by private transport hauliers.

The UIRR operates cross-border intermodal services throughout western Europe and controls 55 per cent of all European combined transport. Local road hauliers are major shareholders in the individual national member companies.

UPDATED

Unilog

Unilog NV
Leuvensesteenweg 443, B-2812 Muizen, Belgium
Tel: +32 15 422011   Fax: +32 15 423829

Key personnel
Commercial Manager: Tony Davis

Services
Operates intermodal services between Belgium, Germany and the UK via the Channel Tunnel.

Unilog has taken delivery of 50 60 ft wagons for joint use with its Multifret wagons. Unilog carries 70 to 80 per cent of its traffic in ISO or 20 ft, 30 ft and 40 ft units, with the rest being a mix of metric 13.6 and 7.15 swapbodies. Carrying ISO containers on metric wagons results in a lot of unused space and Unilog has taken delivery of these wagons from Arbel-Fauvet Rail, Douai, France.

Unilog has started the Northern European Network, a short-distance overnight rail service for containers and swapbodies jointly operated by CNC, Ferryboats and Terminal Athus. The headquarters for both Unilog and NEN is at the new inland terminal of Muizen near Malines, halfway between Antwerp and Brussels. Called Dry Port Muizen it started operation in 1994. and is operated by Ferry Boats (owned mainly by SNCB).

UPDATED

INTERNATIONAL RAILWAY
ASSOCIATIONS AND AGENCIES

INTERNATIONAL RAILWAY ASSOCIATIONS AND AGENCIES

INTERNATIONAL

International Union of Railways (UIC)

Union Internationale des Chemins de Fer
16 rue Jean-Rey, F-75015 Paris, France
Tel: +33 1 44 49 20 51   Fax: +33 1 44 49 20 59
Email: uic-comm@imaginet.fr
Web: http://www.uic.asso.fr

Key personnel
Chairman: Antonio Lorenzo Necci (FS SpA)
Vice-Chairmen: Stig Larsson, Alexsander Janiszewski,
  Prof Jeremiah Kitheka Musava
Chief Executive: M Walrave
Communications Manager: P Véron

European Railway Research Institute (ERRI)
See separate entry

Central Clearing House (BCC)
49A Ave Fonsny, Section 31, B-1060 Brussels, Belgium

Vienna Arsenal Testing Station
Faradaygasse 3, A-1031 Vienna, Austria
Tel: +431 7974 7321   Fax: +431 7974 7594
Head of Vienna Arsenal Testing Station:
  Gerhard Schuecker

UPDATED

International Railway Congress Association (IRCA)

Association Internationale du Congrès des Chemins de Fer
Section 10, 85 Rue de France, B-1060 Brussels, Belgium
Tel: +32 2 520 7831   Fax: +32 2 525 4084

Key personnel
President: E Schouppe (Chief Executive, SNCB)
Vice-Presidents: N Montagu (Deputy Secretary,
  Infrastructure, Department of Transport, UK)
A Poinssot, (Acting Managing Director, Customers,
  SNCF)
Secretary General: A Martens, (Deputy Director-General
  and Board Member, SNCB)

UPDATED

International Union (Association) of Public Transport (UITP)

Union Internationale des Transports Publics
Avenue de l'Uruguay 19, B-1000 Brussels, Belgium
Tel: +32 2 673 6100   Fax: +32 2 660 1072
Email: administration@uitp.com

Key personnel
President: James K Isaac, Birmingham

Vice-Presidents: Elio Gambini, Milan; Günther Girnau,
  Cologne; Jean-Claude Phlypo, Namur; Botond Aba,
  Budapest; Jean-Paul Bailly, Red Diridon, Johannes
  Sloth, Jack C K So
Secretary-General: Pierre Laconte, Brussels

UPDATED

Intergovernmental Organisation for International Carriage by Rail (OTIF)

Secretariat: Central Office for International Carriage by
Rail (OCTI)
Gryphenhübeliweg 30, CH-3006 Berne, Switzerland
Tel: +41 31 351 1762   Fax: +41 31 351 1164
Email: otif@otif.ch

Key personnel
Chairman of Administrative Committee: H R Isliker (CH)
Director-General: M Burgmann (D)

UPDATED

International Container Bureau (BIC)

Bureau International des Containers
167 rue de Courcelles, F-75017 Paris, France
Tel: +33 1 47 66 03 90   Fax: +33 1 47 66 08 91

Key personnel
General Secretary: P Fournier

VERIFIED

International Rail Transport Committee (CIT)

Managing Railway: General Management of the Swiss
Federal Railways, Legal Division
Hochrchulstrasse 43, CH-3030 Berne, Switzerland
Tel: +41 512 202234/202806   Fax: +41 512 203457

Key personnel
President and Chairman: Benedikt Weibel
Secretary: Thomas Leimgruber

UPDATED

IARO

International Air-Rail Organisation
4th Floor, Cardinal Point, Newall Road, Heathrow
TW6 2JS, UK
Tel: +44 181 745 0726   Fax: +44 181 745 1631

Key personnel
Director-General: Andrew Sharp

The IARO represents railways, airports and airlines and is
concerned with rail links to airports. The object of the
organisation is to spread best practice and share
workable ideas to improve airport to city centre journeys.
Core founder members are Heathrow Express,
Netherlands Railways, Piccadilly Line, MTRC Hong Kong,
Heathrow Airport, Gatwick Airport, Manchester Airport,
Birmingham Airport and Halcrow Transmark.

NEW ENTRY

International Union of Private Railway Wagon Owners' Associations (UIP)

Union Internationale d'Associations de Propriétaires de
Wagons de Particuliers
Gojenbergsweg 11, D-21029 Hamburg, Germany
Tel: +49 40 724 2841   Fax: +49 40 724 7271

Key personnel
Secretary-General: Roelf J Janssen

VERIFIED

International Union of Railway Medical Services (UIMC)

c/o International Union of Railways
16 rue Jean-Rey, F-75015 Paris, France
Tel: +33 1 44 49 20 20   Fax: +33 1 44 49 20 29

Key personnel
Acting Director: M A Michel

VERIFIED

Organisation for the Collaboration of Railways (OSJD)

Hoza 63/67, Warsaw, Poland
Tel: +48 22 657 3601   Fax: +48 22 621 9417

Key personnel
Committee Chairman: Dr Ing Andrzej Golaszewski
Secretary: Rastislav Chovan

UPDATED

CONTINENTS

Arab Union of Railways

PO Box 6599, Aleppo, Syria
Tel: +963 21 220302   Fax: +960 21 225697

Key personnel
Chairman: G Drouiche
Deputy Chairman: M G El Khaddour
Secretary-General: Eng Mourhaf Sabouni

Membership comprises: Aqaba Railway of Jordan, Hedjaz Railway of Jordan, Tunisian Railways, Algerian Railways, Syrian Railways, Hedjaz Railway of Syria, Iraqi Railways, Lebanese Railways, General Administration of Projects and Researches of Libya, Egyptian National Railways, Morocco Railways, Société Generale Egyptienne de Materiel des Chemins de Fer, Société Generale de Construction des Chemins de Fer (Syria), Société Kassioun (Syria), Enterprise Nationale de Construction de Materiels & d'Equipements Ferroviaires (Algeria), Entreprise Nationale d'Infrastructures Ferroviaires (Algeria), Société des Travaux Ferroviaires (Tunisia), Union Arabe des Transports Routiers.

VERIFIED

Latin American Railway Association (ALAF)

Asociación Latinoamericana De Ferrocarriles
Avda Belgrano 863, ler piso, 1092 Buenos Aires, Argentina
Tel: +54 1 331 1298/343 0593   Fax: +54 1 331 2747

Key personnel
General Secretary: Ing Agustin R Pigliacampo
Technical-Administrative Secretary: Ing Vigder Sletean
International Transport Department: Alberto Paolini
Accounting Department: Cont Rodolfo Cascio
Administrative Co-ordinator: Dr Jorge Gutracht
Standards Department: Atilio Sanguinetti
International Technical Co-operation Department:
  Ing Jorge O Franco

VERIFIED

Pan American Railway Congress Association (ACPF)

Asociación del Congreso Panamericano de Ferrocarriles
Av 9 de Julio 1925, Piso 13, 1332 Buenos Aires, Argentina
Tel: +54 1 381 4625   Fax: +54 1 814 1823

Key personnel
President: Major General Eng Juan Carlos De Marchi

First Vice-President: Arq Eduardo Santos Castillo
General Secretary: Ing Alfredo Fernandez
Treasurer: Dr Ricardo S Tawil
Special Adviser: Ambassador Horacio Adolfo Basabe (Director of International Organisation, Ministry of Foreign Affairs, Argentina)

VERIFIED

Union of African Railways (UAR)

Avenue Tombalbaye 869, PO Box 687, Kinshasa, Zaire
Tel: +243 12 23861   Fax: +243 12 25166

Key personnel
President: Hanson Sindowe
Vice-Presidents
    North Africa: Sudan Railway Corporation
    West Africa: Mali
    East Africa: Djibouti-Ethiopia Railways
    Central Africa: Congo
    Southern Africa: Tazara
General Secretariat (staff)
    Secretary-General: Robert G Nkana
    Administration and Finance: Canute Peter Shengena
    Translations: Nsanbu Seke

VERIFIED

EUROPEAN

Community of European Railways

Rue des Colonies 2, B-1000 Brussels, Belgium
Tel: +32 2 525 3050   Fax: +32 2 512 5231

Key personnel
President: Heinz Dürr
Secretary-General: Trevor Halvorsen

New members
In 1997 the Association of Train Operating Companies (UK), Banestyrelsen (Denmark), NSB BA (Norway) and Jernbaneverket (Infrastructure management organisation, Norway) joined CER. The former British Rail, UK, ceased to be a member from 1997.
    There are now 22 members of CER.

UPDATED

European Company for the Financing of Railroad Rolling Stock (EUROFIMA)

Rittergasse 20, CH-4001 Basel, Switzerland
Tel: +41 61 287 3340   Fax: +41 61 272 4105

Key personnel
General Manager (Chief Executive Officer): Heinz Weber
Senior Vice-Presidents: André M Bovet,
    Jean-Pierre Phan, Roger Reinhold

Shareholders
DB AG — German Railways Ltd (25%); SNCF — French National Railways (25%); FS — Italian Railways Ltd (13.5%); SNCB — Belgian National Railways (9.8%); NS — Netherlands Railways Ltd (6%); RENFE — Spanish National Railways (5.22%); CFF — Swiss Federal Railways (5%); JZ — Yugoslav Railways (2.3%); SJ — Swedish State Railways (2%); CFL — Luxembourg National Railways (2%); ÖBB — Austrian Federal Railways (2%); CP — Portuguese Railways (1%); OSE — Greek State Railways (0.2%); MÁV — Hungarian State Railways Ltd (0.2%); HZ — Croatian Railways (0.2%); SZ — Slovenian Railways (0.2%); ZBH — Bosnia and Herzegovina Railways (0.2%), FARYM — Macedonian Railways (0.1%); TCDD — Turkish State Railways (0.04%); DSB — Danish State Railways (0.02%); NSB — Norwegian State Railways (0.02%).

Activity
EUROFIMA finances rolling stock purchases for its

shareholder national railways. Rolling stock is supplied to the national railways under equipment financing contracts. These contracts provide for periodical payments by the railways calculated to recover, over the life of a contract, repayments of principal and payments of interest on the funds borrowed, as well as EUROFIMA's expenses.

UPDATED

European Conference of Ministers of Transport (ECMT)

2 rue André Pascal, F-75755 Paris Cedex 16, France
Tel: +33 1 45 24 97 10   Fax: +33 1 45 24 97 42

Key personnel
Chairman of the Council of Ministers: Dr K Lotz (Minister of Transport, Telecommunications and Water Management, Hungary)
First Vice-President: M Wissman (Federal Minister of Transport, Germany)
Second Vice-President: J Trojborg (Minister of Transport, Denmark)
Chairman of the Committee of Deputies: P Scharle (Deputy Secretary for Transport, Ministry of Transport, Telecommunications and Water Management, Hungary)
Secretary-General: Dr G Aurbach

VERIFIED

European Freight Timetable Conference

Czech Railways, Nábřeží L. Svobody 12, CZ-11015 Prague, Czech Republic
Tel: +42 2 2303 2089   Fax: +42 2 2491 2989

Key personnel
President: P Kousal
Secretary: Ing Pavel Vopálka

VERIFIED

European Passenger Train Timetable Conference

Conférence Européenne des Horaires des Trains de Voyageurs (CEH)

c/o Swiss Federal Railways
Hochschulstrasse 6, CH-3030 Berne, Switzerland
Tel: +41 512 202201   Fax: +41 512 203289

Key personnel
President: Prof Dr H P Fagagnini (Swiss Federal Railways)

VERIFIED

European Railway Research Institute (ERRI)

Arthur van Schendelstraat, 754, NL-3511 MK Utrecht, Netherlands
Tel: +31 30 232 4252   Fax: +31 30 236 8914

ERRI carries out research for rail operators.

NEW ENTRY

European Wagon Pool (Europ Agreement)

Communauté d'Exploitation des Wagons Europ (Convention Europ)
SNCB, Frankrijkstraat 85, B-1060 Brussels, Belgium
Tel: +32 2 525 4130   Fax: +32 2 525 4453

Key personnel
President: J Dekempeneer

UPDATED

Union of European Railway Industries

Union des Industries Ferroviaires Européennes (UNIFE)
221 Avenue Louise, Bte 11, B-1050 Brussels, Belgium
Tel: +32 2 626 1260   Fax: +33 2 626 1261
Email: unife@pophost.eunet.be

Key personnel
President: Michel Olivier (France)
Secretary-General: Guillaume Duym

UPDATED

NATIONAL

ARGENTINA

Chamber of Railway Industries

Cámara de Industriales Ferroviarios
Alsina 1607, Buenos Aires
Tel: +54 1 40 4967/5571   Fax: +54 1 40 490958

Key personnel
President: Eng E G Nottage
Secretary: E R Paduto

VERIFIED

AUSTRALIA

Australasian Railway Association Inc

PO Box 94, Market Street, Melbourne 8007
Tel: +61 3 9614 5162   Fax: +61 3 9614 5514

Key personnel
President: R W Dunning
Vice-President: R McCutcheon
Secretary: I R Dobbs
Treasurer: F Small
Director: J Kirk
Deputy Director: B P Williams

UPDATED

The National Committee on Railway Engineering

The Institution of Engineers, Australia
11 National Circuit, Barton, ACT 2600
Tel: +61 62 706555   Fax: +61 62 731488

Key personnel
Chairman: G D Erdos, State Transport Authority, South
    Australia
Members
D J Ferris, Public Transport Corporation, Victoria
R Mitchell, BHP Iron Ore, Western Australia
G C Venn-Brown, Railway Project Engineering Pty Ltd,
    Taree, New South Wales
J Walsh, AN Tasrail, Tasmania
B Bock, Queensland Rail, Queensland
J B Scott, Public Transport Corporation, Victoria
I M Nibloe, TMG International Pty Ltd, Sydney, New South
    Wales
J C B Adams, Consultant

VERIFIED

Rail Track Association of Australia

PO Box 6086, Blacktown, New South Wales 2148
Tel: +61 2 671 6555   Fax: +61 2 671 7875

Key personnel
President: S Maxwell

VERIFIED

AUSTRIA

Federation of Private Railways

Fachverband der Schienenbahnen
PO Box 172, Wiedner Hauptstrasse 63, A-1045 Vienna
Tel: +43 1 501 053165/3166   Fax: +43 50206/50242

Key personnel
Director: Dr Helmut Draxler
Manager: Dr Erik Wolf

UPDATED

Federation of Cable Railways

Fachverband der Seilbahnen
PO Box 172, Wiedner Haupstrasse 63, A-1045 Vienna
Tel: +43 1 501 053165

Key personnel
President: Dr Ingo Karl
Manager: Dr Erik Wolf

VERIFIED

CANADA

Canadian Transportation Agency (CTA)

Ottawa, Ontario K1A ON9
Tel: +1 819 997 0344   Fax: +1 819 953 8353
Web: www.cta-otc.gc.ca

Key personnel
Chairman: Marian Robson
Vice-Chair: Jean Patnamde
Members: Keith Penner, Richard Cashin
Director-General, Air and Accessible Transport: Gavin
    Currie
Director-General, Rail and Marine Transportation:
    Seymour Isenberg
Director-General, Corporate Management:
    Joan McDonald (acting)
General Counsel and Secretary: Marie-Paule Scott

CTA was created in 1996 as part of the Transport Act. It
succeeds the National Transportation Agency and will be
reviewed in 1999 for its performance and effectiveness.
CTA is a quasi-judicial agency that provides regulation to
air and rail carriers in cases where the authority to operate
crosses provincial boundaries (within provinces is
controlled by the provincial authority). In addition to
checking licensing, insurance and passenger-carrying
ability of applicants, the CTA functions as an appeal
board for complaints over service standards for both
freight and passenger. Safety checks are carried out by
Transport Canada, not CTA.

After the Western Transportation Grain Act was
repealed, the CTA assumed the authority to set grain
rates for rail operators.

The CTA is also the repository for the three-year service
plans all inter-province rail carriers are required to have on
file to comply with the Transport Act.

UPDATED

The Railway Association of Canada

800 Rene-Levesque Boulevard West, Suite 1105,
Montréal, Québec H3B 1X9
Tel: +1 514 879 8555   Fax: +1 514 879 1522

Key personnel
Chairman: P M Tellier
Vice-Chairman: R J Ritchie
President: R H Ballantyne

Member companies
Algoma Central Railway inc
Amtrak
Arnaud Railway
BC Rail Ltd
Burlington Northern Santa Fe
Burlington Northern Santa Fe (Manitoba) Inc
Canada and Gulf Terminal Railway Co
Canadian American Railway Co
Canadian National Railways
Canadian Pacific Ltd
Cape Breton & Central Nova Scotia Railway
Cape Breton Development Corp
Cartier Railway Co
Central Western Railway
Conrail
CSX Transportation
ECORAIL Inc
Essex Terminal Railway Co
Goderich-Exeter Railway Co Ltd
GO Transit
New Brunswick Southern Railway Co Ltd
Norfolk Southern Corp
Ontario Northland Transportation Commission
Québec North Shore & Labrador Railway Co
Roberval & Saguenay Railway Co
Société des Chemins de Fer du Québec
Southern Railway of British Columbia
VIA Rail Canada Inc
Wabush Lake Railway
White Pass & Yukon
Windsor & Hantsport Railway
Wisconsin Central Ltd

The Association has now published four issues of *Railway
Trends*, an annual statistical digest of the Canadian rail
industry based on (in 1996) data from 32 Canadian and
US carriers. Salient statistics are as follows. Year is year of
report publication; data is for preceding 12 months.

Generally, measures of productivity for equipment and
labour have shown positive trends. In the last three years,
rationalisation has began to show results and the
accelerating trend by the major railroads to hive off short
lines is reflected in the increase in the number of
companies contributing data.

UPDATED

Canadian Urban Transit Association

55 York Street, Suite 901, Toronto, Ontario M5J 1R7
Tel: +1 416 365 9800   Fax: +1 416 365 1295
Email: transit@cutaactu.on.ca
Web: http://www.cutaactu.on.ca

Key personnel
President and Chief Executive Officer:
    Marc-André Charlebois

YEAR	1988 (base)	1993	1994	1995	1996
Number of railroads reporting	n/a	26	28	30	32
Operating freight revenue (C$ in billions)	6.41	5.77	5.84	6.62	6.48
Net income/(loss) (C$ in millions)	896	(943)	329.4	566.9	387.5
Revenue per ton mile	3.65 c	3.54 c	3.50 c	3.44 c	3.88 c
Originated carloads (in millions)	3.24	2.86	2.98	3.52	3.68
Freight cars in service	129,030	111,683	112,345	113,538	110,704
Locomotives in service	3,663	3,333	3,194	3,258	3,313
Employment	75,267	60,111	57,410	54,427	50,995
Miles of railway operated	50,787	44,182	44,200	43,493	42,273
Revenue ton-miles per employee	2,332	2,706	2,907	3,538	3,758
Intercity and commuter passengers (in millions)	6.998	4.075	3.961	4.027	3.942
Passenger revenue (C$ in millions)	1,4991	883	866	883.5	907.2
Passenger train-miles operated	13,255,000	7,055,000	7,038,000	7,176,000	6,823,000

Quebec office
4612 rue Sainte-Catherine Ouest, Montreal, QC, H3Z 1S3.

The CUTA membership reflects the predominance of local buses on the public transport scene in Canada. Membership by manufacturers, suppliers and consultants also reflects the predominance of the local bus.

UPDATED

FRANCE

Railway Industries Association

Fédération des Industries Ferroviaires (FIF)
12 rue Bixio, F-75007 Paris
Tel: +33 1 45 56 13 53   Fax: +33 1 47 05 29 17

Key personnel
President: J Douffiagues

UPDATED

SYCAFER

Groupement des Installations Ferroviares Fixes
French Track Suppliers and Contractors Association
12 rue Bixio, 75007 Paris, France
Tel: +33 1 39 76 91 94   Fax: +33 1 47 05 52 49

Key personnel
President: Claude Cazenave
Vice-President: Marc-Antane de Dietrich
General Secretary: Yvon Estellé

UPDATED

GERMANY

Association of German Transport Operators

Verband Deutscher Verkehrsunternehmen (VDV)
Kamekestrasse 37-39, D-50672 Cologne
Tel: +49 221 579790   Fax: +49 221 514272

Key personnel
President: Dipl Ing Dieter Lŭdwig
Executive Director: Prof Dr Ing E h Günter Girnaŭ

UPDATED

Association of Privately Owned Wagon Operators

Vereinigung der Privatgüterwagen Interessenten (VPI)
Hochallee 60, D-20149 Hamburg
Tel: +49 40 450 5086   Fax: +49 40 450 5090

Key personnel
General Manager: Henning Traumann
Chairman: Heinrich Sikora
Deputy Chairmen: Dr Wolfgang Dubiel,
Christian van Eeden, Dieter Fischer

VERIFIED

German Railway Industry Association

Verband der Deutschen Bahnindustrie eV
Lindenstrasse 30, D-60325 Frankfurt/Main
Tel: +49 69 72 72 44   Fax: +49 69 72 72 94

Key personnel
President: Dr Eckart Lehmann
Director: Dipl Ing Joachim Körber

VERIFIED

Rolled Steel Association Long Products Division/Railway Material

Walzstahl Vereinigung Oberbau
Breite Strasse 69, D-40213 Düsseldorf
Tel: +49 211 829 209   Fax: +49 211 829 300

Key personnel
Secretary: H Müller

VERIFIED

Switch and Crossing Manufacturers Association

Fachverband Weichenbau
PO Box 1020, D-58010 Hagen
Tel: +49 2331 2008 0   Fax: +49 2331 2008 28

Key personnel
Chairman: Eckhard Bittel

VERIFIED

ITALY

ANIE

Italian Association of Electrotechnical and Electronics Industries
Via Algardi 2, I-20148 Milan, Italy
Tel: +39 2 32641   Fax: +39 2 326 4212

Key personnel
Chairman: Ing Gio Batta Clavarino
General Secretary: Ing Lorenzo Tringali-Casanuova

VERIFIED

College of Italian Railway Engineers

Collegio Ingegneri Ferroviari Italiani
Via G Giolitti 34, I-00185 Rome
Tel: +39 6 488 2129   Fax: +39 6 474 2987
Email: mol1958@mclink.it

Key personnel
President: Dr Ing A Lagana
Secretary: Dr Ing B Cirillo

UPDATED

JAPAN

Japan Overseas Rolling Stock Association (JORSA)

Tekko Building, 1-8-2 Marunouchi, Chiyoda-ku, Tokyo 100
Tel: +81 3 3201 3145   Fax: +81 3 3214 4717

Key personnel
President: H Ohba
Senior Managing Director: S Suzuki
Director, Administration: Y Kurasawa
Director, General Affairs: T Amano

UPDATED

Japan Railway Engineers' Association

Tani Building, 1-28-6 Kameido, Kohtoh-ku, Tokyo 136
Tel: +81 3 5626 2321   Fax: +81 3 5626 2325

Key personnel
Chairman: Dr Eng Masao Nagahama
Deputy Chairmen: Hiroaki Fukuda (General Manager, Nippon Steel Corporation); Ryosuke Hirota (Vice-President, Japan Railway Construction Public Corporation)
Executive General Manager: Masahiro Shintaku

VERIFIED

Japan Society of Mechanical Engineers

Shinanomachi-Rengakan Building, Shinanomachi 35, Shinjuku-ku, Tokyo 160
Tel: +81 3 5360 3500   Fax: +81 3 5360 3508

Key personnel
Secretary: Y Takahashi

VERIFIED

Railway Electrical Engineering Association of Japan

Kimigayo Building 4F, 3-20-15 Asakusabashi Taito-ku, Tokyo 111
Tel: +81 3 3861 8678   Fax: +81 3 3861 8506

Key personnel
President: Ryuji Yukawa
Vice-Presidents: Masanori Ozeki, Takehiko Katta, Hiroshi Takeuchi
Senior Managing Director: Tatsumi Honda
Managing Directors: Tsutomu Sakaguchi, Kazuo Shigihara
Director: Ryoichi Yamada

VERIFIED

SPAIN

Spanish Private Wagon Owners Association

Asociación de Propietarios de Vagones de España
Juan Alvarez Mendizábal 30, 4° Centro, E-28008 Madrid
Tel: +34 1 547 8286   Fax: +34 1 547 8286

Key personnel
President: Emilio Fernández Fernández (Transfesa)
Secretary: Pablo Rodríguez Mosquera
Vice-President: Angel Lozano

Members
Cementos Alfa SA
Calderón de la Barca 4, E-39002 Santander

Cementos Cosmos SA
Brasil 56, E-36204 Vigo

Fertiberia SL
Juan Hurtado de Mendoza 4, E-28036 Madrid

Semat
Musgo 1, Urbanización La Florida, E-28023 Aravaca (Madrid)

Transfesa
Musgo 1, Urbanización La Florida, E-28023 Aravaca (Madrid)

Tudela Veguín SA
Argüelles 25, E-33003 Oviedo

UPDATED

SWITZERLAND

SWISSRAIL Export Association

Tösstalstrasse 163, PO Box 468, CH-8401 Winterthur
Tel: +41 52 233 3525   Fax: +41 52 233 3622

Key personnel
General Manager: E Dürmüller

VERIFIED

UNITED KINGDOM

Association of Consulting Engineers

Alliance House, 12 Caxton Street, London SW1H 0QL
Tel: +44 171 222 6557   Fax: +44 171 222 0750

Key personnel
Chairman: Robert D Reith
Chief Executive: H C Woodrow
Director of Professional Affairs: B V Woodford

UPDATED

Association of Independent Railways Ltd

85 Balmoral Road, Gillingham ME7 4QG
Tel: +44 1634 852672   Fax: +44 1634 852672

Key personnel
Chairman: Ian Allan
Vice-Chairman: A C W Garraway
Secretary: Malcolm Burton

VERIFIED

Association of Wagon Builders and Repairers

48 Clifford Road, Poynton SK12 1HY
Tel: +44 1625 873012

Key personnel
Chairman: D A Jones
Vice-Chairman: D Horgan
Secretary: L T Reddy

VERIFIED

Chartered Institute of Transport

80 Portland Place, London W1N 4DP
Tel: +44 171 467 9400   Fax: +44 171 637 0511
Email: gen@citrans.org.uk

Key personnel
President: S Milne
National Chairman, UK: R A Channing
Director-General and Secretary: R P Botwood
Director, Finance and Administration: M H Bowack

UPDATED

Crown Agents for Overseas Governments and Administrations

St Nicholas House, St Nicholas Road, Sutton SM1 1EL
Tel: +44 181 643 3311   Fax: +44 181 643 8232

Key personnel
Section Head of Railways: J A Wrighton

VERIFIED

Institution of Civil Engineers

1 Great George Street, London SW1P 3AA
Tel: +44 171 222 7722   Fax: +44 171 222 7500

Key personnel
President: David Green
Director-General and Secretary: Roger Dobson

VERIFIED

Institution of Diesel and Gas Turbine Engineers

PO Box 43, Bedford MK40 4JB
Tel: +44 1234 241340   Fax: +44 1234 355493

Key personnel
Secretary: K S Edmanson

VERIFIED

Institution of Electrical Engineers

Savoy Place, London WC2R 0BL
Tel: +44 171 240 1871   Fax: +44 171 240 7735

Key personnel
Secretary: Dr J C Williams

VERIFIED

Institution of Mechanical Engineers Railway Division

1 Birdcage Walk, London SW1H 9JJ
Tel: +44 171 973 1280/1307   Fax: +44 171 973 0182

Key personnel
Chairman: M W J Etwell
Manager: P Lowe

UPDATED

Institution of Railway Signal Engineers

1 Badlake Close, Badlake Hill, Dawlish EX7 9JA
Tel: +44 1626 888096   Fax: +44 1626 888571

Key personnel
President: A D Wilson
General Secretary: R L Weedon

UPDATED

Locomotive & Carriage Institution

69 Avondale Close, Horley RH6 8BN
Tel: +44 1293 773239

Key personnel
President: N J West
Vice-President: R P Metcalfe
Chairman: D Kirkland
General Secretary: J E Lunn

VERIFIED

Permanent Way Institution

4 Reginald Road, Wombwell, Barnsley S73 0HP
Tel: +44 1226 752605   Fax: +44 1226 754287

Key personnel
President: Brian J Garvey
General Secretary: W T Armstrong
Treasurer: B J Newman

UPDATED

Private Wagon Federation

Homelea, Westland Green, Little Hadham SG11 2AG
Tel: +44 1279 843487   Fax: +44 1279 842394

Key personnel
Chairman: L M G Harvey
Secretary-General: G Pratt

VERIFIED

The Railway Forum

Albany House, Petty France, London SW1H 9EA, UK
Tel: +44 171 918 4876   Fax: +44 171 918 4830

Key personnel
Chairman: Sir Derek Hornby
Director-General: David Morphet

The Railway Forum has a broadly based membership in the rail industry covering passenger and freight operators, infrastructure owners and suppliers.

NEW ENTRY

Railway Industry Association

6 Buckingham Gate, London SW1E 6JP
Tel: +44 171 834 1426   Fax: +44 171 821 1640

Key personnel
Chairman: Ray Haines
Director: David Gillan
General Director and Training Manager:
    Steven Kercher
Standards Manager: Colin Band

UPDATED

UNITED STATES OF AMERICA

American Association of Railroad Superintendents

18154 Harwood Avenue, Homewood, Illinois 60430
Tel: +1 708 799 4650

Key personnel
President: J Grant-Wilson
Secretary: P A Weissmann

UPDATED

AASHTO

American Association of State Highway and Transportation Officials
444 North Capitol Street, NW, Suite 249, Washington, DC 20001, USA

Key personnel
Secretary, Standing Committee on Rail Transportation: Otto Sonefeld

AASHTO represents States and the US DOT on safety, state-supported passenger services; high-speed programmes and industry restructuring.

NEW ENTRY

American Public Transit Association (APTA)

1201 New York Avenue, NW, Washington DC 20005
Tel: +1 202 898 4000   Fax: +1 202 898 4070

Key personnel
President: William W Millar
Executive Vice-Presidents:
    EVP & Chief Counsel: Daniel Duff
    EVP, Finance: William L Foster
    EVP & Chief Engineer: Frank J Cihak

An industry effort, PRESS (Passenger Rail Equipment Safety Standards) is an APTA task force started in 1995, and chaired by METRA (see commuter rail section).

UPDATED

American Railway Car Institute

700 N Fairfax Street, Suite 601, Alexandria, Virginia 22314
Tel: +1 703 836 2332   Fax: +1 703 548 0058
Email: rpi@rpi.org

Key personnel
Chairman: Richard G Brown (Trinity Industries)
Vice-Chairman: William L Snelgrove (Union Tank Car Co)
Executive Director: Robert A Matthews

UPDATED

American Railway Engineering Association (AREA)

50 F Street North-West, Washington DC 20001
Tel: +1 202 639 2190   Fax: +1 202 639 2183

Key personnel
President: Phil Ogden
Executive Director: David E Staplin

During 1997 AREA merged with the Roadmasters and Maintenance of Way Association. The new joint organisation continues to operate from the two current addresses but there has been some financial restructuring.

UPDATED

American Short Line Railroad Association

1120 G Street, NW, Suite 520, Washington DC 20005-3889
Tel: +1 202 628 4500   Fax: +1 202 628 6430

Key personnel
President and Treasurer: William E Loftus
Vice-President and General Counsel: Alice C Saylor
Executive Director, Membership Services:
    Kathleen M Cassidy
Executive Director, Federal and Industry Programmes:
    Matthew B Reilly
Executive Director, Traffic and Tariff Programmes:
    K Grant Ozburn
Regional Vice-Presidents
    Hugo, Oklahoma: J S Shaffer
    Mc Cloud, California: J E Forbis
    Panama City Beach, Florida: K E Durden
    Cooperstown, New York: W G Rich
    Iowa City, Iowa: F W Yocum

UPDATED

Association of American Railroads

American Railroads Building, 50 F Street NW,
Washington DC 20001
Tel: +1 202 639 2100   Fax: +1 202 639 2806

Transportation Technology Center
PO Box 11130, Pueblo, Colorado 81001
Tel: +1 719 584 0501   Fax: +1 719 584 0711

Key personnel
Executive Vice-President: Charles E Dettmann
Vice-President and General Counsel:
    Robert W Blanchette
General Solicitor: James C Shultz
Secretary and Treasurer: David B Barefoot
Controller: Mark McRoberts
Vice-Presidents
    Communications Department: Carol Steckback
    Policy, Legislation and Economics Department:
        Karen B Philips
    Research and Test Department: Roy A Allen

The AAR publishes, annually, Railroad Facts, which is a detailed digest of assets, asset utilisation, financial performance, commodities, human resource data and a profile if each Class 1 railway.

UPDATED

Association of Railroad Advertising and Marketing

3706 Palmerston Road, Shaker Heights, Ohio 44122-5016
Tel: +1 216 751 9673   Fax: +1 216 591 0335

Key personnel
President: Arnold F Bornstein
Executive Secretary: Joe D Singer

UPDATED

The High Speed Ground Transportation Association

1301 K Street North West, Suite 1100, East Tower,
Washington DC 20005
Tel: +1 703 414 9200   Fax: +1 703 414 9299

Key personnel
Chairman: Robert J Dietz
President and Chief Executive Officer: Mark R Dysart
Director, Operations & Planning: Patric Anater

The HSGTA has a foundation, the High Speed Rail/ Maglev Foundation at the above address.

UPDATED

National Mediation Board

1301 K Street NW, Suite 250 East, Washington DC 20572
Tel: +1 202 523 5920   Fax: +1 202 523 1494

Key personnel
Chairman: Kenneth B Hipp
Members: Ernest W Dubester, Magdalena G Jacobson
Chief of Staff: Stephen E Crable
Chief Financial Officer: June King
General Counsel: Ronald M Etters
Hearing Officers: Mary L Johnson, Roland Watkins,
    Joyce M Klein

UPDATED

The National Railroad Construction and Maintenance Association Inc

122 C Street NW, Suite 850, Washington DC 20001
Tel: +1 202 638 7790   Fax: +1 202 638 1045

Key personnel
President: Kimberley Madigan
Chairman of the Board: Jim Daloisio
Vice-Chairman: Rick Volkmann

UPDATED

National Railway Labor Conference

Suite 500, 1901 L Street NW, Washington DC 20036
Tel: +1 202 862 7200

Key personnel
Chairman: Robert F Allen   *VERIFIED*

National Transportation Safety Board

490 L'Enfant Plaza SW, Washington DC 20594, USA
Tel: +1 202 382 6600   Fax: +1 202 382 6609
Web: http://www.ntsb.gov

Key personnel
Board Members: Robert T Francis, John J Goglia,
    Jim Hall, John Hammerschmidt, George Black
Chief, Railroad Division: Robert C Lamby

Regional offices
Chicago, Dallas, Fort Worth, Atlanta, Miami, Los Angeles,
Denver, Seattle, Anchorage and Parsippany, New Jersey.

NTSB is an independent Federal accident investigation agency created in 1967. It ascertains probable cause, conducts special studies and assists Federal agencies with rules and regulations.

NEW ENTRY

Operation Lifesaver

1400 King Street, Suite 401, Alexandria, Virginia 22314
Tel: +1 800 537 6224
Web: http://www.oli.osg

Key personnel
President: Gerri Hall

Operation Lifesaver is a national non-profit organisation that uses education and awareness to reduce collisions, injuries and fatalities at level crossings.

NEW ENTRY

Railroad Human Resource Management Association (RHMA)

c/o Association of American Railroads
50 F Street NW, Room 3901, Washington DC 20001
Tel: +1 202 639 2151   Fax: +1 202 639 2806

Key personnel
Chairman: Paul N Austin
Vice-Chairman: Dennis J Cech
Secretary and Treasurer: Penny L Prue   *UPDATED*

Railroad Public Relations Association

17849 Hollow Run Place, Strongsville, Ohio 44136
Tel: +1 216 238 9026   Fax: +1 216 572 8347

Key personnel
Secretary/Treasurer: Milton B Dolinger

VERIFIED

Railroad Retirement Board

844 North Rush Street, Chicago, Illinois 60611-2092
Tel: +1 312 751 4777   Fax: +1 312 751 7154

Key personnel
Chairman: Glen L Bower
Members: V M Speakman, Jerome F Kever
General Counsel: Catherine C Cook
Director of Programs: Bobby V Ferguson
Director of Administration: Kenneth P Boehne
Director of Public Affairs: William G Poulos

UPDATED

Railway Progress Institute

700 N Fairfax Street, Suite 601, Alexandria, Virginia
22314-2098
Tel: +1 703 836 2332   Fax: +1 703 548 0058
Email: rpi@rpi.org

Key personnel
President: Robert A Matthews
Chairman: James J Unger
Vice-Chairman: Ronald L McDaniel   *UPDATED*

Railway Systems Suppliers, Inc

10507 Timberwood Circle, Suite 208, Louisville, Kentucky
40223-5313
Tel: +1 502 327 7774   Fax: +1 502 327 0541
Email: rssi@rssi.org

Key personnel
Chairman and President: Richard J Zemencik
Executive Vice-President: David Fox
First Vice-President: Gary E Ryker
Second Vice-President: Phillip C Hess
Executive Director/Secretary-Treasurer:
    Donald F Remaly

UPDATED

Regional Railroads of America

122 C Street, NW, Suite 850, Washington DC 20001
Tel: +1 202 638 7790   Fax: +1 202 638 1045

Key personnel
Chairman: Peter Gilbertson, Anacostia & Pacific
Vice-Chairman: Mort Fuller, Genesee & Wyoming
Treasurer: Mike Barron, Ann Arbor RR

UPDATED

Roadmasters and Maintenance of Way Association of America

Cary Building, 18154 Harwood Ave, Homewood, Illinois
60430
Tel: +1 708 799 4650

Key personnel
President: Wayne Russell
Secretary: P A Weissmann

UPDATED

CONSULTANCY SERVICES

CONSULTANCY SERVICES

Alphabetical Listing

Accent Marketing & Research
Advanced Railway Research Centre
Alcatel SESA
ALK Associates Inc
Ansaldo Trasporti SpA
Aspen Burrow Crocker
WS Atkins Rail
Atkins China
Austria Rail Engineering
R L Banks & Associates Inc
Barton-Aschman Associates, Inc
Bechtel Corporation
Roland Berger & Partner GmbH
Blue Print Engineering Services
Booz, Allen & Hamilton Inc
Bovis Construction Group
BPE Engineering Ltd
Colin Buchanan
CAM International Inc
CANAC International Inc
Canarail Consultants International Inc
Carmen Systems
CEDG York Ltd
Century Engineering Inc
CIE Consult
Cole, Sherman & Associates Limited
Colston, Budd, Wardrop & Hunt
Coopers & Lybrand (Europe)
CPCS Ltd
Cre'active Design
Daniel, Mann, Johnson & Mendenhall
DCA Design International Ltd
DE-Consult
Delcan Corporation
De Leuw, Cather & Company
Design & Projects International Ltd
Design Research Unit
Design Triangle
Thomas K Dyer Inc
EDS
Edwards & Kelcey Inc
EG & G Dynatrend Inc
Electrack
Electrowatt Engineering Services Ltd
The Engineering Link Ltd
ENOTRAC AG
Envirodyne Engineers Inc
Esveld Consulting Services
EURAIL Consult EEIG
Oscar Faber
Finnish Railway Engineering Ltd
First Engineering
Flow Science Ltd
Fluor Daniel Australia Limited
FM Design Ltd

Frazer-Nash Consultancy Ltd
GEC Alsthom Engineering Research Centre
GEC Alsthom Transport Systems Group
GHD Transmark Australia
GIBBRail
Gotch Consultancy
GRA Incorporated
Halcrow, Sir William, & Partners Ltd
Halcrow Transmark
Hamburg-Consult
Delon Hampton & Associates
Hanson-Wilson Inc
Hatch Mott MacDonald Inc
HDR Engineering Inc
Hill International Inc
Holec Ridderkerk UK Ltd
Holland Railconsult
Hyder Consulting Ltd
ICB
ICF Kaiser Engineers Inc
Ilium Associates, Inc
InfoVision Ltd
Infra Safety Services
Interconsult
Interfleet Technology Ltd
Intermetric
International Rail Consultants
Italferr-SIS TAV SpA
Japan Transportation Consultants Inc
Japan Railway Technical Service (JARTS)
Jones Garrard
KAMPSAX International A/S
AT Kearney Inc
Kennedy & Donkin Transportation Ltd
Lester B Knight & Associates Inc
Laramore, Douglass and Popham
Laser Rail
J W Leas and Associates Inc
LTK Engineering Services
Maguire Group Inc
Martyn Cornwall Design Management
Maunsell
Maunsell Parsons Brinckerhoff Ltd
MBD Design
Mercer Management Consulting Inc
Merz and McLellan Ltd
Metro Consulting
Modjeski & Masters Inc
Morrison Knudsen Corporation
Moss Consult
Mott MacDonald Group
Mouchel Consulting Ltd
The MVA Consultancy
NEA Transport Research & Training
NEL

New Markets
The Nichols Group
Ødegaard & Danneskiold-Samsøe A/S
Parsons Brinckerhoff Inc
Patrick Engineering
Price Waterhouse Management Consultants
Pullman Technology Inc
Queensland Railways Consulting Services
Railcare
Rail India Technical & Economic Services Ltd (RITES)
Rail Sciences
The Railway Consultancy
Railway Engineering Associates Limited
Railway Systems Consultants Ltd
Railway Technology Strategy Centre
Rendel Palmer & Tritton Ltd
RMS Locotec
Roundel Design Group
ScanRail Consult
Science Systems Group
Scott Wilson Kirkpatrick
Serco Railtest
SGTE
Signalling Control UK
Wilbur Smith Associates
Southdowns Environmental Consultants Ltd
Steer Davies Gleave
STV Group
SwedeRail AB
Symonds Group
Systra-Sofretu-Sofrerail
TAMS Consultants Inc
TCI
TecnEcon
TERA
TIFSA
Tilney Lumsden Shane
TMG International Pty Ltd
Tractebel Development
Transcorp
Transport Design Consortium
Transport Design International
Transportation Technology Center
Transurb Consult
Transystem SpA
Trident Consultants Ltd
University of London
Vanness-Brackenridge Group
Vosper Thornycroft (UK) Ltd
Harry Weese Associates
Wendell Cox Consultancy
Wilson, Ihrig & Associates
YTT International Inc
ZT

Company Listing by Country

AUSTRALIA
Colston, Budd, Wardrop & Hunt
Fluor Daniel Australia Limited
GHD Transmark Australia
Queensland Railways Consulting Services
TMG International Pty Ltd

AUSTRIA
Austria Rail Engineering

BELGIUM
Tractebel Development
Transurb Consult

CANADA
CANAC International Inc
Canarail Consultants International Inc
Cole, Sherman & Associates Limited
CPCS Ltd
Delcan Corporation
International Rail Consultants

DENMARK
KAMPSAX International A/S
Ødegaard & Danneskiold-Samsøe A/S
ScanRail Consult

FINLAND
Finnish Railway Engineering Ltd

FRANCE
MBD Design
SGTE
Systra-Sofretu-Sofrerail

GERMANY
Roland Berger & Partner GmbH
DE-Consult
Hamburg-Consult
ICB

HONG KONG
Atkins China

INDIA
Rail India Technical & Economic Services Ltd
  (RITES)

IRELAND
CIE Consult

ITALY
Ansaldo Trasporti SpA
Italferr-SIS TAV SpA
Transystem SpA

JAPAN
Japan Transportation Consultants Inc
Japan Railway Technical Service (JARTS)
YTT International Inc

NETHERLANDS
EDS
Esveld Consulting Services
Holland Railconsult
Infra Safety Services
NEA Transport Research & Training

NORWAY
Interconsult

SPAIN
Alcatel SESA
TIFSA

SWEDEN
Carmen Systems
SwedeRail AB

SWITZERLAND
Electrowatt Engineering Services Ltd
ENOTRAC AG

UK
Accent Marketing & Research
Advanced Railway Research Centre
Aspen Burrow Crocker Ltd
WS Atkins Rail
Blue Print Engineering Services
Bovis Construction Group
BPE Engineering Ltd
Colin Buchanan
Coopers & Lybrand (Europe)
CEDG York Ltd
Cre'active Design
DCA Design International Ltd
Design & Projects International Ltd
Design Research Unit
Design Triangle
The Engineering Link Ltd
EURAIL Consult EEIG
Oscar Faber
First Engineering
Flow Science Ltd
FM Design
Frazer-Nash Consultancy Ltd
GEC Alsthom Engineering Research Centre
GEC Alsthom Transport Systems Group
GIBBRail
Gotch Consultancy
Halcrow, Sir William, & Partners Ltd
Halcrow Transmark
Holec Ridderkerk UK Ltd
Hyder Consulting Ltd
InfoVision Ltd
Interfleet Technology Ltd
Jones Garrard
Kennedy & Donkin Transportation Ltd
Laser Rail
Martyn Cornwall Design Management
Maunsell
Maunsell Parsons Brinckerhoff Ltd
Merz and McLellan Ltd
Metro Consulting
Moss Consult Ltd
Mott MacDonald Group
Mouchel Consulting Ltd
The MVA Consultancy
The Nichols Group
New Markets
Price Waterhouse Management Consultants
Railcare
The Railway Consultancy
Railway Engineering Associates Limited
Railway Systems Consultants Ltd

Railway Technology Strategy Centre
Rendel Palmer & Tritton Ltd
RMS Locotec
Roundel Design Group
Science Systems Group
Scott Wilson Kirkpatrick
Serco Railtest
Signalling Control UK
Southdowns Environmental Ltd
Steer Davies Gleave
Symonds Group
TCI
TecnEcon
Tilney Lumsden Shane
Transcorp
Transport Design Consortium
Transport Design International
Trident Consultants Ltd
University of London
Vosper Thornycroft (UK) Ltd

USA
ALK Associates Inc
R L Banks & Associates Inc
Barton-Aschman Associates, Inc
Bechtel Corporation
Booz, Allen & Hamilton Inc
CAM International Inc
Century Engineering Inc
Daniel, Mann, Johnson & Mendenhall
De Leuw, Cather & Company
Thomas K Dyer Inc
Edwards & Kelcey Inc
EG & G Dynatrend Inc
Electrack
Envirodyne Engineers Inc
GRA Incorporated
Delon Hampton & Associates
Hanson-Wilson Inc
Hatch Mott MacDonald Inc
HDR Engineering Inc
Hill International Inc
ICF Kaiser Engineers Inc
Ilium Associates, Inc
A T Kearney Inc
Lester B Knight & Associates Inc
Laramore, Douglass and Popham
J W Leas & Associates Inc
LTK Engineering Services
Maguire Group Inc
Mercer Management Consulting Inc
Modjeski & Masters Inc
Morrison Knudsen Corporation
Parsons Brinckerhoff Inc
Patrick Engineering
Pullman Technology Inc
Rail Sciences
Wilbur Smith Associates
STV Group
TAMS Consultants Inc
TERA
Transportation Technology Center
Vanness-Brackenridge Group
Harry Weese Associates
Wendell Cox & Consultancy
Wilson, Ihrig & Associates
ZT

Accent Marketing and Research

Gable House, 14-16 Turnham Green Terrace,
London W4 1QP, UK
Tel: +44 181 742 2211   Fax: +44 181 742 1991

Key personnel
Managing Director: Rob Sheldon
Directors: Hugh Inwood, Chris Heywood, Alison Grant
Consultants: Tim Grosvenor (Qualitative Research), Roy Noble (Freight and Distribution)

Capabilities
Accent provides specialised marketing consultancy and research services directly to railway operators and in association with transport and planning consultancies. Accent is a leading exponent of the stated preference research technique in the fields of mode choice, demand forecasting and quality of service assessments.

VERIFIED

Advanced Railway Research Centre

The University of Sheffield, Regent Court, 30 Regent Street, Sheffield S1 4DA, UK
Tel: +44 114 282 5220/1/2   Fax: +44 114 275 5625

Key personnel
Director: Andrew Jablonski

Capability
Enhancement of contact between industry and academia by an information service and a series of seminars; focal point in UK for European land transport projects by small businesses; funding of a programme of railway-related research; teaching and training modules for students and industry professionals.
   Projects include affordable rail vehicles - studies on bodyshell construction and stainless steel crashworthiness; energy absorption of composite structures; proprosals for low-cost light rail systems for urban and rural applications; low-cost infrastructure - studies into wheel/rail contact fatigue and wear measurement of bulk forces in rail.

NEW ENTRY

Alcatel SESA

Alcatel Standard Eléctrica SA
Alcatel Dedicated Integrator for Rail Communications Systems
Ramírez de Prado 5, E-28045 Madrid, Spain

Commercial Office
Grafito 20, E-28850 Torrejón de Ardoz, Spain
Tel: +34 1 677 8228   Fax: +34 1 675 2620

Key personnel
Chief Executive Officer: M A Canalejo
Business Director: F Salcedo
Commercial Director, International: S Terranova

Capabilities
Full range of consultancy services for rail telecommunications systems including: network planning and feasibility studies, detailed planning, design, cost estimation, preparation of complete tender and contract documentation and project management.

VERIFIED

ALK Associates Inc

1000 Herrontown Road, Princeton, New Jersey 08540, USA
Tel: +1 609 683 0220   Fax: +1 609 683 0290
email: hornung@alk.com
Web: http://www.alk.com

Key personnel
Senior Vice-Presidents: Mark A Hornung,
   George C Woodward

Capabilities
ALK specialises in information technology products and services for the transportation industry. Capabilities include strategic planning, operations control systems, locomotive management, marshalling and scheduling, line capacity analysis, and geographic information systems.

Projects
ALK has undertaken a number of strategic planning studies for major railways, especially involving mergers, consolidations, and network rationalisation. It has also developed locomotive management systems for Canadian National, Southern Pacific and Union Pacific (USA). ALK has acted as consultant to Norfolk Southern (USA) on an interline trip planning system, which will preplan the marshalling sequence and train assignments for freight wagons before the beginning of their journey. It will monitor the progress of each wagon and update connecting railways and the shipper of deviations from plan.
   ALK has also undertaken scheduling and line capacity improvement studies for Chinese People's Republic Railways, Pakistan Railways and CSX, MARC and Metra (USA).

UPDATED

Ansaldo Trasporti SpA

425 Via Argine, I-80147 Naples, Italy
Tel: +39 81 565 0111   Fax: +39 81 5650 6889

Key personnel
See entry in *Locomotives and powered passenger vehicles* section

Capabilities

Main contractors, project managers and system engineers for long-distance railways, suburban, metro and mass transit systems.

VERIFIED

Aspen

Aspen Burrow Crocker Ltd
Priory House, 45-51 High Street, Reigate RH2 9RU, UK
Tel: +44 1737 240101　Fax: +44 1737 221502

Key personnel

Chairman: Mike Cottell

Head office

Aspen Associates
Dippen Hall, Eastbourne Road, Blindley Heath, Lingfield RH7 6JX, UK
Tel: +44 1342 893800　Fax: +44 1342 893773

Capabilities

Transport consulting engineers.

UPDATED

WS Atkins Rail Ltd

Berkshire House, 171 High Holborn, London WC1V 7AA, UK
Tel: +44 171 497 1502　Fax: +44 171 379 8563

Key personnel

Chairman: John Doyle
Joint Managing Directors: Anthony Cuming, Peter Busby
Business Development Director: Neil Aspinall

WS Atkins Rail Ltd specialist centres

Civil Engineering, Croydon
Civil Engineering, Holborn, London
Control and systems, Paddington, London
Control and systems, Crewe
Control and systems, York
Control and systems, Birmingham
Electrification, High Holborn, London
Electrification, Derby
Electrification, Croydon
Project Development, High Holborn
Rolling Stock, Derby
Rolling Stock, High Holborn
Training, Croydon

Regional Offices

Midlands
WS Atkins Rail Ltd, Auchinleck House, Five Ways, Birmingham B12 1DJ
Regional Director: Paul Hollingsworth
Tel: +44 121 643 9621　Fax: +44 121 643 9688

Scotland
WS Atkins, Clifton House, Clifton Place, Glasgow G2 2UB
Regional Manager: Martin Grant
Tel: +44 141 332 7030　Fax: +44 141 331 2481

Northern Ireland
WS Atkins, 1 Quayside Office Park, 14 Dargan Crescent, Belfast BT3 9JP
Regional Manager: Alan Skates
Tel: +44 1232 370074　Fax: +44 141 370776

Corporate development

WS Atkins Rail Ltd was formed in 1997 after WS Atkins (NTES), WS Atkins (Cedac), WS Atkins Powertrack and Opal Engineering joined forces.

Capabilities

Include feasibility studies, asset management, rail vehicle certification traffic forecasts, safety and reliability assessments, cost estimates, operations, detailed design of trackwork, rolling stock and depots, civil and structural engineering, architectural design, signalling/communications and systems engineering and supervision of construction.

The core constituents of WS Atkins Rail are: WS Atkins CEDAC specialising in railway civil engineering design, construction supervision and contract management services; WS Atkins NTES providing innovative rolling stock consultancy services for heavy and light rail constructors, owners and operators; and WS Atkins Powertrack providing electrification services for third rail and overhead traction supplies and the associated protection and control facilities.

Projects

Successful infrastructure projects include the platform lengthening, resignalling and electrification work associated with the 'Networker' three-phase regenerative electric trains operating on the intensive commuter lines into London, and for the high-speed international 'Eurostar' trains operating from London Waterloo.

Electrification projects include the North London Line, the new line for Heathrow Express trains, the power supplies for resignalling of commuter lines to the northeast of London. Feasibility studies for NS in the Netherlands and NSB in Norway on converting existing electrification systems to 25 kV AC 50 Hz.

Rolling stock projects include the project engineering support for the 'Networker' family of aluminium bodied trainsets in the UK.

UPDATED

Atkins China

16/F World Trade Centre, 280 Gloucester Road, Causeway Bay, Hong Kong
Tel: +852 2972 1000　Fax: +852 2890 6343

Key personnel

Managing Director: R Collins

Parent company

WS Atkins Consultants Ltd
Woodcote Grove, Ashley Road, Epsom KT18 5BW, UK
Tel: +44 1372 726140　Fax: +44 1372 740055

Capabilities

International consulting engineers for civil, structural and geotechnical engineering, and safety and reliability work. Specialists in driven tunnel works for heavy and light rail rapid transit systems. Capable of handling projects from concept through feasibility, design, tender documentation and assessment stages to supervision of construction. Specialists in driven tunnel works for metro and LRTs.

Projects

Hong Kong Mass Transit Railway; Singapore Mass Rapid Transit; Taipei Rapid Transit System; and Central to Southern District Transit System, Hong Kong.

UPDATED

Austria Rail Engineering

Österreichische Eisenbahn, Transport Planungs- und Beratungsgesellschaft mbH
Zieglergasse 6, PO Box 54, A-1072 Vienna, Austria
Tel: +43 1 526 9331　Fax: +43 1 526 933185

Key personnel

Chairman of the Board: Dr Gernot Grimm
General Manager: Ing Friedrich Pichler

Capabilities

Austria Rail Engineering (ARE) is the international consulting arm of Austrian Federal Railways (ÖBB). Founded in 1979, it provides a wide range of technical and advisory services to governments and private companies around the world. Planning, engineering, operating, marketing and maintenance expertise for rail-borne transportation systems is provided by ARE staff drawn from ÖBB.

Projects

ARE is involved in projects in Kazakhstan, Uzbekistan (TRACECA railway infrastructure), Algeria (technical assistance), Czech Republic (corridor study), Lithuania (management training), Estonia (border facility study) and Uganda (Kampala—Kasese line).

UPDATED

R L Banks & Associates Inc

1717 K Street NW, Washington DC 20006-1515, USA
Tel: +1 202 296 6700　Fax: +1 202 296 3700
email: rlbadc@aol.com

Key personnel

Chief Executive: Robert L Banks
President: Charles H Banks
Vice-Presidents: William W Delaney, George K Withers
Managing Director: David J Shuman

Capabilities

Economic and financial analysis, planning and policy development, privatisation, organisational restructuring, traffic/cost research, tariff restructuring, conceptual engineering, trackage/running rights.

Projects

Recent and current projects include:

Line relocation studies for clients including the state of Vermont and the cities of Indianapolis, Cincinnati, Columbus and Dartmouth USA, involving major railway operators such as Norfolk Southern and Canadian National.

Analyses of operating and financial impact of proposed railway restructuring for several major US operators.

Continuing assistance to the Canadian government and provinces on numerous aspects of railway deregulation and the privatisation of the Canadian National system.

Implementation studies and continuing assistance for commuter rail systems for US cities with projects under way or completed in 10 metropolitan areas, including cities in Maryland, Virginia and California.

Assistance in financing locomotive purchases (US$400 million) for Brazil and South Africa; analysis of viability of privatising locomotive maintenance facilities in Mexico.

Preparation of operating and financial diagnostic profile of RFFSA, Brazil, for international financial institution.

Assistance for US government agency in assessing private transport investment opportunities in central and eastern Europe.

Advice to the World Bank and Zambian government on the development of a regulatory system following railway privatisation.

Participation in economic and engineering feasibility studies for high-speed railway systems in the USA and Canada. Staff experience includes support to the Italian government and the European Union.

UPDATED

Barton-Aschman Associates, Inc

300 West Washington Street, 6th Floor, Chicago, Illinois 60606, USA
Tel: +1 847 491 1000/202 775 6069
Fax: +1 847 475 6053/202 775 6080

Key personnel

President: Clifford C Eby
Senior Vice-President: Brian S Bochner

Capabilities

The company offers a wide variety of transportation planning, engineering and related consulting services. These include rail transit planning, advanced computer travel forecasting and traffic simulation modelling, parking and landscape architectural services for both public and private clients.

Projects

Barton-Aschman is participating in the preparation of major investment studies and environmental documents for rail transit system extensions and route upgrades for Dallas, Texas, and the Miami—Fort Lauderdale—West Palm Beach corridor, Florida, USA.

The firm also recently carried out a rail feasibility study in Caracas, Venezuela, and has begun preparation of a multimodal binational transportation plan covering freight traffic between the USA and Mexico.

Barton-Aschman has also undertaken the first comprehensive transportation study for Shanghai, China, involving the development of travel models for all modes to forecast ridership on major transportation projects such as the new metro.

VERIFIED

Bechtel Corporation

PO Box 193965, San Francisco, California 94119, USA
Tel: +1 415 768 0835   Fax: +1 415 768 4560
Web: http://www.bechtel.com

Subsidiary offices
Hong Kong
Tel: +852 2970 7130
London
Tel: +44 181 846 4271
São Paulo
Tel: +55 11 3048 7651

Capabilities
Bechtel offers a broad spectrum of services including feasibility and environmental studies, architectural/engineering design, project management, engineering management, construction management, start-up and operations, and financial planning in addition to engineering, procurement, and construction.

Bechtel's transportation experience includes over 20 urban rapid transit systems and more than 5,600 miles of railways. The company has been involved in virtually every new transit project in the USA (Washington Metro; Boston rapid transit; San Diego light rail; Sacramento light rail; Atlanta MARTA; San Francisco BART; Baltimore Rapid Transit; and the Los Angeles Metro) as well as in key international transit and rail projects, such as the Caracas Metro, the São Paulo Metro, Taipei Rapid Transit, Athens Metro, South Korea High-Speed Rail and the Western Corridor Railway linking Kowloon (Hong Kong) with northwest New Territories.

UPDATED

Roland Berger & Partner GmbH

PO Box 81 01 49, D-81901 Munich, Germany
Tel: +49 89 92230   Fax: +49 89 922 3202

Key personnel
Senior Partner: Dipl Kfm Roland Berger
Partner: Dipl Ing, Dipl Wirtsch Ing Albrecht Crux

Capabilities
Strategic management consultancy in the railway industry, assisting numerous rolling stock manufacturers throughout Europe as well as giving strategic advice to German railways and urban transit authorities.

VERIFIED

Blue Print Engineering Services

Suite 2c East Mill, Bridgefoot, Belper, Derbyshire DE56 1XG, UK
Tel: +44 1773 828359   Fax: +44 1773 828349
email: 100331.3474@compuserv.com

Key personnel
Senior Partners: S P Chadwick, R P Gibney
Head of Engineering: P A Butler

Capabilities
Blue Print Engineering Services specialises in rolling stock engineering consultancy services.

Blue Print can install specially selected teams of engineers within a client company's locale. It also has expertise in vehicle gauging, from first principle vehicle analysis to structure measurement and clearance assessment.

Other areas of expertise include vehicle dynamics, performance analysis, structural design, bogie design, tender response and preparation of specifications.

UPDATED

Booz, Allen & Hamilton Inc

Transportation Consulting Division
101 California Street, Suite 3300, San Francisco, California 94111, USA
Tel: +1 703 902 5000   Fax: +1 703 902 3306

Key personnel
Vice-Presidents: G Leslie Elliott, Leo J Donovan
    Ghassan Salaneh

Capabilities
Booz, Allen & Hamilton conducts assignments for passenger and freight railways spanning a broad range of functional areas and issues: vehicle engineering; operations and productivity improvement; strategic planning and reliability, maintainability and safety systems.

UPDATED

Bovis Construction Group

Bovis House, Northolt Road, Harrow, Middlesex HA2 0EE, UK
Tel: +44 181 422 3488   Fax: +44 181 423 4356

Key personnel
Chairman: Sir Frank Lampl
Managing Director, Bovis Europe: John Anderson
Executive Directors
    Consultancy: John McCloy
    Commercial: Tony Ring
Business Development Director: Mike Temple
Divisional Director, Railways: Larry Chrimes

Capabilities
Specialist railway project management, consultancy and construction management services on main line, suburban or light railway projects, to government agencies, infrastructure owners and commercial rail entities worldwide. Bovis is currently involved in the management of railway projects valued at over £1,600 million.

Services cover the total railway project process from feasibility assessment, through preconstruction strategic planning to construction completion, and include procurement strategies, value and risk management, cost planning and control, planning and co-ordination, and quality and safety management.

Projects
A two year agreement and management contract with Railtrack plc in the UK valued at £40 million per annum was obtained in April 1996. The works cover the design, management, and implementation of general building, refurbishment, and building services at stations, offices, depots and other railway premises throughout the Midlands and Great Western region, and Scotland; construction management services to the Metro North Commuter Railroad, New York (March 1994) for the US$16 million upgrade at 12 stations to comply with the Americans with Disabilities Act requirements; programme management services (July 1994) to the State Rail Authority of New South Wales, Australia, for the management of the Country Link Capital Works programme, including development of a five year budget plan.

VERIFIED

BPE Engineering Ltd

Denison House, PO Box 29, Doncaster DN1 1PD, UK
Tel: +44 1302 388475   Fax: +44 1302 388495

Other Offices
Birmingham, London and Glasgow

Key personnel
Operations Manager: W Curran
Design and Construction Manager: B Hutchinson
Consulting Manager: M Scully

Capabilities
James Scott (a division of AMEC) offers a complete range of services from feasibility and design through to installation and project management of infrastructure-related packages involving lifts, escalators, switch heating, depot protection, lighting power supplies, vehicle washing machines and all other mechanical and electrical engineering requirements.

Projects
Recent projects include feasibility, design and installation of mechanical and electrical engineering infrastructure on the Great Eastern and London, Tilbury & Southend resignalling schemes, UK; consultancy on mechanical and electrical engineering services associated with the Jubilee Line Extension, UK; and feasibility and design services for EPS regional Eurostar services, UK, including

catenary, signalling, permanent way, civil and mechanical and electrical engineering infrastructure works relating to the provision of vehicle washing machines, toilet discharge facilities, walkways and walkway lighting.

VERIFIED

Colin Buchanan and Partners

59 Queens Gardens, London W2 3AF, UK
Tel: +44 171 258 3799   Fax: +44 171 258 0299

Key personnel
Director, Transportation Engineer: Malcolm Buchanan
Associate Director, Rail Planning: Roland Niblett
Associate, Rail Operations: John Glover

Capability
CPB is an established firm of transport, planning and economics consultants, who provide advice of rail planning. This includes heavy rail, light rail and intermediate capacity modes, and covers new lines, extensions, new stations, passenger surveys, demand forecasting, service design and economic evaluation.

Projects
The firm has been appointed by the Association of Train Operating Companies to carry out the annual London Terminal Census of all trains to and from London. It is traffic adviser to the consortium of banks financing the Croydon Tramlink scheme. Several recent studies for Railtrack, London boroughs and county councils have centred on ways to increase the role of rail in local movement and reduce the congestion caused by the private car. The firm is retained by Millennium Central Ltd to advise on travel arrangements for the proposed Millennium exhibition at Greenwich, including park and ride.

NEW ENTRY

CAM International Inc

215 Philadelphia Street, PO Box 227, Hanover, Pennsylvania 17331, USA
Tel: +1 717 637 5988   Fax: +1 717 637 9329

Key personnel
President: C A McGough III

Capabilities
Planning and equipping of railway electric workshops, including methods development in traction motor and generator repair and maintenance, equipment specification, machine commissioning, operator training, supply of specialised DC motor equipment and workshop upgrades.

Projects
The company has active projects in Egypt and Indonesia.

UPDATED

CANAC International Inc

Subsidiary of Canadian National Railways
1100 University, Suite 500, Montréal, Québec H3B 3A5, Canada
Tel: +1 514 399 5741   Fax: +1 514 399 8298
email: pubmail@ns.canac.com

Key personnel
President and Chief Executive Officer: Frank Trotter
Vice-Presidents
    North American Sales and Services: John Reoch
    Railroad Technologies Division: Gord Patterson
    International Sales and Services: Réjean Bélanger
    Railroad Transportation Institute: Tom Kingsbury

Capabilities
CANAC provides expertise in management (administration, planning, information systems, costing, project control), design and engineering, construction, operation, direct management and maintenance of new or existing railway systems. The company also offers equipment and materials procurement and inspection services and manages the sale of new and used railway supplies around the world.

CANAC's Railway Transportation Institute develops, delivers and evaluates training and performance support for railways and railway-related businesses.

CANAC's Railroad Technologies Division is a research and development facility, employing some 50 scientists and engineering specialists.

Projects

Since 1971 CANAC has undertaken over 500 projects in some 60 countries. Recent and current projects include modernisation of CN's Montréal-Deux Montagnes commuter line, Canada; management of the RCFT system, Togo; operations management for Ferrosur Roca, Argentina; and other projects in China, Kenya, South Korea, Mali and Panama.

UPDATED

Canarail Consultants International Inc

1140 de Maisonneuve Boulevard West, Suite 1050, Montréal, Québec H3A 1M8, Canada
Tel: +1 514 985 0930   Fax: +1 514 985 0929
e-mail: inbox@canarail.com

Key personnel
President: H Bédikian
Vice-President: J D Spielman
Vice-President and Chief Engineer: D Gillstrom
Chief Economist: C A Baillargeon

Capabilities
Canarail provides a full range of railway consultancy services including marketing studies; engineering design; project management; management information systems; training; and maintenance procedures and practices. The company also specialises in railway restructuring/privatisation/commercialisation involving the definition, elaboration and assignment of new authorities.

Projects
Current and recent projects include:

Bangladesh (BR): An organisational reform project to define the long-term role of BR and to formulate a comprehensive plan to transform BR into a viable and market-responsive organisation with management, financial and administrative autonomy and full public accountability. Implementation of recommendations made concerning institutional and organisational restructuring, marketing, tariffs, human resources, railway operations, finance and accounting.

Mali (RCFM): Management of the preventative maintenance and overhaul programmes for RCFM's fleet of General Motors locomotives, with Canarail's renumeration based on performance parameters.

Tanzania (TRC): Development of detailed design and tender documents for new mechanical workshop facilities.

Russian Federation (MPS): Provision of technical support in developing arrangements for the implementation of an X.25 Packet Data Network to improve railway operations and management information systems. Provision of institutional, organisational and financial advisory services for the development of structures for project monitoring and control and for the establishment of a value-added organisation to market the surplus capacity of the network to external users.

Senegal (SNCS): Design and management of the preventative maintenance and overhaul programmes of the SNCS fleet of General Motors locomotives, with Canarail's remuneration determined by the availability rate.

Mali, Mauritania and Senegal: Procurement agent for locomotive spare parts and components.

Guinea Republic (CBG): Performance contract in association with Systra to operate the Boké Railway for the Compagnie des Bauxites de Guinée. Provision of long-term technical assistance to optimise railway operations.

Ivory Coast: Rehabilitation and general overhaul of the fleet of General Motors locomotives operated by the SAGA Group, holder of the operating concession for the SICF system. Provision of technical and training support for depot personnel.

Jamaica (JRC): Determination of the financial viability of the railway and provision of assistance to an investor group in contract negotiations with the Jamaican government to acquire and operate the railway on a commercial basis.

Mongolia (MTZ): Provision of assistance to MTZ in the preparation of a five year plan to form the basis of the development of restructuring options to enable the railway to operate as a business in a competitive market.

Bangladesh (BR): Determination of alignments and the economic and financial viability of constructing links to the Jamuna Bridge from the existing rail networks east and west of the Jamuna River. Preparation of detailed engineering design.

China: Review and update of studies for the construction of a new railway between Daxian and Wanxian.

VERIFIED

Carmen Systems

Carmen Systems AB
Odinsgatan 9, S-41103 Gothenburg, Sweden
Tel: +46 3180 7100   Fax: +46 3180 7120
email: carmen@carmen.se
Web: http://www.carmen.se

Key personnel
Managing Director: Leif Heidenfors
Manager, Railway Marketing: Mathias Kremer

Capabilities
Crew and equipment scheduling systems for railways and airlines.

Projects
Train crew and engine scheduling for Swedish Railways.

NEW ENTRY

CEDG York Ltd

Hudson House, Toft Green, York YO1 1HP, UK
Tel: +44 1904 522164   Fax: +44 1904 523876

Key personnel
Managing Director: Hugh Fenwick
Directors
  Commercial: David Segar
  Engineering, Permanent Way: Ian Kitching
  Engineering, Civil: Trevor Richardson
  Engineering, Electrical and Mechanical: Jim Veitch

London Office
9 Albert Embankment, London SE1 7SN
Tel: +44 171 587 3571   Fax: +44 171 587 0914

Capabilities
A subsidiary of British Steel plc, CEDG York is a multi-disciplinary railway engineering consultancy which provides expertise in track design; bridge design; passenger station and freight depot design; design of new railways; upgrading of existing railways for higher speeds, electrification or heavier axleloads; design and specification of electrical and mechanical equipment and plant for railway operations; quantity surveying, cost planning and project management; and supervision of site activities.

CEDG York enjoys close links with electrification, signalling and telecommunications organisations and is thus able to offer clients a total railway infrastructure package.

Projects
Recent projects include design of works to permit EPS Eurostar trains to operate north of London on the East coast and West coast main lines; feasibility studies for running intermodal trains from the Channel tunnel to London and northwards, via the West coast main line to Glasgow; refurbishment of stations and buildings as part of Railtrack's Backlog Maintenance project, providing architectural, electrical and mechanical, structural, design and quantity surveying services, including the refurbishment of Crewe, Preston and Blackburn stations; bridge assessment work; speed improvement study for GNER to identify potential journey time reductions using tilting trains between London and Edinburgh on the East coast main line; design of facilities to permit driver-only operation of trains; remodelling of railway routes in the Greater Manchester area; design and supervision of electric point heaters; speed improvement study for Northern Ireland Railways; design of track layouts for the Kuala Lumpur Star LRT Phase II project and the New York Port Authority Trans-Hudson scheme.

UPDATED

Century Engineering Inc

32 West Road, Towson, Maryland 21204, USA
Tel: +1 410 823 8070   Fax: +1 410 823 2184

Key personnel
Assistant Vice-President: Anthony R Frascarella

Projects
Baltimore North Corridor Transportation alternative study; Baltimore Mass Transit Systems: Section C; Jones Fork Railroad Extension, Knott County, Kentucky, for CSX; Mass Transit Administration US 301 South Corridor multimodal transportation study.

UPDATED

CIE Consult

Grattan Bridge House, 3 Upper Ormond Quay, Dublin 7, Ireland
Tel: +353 1 703 4701   Fax: +353 1 703 4725
email: ciecnslt@iol.ie

Key personnel
General Manager: Barry Collins
Manager, International Business: Michael Barry
Training Executive: Stephan Clohessy

Capabilities
CIE Consult draws on the expertise of CIE Group companies Iarnród Éireann (the Irish state rail network), Bus Atha Cliath (the Dublin City bus operator) and Bus Éireann (operator of all other bus services) to provide consultancy services in all aspects of public transport management, particularly restructuring and commercial orientation, operations and staff training, civil and mechanical engineering, signalling and telecommunications and the institutional development of transport concerns.

Projects
Recent projects include urban transport components of the World Bank's Transport Rehabilitation Project for Mongolia; provision of a safety case and driver training for National Power, UK; Pakistan Railways Institutional Development Project Phase II (World Bank funding); Lithuanian Railways Transition Management Support Project (EU-Phare funding); consulting assistance in the preparation of the proposed urban transport project for Ukraine (World Bank funding); Irish Aid project for the rehabilitation of the Dondo—Muanza route, Mozambique; marketing training for Polish State Railways; rail infrastructure upgrading study in Estonia.

UPDATED

Cole, Sherman & Associates Limited

75 Commerce Valley Drive East, Thornhill, Ontario, Canada, L3T 7N9
Tel: +1 416 882 4401   Fax: +1 416 882 4399

Key personnel
President: R J Cole
Vice-Presidents: T J Sherman, D E C Wicks

Capabilities
Cole, Sherman & Associates Ltd has specialist staff in planning and research, providing services on such subjects as policy analysis, feasibility planning, corporate planning, economic analysis, technology analysis and management systems development.

Projects
Complete engineering and architectural design of $28 million maintenance-of-way equipment, maintenance and operations centre for CP Rail.

A study on behalf of Illinois Department of Transportation to determine the feasibility for the development of a passenger rail corridor between Chicago and Milwaukee. The study includes market research, route comparison and the analysis of available technology options.

VERIFIED

Colston, Budd, Wardrop & Hunt

Suite 71, Chatswood Village, 47 Neridah Street,
Chatswood, New South Wales 2067, Australia
Tel: +61 2 411 7922   Fax: +61 2 411 2831

Capabilities

Railway operating consultancy; modelling of system performance; proving of computerised schedules; traffic optimisation.

VERIFIED

Coopers & Lybrand (Europe)

Plumtree Court, London EC4A 4HT, UK
Tel: +44 171 212 4743   Fax: +44 171 212 4652/8383

Key personnel

Partner, Transport Consultancy Services:
   Christopher Castles

Capabilities

Coopers & Lybrand provides a range of consulting services to railways and associated industries covering policy and strategic advice (business strategy, restructuring, privatisation, concessioning, regulation and relationships with government); project planning, appraisal and financing; and performance improvement through strengthening organisation structures, management processes, financial and information systems.

UPDATED

CPCS Ltd

CPCS Technologies Ltd
740 Notre Dame Street West, Suite 760, Montréal, Québec H3C 3X6, Canada
Tel: +1 514 876 1900   Fax: +1 514 875 1023

Branch Office

4 Lansing Square, Ontario M2J 1T1, Canada
Tel: +1 416 499 2690   Fax: +1 416 499 2929

Key personnel

Chairman and Chief Executive Officer: G T Fisher
President: D H Page

Capabilities

CPCS Ltd is a privately owned international consulting firm specialising in transportation, telecommunications and commercialisation/privatisation. It provides technical, advisory and training services to governments and the private sector in the planning, engineering, operating, marketing and maintenance of transportation and telecommunications systems. Since its establishment in 1969, CPCS Ltd has successfully completed over 700 projects in over 60 countries around the world.

CPCS Technologies Ltd is the technology and operating company associated with CPCS Ltd, undertaking procurement and assistance in contract operation of railways and other major transportation projects, including privatisation and commercialisation.

Projects

Recent and current work includes:

In Bangladesh, CPCS has been contracted to perform a five year contract valued at close to C$10 million to provide technical assistance in locomotive maintenance and materials management;

Training in transportation management is being provided by CPCS in China and Canada as part of the China Comprehensive Transport Management Training Programme;

For Incofer, Costa Rica, CPCS has recently completed a detailed diagnostic analysis and implemented a costing scheme;

In Indonesia, CPCS has recently completed a World Bank contract to identify and evaluate options for progressively improving the institutional and regulatory framework within which the railways are managed;

Signalling and telecommunications training is being provided for Malaysian State Railways (KTM) personnel to operate and maintain the modern systems installed on a newly double-tracked transit operation;

In Tanzania, CPCS is providing continuing technical assistance and training for improved management and operation of workshops and stores;

In Thailand, CPCS is preparing a feasibility study of the potential for railway expansion in the northeast region of the country;

CPCS continues to provide consulting services to BC Transit and GO Transit, Canada.

As part of management and technical support provided under the Rail Transport Sector Programme in the Southern Africa Development Community (SADC), CPCS is monitoring manufacture, loading, commissioning and on-site performance of Canadian-built locomotives for CFM, Mozambique and participating in the identification, development and implementation of line-of-credit items proposed by SADC railways.

VERIFIED

Cre'active Design

22 New Street, Leamington Spa CV31 1HP, UK
Tel: +44 1926 833113   Fax: +44 1926 832788

Key personnel

Directors: Neil Bates, Tony Hume

Capabilities

Specialising in transport projects, Cre'active Design provides a design resource for transport design with a team of designers, rolling stock engineers and ergonomists.

Cre'active Design offers project management for design work, environmental landscaping and product design, interior and exterior design for refurbished rolling stock, exterior and interior design for new rolling stock, studies of emergency surface stock detrainment procedures and seating studies.

Projects

Recent and current projects include Greater Nottingham Rapid Transit and Croydon Tramlink.

UPDATED

Daniel, Mann, Johnson & Mendenhall

3250 Wilshire Boulevard, Los Angeles, California 90010, USA
Tel: +1 213 381 3663   Fax: +1 213 383 3656

Key personnel

Corporate Vice-President and Director, Transportation:
   Gerald W Seelman

Projects

Leader since 1967 of joint venture for planning, design, construction and management of Baltimore Metro; design and engineering management, in joint venture, of Los Angeles Metro Red Line (full metro), Green Line (Norwalk—El Segundo light rail), Blue Line (Long Beach—Los Angeles light rail) and Blue Line Pasadena Extension; design, engineering and programme management of Oceanside—San Diego commuter rail service; design of F-10 section of Metro rail system for WMATA, Washington DC; design and construction services, in joint venture, for commuter and heavy-rail systems in Taipei, Taiwan; and principal consultant for all facilities on Vancouver Advanced Light Rail Transit system, Canada.

VERIFIED

DCA Design International Ltd

19 Church Street, Warwick CV34 4AB, UK
Tel: +44 1926 499461   Fax: +44 1926 401134

Key personnel

Chairman: David Carter
Managing Director: Michael Groves
Directors: Rob Bassil, John Daly

Capabilities

Multidisciplinary design consultancy specialising in visual, ergonomic and component engineering aspects of transport design. Services include exterior styling, interior design, engineering design, electronic design, corporate design, model-making, ergonomics/human factors, CAD

Mockup of vehicle for London CrossRail project by DCA Design   **1996**

detailed drawing, computer visualising and animation, 'fast track' product design including 3D CAD. Large in-house workshop facilities enable construction of full-size mockups, prototypes and models.

VERIFIED

DE-Consult

Deutsche Eisenbahn-Consulting GmbH
Reinhardtstrasse 18, D-10117 Berlin, Germany
PO Box 39, D-12492 Berlin, Germany
Tel: +49 30 63430/308770   Fax: +49 30 6343 1010/308 77199

Oskar Summer-Strasse 15, D-60596 Frankfurt am Main
PO Box 700254, D-60591 Frankfurt am Main
Tel: +49 69 63190   Fax: +49 69 6319 295

Branch offices
Argentina, Korea, Czech Republic, Colombia, Taiwan

Key personnel
Chairman, Supervisory Board: Roland Heinisch
Chairman, Managing Board: Dr Hermann Lenke
Managing Board Member: Gerd Wiederwald

Corporate development
DE-Consult was founded in 1996. The shareholders are DB AG and Deutsche Bank AG.

Capabilities
A consultancy active in the fields of transport engineering and management, DE-Consult specialises in transport planning, economics and operation, the design of complex transport infrastructure projects for local, regional and long-distance passenger and freight traffic, the innovative design of transport systems, project management and advice on technological matters. The company also offers consultancy services for rolling stock and workshops, as well as asset management and operations management.

DE-Consult services include surveys and feasibility studies, concept and detailed design with emphasis on environmental matters, cost estimates, tender evaluation, construction supervision, acceptance, commissioning, project management, training and finance/marketing consultancy.

Founded in 1966, DE-Consult's shareholders are German Railways (DB AG) and the Deutsche Bank AG. DE-Consult employs a staff of about 1,600 people, mainly engineers and economists.

Projects
Include high-speed rail projects in Germany, Korea and Spain; suburban transport systems in Germany, Bangkok, Athens and Amsterdam; rehabilitation and management projects in Germany, Eastern Europe, Africa, America and Asia; freight transport projects in Germany and Egypt.

UPDATED

Delcan Corporation

133 Wynford Drive, Toronto M3C 1K1, Canada
Tel: +1 416 441 4111   Fax: +1 416 441 4131
email: info@delcan.com
Web: www.interlog.com/~delcan

Overseas offices
Barbados, Ethiopia, Hong Kong, Malawi, Mexico, Taiwan, Turkey, USA (Chicago and Los Angeles) and Venezuela

Key personnel
President and Chief Executive Officer: Peter J Boyd
President, National Engineering Technology:
   David A Vallis
Vice-President, Transportation Division: John C Collings

Capabilities
The Transportation Division provides consulting services in railways and rail transit programme management, planning and engineering including track work, electrification, communications, maintenance facilities, freight terminals, stations and civil engineering.

These services have been provided to urban transit, commuter, intercity passenger and freight railways and now include initiatives to implement a high-speed passenger rail service in Canada.

UPDATED

De Leuw, Cather & Company

A Parsons Transportation Group Company
1133 15th Street NW, Washington DC 20005-2701, USA
Tel: +1 202 775 3300   Fax: +1 202 775 3422

Overseas offices
Abu Dhabi, Bandung, Bangkok, Buenos Aires, Dar es Salaam, Dubai, Gaborone, Islamabad, Izmir, Jakarta, Kaohsiung, Karachi, Khartoum, Kuala Lumpur, Llongwe, London, Manila, Mbabane, Mwanza, Shanghai and Taipei

Key personnel
President: R S O'Neil
Executive Vice-Presidents: G M Randich, V P Lamb
Managers
   International Region: W J Custer Jr
   Eastern Region: A A Patnaude
   Central Region: G M Randich
   Western Region: T E Barron
   Business Development: A Bonds Jr
Sector Manager, Railways: C C De Weese

Capabilities
Services include: feasibility studies; preliminary and final design; site development, surveys, soil investigations; specifications and cost estimates; environmental analysis/permitting; contract documents, construction supervision, construction management and programme management.

VERIFIED

Design and Projects International Ltd

Wessex House, Upper Market Street, Eastleigh SO5 4FD, UK
Tel: +44 1703 625000   Fax: +44 1703 619808

Key personnel
Joint Managing Directors: Peter Smart, Colin Brooks

Capabilities
Design, supply and setting to work of all equipment needed to overhaul, maintain, repair and clean rail vehicles and their components for metro, main line and suburban railway systems; provision of design and consulting services for workshop layouts and special purpose equipment, design and supply of diagnostic test equipment for rail vehicles; supply of maintenance equipment for track work, signalling and all fixed systems.

Projects
The team at Design and Projects International was instrumental in the completion of the following major projects: the workshops for London Docklands Light Railway, and Caracas and Seoul Metros; maintenance equipment for Tuen Mun Light Rail, Hong Kong, and Istanbul LRT. Other contracts include consultancy studies for maintenance depots and facilities for London Underground Ltd; supply of maintenance equipment for the Manchester Metrolink project including layout design of workshop complex; Peitou Depot, Taipei, and Beckton Depot, Docklands Light Railway.

VERIFIED

Design Research Unit

The Old School, Exton Street, London SE1 8UE, UK
Tel: +44 171 633 9711   Fax: +44 171 261 0333

Hong Kong Office
702 World Commerce Centre, Harbour City, 11 Canton Road, Kowloon, Hong Kong
Tel: +852 2377 4737   Fax: +852 2736 6457

Key personnel
Directors: Ian Liddell, Maurice Green, Chris Ellingham, Hugh Crawford, Irvin Morris

Capabilities
Corporate identity, graphics and signage, station planning, landscaping and architectural services.

Projects
Recent projects have included work for London Underground Ltd (Jubilee Line Extension, East London Line Extension and Metropolitan Line); Docklands Light Railway; UK Department of Transport (technical audit of CrossRail and Chelsea—Hackney schemes); and for systems in Athens, Baghdad, Bangkok, Birmingham, Copenhagen, Hong Kong, Kuala Lumpur, Singapore, Taipei and Toronto.

VERIFIED

Design Triangle

The Maltings, Burwell, Cambridge CB5 0HB, UK
Tel: +44 1638 743070   Fax: +44 1638 743493

Associated companies
Peter Bayly Design, Melbourne, Australia
Hippo Design, Montréal, Canada

Key personnel
Partners: Siep Wijsenbeek, Andrew Crawshaw,
   Andrew Clark

Capabilities
Specialist design for the transport industry. Design Triangle is an independent team of industrial designers, engineers and ergonomists. The integrated service encompasses styling, engineering design and ergonomics for operators and manufacturers of public transport and specialist vehicles; industrial design for manufacturers of transport-related products; and design management consultancy for operators.

Projects

Recent projects include front-end design for MTRC Hong Kong refurbishment programme of its rolling stock. The design was originally produced for the Hong Kong Airport Express Link trainsets for MTRC.

UPDATED

Thomas K Dyer Inc

1762 Massachusetts Avenue, Lexington, Massachusetts 02173, USA
Tel: +1 617 862 2075   Fax: +1 617 861 7766

Key personnel

President: Charles L O'Reilly Jr
Vice-Presidents: Glenn E Hartsoe, David C Wuestmann, Robert E Sutton

Capabilities

Dyer provides planning, engineering, design, valuation, construction inspection, research, and computer services in the disciplines of signal and train control systems, track and right-of-way, communications, electric traction (substations, catenary and contact rail) and civil engineering.

Projects

Awarded a task-order contract by the Long Island Rail Road for signal, communications and track design.

Other recent projects include trackwork engineering and design for Phase II of the Baltimore Central Light Rail Line for Baltimore Mass Transit Administration, USA, comprising three extensions totalling over nine miles of track; engineering and design services to modernise the signalling system on SEPTA's Broad Street (Pattison—Fern Rock) metro route, USA, including retrofitting of signalling equipment to existing vehicle fleet; and trackwork design services for Phase II extension (24 miles) of the MetroLink LRT system from East St Louis to Mid-America Airport, USA.

UPDATED

EDS

Electronic Data Systems Nederland BV
PO Box 2233, NL-3500 GE Utrecht, Netherlands
Tel: +31 30 292 4905   Fax: +31 30 297 0354

Key personnel

Principal: Michiel Deerenberg

Capabilities

The travel and transportation division of EDS Northern Europe has established the Rail International Centre of Expertise (RICE) which serves as a database for European railways which are undergoing transformation. RICE also researches new systems, products and services.

NEW ENTRY

Edwards and Kelcey Inc

299 Madison Avenue, PO Box 1936, Morristown, New Jersey 07962-1936, USA
Tel: +1 201 267 0555   Fax: +1 201 275 3555

Key personnel

Director, Mass Transit Division: Peter W Dewes

Capabilities

Rail and transit planning, design and construction. Services include: transit planning; alternatives analysis; signalling and telecommunications; operations; environmental assessment; permitting; community involvement; traction power; electrification; trackwork/ civil engineering; freight movement; and construction services. Edwards and Kelcey has offices in New York, New York; Westchester, Pennsylvania; Boston, Massachusetts; Providence, Rhode Island; Owings Mills, Maryland; Minneapolis, Minnesota; Milwaukee, Wisconsin; and Chicago and Park Ridge, Illinois.

Projects

Metro-North, New Rochelle, New York: Design of a flyover structure to eliminate conflicting movements between Amtrak and Metro-North services at Shell Interlocking, New Rochelle.

SEPTA, Philadelphia, Pennsylvania: Design to replace existing signalling system on the 16 km (9.8 miles) Broad Street metro line.

NJ Transit, Burlington-Gloucester, New Jersey: Major investment study for a 58 km (36 mile) corridor traversing Burlington, Camden and Gloucester counties.

Metro-North, Dover-Wassaic, New York: DEIS/FEIS and environmental permitting for a planned 58 km extension of commuter rail service in Duchess County involving two new stations and a new vehicle storage/maintenance yard.

NJ Transit, Newark, New Jersey: Master plan for Penn Station and surrounding urban area in Newark with emphasis on the importance of linking local land use planning and transit operations.

NJ Transit, Secaucus, New Jersey: Design of rail modifications to enable safe and efficient stopping of certain NJ Transit and Amtrak trains at the proposed Secaucus Transfer station/Allied Junction in the Hackensack Meadowlands.

VERIFIED

EG & G Dynatrend Inc

24 New England Executive Park, Burlington, Massachusetts 01803, USA
Tel: +1 617 272 0300   Fax: +1 617 270 4999

Key personnel

President: Robert Ward

Capabilities

Accessibility and related requirements for people with disabilities; project and construction management for rail systems; application of advanced technologies; and transportation planning and analysis.

VERIFIED

Electrack

A division of Heery International
8201 Corporate Drive, Landover, Maryland 20785, USA
Tel: +1 301 306 0118   Fax: +1 301 577 2052

Key personnel

Vice-President: Don McAlpine

Capabilities

A division of Heery International, Inc, Electrack offers planning, design and construction services for people mover, light rail, monorail, main line and high-speed railway systems. Electrack focuses on the design and construction management of electrification systems, including traction power, operational simulations, catenary and third rail.

Projects

Recent projects include: Design and construction management for a multimodal substation for SEPTA; construction management for the electrification of Amtrak rail lines between Boston and New Haven; catenary system and traction power design for the Denver LRT system; traction power system design for the Baltimore Central LRT line; structural and catenary system design for the reconfiguration of the Hunter Connection, a major interlocking system in Newark, New Jersey, to improve Amtrak and New Jersey Transit service; and the rehabilitation and modernisation of the overhead catenary system on the New Haven line in Connecticut.

VERIFIED

Electrowatt Engineering Ltd

Bellerivestrasse 36, CH-8034 Zurich, Switzerland
Tel: +41 1 385 3322   Fax: +41 1 385 2425
email: easia@loxinfo.co.th

Key personnel

Managing Director: Lothar Garbe
Technical Director: Heinz Saxer

Capabilities

Feasibility studies, environmental studies, modelling and data processing, economic assessment; safety/security consulting, planning and engineering of rail systems; specifications, tender documents, bid evaluations;

supervision of manufacture and installation; project management; planning of timetables; consultancy in contractual aspects of BOT projects.

Projects

Recent projects include a financial restructuring study for Metro Manila LRT Authority; various projects for the Santiago Metro; general consultancy work for the Medellin Metro; the Bangkok Metropolitan Rapid Transit Authority; the Cairo Metro and Kuala Lumpur LRT.

UPDATED

The Engineering Link Ltd

Trent House, The Railway Technical Centre, London Road, Derby DE24 8UP, UK
Tel: +44 1332 263448   Fax: +41 1332 262104

Key personnel

Managing Director: Tony Butler
Engineering Contracts and Projects Director: Martin Gibbard
Engineering Resources Director: Martin Hayhoe
Finance Director: Chris Wright

Capabilities

The Engineering Link is a transport engineering consultancy covering management of major projects and modifications; new build procurement; refurbishment and production improvement; electrical and mechanical engineering; damage repair management; product/ maintenance support; problem solving/expert opinion; risk assessment; audits; depot equipment procurement; feasibility studies; documentation; reliability engineering; data analysis and climatic testing; design validation; and vehicle registration.

Projects

Recent projects undertaken for the UK railway industry include major modifications dealing with environmental issues; fleet overhaul and refurbishment; electrical engineering using CAE systems; and computer simulation.

VERIFIED

ENOTRAC AG

PO Box 23, CH-3661 Uetendorf, Switzerland
Tel: +41 33 345 6222   Fax: +41 33 345 6225

Key personnel

Executive: Heinz Voegeli

ENOTRAC UK Ltd
6th Floor, Times House, Throwley Way, Sutton SM1 4AF, UK
Tel: +44 181 770 3501   Fax: +44 181 770 3502
Executive: Dr Ziad S Mouneimne

Capabilities

ENOTRAC provides consulting services covering systems engineering, feasibility studies, planning, technology evaluation, tender preparation and evaluation, asset replacement strategy, equipment specification, procurement support, software development, field tests, quality assurance, reliability and safety assessments, signalling compatibility studies and operational procedures.

For rolling stock, the services encompass performance evaluation, energy consumption, comparative assessment of traction equipment, rehabilitation and maintenance management.

For maintenance management, ENOTRAC provides Tractivity — a complete computer-based system for vehicle fleet maintenance. The service includes the analysis of operational requirements, software implementation and training.

Power supply services include rating of equipment (substations, catenary), optimum substation spacing, reinforcement requirements, short-circuit calculations and protection, earthing, step and touch voltages, and energy, active and reactive power requirements and magnetic field computation. Optimised design is achieved by a powerful software suite developed in-house for multitrain simulation of complex AC- and DC-supplied networks.

UPDATED

Envirodyne Engineers Inc

168 N Clinton Street, Chicago, Illinois 60661, USA
Tel: +1 312 648 1700   Fax: +1 312 648 1998

Key personnel
Senior Vice-President: Marshall Suloway

Capabilities
Complete engineering services for heavy and light rail transit. In-house expertise in corridor planning, track layout, industrial engineering, elevated and underground, station and line section design.

VERIFIED

Esveld Consulting Services BV

PO Box 331, NL-5300 AH Zaltbommel, Netherlands
Tel: +31 41 80 16369   Fax: +31 41 80 16372

Key personnel
Director: Dr C Esveld

Capability
Consultancy in track technology.

NEW ENTRY

EURAIL Consult EEIG

Co-ordinating Office
42 Upper Grosvenor Street, London W1X 0AP, UK
Tel: +44 171 491 4864   Fax: +44 171 409 3505

Key personnel
Co-ordinator: J C Deacon

Member companies
Kampsax International AS
PO Box 1143, Stamholmen 112, DK-2650 Hvidovre, Copenhagen, Denmark
Tel: +45 36 771070   Fax: +45 36 772828
Manager: J Weber

Dorsch Consult
Hansastrasse 20, D-80686 Munich, Germany
Tel: +49 89 57970   Fax: +49 89 570 4867
Manager: D Koenig

Trademco
4 Papadiamantopoulou Street, GR-115 28 Athens, Greece
Tel: +30 1 724 8048   Fax: +30 1 723 7415
Manager: V Evmolpidis

TYPSA
Plaza del Liceo 3, E-28043 Madrid, Spain
Tel: +34 1 388 2627   Fax: +34 1 388 1686
Manager: A Fernandez-Aller

Thorburn Colquhoun
42 Upper Grosvenor Street, London W1X 0AP, UK
Tel: +44 171 491 4864   Fax: +44 171 409 3505
Manager: J C Deacon

Capabilities
EURAIL Consult EEIG was established in 1992 to combine the experience of five private European companies to provide independent consultancy services for the railway sector throughout Europe. Together the Group employs approximately 2,000 planners, engineers, economists and other specialists. EURAIL Consult EEIG members provide a wide range of engineering services, technical assistance and training to improve management systems, maintenance procedures, costing and pricing policies.

The Group has experience of over 120 railway projects in over 40 countries, covering passenger, freight, and intermodal transport, light rail, high-speed and mass transit.

Projects
These include: study/design for improvements to the Lübeck—Rostock—Stralsund main line, Germany; modernisation of OSE, Greece; tunnel design study for Hong Kong Airport railway; operating and engineering project for Athens—Chalkis suburban railway; technical appraisal for Basque Country High-Speed Network; design appraisal for Munich marshalling yard; a policy study on European transport; a comprehensive public transport study for Valencia, Spain, and infrastructure of the Valencia Metro; governmental advice to the railway department and management training, Armenia; and extensive rail improvements in the United Kingdom including Birmingham New Street Station, Birmingham—Wolverhampton, Bedford Rail Study and Passenger Transport Survey, London Underground Structural Inspections and Cardiff Bay LRT Study.

VERIFIED

Oscar Faber

18 Upper Marlborough Road, St Albans AL1 3UT, UK
Tel: +44 181 784 5784   Fax: +44 181 784 5700

Key personnel
Chairman: Alec Moir

Capabilities
Oscar Faber provides consultancy services in all aspects of transport provision including project identification, planning, design, engineering and management. Resource capabilities cover a wide range of disciplines embracing economics, engineering, financial appraisal, planning, project management, research and statistics, and transportation modelling. The range of services includes: customer and market research; demand forecasting; operation assessment and costing; financial and economic evaluation. The company has a specialist customer survey section whose abilities include revealed and stated preference techniques.

VERIFIED

Finnish Railway Engineering Ltd

PO Box A51, FIN-01019 IVO, Finland
Tel: +358 9 8561 1581   Fax: +358 9 507 1163

Key personnel
Managing Director: Pekka Salo
Marketing Manager: Raimo Mättö

Capabilities
Railway technology consulting.

Projects
Finnish Railway Engineering has carried out efficiency-improvement and computerised ticketing and reservation work for Malayan Railway Administration (KTM); and conducted a rail wear study for Saudi Arabia.

UPDATED

First Engineering

First Engineering Ltd
Floor 7, Buchanan House, 58 Port Dundas Road, Glasgow G4 0HG, Scotland
Tel: +44 141 335 3005   Fax: +44 141 335 3006

Key personnel
Managing Director: Tony Smith
Commercial Director: John Cowie

Corporate development
Formerly known as Scotland Infrastructure Maintenance Co, First Engineering was one of the British Rail Infrastructure Services Units sold off as part of the British Rail privatisation. The company was sold in 1996 to a management buyout team known as TrackAction.

Capabilities
Railway infrastructure and civil engineering consultancy.

Projects include route clearance and structure gauging, Bridgeguard 3 hazard inspection work, inspection of bridges, retaining walls and culverts for Railtrack UK; site investigations throughout Queen Street tunnel, Glasgow, Scotland; design of maintenance repairs on two viaducts for Railtrack Project Delivery (NW).

NEW ENTRY

Flow Science Ltd

Goldstein Research Laboratory, Barton Airport, Eccles, Manchester M30 7RU, UK

Key personnel
Operations Director: Dr D J Smith
Windtunnel Managers: J P Ryall, I Lunnon

Capabilities
Flow Science Ltd is a fluid dynamics consultancy, with expertise in windtunnel testing with moving ground to speeds of 600 m/s. Services include general purpose windtunnel testing for ventilation systems, and so on; earth boundary layer windtunnel for topographic studies, such as cuttings; and investigation of flow around buildings and bridges.

Projects
Recent projects include windtunnel testing of the ICE-2 high-speed trainset design for Krauss-Maffei, Germany.

VERIFIED

Fluor Daniel Australia Pty Ltd

Level 3, 1 Mill Street, Perth,
Western Australia 6000, Australia
Tel: +61 9 278 7613   Fax: +61 9 278 7631

PO Box 222, Dampier, Western Australia 6713, Australia
Tel: +61 91 436455   Fax: +61 91 436496

Key personnel
Managing Director: R M Wright
General Manager: B B Isom
Project Manager, Westrail Contract: D R Giraudo
Manager Operations/Technical Services: D J O'Grady
Resident Manager, Hamersley Iron Project: W E Hardy

Capabilities
Feasibility and operational studies; financial planning; engineering; procurement; construction and project management for railway or integrated multidiscipline projects. Capabilities cover general and heavy-haul trackwork, earthworks, structures, electrification, rail grinding, flaw detection, and track geometry measurement.

Associated divisions offer railway construction, upgrading and maintenance services. Civil and Mechanical Maintenance Pty Ltd (CMM) is the railway upgrading and maintenance division.

UPDATED

FM Design Ltd

1a Lonsdale Square, London N1 1EN, UK
Tel: +44 171 700 3333   Fax: +44 171 700 0597

Key personnel
Directors: Ben Fether, Richard Miles

Capabilities
FM undertakes projects from market analysis through concept generation to detailed design development utilising its own CAD systems, model-making and prototyping capabilities to specification and tender documentation. The consultancy works, where appropriate, in collaboration with operators' and/or manufacturers' in-house teams.

VERIFIED

Frazer-Nash Consultancy Ltd

Stonebridge House, Dorking Business Park, Dorking RH4 1HJ, UK
Tel: +44 1306 885050   Fax: +44 1306 886464
email: fnc@frazer.demon.co.uk

Key personnel
Managing Director: A G Milton
Engineering Director: W T Chester
Technical Director: Dr C C H Guyott
Director for Business Management: G A Beattie

Capabilities
Frazer-Nash Consultancy provides a range of services to the rail industry in the UK and worldwide for the design

and assessment of rolling stock and railway infrastructure. Its principal areas of activity are in the design of bodyshells for rolling stock and infrastructure, with particular emphasis on crashworthiness; noise and vibration; the design and assessment of infrastructure systems and equipment; and safety, reliability and maintainability (SRM) services.

Projects

Support to HM Railways Inspectorate, UK into the effects of low-speed buffer-stop collision at Cannon Street station, London; crashworthiness design of European Nightstock for GEC Alsthom Metro Cammell Ltd; safety case development for luggage stowage for European Passenger Services; concept development and assessment to support the procurement specification for London CrossRail project; design support to Thorn Transit Systems International on the thermal performance of Automated Ticket Machines in hostile environments; crashworthiness design and noise consultancy to CAF for the Heathrow Express emu; structural assessment of the refurbished KCRC rolling stock for GEC Alsthom Metro Cammell Ltd; infrastructure assessment for MTRC and escalator risk assessment work for London Underground.

UPDATED

GEC Alsthom Engineering Research Centre

PO Box 30, Lichfield Road, Stafford ST17 4LN, UK
Tel: +44 1785 56221   Fax: +44 1785 274676

Key personnel

Director: G R Clark
Mechanical Engineering Laboratory Manager:
   M J N Manning
Materials Technology Division Manager:
   Dr A G Foley
Electrical Engineering Division Manager: W G Garlick
Marketing Manager: Dr R J Bassett

Capabilities

Consultancy in electrical, electronic and mechanical engineering and materials technology design; design, testing and qualification of electrical and diesel motive power units and coaches, auxiliary power equipment, suspension systems, control systems, vehicle whole system simulation and systems integration.

UPDATED

GEC Alsthom Transport Systems Group

GEC Alsthom Transport Systems Group
48 rue Albert Dhalenne, F-93482 Saint-Ouen Cedex, Paris, France
Tel: +33 1 41 66 90 00   Fax: +33 1 41 66 96 66
Web: http://www.gecalsthom.com

Key personnel

Managing Director: R N Pierce

38 avenue Kléber, F-75795 Paris Cedex 16
Tel: +33 1 47 55 20 00   Fax: +33 1 47 55 23 26
Managing Director: J Loustau

UK
PO Box 134, Manchester M60 1AH, UK
Tel: +44 161 875 2358   Fax: +44 161 875 2131
Managing Director: R Presley

Capabilities

Main contractors, project managers, system integrators and suppliers of electrical and mechanical equipment and rolling stock for main line, suburban, metro, urban mass transit and rapid transit systems. The Group has experience of taking such projects from initial conception through design and construction to commissioning and subsequent operation, and acts as the focus for GEC Alsthom's Transport Division on major multi-disciplinary rail projects worldwide, be they on a turnkey or a concession (BOT-type) basis. Specialist services include system and feasibility studies, integration of electrical and mechanical equipment with civil works, training of operations and maintenance staff and commissioning of electrical and mechanical subsystems. The Group has a particular strength in financial engineering in support of

major projects and is not averse to taking equity stakes in such projects where appropriate.

Projects

Recent projects include the construction on a turnkey basis of the initial Docklands Light Railway, UK, and participation in the current extension to Lewisham ; the design, construction, operation and maintenance of the Manchester Metrolink LRT system, UK, under a build, operate and transfer (BOT) contract (as a major participant in the concession company) ; undertaking, on a similar BOT basis, the Arlanda Airport Rail Link, Sweden, as the lead member of the A-Train AB consortium ; as part of the KTGV consortium of the Seoul to Pusan High-Speed Railway in South Korea; provision of TGV Trainset, catenaries, substations and signalling; the construction, as part of the Florida Fox consortium, of the high-speed Tampa to Miami Florida Overland Express system in the USA.

UPDATED

GHD Transmark Australia

A joint venture company between Gutteridge Haskins & Davey Pty Ltd and Transmark
39 Regent Street, Railway Square, New South Wales 2000, Australia
Tel: +61 2 698 5355   Fax: +61 2 690 1464

Projects

Illawarra electrification: State Rail Authority of New South Wales (value A$200 million).
   East Hills—Cambelltown railway link: State Rail Authority of New South Wales (value A$80 million).
   Implementation of train radio system: State Rail Authority of New South Wales (value A$80 million).
   Automatic train fare collection: State Rail Authority of New South Wales.
   VFT Sydney access studies: VFT Consortium.
   Ensham Coal Project rail spur line: Queensland Railways (value A$8 million).
   Rail corridor study, Robina to Murwillumbah: Queensland Department of Transport.
   Urban rail development, northern suburbs transit system: Westrail (value A$15-20 million).
   Pyrmont light rail project: Department of Transport, New South Wales (value A$60 million).

VERIFIED

GIBBRail

GIBB Limited, Gibb House, London Road, Reading RG6 1BL, UK
Tel: +44 118 963 5000   Fax: +44 118 935 2517
email: bmgreen@gibb.co.uk

Key personnel

Chairman: Jim Dawson

GIBBRail

Managing Director, International Transportation:
   Tony King
Director, International Rail: Brian Green
Director, UK Rail: Paul Dawkins
Specialist Transport Architect/Designer: Nick Derbyshire

GIBB Business Consulting

Managing Director: Chris Green
Director: Daniel Giblin
Senior Consultant: Tim Eaton
Senior Banker/Project Finance: Martin Blaiklock

GIBB Transportation

Planning Director: Nigel Ash

Offices

Brussels, Sofia, Prague, Magdeburg, Budapest, Dublin, Almaty, Warsaw, Bucharest, St. Petersburg, Madrid, Barcelona, Burgos, Granada, La Coruna, Murcia, Palma de Mallorca, Seville, Sta. Cruz de Tenerife, Toledo, Valencia, Zaragosa, Istanbul, Nanjing, Hong Kong, Jakarta, Nagano-Ken, Colombo, Balangoda, Gaborone, Addis Ababa, Accra, Nairobi, Maseru, Blantyre, Mauritius, Johannesburg, Cape Town, Durban, East London, Port Elizabeth, Khartoum, Kampala, Harare, Bahrain, Amman, Muscat, Riyadh, Abu Dhabi, Dubai and over 40 offices

across the United States of America through the sister company, Law International Inc. with headquarters in Atlanta, Georgia

UK

Reading, Oldbury, Gateshead, Llanelli

Capabilities

GIBB is an independent international consultancy with over 75 years' experience in the consulting, design and management of a wide range of civil engineering, construction and environmental projects. The specialist GIBBRail team has experience in feasibility study, planning and design of high-speed, main line, metro and light rail projects around the world. With support from over 4,500 in-house staff worldwide GIBBRail provides financial and technical advice, civil, structural, mechanical and electrical engineering, transport planning, conceptual perspectives, environmental and economic studies, topographical and geological survey and project and construction management. Transportation architectural services are led by Nick Derbyshire, the award winning architect for Liverpool Street, Bradford Interchange and Ashford International Station. Services provided in relation to railway study and design include: feasibility studies, financial and economic evaluation, investment programmes and revenue forecasting/modelling; 'business case', privatisation advice; transportation planning; railway infrastructure and systems design, layout, design and architecture of stations; passenger flow analysis and intermodal connection facilities; rail and multimodal freight terminals; freight handling, logistics, sector studies; route corridor identification and audit; route optimisation and alignment selection and design for surface and underground routes for high-speed, main line, metro and light rail systems; civil, geotechnical, structural and multidisciplinary engineering; trackwork design; research and analysis of track behaviour, design of track components and support systems; detailed design of complex junction layouts, including production of manufacturers' drawings and setting-out details; depot and workshop design including layouts and maintenance equipment specifications; analysis of railway maintenance and rehabilitation requirements; preparation of railway operating plans, including scheduling, crew rostering, motive power and rolling stock planning; management structures; signalling and train control systems design, including specifications and safety requirements; environmental impact assessment; design of noise and vibration mitigation measures; and safety cases, innovative solutions, value engineering.

Projects

Current and recent projects: United Kingdom privatisation advice, lead adviser on nine of the 25 passenger rail franchises awarded in the UK; design engineer on the Croydon Tramlink; member of a team appointed by the Department of Transport to act as government adviser for the design and construction of the Channel Tunnel Rail Link project; planning, detailed design and construction supervision for Waterloo International Terminal, London; audit for the Department of Transport—the economic justification for the transfer of freight from road to rail; maintenance privatisation, lead adviser on the privatisation of infrastructure maintenance units; strategic advice to Railtrack on the commercial case for infrastructure enhancement; operational advice on Croydon Tramlink; the concept and architectural design of Ashford International station, Kent; revenue forecasting for the Thameslink 2000 scheme; audit of the traffic and revenue forecasts in support of the concession for the Manchester Metro including the extension to Salford Quays and Eccles; engineering design management of the high-speed Channel Tunnel Rail Link and detailed engineering design of the 30 km Folkestone—Ashford section of the route across Kent; validation of the feasibility and costing of terminal options for the Channel Tunnel Rail Link at Stratford; detailed analysis of options and comparison report to government on all aspects of Kings Cross or St. Pancras as the terminus for the Channel Tunnel Rail Link, London; West Coast Main Line Development Study including business case development, track electrification upgrade and funding and financing options; assistance to London Underground in the planning and implementation of LUL's Enhanced Track Replacement Project.

   Advice to SEC (a European consortium of contractors) and the European Commission on the strategy for justifying construction of Trans-European projects; survey and design of upgrading on the Tallinn—Narva line, Estonia; project management of a consortium commissioned to design the upgrading of 100 km of CP's Lisbon—Oporto main line for high-speed services, Loures to Lisbon Corridor Railway Study, Beira-Alta Line Modernisation and Valonge to Cete Railway, Portugal; High-Speed Railway audit and project justification, Madrid—Barcelona, Spain; station planning at Bruxelles Midi Terminal TGV, Belgium; Study to examine the engineering, economic and environmental impact of re-establishing the rail link between Slovenia and Hungary; review of investment in change of gauge facility and freight yard rationalisation, Zahony/Eperjeske, Hungary/Ukraine; feasibility study for the construction of a new bridge over the River Danube between Romania and Bulgaria, taking into account existing road and rail infrastructure; the feasibility for modernisation of route and track layouts together with passenger and freight traffic analyses and projections in Poznan Railway junction complex, Poland; a nine country study to provide a framework for a transport development programme, the Balkan Transportation Study; railway and comparative transport studies on Corridor 6 encompassing Poland, Czech Republic, Slovenia, Hungary and Austria; study and design of a 520 km rail link between Syktyvkar (Komi Republic and Archangel (Russia) involving upgrading existing lines and construction of 200 km of new railway; study to identify optimum site, rail and road accessibility together with the preparation of outline operating plans and rail layout of new intermodal terminal, St. Petersburg; advisers to the Ministry of Railways on the development of a multimodal strategy for the whole of the Russian Federation; appraisal of the Ledmozero—Kochkoma Railway, Finland and the Russian Federation; project engineer for the construction of a new station in St. Petersburg for the new high-speed railway to Moscow.

Privatisation of the transport sector in Indonesia which includes definition of the railway projects suitable for private finance investment; restructuring multimodal services in regard to road/rail integration across Central Asia; advisers to an international bank consortium in respect of the modernisation of the Kazakhstan railways; advisers to the Hong Kong government for railway developments in the Territory including the proposed new Western Corridor Railway and Mass Transit Railway extensions; feasibility study for the development of commuter rail services in Bangkok, Thailand and detailed survey; track, bridges, signalling & telecommunications, rolling stock design and inspection services for a new Citayam—Cibinong freight line in western Java, Indonesia.

Evaluation of Swedish support to Botswana Railways for supply of signalling and telecommunications equipment; track maintenance system reviews in Tanzania and Zambia; and national transportation study in Namibia.

UPDATED

Gotch Consultancy

21 Alleyn Road, London SE21 8AB, UK
Tel: +44 181 766 7999   Fax: +44 181 766 7999

Key personnel
Principal Consultant: Jeremy Gotch

Capabilities
Gotch Consultancy undertakes operational or research and analysis assignments in the fields of transport and distribution management. Specific areas of expertise include: international rail and intermodal freight; European transport economics including Channel Tunnel impact and rail privatisation and open access; investment appraisal; quality assurance; and mergers and acquisitions.

VERIFIED

GRA Incorporated

115 West Avenue, Suite 201, Jenkintown, Pennsylvania 19046, USA
Tel: +1 215 884 7500   Fax: +1 215 884 1385
email: gramail@gra-inc.com
Web: http://www.gra-inc.com/~gra

Key personnel
President: Frank Berardino
Executive Vice-Presidents: Richard Golaszewski,
   John J Grocki, Chris A Frankel

Associates: W Bruce Allen, Aaron J Gellman,
   Paul Banner, Geoffrey Zeh

Capabilities
Rail economics including: rates and pricing, costing, cost allocation and financial analysis; special studies of operations and maintenance, including short line operations; privatisation; asset valuation, disposition, rehabilitation and financing analysis; traffic analysis; reorganisation planning and economics; high-speed rail feasibility studies.

Projects
GRA projects include: rail line ecomomics and costing; economic study of freight car hire charges; short line operations studies; analysis of reorganisation possibilities for a bankrupt wagon leasing firm; expert witness testimony on rates and economics; economic impacts of new and altered rail corridors; several valuation studies of transportation assets; privatisation studies of government-owned transport assets.

UPDATED

Halcrow

Sir William Halcrow & Partners Ltd
Vineyard House, 44 Brook Green, London W6 7BY, UK
Tel: +44 171 602 7282   Fax: +44 171 603 0095

Key personnel
Railways and Tunnels Directors: A J Runacres,
   R N Craig, P S Coventry, P Jenkin, G P Gittoes

Halcrow Fox
(address as above)
Tel: +44 171 603 1618   Fax: +44 171 603 5783
Railways Directors: R J Airport, S Hammerton

Halcrow Transmark Ltd
(address as above)
Tel: +44 181 970 1800   Fax: +44 181 970 1812
Railways Directors: D S Kennedy, P S Coventry,
   J B Powell, A J Buckoke, K H Lockwood, S Munday,
   J A Baggs, R S Hoad, G Hornby, T P Worrall

Principal subsidiaries
HGA Ltd
Burderop Park, Swindon SN4 0QD, UK
Tel: +44 1793 814756   Fax: +44 1793 815020
Managing Director: T J Tovey

International site offices and local representation in Argentina, Australia, Bangladesh, Barbados, Belgium, Bulgaria, Chile, Costa Rica, Denmark, Dominican Republic, Egypt, Ethiopia, Ghana, Guyana, Hong Kong, Hungary, India, Indonesia, Iran, Italy, Kazakhstan, Korea, Latvia, Lithuania, Malaysia, Morocco, Nepal, Pakistan, Paraguay, Peru, Philippines, Poland, Qatar, Romania, Russian Federation, Slovakia, Slovenia, Sri Lanka, St Lucia, Sweden, Syria, Tanzania, Thailand, Trinidad, Tunisia, Turkey, Ukraine, United Arab Emirates, Venezuela, Vietnam, Yemen Arab Republic.

Capabilities
Appraisal, design and construction supervision of civil, structural, mechanical and electrical engineering and environmental services.

Its rail group combines the railway engineering design capability of Sir William Halcrow & Partners; the capability in railway operations, electrical and mechanical engineering and management of Halcrow Transmark (see entry in this section); and the planning and evaluation services offered by Halcrow Fox. The rail group has experience in the planning, evaluation, specification, design, construction and commissioning of railways, metros and light rail systems.

Halcrow Fox offers urban and light rail planning and evaluation, including investment policy reviews, alignment planning, passenger and revenue forecasts, and environmental and development impact studies.

Transmark, operating as Transmode in the USA and GHD-Transmark in Australia and New Zealand, offers initial research, forecasting, feasibility studies, planning and design, construction supervision, and specification of equipment. Transmark also devises management and operational systems and provides staff training for new technology.

Projects
Current railway schemes include:
   Channel Tunnel Rail Link, UK: engineering, planning and design and equipment impact studies for Union Railways. Founder member of London & Continental Railways, jointly responsible for the design and construction of the Channel Tunnel Rail Link; CrossRail, London, UK: detailed design and advice during construction of 5 km of twin-bored running tunnels between London Bridge and Canary Wharf with cut-and-cover station at Bermondsey and major underground crossover structure for LUL; East London Line: engineering feasibility studies and preparation of parliamentary plans for LUL; Post Office Railway (underground small gauge), UK: surveys, maintenance and safeguarding of tunnels; Edinburgh South Suburban Rail Study, UK: investigation of the scope for improvements in services and infrastructure; Leeds Supertram; design review, performance simulation and development of rolling stock functional specification and system operating plan for Badgerline Transit Developments; Greater Manchester Passenger Transport Executive; assistance with project development (including operational and revenue forecasting), project management and engineering liaison; GEOGIS validation and look-out protection: validation of information held on the GEOGIS asset database for Railtrack North West and Midlands Zones; LUL station congestion programme: joint studies with LUL to develop designs for improvements to over 30 existing stations and to assist in the assessment of their safety; Midland Parkway study.

Lisbon North—South Line, Portugal: installation of a new railway on the lower deck of the existing road suspension bridge across the River Tagus, connecting existing railway lines on the north and south banks; pre-investment study, Czech Republic: study for Czech Railways to forecast future levels of national and international passenger and freight traffic along the country's four main rail corridors; CIS rail strategy study for EC TACIS programme to identify key rail corridors in Russia, Belarus, Ukraine and Moldova; Tsing Yi and East Lantau Tunnels, Hong Kong: detailed design and supervision for Mass Transit Railway Corporation (MTRC); Lat Krabang inland container depot project, Thailand: design and project management of an inland container depot in Bangkok; Malayan double-tracking projects: planning and project management of double-tracking of suburban railway lines around Kuala Lumpur; Kuala Lumpur to Sepang Airport, Malaysia: tender design of 48 km high-speed rail link for a private consortium; railway rehabilitation and extension, Java, Indonesia; State Rail train radio project, Australia: project management and specialist technical inputs to a secure radio communications system; and Pyrmont light rail system, Australia: consortium project management and design engineering.

Other projects have been carried out in Greece, Hong Kong, Malaysia and Denmark.

UPDATED

Halcrow Transmark

Transportation Systems and Market Research Limited
Vineyard House, 44 Brook Green, London W6 7BY, UK
Tel: +44 181 970 1800   Fax: +44 181 970 1811

Parent company
Sir William Halcrow & Partners Ltd
(See entry in this section)

Key personnel
Executive Chairman: P S Coventry
Directors: D S Kennedy, P S Coventry, J B Powell,
   K H Lockwood, R Hoad, T Worrall

Capabilities
Halcrow Transmark was formed in 1969 to undertake transport consultancy, give technical advice and carry out market research throughout the world. Halcrow Transmark operates under the name of Transmode in the USA and GHD-Transmark Australia in Australia and New Zealand.

Projects have been undertaken across the full range of heavy and light rail disciplines, from provision of advice by a single specialist to technical assistance programmes and major multidisciplinary studies. Training has been an important element in many projects and is undertaken both in the UK and overseas.

Clients include national and state governments; railway administrations; the World Bank and the various development banks; the Overseas Development Administration and many other funding agencies. Halcrow Transmark has also worked with local authorities and private industries such as mining companies and mineral railways, and has advised consortia led by financial institutions and corporate groups, particularly in the areas of privatisation and investment.

Projects

Typical projects include:

Australia: State Railway Authority of New South Wales Train Radio, project management and specialist technical inputs to a secure radio communications system; Pyrmont LRT system, consortium project management and design engineering; project management/support for a national computerised passenger rail ticketing and reservations system (including timetable and fares enquiry functions) for Computer Science Corporation of New South Wales;

Czech Republic: pre-investment study for Czech Railways;

Denmark: Copenhagen LRT system, technical advice on line installations, including signalling, telecommunications, civil engineering and safety systems;

Greece: project management for major infrastructure projects;

Hong Kong: rolling stock project management consultancy;

India: analysis of railway operational constraints;

Indonesia: railway rehabilitation and extension, Java;

Italy: feasibility study for Padova—Chioggia rail service;

Malawi: establishment of investment plan for rehabilitation of physical assets of Malawi Railways and provision of General Manager;

Malaysia: double-tracking and electrification of KTM network around Kuala Lumpur; LRT rolling stock design supervision;

Portugal: installation of new railway on lower deck of existing road suspension bridge across the River Tagus to connect lines on north and south banks;

Thailand: design and project management of inland container depot; detailed engineering design for new rail routes;

Ukraine: study for design and development of UZ telecommunications networks;

UK: design and construction of Channel Tunnel Rail Link; privatisation advice to banks, contractors and independent operators; contractual, incentive regime and benchmarking advice to Railtrack, infrastructure contractors and operating companies; detailed design of permanent way, structures, overhead line equipment, signalling and telecommunications for Railtrack; study and design of LRT systems in Manchester and Cardiff;

USA: operations and signalling assistance in the remodelling of Grand Central Terminal, New York; implementation of a new regional control system for Metro-North;

Vietnam: feasibility study for Hanoi—Dong Dang rail route rehabilitation.

UPDATED

Hamburg-Consult

Gesellschaft für Verkehrsberatung und Verfahrenstechniken mbH
Steinstrasse 20, PO Box 102720, D-20019 Hamburg, Germany
Tel: +49 40 278450   Fax: +49 40 2784 5410

Key personnel

Chairman: Holger Albert
Managing Directors: Fritz Pasquay, Willi Nibbe
Vice-Directors: Walter Keudel, Karl-Heinz Höffler,
    Claus D Jahnke, Gerhard Schenk

Capabilities

Hamburg-Consult is a subsidiary of the public transport company Hamburger Hochbahn Aktiengesellschaft (HHA), and works in close connection with the management of the parent company as well as other affiliated local railway companies.

VERIFIED

Delon Hampton & Associates

800 K Street NW, North Lobby, Suite 720,
Washington DC 20001, USA
Tel: +1 202 898 1999

Key personnel

Chairman of the Board and Chief Executive Officer:
    Delon Hampton

Capabilities

Design, planning and inspection of rapid transit and light rail systems and other transportation infrastructure

Projects

Prime consultant for design of four stations and several tunnel sections for Los Angeles heavy rail system; subconsultant for design of Section E-7a of the Washington Metro; subconsultant for the Howard-Dan Ryan rail extension for the Chicago Transit Authority; prime consultant for station and section design of the Southwest Transit project, Chicago, Illinois; prime consultant for aerial structure design of the Long Beach—Los Angeles LRT system.

VERIFIED

Hanson-Wilson Inc

3100 Broadway Suite 900, Kansas City, Missouri 64111, USA
Tel: +1 816 561 9054   Fax: +1 816 561 0654

Key personnel

President: James G Gibbs
Vice-President: Gary J Potts

Capabilities

Complete railroad services — design, design/build and construction management for freight railways, light rail and commuter rail providers. Includes: intermodal, automotive transfer, and fuelling facilities; capacity improvement programmes; track design, evaluation and inspection; bridge design, evaluation and inspection; environmental/waste management; survey, mapping and photogrammetry; and catenary design.

Projects

Willow Springs Intermodal Facility, Willow Springs, Illinois (design and construction management); Harvard Yard Intermodal Facility, West Memphis, Arkansas (design and construction management); Belen Yard, Belen, New Mexico, eastbound main line fuelling facility (two phases) and yard revisions (design and construction management); Capacity Improvement Project, various locations for additional main line trackage (design and construction management); Southwest Corridor Freight Rail Relocation, Denver, Colorado: preliminary track design for 8 miles of three main tracks and complete design of bridges; Metropolitan Transit Development Board, San Diego, California: 3.5 miles of light rail and relocation of existing freight tracks (construction management and design review services), including maintenance of traffic for freight rail and Amtrak services; Kansas City Auto Transfer Facility, Kansas City, Kansas: 30-acre automotive distribution facility (design and construction management); Ebony Intermodal Facility, Ebony, Arkansas: design-build of new intermodal facility (design and construction services); and Automated Equipment Identification (AEI) System, throughout Mexico (site design, construction and installation of system).

NEW ENTRY

Hatch Mott MacDonald Inc

6140 Stoneridge Mall Road, Suite 250, Pleasanton, California 94588, USA
Tel: +1 510 469 8010   Fax: +1 510 469 8011

Key personnel

President and Chief Executive Officer: Gordon A Smith
Chief Operating Officer and Director, Western
    Operations: Peter Wickens
Director, Eastern Operations: Jan J Feberwee

Canada office
2800 Speakman Drive, Sheridan Science & Technology Park, Mississauga, Ontario, L5K 2R7
Tel: +1 905 855 2010   Fax: +1 905 855 2607

Capabilities

Engineering consulting services, project and construction management and planning and architectural services for rail and transit systems. Services include: planning, route selection and environmental assessment; civil engineering, including alignment, trackwork, structures, bridges and elevated guideways; tunnels in soft ground or rock, including planning, architecture and safety; building services; systems engineering including signalling, telecommunications, traction power and distribution, tunnel ventilation; programme and project management; and construction management.

Projects

Recent and current projects include: programme management services for Toronto Transit Commission's Rapid Transit Expansion Programme; design, project management and construction management for CN North America's St Clair River Tunnel between Sarnia, Canada and Port Huron, USA; construction management services for the construction of the Denver LRT system; application engineering services for the installation of an enhanced speed enforcement system at priority locations systemwide for New York City Transit Authority; detailed design of Ocean Parkway interlocking as part of the Brighton Beach Line resignalling programme for New York City Transit Authority; construction management services for the traction power system for the Montréal—Deux Montagnes route modernisation; and consulting and oversight services to Santa Clara County Transportation Agency on the design of trackwork, signals and telecommunications for the 12 mile Tasman Corridor LRT extension.

UPDATED

HDR Engineering Inc

103 Orinoco Street, Alexandria, Virginia 22314-2096, USA
Tel: +1 703 518 8500   Fax: +1 703 548 0527

Key personnel

Vice-President: Tom Smithberger

Capabilities

Railroad structures design and inspection; railroad trackwork design and inspection; construction administration services; metro (line and station) designs; terminal and transfer facilities design; and light rail and people mover design.

VERIFIED

Hill International Inc

1 Levitt Parkway, Willingboro, New Jersey 08046 USA
Tel: +1 609 871 5800   Fax: +1 609 871 1261

Key personnel

Chairman: Irvin E Richter

Capabilities

Engineering consultancy; project and construction management; project management supervision; construction claims analysis; expert witness testimony; claims prevention and dispute resolution.

Projects

Projects include: Istanbul LRT line, Turkey; Frankford Elevated reconstruction, Norristown Line reconstruction and RRD main line improvement programme, Philadelphia, USA; Los Angeles Metro Rail, USA; Tren Urbano rapid transit study, San Juan, Puerto Rico; Kearny rail connection, Kearny, USA; and Long Island Rail Road Richmond Hill improvements, Queens, USA.

UPDATED

Holec Ridderkerk UK Ltd

Dogpool Lane, Stirchley, Birmingham B30 2XJ, UK
Tel: +44 121 471 1047   Fax: +44 121 414 1369

Key personnel

See entry in *Locomotives and powered passenger vehicles* section

Capabilities

Design, engineering, systems integration and marketing of electric multiple-units. Diesel multiple-units, metro vehicles, passenger coaches, light rail vehicles and tramcars. Consultancy services are also provided in specialist areas and for vehicle subsystems.

Particular mention is made of familiarity with the current UK position concerning Railtrack group standards and safety case issues.

Projects

The Class 323 emu equipped with a three-phase 25 kV 50 Hz AC regenerative traction package is the first emu to gain acceptance in the UK from Railtrack's Electrical Engineering and Control Systems Safety Assessment Panel for nationwide operation on overhead electrified routes. The traction and control systems have been supplied by Holec Machines and Apparaten BV, Netherlands (a sister company of Holec Ridderkerk UK Ltd), and do not require a separate Interference Current Monitoring Unit.

The traction and train subsystems have been configured so that they are compatible with lineside signalling and telecommunications infrastructure. With no infrastructure changes necessary to these systems, the Class 323 is non-route specific. Work has begun to gain comparable acceptance for the UK 750 V DC third rail system and for dual-voltage operation.

UPDATED

Holland Railconsult

PO Box 2855, NL-3500 GW Utrecht, Netherlands
Tel: +31 30 235 6618/4835   Fax: +31 30 235 7232/5800

Key personnel
Communications Officer: Marleen Peters

Capabilities
Holland Railconsult was formerly the Engineering Department of Netherlands Railways. The consultancy has extensive expertise in civil engineering track construction and signalling issues.

UPDATED

Hyder Consulting

Hyder Consulting Ltd
2-3 Cornwall Terrace, Regents Park, London NW1 4QP, UK
Tel: +44 171 544 6600   Fax: +44 171 470 0019

Key personnel
Divisional Director: M Renfrew

Acer Consultants (Far East) Ltd
3/F Somerset House, Taikoo Place, 979 King's Road, Quarry Bay, Hong Kong
Tel: +852 2911 2233   Fax: +852 2805 5028
Key Contact: Kenneth Lau

Overseas offices
Germany, Cyprus, Spain, Ireland, Turkey, Australia, Egypt, Bahrain, Kuwait, Qatar, Saudi Arabia, United Arab Emirates, Pakistan, Malaysia, Singapore, Thailand, USA and Taiwan

Capabilities
Management and advisory services including: economic and financial appraisal, operations and research management, tariff negotiation, public transportation planning, traffic modelling and forecasting, operations audits and productivity enhancements, technical audits and quality audits, maintenance management, environmental impact assessment, safety and reliability audits, training and certification, value engineering, problem solving and troubleshooting.

Project planning and design including: design management, concept design and system selection, feasibility studies, outline designs and specifications for legislative approval, preparation of applications for grants (or other funding) as admissible, operations and system planning, alignment and permanent way engineering, civil and structural engineering, station planning, electrical and mechanical engineering, signalling and control systems engineering, rolling stock, freight terminal and depot design.

Project implementation including: preparation of contract documents, preparation of specifications, tender invitations and adjudication, project management and cost control, supervision and quality control of construction contracts, monitoring and quality control of

procurement contracts, testing and commissioning, training and certification, operations and maintenance management.

Areas of activity include main line, regional and suburban railway services; metros and urban transit systems including light rail and people movers; heavy-haul freight, general merchandise, unitised loads, bimodal and intermodal technologies.

Projects

Typical rail projects currently in hand are:
Istanbul Metro, Turkey: Electrical and mechanical systems design; supervision of implementation; commissioning and acceptance.

LAR Lai King Station, Hong Kong: detailed design of all E&M services and civil and structural aspects for the Lai King station which is the interchange station of the Tsuen Wan line and Lantau Airport line.

Ankara LRT, Turkey: supervision of supply and installation of rolling stock, E&M subsystems, commissioning and acceptance.

Kuala Lumpur LRT system, Malaysia: Checking engineer for the contracting consortium on Line 1, Stage 2.

Projects have also been carried out for Railtrack, UK and Jubilee Line Extension.

NEW ENTRY

ICB

Ingenieur-Consult Verkehrstechnik GmbH
Rudower Chaussee 4, Haus 8, D-12489 Berlin, Germany
Tel: +49 30 670 5990   Fax: +49 30 670 59911
email: icb-gmbh.berlin@t-online.de

Key personnel
Managers: Dipl Ing Rainer Patzig/Dipl Ing Thomas Just

Hamburg office
Teilfeld 5, D-20459 Hamburg
Tel: +49 30 374 9340   Fax: +49 30 374 2623

Capabilities
Railway and transport engineering including planning and implementation of railway projects; taking over building supervision from railway organisations; tender preparation; traffic development planning; project co-ordination.

Projects
Include work in Germany, Russia and Malaysia.

NEW ENTRY

ICF Kaiser Engineers Inc

9300 Lee Highway, Fairfax, Virginia 22031-1207, USA
Tel: +1 703 934 3465   Fax: +1 703 934 3029

Key personnel
President, Engineering and Construction Group:
    David Watson
Executive Vice-President, Infrastructure: Charles B Mudd
Senior Vice-President, Railroads: John Bergerson

Capabilities
Consultancy services for freight railways, light rail, metro, commuter rail and automated guideway transit systems including programme management; planning and design; systems engineering; construction and procurement management.

Projects
Lafayette Railroad relocation (conceptual and preliminary engineering, final design); Gainesville Regional Utilities freight railway (planning, design, permitting, right-of-way acquisition); freight railway, Portugal (project management, engineering, construction management); Boston Southwest Corridor freight/passenger line (preliminary engineering, final design, services during construction); Taipei Metro (general consultant, technology transfer); Chicago Southwest Corridor (co-ordinating consultant, new rail link to Midway Airport); Exchange Place station, New Jersey (construction); Park Avenue tunnel rehabilitation, New York (construction management); Jubilee Line Extension, London (electrical and mechanical design); Chicago Circulator (light rail programme management); Los Angeles Metro and LRT (programme management and design); Baltimore Metro

(programme management; design, construction management); Dade County (Miami) Metrorail (programme management, design, construction management); Jacksonville Automated Guideway Express (people mover programme management, design and construction management).

UPDATED

Ilium Associates, Inc

500 108th Ave NE, Suite 2450, Bellevue, Washington 98004, USA
Tel: +1 206 646 6525   Fax: +1 206 646 6522

Key personnel
President: Carolyn Perez Andersen
Vice-President: Robert M Prowda

Capabilities
Consumer research and analysis; preparation of marketing strategies and plans; project planning, graphic design of signage systems, corporate identities including vehicle graphics and uniforms; brochures, posters and map design.

VERIFIED

InfoVision Ltd

Slack Lane, Derby DE22 3FL, UK
Tel: +44 1332 347123   Fax: +44 1332 345110
email: welcome@infovision.co.uk

Key personnel
Chairman and Chief Executive: Peter Crawford
Sales & Marketing Director: Alastair Fox
Operations & Systems Development Director: Jeff Luff
Financial Director: John Stride

Capabilities
Provision of technical documentation in electronic format, druid rail information retrieval software for rapid access to equipment operating and maintenance manuals, illustrated parts catalogues and servicing schedules. Origination of information and conversion of legacy data.

Consultancy services covering all aspects of technical documentation. Specification, planning and production of system and equipment operating and maintenance manuals and illustrated parts catalogues.

Projects
Recent projects include consultancy and supply of software to rail operators in the UK, KCRC (Hong Kong) and MTRC (Hong Kong).

UPDATED

Infra Safety Services

PO Box 1075, NL-3300 BB Dordrecht, Netherlands
Tel: +31 78 654 0655   Fax: +31 78 651 4421

Key personnel
Director: C J de Graaff
General Manager: J F A M Weijtmans

Capability
Infra Safety Services provides a total package for securing the work area. The company draws up and executes safety plans, and develops high-standard systems such as ARW 5/2 and Minimel 90 or PWA.

NEW ENTRY

Interconsult

Interconsult AS
Grenseveien 90, PO Box 6412 Etterstad, N-0605 Oslo, Norway
Tel: +47 22 635900   Fax: +47 22 635990

Key personnel
Group Managing Director: Frode Kværneng
Head of Transport Branch: Pål Stabell
Head of Railway Department: Karstein Søreide
Managing Director, Interconsult International AS:
    Ole K Paulsen

Capabilities
Planning consultancy services for railway operators.

Projects

Recent projects include: appraisal of options for rail traffic to and from Lillehammer, Norway, to serve Winter Olympics (1993); appraisal of options for rail link between Oslo and new airport under construction at Gardermoen, Norway (1994); and development of computer systems for monitoring and maintaining bridges and points/switches using hand-held intelligent terminals, digital cameras and light pens (1994-95).

VERIFIED

Interfleet Technology Ltd

Trent House, CP 100, Railway Technical Centre, London Road, Derby DE24 8UP, UK
Tel: +44 1332 264061   Fax: +44 1332 262824

Key personnel

International Projects Director: Jonathan Wragg
Principal Engineer: Ian Myrloi

Capabilities

Specialist engineering and design; in-service support; vehicle development; project engineering, management and strategic services.

Projects

Recent projects have included consultancy work for CAF (Spain), Union Carriage & Wagon (South Africa) and GHD Transmark Australia.

Interfleet secured a contract in 1997 to provide nine years of technical support expertise for Heathrow Express Trains.

UPDATED

Intermetric

Intermetric GmbH
Industriestrasse 24, D-70565 Stuttgart, Germany
Tel: +49 711 780 0392   Fax: +49 711 780 0397

Products

Track geometry design; surveying; plans; geotechnical measuring.

NEW ENTRY

International Rail Consultants

1190 Hornby Street, Vancouver, British Columbia V6Z 2H6, Canada
Tel: +1 604 684 9311   Fax: +1 604 688 5913
email: IRC@sandwell.com

Key personnel

Directors: P M August, M J C Leeper
Director and Business Development Officer: K Spata

Capabilities

Established in 1985 as a joint venture, International Rail Consultants combines the consulting experience of the Swan Wooster Division of Sandwell Inc with the operational experience of BC Rail.

International Rail offers experience in many aspects of railway planning, management, economics, operations, engineering and construction, including: fixed plant design, construction and maintenance; railway electrification; intermodal systems; port and terminal developments; telecommunications; operations and train control; economic and financial analysis, strategic planning; computerised systems design, EDI, MIS; inventory management; equipment procurement, rebuilding and maintenance; general management, organisation and restructuring; privatisation and commercialisation; and manpower development and training programmes.

Projects

In 1996, International Rail was involved in projects in southern Africa, Bangladesh, China, Colombia, Philippines, Thailand, Peru, Argentina, Australia, USA and Canada.

UPDATED

Italferr-SIS TAV SpA

Via Marsala 53, I-00185 Rome, Italy
Tel: +39 6 49751   Fax: +39 6 4975 2437
email: itf.com@italferr.it

Key personnel

Chairman: Livio Vido
Vice-Chairman and Managing Director: Bruno Cimino
Managing Director: Carlo Ianniello
General Managers: Giovanni Marengo/
   Alessandro Rizzardi
Commercial Director: Gaetano Piepoli

Capabilities

Italferr-SIS TAV SpA is the consulting engineering subsidiary of Italian Railways (FS) founded in Rome in 1984. Shareholders are FS (94 per cent) and Istituto Bancario San Paolo di Torino (6 per cent).

Italferr services cover management and personnel; finance and economics; operations; commercial policy, costs and tariffs; management information systems; traffic control systems, signalling and telecommunications; permanent way; electrification; traction and rolling stock; port rail facilities and ferry services; stations, marshalling yards and intermodal terminals; workshop and depot facilities.

Feasibility study on the development of the railway and combined transport on corridor IV, Bulgaria, Hungary; Modernisation of electric traction supply system for the E20 railway line (Kunowice—Warsaw section), Poland (EU Phare); ETCS pilot installation on the E20 rail line (Kunowice—Warsaw section), Poland (EU Phare); study of the Ukraine section of the Trieste—Budapest—Kiev rail corridor; study of the competition of railway transport on the Casablance—Rabat—Fes axis, Morocco (IBRD); Perugia S Anna—Perugia Fontivegge rapid transit system; Bologna—Verona railway belt line.

UPDATED

Japan Transportation Consultants Inc

5-2 Nishi Kanda 2-chome, Chiyoda-ku, Tokyo 101, Japan
Tel: +81 3 3263 9470   Fax: +81 3 3263 9472

Key personnel

Manager, Overseas Services: E Kurakawa

VERIFIED

JARTS

Japan Railway Technical Service
Taiyokan Building, 2-27-8 Hongo 2-chome,
Bunkyo-ku, Tokyo 113, Japan
Tel: +81 3 5684 3171   Fax: +81 3 5684 3170/3180
email: jarts@po.iijnet.or.jp

Key personnel

Chairman: Akira Miki
President: Hiroshi Okada
Senior Executive Vice-President: Sadaaki Kuroda
Executive Vice-President: Naofumi Takashige

Capabilities

JARTS was established for the purpose of co-operating with the international community in the development of urban, suburban, and main line railways, operating under the guidance of Japan's Ministry of Transport and in co-operation with the Japan Railways Group (formerly Japanese National Railways), the Japan Railway Construction Public Corporation and the Teito Rapid Transit Authority.

Fields of activity include: studies, surveys, projects and management relating to railways, metros and monorails; construction of new lines; track modernisation and upgrading; electrification; dieselisation; modernisation of rolling stock; automatic train control and centralised traffic control; seat reservation systems; marshalling yard automation; holding of overseas seminars, making PR films, introducing Japanese railway technology and training of personnel.

Projects

Recent and current projects include:
   Argentina: consulting project on rail privatisation in the Buenos Aires Metropolitan area (1992-2003);
   Egypt: master plan study for ENR.

Vietnam: feasibility study on the rehabilitation and improvement of rail services.
Thailand: study of improvement plan for rail transport.

UPDATED

Jones Garrard Ltd

116 Regent Road, Leicester LE1 7LT, UK
Tel: +44 116 254 2390   Fax: +44 116 255 6658

Key personnel

Directors: Michael Rodber, Chris Harris

Capabilities

Exterior and interior industrial design of rail vehicles, from concept through to implementation as new vehicle design projects, refurbishment, component design and development and overall project management. Specific services include design proposals, design development, component definition, specifications, mockups and prototypes, trial installations and project management of all stages of the design and procurement process. Also design, development and production of passenger emergency equipment, particularly detrainment systems.

Projects

Exterior design of Channel Tunnel Eurostar high-speed trainset for EPS, SNCF and SNCB; external design of AVE high-speed trainset for RENFE; interior design of Stockholm metro trainsets; Hong Kong Airport Express and Lantao Airport trains; interior design of Channel Tunnel overnight trains; Arlanda Airport trains; refurbishment of mass transit rolling stock for MTRC and KCRC (Hong Kong), London Underground Ltd and Glasgow Underground (UK); and various ergonomic and safety systems and detrainment systems for mass transit rolling stock.

VERIFIED

KAMPSAX International A/S

PO Box 1143, Stamholmen 112, DK-2650 Hvidovre, Copenhagen, Denmark
Tel: +45 36 390700   Fax: +45 36 772829
email: kampsax@inet.uni-c.dk

Subsidiary and Associate Companies

Denmark, China and Indonesia.

Key personnel

Managing Director: Hugo Larsen
Deputy Managing Director: Søren Nysom
Chief Railway Engineer: Jan Webèr

Capabilities

A member of EURAIL Consult (see entry in this section), Kampsax undertakes design and supervision, and covers planning, maintenance, and training activities.

Projects

Current and recent projects include: provision of Stockholm Underground with a signalling specialist from 1995 to 1996 for rehabilitation of Roslagsbanen.

Between 1988 and 1991 Kampsax undertook the detailed engineering design and construction supervision of a 175 km branch line from Francistown to Sua Pan in Botswana. The project comprised construction of a single track freight railway line from south of Francistown to Sua Pan in the Makgadikgadi depression.

For the Danish State Railways, Kampsax carried out detailed design and engineering for the signalling control and communications system for the Ballerup—Frederikssund line on the Copenhagen urban rail system.

Kampsax has been retained to provide technical assistance and project management services for the operation of maintenance depot servicing Botswana Railway's 32 diesel-electric locomotives.

UPDATED

A T Kearney Inc

222 West Adams, Chicago, Illinois 60606, USA
Tel: +1 312 648 0111   Fax: +1 312 223 6200

Key personnel
Vice-President and Managing Director of
    Transportation: Justin F Zubrod Sr

Capabilities
A T Kearney is a rail transportation consulting firm with
more than 30 offices in North America, Europe and Asia.

VERIFIED

Kennedy & Donkin Transportation Ltd

Westbrook Mills, Godalming GU7 2AZ, UK
Tel: +44 1483 425900   Fax: +44 1483 425136

Key personnel
Managing Director: John R Springate
Business Development Director: Rowland R Vye
Transportation Director: Robert A Gray

Offices in 17 countries

Capabilities
Feasibility studies, system design and engineering. The
staff includes engineers, economists, operators and
planners with a wide range of experience in the planning,
design, operation and management of railways, LRT and
metro systems. Also, bridge inspection, assessment and
remediation; civil and structural services covering
infrastructure and permanent way, stations, offices and
depots; design and supervision of bridges and tunnels.

Projects
Hong Kong: installation supervision of automatic or
automatic train protection and bidirectional operation for
KCRC Hong Kong.
    Thailand, Bangkok MRT: specification and tender
evaluation for the elevated metro developed by the
Tanayong Group.
    Hong Kong: system-wide power supply and distribution
review including effects of Lantau Airport extension on
the system.
    Philippines: responsible for planning and feasibility
studies and design and construction management for
Manilla LRT (jointly with Electrowatt, Switzerland).
    UK: projects include DLR, London; Manchester
Metrolink, Phase 2; Central, Northern and Jubilee Lines,
London Underground; signalling and capacity
improvements on Felixstowe line, for Railtrack;
performance requirement for low-maintenance DC circuit
breakers for Railtrack; project representative for Channel
Tunnel Rail Link — acting as agent for Department of
Transport.
    Other projects have been carried out in Bulgaria,
Pakistan, Lithuania, Slovenia, Algeria, Nigeria and Russia.

UPDATED

Lester B Knight & Associates Inc

549 W Randolph Street, Chicago, Illinois 60606, USA
Tel: +1 312 346 2100   Fax: +1 312 648 1085

Key personnel
Vice-Presidents: Dominick J Gatto, Lee A Hoyt

Capabilities
Transport and environmental studies; railroads and rapid
transit systems planning, design and construction,
engineering and management; operations and
maintenance.

VERIFIED

Laramore, Douglass and Popham

332 South Michigan Ave, Suite 400, Chicago, Illinois
60604, USA
Tel: +1 312 427 8486   Fax: +1 312 427 8474
email: rth@ldpgroup.com

9 East 41st Street, Suite 300, New York, New York 10017,
USA
Tel: +1 212 867 4122   Fax: +1 212 867 4481

Key personnel
President: Robert H Steinberger
Senior Vice-President: Richard T Harvey

Capabilities
Design and project management for electrified rapid
transit and electric railway traction power supply and
distribution systems.

Projects
Include CTA Chicago Green Line rehabilitation consisting
of four new traction power substations and 10
rehabilitation substations; MBTA Boston Red Line
breaker replacement and Kenmore substation
replacement.

UPDATED

Laser Rail

Laser Rail Ltd
Jessop House, 39 Smedley Street East, Matlock
DE4 3FQ, UK
Tel: +44 1629 760750   Fax: +44 1629 760751

Key personnel
Director: David M Johnson

Corporate development
Laser Rail was established in 1989 by David Johnson in
response to a rapidly growing need to manage the
implementation of new technology into the commercial
rail environment.

Capabilities
Interactive track design gauging system software for
gauging applications, including route enhancement.
Computerised systems for designing track geometry, for
both renewal and maintenance. Track geometry
measurement and database systems for track
assessment, redesign and monitoring of both track
performance and maintenance machinery.
    Laser Rail operates a range of computer facilities as
part of its services. It also provides training and
certification to various levels of competency and is
available in-house and can be supplied as part of the
overall support package.

UPDATED

J W Leas and Associates Inc

1084 East Lancaster Avenue, Rosemont, Pennsylvania
19010, USA
Tel: +1 610 525 1952   Fax: +1 610 527 9136

Key personnel
President: J Wesley Leas

Capabilities
Fare collection system studies; fare structure analyses;
fare collection equipment and media specifications,
production monitoring and testing; revenue service
appraisal and revenue control procedures for rapid and
mass transit operations.

Projects
Implemented system for a multi-operator universal ticket
to serve the needs of BART, CCCTA and other transit
agencies in the San Francisco Bay area; created system
recommendation, equipment requirements, cost
analysis, technical specifications and performance
monitoring for the recommended fare collection system
for Los Angeles–Long Beach LRT (Blue Line);
recommended fare collection system features and
specified the equipment and fare media, monitored
production and revenue testing for the LACMTA system
bus and rail operations in Los Angeles; prepared
specifications for electronic registering fareboxes with

ticket processing units for Harris County MTA of Houston
and Seattle Metro; prepared technical specifications and
monitored revenue testing of new ticket vending
machines for commuter rail operation for SCRRA in Los
Angeles area; assisted MTA Baltimore in implementing
fare collection for heavy rail extension and participated in
specifying fare collection equipment and media for new
Central Light Rail Line; studied fare collection needs and
proposed procurement specifications for rapid transit,
light rail and commuter rail service for MBTA in Boston
and made appropriate recommendations.

VERIFIED

LTK Engineering Services

A member of the Klauder Group
Two Valley Square, Suite 300, 512 Township Line Road,
Blue Bell, Pennsylvania 19422, USA
Tel: +1 215 542 0700   Fax: +1 215 542 7676

Key personnel
President: George N Dorshimer
Vice-President, Western Region: John S Gustafson
Vice-President, Eastern Region: Frederick H Landell
Director, Business Development: David H Oglevee

Capabilities
LTK offers a wide variety of engineering, managerial and
planning services tailored specifically to meet the needs
of the rail transport industry. LTK expertise includes:
design, specification, manufacture, installation and
construction management for rail vehicles of all kinds;
traction electrification systems; signalling and train
control systems; telecommunications systems; fare
collection equipment; and vehicle maintenance facilities.

Projects
LTK has recently provided engineering and managerial
support for the following rail vehicle procurement
programmes: high-speed trainsets for Amtrak Northeast
Corridor services; new-generation metro trainsets for New
York City Transit Authority; low-floor LRVs for Portland,
Oregon; P2000 LRVs with capability for upgrade to full
automation for Los Angeles County Metropolitan
Transportation Authority; LRVs for Dallas Area Rapid
Transit; rapid transit cars for Southeastern Pennsylvania
Transportation Authority and Massachusetts Bay
Transportation Authority; double-deck push-pull coaches
and diesel-electric locomotives for Southern California
Regional Rail Authority; and M-6 trainsets for Metro-North.
    LTK has recently provided railway and rail transit
systems engineering for a variety of projects including:
Newark-Elizabeth rail link, New Jersey Transit; Westside
and Hillsborough extensions of Portland LRT system; and
signalling modernisation projects for SEPTA's Broad
Street metro line and CTA's Green Line. Other clients
have included Walt Disney Corporation, Canadian
National and the World Bank.

UPDATED

Maguire Group Inc

225 Foxborough Blvd, Foxborough, Massachusetts
02035, USA
Tel: +1 508 543 1700   Fax: +1 508 543 5157

Key personnel
President: Richard J Repeta

Projects
Vermont Avenue Station design ($30 million) for Los
Angeles Metro Wilshire Line; tunnel ventilation shafts ($9
million) for Massachusetts Bay Transportation Authority
(MBTA); Red Line extension tunnel section ($110 million)
with an associate firm, for Massachusetts Bay
Transportation Authority (MBTA).

VERIFIED

Martyn Cornwall Design Management

Top Floor, Jamaica Wharf, 2 Shad Thames, London SE1 2YU, UK
Tel: +44 171 234 0612   Fax: +44 171 403 3868

Key personnel
Director: Martyn Cornwall
Production Director: David French

Capabilities
Provision of comprehensive design management services to the railway industry, including strategic advice and planning of all aspects of design; execution of design projects; commissioning of design projects; design and project management.

Projects
Recent projects include the development and implementation of corporate identities for businesses formed out of the former British Rail.

VERIFIED

Maunsell

Maunsell House, 160 Croydon Road, Beckenham BR3 4DE, UK
Tel: +44 181 663 6565   Fax: +44 181 663 6723
email: gmplon@maunsell.co.uk

Key personnel
Chief Executive (International): J W Downer
Chief Executive (Europe): P J Jarvis
Chief Executive (Middle East): S Al-Kubaisi

9th Floor, 161 Collins Street, Melbourne, Victoria 3000, Australia
Tel: +61 39 653 1234   Fax: +61 39 654 7117
Chief Executive: D N Odgers

1 Kowloon Park Drive, Kowloon, Hong Kong
Tel: +852 376 2299   Fax: +852 376 2070
Chief Executive: F S Y Bong

03/00 The Concourse, 300 Beach Road, Singapore 199555
Tel: +65 299 2466   Fax: +65 299 0297
Chief Executive: G Forrest Brown

Other offices
Birmingham, Cardiff, Haslemere, Manchester, Newcastle, Norwich, Oxted, Sheffield, Witham, Adelaide, Brisbane, Canberra, Perth, Sydney, Paris, Shanghai, Jakarta, Dublin, Tokyo, Beirut, Kuala Lumpur, Karachi, Doha, Ho Chi Minh City, Singapore, Bangkok, Abu Dhabi, Dubai, and Manila

Capabilities
Maunsell, which employs over 2,700 people, provides civil and structural engineering, permanent way, power supply, signalling communications and control system and rolling stock consultancy services.

The range of services offered includes feasibility studies, design, contract documentation, construction management, inspection services and remedial engineering.

Maunsell's experience includes the engineering of mass transit systems, heavy-haul railways, train maintenance facilities, passenger station and maintenance facilities and mass transit stations, repair and upgrading of existing systems.

Projects
Recent projects include: Copenhagen Mini Metro, Denmark; independent specialist advice for Channel Tunnel Rail Link, UK; Bukit Panjang LRT, Singapore; London Underground Ltd's (LUL) Jubilee Line Extension, Green Park—Waterloo section, UK; MRT south contract, Bangkok; Heathrow Express trackbed and tracklaying; Tseung Kwan O extension, Mass Transit Railway, Hong Kong; numerical modelling of tunnels on LUL Northern Line, UK; and design of Siu Ho Wan Depot, Hong Kong; Mass Rapid Transit Woodlands Extension, Singapore.

UPDATED

Maunsell Parsons Brinckerhoff Ltd

Downsview House, 145 Station Road East, Oxted RH8 0QE, UK
Tel: +44 1883 730157   Fax: +44 1883 722914

Key personnel
Managing Director: R Chaning Pearce
Directors: P J Jarvis, A R Umney, P R Nagle, D Palmer

Capabilities
Planning, design, procurement, construction, operation and maintenance of railways and other transport systems, particularly light rail and urban mass transport. The company combines the resources of Maunsell and Parsons Brinckerhoff International Inc. The Maunsell Group, employing over 2,300 members of staff, is prominent in civil and structural engineering, while Parsons Brinckerhoff, with over 4,800 staff, has extensive systems experience in many operating mass transit railways.

Expertise includes: feasibility studies; applications under the UK Transport and Works Act legislation and support for UK Parliamentary Inquiries; signalling, telecommunications and control systems; traction power; rolling stock; depots; permanent way; fare collection; operational studies; safety and reliability; asset surveys and management; hazard analysis; rules and procedures; maintenance standards and specifications; alignment and trackwork; tunnels; elevated structures; station architecture and services; drainage; lighting; HVAC; lifts and escalators; tunnel ventilation; fire and life safety; quality assurance; inspection testing and commissioning; and systems assurance.

Projects
Recent and current projects include: Jubilee Line Extension, London: design audit of E&M systems and design of system-wide tunnel ventilation (with support for systems assurance), review of design proposals for Stratford Market Depot; East London Line Extension; outline design including a new servicing facility and control centre, assistance to London Underground Ltd (LUL) with submission under Transport and Works Act; Croxley Link: cost estimate for project, including pedestrian control and assessment of an existing bridge; Central Line, London Underground Ltd: services of resident engineers and senior staff for installation, inspection and testing of replacement signalling systems and new control room; London Tilbury & Southend Line, Railtrack: project and design management services for resignalling of 90 miles of commuter railway; Docklands Light Railway, London: reliability studies; feasibility and design studies for LRT projects for various UK local authorities and London Underground Ltd; preparation of standards and specifications for design and maintenance of signalling equipment, rolling stock and civil and structural works.

UPDATED

MBD Design

11 rue Victor Hugo, F-93177 Bagnolet Cedex, France
Tel: +33 1 48 57 30 00   Fax: +33 1 48 57 41 31

Key personnel
Marketing Manager: Yves Domergue
Engineering Process Manager: Alain Domergue

Capabilities
MBD Design accepts commissions from network authorities and rolling stock manufacturers for both long- and short-term railway transportation projects.

Projects
Design studies have been undertaken for: the Paris suburban Z2N double-deck train; SYBIC locomotive for SNCF; MF88 for Paris Metro; TER (regional express train) dmu; EOLE three-door double-deck cars for the Paris RER.

VERIFIED

Mercer Management Consulting Inc

1166 Avenue of the Americas, New York, New York 10036, USA

Transportation Group
33 Hayden Avenue, Lexington, Massachusetts 02173, USA
Tel: +1 617 861 7580   Fax: +1 617 862 3935

Key personnel
Vice-President: Hugh Randall

UK Office
1 Grosvenor Place, London SW1X 7HJ, UK
Tel: +44 171 235 5444   Fax: +44 171 245 6933
Vice-President: Matthew Vanderbroeck

Capabilities
Mercer's Transportation Group assists railways and other transport undertakings in the following areas: strategy development; privatisation and commercialisation planning and implementation; organisational restructuring and management development; process re-engineering; operations enhancement and cost reduction; marketing and market research; information management; acquisition and alliance planning; and litigation support. Clients include railways and their suppliers and customers around the world.

VERIFIED

Merz and McLellan Ltd

A Parsons Brinckerhoff company
Amber Court, William Armstrong Drive, Newcastle Business Park, Newcastle upon Tyne NE4 7YQ, UK
Tel: +44 191 226 1899   Fax: +44 191 226 1104

Key personnel
Chairman: Malcolm Kennedy
Managing Director: Paul Cheesmond
Deputy Managing Director: Eric Burton

Overseas offices
Abu Dhabi, Qatar, Singapore, Sudan, Switzerland and Zimbabwe

Capabilities
The company's capabilities are associated with the fixed and mobile electrical and mechanical components of transport systems. Current activities include system and engineering feasibility studies and specifications of passenger transport vehicles, power supply and distribution systems including overhead line equipment, signalling, communications and SCADA systems, and fare-collection equipment. Other components of transport systems covered by the firm's expertise include lifts, escalators and baggage-handling equipment. In addition, the firm offers a comprehensive service in the engineering and design of electrical and mechanical fixed systems such as environmental control and building services in passenger, maintenance and office facilities, and tunnel ventilation and pumping systems.

Projects
Current or recent activities include: London Underground Ltd's East London Line study (E&M works); power study for Tyne & Wear Metro; Cleveland LRT; South Yorkshire Supertram; and research & development projects in light rail under the Eureka Programme for the Department of Trade and Industry, UK.

UPDATED

Metro Consulting

Metro Consulting Ltd
11 Carteret Street, London SW1 9DL, UK
Tel: +44 1 171 222 2526   Fax: 44 171 222 2527

Key personnel
Managing Director: W A E Bray
Development Director: Ron Taylor
General Manager, Sales & Marketing: Harvey Robinson

Capabilities
Management services, railway engineering, safety assessment, asset management and information, graphic

design, including training, signalling, communications, station control and infrastructure management.

Projects
Include management assignments for London Underground, Railtrack and in Hong Kong. These have included assignments in business planning, restructuring and reorganisation, risk assessments, quality and safety management activities, management information systems, engineering and technology strategies.

NEW ENTRY

Modjeski & Masters Inc

PO Box 2345, Harrisburg, Pennsylvania 17105, USA
Tel: +1 717 790 9565   Fax: +1 717 790 9564
email: modkeski@acl.com
Web: http://wwwmodjeski

Key personnel
President & Chief Engineer: Dr J M Kulicki

Capabilities
Rail structures; design and maintenance inspections, fixed and movable bridges.

UPDATED

Morrison Knudsen Corporation

MK Centennial
PO Box 1307, Arvada, Colorado 80001, USA
Tel: +1 303 420 0221   Fax: +1 303 420 2308

Key personnel
President: L R Thomas
Senior Vice-President, Rail and Transit: P Hackley

Capabilities
Morrison Knudsen Corporation (MK) has been involved in the design of various heavy civil engineering projects, including railways and their associated facilities, since 1915. Comprehensive programmes for improving the safety, speed and economic performance of railway services have been developed from extensive studies and economic evaluations determining the size, capacity, location and disposition of various elements making up a railway system.

Construction services: Construction of both surface and underground railways, undertaken on an individual basis or as part of a turnkey design/construct agreement. MK was responsible for the design, procurement and construction of the 144 km El Cerrejon Coal Railway in Colombia. This included the provision of main line, yard, siding and loading/unloading trackage, 30 major bridge structures, signalling systems, workshop facilities and rolling stock; optimisation of track structure components; and operational and maintenance analysis.

Electrification services: In the field of high-voltage railway electrification, MK has undertaken 2,400 track-km of electrification design and has recently conducted feasibility studies for a further 6,880 route-miles of electrification. MK has been the principal designer or a primary participant in the design of the five railway electrification systems operating at 50 kV AC around the world.

Rehabilitation and maintenance services: All aspects of track and structure rehabilitation and maintenance.

Operations and maintenance: MK has operated and maintained (trackage, signalling and personnel training) railways in the USA and elsewhere. These include: Burlington Northern, Vermont Northern, Black Mesa & Lake Powell, Craig Mine, Beluga Coal Project (USA); Hamersley Iron Ore, Mount Newman, Robe River (Australia); Québec North Shore & Labrador (Canada); Orinoco (Venezuela).

Consulting services: MK is experienced in the development of comprehensive transport analysis; services cover a wide range of modes, commodities and objectives.

Projects
Dallas Light Rail Project: system design, including rolling stock, signalling and train control systems; Baltimore Light Rail System: engineering and construction management; Tasman Corridor Light Rail Extension, San Jose: general design consultant in conjunction with joint-venture partner; BART, San Francisco: detailed design of extensions; Taiwan High-Speed Rail Project: selected to negotiate a contract for programme management consultancy service.

VERIFIED

Moss Consult

Moss Consult Ltd
Moss House, North Heath Lane, Horsham, West Sussex, RH12 5QE, UK
Tel: +44 1403 259511   Fax: +44 1403 211493
email: mcl@moss.co.uk

Key personnel
Sales Manager: John Boyle

Capabilities
Civil engineering 3-D modelling system. Gauging software for accurate measurement of tunnels, bridges and other structures.

NEW ENTRY

Mott MacDonald Group

St Anne House, 20/26 Wellesley Road, Croydon CR9 2UL, UK
Tel: +44 181 686 5041   Fax: +44 181 681 5706
email: railways@mottmac.com
Web: http://www.mottmac.com

International Offices
Australia, Bangladesh, Bulgaria, Czech Republic, Denmark, Hong Kong, India, Indonesia, Ireland, Oman, Pakistan, Portugal, Singapore, Spain, Sri Lanka, Taiwan, Thailand, United Arab Emirates and the USA

Key personnel
Group Board Directors: R Beresford, T J Thirlwall,
    P M Chesworth, R B Fox, D Gadd CBE (non-executive),
    M O Blackburn, J A Lowe (non-executive).
Main Board Directors: W A Perkins, J D Hayward,
    R E Williams, I H Elliott
Divisional Directors, Railways Division: J D Corrie,
    A D Millership, G J D Porter, J S Sheldon, W A Perkins,
    J D Hayward, D R Phillips, M D Groundsell, D A Henson,
    T A Pope, N Rhodes, R S Staniforth, A West, D P White
Divisional Directors, Transportation and Planning
    Division: M Wallwork, N G Bristow, R F Davies,
    R S Mansfield, R E Williams, I H Elliott, P J Carden

Capabilities
Mott MacDonald is a multidisciplinary engineering consultancy with a worldwide staff resource of over 4,200 including chartered engineers, transportation planners, computer specialists, environmental scientists and support staff.

Capabilities encompass investigations, studies and technical feasibility reports, project definition, financial and environmental appraisal; safety assessment; preliminary and detailed design, contract preparation and tendering supervision, project scheduling, specification and procurement, quality control, cost and budget control, project implementation and construction management. The Group undertakes management and operational planning in the areas of traffic engineering, rail and transit operation and management related to different modes, inspection and testing of equipment during manufacture; investment planning, including development of transport models, traffic forecasting, evaluation techniques on economics, financial, technical and environmental grounds and modal choice techniques.

Projects
Lantau Airport Railway, Hong Kong: design of Tsing Ma Bridge and design supervision for Kap Shui Mun Bridge; Great Belt Crossing, Denmark: preliminary and detailed design of 8 km of rail tunnel to link Sprøgo to Zeeland beneath the Eastern Channel of the Great Belt; Channel Tunnel Rail Link: engineering design for tunnels; Heathrow Express: civil, mechanical and engineering design for 12 km of tunnel (plus open cut-and-cover works) with two underground stations; provision of an in-house developed geological and Geotechnical Data Management System (GDMS); Linha do Norte Upgrading, Portugal: preliminary and detailed design works for 105 km section of railway including all bridgeworks, maintenance facilities and track realignment; rolling stock procurement for Royal Mail: study comprising technical evaluation, advice on rolling stock procurement and examination of alternative sourcing and funding implications; Banverket, Sweden: signalling and ATP design services; Railtrack, UK: safety of dual-voltage earthing arrangements on the North London line; London Underground Ltd, UK: asset and condition survey of earth structures; Taipei Department of Rapid Transit Systems, Taiwan: consultancy services, for mechanical and electrical commissioning.

Railtrack, UK: design and enabling works for Croydon Tramlink; LTS Rail, UK: procurement of new rolling stock; OPRAF, UK: tilting train studies and specifications for West Coast Main Line; Bangkok MRTA, Thailand: project management for 20 km underground metro system; Department of Transport, UK: project representative for Channel Tunnel Rail Link; DART Ireland: power supply design for Greystones extension; North East Line, Singapore: overhead catenary system design; PowerGen, UK: trackwork, signalling and telecoms design for Hams Hall National Distribution Park; Railtrack plc, UK: civil engineering and signalling design for Ivanhoe and Robin Hood lines; PRaK, Czech Republic: feasibility study for rail link to Prague airport.

UPDATED

Mouchel Consulting Ltd

West Hall, Parvis Road, West Byfleet KT14 6EZ, UK
Tel: +44 1932 337000   Fax: +44 1932 356122

Key personnel
Chairman: Colin Coulson
Deputy Chairman: Jim Harding
Director, Environment: Paul Driver
Director, Transportation: Bill Wyley
Director, Civil and Power: David Thompson

Capabilities
Mouchel is a multidisciplinary consultancy specialising in transport and civil engineering. Areas of expertise include transport planning, demand forecasting, economic assessment of projects, development impact studies, civil and structural design, communications and signalling systems, project management and environmental consultancy.

Projects
Recent major transport projects include a major railway development study, Hong Kong: rail patronage forecast, Gwent, UK; LRT studies and patronage forecast, Gloucester and Cheltenham, UK; viability study of a railway line, Devon, UK; rail interchange feasibility study and economic assessment, London Docklands, UK; advice on rail transport needs for a specialist energy sector firm; temporary station feasibility study, Canning Town, Docklands Light Railway, UK; Ashford International station, UK; heritage tramway study, Weymouth, UK; Southwark station, Jubilee Line Extension, London, UK; advance works for Canary Wharf station, Jubilee Line Extension, London, UK; rail corridor revitalisation, Dyfed and West Glamorgan, UK; and load assessment of bridges under and over railway lines for Railtrack, UK.

UPDATED

The MVA Consultancy

MVA House, Victoria Way, Woking GU21 1DD, UK
Tel: +44 1483 728051   Fax: +44 1483 755207
email: consultancy@mva.co.uk
Web: http://www.mva-group.com

Overseas offices
Paris, Hong Kong and Kuala Lumpur

Associated companies
MVA Consultants SA
MVA Systematica
MVA Asia
The MVA Consultancy Sdn Bhd

Key personnel
Chairman: Martin G Richards
Managing Director: Michael Roberts

Directors: David Ashley, Dr Denvil Coombe, Geoff Copley, Andrew Last, Prof Tony May, Hugh Munro, Hugh Neffendorf, John Segal, John Wicks

Divisional Directors: Michael Brewer, Martin Dix, Clive Gilliam, Peter Hague, Dr Eileen Hill, Bil Harrison, Steve Lowe, Andrew Skinner, Mike Slinn, Peter Stanley, Steve Williamson

Company Secretary: Dan Samter

Capabilities

Advice to private and public sector companies worldwide on the planning, operation and marketing of transport systems and related facilities, including LRT and heavy rail. Services include: policy and planning studies, demand forecasting, economic and financial reviews, consumer needs and attitudes, market research, marketing strategy formulation, fare systems, ticketing (including concessionary fares and operator reimbursement) and route/network planning. Through MVA Systematica, MVA provides software for the planning and operational management of transport systems.

The MVA Consultancy and MVA Systematica, together with MVA Consultants SA, MVA Asia and The MVA Consultancy Sdn Bhd (Malaysia), are part of The MVA Group. Through an established relationship, MVA has access to the expertise and knowledge of French consultants Systra (urban transport and railways).

Projects

MVA's recent clients have included: the former Network SouthEast, InterCity, Regional Railways and ScotRail businesses, OPRAF (UK), InterCity CrossCountry, InterCity East Coast, London Transport, Northern Ireland Railways, North London Railways, South West Trains, Union Railways, over 100 local authorities and all seven Passenger Transport Executives in the UK, UK Department of Transport, Eurotunnel, Netherlands Ministry of Transport, Netherlands Railways, Polish Railways, RATP Paris, Regione Lombardia (Italy), Russian Railways, Córas Iompair Éireann (Ireland), OSE (Greece), Singapore Ministry of Communications, Hong Kong Mass Transit Railway Corporation, Kowloon—Canton Railway, Provisional Office of High-Speed Rail (Taiwan), Taipei Transit System Co (TRTC) and Bangkok Transit System Corporation Ltd.

UPDATED

NEA Transport Research and Training

Polakweg 13, PO Box 1969, NL-2280 DZ Rijswijk, Netherlands
Tel: +31 70 398 8388   Fax: +31 70 395 4186
email: email@nea.nl

Key personnel

Managing Director: Dr Henk den Harder
Director, Training and Education: Menno M Menist
Director, General Transport Economics Research: Pieter B D Hilferink
Director, Transport Sector Research: Ad Rosenbrand

Capabilities

NEA is an independent organisation specialising in research, consultancy and training services in the transport field. NEA's training experience includes development of course materials and case studies and training-needs assessments. Research and consultancy work has included modelling, forecasting and evaluation of international freight flows, including simulation, scenario building and economic impact analysis.

Projects

Training and consultancy assignments have been undertaken for governments, international agencies and organisations and the private sector across Europe and in countries including: Indonesia, Bhutan, China, Vietnam, Malaysia, Singapore, Bangkok, Bangladesh, Ghana, Tanzania, Mozambique, Botswana, Malawi, Swaziland, Zambia and Zimbabwe.

UPDATED

NEL

National Engineering Laboratory
Scottish Enterprise Technology Park, East Kilbride, Glasgow G75 0QU, UK
Tel: +44 1355 220222   Fax: +44 1355 272999
email: info@nel.co.uk

Key personnel

Managing Director: W Paton
Business Development Manager—Consultancy: Stewart Kane

Capabilities

NEL employs 242 people and offers transport engineering technology; noise engineering; structural analysis and testing; emission reduction, fuel systems, cooling techniques; environmental engineering and testing; quality accreditation.

Projects

Include development of rail sensors for Glasgow Underground.

NEW ENTRY

New Markets

New Markets Ltd
18-20 Barton Street, Tewkesbury GL20 5PP, UK
Tel: +44 1684 291544   Fax: +44 1684 291545

Key personnel

Managing Director: Ted Elwes
Rail Manager: David Richman

Capabilities

New Markets offers product marketing and sales support; product diversification programmes; new product development and technology licencing; acquisitions and joint ventures; and subcontracting as well as market and technical consultancy.

Projects

These have been completed for major companies in Australia, Germany, Switzerland and the UK.

UPDATED

The Nichols Group

2 Saville Row, London W1X 1AF, UK
Tel: +44 171 494 1511   Fax: +44 171 494 2675

Key personnel

Chairman: Mike Nichols
Managing Director, Nichols Transportation Ltd: Robb Busby
Managing Director, Nichols Associates Ltd: Peter Hansford
Manager, Nichols Resources Ltd: David Waboso

Capabilities

The Nichols Group provides services through three distinct companies. Nichols Transportation is a strategic transportation consultancy advising clients on the planning, funding, management and operation of railways and light rail systems. Nichols Associates is a project management consultancy specialising in the creation, promotion and management of major infrastructure projects. Nichols Resources provides project management professionals as flexible resources to the railway industry and services include interim management, outsourcing and human resources consulting.

Projects

Recent contracts include programme management for the sale of 13 former British Rail Infrastructure Services companies, UK; development and implementation of a system for assessing and accrediting the skills of project managers for London Underground Ltd, UK; management of the award of the concession to build and operate the Lewisham Extension of the Docklands Light Railway, UK; and advice to potential private sector purchasers and operators on all aspects of tender preparation as part of the rail privatisation process, UK.

VERIFIED

Ødegaard & Danneskiold-Samsøe A/S

Kroghsgade 1, DK-2100 København Ø, Denmark
Tel: +45 35 266011   Fax: +45 35 265018

Key personnel

Managing Director: John Ødegaard
Sales Manager: Ulrik Danneskiold-Samsøe
Senior Consultants: Henrik W Thrane, Uffe Degn

Capabilities

Consulting engineers, specialising in noise and vibration control of trains and other modes of transport. The company's services apply to all phases of the life of a train, from design through to operation. Services offered include: design advice, noise and vibration analyses and troubleshooting.

VERIFIED

Parsons Brinckerhoff Inc

One Penn Plaza, New York, NY 10119-0061, USA
Tel: +1 212 465 5000   Fax: +1 212 465 5096

Key personnel

President: Thomas J. O'Neill
Chair: Robert Prieto
Controller: Richard A. Schrader
Operation Manager: Gary Griggs (New York)

Other offices

San Francisco, California
Tel:+1 415 243 4634
Operation Manager: Anthony Daniels

Herndon, Virginia
Tel: +1 703 742 5701
Operation Manager: Christopher Reseigh

London
Tel: +44 1 71 242 2898
Operation Manager: Paul Nagle

Newcastle upon Tyne, UK
Tel: +44 1 91 226 1899
Operation Manager: Paul Cheesmond

Hong Kong
Tel: +852 2 579 8700
Operation Manager: Keith Hawksworth

Major subsidiary companies

Parsons Brinckerhoff Quade & Douglas, Inc
Parsons Brinckerhoff Construction Services, Inc
Parsons Brinckerhoff Energy Services, Inc
Parsons Brinckerhoff International, Pte. Ltd
Parsons Brinckerhoff Ltd
PB Farradyne Inc
PB Transit & Rail Systems, Inc

Corporate Offices

United States, United Kingdom, Japan, Singapore, Hong Kong, China, Thailand, Turkey, Australia, Malaysia, Spain, Argentina, Egypt, Sudan, Zimbabwe, Indonesia, Philippines, Mexico

Capabilities

Multidisciplinary planning, design, programme and construction management and operations and maintenance services for urban transport.

Projects

Representative project experience includes:
Metropolitan Atlanta Rapid Transit Authority (MARTA) Transit System, Atlanta, Georgia: For more than 30 years, PB in joint venture has provided planning, design, and construction management services for MARTA a $3.3 billion rapid transit system encompassing 96 km of rapid transit lines, one express busway, 45 rail passenger stations, park-and-ride facilities for more than 33,000 vehicles, and 282 rapid transit rail vehicles.
Frankford Elevated Reconstruction, Philadelphia, Pennsylvania: In a joint venture, PB provided design and construction management services for this award-winning project. This was the first reconstruction of an elevated rail line in the USA that maintained normal operations through construction.
Tren Urbano, San Juan, Puerto Rico:
As a subcontractor, Parsons Brinckerhoff is providing

programme management and design services for the systems and test track turnkey contract. The company will provide management and interface co-ordination of all systemwide elements, including vehicles, train control, electrification, trackwork, and communication systems as they relate to the fixed facilities of this double-track heavy rail system.

Los Angeles Metro, Los Angeles, California: In a joint venture, PB is providing the design of the heavy and light rail components. Critical to its efforts is the seismic engineering aspects to develop an earthquake-resistant public transit system.

Greater Cairo Metro, Cairo, Egypt: PB, in a joint venture, is managing the fast track design/build of this 16.4 km heavy rail line. Phase 1A is completed and is open for revenue service, with Phase 1B scheduled to open in mid-1997. PB's contract was extended to include Phase 2 of the project.

Taipei MRT, Taipei, Taiwan: PB led the general engineering consultant joint venture in all project phases from system planning through operations planning on this 54 mile heavy and light rail transit network.

Westside Light Rail Extension, Portland, Oregon: PB is currently providing construction management services for this 18.5 km extension.

Kowloon Canton Railway Corporation, Hong Kong: PB in a joint venture provided planning, design, and support services during construction of the Kowloon-Canton Railway Corporation's maintenance facility.

Bay Area Rapid Transit (BART) Extension, San Francisco: PB is a member of the general engineering consultant (GEC) joint venture guiding the $2.5 billion BART Extensions Program begun in the 1980s, involving 30 miles of rapid rail line and 10 stations.

Airport Access, New York: As general engineering consultant during this design-build-operate-maintain (DBOM) programme, PB is providing a wide range of planning, design, environmental analysis, construction management, and procurement activities, while also helping to operate a programme office jointly with the client's staff members.

Singapore MRT, Singapore:
PB is providing mechanical/electrical consultancy services for the engineer's design of the tunnel ventilation system and station environmental control system for 16 underground stations on the Singapore subway 20 km North East Line. This is PB's second major environmental control/tunnel ventilation contract on the Singapore MRT system.

NEW ENTRY

Patrick Engineering

Patrick Engineering Inc
4985 Varsity Drive, Lisle, Illinois 60532-4144, USA
Tel: +1 708 434 7050   Fax: +1 708 434 8400
email: lhh@patrickengineering.com
Web: http://www.patrickengineering.com

Key personnel
President: Daniel P Dietzler
Vice-President, Transportation & Design Services:
   Ted W Lachus
Chief Railroad Engineer: Steve P Heath

Capabilities
Project management, professional engineering and architectural services including civil, structural, mechanical, electrical and environmental engineering; architectural and surveying services including GPS; geotechnical investigations and drilling; design/build services for industrial systems and other railway projects. Patrick Engineering has provided services for Class I and short line railways in the USA and Canada and in Central America.

Projects
Recent projects include: intermodal yard and paving design; project management and resident engineering; retaining-wall design; station tower and office design; environmental assessments and site remediation; track design; curve reduction studies; capacity improvement; automotive and tank car unloading facilities, including secondary spill containment; coal handling facilities; waste transport facilities; drainage studies; commuter station and parking facilities; rail yard surveying; embankment stability analyses; economic study of waste transport by rail; grade raising projects; level crossings.

UPDATED

Price Waterhouse Management Consultants

1 Milton Gate, Moor Lane, London EC2Y 9PB, UK
Tel: +44 171 939 3000   Fax: +44 171 638 1358

Key personnel
Partner, Rail Practice: Richard P B Smith

Capabilities
Consultancy and implementation services in business strategy and planning, financial management, organisation development and human resources, information technology consultancy, marketing and change management.

VERIFIED

Pullman Technology Inc

16412 Lathrop Avenue, Harvey, Illinois 60426, USA
Tel: +1 708 339 8600   Fax: +1 708 339 8607

Capabilities
Full range of consulting services, design and engineering, manufacturing engineering, quality control and testing, engineering analysis, spare parts, technical publications, specification documentation, customer engineering representation, and Computer Aided Design (CAD), relating to commuter, rapid transit and tour train operations.

VERIFIED

Queensland Railways Consulting Services

13th Floor, 127 Creek Street, Brisbane, Queensland 4000, Australia
Tel: +61 7 235 1336   Fax: +61 7 235 3346
email: qrcs@thehub,com.au

Key personnel
Executive Manager, Strategic Issues: David George
Manager, QR Consulting Services: Mike Garrett

Capabilities
Queensland Railways offers expertise in all areas of railway operations from the feasibility and planning stages through to project management, commissioning, operating and maintenance.

UPDATED

Railcare Ltd

3 Ibstock Road, Coventry, CV6 6NL, UK
Tel: +44 1203 364897   Fax: +44 1203 644074/364898
email: marketing.railcare@dial.pipex.com

Key personnel
Managing Director: B Turnbull
Business Development Director: P L Robinson

Capabilities
Rail vehicle exterior and interior design.

UPDATED

Rail India Technical & Economic Services Ltd (RITES)

New Delhi House, 27 Barakhamba Road, New Delhi 110001, India
Tel: +91 11 331 4261   Fax: +91 11 331 5286
email:S=rites;G=in;A=vsnl;P=globalnet;O=gndel

Key personnel
Chairman: G K Malhotra
Managing Director: B I Singhal
Directors
   Technical: Ravi Kaul
   Finance: T P Mani

Capabilities
Consultancy and engineering services for railways and other transport systems. Services include: transportation studies and traffic surveys, design and detailed engineering, investment planning, organisational restructuring, privatisation, planning and estimation of fleet requirements and other infrastructure facilities.

Projects
Package exports, comprising supply of rolling stock and equipment, after-sales service, training and maintenance support to Bangladesh, Nepal, Vietnam, Sri Lanka, Peru and Chile; technical and management assistance to rail systems in Tanzania, Zambia, Botswana, Cambodia, Mozambique, Nepal, Swaziland and Saudi Arabia; technical support with wagon couplers for Malaysian Railways; advice on setting up inland container terminals in Nepal; training programmes for Tanzania Railways Corporation; report on mass transit system for Delhi.

UPDATED

Rail Sciences

Rail Sciences Inc
3 North Clarendon Avenue, Avondale Estates, GA 30002-1151, USA
Tel: +1 404 294 5300   Fax: +1 404 294 5423
email: railsciences@worldnet.att.net
email: info@railsciences.com
Web: www.railsciences.com

Key personnel
President: Gary P Woolf
Vice President: Warren B Egan

Capabilities
Railway consultancy specialising in the application of advanced analytical techniques to solve operational problems; accident and derailment analysis, rail line capacity simulation modelling, schedule feasibility, vehicle dynamics, operational planning and analysis, computer model development, dispatching control systems, driver training, testing and data acquisition, mechanical inspections.

Projects
Include accident analysis for Canadian National; lateral force detection and rail grinding tests for BC Rail, derailment training for SNIM, Mauretania, derailment studies for Union Pacific, line capacity for Conrail, derailment analysis for Alaska Railroad, braking distance analysis for BHP Australia, E-P braking study for Southern Pacific.

UPDATED

The Railway Consultancy Ltd

43a Palace Square, Crystal Palace, London SE19 2LT, UK
Tel: +44 181 653 1097   Fax: +44 181 653 1097
email: 106351,377@compuserv.com

Key personnel
Managing Director: Dr Nigel G Harris

Capabilities
Demand, revenue and passenger benefit estimation for both train and station services; operational consultancy (for both train and station services including simulations, timetable preparation, disruption and contingency planning); transport policy and management advice; business planning, including project appraisal and economic assessments; specification and design of IT systems to assist the railway planning process; training courses on railway and transport planning issues.

Projects
Franchise bid preparation; economic assessment of different urban transport technologies for UK Department of Transport; design of database to hold information on operational incidents for London Underground Ltd, UK; fares regulation analysis for MTRC Hong Kong; demand estimation for proposed station at Milhouses for South Yorkshire PTE; track quality training programme for LUL; study completed on the impacts of the privatisation of British Rail.

UPDATED

Railway Engineering Associates Limited

68-82 Boden Street, Glasgow G40 3PX, UK
Tel: +44 141 554 3868   Fax: +44 141 556 5091

Key personnel
Principal Consultants: Henry Maxwell, Donald McCallum

Capabilities
Specialist railway engineering consultancy services for companies involved in railway works or works involving encroachment on to operational railway land. Expertise includes permanent way design, bridge/structure design, station and depot design.

Projects
Recent projects include: Chalmerston Link: new railway (2 km) for British Coal, UK; Mossend Euroterminal, UK: Bristol Avonmouth, UK: outline design of freight terminal and design of level crossings; Daventry International Freight Terminal, UK: general railway advice and design.

VERIFIED

Railway Systems Consultants Ltd

Church View, Knockhundred Row, Midhurst GU29 9DQ, UK
Tel: +44 1730 813280   Fax: +44 1730 817152
email: rscuk@compuserv.com

Key personnel
Director: Nico M J Dekker

Capabilities
Rapid transit, including guided bus. people movers, light and heavy rail. Feasibility and outline design studies, including systems engineering, power systems, command control and communications, rolling stock, operations and maintenance, highway traffic management and urban design. Systems, subsystems, business and operational specification. Preparation of tender and contract documentation, tender evaluation and negotiation, contract monitoring and supervision.

Projects
Cross River Partnership, London: definition and evaluation of rapid transit route alignments between the Oval, Elephant & Castle, Waterloo, Euston and Kings Cross, including operational, traffic management and urban design aspects.

Croydon Tramlink, UK: project development, including system-wide performance specification. Evaluation of EMC and stray-current protection options. Overhead line studies to evaluate indicative engineering designs and associated aesthetic qualities. Pre-qualification and tender assessment of technical aspects of bidders. Technical monitoring of the concessionaire on behalf of London Transport.

Docklands Light Railway, London: assessment of performance derogation to be offered to franchisees due to system reliability deficiencies.

Nottingham Express Transit (LRT): overhead line design studies. Track sharing option evaluation with Railtrack.

Utrecht, Netherlands: independent appraisal of rapid transit network proposals. Birmingham International Airport, UK: technical and operational advice with regard to upgrading people mover and replacement options. Preparation of tender and contract documents, subsequent tender assessment.

Channel Tunnel Rail Link: operational assessment of tenders, including tender negotiation and development of domestic train service specification.

NEW ENTRY

Railway Technology Strategy Centre

Centre for Transport Studies, University of London Department of Civil Engineering, Imperial College of Science Technology and Medicine, London SW7 2BU, UK
Tel: +44 171 823 9942   Fax: +44 171 594 6102
email: m.lawson@ic.ac.uk

Key personnel
Chairman: Professor T M Ridley

Director: William R Steinmetz
Senior Associates: Michael Hamlyn, Nigel Harris, Robin Hirsch, Paul Cheesman, Roger Clutton

Capabilities
The Railway Technology Strategy Centre (RTSC) was established in 1992 with funding from the former British Rail and now carries out projects on strategic, technology and economic issues for BR successors.

Projects
The RTSC has developed a programme to assist metros in identifying and implementing the best practice through detailed case studies and benchmarking comparisons. The metros involved in this exercise are Berlin, Hong Kong, London, New York, Paris, Mexico City, São Paulo and Tokyo.

The RTSC has been selected to prepare and maintain the UITP World Urban Transport Databank.

Other work includes work on train control technology for Railtrack UK and a study on technologies for moving people in urban areas, prepared for the Department of Transport, UK.

NEW ENTRY

Rendel Palmer & Tritton Ltd

61 Southwark Street, London SE1 1SA, UK
Tel: +44 171 928 8999   Fax: +44 171 928 5566

Overseas offices
Bangladesh, Canada, Hong Kong, Indonesia, Libya, Malaysia, Singapore, Turkey, United Arab Emirates, USA

Key personnel
Chairman and Managing Director: D W Hookway
Directors: D Carmichael, A R Clark, P J Clark, R B Claxton, R J Day, D W Fletcher, D J Head, J M H Kelly, G R D Marshall, A J Parfitt, J F Smith, R G R Tappin

Capabilities
Rendel Palmer & Tritton has wide experience of railway planning, design and maintenance of metros and LRT systems. Main areas of activity include: feasibility, economic and investment studies; survey, design and construction supervision for freight and urban railways; reconstruction, development and rehabilitation of railway infrastructure; and modernisation programmes for motive power, rolling stock and other equipment. Rendel Palmer & Tritton has also had a broad range of experience in the design and equipping of container and freight terminals; the design and development of loading and unloading installations for bulk transport; and in the development of railway containerisation and rail/port links.

VERIFIED

RMS Locotec

Rail Management Services
Vanguard Works, Bretton Street, Dewsbury WF12 9BJ, UK
Tel: +44 1924 465050   Fax: +44 1924 465422

Key personnel
Managing Director: John Hummel
Operations Director: Laurence Crossan
Sales Executive: Roger A Raylor

Capabilities
RMS was established to meet the demand for rail management services due to the impending changes in the UK rail industry, primarily on the freight side. The services offered cover feasibility studies, project management, operations and commercial studies and specialist engineering services.

RMS can provide an entire rail operations and maintenance package, including provision of labour and resources, management of rail traffic, provision of an interface with rail operators and other suppliers, and management of fleets of locomotives, wagons or carriages. It can provide safety systems and offers staff training and certification for rail operations.

RMS is currently carrying out feasibility studies and costings of private rail operations for a number of major rail users.

VERIFIED

Roundel Design Group

7 Rosehart Mews, Westbourne Grove, London W11 3TY, UK
Tel: +44 171 221 1951   Fax: +44 171 221 1843

Key personnel
Managing Director: Michael Denny
Directors: John Bateson, Harold Batten

Capabilities
Corporate identity design for transport industries including service branding, livery design, information design and corporate communications.

Projects
Design of corporate guidelines for London Underground Ltd train interiors; information design for Docklands Light Railway and InterCity; corporate identity for Finnish State Railways (VR). Other recent clients include Adtranz, Sweden; KCRC, Hong Kong; and EPS, UK.

VERIFIED

ScanRail Consult

Soelvgade 40 E 3, DK-1349 Copenhagen, Denmark
Tel: +45 33 14 04 00 ext 155555   Fax: +45 33 32 30 84

Key personnel
Chairman of the Board: Erik Elsborg
Director: Preben Olesen

Capabilities
ScanRail Consult is an independent organisation within the Danish National Railway Agency. With approximately 500 engineers, planners, strategic business consultants, architects and assistants, ScanRail Consult covers a wide range of strategic planning, transport management and mechanical expertise related to railway systems.

Competence areas include: planning and design, supervision and rehabilitation, feasibility studies and cost/benefit analyses, construction management, project management, quality and environmental management, validation and safety assessment, management and training, business and management consultancy in transport and railways, consultancy services for restructuring and commercialisation for railways and transport related businesses.

ScanRail Consult is actively taking part in international research and development within its competence areas. Furthermore, ScanRail Consult assists the European Commission, UIC and ERRI in the development of European codes and standards for railway systems.

Projects
Some of ScanRail Consult's current and recent projects are:

European Commission: the implementation of a Technology Whitebook for the future train and railway systems in Europe; evaluation of railway related proposals within the RTD programmes of the European Commission; participating in projects under the 4th Framework Programme and providing assistance under the 5th Framework Programme; technical support to UIC and ERRI.

ScanRail Consult is rendering consultancy services in Eastern Europe, the Baltics and Africa. In Denmark all planning and engineering for the Danish National Railway Agency and the Danish Ministry of Transport is part of ScanRail Consult's total portfolio of projects. This includes building new and upgrading existing lines in Denmark and construction of high-speed main lines.

ScanRail Consult has also been rendering consultancy services to the building of the Øresund Fixed Link (bridge-tunnel) between Denmark and Sweden.

ScanRail Consult has played a significant role as consultant on the railway part of the Great Belt Link.

NEW ENTRY

Science Systems Group

23 Clothier Road, Brislington, Bristol BS4 5SS, UK
Tel: +44 117 971 7251   Fax: +44 117 972 1846

Key personnel
Managing Director: Dr M D Love
Operations Director: B T Evans
Business Development Director: Peter J M Turner
Business Development Executive: Richard C Jones

Capabilities

All aspects of software development and project management for train control systems, control centres, simulation, passenger information and automatic fare collection.

Projects

Work has been carried out on London Underground Central Line and Jubilee Line Extension; Seoul subway system; trainer's interface software (LUL); Docklands Light Railway, London.

UPDATED

Scott Wilson Kirkpatrick

Scott House, Basing View, Basingstoke RG21 2JG, UK
Tel: +44 1256 461161   Fax: +44 1256 460582

Key personnel

Director, Railways: Martin Nielsen

Principal subsidiaries

Scott Wilson MainLine
Infrastructure Design Group
SWK Pavement Engineering Ltd
Scott Wilson Kirkpatrick (Mechanical & Electrical) Ltd

Capabilities

Permanent way engineering and research; business management and restructuring; transport economics; railway operations; railway safety; railway, civil, structural and hydraulic engineering; environmental impact; electrification; signalling and telecommunications; passenger rail and LRT; and freight and materials handling.

Also management consultancy, covering business and management structures, cost and safety audits, technical assistance and training, public consultation, operations audits, locomotive and rolling stock utilisation and facilities management; advisory services, including funding advice, expert witnesses, consultation and liaison, procurement, forms of contract, tariff negotiation, value engineering, pre- and post-contract management, quality management and quantity surveying; feasibility studies; construction and site management; and technical assistance and training including railway management, timetabling, HRD, finance and fleet management, operational research, procurement and technical standards.

Projects

Current and recent projects include rail access to airports serving London, Manchester, Liverpool, Glasgow UK and Hong Kong; light rail and metro systems in London, Nottingham, Liverpool, Birmingham, Croydon UK, Mauritius, Johannesburg, Delhi and Hong Kong; commuter operations serving London, Nottingham, Swansea, Norfolk, Leicestershire and Glasgow, UK; train maintenance depots in Reading, Plymouth and Aylesbury (UK) and Tanzania; high-speed rail including the Channel Tunnel Rail Link and EPS North of London Eurostar loading gauge improvements, UK; experimental and research projects including a test track for London Underground Ltd, UK, and trenchless track drainage; freight projects in the UK, Botswana and Tanzania; and technical assistance to the Russian Federation, Kazakhstan and Tanzania.

UPDATED

Serco Railtest

Serco Railtest Ltd
PO Box 243, rtc Business Park, London Road, Derby DE24 8ZZ, UK
Tel: +44 1332 262626   Fax: +44 1332 264608
email: serco.railtest@ems.rail.co.uk

Key personnel

Managing Director: Lee Bartholomew
Sales and Marketing: Barry Winchurch

Capabilities

Acceptance testing of all types of rail vehicles and components, including on-track plant; evaluation and commissioning of new and modified traction and rolling stock; independent infrastructure assessment service covering high-speed track geometry, structure gauging,

ultrasonic rail inspection, overhead line inspection and track inspection.

Rail Operations, providing test train planning and operation and management of the Old Dalby Test Track and Development Centre.

Also offering comprehensive technical data and document management services.

UPDATED

SGTE

Société Générale de Techniques et d'Etudes
Parc Saint Christophe, 10 avenue de l'Entreprise, Pôle Galilée 3, F-95865 Cergy-Pontoise Cedex, France
Tel: +33 1 34 24 44 00   Fax: +33 1 34 24 42 90

Key personnel

Chairman: Alain Nicolaïdis
General Manager: Bernard Bodin
Executive Manager: Claude Antoine

Capabilities

Planning, project design, works supervision and project management of rail and urban transit systems.

Projects

Third line for the Caracas Metro: project management on behalf of Frameca Consortium; Athens Mass Transit: member of the Engineering Subgroup of the Franco-German Consortium; Algiers Metro: management of the consortium in charge of the supervision of civil work and infrastructure installation; maintenance assistance, safety and reliability studies for the Channel Tunnel; Cairo Metro: member of the Engineering Subgroup; and railway upgrading projects in Germany for the Berlin—Leipzig—Halle—Erfurt link. Extending and upgrading urban transport in Berlin and Lisbon; assistance to management and supervision of works for KNR high-speed line, Korea.

UPDATED

Signalling Control UK

PO Box 408, Network Technical Centre, Wellesley Grove, Croydon CR9 1XP, UK
Tel: +44 181 666 6300   Fax: +44 181 666 6133

Key personnel

Managing Director: R Williams

Capabilities

SCUK owns one of the former British Rail signal design offices and has wide expertise in signalling matters.

VERIFIED

Wilbur Smith Associates

Nationsbank Tower, PO Box 92, 1301 Gervais Street, Columbia, South Carolina 29202, USA
Tel: +1 803 738 0580   Fax: +1 803 251 2064

Key personnel

President: Robert A Hubbard

Capabilities

Transportation consulting services covering rail, road, air and water systems, extending from planning, pre-feasibility and preliminary engineering through development of final design, contract documents, construction and maintenance services, training and technical assistance and field supervision. Management consultation services include planning, programming, budgeting and supervision of contractors and subcontractors. Services also include transit vehicle/station/facility design, design of architectural graphics and related visual communications systems, and interior space planning.

Projects

Total planning of Singapore MRT system plus design of phase 11A (in joint venture with DCIL); Los Angeles: Santa Barbara rail corridor study, phases I and II for Southern California Association of governments; Virginia Rail programme needs for Virginia Department of Highways and Transportation; Washington State on-call freight rail services for Washington State Department of Transport (DOT); Detroit: Chicago rail passenger demand forecasts in association with URS Consultants and PBQD; Southeast Florida rail corridor study for Florida DOT;

Metro 12E section design for Washington, DC Metro Area Transit Authority; Georgia rail system evaluation for GA DOT; Hong Kong Aberdeen LRT feasibility study; HSST rail patronage analysis for HSST Nevada Corridor; Ohio high-speed rail ridership study for Ohio High-Speed Rail Authority; Florida rail system plan for FDOT; passenger train operating speed improvements for North Carolina DOT; Chicago—Milwaukee high-speed rail, sub to Environdyne Engineers for Illinois and Wisconsin DOTs; Florida alternative passenger route assessments (all speeds) and update of Florida rail system plan for Florida DOT; statewide passenger study for Washington DOT; nationwide high-speed rail study, Thailand; Caracas Metro transportation planning services, Venezuela; Bangkok mass transit master planning study, Thailand; Sentosa Island LRT system study, Singapore; Richmond Multimodal Transportation Center for City of Richmond, Virginia; inland access to Wilmington and Morehead City terminals for North Carolina Port Authority; California high-speed rail economic impacts for Caltrans; and on-call services for North Carolina Railroad.

VERIFIED

Southdowns Environmental Consultants Ltd

Suite A3, 16 Station Street, Lewes, East Sussex BN7 2DB, UK
Tel: +44 1273 488186   Fax: +44 1273 488187
email: secl@tcp.co.uk

Key personnel

Director: Patrick Williams

Capabilities

Southdowns Environmental Consultants Ltd specialises in the measurement, calculation, evaluation and mitigation of environmental noise and vibration impacts from railways.

UPDATED

Steer Davies Gleave

32 Upper Ground, London SE1 9PD, UK
Tel: +44 171 919 8500   Fax: +44 171 827 9850/1/2
email: sdginfo@sdg.co.uk

Key personnel

Managing Director: Jim Steer
Directors: Brian Martin, Charles Russell, Peter Twelftree, Luis Willumsen

Capabilities

Steer Davies Gleave is an independent specialist transport consultancy offering a multidisciplinary, problem-solving approach to railway management, operations and planning issues. The practice has capabilities in policy and business development strategy, including in the context of privatisation and open-access regimes for railway networks.

Projects

Recent and current projects include: Tyne & Wear Metro Sunderland Extension, UK; Dublin LRT system, Ireland; and public transport strategy in Rome, Italy; track charging systems, EU; passenger rail franchises, UK; Eurostar market appraisals; Santiago—Valparaiso high-speed rail link, Chile

UPDATED

STV Group

205 West Welsh Drive, Douglasville, Pennsylvania 19518, USA
Tel: +1 610 385 8200   Fax: +1 610 385 8501

STV Incorporated

225 Park Avenue South, New York, New York 10003, USA
Tel: +1 212 777 4400   Fax: +1 212 529 5237

Key personnel

Chairman and Chief Executive Officer: M Haratunian
President and Chief Operating Officer: D M Servedio
Key Rail Staff: W F Matts, K Bossung, O Allen, M Gagliardi

Capabilities

Transport planning; system and facility design; rolling stock engineering; operations and maintenance analysis.

UPDATED

SwedeRail AB

Klarabergsviadukten 78, S-105 50 Stockholm, Sweden
Tel: +46 8 762 3781   Fax: +46 8 106243

Overseas offices
Botswana, Tanzania and India

Key personnel
President: Bernt Andersson
Vice-President: Sunit Ray
Senior Consultants: Bo Marklund, Robert Hallenborg,
   Björn Andersson, Jan Gullbrandsson, Ulf Halloff,
   Kaj Hallgren

Corporate development
SwedeRail has acquired ASG Transport Development
AB, specialists in road transport and logistics.

Capabilities
SwedeRail is a subsidiary of Swedish State Railways (SJ)
and the Swedish National Rail Administration (BV).
Capabilities include project identification, feasibility
studies, market survey and analysis, design, cost
estimates and cost flow requirements, detailed project
engineering, management support, technical support,
project monitoring supervision on or off site,
implementation and commissioning services, human
resources development training in Sweden and abroad,
economic and financial evaluation, efficiency
development, restructuring, optimisation studies, quality
assurance and control, environmental rehabilitation and
training.

Projects
Feasibility study and preliminary engineering for
rehabilitation and electrification of railways in Southern
Mozambique and Swaziland; feasibility study, design and
final construction of electrification of Tumbler Ridge coal
line of British Columbia Railways in Canada; study of
railway rolling stock in the nine SADCC states of Africa;
identification and installation of trainworking and
telecommunication systems for Botswana Railways;
diagnostic study in organisational development and
manpower training programmes in railway maintenance
for Indian Railways; management support to Tanzania-
Zambia Railways Authority (TAZARA) including technical
assistance; an advanced training programme in railway
maintenance, organised annually in Sweden for senior
managers and technical specialists from developing
railways of the world (Rail Tech); design and
environmental rehabilitation of battery workshops,
Pakistan; consultancy in railway restructuring studies;
management support to developing railways.

UPDATED

Symonds Group

Symonds House, Wood Street, East Grinstead
RH19 1UU, UK
Tel: +44 1342 327161   Fax: +44 1342 313500/315927

International Offices
Australia, New Zealand, Hong Kong, Malaysia, Oman,
Indonesia, Hungary, Kenya, Philippines, India and
Bangladesh

Key personnel
Director, Railway & Transit Projects: Roger Sawyers
Manager, Rail Management and Policy: Ian Brooker

Capabilities
Multidisciplinary consultants experienced in rail
management and policy, and in the evaluation, design
and commissioning of major infrastructure projects.

Projects
Include the Oresund Tunnel fixed road/rail link between
Denmark and Sweden; Arlandabanen rail link, Stockholm;
Kuala Lumpur LRT; Budapest Metro; Leeds Supertram;
Docklands Light Transit Lewisham extension; West Coast
Main Line freight study; advice to rail franchisees
including CGEA.

UPDATED

Systra-Sofretu-Sofrerail

5 avenue du Coq, F-75009 Paris, France
Tel: +33 1 40 16 63 33   Fax: +33 1 40 16 64 44
email: sit@systra.worldnet.net

Key personnel
Chairman and Chief Executive Officer:
   Pierre Louis Rochet
Executive Vice-President, Development: Maurice Simony
Executive Vice-President, Gérard Mermillod
Vice-President, Finance & Legal Affairs: Christian Bret
Vice-President, Engineering & Human Resources: Serge
   Dassonville

Other offices
China, Czech Republic, Italy, Taiwan

Associated companies
Canarail, Canada
Systra SpA, Italy
Systra, USA
MVA Group (UK, France, Hong Kong, Malaysia)
Tifsa, Spain

Capabilities
Systra-Sofretu-Sofrerail combines the expertise of Sofretu
and Sofrerail, the engineering consultancies created by
RATP, Paris and SNCF.
   Capabilities include high-speed trains, conventional
rail, mass transit, metro, light rail, automatic guided transit
systems and buses.
   Systra-Sofretu-Sofrerail offers consulting engineering
services for planning and organising transport, from
master plans through to operating systems design;
engineering of civil works, systems and their interfaces;
construction management, testing and commissioning of
equipment; planning operations and maintenance;
training of personnel; start up of operations.

Projects
Europe
UK: engineering and associated services to London &
Continental Railways.
Belgium: assistance to TUC-Rail for the Brussels—French
border high-speed line; study of Brussels regional
network.
Bosnia: technical assistance in rehabilitation of Sarajevo—
Mostar—Ploče line.
Bulgaria: staff training.
France: project management for Line 2 and Mongy
tramway upgrade, Lille; prime contractor for Orléans LRT
first line.
Greece: assistance in restructuring of OSE.
Hungary: feasibility study of Budapest metro network.
Italy: technical assistance to Italferr for high-speed
projects; general engineering consultant for all urban
transport projects in Rome.
Portugal: design for the Northern Line; new station design
in Lisbon.

Africa and Asia
Bangladesh: track maintenance training.
Egypt: assistance in operation and maintenance for the
Cairo metro line 2.
Ivory Coast: assistance to Sitarail for start up of new rail
network.
China: construction engineering for Guangzhou metro
Line 1; signalling study in Hong Kong.
Indonesia: feasibility study for Jakarta—Surabaya high-
speed corridor; inspection and supervision of Tangerang
line, Jakarta.
Korea: design for Korean high-speed line infrastructure;
staff training.
Philippines: general consultant for the construction of the
Manila LRT.
Taiwan: detailed design of the Taipei—Khaoshiung high-
speed line.

Americas
Chile: technical assistance for the rehabilitation of Chilean
railways and maintenance management; design and
engineering for the Santiago metro Line 5.
Mexico: assistance to Covitur in commissioning Line B of
Mexico City metro.

UPDATED

TAMS Consultants Inc

655 Third Avenue, New York, New York 10017, USA
Tel: +1 212 867 1777   Fax: +1 212 697 6354
email: marketing@tamsconsultants.com
Web: http://www.tamsconsultants.com

Key personnel
President: Anthony R Dolcimascolo
Principals: Patrick J McAward Jr, Lyle H Hixenbaugh,
   Edward C Regan, G Barrie Heinzenknecht,
   Ronald H Axelrod, Frank A Baragona, Eric Cole,
   E Patrick Sorensen

Capabilities
TAMS offers international services in engineering,
architecture, and planning. The firm has worked in more
than 100 countries, providing comprehensive services for
major ports, highways, railroads, bridges, airports, dams,
agricultural and regional development, waste
management, and urban planning projects.
   TAMS has broad experience in the planning, design,
and inspection of railroad facilities, ranging from the
engineering of more than 4,000 km of railroads
throughout the world to the design of major tunnels and
stations. Projects include planning new lines through
jungle or desert and rapid transit systems in US cities.
Services provided by TAMS include location and
alignment, trackwork, bridges, tunnels, and marshalling
yards.

UPDATED

TCI

Transportation Consultants International
1 Eversholt Street, London NW1 2DN, UK
Tel: +44 171 214 9380   Fax: +44 171 214 9389

Key personnel
Chairman: Jonathan Cohen
Group Managing Director: Dick Keegan

Other TCI companies
TCI Consultants (address above)
Tel: +44 171 214 9464   Fax: +44 171 214 9020
Managing Director: Bob Walters

TCI Signalling Ltd
Suite 2, 7-11 Station Road, Reading RG1 1LG, UK
Tel: +44 118 950 7059   Fax: +44 118 959 6716
Managing Director: Francis O'Hara

TCI Operational Research Ltd
3rd Floor, A Block, Macmillan House, Paddington Station,
London W2 1FT
Tel: +44 171 313 0622   Fax: +44 171 922 4249
Managing Director: Mike Lee

TCI Forecast Ltd
The Old Chapel, 635 Gloucester Road, Horfield, Bristol
BS7 0BJ
Tel: +44 117 952 2618   Fax: +44 117 952 2618
Directors: Tim Lyons, Steve Wedlock, Tony Poulton

Capabilities
TCI provides project management and consulting
services for clients operating within rail and rail-related
areas of business. The company provides specialist staff
from a wide spectrum of railway backgrounds covering
railway and engineering disciplines including track, rolling
stock, signalling, operations, financial and economic
analysis and management skills such as safety,
investment appraisal and market research. TCI will deliver
projects on a turnkey basis or meet specific needs
including risk assessment, safety case preparation,
interface management, training, feasibility studies,
project management, construction management,
operational research and signalling and
telecommunications.

Projects
Current and recent projects include:
   Interface management for the Heathrow Express link.
   ATP and resignalling schemes for the Kowloon—
Canton Railway Corporation Hong Kong.
   Procurement management for Great Western Holdings
for new diesel trains and refurbishment of existing fleet.
   Signalling design, testing and commissioning for a new
Royal Mail terminal at Stafford station, UK.

Train describer alterations for cab secure radio throughout the south of England for Vauhgan Harmon systems Ltd.

Project planning for the West Coast Main Line route modernisation core programme including the development of a transmission-based train control system.

Advice and research for UK train operating companies on forecasting passenger demand and maintenance of the handbook of best practice in this field.

UPDATED

TecnEcon Ltd

Glen House, 125 Old Brompton Road, London SW7 3RP, UK
Tel: +44 171 373 7755   Fax: +44 171 370 3328
email: tecnecon@dial.pipex

Key personnel
Managing Director: Jeff Ody
Commercial Director: Alan Power
Director, Transport Planning Services: Philip Bates
International Transport Planning: Stephen Rutherford
Transport Planning, South-East: Eddie Strankalis
Public Transport: Hermann Maier
Traffic and Parking Studies, South-East: David Warriner
European Transport: Jean Pierre Soulie

Middle East Regional Office
PO Box 52750, Dubai, United Arab Emirates

Capabilities
Multimodal urban transport planning specialists in modelling and operational studies, economic and financial appraisal; market research into public transport attitudes and product development in relation to real-time passenger information systems; technical assistance and policy advice to international lending agencies, governments and transport operators.

Projects
London Docklands: demand modelling for metro system extensions.

Metro, Leeds: demand and revenue forecasts.

TecnEcon has been commissioned by London Underground to model pedestrian movement and delays at a number of stations on the Victoria line, including Oxford Circus.

Tyne & Wear Metro commissioned TecnEcon in 1995/96 to estimate the sensitivity of travel demand to price changes. The study involved a time series analysis of ticket sales data for each of the six fares. The results were used to determine fare scales and to form a basis of a medium review of commercial and pricing strategy.

NEW ENTRY

TERA

Transportation and Economic Research Associates Inc
PO Box 16438, Washington DC, 20041-6438, USA
Tel: +1 703 860 3467   Fax: +1 703 713 6684
Web: www.teraus.com

Key personnel
President: Asil Gezen

Capabilities
Include transport economics and planning studies simulation and modelling of transport systems; analyses of regulatory impacts; evaluations of existing infrastructure performance and new needs; business planning and feasibility studies.

Projects
Include feasibility studies, infrastructure evaluations, trade/traffic forecasting, operational and financial assessments in Albania, Macedonia, Bulgaria, Romania, Poland, Russia, Tunisia, USA, Latvia, Lithuania, Estonia, Georgia, India, Venezuela, Belarus, Hungary, Brazil and Turkmenistan.

NEW ENTRY

TIFSA

Tecnología e Investigación Ferroviaria SA
Capitan Haya 1-5 planta, E-28020 Madrid, Spain
Tel: +34 1 555 9562   Fax: +34 1 555 1041

Key personnel
President: Reyes Fernández Durán
Marketing Manager: Juan Pintó
Directors: A Fernández Gil, J Batanero, J Figuera, J A Hurtado

Capabilities
Consultancy services including institutional development, market studies, planning, training programmes, design of business plans, restructuring, infrastructure projects, signalling and telecommunications systems, high-speed railway systems, technical assistance for construction and maintenance, rolling stock engineering (including development, inspection and maintenance programmes) and environmental services including audits, soil contamination, impact studies and risk assessment.

Projects
Recent projects include work for clients in Spain (central and regional governments, RENFE, FEVE, Bilbao Metro, La Coruna Light Rail and Catalonian Railways), with the European Commission (DGI, III, VII, VIII, Phare and Tacis programmes), BERD, Russia, Slovenia, Belarus, Poland, Hungary, Greece, Mexico, Argentina and USA.

UPDATED

Tilney Lumsden Shane

5 Heathmans Road, London SW6 4TJ, UK
Tel: +44 171 731 6946   Fax: +44 171 736 3356
email: 106440.2232@compuserv.com

Key personnel
Directors: Marvin Shane, Kathy Tilney, Roger Edey, Heather Shane

Capabilities
Design of interiors for transport systems and of environments suitable for high passenger densities; design of specialist rail vehicles including concepts, engineering development and textile design. Rail project design includes passenger flow analysis, CAD drawing production, mockup build supervision, technical and procurement specification.

Projects
Refurbishment design for London Underground Ltd Victoria, Bakerloo, Northern and Piccadilly lines; Channel Tunnel Eurostar bar/buffet design; Channel Tunnel Nightstock train design for EPS, SNCF, NS and DB AG; metro train interior concepts for Adtranz; light rail system blueprint design for Centro, UK; layout and interior design for Hong Kong Airport express train; and various office and retail projects for railway operators.

UPDATED

TMG International Pty Ltd

13th Floor 39-41 York Street, Sydney, NSW 2000, Australia
Tel: +61 2 262 4111   Fax: +61 2 262 4110

Key personnel
Directors: Dale Coleman, Keith Walker, Warwick Talbot, Ian Nibloe, Alex Wardrop

TMG International (UK) Ltd
42 Shad Thames, London, SE1 2YA, UK
Tel: +44 171 403 1928   Fax: +44 171 403 4564
Directors: Peter Coysten, Michael Hamlyn, David Hyland, Ian Hodgson

TMG International (HK) Ltd
702 Tung Wah Mansions, 199-203 Hennessey Road, Hong Kong
Tel: +852 511 3306   Fax: +852 507 2885
Directors: Graham Davies, David Hyland

Capabilities
TMG is a railway and public transport policy, planning and operations consultancy. It offers services worldwide in transport planning, economic feasibility studies, project management, project planning, railway engineering and railway and public transport operations analysis and modelling.

Projects
TMG has developed a risk-based appraisal system for infrastructure renewal projects for railways in Australia, Hong Kong, New Zealand and UK. This system allows the effect of not doing any project on the safety and reliability of the system to be quantified, and the ranking of projects to give the optimum return on investment.

VERIFIED

Tractebel Development

Avenue Ariane 7, B-1200 Brussels, Belgium
Tel: +32 2 773 7511   Fax: +32 2 773 7990

Key personnel
Projects Manager: M Brismeé

Capabilities
Town and country planning, freight/passenger transport systems.

NEW ENTRY

Transcorp

1a Lonsdale Sq, London N1 1EN, UK
Tel: +44 171 466 4433   Fax: +44 171 700 0597
email: tcorp@fmgroup.co.uk

Key personnel
Executives: Neil Bates, Tony Hume, David King, Peter Trickett

Capabilities
Transcorp is a consortium of companies providing a design resource for passenger-focused transport. This includes exterior and interior design, brand creation, architectural design, ergonomics and engineering.

Projects
Clients include Bombardier, Eurotransit, Chiltern Railways, Ganz-Hunslet, greater Nottingham Rapid Transit, Holec Ridderkerk, London Underground, Manchester Metrolink, Kinki Sharyo, Jenbacher, KCRC Hong Kong, SNCF and London and Continental.

NEW ENTRY

Transport Design Consortium

5 Heathmans Road, London SW6 4TJ, UK
Tel: +44 171 731 8190   Fax: +44 171 736 3356

Member companies
Jones Garrard Ltd
Roundel Design Group
Tilney Lumsden Shane Ltd

Key personnel
Styling/Industrial Design: Roger Jones
Corporate and Graphic Design: Michael Denny
Interior/Environmental Design: Marvin Shane

Capabilities
Transport Design Consortium provides consultancy expertise in styling; engineering, environmental, graphic, industrial and interior design; corporate identity and project management for the rail industry, including ergonomics, mockup building, technical and procurement specifications.

Projects
Recent and current rail projects:
Brush: design support, Class 60 locomotive;
Centro: definition of design standards and criteria for a light rail system in the West Midlands, to include all aspects of the system and its environment;
BAA: rolling stock design, Heathrow Express project;
London Underground Ltd: refurbishment of 1967-72 rolling stock on the Victoria, Northern and Bakerloo Lines; refurbishment of 1973 rolling stock on the Piccadilly Line; interior design guidelines for new and refurbished rolling stock; feasibility study on platform edge door screens; study of emergency detrainment procedures;

RENFE: external design of AVE high-speed trainset;

EPS/SNCB/SNCF, GEC Alsthom: external, cab and bar/buffet design and engineering of Eurostar high-speed trainset;

GEC Alsthom: Channel Tunnel overnight coaches for EPS;

Hong Kong MTRC: airport express and suburban trains to serve proposed new airport.

VERIFIED

Transport Design International

12 Waterloo Park Estate, Bidford-on-Avon B50 4JH, UK
Tel: +44 1789 490591   Fax: +44 1789 490592

Joint Venture Companies
Warwick Design Consultants Ltd, UK
Design Resource Australia Pty Ltd, Australia
Index Industrial Design and Development Inc, USA
Minitram Systems, UK

Key personnel
Executives: Martin Pemberton (UK),
John Brown (Australia), André Grasso (USA)

Capabilities
Comprehensive transport design service for the development of new vehicles and products from concept through to production. With offices in the UK, Australia and the USA, Transport Design International employs specialist industrial designers, ergonomists and mechanical and electronic engineers and maintains full workshop and prototyping facilities within each studio complex. Typical commissions involve feasibility analysis, layout and design of vehicle interiors including: driving cabs and control desks, passenger seating, onboard catering and information and entertainment facilities. Exterior styling is also undertaken, and scale models and full-size mockups of complete vehicles are produced in-house and delivered on site.

The group's designers are also experienced in working with architectural teams to create complete station environments encompassing: ticket offices, platform furniture, retail kiosks and service counters, ticketing equipment including validators and barriers, public information systems and signage and graphics. Research and sourcing of new materials and technologies is also undertaken, to satisfy particular performance requirements such as safety and statutory standards, weight restrictions and maintenance procedures.

Projects
Current and recent projects include: London Underground Ltd; design of refurbishment of Piccadilly Line metro trainsets, including construction of full-size interior mockups; London Underground Ltd/GEC Alsthom Metro-Cammell: design of metro trainsets for Jubilee Line Extension, including construction of full-size interior mockups; Queensland Rail: feasibility studies on design of tilting trainsets for Brisbane—Rockhampton service and new designs for emus; SRA New South Wales: new designs for fourth-generation Tangara emus, XPT seating and suburban rolling stock refurbishment; PTC Melbourne: fleet refurbishment; and several light rail schemes in Asia and the UK.

VERIFIED

Transportation Technology Center

Association of American Railroads, Research & Test Department, PO Box 11130, Pueblo, Colorado 81001, USA
Tel: +1 719 584 0554   Fax: +1 719 584 0711

Key personnel
Chief, Quality and New Business Development:
    Peter C L Conlon

Capabilities
Contract research, development, testing, consulting and training services for passenger and freight railways and railway supply organisations.

VERIFIED

Transurb Consult

60 Rue Ravenstein b 18, B-1000 Brussels, Belgium
Tel: +32 2 512 3047   Fax: +32 2 513 9419

Key personnel
General Manager: Pierre M De Smet

Capabilities
Transurb Consult was formed in 1973 to bring together the various aspects of Belgian transport technology. Its capital is equally apportioned between Belgian Railways (SNCB), Luxembourg Railways (CFL), the Brussels Public Transport Company (STIB), the public transport companies of the Walloon and Flemish Regions (TEC and De Lijn). The private sector is mainly represented by Tractebel, a major holding company in Belgium, and by specialised private research offices dealing with all aspects of transportation.

VERIFIED

Transystem SpA

Via Giulini 3, I-20123 Milan, Italy
Tel: +39 2 860546   Fax: +39 2 876541

Key personnel
Managing Director: Luciano Pistone
Manager Technical Director: Georgio Beltrami
Marketing Manager: Alberto Mirri

Capabilities
Transystem operates in the field of infrastructure design and erection, permanent way, signalling, automation and computerised train control, overhead and third-rail contact line, power supply, auxiliary installation, workshops and depot yard. Transystem also produces and uses models and original package programmes for planning and design activities.

VERIFIED

Trident Consultants Ltd

84 Uxbridge Road, Ealing, London W13 8RH, UK
Tel: +44 181 579 7381   Fax: +44 181 840 0587

Key personnel
Managing Director: Dr Rod Bayliss
Operations Director: Dr Phil Proctor
Marketing Director: David Bolton

Principal subsidiary
Trident Consultants Far East (M) Sdn Bhd,
Ampang, Malaysia
Tel: +60 3 452 1121   Fax: +60 3 452 5792

Capabilities
Trident is a technical risk management consultancy specialising in the control and mitigation of risk to personnel, assets and revenue in heavy and light rail and mass transit systems. The consultancy provides specialist services in safety studies, quantified risk assessment, safety management consultancy, safety case preparation, reliability and availability studies, and human performance and behaviour assessment.

Projects
Trident's client list includes GATX, London Underground Ltd and Hong Kong MTRC.

UPDATED

University of London

Railway Technology Strategy Centre
Centre for Transport Studies, Department of Civil Engineering, Imperial College of Science, Technology & Medicine, London SW7 2BU, UK
Tel: +44 171 823 9942   Fax: +44 171 594 6102

Key personnel
Director: William R Steinmetz

Capabilities
In 1993, Imperial College established a Railway Technology Strategy Centre (RTSC) to contribute to the development of railway strategies, with particular emphasis on investment strategies, new technologies and unit cost reduction. The RTSC forms part of the University of London Centre for Transport Studies, formed by Imperial and University Colleges to develop intercollegiate research and teaching.

Initial contracts were with the former British Rail Technology Strategy Group, and the client base has been expanded to include Railtrack, London Underground Ltd and one of the three rolling stock leasing companies (ROSCOs).

Projects
Recent and current projects include development of a train control strategy (TCAM) and assistance on signalling equipment assessment to prioritise renewals (SICA system) for Railtrack.

VERIFIED

Vanness-Brackenridge Group

9652 Preston Trail W, Ponte Vedra Beach, FL 32082, USA
Tel: +1 904 280 1898   Fax: +1 904 280 1899

Key personnel
Principals: J Christopher Rooney, T Stephen O'Connor

Capabilities
Consultancy services for railways, governments and bilateral lending agencies concerning restructuring and strategic planning issues. The Vanness-Brackenridge Group has experience in railway restructuring, strategic planning, financial modelling, market analysis, organisational restructuring and policy development.

Projects
The Vanness-Brackenridge Group has served clients in 15 countries including Argentina, Australia, Bolivia, Brazil, Canada, Chile, Ecuador, South Korea, Mexico, Myanmar (Burma), New Zealand, Spain, Sri Lanka, Thailand and USA. Recent projects include:

Secretariat of Works and Public Services, Argentina: supervision of the analysis of the business and financial viability of creating five regional freight networks from the national Ferrocarriles Argentinos system.

Ferrocarriles Metropolitanos, Argentina: supervision of activities of Amtrak and New Zealand Rail advisers in the formulation of business strategies and financial budgets for Buenos Aires suburban passenger services on the Sarmiento and San Martín systems.

Canadian National Railways: advice as part of a continuing assignment to address strategic marketplace, competitive and organisational issues.

Companhia Vale do Rio Doce, Brazil: management of a long-term engagement to transform the Vitória a Minas Railway (EVFM) from an industrial system into a full-service operation offering general freight and passenger services.

Conrail, USA: supervision of technical staff preparing for privatisation.

Chilean State Railways (EFE): analysis for the Inter-American Development Bank of the feasibility of restructuring EFE.

Bolivian National Railways (ENFE): analysis of an open access policy for operating private freight services over ENFE infrastructure.

State Railways of Ecuador (ENFE): advice to the Ecuadorean government and the Inter-American Development Bank concerning the best strategy for ENFE's future development.

National Railways of Mexico (FNM): analysis for the Mexican Secretariat of Transport and Communications of various strategies for FNM privatisation.

New Zealand Rail (NZR): Participation in the sale of NZR to a consortium including Wisconsin Central Transportation.

Sri Lanka Railway (SLR): advice to Sri Lanka Ministry of Transport and World Bank on the restructuring of SLR.

State Railway Authority of New South Wales, Australia: study of current operations and proposed reforms.

UPDATED

Vosper Thornycroft (UK) Ltd

Vosper House, 223 Southampton Road, Portsmouth PO6 4QA, UK
Tel: +44 1705 379481   Fax: +44 1705 381124

Key personnel
Rail Product Manager: Cliff Shorter

Capabilities
Training technology, simulation, computer-based training, training management and course design. Products for the railway industry include computer-based training for maintenance and faulting of lineside telephones; third rail safety management; human factors studies to improve safety training; train driver competency assessment package; training needs analysis; confidential incident reporting system; computer-based training for faulting of automatic level crossings; basic accident investigation course; computer-based training for train layout; and signals and symbols training package.

VERIFIED

Harry Weese Associates

10 W Hubbard Street, Chicago, Illinois 60610, USA
Tel: +1 312 467 7030   Fax: +1 312 467 7051
email: hwa@worldnet.att.net

Key personnel
President: James A Torvik

Projects
Washington Metro: general architectural consultant for 160 km, 86-station system.

Toronto Transit Commission: member of consultant team for the 'Let's Move Programme', a 120 km, 54-station addition to the existing TTC system.

Chicago & North Western Passenger Terminal, Chicago: five year rehabilitation programme in progress, including the replacement of platforms and canopies, lighting, trackwork and mechanical systems and the repair of two classical brick facades.

UPDATED

Wendell Cox Consultancy

PO Box 8083, Belleville, Illinois 62222, USA
Tel: +1 618 632 8507   Fax: +1 618 632 8538
e-mail: policy@i1.net

Key personnel
Principal: Wendell Cox
Associate: Jean Love

Capabilities
Urban transport organisational design; competitive tendering; deregulation; strategic planning; public transport legislation, planning and policy; privatisation; submission of private proposals and bids; and service costing.

Projects
These have included: Urban rail efficiency studies in Phoenix, Seattle, Salt Lake City and Chicago; performance audits for British Columbia Transit and Indiana University; development of competitive pricing procedures for Transit New Zealand; analysis of North American light rail experience for New South Wales, Ministry of Transport; analysis of public transport privatisation potential for the New York State Senate; technical assistance programmes for the United States Department of Transportation Federal Transit Administration; developed proposal for privately operated commuter express bus system in Honolulu; drafted community mobility programme for Suburban Mobility Authority, Detroit; drafting of legislation for competitive tendering for Denver Regional Transportation District and also, competitive tendering and deregulation seminars for legislators, local public officials and public transport managers in the USA, Canada, New Zealand and Australia.

VERIFIED

Wilson, Ihrig & Associates

5776 Broadway, Oakland, California 94618 USA
Tel: +1 510 658 6719   Fax: +1 510 652 4441

Key personnel
President: George Paul Wilson
Principal: Steven L Wolfe

Capabilities
Acoustical design of stations, line sections and facilities; vehicle noise, vibration and ride quality evaluation; assessment and prediction of ground-borne vibration; track fastener design, testing and specification; noise and vibration criteria development.

Projects
These have included rail transit projects in USA, Canada, UK, Hong Kong, Australia, Greece, and Brazil.

VERIFIED

YTT International Inc

2-33-4 Musashi-dai, Fuchu, Tokyo 183, Japan
Tel: +81 423 281515   Fax: +81 423 280808

Key personnel
President: Yojiro Tawaragi
Board of Directors: Akira Nakayasu, Seizo Shirai, Iwao Yamamoto
Manager, International Projects: Nicholas M Iadanza
Chief Co-ordinator: Douglas W Martin
General Affairs: Sumiko Hanamura

Capabilities
Engineering, construction supervision and project management for rail vehicle projects; feasibility, planning, technical interface and co-ordination; rail vehicle specifications, inspection, testing, quality control and assurance.

Projects
Recent projects include preparation of the specification for diesel commuter trainsets for railways in southeast Asia; quality assurance and testing services at the manufacturer's plant for 20 LRVs and 17 bi-level stainless steel coaches for MBTA Boston; 37 stainless steel gallery cars for Chicago Metra and HBLRTS low-floor LRVs for New Jersey Transit; preliminary design, detailed design,

planning, preparation of technical specification documents and construction supervision of rail vehicles for the Philippines; and consulting and engineering services for the manufacture of commuter rail vehicles for Indonesia.

UPDATED

ZT

Zeta-Tech Associates Inc
900 Kings Highway North, PO Box 8407, Cherry Hill, New Jersey 08002, USA
Tel: +1 609 779 7795   Fax: +1 609 779 7436
email: zetatech@zetatech.com
Web: http://www.zetatech.com

Key personnel

President: Dr Allan M Zarembski
Vice-President of Costing and Economic Analysis:
   Randolph R Resor

Director of Training and Field Engineering:
   Donald Holfeld
Director of Engineering Analysis: Joseph W Palese
Senior Engineer: Pradeep K Patel
Project Engineers: Sunil Kondapalli, Leonid Katz
Programmer/Analyst: Nick Forte
Office Administrator: Kim Corrigan
Administrative Assistant: Katy White

Capabilities

Zeta-Tech Associates is a technical consulting and applied technology company directed at the railway and transportation industries. Its expertise covers:

Track and track systems covering fasteners and fastener systems; sleepers; track strength; track buckling; track maintenance; and track geometry;

Vehicle/track interaction; freight wagon systems; inspection and measurement systems; fatigue design and analysis of structures; applied economics; technical marketing; computer simulation and modelling; transportation cost analysis;

Operations analysis including train simulation modelling freight and passenger equipment; and benefit analysis of improved operations, equipment, advanced train control systems;

Costing including development of detailed operating costs, cost allocation and life cycle costing;

Technical training for all areas of the railway/transit industry, including needs assessment, training material development, training delivery and training evaluation;

Maintenance planning, comprising the development and application of computer software for use in forecasting component failure and planning of maintenance requirements, including database development and track component degradation/failure modelling.

UPDATED

ADDENDA

Alphabetical Listing

Aluminium Inductors Ltd
ANF-Industrie
BN
Bombardier Inc

BWS
DSC
LTS
Optech

Partner Jonsered
SAB WABCO
SILSAN AS
Talbot

Classified Listing

LOCOMOTIVES AND POWERED PASSENGER VEHICLES
ANF-Industrie
BN
Bombardier Inc

DIESEL ENGINES, TRANSMISSION AND FUELLING SYSTEMS
SILSAN AS

ELECTRIC TRACTION EQUIPMENT
Aluminium Inductors Ltd

FREIGHT VEHICLES AND EQUIPMENT
Talbot

BRAKES AND DRAWGEAR
SAB WABCO

BOGIES AND SUSPENSIONS, WHEELS AND AXLES
ANF-Industrie

SIGNALLING
DSC

PASSENGER INFORMATION SYSTEMS
LTS
Optech

PERMANENT WAY EQUIPMENT
BWS
Partner Jonsered

Aluminium Inductors

Aluminium Inductors Ltd
29 Lower Coombe Street, Croydon CR0 1AA, UK
Tel: +44 181 680 2100   Fax: +44 181 681 1577

Products
Transformers, inverter-based supply systems. A power conversion system designed by R-R Industrial Controls, Gateshead, UK, has a new-design of transformer to cut weight and boost efficiency.

In association with R-R Industrial Controls advanced high-density inverter-based supply systems for trains are being developed to cope with both alterations in rail traction DC supply environment and the provision of reliable power for emergency battery chargers, three-phase fan motors for air conditioning and motors for air compressor braking systems.

The systems make use of IGBT switching circuits.

NEW ENTRY

ANF-Industrie

ANF-Industrie
PO Box 1, F-59154 Crespin, France
Tel: +33 27 23 53 00   Fax: +33 3 27 35 16 24

Key personnel changes
Chairman: Bernard Dolphin

Directors
Heavy Rail Product Line: Claude Maire
Mass Transit: Francis Ancelet
Purchasing: Philippe Noirot-Cosson

Extra contracts
64 bogies have been delivered for Istanbul metro; half-life overhaul of 770 bogies has been carried out for Caracas metro.

UPDATED

BN

BN Division of Bombardier Eurorail
Avenue Louise 65, B-1050 Brussels, Belgium
Tel: +32 2 535 5511   Fax: +32 2 539 0428

Key personnel changes
Commercial Director: M Van Vooren
Engineering Director: M Thomas
Operations Director: A Lanckriet

Contract Management Railway Material:
J Van der Bussche
Manager, Advanced Engineering and R&D: D Versteyhe

UPDATED

Bombardier Inc

Bombardier Inc
1101 Parent Street, Saint-Bruno, Quebec J3V 6E6, Canada
Tel: +1 514 441 2020   Fax: +1 514 441 1515

Contracts
In September 1997, the MTA Metro-North Railroad of New York awarded a contract to Bombardier for the manufacture and supply of 50 commuter cars. In July 1997, in association with GEC Alsthom, Bombardier has won an order to supply six high-speed electric locomotives to be operated by Maryland Rail Commuter Service (MARC). The design of the locomotive is unique in North America and features a host of unprecedented advantages. In April 1997, Bombardier had been awarded a contract from the MTA/New York City Transit for the supply of 680 rapid transit cars. The contract comes with an option for up to 200 additional vehicles. The R142 rapid transit cars are customised to MTA/NYCT specifications to provide the highest degree of reliable and safe service, operational flexibility and ease of maintenance. In December 1996, Bombardier was selected by GO Transit for a seven-year maintenance contract of its fleet of rolling stock, consisting of 39 General Motors locomotives and 282 Bombardier Bi-Level commuter coaches. The Bombardier/GEC Alsthom consortium has been selected for the supply of high-speed equipment for Amtrak's Northeast Corridor (NEC) route between Washington DC, New York City, and Boston. The contract calls for the design and manufacture of up to 18 American Flyer trainsets, each consisting of two power cars and six coaches, and 15 electric locomotives. It also includes the design, construction and installation of up to three maintenance facilities for the rolling stock. In addition to being responsible for the complete design of the coaches, Bombardier will manufacture the locomotives, power cars and coaches and will undertake the integration of the trainsets.

Other orders include 50 push-pull commuter cars for the MTA Metro-North Railroad of New York; 99 Comet IV cars for the New Jersey Transit; 8 bi-level cars for the San Joaquin Regional Rail Commission, California; 72 American Flyer coaches for Amtrak NorthEast Corridor; 6 bi-level cars for the North San Diego County Transit District, California; 15 cars for the MTA Metro-North Railroad, New York; 25 bi-level cars for the Southern California Regional Rail Authority, California.

UPDATED

BWS

Entry to be deleted from *Permanent way equipment* section.

UPDATED

DSC moves

Following the acquisition of DSC Communications Dedicom, Denmark by Sasib Railway, Italy, Dedicom has become Sasib Railway Dedicom and is now based at Priorparken 530, 2605 Brondby, Denmark (Tel: +45 43 43 84 00 Fax: +45 43 43 84 01).

NEW ENTRY

LTS

Linné Trafiksystem AB
PO Box 654, Hamngatan 9, S-58107 Lonköping, Sweden
Tel: +46 31 896960   Fax +46 31 494465

Key personnel
Managing Director: Bengt Rodung
Sales Director: Stefan Bertling

Products
Turnkey supplier of intelligent transport planning and passenger information systems; VIPS computer tool for public transport planning; Linaria/Dynamite system for automatic passenger information.

Contracts
The Linaria/Dynamite system has been installed in 30 cities.

NEW ENTRY

Optech

Optech
11 Queens Brook, Spa Road, Bolton BL1 4AY, UK
Telephone: +44 1204 381119   Fax: +44 1204 381306

Key personnel
General Manager: Andy Devlin

Products
CCTV, audio data, computer control and SCADA systems, including the Help Point system for LRT and metros. The Help Point system has three buttons — fire, emergency and information. When the call is answered a camera overlooking the help point is switched on and the conversation recorded.

Contracts
Passenger Help Points have been supplied to Greater Manchester Metrolink, Docklands Light Railway and London Underground Ltd.

NEW ENTRY

Partner Jonsered

Partner Jonsered Power Products UK
Oldends Lane, Stonehouse GL10 3SY, UK
Tel: +44 1453 820305/306   Fax: +44 1453 971577

Key personnel
Marketing Manager: Shirley Pitts

Products
Hand-held power tools for rail maintenance/installation.

NEW ENTRY

SAB WACO

SAB WABCO
Roskildevagen 1B, PO Box 193, S-201 21 Malmo, Sweden
Tel: +46 40 350460   Fax: +46 40 303803

Key personnel
President: Johan Halling
Senior Vice-President, and Administration: Rolf Lundahl
Senior Vice-President, Marketing: Lars Blecko
Senior Vice-President, Business Development Manager:
    Mils Lennart Nilsson
Senior Vice-President, Technology: Heinz Ziegler

Subsidiaries
SAB WABCO AB
SAB WABCO International AB
SAB WABCO SA
SAB WABCO NV
SAB IBERICA SA, SAB WABCO SA
SAB IBERICA SA, Spain
SAB WABCO D&M Products Ltd
SAB WABCO Products Ltd
SAB WABCO D&M Ltd
SAB WABCO Ltd
Davies & Metcalfe Ltd
SAB WABCO SpA
SAB WABCO do Brazil SA
Suecobras Ind. e comercio Ltda
SAB WABCO CS sro
SAB WABCO D&M Engineering Ltd
SAB WABCO BSI Verkehrstechnik Products GmbH

SAB WABCO BSI Verkehrstechnik GmbH
Gutehoffnungshutte Radsatz GmbH
SAB WABCO Woojin Ltd
SAB WABCO India Ltd

Associated companies
FACTO AG, Switzerland

Products
Complete range of braking systems for all types of locomotives, passenger and freight vehicles, including LRVs and guided vehicles with rubber tyres; UIC approved automatic airbrakes to the requirements of most railway administrations; electropneumatic, electrohydraulic, electromechanical and all-electric brake systems; vacuum and combined brake systems; air supply equipment, reciprocating and screw compressors, air treatment devices and accessories; airbrake control devices; automatic slack adjusters, variable load devices; friction brake devices, tread brakes, brake discs, calliper assemblies, disc brake actuators with spring, hydraulic or mechanically operated parking; friction materials; electromagnetic track brakes; UIC approved.

Automatic door systems; sliding door systems (external and internal); plug-sliding door systems; swing-plug door systems. All available in single or double leaf, electropneumatic or electric. Automatic retracting and fixed steps.

Wheel products: solid wheels, wheelsets, resilient and low-noise wheels, running gear.

Microprocessor-controlled wheelslide protection devices, anti-slip and speed controls; automatic test equipment for brake controls; automatic computer-controlled systems for marshalling yards; transit car coupling systems.

Recent contracts
High-speed trains: complete brake systems for Pendolino trains, TGV South Korea, TGV France and brake equipment for X2000 Sweden and ICE Germany. Dmus and emus: brake systems and brake equipment for vehicles to: Australia, France, Germany, Hungary, Italy, Netherlands, Spain, Sweden, Taiwan and United Kingdom.
Container wagons: complete brake systems for among others AAE, RoadRailer and NS.
Freight cars: complete brake systems and brake equipment for many railways around the world.
LRV/Trams: electro-hydraulic brake systems to Cologne, Strasbourg, Grenoble and Val de Seine; electromechanical system to Hungary and Czech Republic; electrohydraulic brake systems, wheels and door systems for Hungary and Czech Republic, wheels for Darmstadt, Nuremberg, Vienna, wheels and door systems for Manila and door systems for Den Haag.
Metros: electropneumatic brake systems for Paris metro, Rome metro, Santiago metro and Teheran metro, electropneumatic brake systems for Stockholm metro.
Locomotives: complete brake systems to Italy and France, wheels for EuroSprinter, Germany.

UPDATED

SILSAN

SILSAN AS
PO Box 127, TR-01322 Adana, Turkey
Tel: +90 322 4410012   Fax: +90 322 4410086

Key personnel
Sales: Caghan Bacaksizlar

Products
Diesel engine components including cylinder liners for engines from Europe, USA and other countries.

NEW ENTRY

Talbot

Entry to be deleted from *Freight vehicles and equipment* section.

UPDATED

Index

Printed and bound in Great Britain by Butler & Tanner Ltd, Frome and London